TEACHER'S EDITION

PRENTICE HALL

TEXAS MATHEMATICS
COURSE 2

Randall I. Charles   Darwin Mills
Mark Illingworth   Alma Ramirez
Bonnie McNemar   Andy Reeves

PEARSON

Prentice
Hall

Boston, Massachusetts
Upper Saddle River, New Jersey

Acknowledgments appear on pp. T738–T739, which constitute an extension of this copyright page.

ISBN 0-13-134009-3
1 2 3 4 5 6 7 8 9 10   09 08 07 06

Prentice Hall Math Course 2
Teacher's Edition Contents

Texas Mathematics Teacher Handbook

Texas Student Edition With Teacher Notes

1 2 3 4 5 6 7 8 9 10   10 09 08 07 06

Authors

Series Author

Randall I. Charles, Ph.D., is Professor Emeritus in the Department of Mathematics and Computer Science at San Jose State University, San Jose, California. He began his career as a high school mathematics teacher, and he was a mathematics supervisor for five years. Dr. Charles has been a member of several NCTM committees and is the former Vice President of the National Council of Supervisors of Mathematics. Much of his writing and research has been in the area of problem solving. He has authored more than 75 mathematics textbooks for kindergarten through college. *Scott Foresman-Prentice Hall Mathematics Series Author Kindergarten through Algebra 2*

Program Authors

Mark Illingworth has taught in both elementary and high school math programs for more than twenty years. During this time, he received the Christa McAuliffe sabbatical to develop problem solving materials and projects for middle grades math students, and he was granted the Presidential Award for Excellence in Mathematics Teaching. Mr. Illingworth's specialty is in teaching mathematics through applications and problem solving. He has written two books on these subjects and has contributed to math and science textbooks at Prentice Hall.

Bonnie McNemar is a mathematics educator with more than 30 years' experience in Texas schools as a teacher, administrator, and consultant. She began her career as a middle school mathematics teacher and served as a supervisor at the district, county, and state levels. Ms. McNemar was the director of the Texas Mathematics Staff Development Program, now known as TEXTEAMS, for five years, and she was the first director of the Teachers Teaching with Technology (T^3) Program. She remains active in both of these organizations as well as in several local, state, and national mathematics organizations, including NCTM.

Darwin Mills, an administrator for the public school system in Newport News, Virginia, has been involved in secondary level mathematics education for more than fourteen years. Mr. Mills has served as a high school teacher, a community college adjunct professor, a department chair, and a district level mathematics supervisor. He has received numerous teaching awards, including teacher of the year for 1999–2000, and an Excellence in Teaching award from the College of Wooster, Ohio, in 2002. He is a frequent presenter at workshops and conferences. He believes that all students can learn mathematics if given the proper instruction.

Alma Ramirez is co-director of the Mathematics Case Project at WestEd, a nonprofit educational institute in Oakland, California. A former bilingual elementary and middle school teacher, Ms. Ramirez has considerable expertise in mathematics teaching and learning, second language acquisition, and professional development. She has served as a consultant on a variety of projects and has extensive experience as an author for elementary and middle grades texts. In addition, her work has appeared in the 2004 NCTM Yearbook. Ms. Ramirez is a frequent presenter at professional meetings and conferences.

Andy Reeves, Ph.D., teaches at the University of South Florida in St. Petersburg. His career in education spans 30 years and includes seven years as a middle grades teacher. He subsequently served as Florida's K–12 mathematics supervisor, and more recently he supervised the publication of The Mathematics Teacher, Mathematics Teaching in the Middle School, and Teaching Children Mathematics for NCTM. Prior to entering education, he worked as an engineer for Douglas Aircraft.

Contributing Author

Denisse R. Thompson, Ph.D., is a Professor of Mathematics Education at the University of South Florida. She has particular interests in the connections between literature and mathematics and in the teaching and learning of mathematics in the middle grades. Dr. Thompson contributed to the Guided Problem Solving features.

T5

Texas Mathematics Program Advisors

Prentice Hall wishes to thank the following educators for their ongoing advice in the development of the Texas edition of Prentice Hall Mathematics. Their valuable insights have helped ensure that this mathematics series meets the needs of Texas students and their teachers.

Pam Amato
Staff Developer
El Paso ISD
El Paso, Texas

Alice Ames
Bellfort Academy
Houston, Texas

Bobby Atchley
Shirley Hall Middle School
Weatherford ISD
Weatherford, Texas

Roberto D. Ayala
Assistant Principal
W. H. Atwell Middle School
Dallas ISD
Dallas, Texas

Debbie Boswell
Hutto Middle School
Hutto ISD
Hutto, Texas

Patty J. Copeland
Math/Science Curriculum
 Specialist
Diboll ISD
Diboll, Texas

Leah Cramer
Team Leader
Jasper High School
Plano ISD
Plano, Texas

Deborah E. Ekwo, Ed.D.
Instructional Coordinator/
 Coach
Professional Development
 Services
Houston ISD
Houston, Texas

Farica Erwin
W. H. Taft High School
Northside ISD
San Antonio, Texas

Sandra Freriks
West Texas High School
Plemons-Stinnett-Phillips
 Consolidated ISD
Stinnett, Texas

Mary Alice Hatchett
K–12 Math Consultant
Georgetown, Texas

Jacelyn Hepburn
W. E. Greiner Middle School
Dallas ISD
Dallas, Texas

Vickie Johnson
Manor Middle School
Manor ISD
Manor, Texas

Jeanne Kirk
Mathematics Coordinator
 (retired)
W. H. Taft High School
Northside ISD
San Antonio, Texas

Kelli Mallory
Coordinator of Secondary
 Mathematics
Frisco ISD
Frisco, Texas

Susan Allen Navarrette
Hornedo Middle School
El Paso ISD
El Paso, Texas

Verónica V. Orduño
J. G. Cigarroa Middle School
Laredo ISD
Laredo, Texas

Pamela Palmer
Memorial High School
Spring Branch ISD
Houston, Texas

Merle Picone
District Math Specialist
Brenham ISD
Brenham, Texas

Arnolia Robinson
Marshall Middle School
Houston ISD
Houston, Texas

Alan Roemer
Weatherford HighSchool
Weatherford ISD
Weatherford, Texas

Maria L. Zsohar
Math Specialist
Richardson ISD
Dallas, Texas

Reviewers

Course 2 Reviewers

Donna Anderson
Math Supervisor, 7–12
West Hartford Public Schools
West Hartford, Connecticut

Nancy L. Borchers
West Clermont Local Schools
Cincinnati, Ohio

Kathleen Chandler
Walnut Creek Middle School
Erie, Pennsylvania

Jane E. Damaske
Lakeshore Public Schools
Stevensville, Michigan

Frank Greco
Parkway South Middle School
Manchester, Missouri

Rebecca L. Jones
Odyssey Middle School
Orlando, Florida

Marylee R. Liebowitz
H. C. Crittenden Middle School
Armonk, New York

Kathy Litz
K. O. Knudson Middle School
Las Vegas, Nevada

Don McGurrin
Wake County Public School System
Raleigh, North Carolina

Ron Mezzadri
K–12 Mathematics Supervisor
Fair Lawn School District
Fair Lawn, New Jersey

Sylvia O. Reeder-Tucker
Prince George's County Math
   Department
Upper Marlboro, Maryland

Julie A. White
Allison Traditional Magnet Middle
   School
Wichita, Kansas

Charles Yochim
Bronxville Middle School
Bronxville, New York

Course 2 Reviewers

Cami Craig
Prince William County Public Schools
Marsteller Middle School
Bristow, Virginia

Donald O. Cram
Lincoln Middle School
Rio Rancho, New Mexico

Pat A. Davidson
Jacksonville Junior High School
Jacksonville, Arkansas

Yvette Drew
DeKalb County School System
Open Campus High School
Atlanta, Georgia

Robert S. Fair
K–12 District Mathematics Coordinator
Cherry Creek School District
Greenwood Village, Colorado

Michael A. Landry
Glastonbury Public Schools
Glastonbury, Connecticut

Nancy Ochoa
Weeden Middle School
Florence, Alabama

Charlotte J. Phillips
Wichita USD 259
Wichita, Kansas

Mary Lynn Raith
Mathematics Curriculum Specialist
Pittsburgh Public Schools
Pittsburgh, Pennsylvania

Tammy Rush
Consultant, Middle School
   Mathematics
Hillsborough County Schools
Tampa, Florida

Judith R. Russ
Prince George's County Public Schools
Capitol Heights, Maryland

Tim Tate
Math/Science Supervisor
Lafayette Parish School System
Lafayette, Louisiana

Dondi J. Thompson
Alcott Middle School
Norman, Oklahoma

Candace Yamagata
Hyde Park Middle School
Las Vegas, Nevada

Course 2 Reviewers

Linda E. Addington
Andrew Lewis Middle School
Salem, Virginia

Jeanne Arnold
Mead Junior High School
Schaumburg, Illinois

Sheila S. Brookshire
A. C. Reynolds Middle School
Asheville, North Carolina

Jennifer Clark
Mayfield Middle School
Putnam City Public Schools
Oklahoma City, Oklahoma

Nicole Dial
Chase Middle School
Topeka, Kansas

Christine Ferrell
Lorin Andrews Middle School
Massillon, Ohio

Virginia G. Harrell
Education Consultant
Hillsborough County, Florida

Jonita P. Howard
Mathematics Curriculum Specialist
Lauderdale Lakes Middle School
Lauderdale Lakes, Florida

Patricia Lemons
Rio Rancho Middle School
Rio Rancho, New Mexico

Susan Noce
Robert Frost Junior High School
Schaumburg, Illinois

Carla A. Siler
South Bend Community School Corp.
South Bend, Indiana

Kathryn E. Smith-Lance
West Genesee Middle School
Camillus, New York

Kathleen D. Tuffy
South Middle School
Braintree, Massachusetts

Patricia R. Wilson
Central Middle School
Murfreesboro, Tennessee

Patricia Young
Northwood Middle School
Pulaski County Special School District
North Little Rock, Arkansas

Content Consultants

Ann Bell
Mathematics
Prentice Hall Consultant
Franklin, Tennessee

Blanche Brownley
Mathematics
Prentice Hall Consultant
Olney, Maryland

Joe Brumfield
Mathematics
Prentice Hall Consultant
Altadena, California

Linda Buckhalt
Mathematics
Prentice Hall Consultant
Derwood, Maryland

Andrea Gordon
Mathematics
Prentice Hall Consultant
Atlanta, Georgia

Eleanor Lopes
Mathematics
Prentice Hall Consultant
New Castle, Delaware

Sally Marsh
Mathematics
Prentice Hall Consultant
Baltimore, Maryland

Bob Pacyga
Mathematics
Prentice Hall Consultant
Darien, Illinois

Judy Porter
Mathematics
Prentice Hall Consultant
Fuquay Varina, North Carolina

Rose Primiani
Mathematics
Prentice Hall Consultant
Harbor City, New Jersey

Jayne Radu
Mathematics
Prentice Hall Consultant
Scottsdale, Arizona

Pam Revels
Mathematics
Prentice Hall Consultant
Sarasota, Florida

Barbara Rogers
Mathematics
Prentice Hall Consultant
Raleigh, North Carolina

Michael Seals
Mathematics
Prentice Hall Consultant
Edmond, Oklahoma

Margaret Thomas
Mathematics
Prentice Hall Consultant
Indianapolis, India

CHAPTER 1

Decimals and Integers

TEKS ★ TAKS

Number, Operation, and Quantitative Reasoning
TEKS (7.1)(A), (7.2)(A), (B), (C), (F), (G) TAKS Obj. 1

Patterns, Relationships, and Algebraic Thinking
TEKS (7.3)(B) TAKS Obj. 2

Probability and Statistics
TEKS (7.12)(A), (B) TAKS Obj. 5

Underlying Processes and Mathematical Tools
TEKS (7.13)(A), (C), (D), (7.14)(A), (7.15)(B) TAKS Obj. 6

Exponents, Factors, and Fractions

TEKS ★ TAKS

Number, Operation, and Quantitative Reasoning
TEKS (7.1)(A), (7.1)(B), (7.1)(C), (7.2)(E) *TAKS* Obj. 1

Underlying Processes and Mathematical Tools
TEKS (7.13)(A), (7.13)(C), (7.13)(D) *TAKS* Obj. 6

Operations With Fractions

(TAKS) Prep and Assessment

Student Support

Vocabulary

GO Online

GPS Guided Problem Solving

TEKS ★ (TAKS)

Number, Operation, and Quantitative Reasoning
TEKS (7.2)(A), (7.2)(B), (7.2)(F), (7.2)(G) (TAKS) Obj. 1

Patterns, Relationships, and Algebraic Thinking
TEKS (7.3)(B) (TAKS) Obj. 2

Underlying Processes and Mathematical Tools
TEKS (7.13)(D), (7.14)(A)
(TAKS) Obj. 6

Equations and Inequalities

TAKS Prep and Assessment

TEKS ★ TAKS

Number, Operation, and Quantitative Reasoning
TEKS (7.2)(F) TAKS Obj. 1

Patterns, Relationships, and Algebraic Thinking
TEKS (7.5)(A), (7.5)(B)
TAKS Obj. 2

Underlying Processes and Mathematical Tools
TEKS (7.13)(C), (7.13)(D), (7.14)(A) TAKS Obj. 6

CHAPTER 5

Ratios, Rates, and Proportions

Student Support

Vocabulary

GO Online

GPS Guided Problem Solving

TEKS ★ TAKS

Number, Operation, and Quantitative Reasoning
TEKS (7.2)(D), (G) *TAKS* Obj. 1

Patterns, Relationships, and Algebraic Thinking
TEKS (7.3)(B), (7.4)(A)
TAKS Obj. 2

Geometry and Spatial Reasoning
TEKS (7.6)(D) *TAKS* Obj. 3

Probability and Statistics
TEKS (7.11)(B) *TAKS* Obj. 5

Underlying Processes and Mathematical Tools
TEKS (7.13)(A), (D), (7.14)(A), (7.15)(A) *TAKS* Obj. 6

TAKS Prep and Assessment

CHAPTER 6

Percents

Student Support

Vocabulary

Vocabulary Review 274, 279, 284, 290, 294, 298, 304, 310
New Vocabulary 274, 304, 310
Vocabulary Tip 274
Exercises 306, 312

GO Online

Video Tutor Help 298, 305
Active Math 280, 294
Homework Help 277, 283, 287, 293, 297, 301, 306, 314
Lesson Quiz 277, 283, 287, 293, 297, 301, 307, 313
Vocabulary Quiz 316
Chapter Test 318

(TAKS) **Prep** 319

GPS Guided Problem Solving

Exercises 276, 282, 286, 292, 296, 300, 306, 313
Solving Percent Problems 302

TEKS ★ TAKS

Number, Operation, and Quantitative Reasoning
TEKS (7.1)(A), (7.1)(B)
(TAKS) Obj. 1

Patterns, Relationships, and Algebraic Thinking
TEKS (7.3)(A), (7.3)(B)
(TAKS) Obj. 2

Probability and Statistics
TEKS (7.11)(B) (TAKS) Obj. 5

Underlying Processes and Mathematical Tools
TEKS (7.13)(D), (7.14)(A)
(TAKS) Obj. 6

CHAPTER 7

Geometry

TEKS ★ TAKS

Patterns, Relationships, and Algebraic Thinking
TEKS (7.3)(A) TAKS Obj. 2

Geometry and Spatial Reasoning
TEKS (7.6)(A), (7.6)(B), (7.6)(D), (7.8)(C) TAKS Obj. 3

Probability and Statistics
TEKS (7.11)(A), (7.11)(B) TAKS Obj. 5

Underlying Processes and Mathematical Tools
TEKS (7.13)(D), (7.14)(A), (7.15)(A), (7.15)(B) TAKS Obj. 6

TAKS Prep and Assessment

CHAPTER 8

Measurement

TAKS Prep and Assessment

Student Support

Vocabulary

GO Online

GPS Guided Problem Solving

TEKS ★ TAKS

Number, Operation, and Quantitative Reasoning
TEKS (7.1)(C) **TAKS** Obj. 1

Patterns, Relationships, and Algebraic Thinking
TEKS (7.4)(A) **TAKS** Obj. 2

Geometry and Spatial Reasoning
TEKS (7.6)(C), (7.8)(A), (7.8)(B), (7.8)(C) **TAKS** Obj. 3

Measurement
TEKS (7.9)(A), (B), (C)
TAKS Obj. 4

Underlying Processes and Mathematical Tools
TEKS (7.13)(D), (7.14)(A)
TAKS Obj. 6

Table of Contents

CHAPTER 9

Patterns and Rules

TEKS ★ TAKS

Patterns, Relationships, and Algebraic Thinking
TEKS (7.4)(A), (7.4)(B), (7.4)(C), (7.5)(B) TAKS Obj. 2

Probability and Statistics
TEKS (7.11)(B) TAKS Obj. 5

Underlying Processes and Mathematical Tools
TEKS (7.13)(A), (7.13)(C), (7.14)(A), (7.15)(A), (7.15)(B) TAKS Obj. 6

TAKS Prep and Assessment

Graphing in the Coordinate Plane

Student Support

TEKS ★ TAKS

Patterns, Relationships, and Algebraic Thinking
TEKS (7.4)(B) TAKS Obj. 2

Geometry and Spatial Reasoning
TEKS (7.7)(A), (7.7)(B) TAKS Obj. 3

Measurement
TEKS (7.9)(A) TAKS Obj. 4

Probability and Statistics
TEKS (7.11)(B) TAKS Obj. 5

Underlying Processes and Mathematical Tools
TEKS (7.13)(A), (7.14)(A) TAKS Obj. 6

TAKS Prep and Assessment

Contents   **xix**

CHAPTER 11

Displaying and Analyzing Data

Student Support

Vocabulary

Vocabulary Review 532, 538, 544, 550, 554, 560, 567

New Vocabulary 532, 538, 544, 550, 567

Vocabulary Tip 533, 551

Exercises 534, 540, 546, 551, 555, 568

GO Online

Video Tutor Help 567

Active Math 554

Homework Help 536, 541, 547, 552, 556, 564, 570

Lesson Quiz 535, 541, 547, 553, 555, 563, 569

Vocabulary Quiz 572

Chapter Test 574

Math at Work 565

   TAKS Prep 575

GPS Guided Problem Solving

Exercises 535, 541, 546, 552, 555, 563, 569

Describing Data 558

TEKS ★ TAKS

Patterns, Relationships, and Algebraic Thinking
TEKS (7.3)(B) **TAKS** Obj. 2

Probability and Statistics
TEKS (7.11)(A), (7.11)(B), (7.12)(A), (7.12)(B) **TAKS** Obj. 5

Underlying Processes and Mathematical Tools
TEKS (7.13)(D), (7.14)(B)
TAKS Obj. 6

TAKS Prep and Assessment

  TAKS Strategies: Interpreting Data, 571

Chapter Review, 572

Chapter Test, 574

  TAKS Tune-Up, 536, 542, 547, 553, 556, 564, 570, 575–577

CHAPTER 12

Using Probability

Student Support

Vocabulary

Vocabulary Review 580, 586, 591, 598, 606, 610
New Vocabulary 580, 586, 591, 598, 606, 610
Vocabulary Builder 603
Vocabulary Tip 580, 610
Exercises 582, 588, 593, 600, 608, 611

GO Online

Video Tutor Help 581, 586
Active Math 599, 606
Homework Help 582, 589, 594, 602, 609, 612
Lesson Quiz 583, 589, 595, 601, 609, 613
Vocabulary Quiz 616
Chapter Test 618
TAKS Prep 619

GPS Guided Problem Solving

Exercises 582, 588, 594, 601, 608, 612
Practice With Probability 604

TEKS ★ TAKS

Number, Operation, and Quantitative Reasoning
TEKS (7.1)(B) TAKS Obj. 1

Probability and Statistics
TEKS (7.10)(A), (7.10)(B), (7.11)(B) TAKS Obj. 5

Underlying Processes and Mathematical Tools
TEKS (7.13)(A), (7.13)(D), (7.14)(A) TAKS Obj. 6

TAKS Prep and Assessment

Connect Your Learning
through problem solving, activities, and the Web

Applications: Real-World Applications

Applications: **Math at Work and Careers**

Applications: **Interdisciplinary Applications**

Activity Labs

Activity Labs: **Hands On**

Activity Labs: **Technology**

Activity Labs: **Data Analysis**

Activity Labs: Data Collection

Activity Labs: Algebra Thinking

Activities: **Chapter Projects**

Problem Solving Strategies

Guided Problem Solving Features

Go Online

Throughout this book you will find links to the Prentice Hall Web site. Use the Web Codes provided with each link to gain direct access to online material. Here's how to *Go Online*:

1. Go to PHSchool.com
2. Enter the Web Code
3. Click Go!

Lesson Web Codes

Lesson Quiz Web Codes: There is an online quiz for every lesson. Access these quizzes with Web Codes ara-0101 through ara-1206 for Lesson 1-1 through Lesson 12-6. See page 89.

Homework Help Online Web Codes: For every lesson, there is additional support online to help students complete their homework. Access this homework help online with Web Codes are-0101 through are-1206 for Lesson 1-1 through Lesson 12-6. See page 297.

Lesson Quizzes
Web Code format: ara-0204   02 = Chapter 2   04 = Lesson 4

Homework Help Online
Web Code format: are-0605   06 = Chapter 6   05 = Lesson 5

Chapter Web Codes

Chapter	Vocabulary Quizzes	Chapter Tests	Chapter Projects	TAKS Tune-up Cumulative Practice
1	arj-0151	ara-0152	ard-0161	arq-0156
2	arj-0251	ara-0252	ard-0261	arq-0256
3	arj-0351	ara-0352	ard-0361	arq-0356
4	arj-0451	ara-0452	ard-0461	arq-0456
5	arj-0551	ara-0552	ard-0561	arq-0556
6	arj-0651	ara-0652	ard-0661	arq-0656
7	arj-0751	ara-0752	ard-0761	arq-0756
8	arj-0851	ara-0852	ard-0861	arq-0856
9	arj-0951	ara-0952	ard-0961	arq-0956
10	arj-1051	ara-1052	ard-1061	arq-1056
11	arj-1151	ara-1152	ard-1161	arq-1156
12	arj-1251	ara-1252	ard-1261	
TAKS Practice Test				arq-1254

Additional Web Codes

Video Tutor Help:
Use Web Code are-0775 to access engaging online instructional videos to help bring math concepts to life. See page 126.

Data Updates:
Use Web Code arg-9041 to get up-to-date government data for use in examples and exercises. See page 541.

Math at Work:
For information about each Math at Work feature, use Web Code arb-2031. See page 345.

TEKS ★ TAKS Overview

This Overview summarizes important changes in the TEKS and provides the TAKS Blueprint (an outline of topics covered from the Texas Board of Education). Succeeding pages show the detailed instructional support for TEKS and the comprehensive practice for TAKS found in *Prentice Hall Course 2 Mathematics*.

Implementation Timeline

1998   Texas State Board of Education implemented the Texas Essential Knowledge and Skills (TEKS) for Mathematics

2003   Texas Assessment of Knowledge and Skills (TAKS) was the first administration of TAKS tests

2005   TEKS revised by the State Board of Education

2006   Revised TEKS implemented in 2006–2007 school year

2008   Potential date for revised TAKS items to appear in statewide testing

What's New in the 2005 TEKS for Grade 7?

New Emphasis for the Course

- Problem solving is to occur "in meaningful contexts." Throughout this text, you will find meaningful real-world contexts that give students reasons to study math. See, for example, the "Why Learn This" section that starts each lesson.

- Students are to use graphing technology. See pages 460 and 502 for examples of support.

- One of the primary focal points at Grade 7 is now described for clarity as "using *direct* proportional relationships." You will find support for direct proportional relationships in Lessons 5-1, 5-2, 5-3, 5-4, 5-5, 5-6, 9-1, and 9-5.

Important Changes in Specific Student Expectations

- **TEKS** (7.4)(C) Students will . . . use words and symbols to describe the relationship between the terms in an arithmetic sequence.

    Arithmetic sequences are found in Lessons 9-2 and 9-3. Item 29 on page 455 is an example of a TAKS Tune-Up item supporting this expectation.

- **TEKS** (7.5)(B) Students will . . . formulate an equation when given a problem situation.

    The "Words to Equation" model found in Lessons 4-3, 4-4, 4-6, and many others will help your students achieve this student expectation. Also see TAKS Tune-Up items on pages 177, 198, and 218.

- **TEKS** (7.7)(B) Students . . . graph reflections across the horizontal or vertical axis.

    Students reflect points and figures in Lesson 10-6. TAKS Tune-Up items on pages 525 and 526 give students practice.

- **TEKS** (7.9)(B and C) These expectations identify the types of three-dimensional figures students are to study—prisms (triangular and rectangular) and cylinders.

  (B) connect models for volume of prisms (triangular and rectangular) and cylinders to formulas of prisms (triangular and rectangular) and cylinders; and

  (C) estimate measurements and solve application problems involving volume of prisms (rectangular and triangular) and cylinders.

    Students learn this content in Lesson 8-10. See TAKS Tune-Up on pages 425, 433, and 623 for samples of items that allow students to practice these concepts.

- **TEKS** (7.10)(A and B) These expectations change the scope of students' work.

  (A) construct sample spaces for simple or composite experiments

  (B) find the probability of independent events (Note: This is not tested)

    Students learn this content in Chapter 12. See TAKS Tune-Up on pages 602, 609, and 623 for samples of items that allow students to practice these concepts.

- **TEKS** (7.11)(A) These expectations now list specific types of representations that students are to study.

  (A) select and use an appropriate representation for presenting and displaying relationships among collected data, including line plot, line graph, bar graph, stem and leaf plot, circle graph, and Venn diagrams, and justify the selection

    Students learn this content in Lessons 7-7, 11-1, 11-2, 11-3, and 11-6. See TAKS Tune-Up on pages 357, 536, 553, and 576 for samples of items that allow students to practice these graphs.

 Blueprint for Grade 7

This chart shows how many items appear on the TAKS test for each TAKS Objective.

TAKS Objectives	Number of Items on Grade 7 TAKS Test for This Objective
Objective 1: Numbers, Operations, and Quantitative Reasoning	10
Objective 2: Patterns, Relationships, and Algebraic Reasoning	10
Objective 3: Geometry and Spatial Reasoning	7
Objective 4: Measurement	5
Objective 5: Probability and Statistics	7
Objective 6: Mathematical Processes and Tools	9
Total number of items	48

(Source: *TAKS Information Booklet, August 2004*)

Focal Points of Grade 7 TEKS

In *Prentice Hall Course 2 Mathematics*, you will find support for teaching the focal points for Grade 7 as identified in the TEKS:

- using direct proportional relationships in number, geometry, measurement, and probability

- applying addition, subtraction, multiplication, and division of decimals, fractions, and integers

- using statistical measures to describe data

These focal points are strongly supported in the text. Introductory Activity Labs allow students to explore concepts before a lesson. Within lessons, students' understanding is deepened, and they have ample opportunities for practice. Activity Labs that follow lessons allow students to expand their knowledge of concepts learned in a lesson. The following will give you an overview of how the focal points are developed in this text.

Direct Proportional Relationships

In Chapters 5, 6, and 11, students will study direct proportional relationships related to number, geometry, and measurement. In Chapter 12, they will study probability.

> Activity Labs develop students' conceptual understanding.

Operations With Decimals, Integers, and Fractions

In Chapter 1, students practice adding and subtracting decimals, and they extend these skills to multiplying and dividing decimals and operations with integers. In Chapter 3, students review adding and subtracting fractions and learn to multiply and divide fractions. Throughout the year, students will apply their knowledge of operations with decimals, integers, and fractions to solve real-world problems.

> Examples support problem solving.

Statistical Measures

In Chapter 1, students learn to find mean, median, mode, and range, including how to determine which is the best measure to describe a set of data. They use these concepts in Chapter 11 and exercises throughout the year.

> Practice exercises develop and maintain skills.

Manipulative Materials and Technology

In Grades 6-8, students are to develop conceptual understanding using manipulative materials and graphing technology. In *Prentice Hall Course 2 Mathematics,* students use both of these tools to develop their understanding of the Grade 7 TEKS.

> Simple manipulatives support the development of conceptual understanding.

> Graphing technology can be a powerful tool for deepening students' understanding of a concept.

TEKS Progression in Middle Grades

The table below highlights the skills found in the TEKS. Grade 5 is included so that you know what to expect of students as they enter the sixth grade. Knowing what your students were responsible for learning the previous year will help you to teach new skills based on prior learning. Students are expected to use all these skills in appropriate problem situations.

Grade 5	Grade 6	Grade 7	Grade 8
Number, operation, and quantitative reasoning			
Comparing and Ordering			
• comparing and ordering whole numbers and fractions (5.1)(A) (5.2)(B)	• comparing and ordering nonnegative rationals (6.1)(A)	• comparing and ordering integers and positive rational numbers (7.1)(A)	• comparing and ordering rational numbers including integers, percents, and positive and negative fractions and decimals (8.1)(A)
Equivalent Forms			
• generating equivalent fractions (5.2)(A)	• generating equivalent rational numbers including whole numbers, fractions, and decimals (6.1)(B)	• generating equivalent rational numbers including fractions, decimals, whole numbers, and percents (7.1)(B)	• selecting and using appropriate forms of rational numbers (8.1)(B)
Factors and Multiples			
• writing prime factorizations of whole number and common factors of a set of whole numbers (5.3)(D)	• writing prime factorizations using exponents (6.1)(D) • identifying common factors and the greatest common factor of a set of positive integers (6.1)(E) • identifying common multiple and the least common multiple of a set of positive integers. (6.1)(F)		
Real Numbers			
		• representing squares and square roots using geometric models (7.1)(C)	• approximating the value of irrational numbers (8.1)(C)
Operations			
• adding and subtracting whole numbers and decimals (5.3)(A) • multiplying whole numbers (5.3)(B) • modeling addition and subtraction of fractions with like denominators (5.3)(E)	• multiplying and dividing whole numbers (6.2)(C) • modeling addition and subtraction of fractions (6.2)(A) • adding and subtracting fractions and decimals (6.2)(B)	• modeling multiplication and division situations with fractions and decimals (7.2)(A) • adding, subtracting, multiplying, and dividing fractions and decimals (7.2)(B) • modeling addition, subtraction, multiplication, and division of integers (7.2)(C)	

Grade 5	Grade 6	Grade 7	Grade 8
Number, operation, and quantitative reasoning, continued			
Operations, continued			
	• multiplying and dividing whole numbers including equivalent ratios and rates (6.2)(C) • using order of operations to simplify whole number expressions (6.2)(E)	• dividing to find unit rates and ratios in proportional relationships (7.2)(D) • simplifying numerical expressions involving order of operations and exponents (7.2)(E) • selecting and using appropriate operations and justifying the selections (7.2)(F)	• multiplying by a constant factor (unit rate) (8.2)(D) • selecting appropriate operations involving rational numbers and justifying the selections (8.2)(A)
Rounding, Estimating, and Determining Reasonableness			
• rounding whole numbers and decimals through tenths (5.4)(A)	• estimating and rounding to approximate reasonable results where exact answers are not required (6.2)(D)	• determining reasonableness of a solution to a problem (7.2)(G)	• evaluating a solution for reasonableness (8.2)(C)
Patterns, relationships, and algebraic thinking			
Proportional Relationships			
	• representing ratios and percents with concrete models, fractions, and decimals (6.3)(B) • using ratios (6.3)(A) • using ratios to make predictions (6.3)(C)	• estimating and finding solutions involving proportional relationships (7.3)(B) • estimating and finding solutions involving percent (7.3)(A)	• estimating and finding solutions involving percents and other proportional relationships (8.3)(B) • comparing and contrasting proportional and nonproportional linear relationships (8.3)(A)
Representing Relationships			
	• using tables of data to generate formulas involving perimeter, area, volume of a rectangular prism, etc. (6.4)(B) • using tables and symbols to represent relationships (6.4)(A)	• generating formulas and graphing data involving unit conversions, perimeter, area, circumference, volume, and scaling (7.4)(A),(7.4)(B) • using words and symbols to describe the relationship between the terms and their positions in an arithmetic sequence (7.4)(C)	• generating a different representation of data given another representation of data (such as a table, graph, equation, or verbal description) (8.4) • finding and evaluating an algebraic expression to determine any term in an arithmetic sequence (8.5)(B)
Equations			
	• using letters to represent an unknown in an equation and formulate equations (6.5) • formulating equations described by linear relationships (6.5)	• using concrete and pictorial models to solve equations and use symbols to record the actions (7.5)(A) • formulating problem situations when given a simple equation and formulate an equation when given a problem situation (7.5)(B)	• predicting, finding, and justifying solutions to application problems using appropriate tables, graphs, and algebraic equations (8.5)(A)

Grade 5	Grade 6	Grade 7	Grade 8
Geometry and spatial reasoning			
Angles and Figures			
• using critical attributes to define geometric shapes or solids (5.7)(B)	• measuring angles (6.8)(C) • classifying angles as acute, obtuse, or right (6.6)(A) • identifying relationships involving angles in triangles and quadrilaterals (6.6)(B)	• classifying pairs of angles as complementary or supplementary (7.6)(A) • classifying triangles and quadrilaterals (7.6)(B) • classifying three-dimensional figures, including pyramids, cones, prisms, and cylinders (7.6)(C) • sketching three-dimensional figures when given the top, side, and front views (7.8)(A) • making a net of the surface area of a three-dimensional figure (7.8)(B)	• drawing three-dimensional figures from different perspectives (8.7)(A)
Coordinate Plane and Transformations			
• sketching the results of translations, rotations, and reflections (5.8)(A) • describing the transformation that generates one figure from the other (5.8)(B)	• locating and naming points on a coordinate plane using ordered pairs of non-negative rational numbers (6.7)	• locating and naming points on a coordinate plane using ordered pairs of integers (7.7)(A) • graphing reflections and graphing translations (7.7)(B) • using geometric concepts and properties to solve problems in fields such as art and architecture (7.8)(C)	• locating and naming points on a coordinate plane using ordered pairs of rational numbers (8.7)(D) • generating similar figures using dilations (8.6)(A) • graphing dilations, reflections, and translations (8.6)(B) • using geometric concepts and properties to solve problems in fields such as art and architecture (8.7)(B)
Measurement			
Converting Measures			
• describing numerical relationships between units of measure within the same measurement system (5.11)(B)	• converting measures within the same measurement system (6.8)(D)		
Lengths and Area			
	• describing the relationship between radius, diameter, and circumference of a circle (6.6)(C) • solving problems involving length (including perimeter), area, time, temperature, volume, and weight (6.8)(B) • estimating measurements (including circumference) and evaluate reasonableness of results (6.8)(A)	• estimating measurements and solving application problems involving length (including perimeter and circumference) and area of polygons and other shapes (7.9)(A)	

Grade 5	Grade 6	Grade 7	Grade 8
Volume and Surface Area			
• measuring volume using concrete models of cubic units (5.10)(A)		• connecting models and solving problems involving volume of prisms (rectangular and triangular) and cylinders (7.9)(B), (7.9)(C)	• connecting models of prisms, cylinders, pyramids, spheres, and cones to formulas for volume of these objects (8.8)(B) • estimating measurements and using formulas to solve problems involving lateral and total surface area and volume (8.8)(C)
Probability and statistics			
Probability			
• using fractions to describe the results of an experiment (5.12)(A) • using experimental results to make predictions (5.12)(B)	• constructing sample spaces using lists and tree diagrams (6.9)(A) • finding the probabilities of a simple event and its complement (6.9)(B)	• constructing sample spaces for simple or composite experiments (7.10)(A) • finding the probability of independent events (7.10)(B)	• finding the probabilities of dependent and independent events (8.11)(A) • using theoretical probabilities and experimental results to make predictions and decisions (8.11)(B) • selecting and using different models to simulate an event (8.11)(C)
Representing Data			
• using tables of related number pairs to make line graphs (5.13)(A) • graphing a given set of data using an appropriate graphical representation such as a picture or line (5.13)(C)	• selecting and using an appropriate representation for data including line plot, line graph, bar graph, and stem and leaf plot (6.10)(A) • solving problems by collecting, organizing, displaying, and interpreting data (6.10)(D) • sketching circle graphs to display data (6.10)(C)	• selecting and using an appropriate representation for presenting and displaying relationships among collected data, including line plot, line graph, bar graph, stem and leaf plot, circle graph, and Venn diagrams, and justify the selection (7.11)(A)	• selecting and using an appropriate representation for presenting and displaying relationships among collected data including line plots, line graphs, stem and leaf plots, circle graphs, bar graphs, box and whisker plots, histograms, and Venn diagrams with and without the use of technology (8.12)(C)
Mean, Median, Mode, and Range			
• describing characteristics of data presented in tables and graphs including the shape and spread of the data and the middle number (5.13)(B)	• identifying mean, median, mode, and range of a set of data (6.10)(B)	• describing a set of data using mean, median, mode, and range (7.12)(A) • choosing among mean, median, mode, or range to describe a set of data (7.12)(B)	• selecting the appropriate measure of central tendency or range to describe a set of data (8.12)(A)

This year you will take the test called the Texas Assessment of Knowledge and Skills, or TAKS. The TAKS test checks your understanding of the learning requirements in the Texas Essential Knowledge and Skills, or TEKS, for Grade 7. Your textbook helps you get ready for TAKS every day in every lesson. Here is how.

1 At the beginning of each lesson

Review the TEKS and TAKS at the beginning of every lesson. This list will tell you what you will be learning.

TEKS ★ TAKS

- **(7.3)(B)** To estimate and find solutions to application problems involving proportional relationships such as similarity **TAKS** Obj. 2
- **(7.6)(D)** To use critical attributes to define similarity **TAKS** Obj. 3

🔊 **New Vocabulary** polygon, similar polygons, indirect measurement

2 Within a lesson

Examples in multiple-choice and griddable format will help prepare you for the types of questions you will see on TAKS.

2 **TAKS** **Multiple Choice** A 6-ft-tall person standing near a flagpole casts a shadow 4.5 ft long. The flagpole casts a shadow 15 ft long. What is the height of the flagpole?

Ⓐ 11.25 ft   Ⓑ 18 ft   Ⓒ 20 ft   Ⓓ 360 ft

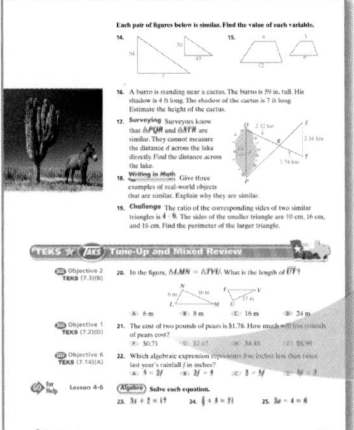

3 At the end of each lesson

The TAKS Tune-Up sections will help you review concepts tested on TAKS. For more help, a TAKS Mathematics Formula Chart similar to the one you are allowed to use for the test is at the end of your textbook.

TAKS Objective 1
TEKS (7.2)(D)

21. The cost of two pounds of pears is $1.78. How much will five pounds of pears cost?

Ⓕ $0.71   Ⓖ $2.67   Ⓗ $4.45   Ⓙ $8.90

4 At the end of each chapter

TAKS Tune-Up Cumulative Practice provides three
pages of practice test items. You will also find

TAKS Tips

TAKS tips help you solve TAKS items like the ones you will see on the test.

Vocabulary Builder

The Vocabulary Builder reviews math terms that you may see on the TAKS test.

Vocabulary Builder

As you solve test items, you must understand
the meanings of mathematical terms. Match
each term with its mathematical meaning.

A. proportion   **I.** a ratio that compares
two quantities

B. ratio   measured in different

TAKS GO for Help Guide

The handy Help Guide shows where you can go for
help with any questions you missed.

TAKS GO for Help Guide

TAKS Objective	Item Numbers	GO To	TAKS Objective	Item Numbers	GO To
Obj. 5: (7.11)(B)	1	Lesson 2-3	Obj. 6: (7.13)(B)	11	Lesson 5-4
	2–3	Lesson 3-4		12	Lesson 5-5
Obj. 1: (7.5)(B)	4–5	Lesson 4-4	Obj. 2: (7.3)(B)	13	Lesson 5-4
Obj. 1: (7.2)(D)	6	Lesson 5-2		14	Lesson 5-6
	7–8	Lesson 5-4			
Obj. 1: (7.2)(E)	9	Lesson 2-1			
	10	Lesson 1-9			

For additional TAKS Practice, see the *TAKS Review and Preparation Workbook*.

Texas Essential Knowledge and Skills

Where You Learn The following section states the Texas Essential Knowledge and Skills for Grade 7 and some examples of where these TEKS are located in the 7th grade text.

TEKS	WHERE YOU LEARN
Number, operation, and quantitative reasoning	
(7.1) The student represents and uses numbers in a variety of equivalent forms. The student is expected to	
(A) compare and order integers and positive rational numbers;	**Lessons:** 1-6, 2-4, 2-6, 2-7, 6-2 **Activity Labs:** 2-4a, 2-6a, 2-6b, 6-2a
(B) convert between fractions, decimals, whole numbers, and percents mentally, on paper, or with a calculator; and	**Lessons:** 2-6, 2-7, 6-1, 6-2, 6-3, 6-4, 6-6, 6-7, 6-8, 12-1 **Activity Lab:** 2-6a **Guided Problem Solving:** Chapter 6
(C) represent squares and square roots using geometric models.	**Lessons:** 2-1, 8-6
(7.2) The student adds, subtracts, multiplies, or divides to solve problems and justify solutions. The student is expected to	
(A) represent multiplication and division situations involving fractions and decimals with models, including concrete objects, pictures, words, and numbers;	**Lessons:** 1-3, 1-4, 3-4, 3-5 **Activity Labs:** 1-3a, 1-4a, 3-4a, 3-5a **Guided Problem Solving:** Chapter 3
(B) use addition, subtraction, multiplication, and division to solve problems involving fractions and decimals;	**Lessons:** 1-2, 1-3, 1-4, 1-5, 3-2, 3-3, 3-4, 3-5, 3-6, 3-7 **Activity Labs:** 3-2a, 3-6b **Guided Problem Solving:** Chapter 3
(C) use models, such as concrete objects, pictorial models, and number lines, to add, subtract, multiply, and divide integers and connect the actions to algorithms;	**Lessons:** 1-7, 1-8 **Activity Labs:** 1-7a, 1-8a
(D) use division to find unit rates and ratios in proportional relationships such as speed, density, price, recipes, and student-teacher ratio;	**Lessons:** 5-1, 5-2, 5-3, 5-4 **Activity Lab:** 5-4a **Guided Problem Solving:** Chapter 5
(E) simplify numerical expressions involving order of operations and exponents;	**Lesson:** 2-1 **Activity Lab:** 2-1b

TEKS	WHERE YOU LEARN
Number, operation, and quantitative reasoning	
(F) select and use appropriate operations to solve problems and justify the selections; and	**Lessons:** 1-4, 1-7, 1-8, 3-2, 3-3, 3-4, 4-1 **Activity Labs:** 1-8a, 3-6b **Guided Problem Solving:** Chapter 1
(G) determine the reasonableness of a solution to a problem.	**Lessons:** 1-2, 1-3, 3-2, 3-3, 3-5, 5-2 and Check for Reasonableness features throughout Examples

TEKS	WHERE YOU LEARN
Patterns, relationships, and algebraic thinking	
(7.3) The student solves problems involving direct proportional relationships. The student is expected to	
(A) estimate and find solutions to application problems involving percent; and	**Lessons:** 6-3, 6-4, 6-5, 6-6, 6-7, 6-8 **Activity Labs:** 6-4a, 6-8a **Guided Problem Solving:** Chapters 6, 7
(B) estimate and find solutions to application problems involving proportional relationships such as similarity, scaling, unit costs, and related measurement units.	**Lessons:** 1-5, 3-6, 5-1, 5-2, 5-3, 5-4, 5-5, 5-6, 6-5, 11-5 **Activity Labs:** 3-7b, 5-4a, 5-6a, 5-6b **Guided Problem Solving:** Chapter 5
(7.4) The student represents a relationship in numerical, geometric, verbal, and symbolic form. The student is expected to	
(A) generate formulas involving unit conversions, perimeter, area, circumference, volume, and scaling;	**Lessons:** 5-6, 8-2, 8-3, 8-4 **Activity Labs:** 8-2a, 8-5a, 8-10b, 9-4a
(B) graph data to demonstrate relationships in familiar concepts such as conversions, perimeter, area, circumference, volume, and scaling; and	**Lessons:** 9-1, 9-5, 9-6, 10-4 **Activity Labs:** 9-1a, 10-2b
(C) use words and symbols to describe the relationship between the terms in an arithmetic sequence (with a constant rate of change) and their positions in the sequence.	**Lessons:** 9-2, 9-3 **Activity Lab:** 9-2a

TEKS	WHERE YOU LEARN

Patterns, relationships, and algebraic thinking

(7.5) The student uses equations to solve problems. The student is expected to

(A)	use concrete and pictorial models to solve equations and use symbols to record the actions; and	**Lessons:** 4-3, 4-4, 4-5, 4-6 **Activity Labs:** 4-3a, 4-6a **Guided Problem Solving:** Chapter 4
(B)	formulate problem situations when given a simple equation and formulate an equation when given a problem situation.	**Lessons:** 4-2, 4-3, 4-4, 4-5, 4-6, 9-5

TEKS	WHERE YOU LEARN

Geometry and spatial reasoning

(7.6) The student compares and classifies two- and three-dimensional figures using geometric vocabulary and properties. The student is expected to

(A)	use angle measurements to classify pairs of angles as complementary or supplementary;	**Lesson:** 7-2
(B)	use properties to classify triangles and quadrilaterals;	**Lessons:** 7-3, 7-4
(C)	use properties to classify three-dimensional figures, including pyramids, cones, prisms, and cylinders; and	**Lesson:** 8-8
(D)	use critical attributes to define similarity.	**Lessons:** 5-5, 7-5 **Activity Labs:** 5-5a, 5-5b

(7.7) The student uses coordinate geometry to describe location on a plane. The student is expected to

(A)	locate and name points on a coordinate plane using ordered pairs of integers; and	**Lessons:** 10-1, 10-5, 10-6 **Activity Lab:** 10-1b
(B)	graph reflections across the horizontal or vertical axis and graph translations on a coordinate plane.	**Lessons:** 10-5, 10-6

(7.8) The student uses geometry to model and describe the physical world. The student is expected to

(A)	sketch three-dimensional figures when given the top, side, and front views;	**Activity Lab:** 8-8a
(B)	make a net (two-dimensional model) of the surface area of a three-dimensional figure; and	**Lesson:** 8-9

TEKS	WHERE YOU LEARN
Geometry and spatial reasoning	
(C) use geometric concepts and properties to solve problems in fields such as art and architecture.	**Lessons:** 5-6, 7-3, 7-4, 7-5, 8-1, 8-5, 8-8 **Activity Lab:** 5-6a

TEKS	WHERE YOU LEARN
Measurement	
(7.9) The student solves application problems involving estimation and measurement. The student is expected to	
(A) estimate measurements and solve application problems involving length (including perimeter and circumference) and area of polygons and other shapes;	**Lessons:** 8-1, 8-2, 8-3, 8-4, 8-5 **Activity Lab:** 10-1b **Guided Problem Solving:** Chapter 8
(B) connect models for volumes of prisms (triangular and rectangular) and cylinders to formulas of prisms (triangular and rectangular) and cylinders; and	**Lesson:** 8-10
(C) estimate measurements and solve application problems involving volume of prisms (rectangular and triangular) and cylinders.	**Lesson:** 8-10

TEKS	WHERE YOU LEARN
Probability and statistics	
(7.10) The student recognizes that a physical or mathematical model can be used to describe the experimental and theoretical probability of real-life events. The student is expected to	
(A) construct sample spaces for simple or composite experiments; and	**Lessons:** 12-3, 12-4 **Activity Labs:** 12-3b, 12-4a
(B) find the probability of independent events.	**Lessons:** 12-1, 12-2, 12-3, 12-4 **Activity Labs:** 12-2a, 12-2b, 12-3b
(7.11) The student understands that the way a set of data is displayed influences its interpretation. The student is expected to	
(A) select and use an appropriate representation for presenting and displaying relationships among collected data, including line plot, line graph, bar graph, stem and leaf plot, circle graph, and Venn diagrams, and justify the selection; and	**Lessons:** 7-7, 11-1, 11-2, 11-3, 11-6 **Activity Labs:** 7-7b, 11-1b, 11-2b, 11-3b, 11-5b, 11-7a

TEKS ★ TAKS in Your Textbook

TEKS	WHERE YOU LEARN
Probability and statistics	
(B) make inferences and convincing arguments based on an analysis of given or collected data.	**Lessons:** 7-7, 9-1, 11-1, 11-2, 11-3, 11-5, 11-6, 12-2 **Activity Labs:** 5-3b, 6-4a, 6-8a, 11-1b, 11-5b, 11-7a, 12-3b **Guided Problem Solving:** Chapters 7, 10, 11, 12
(7.12) The student uses measures of central tendency and range to describe a set of data. The student is expected to	
(A) describe a set of data using mean, median, mode, and range; and	**Lessons:** 1-10, 11-3
(B) choose among mean, median, mode, or range to describe a set of data and justify the choice for a particular situation.	**Lessons:** 1-10, 11-6 **Guided Problem Solving:** Chapter 11

TEKS	WHERE YOU LEARN
Underlying processes and mathematical tools	
(7.13) The student applies Grade 7 mathematics to solve problems connected to everyday experiences, investigations in other disciplines, and activities in and outside of school. The student is expected to	
(A) identify and apply mathematics to everyday experiences, to activities in and outside of school, with other disciplines, and with other mathematical topics;	**Lesson:** 1-1 **Activity Labs:** 5-6b, 9-8b **Guided Problem Solving:** Chapters 1–12 and Application Examples throughout the text
(B) use a problem-solving model that incorporates understanding the problem, making a plan, carrying out the plan, and evaluating the solution for reasonableness;	**Problem Solving Handbook**
(C) select or develop an appropriate problem-solving strategy from a variety of different types, including drawing a picture, looking for a pattern, systematic guessing and checking, acting it out, making a table, working a simpler problem, or working backwards to solve a problem; and	**Problem Solving Handbook** **Guided Problem Solving:** Chapters 1, 2, 3, 4, 6, 9, 10
(D) select tools such as real objects, manipulatives, paper/pencil, and technology or techniques such as mental math, estimation, and number sense to solve problems.	**Lessons:** 1-1, 4-2, 4-5, 5-4, 6-4, 8-6, 12-2 **Activity Labs:** 2-1b, 3-2a, 3-5a, 4-1b, 4-3a, 4-6a, 5-5b, 6-7b, 7-2a, 8-8a, 11-2b, 12-2a, 12-2b

TEKS	WHERE YOU LEARN
Underlying processes and mathematical tools	
(7.14) The student communicates about Grade 7 mathematics through informal and mathematical language, representations, and models. The student is expected to	
(A) communicate mathematical ideas using language, efficient tools, appropriate units, and graphical, numerical, physical, or algebraic mathematical models; and	**Lessons:** 1-5, 1-6, 3-6, 6-1, 8-1, 8-6, 9-5, 9-6, 10-4 **Activity Labs:** 3-4a, 3-7a, 3-7b, 4-2b, 5-5a, 5-6a, 8-2a, 8-10b, 10-5a **Vocabulary Builder:** Chapters 3, 4, 5, 7, 10, 12
(B) evaluate the effectiveness of different representations to communicate ideas.	**Lessons:** 11-1, 11-2 **Activity Labs:** 11-2b, 11-3b
(7.15) The student uses logical reasoning to make conjectures and verify conclusions. The student is expected to	
(A) make conjectures from patterns or sets of examples and nonexamples; and	**Lessons:** 9-2, 9-3 **Activity Labs:** 4-1a, 5-5a, 7-3a, 9-2a, 9-4a **Guided Problem Solving:** Chapter 9
(B) validate his/her conclusions using mathematical properties and relationships.	**Lessons:** 7-3, 7-4, 9-2, 9-3 **Activity Lab:** 1-9b

TEKS ★ in Your Textbook

Grade 7 TAKS Mathematics Objective 1

This objective provides the basic building blocks within the TEKS—**numbers, operations, and quantitative reasoning**—from which all mathematical understanding stems.

As discussed in the *TAKS Information Booklet for Mathematics Grade 7,* students at this level should:

- Understand the value of digits based on their positions in numbers, including rational numbers, in order to read and work with numbers. *See* **TEKS** (7.1)(A).

- Know how to use both negative and positive integers in real-world problem solving. *See* **TEKS** (7.1)(B).

- Understand squares and square roots to work with more abstract expressions and equations. *See* **TEKS** (7.1)(C).

- Use more abstract and complicated numbers as they work with and distinguish among the four basic operations and the order in which they are used. *See* **TEKS** (7.2)(A), (7.2)(B), (7.2)(C), (7.2)(D), (7.2)(E), (7.2)(F).

- Develop a sense of the reasonableness of answers. Quantitative reasoning is knowing when an answer makes sense and is one purpose for rounding numbers to estimate. *See* **TEKS** (7.2)(G).

Texas Assessment of Knowledge and Skills

Where You Practice TAKS Tune-Up features provide ongoing TAKS practice in every lesson and at the end of every chapter.

TAKS OBJECTIVES	WHERE YOU PRACTICE
Obj. 1. The student will demonstrate an understanding of numbers, operations, and quantitative reasoning.	
(7.1) Number, operation, and quantitative reasoning. The student represents and uses numbers in a variety of equivalent forms. The student is expected to	
(A) compare and order integers and positive rational numbers;	**Pages:** 34, 47, 65, 90, 94, 115, 116, 129, 157, 223, 224, 320, 334, 619
(B) convert between fractions, decimals, whole numbers, and percents mentally, on paper, or with a calculator; and	**Pages:** 100, 116, 165, 213, 277, 287, 319, 320, 327, 371, 383, 507, 595, 622
(C) represent squares and square roots using geometric models.	**Pages:** 403, 413, 432, 445, 619
(7.2) Number, operation, and quantitative reasoning. The student adds, subtracts, multiplies, or divides to solve problems and justify solutions. The student is expected to	
(A) represent multiplication and division situations involving fractions and decimals with models, including concrete objects, pictures, words, and numbers;	**Pages:** 17, 23, 64, 116, 123, 129, 145, 163, 164, 172, 241, 293, 301, 522
(B) use addition, subtraction, multiplication, and division to solve problems involving fractions and decimals;	**Pages:** 11, 23, 30, 34, 59, 64, 71, 78, 85, 100, 105, 117, 123, 129, 133, 139, 159, 163, 164, 190, 213, 225, 231, 248, 277, 315, 364, 425, 449, 602, 622
(C) use models, such as concrete objects, pictorial models, and number lines, to add, subtract, multiply, and divide integers and connect the actions to algorithms;	**Pages:** 42, 47, 51, 57, 65, 90, 198, 287, 321, 327, 501, 621
(D) use division to find unit rates and ratios in proportional relationships such as speed, density, price, recipes, and student-teacher ratio;	**Pages:** 7, 235, 241, 248, 255, 265, 270, 357, 475, 529
(E) simplify numerical expressions involving order of operations and exponents;	**Pages:** 51, 64, 71, 157, 204, 271, 483, 522, 564, 621
(F) select and use appropriate operations to solve problems and justify the selections; and	**Pages:** 11, 17, 59, 159, 198, 213, 224, 339, 425, 609
(G) determine the reasonableness of a solution to a problem.	**Pages:** 90, 225, 513, 619, 623

This objective combines the basic algebra concepts within the TEKS—**patterns, relationships, and algebraic thinking.**
As discussed in the *TAKS Information Booklet for Mathematics Grade 7,* students at this level should:

- Estimate, find solutions, describe relationships, and graph data. *See* **TEKS** (7.3)(A), (7.3)(B), (7.4)(B).

- Use proportional relationships to calculate percent in everyday situations. *See* **TEKS** (7.3)(A), (7.3)(B).

- Generate formulas involving conversions. *See* **TEKS** (7.4)(A).

- Understand how terms in a sequence are related. *See* **TEKS** (7.4)(C).

- Use models, expressions with variables, and simple equations to solve problems. *See* **TEKS** (7.5)(A), (7.5)(B).

TAKS OBJECTIVES	WHERE YOU PRACTICE
Obj. 2. The student will demonstrate an understanding of patterns, relationships, and algebraic reasoning.	
(7.3) Patterns, relationships, and algebraic thinking. The student solves problems involving direct proportional relationships. The student is expected to	
(A) estimate and find solutions to application problems involving percent; and	**Pages:** 293, 297, 301, 307, 314, 371, 378, 477, 547, 619, 622, 623
(B) estimate and find solutions to application problems involving proportional relationships such as similarity, scaling, unit costs, and related measurement units.	**Pages:** 30, 65, 94, 248, 255, 263, 265, 271, 283, 321, 339, 344, 371, 408, 556, 589, 621, 622
(7.4) Patterns, relationships, and algebraic thinking. The student represents a relationship in numerical, geometric, verbal, and symbolic form. The student is expected to	
(A) generate formulas involving unit conversions, perimeter, area, circumference, volume, and scaling;	**Pages:** 327, 383, 387, 397, 403, 432, 459, 482, 536, 620, 621, 623
(B) graph data to demonstrate relationships in familiar concepts such as conversions, perimeter, area, circumference, volume, and scaling; and	**Pages:** 440, 459, 481, 482, 494, 507, 527, 528
(C) use words and symbols to describe the relationship between the terms in an arithmetic sequence (with a constant rate of change) and their positions in the sequence.	**Pages:** 445, 455, 475, 482, 528, 570, 619, 621
(7.5) Patterns, relationships, and algebraic thinking. The student uses equations to solve problems. The student is expected to	
(A) use concrete and pictorial models to solve equations and use symbols to record the actions; and	**Pages:** 184, 204, 208, 219, 224, 231, 297, 370, 583, 620
(B) formulate problem situations when given a simple equation and formulate an equation when given a problem situation.	**Pages:** 177, 184, 198, 218, 223, 224, 270, 283, 364, 464, 513

TEKS ★ *TAKS* in Your Textbook

TAKS Texas Assessment of Knowledge and Skills **XXXV**

Grade 7 ⓣₐₖₛ Mathematics Objective 3

This objective combines the fundamental concepts of size and shape found within the TEKS—**geometry and spatial reasoning**—from which all geometric understanding is built.

As discussed in the *TAKS Information Booklet for Mathematics Grade 7,* students at this level should:

- Know how to classify shapes, solids, and pairs of angles. *See* **TEKS** (7.6)(A), (7.6)(B), (7.6)(C).

- Use properties to define similarity. *See* **TEKS** (7.6)(D).

- Learn how to plot points on a coordinate grid using ordered pairs of integers. These concepts build spatial reasoning skills that help develop an understanding of distance, location, area, and volume. *See* **TEKS** (7.7)(A), (7.7)(B), (7.8)(A), (7.8)(B), (7.8)(C).

TAKS OBJECTIVES		WHERE YOU PRACTICE
Obj. 3. The student will demonstrate an understanding of geometry and spatial reasoning.		
(7.6)	**Geometry and spatial reasoning.** The student compares and classifies two- and three-dimensional figures using geometric vocabulary and properties. The student is expected to	
(A)	use angle measurements to classify pairs of angles as complementary or supplementary;	**Pages:** 334, 349, 357, 365, 370, 392, 471, 517, 529, 602, 619
(B)	use properties to classify triangles and quadrilaterals;	**Pages:** 339, 344, 353, 365, 370, 455, 570, 575, 576, 621
(C)	use properties to classify three-dimensional figures, including pyramids, cones, prisms, and cylinders; and	**Pages:** 413, 433, 489, 564, 619, 623
(D)	use critical attributes to define similarity.	**Pages:** 263, 349, 483, 619
(7.7)	**Geometry and spatial reasoning.** The student uses coordinate geometry to describe location on a plane. The student is expected to	
(A)	locate and name points on a coordinate plane using ordered pairs of integers; and	**Pages:** 489, 501, 522, 523, 620
(B)	graph reflections across the horizontal or vertical axis and graph translations on a coordinate plane.	**Pages:** 513, 517, 527, 528
(7.8)	**Geometry and spatial reasoning.** The student uses geometry to model and describe the physical world. The student is expected to	
(A)	sketch three-dimensional figures when given the top, side, and front views;	**Pages:** 431, 613, 621
(B)	make a net (two-dimensional model) of the surface area of a three-dimensional figure; and	**Pages:** 418, 576
(C)	use geometric concepts and properties to solve problems in fields such as art and architecture.	**Pages:** 139, 307, 427, 449, 475, 556

Grade 7 TAKS Mathematics Objective 4

TAKS OBJECTIVES		WHERE YOU PRACTICE
Obj. 4. The student will demonstrate an understanding of the concepts and uses of measurement.		
(7.9) **Measurement.** The student solves application problems involving estimation and measurement. The student is expected to		
(A)	estimate measurements and solve application problems involving length (including perimeter and circumference) and area of polygons and other shapes; and	**Pages:** 365, 378, 383, 387, 392, 397, 427, 431, 432, 529, 536, 620, 621
(C)	estimate measurements and solve application problems involving volume of prisms (rectangular and triangular) and cylinders.	**Pages:** 425, 433, 440, 577, 623

This objective includes the concepts within the TEKS from which students develop an understanding of **measurement**. As discussed in the *TAKS Information Booklet for Mathematics Grade 7,* students at this level should:

- Continue to develop measurement skills by solving application problems involving estimation and measurement. *See* **TEKS** (7.9)(A), (7.9)(C).

- Identify reasonableness of answers and solve more difficult problems. *See* **TEKS** (7.9)(A), (7.9)(C).

TEKS ★ TAKS in Your Textbook

Grade 7 TAKS Mathematics Objective 5

This objective includes the concepts within the TEKS that help students become informed consumers of data and information using their understanding of **probability and statistics**.

As discussed in the *TAKS Information Booklet for Mathematics Grade 7,* students at this level should:

- Use experimental and theoretical probability to make predictions by constructing sample spaces for compound events. See **TEKS** (7.10)(A).

- Select graphical representations for data and make inferences by analyzing the data presented. See **TEKS** (7.11)(A).

- Recognize appropriate and accurate representations of data in everyday situations and in information related to science and social studies. See **TEKS** (7.11)(A).

- Calculate measures of central tendency for real-world applications (for example, average grades, figure sports statistics, and determine election results). See **TEKS** (7.12)(A), (7.12)(B).

TAKS OBJECTIVES	WHERE YOU PRACTICE
Obj. 5. The student will demonstrate an understanding of probability and statistics.	
(7.10) Probability and statistics. The student recognizes that a physical or mathematical model can be used to describe the experimental and theoretical probability of real-life events. The student is expected to	
(A) construct sample spaces for simple or composite experiments.	**Pages:** 595, 602, 609, 615, 623
(7.11) Probability and statistics. The student understands that the way a set of data is displayed influences its interpretation. The student is expected to	
(A) select and use an appropriate representation for presenting and displaying relationships among collected data, including line plot, line graph, bar graph, stem and leaf plot, circle graph, and Venn diagrams, and justify the selection; and	**Pages:** 357, 536, 553, 576
(B) make inferences and convincing arguments based on an analysis of given or collected data.	**Pages:** 109, 117, 269, 270, 319, 320, 369, 370, 471, 542, 547, 556, 564, 570, 571, 575, 577, 589, 615, 620
(7.12) Probability and statistics. The student uses measures of central tendency and range to describe a set of data. The student is expected to	
(A) describe a set of data using mean, median, mode, and range; and	**Pages:** 57, 59, 63, 65, 100, 115, 116, 123, 133, 190, 277, 315, 321, 344, 517, 571, 595, 613, 620, 622
(B) choose among mean, median, mode, or range to describe a set of data and justify the choice for a particular situation.	**Pages:** 145, 177, 235, 433, 622

Grade 7 **TAKS** Mathematics Objective 6

This objective incorporates the **underlying processes and mathematical tools** within the TEKS that are used in finding mathematical solutions to real-world problems.

As discussed in the *TAKS Information Booklet for Mathematics Grade 7,* students at this level should:

- Recognize mathematics as it occurs in real-world problem situations, generalize from mathematical patterns and sets of examples, select an appropriate approach to solving a problem, solve the problem, and then determine whether the answer is reasonable. *See* **TEKS** (7.13)(A), (7.13)(B), (7.13)(C).

- Express problem situations in mathematical language and symbols. This is essential to finding solutions to real-world problems. *See* **TEKS** (7.14)(A).

- Use logical reasoning to make conjectures and verify conclusions. *See* **TEKS** (7.15)(A), (7.15)(B).

TAKS OBJECTIVES	WHERE YOU PRACTICE
Obj. 6. The student will demonstrate an understanding of the mathematical processes and tools used in problem solving.	
(7.13) Underlying processes and mathematical tools. The student applies Grade 7 mathematics to solve problems connected to everyday experiences, investigations in other disciplines, and activities in and outside of school. The student is expected to	
(A) identify and apply mathematics to everyday experiences, to activities in and outside of school, with other disciplines, and with other mathematical topics;	**Pages:** 51, 63, 64, 78, 133, 157, 184, 314, 371, 471, 482, 483, 621, 622
(B) use a problem-solving model that incorporates understanding the problem, making a plan, carrying out the plan, and evaluating the solution for reasonableness; and	**Pages:** 42, 105, 111, 116, 117, 145, 164, 165, 204, 208, 219, 231, 241, 269, 271, 307, 583, 620
(C) select or develop an appropriate problem-solving strategy from a variety of different types, including drawing a picture, looking for a pattern, systematic guessing and checking, acting it out, making a table, working a simpler problem, or working backwards to solve a problem.	**Pages:** 85, 139, 151, 235, 265, 315, 477, 553, 619
(7.14) Underlying processes and mathematical tools. The student communicates about Grade 7 mathematics through informal and mathematical language, representations, and models. The student is expected to	
(A) communicate mathematical ideas using language, efficient tools, appropriate units, and graphical, numerical, physical, or algebraic mathematical models.	**Pages:** 11, 111, 172, 225, 255, 263, 301, 320, 321, 353, 408, 464, 583, 621, 622
(7.15) Underlying processes and mathematical tools. The student uses logical reasoning to make conjectures and verify conclusions. The student is expected to	
(A) make conjectures from patterns or sets of examples and nonexamples; and	**Pages:** 151, 165, 353, 418, 449, 619
(B) validate his/her conclusions using mathematical properties and relationships.	**Pages:** 7, 413, 542, 619

TEKS ★ TAKS in Your Textbook

T47

Differentiate Instruction with Ease

Students develop and learn in different ways at different paces. Accessible content, presented in a variety of formats, acknowledges these unique differences while providing options for learning. The goal of *Prentice Hall Mathematics* is for all students to be successful and for you to have the tools you need to accomplish this. *Prentice Hall Mathematics* Grade 6 through Algebra 2 provides better solutions for meeting the needs of every student in the classroom by achieving two goals:

- Providing superior teacher support materials for planning how to effectively differentiate instruction
- Providing unique resources for the various populations of students.

Differentiated Instruction
Solutions for All Learners

Adapted Resources for Differentiating Instruction

In addition to the support provided in the Teacher's Editions, Prentice Hall has created resources developed uniquely for Below Level and Special Needs students.

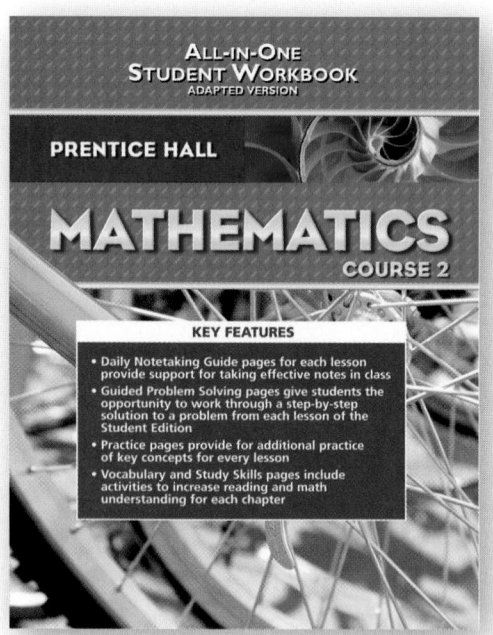

All-in-One Student Workbook Adapted Version

This resource includes adapted practice and adapted daily notetaking worksheets to support special needs students. By providing these critical resources ready for you to use, you can cover the same mathematical content with the students, but provide a more appropriate resource for them to take notes and practice the lesson's mathematics.

Differentiated Assessments

Prentice Hall Mathematics also recognizes the importance of not only differentiating instruction, but also differentiating the assessments used to monitor student progress and inform future instruction. To achieve this, three versions of each chapter test are provided: L2 for Below Level L3 for All Students and L4 for Advanced Learners.

Texas *ExamView* Test Generator

To provide the ultimate flexibility in creating assessments and practice worksheets for all students, the *Texas Prentice Hall Mathematics ExamView* Test Banks contain adapted items written exclusively for your Special Needs and Below Level students. A TAKS Practice Test is also provided.

Texas *Prentice Hall Mathematics* Teacher's Editions offer comprehensive support in differentiating instruction.

L1 Special Needs
L2 Below Level
L3 All Students
L4 Advanced Learners
ELL English Language Learners

Prentice Hall Mathematics uses a consistent method for identifying resources for differentiating instruction. This consistency helps you to easily identify and choose the appropriate resources for your students.

Planning and Using Differentiated Resources

These chapter level support pages provide you an easy-to-read overview of the resources available and suggested ways in the instructional lesson to use the resources. All Texas ancillaries are clearly identified.

Differentiated Instruction

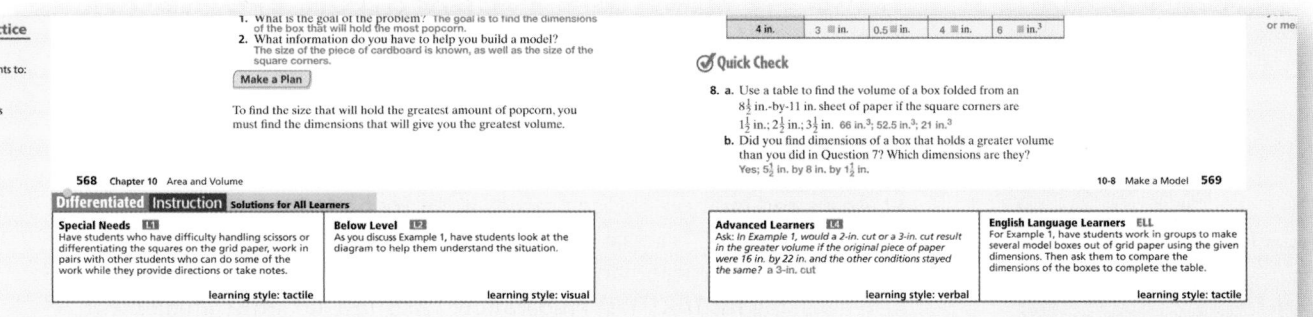

Differentiated Instruction teaching notes

These useful notes help you differentiate the lesson for all learners, including Special Needs, Below Level, Advanced, and English Language Learners.

Assessment to Inform Instruction

Assessment is integral to mathematics instruction. Student assessment should occur often and with a variety of different measures. *Prentice Hall Mathematics* provides an ongoing assessment strand that addresses assessment *for* learning and assessment *of* learning. The formative assessment features (before and during instruction) offer a variety of methods for teachers to assess student understanding and inform future instruction. The summative assessment features (after instruction) document student mastery of mathematical concepts and skills and further prepare students for success in today's tests.

Instant Check System" for Ongoing Assessment

This unique feature of *Prentice Hall Mathematics* ensures that students make progress every day, in every lesson. It helps teachers assess necessary prerequisite skills and monitor student understanding. The Instant Check System™ assessments include:
- Check Your Readiness – Assesses prerequisite skills for each chapter
- Check Skills You'll Need – Assesses prerequisite skills for each lesson
- Quick Check – Assesses student understanding after every example in the book
- Check Point – Assesses understanding after completing lessons

Texas All-in-One
Progress Monitoring Assessments

This comprehensive teacher support resource contains all the program assessments needed to evaluate student understanding, monitor student progress, and inform future instruction. The following assessments are included:
- Pre-Course Screening Test
- Texas Benchmark Tests to document progress at 6-week intervals
- Quarter, Mid-Course, and Final Tests – regular and adapted for special needs
- TAKS Strategy Practice
- TAKS Practice Tests
- Comprehensive Report Forms
- Answers to all of the tests

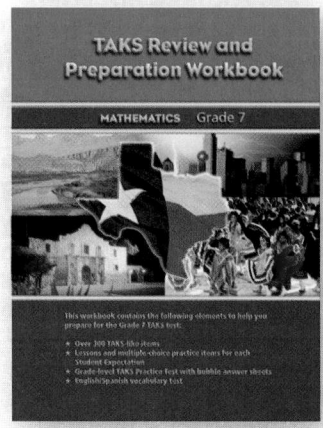

TAKS Review and Preparation Workbook

Prentice Hall Mathematics recognizes how critical it is for teachers to prepare every student for TAKS success.

This workbook contains the following elements to help you prepare students for the Grade 7 TAKS test:
- Over 300 TAKS-like items
- Lessons and multiple-choice practice items for each Student Expectation.
- Grade-level TAKS Practice Test with bubble answer sheets.
- English/Spanish vocabulary list.

Also available for TAKS Test Preparation: TAKS Test-Taking Strategies with Transparencies and TAKS Daily Review Transparencies

Help All Students Become Problem Solvers

One of the major goals of a mathematics program is to develop students' ability to solve problems in class, on assessments, in the context of real-world situations, and outside the classroom. *Prentice Hall Mathematics* helps support this goal by embedding problem-solving instruction in every lesson, providing targeted support for problem-solving strategies throughout the Student Edition, and including sufficient problems to help students practice and reinforce problem solving skills.

Guided Problem Solving Features

These features throughout the Student Edition provide scaffolded support in solving problems. The student walks through how to solve one representative problem, focusing on both the reasoning and the computation that must be done.

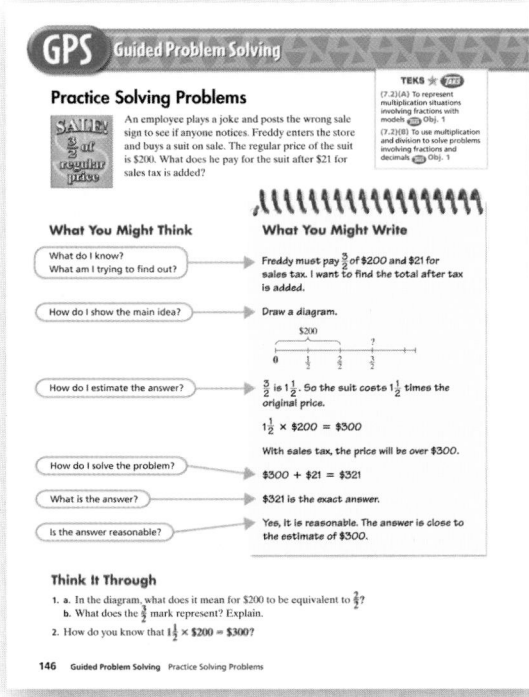

Activities and Activity Labs

Throughout the Student Edition are in-lesson activities and full feature Activity Labs. These provide students an opportunity to complete more in-depth problems and applications of the mathematical content they're learning.

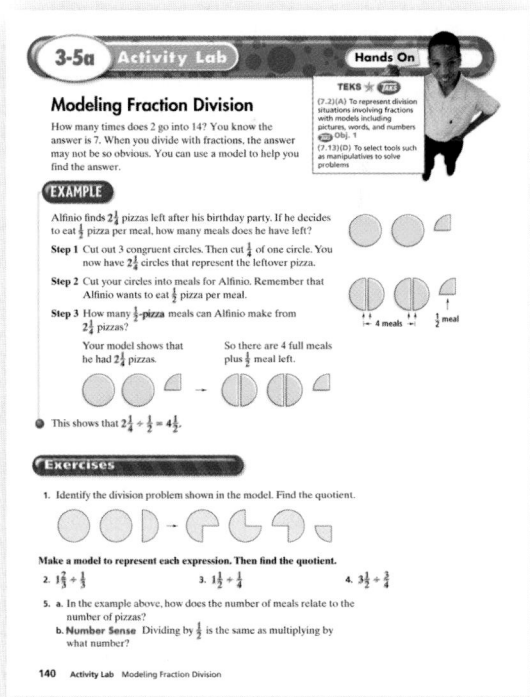

Problem Solving Practice

Every lesson in the Student Edition includes a comprehensive, leveled exercise set. This provides students the opportunity to solve a variety of problems and apply problem solving strategies on a daily basis. Furthermore, additional problems have been added to the end of each book in the Extra Skill and Word Problem Practice section.

Technology — not simply added, but added value

Take Learning to a New Level

Texas Student Express CD-ROM
A suite of learning tools to help students study, learn, and succeed in class. An interactive textbook with instructional videos, built-in activities, vocabulary support, and instant feedback assessments make this the most powerful student study tool available. Interactive Text also available online.

Video Homework Tutor and Online Active Math
Video Homework Tutor provide built-in homework help for every lesson. Narrated by real teachers, these engaging interactive tutorials cover the key concepts of each day's lesson. Additionally, Online Active Math interactive provide an opportunity to explore math concepts.

Use Assessment Technology to Inform Instruction

Texas ExamView 5.0
The most powerful test generator available—with the most comprehensive test banks. Create and modify custom-made tests with ease. Access the Math Art folder to instantly add math images to your questions. Also-instantly translate any test into Spanish. A TAKS Practice Test is also provided.

MindPoint Quiz Show
This creative product allows teachers to involve the entire class in a fun, end-of-chapter review game.

Online at PHSchool.com

Success Tracker" Online
Personalized for each student with individual assessment, diagnosis, and remediation. Color-coded reports make it easy for teachers to monitor progress.

Superior Planning and Teaching Tools

Texas TeacherEXPRESS" CD-ROM
powered by LessonView planning software
An Interactive Teacher's Edition, LessonView planning software, correlations to the Teks, instructional tools, plus professional development to help teachers plan, teach, and assess.

Texas PresentationEXPRESS CD-ROM with QuickTake
This innovative component includes all the transparencies in interactive, PowerPoint format, making it easier for you to teach and to customize based on your teaching preferences. QuickTake assessments are embedded in every lesson, allowing teachers to quickly and easily monitor student progress. Includes Chapter level TAKS items for use with QuickTake.

Worksheets Online
All program worksheets are also conveniently posted online so you and your students can access them anywhere - one more way to make your planning and assignment management easier.

Professional Development
that meets your needs

In-Service On Demand

Now, you have the freedom to access your Prentice Hall in-service training online, anytime, anywhere, at PHSchool.com. This online tutorial library offers in-service training specifically for the Prentice Hall textbook and technology you're teaching with right now.

In-service designed around you!

In-Service On Demand is Prentice Hall's new Web site of in-service training tutorials for your Prentice Hall products. Now you can access the same training for using your Prentice Hall textbook and technology that you would learn in a traditional in-service—from the convenience of your computer!

In-Service for your Prentice Hall program!

The In-Service On Demand library features video-based tutorials to help you maximize the effectiveness of the Prentice Hall program you use. This extensive library is continually being updated with tutorials for Prentice Hall's newest products! Visit the site as often as you like!

In-Service is just a click away!

1. Go to PHSchool.com and click on In-Service On Demand.
2. Select mathematics and then select your *Prentice Hall Mathematics* book.
3. Watch the video-based tutorials and get the in-service training you need when and where it's convenient for you.
4. Download and print PDF tutorial guides on what you've just seen.

Day-to-Day Professional Development

Math Background in Teacher's Edition

Support instruction at the chapter and lesson level as every Chapter of Prentice Hall Mathematics begins with Math Background related to the content of the chapter in both middle school and high school.

Sustained Development of Mathematics Content

Math Across the Grades

Deepen teacher content knowledge as it relates to the PreK–Algebra curriculum, particularly how mathematics concepts and skills are developed across the grades in the Scott Foresman and Prentice Hall Mathematics programs.

Research-Based and Proven Effective

The stakes for mathematics educators are high. You are expected to raise student achievement. Prentice Hall Mathematics programs are backed by efficacy research to give you the confidence to meet this challenge.

In developing Prentice Hall programs, the use of research is a guiding, central construct. This research was conducted in three phases:

1 Exploratory Needs Assessment
(Quantitative and Qualitative)

Key research events include —
- Teacher interviews
- Classroom observations
- Mail surveys
- Reviews of educational research

2 Formative, Prototype Development and Field Testing
(Quantitative and Qualitative)

Key research events include —
- Field testing of prototypes
- Classroom observations
- Teacher reviews
- Supervisor reviews
- Educator advisory panels

3 Summative, Validation Research
(Experimental and Quasi-Experimental Study Designs & Qualitative Research)

Key research events include —
- Pre-publication learner verification research
- Post-publication efficacy studies
- Classroom observations
- Evaluation of in-market results on standardized tests
- Effect size studies

The facing page contains an example of the latest research carried out for Prentice Hall Middle School Mathematics.

2005 Research Results: Prentice Hall Middle School Mathematics

Independent research confirms Middle School students using Prentice Hall Mathematics achieve greater success in mathematics

Results of independent research indicate that students using Prentice Hall Mathematics Course 2 showed significant improvement, outperforming students using other mathematics programs. The randomized control trial, conducted by PRES Associates, Inc., a national educational evaluation firm with central offices in Jackson, WY, confirmed students using the Prentice Hall curricula showed greater improvement from pre- to post-tests than their counterparts using other programs as measured by two different standardized assessments. Improvement was evident on all mathematics objectives measured. Additionally, the program was especially effective with low-performing students.

The study is part of a multi-year research effort commissioned by the publisher and is one of many slated to evaluate the effectiveness of Prentice Hall's educational materials across disciplines and grade levels. Participants represented a mix of urban and urban-fringe districts with diverse socio-economic, ethnic, and academic backgrounds.

Among the key findings, PRES Associates reported:

- Student performance significantly improved from the beginning of the school year to its end as measured by the TerraNova Basic Multiple Assessment, chosen because it is aligned to national NCTM standards and has proven reliability and validity.
- Students using Prentice Hall Mathematics Course 2 improved to a greater extent in pre- to post-test scores than those using other programs.
- Assessment results suggest that Prentice Hall Mathematics Course 2 is particularly effective with low-performing students, as evidenced by the significant gains in low-performing student test scores.
- Prentice Hall Mathematics Course 2 students reported feeling significantly more comfortable with math than students using other programs. They also reported higher math aspirations (i.e., plans to take advanced math in high school).
- Teachers participating in the study reported that Prentice Hall Mathematics Course 2 provided significantly better assistance than other programs in the following areas (1) individualizing instruction, (2) reinforcing previously taught concepts, (3) providing test preparation, and (4) making connections to real-life.
- Teachers identified many aspects of the Prentice Hall program as effective, including the Guided Problem Solving workbook, Check Skills You'll Need exercises, and Check Understanding exercises.

The study was designed to fully meet the evidence criteria put forth by the What Works Clearinghouse, the Federal agency established in 2002 to provide the educators and the public with a trusted source of scientific evidence of what works in education. This study was designed so that accurate and appropriate inferences could be made regarding the effectiveness of the Prentice Hall Mathematics Course 2 program.

Visit PHSchool.com/MathResearch for the full report and additional research in support of Prentice Hall Mathematics programs.

Mathematics Strands

The following 10 strands are from the NCTM Principles and Standards. The Background and Progression sections highlight content students usually have mastered when they enter middle grades and the progression expected using *Prentice Hall Mathematics Courses 1, 2,* and *3*.

Number and Operations

- Understand numbers, ways of representing numbers, relationships among numbers, and number systems
- Understand meanings of operations and how they relate to one another
- Compute fluently and make reasonable estimates

Background and Progression Students usually enter middle grades with computational facility with whole numbers, and varying degrees of mastery of fractions and decimals.

In *Course 1*, students reach mastery of all decimal and fraction operations. They work with percents and develop estimation skills. Concepts of scale and ratio are introduced. (Chapters 1, 5, 6, and 7)

In *Course 2*, students reach mastery of integer operations, rates, and ratios. They work with percent applications and exponents. (Chapters 1, 2, 5, and 6)

In *Course 3*, students reach mastery of percent and proportion applications. They continue to work with exponents, including using square roots. (Chapters 2, 3, and 4)

Algebra

- Understand patterns, relations, and functions
- Represent and analyze mathematical situations and structures using algebraic symbols
- Use mathematical models to represent and understand quantitative relationships
- Analyze change in various contexts

Background and Progression Students usually enter middle grades having represented patterns through words, tables, and graphs. They also have some experience with symbolic representation of unknown quantities.

In *Course 1*, students use variables in equations and patterns. Models are introduced for percents, proportions, integers, and properties of equality. (Chapters 3, 7, and 11)

In *Course 2*, students continue to use models, tables, graphs, and symbolic notation to represent algebraic relationships. They solve equations and interpret the slope of a line. (Chapters 4, 9, and 10)

In *Course 3*, students solve equations and use equivalent forms for expressions containing parentheses, like terms, and exponents. They relate slope and y-intercept to graphs and linear relationships. (Chapters 1, 6, 11, and 12)

Geometry

- Analyze characteristics and properties of two- and three-dimensional geometric shapes and develop mathematical arguments about geometric relationships
- Specify locations and describe spatial relationships using coordinate geometry and other representational systems
- Apply transformations and use symmetry to analyze mathematical situations
- Use visualization, spatial reasoning, and geometric modeling to solve problems

Background and Progression Students entering middle grades have usually mastered names and characteristics of common polygons and simple solids.

In *Course 1*, students use grids, nets, and block diagrams to build concepts of area and volume. They explore symmetry and transformations. The coordinate plane is introduced. (Chapters 8 and 9)

In *Course 2*, students continue to use two-dimensional representations of three-dimensional figures. They study congruent and similar figures and transformations. (Chapters 5, 7, 8, and 10)

In *Course 3*, students draw inferences about lengths, areas, and volumes of similar two- and three-dimensional figures. They study both reflectional and rotational symmetry. (Chapters 3, 7, and 8)

Measurement

- Understand measurable attributes of objects and the units, systems, and processes of measurement
- Apply appropriate techniques, tools, and formulas to determine measurements

Background and Progression Students entering middle grades have usually worked with customary and metric units. They often know formulas for the perimeter and area of simple figures.

In *Course 1*, students choose units, convert units, and estimate measures within the customary and metric systems. They develop and use formulas related to polygons. They explore surface area and volume. (Chapters 6 and 9)

In *Course 2*, students develop and use formulas to find areas of irregular figures, and to find surface area and volume of prisms and cylinders. (Chapters 5 and 8)

In *Course 3*, students continue to convert units. They extend their understanding of formulas to include pyramids, cones, and spheres. (Chapters 4, 7, and 8)

Data Analysis and Probability

- Formulate questions that can be addressed with data and collect, organize, and display relevant data to answer them
- Select and use appropriate statistical methods to analyze data
- Understand and apply basic concepts of probability

Background and Progression Students in middle grades have experience with gathering, displaying, and analyzing data. They have used simple probabilities to express the likelihood of an event.

In *Course 1*, students master measures of central tendency, simple line graphs, bar graphs, and probabilities. They make line plots, circle graphs, and stem-and-leaf plots. (Chapters 2, 7, and 10)

In *Course 2*, students continue to study line plots, stem-and-leaf plots, and bar graphs. They analyze survey techniques for bias, and make scatter plots to analyze data. (Chapter 11)

In *Course 3*, students place and interpret trend lines on scatter plots. They also develop probability concepts for compound events. (Chapters 9 and 10)

Problem Solving

- Build new mathematical knowledge through problem solving
- Solve problems that arise in mathematics and in other contexts
- Apply and adapt a variety of appropriate strategies to solve problems
- Monitor and reflect on the process of mathematical problem solving

Background and Progression *Throughout Prentice Hall Mathematics*, students use a consistent framework for problem solving, which identifies four phases: Understand the Problem, Make a Plan, Carry Out the Plan, Check the Answer.

In each course, students learn specific strategies and apply them to a variety of problems. They practice and apply these strategies through guided problem solving. (Problem Solving Handbook)

Reasoning and Proof

- Recognize reasoning and proof as fundamental aspects of mathematics
- Make and investigate mathematical conjectures
- Develop and evaluate mathematical arguments and proofs
- Select and use various types of reasoning and methods of proof

Background and Progression At the elementary level, students use mathematical reasoning in the development of number sense and classification skills.

In *Prentice Hall Mathematics*, reasoning is an integral part of students' daily work. Every lesson contains a mix of Reasoning, Number Sense, and Error Analysis exercises. Students have the opportunity to explain their thinking using mathematical concepts and properties. Activities throughout the program provide students with opportunities to use inductive reasoning.

Communication

- Organize and consolidate their mathematical thinking through communication
- Communicate their mathematical thinking coherently and clearly to peers, teachers, and others
- Analyze and evaluate the mathematical thinking and strategies of others
- Use the language of mathematics to express mathematical ideas precisely

Background and Progression To effectively communicate mathematically, students need ample opportunity to express math in words, in symbols, through models, and orally.

Prentice Hall Mathematics integrates a vocabulary strand that includes short help tips related to vocabulary and symbols as well as full-page features.

Students also have opportunities to write about mathematics. Many exercises ask students to justify their work, explain a process, or draw a conclusion.

Connections

- Recognize and use connections among mathematical ideas
- Understand how mathematical ideas interconnect and build on one another to produce a coherent whole
- Recognize and apply mathematics in contexts outside of mathematics

Background and Progression By the upper elementary grades, most students are able to distinguish which one of several approaches might be best to solve a problem.

In *Prentice Hall Mathematics*, students use alternative methods in More Than One Way features (every chapter). These situations give a rich mix of numeric, algebraic, geometric, and experimental approaches to problems. Each lesson also includes real-world Examples and exercises that provide contexts in mathematics.

Representation

- Create and use representations to organize, record, and communicate mathematical ideas
- Select, apply, and translate among mathematical representations to solve problems
- Use representations to model and interpret physical, social, and mathematical phenomena

Background and Progression Students entering middle grades have experience using concrete and visual models to help develop number concepts.

In *Prentice Hall Mathematics*, visualization continues with consistent modeling of numbers, operations, and relationships.

Algebraic relationships are represented through tables, patterns, graphs, words, and notation. The use of variables is introduced gradually through the program.

By the end of *Course 3*, students have learned to identify the most appropriate vehicle for presenting data, which means choosing among various types of graphs.

Course 2 Texas Leveled Pacing Chart

This Texas Leveled Pacing Chart is provided as a guide to help you customize your course and to provide for differentiated instruction. This chart covers the content of the book and helps students cover the TEKS they need for success on the TAKS test.

The suggested number of days for each chapter is based on a traditional 45-minute class period and on a 90-minute block period. The total of 160 days of instruction leaves time for assessments, projects, assemblies, or other special days that vary from school to school.

✓ Content to prepare for the TAKS test
✓ Reviews previous year
✓ Content to cover after the TAKS test or for Enrichment

Differentiated Instruction

	TEKS	Core	Advanced
Chapter 1 Decimals and Integers Traditional 17 days Block 9 days			
1-1 Using Estimation Strategies	(7.13)(A), (7.13)(D)	✓	✓
1-2 Adding and Subtracting Decimals	(7.2)(B), (7.2)(G)	✓	✓
Extension: Using Mental Math			✓
1-3a Activity Lab, Hands On: Modeling Decimal Multiplication	(7.2)(A)	✓	✓
1-3 Multiplying Decimals	(7.2)(A), (7.2)(B), (7.2)(G)	✓	✓
1-4a Activity Lab, Hands On: Modeling Decimal Division	(7.2)(A)	✓	✓
1-4 Dividing Decimals	(7.2)(A), (7.2)(B), (7.2)(F)	✓	✓
Guided Problem Solving: Choosing Operations	(7.2)(F), (7.13)(C)	✓	✓
1-5 Measuring in Metric Units	(7.2)(B), (7.3)(B), (7.14)(A)	✓	✓
1-6 Comparing and Ordering Integers	(7.1)(A), (7.14)(A)	✓	✓
Vocabulary Builder: Learning New Math Terms			✓
1-7a Activity Lab, Hands On: Modeling Integer Addition and Subtraction	(7.2)(C)	✓	✓
1-7 Adding and Subtracting Integers	(7.2)(C), (7.2)(F)	✓	✓
1-8a Activity Lab, Hands On: Modeling Integer Multiplication	(7.2)(C), (7.2)(F)	✓	✓
1-8 Multiplying and Dividing Integers	(7.2)(C), (7.2)(F)	✓	✓
1-9 Order of Operations and the Distributive Property	Prepares for (7.2)(E)	✓	
1-9b Activity Lab, Algebra Thinking: Properties and Equality	(7.15)(B)	✓	✓
1-10 Mean, Median, Mode, and Range	(7.12)(A), (7.12)(B)	✓	✓
1-10b Activity Lab, Data Analysis: Box-and-Whisker Plots	Prepares for (8.12)(C)		✓
Using the Problem Solving Plan	(7.13)(B), (7.13)(C)	✓	
Chapter 2 Exponents, Factors, and Fractions Traditional 14 days Block 7 days			
2-1 Exponents and Order of Operations	(7.1)(C), (7.2)(E)	✓	✓
2-1b Activity Lab, Technology: Using a Scientific Calculator	(7.2)(E), (7.13)(D)	✓	✓
2-2a Activity Lab: Divisibility Tests	Prepares for (7.2)(B)	✓	
2-2 Prime Factorization	Prepares for (7.2)(B)	✓	
Guided Problem Solving: Using LCM and GCF	(7.13)(A), (7.13)(C)	✓	✓
2-3 Simplifying Fractions	Prepares for (7.2)(B)	✓	
2-4a Activity Lab, Hands On: Comparing Fractions	(7.1)(A)	✓	✓
2-4 Comparing and Ordering Fractions	(7.1)(A)	✓	✓
2-5 Mixed Numbers and Improper Fractions	Prepares for (7.1)(A)	✓	
2-6a Activity Lab: Comparing Fractions and Decimals	(7.1)(A), (7.1)(B)	✓	✓
2-6 Fractions and Decimals	(7.1)(A), (7.1)(B)	✓	✓
2-6b Activity Lab, Data Analysis: Using Tables to Compare Data	(7.1)(A)	✓	✓
2-7 Rational Numbers	(7.1)(A), (7.1)(B)	✓	✓
2-8 Scientific Notation		✓	✓
Extension: Negative Exponents			✓
Problem Solving Strategy: Draw a Picture	(7.13)(B), (7.13)(C)	✓	✓
Chapter 3 Operations With Fractions Traditional 13 days Block 7 days			
3-1 Estimating With Fractions and Mixed Numbers	Prepares for (7.2)(B)	✓	
Vocabulary Builder: High-Use Academic Words	(7.14)(A)	✓	✓
3-2a Activity Lab, Hands On: Using Fraction Models	(7.2)(B), (7.13)(D)	✓	✓
3-2 Adding and Subtracting Fractions	(7.2)(B), (7.2)(F), (7.2)(G)	✓	✓
3-3 Adding and Subtracting Mixed Numbers	(7.2)(B), (7.2)(F), (7.2)(G)	✓	✓

	TEKS	Core	Advanced
3-4a Activity Lab, Hands On: Modeling Fraction Multiplication	(7.2)(A), (7.14)(A)	✓	✓
3-4 Multiplying Fractions and Mixed Numbers	(7.2)(A), (7.2)(B), (7.2)(F)	✓	✓
3-5a Activity Lab, Hands On; Modeling Fraction Division	(7.2)(A), (7.13)(D)	✓	✓
3-5 Dividing Fractions and Mixed Numbers	(7.2)(A), (7.2)(B), (7.2)(G)	✓	✓
Guided Problem Solving: Practice Solving Problems	(7.2)(A), (7.2)(B)	✓	✓
3-6 Changing Units in the Customary System	(7.2)(B), (7.3)(B), (7.14)(A)	✓	✓
3-6b Activity Lab, Algebra Thinking: Solving Puzzles	(7.2)(F), (7.2)(B)	✓	✓
3-7a Activity Lab: Choosing Appropriate Units	(7.14)(A)	✓	✓
3-7 Precision	(7.2)(B)	✓	✓
3-7b Activity Lab: Estimating in Different Systems	(7.3)(B), (7.14)(A)	✓	✓
Problem Solving Strategy: Look for a Pattern	(7.13)(B), (7.13)(C), (7.15)(A),	✓	✓

Chapter 4 Equations and Inequalities   Traditional 15 days   Block 8 days

	TEKS	Core	Advanced
4-1a Activity Lab: Describing Patterns	(7.15)(A)	✓	✓
4-1 Evaluating and Writing Algebraic Expressions	(7.2)(F), Prepares for (7.5)(B)	✓	✓
4-1b Activity Lab, Technology: Using Spreadsheets	(7.13)(D)	✓	✓
4-2 Using Number Sense to Solve Equations	(7.5)(B), (7.13)(D)	✓	✓
4-2b Activity Lab, Algebra Thinking: Keeping the Balance	(7.14)(A), Prepares for (7.5)(A)	✓	✓
4-3a Activity Lab, Hands On: Modeling Equations	(7.5)(A), (7.13)(D)	✓	✓
4-3 Solving Equations by Adding or Subtracting	(7.5)(A), (7.5)(B)	✓	✓
Vocabulary Builder: High-Use Academic Words	(7.14)(A)	✓	✓
4-4 Solving Equations by Multiplying or Dividing	(7.5)(A), (7.5)(B)	✓	✓
Guided Problem Solving: Practice Solving Problems	(7.5)(A), (7.13)(C)	✓	✓
4-5 Exploring Two-Step Problems	(7.5)(A), (7.5)(B), (7.13)(D)	✓	✓
4-6a Activity Lab, Hands On: Modeling Two-Step Equations	(7.5)(A), (7.13)(D)	✓	✓
4-6 Solving Two-Step Equations	(7.5)(A), (7.5)(B)	✓	✓
4-7 Graphing and Writing Inequalities		✓	✓
4-8a Activity Lab, Data Analysis: Inequalities in Bar Graphs		✓	✓
4-8 Solving Inequalities by Adding and Subtracting		✓	✓
4-9 Solving Inequalities by Multiplying and Dividing		✓	✓
Problem Solving Strategy: Systematic Guess and Check	(7.13)(B), (7.13)(C), (7.15)(B)	✓	✓

Chapter 5 Ratios, Rates, and Proportions   Traditional 12 days   Block 6 days

	TEKS	Core	Advanced
5-1 Ratios	(7.2)(D), (7.3)(B)	✓	✓
5-2 Unit Rates and Proportional Reasoning	(7.2)(D), (7.2)(G), (7.3)(B)	✓	✓
Extension: Using Conversion Factors			✓
5-3 Proportions	(7.2)(D), (7.3)(B)	✓	✓
5-3b Activity Lab, Algebra Thinking: Interpreting Rates Visually	(7.11)(B)	✓	✓
5-4a Activity Lab, Data Collection: Using Proportions With Data	(7.2)(D), (7.3)(B)	✓	✓
5-4 Solving Proportions	(7.2)(D), (7.3)(B), (7.13)(D)	✓	✓
Guided Problem Solving: Proportions and Equations	(7.2)(D), (7.3)(B)	✓	✓
5-5a Activity Lab, Hands On: Exploring Similar Figures	(7.6)(D), (7.14)(A), (7.15)(A)	✓	✓
5-5 Using Similar Figures	(7.3)(B), (7.6)(D)	✓	✓
5-5b Activity Lab, Technology: Drawing Similar Figures	(7.6)(D), (7.13)(D)	✓	✓
Vocabulary Builder: Learning Vocabulary		✓	✓
5-6a Activity Lab, Hands On: Scale Drawings and Models	(7.3)(B), (7.4)(A), (7.8)(C)	✓	✓
5-6 Maps and Scale Drawings	(7.3)(B), (7.4)(A), (7.8)(C)	✓	✓
5-6b Activity Lab: Plan a Trip	(7.3)(B), (7.13)(A)		✓
Problem Solving Strategy: Act It Out	(7.13)(B), (7.13)(C), (7.15)(B)	✓	✓

Chapter 6 Percents   Traditional 13 days   Block 6 days

	TEKS	Core	Advanced
6-1 Understanding Percents	(7.1)(B), (7.14)(A)	✓	✓
6-2a Activity Lab, Hands On: Rational Number Cubes	(7.1)(A), Prepares for (7.1)(B)	✓	✓
6-2 Percents, Fractions, and Decimals	(7.1)(A), (7.1)(B)	✓	✓
6-3 Percents Greater Than 100% or Less Than 1%	(7.1)(B), (7.3)(A)	✓	✓
6-4a Activity Lab, Data Analysis: Using Percent Data in a Graph	(7.3)(A), (7.11)(B)	✓	✓
6-4 Finding a Percent of a Number	(7.1)(B), (7.3)(A), (7.13)(D)	✓	✓

	TEKS	Core	Advanced
6-5 Solving Percent Problems Using Proportions	(7.3)(A), (7.3)(B)	✓	✓
6-6 Solving Percent Problems Using Equations	(7.1)(B), (7.3)(A)	✓	✓
Guided Problem Solving: Solving Percent Problems	(7.1)(B), (7.3)(A)	✓	✓
6-7 Applications of Percent	(7.1)(B), (7.3)(A)	✓	✓
6-7b Activity Lab, Algebra Thinking: Percent Equations	(7.13)(D)	✓	✓
6-8a Activity Lab, Data Analysis: Exploring Percent of Change	(7.3)(A), (7.11)(B)	✓	✓
6-8 Finding Percent of Change	(7.1)(B), (7.3)(A)	✓	✓
Problem Solving Strategy: Make a Table	(7.13)(B), (7.13)(C), (7.15)(B)	✓	✓

Chapter 7 Geometry   Traditional 13 days   Block 6 days

	TEKS	Core	Advanced
7-1 Lines and Planes	Prepares for (7.6)(A)	✓	
Vocabulary Builder: High-Use Academic Words	(7.14)(A)	✓	✓
7-2a Activity Lab, Hands On: Measuring Angles	(7.13)(D), Prepares for (7.6)(A)	✓	✓
7-2 Identifying and Classifying Angles	(7.6)(A)	✓	✓
7-3a Activity Lab, Hands On: Sides and Angles of a Triangle	(7.15)(A), Prepares for (7.6)(B)	✓	✓
7-3 Triangles	(7.6)(B), (7.8)(C), (7.15)(B)	✓	✓
7-4 Quadrilaterals and Other Polygons	(7.6)(B), (7.8)(C)	✓	✓
7-5 Congruent Figures	(7.6)(D), (7.8)(C)	✓	✓
7-6 Circles	Prepares for (7.9)(A)	✓	
7-7 Circle Graphs	(7.11)(A), (7.11)(B)	✓	✓
Guided Problem Solving: Percents and Circle Graphs	(7.3)(A), (7.11)(B)	✓	✓
7-7b Activity Lab, Data Collection: Making a Circle Graph	(7.11)(A)	✓	✓
7-8 Constructions			✓
Problem Solving Strategy: Work a Simpler Problem	(7.13)(B), (7.13)(C), (7.15)(A)	✓	✓

Chapter 8 Measurement   Traditional 16 days   Block 8 days

	TEKS	Core	Advanced
8-1 Estimating Perimeter and Area	(7.9)(A), (7.8)(C), (7.14)(A)	✓	✓
8-2a Activity Lab, Hands On: Generating Formulas for Area	(7.4)(A), (7.14)(A)	✓	✓
8-2 Area of a Parallelogram	(7.4)(A), (7.9)(A)	✓	✓
8-3 Perimeter and Area of a Triangle	(7.4)(A), (7.9)(A)	✓	✓
8-4 Areas of Other Figures	(7.4)(A), (7.9)(A)	✓	✓
8-5a Activity Lab, Hands On: Modeling a Circle	(7.4)(A)	✓	✓
8-5 Circumference and Area of a Circle	(7.8)(C), (7.9)(A)	✓	✓
Guided Problem Solving: Areas of Irregular Figures	(7.9)(A)	✓	✓
8-6 Square Roots and Irrational Numbers	(7.1)(C), (7.13)(D), (7.14)(A)	✓	✓
8-7a Activity Lab, Hands On: Exploring Right Triangles		✓	✓
8-7 The Pythagorean Theorem	Prepares for (8.9)(A)		✓
8-8a Activity Lab, Hands On: Three Views of an Object	(7.8)(A), (7.13)(D)	✓	✓
8-8 Three-Dimensional Figures	(7.6)(C), (7.8)(C)	✓	✓
8-9 Surface Areas of Prisms and Cylinders	(7.8)(B), Prepares for (8.8)(C)	✓	✓
Extension: Patterns in 3-Dimensional Figures			✓
8-10 Volumes of Prisms and Cylinders	(7.9)(B), (7.9)(C)	✓	✓
8-10b Activity Lab, Hands On: Generating Formulas for Volume	(7.4)(A), (7.14)(A)	✓	✓
Problem Solving Strategy: Work Backward	(7.13)(B), (7.13)(C), (7.15)(B)	✓	✓

Chapter 9 Patterns and Rules   Traditional 13 days   Block 6 days

	TEKS	Core	Advanced
9-1a Activity Lab, Data Analysis: Scales and Intervals	(7.4)(B)	✓	✓
9-1 Patterns and Graphs	(7.4)(B), (7.11)(B)	✓	✓
9-2a Activity Lab, Hands On: Finding Patterns	(7.4)(C), (7.15)(A)	✓	✓
9-2 Number Sequences	(7.4)(C), (7.15)(A)	✓	✓
9-3 Patterns and Tables	(7.4)(C), (7.15)(A), (7.15)(B)	✓	✓
9-4a Activity Lab: Generating Formulas From a Table	(7.4)(A), (7.15)(A)	✓	✓
9-4 Function Rules	Prepares for (A.1)(C)		✓
9-5 Using Tables, Rules, and Graphs	(7.4)(B), (7.5)(B), (7.14)(A)	✓	✓

	TEKS	Core	Advanced
9-5b Activity Lab, Technology: Three Views of a Function			✓
9-6 Interpreting Graphs	(7.4)(B), (7.14)(A)	✓	✓
Guided Problem Solving: Practice Solving Problems	(7.13)(C), (7.15)(A)	✓	✓
9-7 Simple and Compound Interest		✓	✓
9-8 Transforming Formulas		✓	✓
9-8b Activity Lab, Algebra Thinking: More About Formulas	(7.13)(A)	✓	✓
Problem Solving Strategy: Write an Equation	(7.13)(B), (7.13)(C), (7.15)(B)	✓	✓
Chapter 10 Graphing in the Coordinate Plane Traditional 12 days Block 6 days			
10-1 Graphing Points in Four Quadrants	(7.7)(A)	✓	✓
10-1b Activity Lab: Geometry in the Coordinate Plane	(7.7)(A), (7.9)(A)	✓	✓
10-2 Graphing Linear Equations		✓	✓
Guided Problem Solving: Practice Solving Problems	(7.11)(B), (7.13)(A)	✓	✓
10-2b Activity Lab, Data Analysis: Representing Data	(7.4)(B)	✓	✓
10-3 Finding the Slope of a Line			✓
10-3b Activity Lab, Technology: Exploring Slope			✓
10-4 Graphing Nonlinear Relationships	(7.4)(B), (7.14)(A)	✓	✓
Vocabulary Builder: High-Use Academic Words	(7.14)(A)	✓	✓
10-5a Activity Lab: Slides, Flips, and Turns	(7.14)(A), Prepares for (7.7)(B)	✓	✓
10-5 Translations	(7.7)(A), (7.7)(B)	✓	✓
10-6 Line Symmetry and Reflections	(7.7)(A), (7.7)(B)	✓	✓
Extension: Exploring Tessellations			✓
10-7 Rotational Symmetry and Rotations			✓
Chapter 11 Displaying and Analyzing Data Traditional 12 days Block 6 days			
11-1 Reporting Frequency	(7.11)(A), (7.11)(B), (7.14)(B)	✓	✓
11-1b Activity Lab: Venn Diagrams	(7.11)(A), (7.11)(B)	✓	✓
11-2 Spreadsheets and Data Displays	(7.11)(A), (7.11)(B)	✓	✓
11-2b Activity Lab, Technology: Graphing Using Spreadsheets	(7.11)(A), (7.13)(D), (7.14)(B)	✓	✓
11-3 Stem-and-Leaf Plots	(7.11)(A), (7.11)(B), (7.12)(A)	✓	✓
11-3b Activity Lab, Data Analysis: Choosing the Best Display	(7.11)(A)	✓	✓
11-4a Activity Lab, Data Collection: Writing Survey Questions			✓
11-4 Random Samples and Surveys			✓
11-5 Estimating Population Size	(7.3)(B), (7.11)(B)	✓	✓
Guided Problem Solving: Describing Data	(7.11)(B), (7.12)(B)	✓	✓
11-5b Activity Lab, Data Analysis: Graphing Population Data	(7.11)(A), (7.11)(B)	✓	✓
11-6 Using Data to Persuade	(7.11)(A), (7.11)(B), (7.12)(B)	✓	✓
11-7a Activity Lab, Data Collection: Two Variable Data Collection	(7.11)(A), (7.11)(B)	✓	✓
11-7 Exploring Scatter Plots	Prepares for (8.12)(B)		✓
Chapter 12 Using Probability Traditional 10 days Block 5 days			
12-1 Probability	(7.1)(B), (7.10)(B)		
Extension: Odds			✓
12-2a Activity Lab, Hands On: Exploring Experimental Probability	(7.10)(B), (7.13)(D)	✓	✓
12-2 Experimental Probability	(7.10)(B), (7.11)(B), (7.13)(D)	✓	✓
12-2b Activity Lab, Technology: Random Numbers	(7.10)(B), (7.13)(D)	✓	✓
12-3 Sample Spaces	(7.10)(A), (7.10)(B)	✓	✓
12-3b Activity Lab, Data Analysis: Using Data to Predict	(7.10)(A), (7.10)(B), (7.11)(B)	✓	✓
12-4a Activity Lab, Hands On: Exploring Multiple Events	(7.10)(A)	✓	✓
12-4 Compound Events	(7.10)(A), (7.10)(B)	✓	✓
Vocabulary Builder: High-Use Academic Words	(7.14)(A)	✓	✓
Guided Problem Solving: Practice With Probability	(7.11)(B), (7.13)(A)	✓	✓
12-5 Permutations			✓
12-6 Combinations			✓

Using Your Book for Success

Welcome to *Prentice Hall Course 2*. There are many features built into the daily lessons of this text that will help you learn the important skills and concepts you will need to be successful in this course. Look through the following pages for some study tips that you will find useful as you complete each lesson.

Getting Ready to Learn

Check Your Readiness

Complete the *Check Your Readiness* exercises to see what topics you may need to review before you begin the chapter.

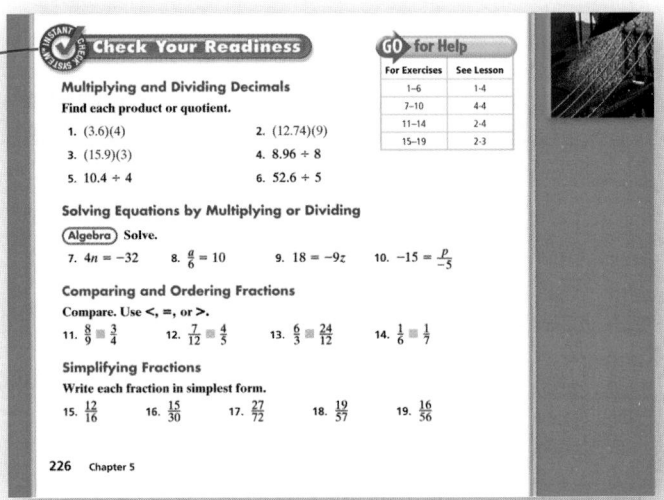

Check Skills You'll Need

Complete the *Check Skills You'll Need* exercises to make sure you have the skills needed to successfully learn the concepts in the lesson.

New Vocabulary

New Vocabulary is listed for each lesson, so you can pre-read the text. As each term is introduced, it is highlighted in yellow.

Built-In Help

Go for Help

Look for the green labels throughout your book that tell you where to "Go" for help. You'll see this built-in help in the lessons and in the homework exercises.

Video Tutor Help

Go online to see engaging videos to help you better understand important math concepts.

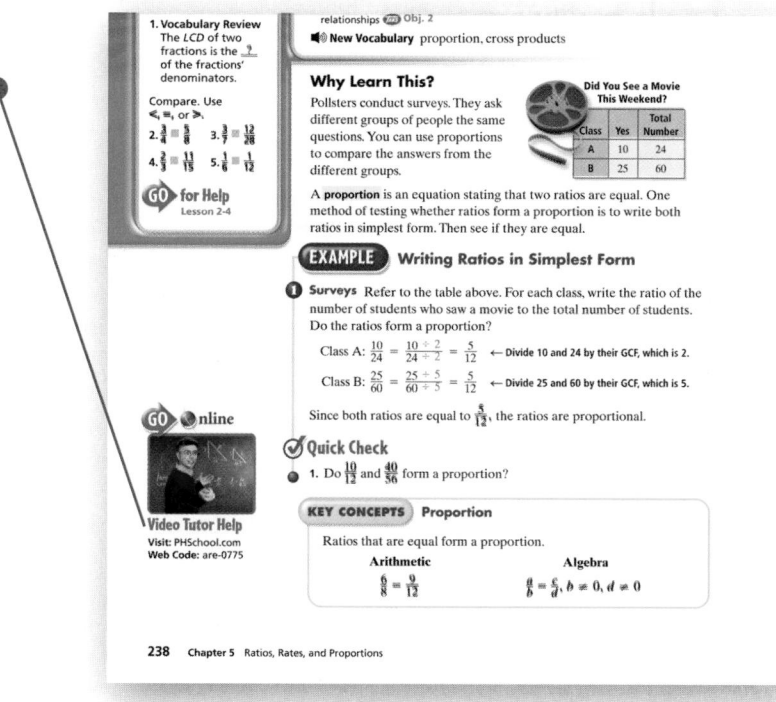

Understanding the Mathematics

Quick Check

Every lesson includes numerous examples, each followed by a *Quick Check* question that you can do on your own to see if you understand the skill being introduced. Check your progress with the answers at the back of the book.

Understanding Key Concepts

Frequent *Key Concept* boxes summarize important definitions, formulas, and properties. Use these to review what you've learned.

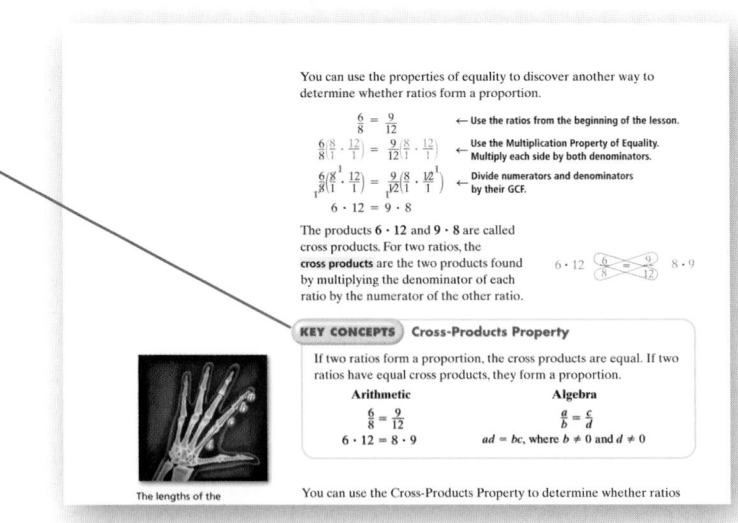

Online Active Math

Make math come alive with these online activities. Review and practice important math concepts with these engaging online tutorials.

Vocabulary Support

Understanding mathematical vocabulary is an important part of studying mathematics. *Vocabulary Tips* and *Vocabulary Builders* throughout the book help focus on the language of math.

Understanding the Mathematics

Guided Problem Solving

These features throughout your Student Edition provide practice in problem solving. Solved from a student's point of view, this feature focuses on the thinking and reasoning that goes into solving a problem.

Activity Labs

Activity Labs throughout the book give you an opportunity to explore a concept. Apply the skills you've learned in these engaging activities.

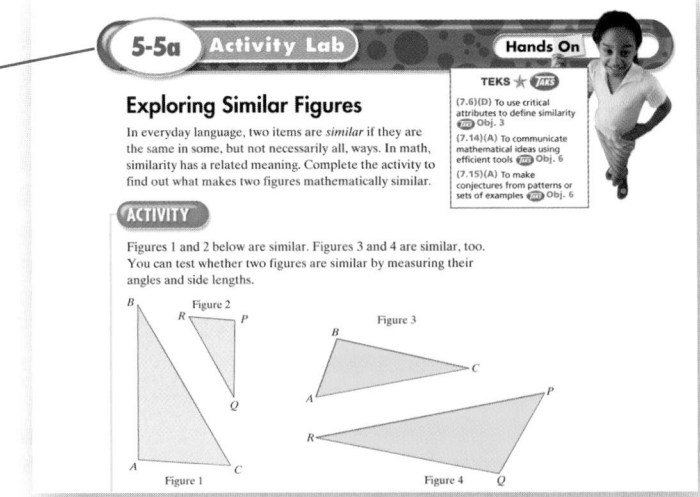

Practice What You've Learned

There are numerous exercises in each lesson that give you the practice you need to master the concepts in the lesson. The following exercises are included in each lesson.

Check Your Understanding

These exercises help you prepare for the Homework Exercises.

Practice by example

These exercises refer you back to the Examples in the lesson, in case you need help with completing these exercises.

Apply your skills

These exercises combine skills from earlier lessons to offer you richer skill exercises and multi-step application problems.

Challenge

This exercise gives you an opportunity to extend and stretch your thinking.

TAKS Tune-Up

TAKS Tune-Up exercises give you daily practice with the types of test question formats that you will encounter on the *TAKS* test.

Intervention This Diagnostic Test covers pre-course skills that students need to succeed in this math program. For intervention, direct students to the following pages from the Skills Handbook in the back of their textbooks.

Exercise	Page
1, 2	658
3, 4	659
5–7	654
8	655
9–11	660
12–14	661
15–18	662
19–22	663
23–27	664
28–33	665
34–37	666

Beginning-of-Course Diagnostic Test

1. Write the value of the underlined digit in 523.6<u>5</u>4.

2. Write the value of the underlined digit in 402.<u>6</u>59.

3. Write a number for fifty-one and six thousandths.

4. Write 7.325 in words.

Use < or > to compare the whole numbers.

5. 2,648 ▨ 264

6. 625 ▨ 6,250

7. 42,509 ▨ 42,709

8. Round 75,845 to the nearest thousand.

9. Round 256.24 to the nearest whole number.

10. Round 546.256 to the nearest tenth.

11. Round 2.5879 to the nearest hundredth.

Multiply.

12. 4.6
   $\times\ 0.7$

13. 0.421
   $\times\ 5.6$

14. 3.08×12.4

15. 0.7
   $\times\ 0.02$

16. 0.032×0.06

17. 0.28×0.07

18. 0.06×0.2

1. 5 hundreths

2. 6 tenths

3. 51.006

4. seven and three hundred twenty-five thousandths

5. >

6. <

Divide.

19. $5\overline{)10.16}$

20. $13\overline{)34.918}$

21. $27.05 \div 2$

22. $0.036 \div 24$

Multiply.

23. $0.07 \times 1,000$

24. 478.24×0.01

25. 0.001×0.04

26. $0.9 \times 1,000$

27. 6.04×0.01

Divide.

28. $0.832 \div 0.26$

29. $0.5031 \div 0.039$

30. $0.42\overline{)0.273}$

31. $0.03\overline{)0.144}$

32. $0.00027 \div 0.18$

33. $0.018 \div 0.9$

Add or subtract. Write the answer in simplest form.

34. $\dfrac{5}{9} + \dfrac{2}{9}$ 35. $\dfrac{7}{12} - \dfrac{3}{12}$

36. $5\dfrac{4}{8} + 4\dfrac{6}{8}$ 37. $4\dfrac{8}{10} - 2\dfrac{6}{10}$

15. 0.014
16. 0.00192
17. 0.0196
18. 0.012
19. 2.032
20. 2.686
21. 13.525
22. 0.0015
23. 70
24. 4.7824
25. 0.00004
26. 900
27. 0.0604
28. 3.2
29. 12.9
30. 0.65
31. 4.8
32. 0.0015
33. 0.02
34. $\dfrac{7}{9}$
35. $\dfrac{1}{3}$
36. $10\dfrac{1}{4}$
37. $2\dfrac{1}{5}$

Diagnostic Test

7. $<$
8. 76,000
9. 256
10. 546.3
11. 2.59
12. 3.22
13. 2.3576
14. 38.192

Using the Problem Solving Plan

Throughout this text, students will be encouraged to use the four-step problem-solving plan that is outlined in this lesson. This approach gives students a simple yet effective framework for organizing their work in the process of solving a problem. Rather than having students haphazardly approach the task of problem solving, this four-step plan gives them an organized procedure to follow for a wide range of problems.

Guided Instruction

Students should remember these key phrases: Understand the Problem; Make a Plan; Carry out the Plan; Check for Reasonableness.

Call attention to the list of problem-solving strategies in the text. Ask for an example of each.

Have students brainstorm strategies that they can use to solve real-world problems such as Make a Table. Write up their ideas on poster board and display them in the room for students' reference.

Error Prevention!

Students often focus on one condition of a problem and forget another. Stress the importance of checking that a proposed solution satisfies all the conditions of the problem.

TEKS **TAKS**

(7.13)(B) To use a problem-solving model that incorporates understanding the problem, making a plan, carrying out the plan, and evaluating the solution for reasonableness **TAKS** Obj. 6

(7.13)(C) To select or develop an appropriate problem-solving strategy **TAKS** Obj. 6

USING THE Problem Solving Plan

One of the most important skills you can have is the ability to solve problems. An integral part of learning mathematics is how adept you become at unraveling problems and looking back to see how you found the solution. Maybe you don't realize it, but you solve problems every day—some problems are easy to solve, and others are challenging and require a good plan of action. In this Problem Solving Handbook you will learn how to work though mathematical problems using a simple four-step plan:

THE 4-STEP PLAN

1. **Understand** **Understand the problem.**
   Read the problem. Ask yourself, "What information is given? What is missing? What am I being asked to find or to do?"

2. **Plan** **Make a plan to solve the problem.**
   Choose a strategy. As you use problem solving strategies throughout this book, you will decide which one is best for the problem you are trying to solve.

3. **Carry Out** **Carry out the plan.**
   Solve the problem using your plan. Organize your work.

4. **Check** **Check the answer to be sure it is reasonable.**
   Look back at your work and compare it against the information and question(s) in the problem. Ask yourself, "Is my answer reasonable? Did I check my work?"

Problem Solving Strategies

Creating a good plan to solve a problem means that you will need to choose a strategy. What is the best way to solve that challenging problem? Perhaps drawing a diagram or making a table will lead to a solution. A problem may seem to have too many steps. Maybe working a simpler problem is the key. There are a number of strategies to choose from. You will decide which strategy is most effective.

As you work through this book, you will encounter many opportunities to improve your problem solving and reasoning skills. Working through mathematical problems using this four-step process will help you to organize your thoughts, develop your reasoning skills, and explain how you arrived at a particular solution.

Putting this problem solving plan to use will allow you to work through mathematical problems with confidence. Getting in the habit of planning and strategizing for problem solving will result in success in future math courses and high scores on those really important tests!

Good Luck!

THE STRATEGIES

Here are some examples of problem solving strategies. Which one will work best for the problem you are trying to solve?

- **Draw a Picture**
- **Look for a Pattern**
- **Systematic Guess and Check**
- **Act It Out**
- **Make a Table**
- **Work a Simpler Problem**
- **Work Backward**
- **Write an Equation**

Data Analysis Connection
Point out that problem-solving strategies are used to solve many types of problems, mathematical and non-mathematical.
Ask questions such as:
- *What are some real-world problems that scientists, mathematicians, professional athletes and coaches, or other professionals might need to analyze?* Accept all reasonable answers.

Differentiated Instruction

Visual Learners
To help students remember the four steps of the Problem-Solving Plan, display these phrases on a poster and have students suggest graphics to illustrate each. For instance, they might suggest a telescope to signal Check for Reasonableness.

TEKS ★ TAKS Resources

Dana Center TEKS Toolkit Clarifying Activities (7.13)(B), (7.13)(C)
Visit: PHSchool.com
Web Code: aqq-9045

Draw a Picture

The *Draw a Picture* strategy often helps students to clarify relationships among the numbers in a problem and to see the conditions of the problem more clearly.

Guided Instruction

Explain to students that a picture could be a table, diagram, or sketch. Different pictures are better for different situations, so students will have to choose the most appropriate picture to use to help them solve the problem.

Have volunteers read the text. Call attention to the problem solving steps:
• Understand the Problem
• Make a Plan
• Carry Out the Plan
• Check the Answer

Ask students questions such as:
• *What other kinds of pictures could you use to help you solve this problem?*
• *Could you solve this problem without a picture? How does the picture help you?*

TEKS ★ TAKS Resources

Dana Center TEKS Toolkit Clarifying Activities (7.13)(B), (7.13)(C)
Visit: PHSchool.com
Web Code: aqq-9045

TEKS ★ TAKS
(7.13)(B) To use a problem-solving model that incorporates understanding the problem, making a plan, carrying out the plan, and evaluating the solution for reasonableness **TAKS Obj. 6**
(7.13)(C) To select or develop an appropriate problem-solving strategy, including looking for a pattern **TAKS Obj. 6**

Draw a Picture

When to Use This Strategy You can *Draw a Picture* to show a problem visually. A picture often helps you understand a problem better.

A worm is trying to escape from a well 10 ft deep. The worm climbs up 2 ft per day, but each night it slides back 1 ft. How many days will the worm take to climb out of the well?

Understand The total distance to travel is 10 ft. The worm gains 2 ft during the day, but loses 1 ft each night. The goal is to find out how many days the worm will take to get out of the well.

Plan Draw a picture to track the worm's position from day to day.

Carry Out
The worm reaches 10 ft and climbs out of the well at the end of the ninth day.

Worm's Progress

Check You might think that the worm progresses 1 ft each day and so needs 10 days to escape. The worm does move a total of 1 ft each day, except on the ninth day. On the ninth day, it climbs 2 ft to the edge of the well.

● Practice

1. Suppose the worm in the example above climbs up 3 ft per day and slides back 2 ft per night. How many days will it take for the worm to climb out of the 10-ft well?

2. You schedule the games for your basketball league's tournament. If a team loses a game, it is eliminated. There are 32 teams. How many games do you need to schedule to determine the league champion?

3. There are 10 girls and 8 boys in a club. The club advisor can send one boy and one girl to a conference. How many different pairs of students can go to the conference?

1. 8 days

2. 31 games

3. 80 pairs

TEKS ★ TAKS

(7.13)(B) To use a problem-solving model that incorporates understanding the problem, making a plan, carrying out the plan, and evaluating the solution for reasonableness TAKS Obj. 6

(7.13)(C) To select or develop an appropriate problem-solving strategy, including looking for a pattern TAKS Obj. 6

(7.15)(A) To make conjectures from patterns or sets of examples TAKS Obj. 6

(7.15)(B) To validate his/her conclusions using mathematical properties and relationships TAKS Obj. 6

Look for a Pattern

When to Use This Strategy Certain problems allow you to look at similar cases. You can *Look for a Pattern* in the solutions of these cases to solve the original problem.

Geometry What is the sum of the measures of the angles of a 12-sided polygon?

Understand The goal is to find the sum of the measures of the angles of a 12-sided polygon. The sum of the measures in a triangle is 180°.

Plan Draw polygons with 3, 4, 5, and 6 sides. Divide each polygon into triangles by drawing diagonals from one vertex. Look for a pattern.

Carry Out The diagrams below show polygons divided into triangles.

3 sides	4 sides	5 sides	6 sides

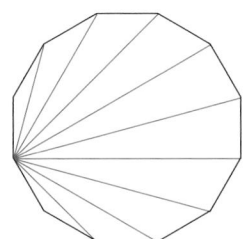

The number of triangles formed is two less than the number of sides of the polygon. This means that the sum of the measures of the angles of each polygon is the number of triangles times 180°. For a 12-sided polygon, the number of triangles is $12 - 2 = 10$. The sum of the measures of the angles is $10 \times 180° = 1,800°$.

Check Draw a diagram to check that exactly ten triangles are formed when you draw diagonals from one vertex of a 12-sided polygon.

● Practice

1. The figure at the right shows a pattern of black and white tiles. How many black tiles will you need for nine rows?

2. The figure at the left has four rows of small triangles. How many small triangles will you need for eight rows?

3. In a 3×3 grid, there are 14 squares of different sizes. There are nine 1×1 squares, four 2×2 squares, and one 3×3 square. How many squares of different sizes are in a 5×5 grid?

Problem Solving Handbook li

Look For a Pattern

Patterns are fundamental to all of mathematics. *Look for a Pattern* is a good problem-solving strategy to use when teaching about number patterns, sequences, and similarities among geometric figures.

Guided Instruction

Tell students that when a problem asks them to analyze numerical or geometric relationships, they can use the strategy of looking for a pattern.

Have students read the problem and list the problem-solving steps they will use:
- Understand the Problem
- Make a Plan
- Carry Out the Plan
- Check the Answer

Some students may find making a table helpful.

Error Prevention!

Students may divide 12 by 3 and multiply this result of 4 by 180° to find the sum of the angles for a 12-sided polygon. This falsely assumes that only 4 triangles form the 12-sided polygon. This further emphasizes the need to draw a diagram.

1. 45 black tiles

2. 64 small triangles

3. 55 squares

TEKS ★ TAKS Resources

Dana Center TEKS Toolkit Clarifying Activities (7.13)(B), (7.13)(C), (7.15)(A), (7.15)(B)
Visit: PHSchool.com
Web Code: arq-9045

Problem Solving Handbook

Systematic Guess and Check

For the *Systematic Guess and Check* strategy, students make a reasonable estimate of the answer, check if the estimate satisfies the conditions of the problem, and change the number, if necessary. Students arrive at the correct solution by making increasingly more reasonable guesses.

Guided Instruction

Discuss with students how to complete a jigsaw puzzle. Talk about what to do if the piece does not fit properly in the jigsaw puzzle, that is, going back and trying another piece until one is found that does fit.

Elicit the problem solving steps:
• Understand the Problem
• Make a Plan
• Carry Out the Plan
• Check the Answer

Example

Discuss the triangular shape of the sails. Ask questions, such as:
• What other shape sails have you seen?
• Where did you see them?
• What have you noticed about the size of the sail and the size of the boat?
• Why do you suppose there is a relationship between them?

Practice

Remind students to use the result of the first time they check an answer to improve subsequent guesses.

TEKS ★ TAKS Resources

Dana Center TEKS Toolkit Clarifying Activities (7.13)(B), (7.13)(C), (7.15)(B)
Visit: PHSchool.com
Web Code: arq-9045

T74

TEKS ★ TAKS

(7.13)(B) To use a problem-solving model that incorporates understanding the problem, making a plan, carrying out the plan, and evaluating the solution for reasonableness **TAKS Obj. 6**

(7.13)(C) To select or develop an appropriate problem-solving strategy, including systematic guessing and checking **TAKS Obj. 6**

(7.15)(B) To validate his/her conclusions using mathematical properties and relationships **TAKS Obj. 6**

Systematic Guess and Check

When to Use This Strategy The strategy *Systematic Guess and Check* works well when you can start by making a reasonable estimate of the answer.

Construction A group of students is building a sailboat. The students have 48 ft^2 of material to make a sail. They design the sail in the shape of a right triangle as shown at the right. Find the length of the base and the height.

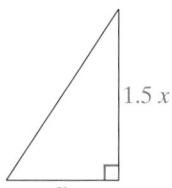

Understand The diagram shows that the height is 1.5 times the length of the base.

Plan Test possible dimensions of the triangle formed by the boom (base), the mast (height), and the sail. Check to see if they produce the desired area. Organize your results in a table.

Carry Out

Boom	Mast	Area	Conclusion
6	9	$\frac{1}{2} \cdot 6 \cdot 9 = 27$	Too low
10	15	$\frac{1}{2} \cdot 10 \cdot 15 = 75$	Too high
8	12	$\frac{1}{2} \cdot 8 \cdot 12 = 48$	✔

Check A triangle with a base length of 8 ft and a height of 12 ft has an area of 48 ft^2.

● Practice

1. The width of a rectangle is 4 cm less than its length. The area of the rectangle is 96 cm^2. Find the length and width of the rectangle.

2. A dance floor is a square with an area of 1,444 ft^2. What are the dimensions of the dance floor?

3. You are building a rectangular tabletop for a workbench. The perimeter of the tabletop is 22 ft. The area of the tabletop is 24 ft^2. What are the dimensions of the tabletop?

4. **Measurement** You want to put up a fence around a rectangular garden. The length of the garden is twice its width. If the garden has an area of 2,450 ft^2, how much fencing material do you need?

1. 12 cm; 8 cm

2. 38 ft × 38 ft

3. 8 ft × 3 ft

4. 210 ft

Act It Out

When to Use This Strategy You can use the strategy *Act It Out* to simulate a problem.

A cat is expecting a litter of four kittens. The probabilities of male and female kittens are equal. What is the probability that the litter contains three females and one male?

Understand Your goal is to find the experimental probability that the litter of four kittens contains three females and 1 male.

Plan Act out the problem by tossing a coin. Let heads represent a male and tails represent a female. Toss the coin 100 times. Separate the results into groups of 4 to represent the four kittens in a litter.

Carry Out The table below shows 25 "litters" of 4.

T T H H	(H T T T)	H T H H	(H T T T)	T H T H
T T H H	H H H T	H H T T	(T H T T)	H H H H
H H T T	(T T T H)	T H T H	H T H H	H T H T
(T H T T)	H T H T	T H H T	H H H H	H H H H
T H H H	T T T T	T H H T	H T H H	(T T T H)

Six groups out of twenty-five contain three females and one male. So $P(3 \text{ females and } 1 \text{ male}) = \frac{6}{25}$. The experimental probability is 0.24.

Check Make a list of all 16 possible outcomes. Of these outcomes, only 4 have three females and one male. So the theoretical probability is $\frac{4}{16}$, or 0.25. This is close to the experimental value.

● Practice

1. A sports jersey number has two digits. Even and odd digits are equally likely. Use a simulation to find the probability that both digits are even.

2. You are taking a 4-question true-or-false quiz. You do not know any of the answers. Use a simulation to find the probability that you guess exactly 3 out of 4 answers correctly.

3. A restaurant gives away a model car with each meal. You are equally likely to get any of the five cars. Use a simulation to find the probability that you get two of the same car after two meals.

Act It Out

Simulations use mathematical models to find experimental probabilities for events for which it is difficult to collect data directly. To design a simulation, model the possible number of outcomes by selecting a device such as coins, number cubes, or spinners. Then collect data. The more trials that are performed, the more reliable the results of the simulation will be.

Guided Instruction

When simulating or acting out a problem, students should be sure to choose a device that matches the problem. In this case, a coin makes sense since it has two outcomes, heads or tails, and each is equally likely. Have students note how each of the following steps is used to solve the problem:
- Understand the Problem
- Make a Plan
- Carry Out the Plan
- Check the Answer

Differentiated Instruction

Special Needs **L1**
Some students may be uncomfortable with the idea that finding experimental probability may not yield the same right answer for everyone. Discuss the meaning of the word "experiment" and how the number of favorable outcomes may differ each time.

1–3. Check students' work

Problem Solving Handbook

T75

Make a Table

Making a table helps you organize the information given in a problem. Once the information is organized, you can use logical reasoning to observe patterns and extend the table.

Guided Instruction

Be sure students understand what the rate of change or decrease is and how to find it. Call attention to the use of problem-solving steps:
- Understand the Problem
- Make a Plan
- Carry Out the Plan
- Check the Answer

Have students identify where in the problem each is used.

Emphasize the fact that students should think about making a table when they are asked to compare two or more things, or when the numbers they are using change according to a pattern.

Differentiated Instruction

Special Needs   L1

Some students may prefer to do their problem solving mentally rather than making tables. Assure students that they are practicing strategies that allow them to organize their thinking, which becomes essential with more complicated problems. Encourage students to continue to use mental math to predict the solution to a problem.

TEKS ★ ⓣⒶⓀⓈ Resources

Dana Center TEKS Toolkit Clarifying Activities (7.13)(B), (7.13)(C), (7.15)(B)
Visit: PHSchool.com
Web Code: arq-9045

TEKS ★ ⓣⒶⓀⓈ

(7.13)(B) To use a problem-solving model that incorporates understanding the problem, making a plan, carrying out the plan, and evaluating the solution for reasonableness ⓣⒶⓀⓈ **Obj. 6**

(7.13)(C) To select or develop an appropriate problem-solving strategy, including making a table ⓣⒶⓀⓈ **Obj. 6**

(7.15)(B) To validate his/her conclusions using mathematical properties and relationships ⓣⒶⓀⓈ **Obj. 6**

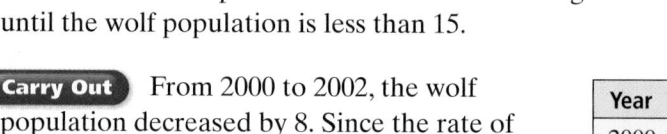

Make a Table

When to Use This Strategy A real-world problem may ask you to examine a set of data and draw a conclusion. In such a problem, you can *Make a Table* to organize the data.

Biology A wildlife preserve surveyed its wolf population in 1996 and counted 56 wolves. In 2000, there were 40 wolves. In 2002, there were 32 wolves. If the wolf population changes at a constant rate, in what year will there be fewer than 15 wolves?

Understand Given the wolf population in 1996, 2000, and 2002, you want to find the year in which there will be fewer than 15 wolves.

Plan Find the rate of change. *Make a Table* to organize the information in the problem. Use the rate of change to extend the table until the wolf population is less than 15.

Carry Out From 2000 to 2002, the wolf population decreased by 8. Since the rate of decrease is constant, you can say that every 2 years, the population decreases by 8.

In the beginning of 2006, there will be about 16 wolves. The population will be less than 15 later that year.

Year	Wolves
2000	40
2002	$40 - 8 = 32$
2004	$32 - 8 = 24$
2006	$24 - 8 = 16$

Check For there to be 15 wolves, the population must decrease by $56 - 15$ wolves, or 41 wolves. The population decreases by 4 wolves per year. Let x represent the number of years until there are 15 wolves. Solve $4x = 41$. The value of x is about 10 years. So $1996 + 10 = 2006$.

● Practice

1. **Business** You are starting a business selling lemonade. You know that it costs $6 to make 20 c of lemonade and $7 to make 30 c of lemonade. How much will it cost to make 50 c of lemonade?

2. You have $10 saved and plan to save an additional $2 each week. How much will you have after 7 weeks?

3. A driver of a car slows to a stop. The decrease in speed is constant. When the driver first applies the brakes, the car is going 50 mi/h. After 5 s, the car is traveling 30 mi/h. About how long does it take the car to stop?

1. $9

2. $24

3. $12.5 s

Work a Simpler Problem

When to Use This Strategy If a problem seems to have many steps, you may be able to *Work a Simpler Problem* first. The result may give you a clue about the solution of the original problem.

When you simplify 3^{50}, what number is in the ones place?

Understand You know that 3^{50} is a large number to calculate. You need to find the number in the ones place.

Plan It is not easy to simplify 3^{50} with paper and pencil. Simplify easier expressions such as 3^2, 3^3, and 3^4, to see what number is in the ones place.

Carry Out The table shows the values of the first 10 powers of 3. Notice that the ones digits in the value column repeat in the pattern 3, 9, 7, and 1. Every fourth power of 3 has a ones digit of 1. Since 4 is divisible by 4, 3^{48} has a ones digit of 1. Then the ones digit of 3^{49} is 3 and the ones digit of 3^{50} is 9.

Check When the exponent of 3 is 2, 6, or 10, the ones digit is 9. The numbers 2, 6, and 10 are divisible by 2 but not by 4. Since 50 is divisible by 2 but not by 4, the ones digit of 3^{50} is 9.

Power	Value
3^1	3
3^2	9
3^3	27
3^4	81
3^5	243
3^6	729
3^7	2,187
3^8	6,561
3^9	19,683
3^{10}	59,049

● Practice

1. **a.** What is the pattern for the ones digit of any power of 8?
   b. When you simplify 8^{63}, what number is in the ones place?

2. **a.** What is the pattern for the ones digit of any power of 7?
   b. When you simplify 7^{21}, what number is in the ones place?

3. The table shows the values of powers of 2 with even exponents from 10 to 20. What is the ones digit of 2^{80}?

4. What is the value of $(-1)^{427}$? Explain.

5. When you simplify 10^{347}, what digit is in the ones place?

6. Find the sum of the first 10 powers of 10, that is, the sum of $10^1 + 10^2 + 10^3 + \ldots 10^{10}$.

Power	Value
2^{10}	1,024
2^{12}	4,096
2^{14}	16,384
2^{16}	65,536
2^{18}	262,144
2^{20}	1,048,576

Work a Simpler Problem

When reading a problem, students sometimes see only a tangle of numbers and mysterious operations. Solving a *simpler problem* may reduce anxiety over large numbers or operations involved and help to focus attention on the nature of the operations.

Guided Instruction

Tell students that this strategy will help them when they face a complex problem. Often, it will be used in conjunction with another strategy, such as *Make a Table*. Explain that this strategy also is helpful when finding numerical or geometric patterns.

Ask volunteers to read the parts of the problem identifying each of the problem-solving steps:
- Understand the Problem
- Make a Plan
- Carry Out the Plan
- Check the Answer

Remind students that the simpler problem they set up needs to be similar to the original problem.

Differentiated Instruction

Below Level   **L2**
The problem in this lesson might frustrate students who have a brief attention span, especially if they cannot immediately perceive the correct pattern. Have each student work with a partner with whom they can discuss any patterns they see.

TEKS ★ **TAKS Resources**

Dana Center TEKS Toolkit Clarifying Activities (7.13)(B), (7.13)(C), (7.15)(B)
Visit: PHSchool.com
Web Code: arq-9045

Problem Solving Handbook

1a. 8, 4, 2, 6, 8, 4, 2, 6, . . .

1b. 2

2a. 7, 9, 3, 1, 7, 9, 3, 1, . . .

2b. 7

3. 6

4. −1; all odd powers of −1 are negative.

5. 0

6. 11,111,111,110

T77

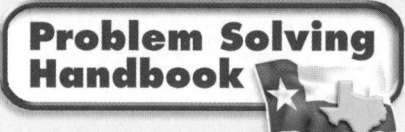

Work Backward

In some problem-solving situations, it may be helpful to work backward. These situations often involve a time of day or a known end result of a process. To solve these problems, begin with the final result and work backward to the beginning.

Guided Instruction

Give students exercises like these to practice converting between minutes and fractional hours:

30 min $\frac{1}{2}$ h   45 min $\frac{3}{4}$ h

20 min $\frac{1}{3}$ h $\frac{2}{3}$ h 40 min

$\frac{1}{4}$ h 15 min $1\frac{1}{2}$ h 90 min

Then elicit problem-solving steps:
- Understand the Problem
- Make a Plan
- Carry Out the Plan
- Check the Answer

Have students explain how each one is used in the example.

Visual Learners
Have students sketch a series of clocks to help them keep track of changing times with each step as they test their estimates.

1. 3:30 P.M.
2. $26.70
3. 14

TEKS ★ (TAKS) Resources

Dana Center TEKS Toolkit Clarifying Activities (7.13)(B), (7.13)(C), (7.15)(B)
Visit: PHSchool.com
Web Code: arq-9045

TEKS ★ (TAKS)

(7.13)(B) To use a problem-solving model that incorporates understanding the problem, making a plan, carrying out the plan, and evaluating the solution for reasonableness **(TAKS) Obj. 6**

(7.13)(C) To select or develop an appropriate problem-solving strategy, including working backward **(TAKS) Obj. 6**

(7.15)(B) To validate his/her conclusions using mathematical properties and relationships **(TAKS) Obj. 6**

Work Backward

When to Use This Strategy You can use the strategy *Work Backward* when a problem asks you to find an initial value.

You and your friends are going to dinner and then to a play that starts at 8:00 P.M., It will take $\frac{3}{4}$ h to drive to the restaurant and $1\frac{1}{4}$ h to eat and drive to the theater. You want to arrive at the theater 15 min before the play starts. At what time should you leave?

Understand Your goal is to find out what time you should leave home to arrive 15 min early for the 8:00 P.M. play. It takes $\frac{3}{4}$ h to drive to the restaurant and $1\frac{1}{4}$ h to eat and drive to the theater.

Plan You know that the series of events must *end* at 8:00 P.M. It makes sense to *Work Backward* to find when you must leave your house.

Carry Out

Concert starts.	Arrive at theater.	Arrive at dinner.	Leave home.
8:00 P.M.	7:45 P.M.	6:30 P.M.	5:45 P.M.

Working backward shows that when you leave at 5:45 P.M., you will get to the play 15 min early.

Check Find the total time it takes for the series of events to happen. $\frac{3}{4} + 1\frac{1}{4} + \frac{1}{4} = 2\frac{1}{4}$. Subtract $2\frac{1}{4}$ h from 8:00 P.M., and you get 5:45 P.M.

● Practice

1. After school today, you spent $1\frac{3}{4}$ h at band practice and then a half hour in the library. It took you 15 min to get home at 6:00 P.M. What time did you start practice?

2. Your friend spends one third of her money on lunch. You then give her $2.50 to repay a loan. After school, your friend spends $4.00 for a movie and $2.50 for a snack. She has $4.90 left. How much money did she have before lunch?

3. If you start with a number, add 5, and then multiply by 7, the result is 133. What was the original number?

TEKS ★ TAKS

(7.13)(B) To use a problem-solving model that incorporates understanding the problem, making a plan, carrying out the plan, and evaluating the solution for reasonableness **TAKS Obj. 6**

(7.13)(C) To select or develop an appropriate problem-solving strategy, including solving a simpler problem **TAKS Obj. 6**

(7.15)(B) To validate his/her conclusions using mathematical properties and relationships **TAKS Obj. 6**

Write an Equation

When to Use This Strategy You can *Write an Equation* to represent a real-world situation that involves two variables.

The cost of materials needed to make one toboggan is $8. A craftsman has a budget of $2,000. How many toboggans can he make?

Understand Your goal is to find the number of toboggans the craftsman can make given his budget and the cost of materials.

Plan *Write an Equation* to model the situation. Then solve the equation.

Carry Out Write an equation to represent the number of toboggans.

Words   amount budgeted divided by cost of materials is the number of toboggans

Let b = amount budgeted. Let n = number of toboggans.

Equation b ÷ $8   = n

$$\frac{b}{8} = n$$

$$\frac{2,000}{8} = n \quad \leftarrow \text{Substitute } b \text{ for 2,000.}$$

$$250 = n \quad \leftarrow \text{Simplify.}$$

The craftsman can make 250 toboggans.

Check The total cost of making 250 toboggans is 250 · $8, or $2,000. This equals the craftsman's budget. The answer checks.

● Practice

1. Family membership at a science museum costs $89 per year. The shows at the museum theater cost $22.50 per family each visit. How many shows can a family see if its yearly budget is $300?

2. A pair of boots costs $10 more than twice the cost of a pair of shoes. The boots cost $76.50. How much do the shoes cost?

3. Your family's car can travel 23 mi using 1 gal of gas. To the nearest gallon, how many gallons of gas will your car need for a 540-mi trip?

Write an Equation

Many real-world problems describe relationships between numbers. You can often find a solution by using the strategy *Write an Equation*. Equations use variables to represent values that are unknown or subject to change.

Guided Instruction

Tell students that writing an equation is a good way to organize the information needed to solve the problem.

Point out the translation of words to equation shown in the problem. Have students identify where each of the problem-solving steps below is used.
- Understand the Problem
- Make a Plan
- Carry Out the Plan
- Check the Answer

Error Prevention!

When choosing variables for equations, suggest that it helps to use variables that have meaning in the problem, such as *d* for days.

1. 9 shows
2. $33.25
3. 23 gal

TEKS ★ TAKS Resources

Dana Center TEKS Toolkit
Clarifying Activities (7.13)(B),
(7.13)(C), (7.15)(B)
Visit: PHSchool.com
Web Code: arq-9045

Problem Solving Handbook

T79

1 Decimals and Integers

Chapter at a Glance

Lesson Titles, Objectives, and Features	Assessment	NCTM Standards	TEKS ★ 𝒯𝒜𝒦𝒮
1-1 **Using Estimation Strategies** • To estimate using rounding, front-end estimation, and compatible numbers	Lesson Quiz	1, 4, 5, 6, 7, 8, 9, 10	**TEKS** (7.13)(A) 𝒯𝒜𝒦𝒮 **Obj. 6** **TEKS** (7.13)(D)
1-2 **Adding and Subtracting Decimals** • To add and subtract decimals and to do mental math using the properties of addition **Extension:** Using Mental Math	Lesson Quiz	1, 2, 4, 6, 7, 8, 9, 10	**TEKS** (7.2)(B), (7.2)(G) 𝒯𝒜𝒦𝒮 **Obj. 1**
1-3a Activity Lab: Modeling Decimal Multiplication **1-3** **Multiplying Decimals** • To multiply decimals and to do mental math using the properties of multiplication	Lesson Quiz Checkpoint Quiz 1	1, 2, 6, 7, 8, 9, 10	**TEKS** (7.2)(A), (7.2)(B), (7.2)(G) 𝒯𝒜𝒦𝒮 **Obj. 1**
1-4a Activity Lab, Hands On: Modeling Decimal Division **1-4** **Dividing Decimals** • To divide decimals and to solve problems by dividing decimals **Guided Problem Solving:** Choosing Operations	Lesson Quiz	1, 2, 6, 7, 8, 9, 10	**TEKS** (7.2)(A), (7.2)(B), (7.2)(F), (7.13)(C) 𝒯𝒜𝒦𝒮 **Obj. 1, 6**
1-5 **Measuring in Metric Units** • To use and convert metric units of measure	Lesson Quiz	1, 4, 5, 6, 7, 8, 9, 10	**TEKS** (7.2)(B), (7.3)(B), (7.14)(A) 𝒯𝒜𝒦𝒮 **Obj. 1, 2, 6**
1-6 **Comparing and Ordering Integers** • To compare and order integers and to find absolute values	Lesson Quiz Checkpoint Quiz 2	1, 2, 4, 5, 6, 7, 8, 9, 10	**TEKS** (7.1)(A), (7.14)(A) 𝒯𝒜𝒦𝒮 **Obj. 1, 6**
1-7a Activity Lab, Hands On: Modeling Integer Addition and Subtraction **1-7** **Adding and Subtracting Integers** • To add and subtract integers and to solve problems involving integers	Lesson Quiz	1, 5, 6, 7, 8, 9, 10	**TEKS** (7.2)(C), (7.2)(F) 𝒯𝒜𝒦𝒮 **Obj. 1**
1-8a Activity Lab, Hands On: Modeling Integer Multiplication **1-8** **Multiplying and Dividing Integers** • To multiply and divide integers and to solve problems involving integers	Lesson Quiz	1, 4, 5, 6, 7, 8, 9, 10	**TEKS** (7.2)(C), (7.2)(F) 𝒯𝒜𝒦𝒮 **Obj. 1**
1-9 **Order of Operations and the Distributive Property** • To use the order of operations and the Distributive Property **1-9b Activity Lab, Algebra Thinking:** Properties and Equality	Lesson Quiz	1, 2, 6, 7, 8, 9, 10	**TEKS** (7.15)(B) 𝒯𝒜𝒦𝒮 **Obj. 6;** Prepares for **TEKS** (7.2)(E)
1-10 **Mean, Median, Mode, and Range** • To describe data using mean, median, mode, and range **1-10b Activity Lab, Data Analysis:** Box-and-Whisker Plots	Lesson Quiz	1, 4, 5, 6, 7, 8, 9, 10	**TEKS** (7.12)(A), (7.12)(B) 𝒯𝒜𝒦𝒮 **Obj. 5;** Prepares for **TEKS** (8.12)(C)
𝒯𝒜𝒦𝒮 **Tune-Up: Cumulative Practice**			

NCTM Standards 2000

1 Number and Operations	**2** Algebra	**3** Geometry	**4** Measurement	**5** Data Analysis and Probability
6 Problem Solving	**7** Reasoning and Proof	**8** Communication	**9** Connections	**10** Representation

Correlations to Standardized Tests

All content for these tests is contained in *Prentice Hall Math,* Course 2. This chart reflects coverage in this chapter only.

	1-1	1-2	1-3	1-4	1-5	1-6	1-7	1-8	1-9	1-10
Terra Nova CAT6 (Level 17)										
Number and Number Relations	✔	✔	✔	✔	✔	✔	✔	✔	✔	✔
Computation and Numerical Estimation	✔	✔	✔	✔	✔	✔	✔	✔	✔	✔
Operation Concepts	✔	✔	✔	✔	✔	✔	✔	✔	✔	✔
Measurement	✔				✔	✔	✔	✔		
Geometry and Spatial Sense										
Data Analysis, Statistics, and Probability	✔				✔	✔	✔	✔		✔
Patterns, Functions, Algebra	✔	✔	✔	✔		✔	✔	✔	✔	
Problem Solving and Reasoning	✔	✔	✔	✔	✔	✔	✔	✔	✔	✔
Communication	✔	✔	✔	✔	✔	✔	✔	✔	✔	✔
Decimals, Fractions, Integers, Percent									✔	
Order of Operations	✔	✔	✔	✔	✔	✔	✔	✔	✔	✔
Terra Nova CTBS (Level 17)										
Decimals, Fractions, Integers, Percents	✔	✔	✔	✔	✔	✔	✔	✔	✔	
Order of Operations, Numeration, Number Theory	✔	✔	✔	✔	✔	✔	✔	✔	✔	✔
Data Interpretation	✔			✔	✔	✔	✔	✔	✔	✔
Pre-algebra		✔	✔	✔		✔			✔	
Measurement	✔	✔	✔	✔	✔	✔	✔	✔		
Geometry										
ITBS (Level 13)										
Number Properties and Operations	✔	✔	✔	✔	✔	✔	✔	✔	✔	✔
Algebra		✔	✔	✔		✔			✔	
Geometry										
Measurement	✔	✔			✔	✔	✔	✔		
Probability and Statistics	✔	✔		✔	✔	✔	✔	✔	✔	✔
Estimation	✔	✔	✔	✔	✔	✔				
SAT 10 (Int 3 Level)										
Number Sense and Operations	✔	✔	✔	✔	✔	✔	✔	✔	✔	✔
Patterns, Relationships, and Algebra	✔	✔	✔	✔	✔	✔	✔	✔	✔	✔
Data, Statistics, and Probability	✔	✔		✔	✔	✔	✔	✔	✔	✔
Geometry and Measurement	✔	✔	✔	✔	✔	✔	✔	✔		
NAEP										
Number Sense, Properties, and Operations		✔	✔	✔				✔	✔	
Measurement					✔					
Geometry and Spatial Sense										
Data Analysis, Statistics, and Probability										
Algebra and Functions										

CAT6 California Achievement Test, 6th Ed.   **CTBS** Comprehensive Test of Basic Skills   **ITBS** Iowa Test of Basic Skills, Form M
SAT10 Stanford Achievement Test, 10th Ed.   **NAEP** National Assessment of Educational Progress 2005 Mathematics Objectives

TEKS Math Background

Focus on the TEKS

- New at Grade 7 is the use of number lines to add, subtract, multiply, and divide integers (7.2)(C). Students compare integers in Lesson 1-6 to prepare for using integers with all four operations in Lessons 1-7 and 1-8 (7.2)(C). Special attention should be given to these lessons.

- At Grade 7, students extend Grade 6 skills to describe sets of data using mean, median, mode, and range (7.12)(A). Analysis of TAKS results shows that students still struggle with this student expectation.

  In Lesson 1-10, students find a measure of central tendency for a set of data. Place special emphasis on this lesson because it focuses on (7.12)(A).

1-1 Using Estimation Strategies

TEKS ★ TAKS (7.13)(A) Obj. 6; (7.13)(D)

Math Understandings
- Estimation is used when an exact answer is not needed.
- Estimation is used with mental math to check answers.
- Most estimation techniques involve replacing numbers with ones that are close and easy to compute with mentally.

The symbol ≈ means "is approximately equal to" and is used with estimated answers.

Estimation strategies in addition include **estimation by rounding**, **front-end estimation**, and **using compatible numbers**.

Estimation strategies in multiplication and division include **estimation by rounding** and **using compatible numbers**.

Example: To estimate 37×54, students can use compatible numbers to change 37 to 40 and 54 to 50, and use the basic fact 4×5 to estimate 40×50 as about 2,000.

1-2, 1-3, 1-4 Adding, Subtracting, Multiplying, and Dividing Decimals

TEKS ★ TAKS (7.2)(A), (7.2)(B), (7.2)(F), (7.2)(G), Obj. 1

Math Understandings
- The properties of addition and multiplication can help you compute with decimals mentally.

Properties of Addition and Multiplication	
Arithmetic	**Algebra**
Commutative Property	
$2 + 3 = 3 + 2$	$a + b = b + a$
$2 \cdot 3 = 3 \cdot 2$	$a \cdot b = b \cdot a$
Associative Property	
$(2 + 3) + 4 = 2 + (3 + 4)$	$(a + b) + c = a + (b + c)$
$(2 \cdot 3) \cdot 4 = 2 \cdot (3 \cdot 4)$	$(a \cdot b) \cdot c = a \cdot (b \cdot c)$
Identity Property	
$6 + 0 = 6$	$a + 0 = a$
$6 \cdot 1 = 6$	$a \cdot 1 = a$
Zero Property	
$5 \cdot 0 = 0$	$a \cdot 0 = 0$
$0 \cdot 5 = 0$	$0 \cdot a = 0$

To add or subtract decimals, align the decimal points.

To multiply decimals, first multiply as if the factors were whole numbers. Then, mark off from right to left in the product, the sum of the number of decimal places in both factors.

To divide decimals, rewrite the divisor as a whole number by multiplying both the divisor and the dividend by a power of 10. Annex zeros in the dividend as needed. Place the decimal point in the quotient above the decimal point in the dividend.

1-5 Measuring in Metric Units

TEKS ★ TAKS (7.2)(B), (7.3)(B), (7.14)(A) Obj. 1, 2, 6

Math Understandings
- The metric system of measurement is a decimal system based on powers of ten.
- The **meter** is the basic unit for length; **gram** is the basic unit of mass; and **liter** is the basic unit of capacity.
- The prefixes *deci, centi,* and *milli* describe measures that are less than a basic unit. The prefixes *deca, hecto,* and *kilo* describe measures that are more than a basic unit.

1-6 Comparing and Ordering Integers

TEKS ★ *TAKS* (7.1)(A), (7.14)(A) Obj. 1, 6

Math Understandings

- Integers are the set of positive whole numbers (positive integers), their opposites (negative integers), and zero (neither positive nor negative).

When numbers are compared on a number line, the numbers increase from left to right. The **absolute value** of a number is its distance from zero on a number line.

1-7 / 1-8 Adding, Subtracting, Multiplying, and Dividing Integers

TEKS ★ *TAKS* (7.2)(C), (7.2)(F) Obj.1

Math Understandings

- Absolute value, properties, and the number line can be used to show why the rules for operations with integers make sense.

The product or quotient of two numbers with the same sign is positive; for two numbers with different signs, it is negative.

1-9 Order of Operations and the Distributive Property

TEKS ★ *TAKS* Prepares for (7.2)(E)

Math Understandings

- Mathematicians have agreed upon an order of operations to avoid confusion.
- The Distributive Property allows you to evaluate expressions that have a number multiplying a sum or a difference.

The Order of Operations

- Work inside grouping symbols.
- Multiply and divide in order from left to right.
- Add and subtract in order from left to right.

The Distributive Property	
Arithmetic	Algebra
$9(4 + 5) = 9(4) + 9(5)$	$a(b + c) = a(b) + a(c)$
$5(8 - 2) = 5(8) - 5(2)$	$a(b - c) = a(b) - a(c)$

1-10 Mean, Median, Mode, and Range

TEKS ★ *TAKS* (7.12)(A), (7.12)(B) Obj. 5

Math Understandings

- There are different numerical methods for describing the "center" of a numerical data set.
- The mean, median, and mode are common measures for the central tendency of a data set.
- The range of a set of data is the difference between the greatest and least values.

The **mean** of a data set is the sum of the data values divided by the number of data items. The **median** of a data set is the middle value when the data are arranged in numerical order. The median for an even number of data items is the mean of the two middle items. The **mode** of a data set is the data item that occurs most often. There can be more than one mode for a data set. The **range** of a data set describes the spread of the data, the difference between the greatest and least values.

Additional Professional Development Opportunities

Math Background Notes for Chapter 1: Every lesson has a Math Background in the PLAN section.

Research Overview, Mathematics Strands
Additional support for these topics and more is in the front of the Teacher's Edition.

LessonLab
LessonLab, a Pearson Education company, offers comprehensive, facilitated professional development designed to help teachers to improve student achievement. To learn more, please visit lessonlab.com.

Texas Chapter 1 Resources

	1-1	1-2	1-3	1-4	1-5	1-6	1-7	1-8	1-9	1-10	For the Chapter
Print Resources											
L3 Practice	•	•	•	•	•	•	•	•	•	•	
L1 Adapted Practice	•	•	•	•	•	•	•	•	•	•	
L3 Guided Problem Solving	•	•	•	•	•	•	•	•	•	•	
L2 Reteaching	•	•	•	•	•	•	•	•	•	•	
L4 Enrichment	•	•	•	•	•	•	•	•	•	•	
L3 Daily Notetaking Guide	•	•	•	•	•	•	•	•	•	•	
L1 Adapted Daily Notetaking Guide	•	•	•	•	•	•	•	•	•	•	
L3 Vocabulary and Study Skills Worksheet	•		•			•		•		•	•
L3 Daily Puzzles	•	•	•	•	•	•	•	•	•	•	
L3 Activity Labs	•	•	•	•	•	•	•	•	•	•	
L3 Checkpoint Quiz			•			•					
L3 Chapter Project											•
L2 Chapter Test											•
L3 Chapter Test											•
L4 Alternative Assessment											•
L3 Cumulative Review											•
Spanish Resources ELL											
L3 Practice	•	•	•	•	•	•	•	•	•	•	
L3 Vocabulary and Study Skills Worksheet	•		•			•		•		•	•
L3 Checkpoint Quiz			•			•					
L2 Chapter Test											•
L3 Chapter Test											•
L4 Alternative Assessment											•
L3 Cumulative Review											•
Transparencies											
Check Skills You'll Need	•	•	•	•	•	•	•	•	•		
Additional Examples	•	•	•	•	•	•	•	•	•	•	
Problem of the Day	•	•	•	•	•	•	•	•	•		
TAKS Daily Review	•	•	•	•	•	•	•	•	•	•	
Classroom Aid		•	•	•				•	•		
Student Edition Answers	•	•	•	•	•	•	•	•	•	•	•
Lesson Quiz	•	•	•	•	•	•	•	•	•		
TAKS Strategies											•
Technology											
Texas Interactive Textbook Online	•	•	•	•	•	•	•	•	•	•	•
Texas StudentExpress CD-ROM	•	•	•	•	•	•	•	•	•	•	•
Success Tracker™ Online Intervention	•	•	•	•	•	•	•	•	•	•	•
TeacherExpress CD-ROM	•	•	•	•	•	•	•	•	•	•	•
PresentationExpress CD-ROM	•	•	•	•	•	•	•	•	•	•	•
Texas ExamView CD-ROM with QuickTake	•	•	•	•	•	•	•	•	•	•	•
MindPoint Quiz Show CD-ROM	•	•	•	•	•	•	•	•	•	•	•
Prentice Hall Web Site: PHSchool.com	•	•	•	•	•	•	•	•	•	•	•

Also available: **TAKS Tune-Up Kit**
- TAKS Daily Review Transparencies
- TAKS Review and Preparation Workbook
- TAKS Strategies with Transparencies
- Texas Progress Monitoring Assessments
- Texas ExamView CD-ROM
- MindPoint Quiz Show CD-ROM

Other Resources
Algebra Readiness Tests
All-in-One Student Workbook
All-in-One Student Workbook, Adapted Version
Multilingual Handbook

Solution Key
Math Notes Study Folder
Spanish Cumulative Assessment

Where You Can Use the Lesson Resources

Here is a suggestion, following the four-step teaching plan, for how you can incorporate Differentiated Instruction Resources into your teaching.

	Instructional Resources L3	Differentiated Instruction Resources
1. Plan		
Preparation Read the Math Background in the Teacher's Edition to connect this lesson with students' previous experience. **Starting Class** **Check Skills You'll Need** Assign these exercises to review prerequisite skills. **TEKS** ★ **TAKS** Review the full text of the TEKS student expectations and TAKS objectives covered in this lesson. **New Vocabulary** Help students pre-read the lesson by pointing out the new terms introduced in the lesson.	**TEKS Math Background** **Math Understandings** **Transparencies & PresentationExpress CD-ROM** Check Skills You'll Need Problem of the Day TAKS Daily Review **Resources** Vocabulary and Study Skills	**Spanish Support** ELL Vocabulary and Study Skills
2. Teach		
L3 Guided Instruction Use the Activity Labs to build conceptual understanding. Teach each Example. Use the Teacher's Edition side column notes for specific teaching tips, including Error Prevention notes. Use the Additional Examples found in the side column (and on transparency and PowerPoint) as an alternative presentation for the content. After each Example, assign the Quick Check exercise for that Example to get an immediate assessment of student understanding. Use the Closure activity in the Teacher's Edition to help students attain mastery of lesson content.	**Student Edition** Activity Lab **Resources** Daily Notetaking Guide Activity Lab **Transparencies & PresentationExpress CD-ROM** Additional Examples Classroom Aids **Texas ExamView CD-ROM with QuickTake**	**Teacher's Edition** Every lesson includes suggestions for working with students who need special attention. L1 Special Needs L2 Below Level L4 Advanced Learners ELL English Language Learners **Resources** L1 Adapted Daily Notetaking Guide **Multilingual Handbook**
3. Practice		

Assignment Guide
Check Your Understanding
Use these questions to check students' understanding before you assign homework.
Homework Exercises
Assign homework from these leveled exercises in the Assignment Guide.
  A Practice by Example
  B Apply Your Skills
  C Challenge
  TAKS Tune-Up and Mixed Review
Homework Quick Check
Use these key exercises to quickly check students' homework.
	Transparencies & PresentationExpress CD-ROM
	Student Answers
	Resources
	Practice
	Guided Problem Solving
	Vocabulary and Study Skills
	Activity Lab
	Daily Puzzles
	Texas ExamView CD-ROM with QuickTake
		Spanish Support
		ELL Practice
		ELL Vocabulary and Study Skills
		Resources
		L1 Adapted Practice
		L4 Enrichment

4. Assess & Reteach		
Lesson Quiz Assign the Lesson Quiz to assess students' mastery of the lesson content. **Checkpoint Quiz** Use the Checkpoint Quiz to assess student progress over several lessons.	**Transparencies & PresentationExpress CD-ROM** Lesson Quiz **Resources** Checkpoint Quiz	**Resources** L2 Reteaching ELL Checkpoint Quiz Success Tracker™ Online Intervention **Texas ExamView CD-ROM with QuickTake**

KEY   L1 Special Needs   L2 Below Level   L3 For All Students   L4 Advanced, Gifted   ELL English Language Learners

CHAPTER 1 — Decimals and Integers

Check Your Readiness

Answers are in the back of the textbook.

For intervention, direct students to:

Comparing and Ordering Whole Numbers
Skills Handbook, p. 654

Dividing Whole Numbers
Skills Handbook, p. 657

Place Value and Decimals
Skills Handbook, p. 658

Reading and Writing Decimals
Skills Handbook, p. 659

Rounding Decimals
Skills Handbook, p. 660

What You've Learned
TEKS ★ TAKS

- **(6.1)(A)** In a previous course, you learned to compare and order non-negative rational numbers. **TAKS Obj. 1**
- **(6.2)(B)** You used addition and subtraction to solve problems involving decimals. **TAKS Obj. 1**
- **(6.8)(D)** You converted measures within the metric system. **TAKS Obj. 4**

Check Your Readiness

For Exercises	See Skills Handbook
1–2	p. 654
3–6	p. 657
7–11	p. 658
12–16	p. 659
17–21	p. 660

GO for Help

Comparing and Ordering Whole Numbers

Use > or < to compare the whole numbers.

1. 72 $<$ 720
2. 3,972 $>$ 3,927

Dividing Whole Numbers

Find each quotient.

3. $8\overline{)296}$ 37
4. $9\overline{)684}$ 76
5. $11\overline{)2,376}$ 216
6. $68\overline{)14,552}$ 214

Place Value and Decimals

Write the value of the underlined digit.

7. 24.3̲5
tenths
8. 4.086̲
thousandths
9. 179̲.8
ones
10. 59.0̲3
hundredths
11. 1.0467̲
ten-thousandths

Reading and Writing Decimals

Write each number in words. Use *tenths*, *hundredths*, or *thousandths*.
12–16. See margin.

12. 421.5
13. 5,006.25
14. 15.004
15. 0.329
16. 710.413

Rounding Decimals

Round to the nearest hundredth.

	34.12	278.79	3.60	81.80	17.00
	17. 34.124	**18.** 278.786	**19.** 3.602	**20.** 81.796	**21.** 16.999

12. four hundred twenty-one and five tenths

13. five thousand six and twenty-five hundredths

14. fifteen and four thousandths

15. three hundred twenty-nine thousandths

16. seven hundred ten and four hundred thirteen thousandths

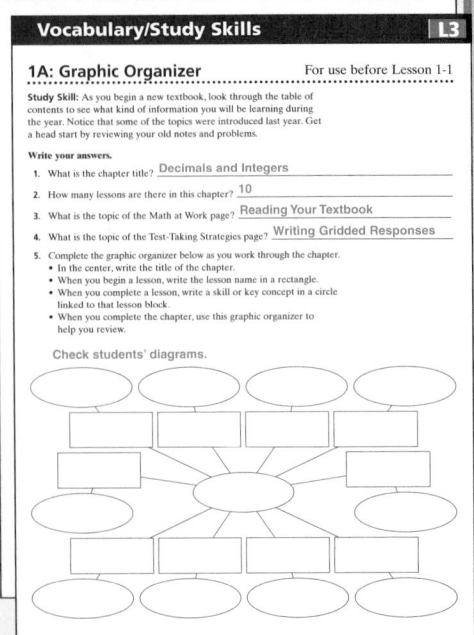

Spanish Vocabulary/Study Skills   ELL

Vocabulary/Study Skills   L3

1A: Graphic Organizer   For use before Lesson 1-1

Study Skill: As you begin a new textbook, look through the table of contents to see what kind of information you will be learning during the year. Notice that some of the topics were introduced last year. Get a head start by reviewing your old notes and problems.

Write your answers.

1. What is the chapter title? Decimals and Integers
2. How many lessons are there in this chapter? 10
3. What is the topic of the Math at Work page? Reading Your Textbook
4. What is the topic of the Test-Taking Strategies page? Writing Gridded Responses
5. Complete the graphic organizer below as you work through the chapter.
   • In the center, write the title of the chapter.
   • When you begin a lesson, write the lesson name in a rectangle.
   • When you complete a lesson, write a skill or key concept in a circle linked to that lesson block.
   • When you complete the chapter, use this graphic organizer to help you review.

Check students' diagrams.

Number, Operation, and Quantitative Reasoning
TEKS **(7.1)(A), (7.2)(A),**
(7.2)(B), (7.2)(C), (7.2)(F),
(7.2)(G)
TAKS **Obj. 1**

Patterns, Relationships, and Algebraic Thinking
TEKS **(7.3)(B)**
TAKS **Obj. 2**

Probability and Statistics
TEKS **(7.12)(A), (7.12)(B)**
TAKS **Obj. 5**

Underlying Processes and Mathematical Tools
TEKS **(7.13)(A), (7.13)(C),**
(7.14)(A), (7.15)(B),
TAKS **Obj. 6; TEKS (7.13)(D)**

Chapter 1 Overview

In this chapter, students will build on their knowledge of mental math and estimation strategies as they compute with decimals and measures in metric units. They apply their prior knowledge of algebraic properties and number sense as they learn to compare and order integers, and to add, subtract, multiply, and divide them. They also apply skills learned in the chapter to find measures of central tendency and range.

Activating Prior Knowledge

In this chapter, students will build on their knowledge of decimal concepts and of estimation strategies to compute with decimals and metric measurements. They also draw upon their understanding of integers to compute with them. Ask questions such as:

- *How can you estimate sums of whole numbers?* One way: round each addend to the greatest place and add.
- *How can you estimate the product of two whole number factors?* One way: round each factor to a number that makes the computation easier.

What You'll Learn Next
TEKS ⭐ TAKS

- **(7.1)(A)** In this chapter, you will learn to compare and order integers. **TAKS** **Obj. 1**

- **(7.2)(B)** You will use addition, subtraction, multiplication, and division to solve problems involving decimals. **TAKS** **Obj. 1**

- **(7.3)(B)** You will find solutions to application problems involving related measurement units. **TAKS** **Obj. 2**

TAKS Tune-Up On pages 63–65, you will review and practice vocabulary and *TAKS* objectives you have learned.

🔊 Key Vocabulary

- absolute value (p. 31)
- additive inverses (p. 38)
- compatible numbers (p. 5)
- integers (p. 31)
- mean (p. 53)
- median (p. 54)
- mode (p. 54)
- opposites (p. 31)
- order of operations (p. 48)
- outlier (p. 53)
- range (p. 55)

Chapter 1   **3**

3

TEKS ⭐ TAKS

(7.13)(A) To apply mathematics to everyday experiences TAKS Obj. 6

(7.13)(D) To select techniques such as estimation to solve problems

Dana Center TEKS Toolkit Clarifying Activities (7.13)(A), (7.13)(D)
Visit: PHSchool.com
Web Code: arq-9045

TEKS Math Background

Learning to estimate the result of a computation is as important as learning to calculate the exact result. *Rounding* is probably the most commonly used estimation technique. When estimating sums and differences, however, *front-end estimation* often yields a better estimate than rounding. Also, when estimating quotients, it is frequently easier to work with *compatible numbers* instead of rounded numbers. In this lesson, students have an opportunity to practice all three techniques.

More Math Background: p. 2C

Lesson Planning and Resources

See p. 2E for a list of the resources that support this lesson.

Bell Ringer Practice

☑ **Check Skills You'll Need**
Use student page, transparency, or PowerPoint.

TAKS **Daily Review 1**
Use transparency.

1-1 Using Estimation Strategies

☑ **Check Skills You'll Need**

1. Vocabulary Review
How is an estimate different from a guess? See below.

Round to the place of the underlined digit.

2. 8<u>2</u>,729
83,000

3. <u>4</u>49
400

4. 24,1<u>0</u>6
24,110

5. 3,<u>5</u>28
3,500

 for Help

Skills Handbook
p. 655

Check Skills You'll Need

1. An estimate is an answer with a calculation; a guess is an answer without a calculation.

 for Help

For help with rounding decimals, go to Skills Handbook p. 660.

TEKS ⭐ TAKS

• **(7.13)(A)** To apply mathematics to everyday experiences TAKS Obj. 6
• **(7.13)(D)** To select techniques such as estimation to solve problems

🔊 **New Vocabulary** compatible numbers

Why Learn This?

You can estimate an answer before you calculate it. Sometimes an estimate is all you need.

You can use rounding to estimate sums, differences, and products. You can use a number line to help you round decimals.

4.7 is between 4.0 and 5.0. You can round 4.7 to 5.0.

When you estimate, use the symbol ≈, which means "is approximately equal to."

EXAMPLE Estimating by Rounding

1 **Biology** The span of an eagle ray's fins is 3.27 m. The span of her baby's fins is 0.88 m. Estimate the difference between the spans. Round to the nearest whole number before you find the difference.

$$3.27 - 0.88 \approx 3 - 1 \quad \leftarrow \text{Round to the nearest whole number.}$$
$$= 2 \quad \leftarrow \text{Subtract.}$$

The difference in spans is about 2 m.

☑ **Quick Check**

1. Estimate. First round to the nearest whole number.
   a. $1.75 + 0.92$ 3   **b.** $14.34 - 7.8$ 6   **c.** 4.90×6.25 30

Differentiated Instruction Solutions for All Learners

Special Needs L1
In Example 2, write the extra step of adding $7 and $2 for students so that they can see where the $9 estimate came from.

learning style: visual

Below Level L2
Have students visualize rounding on a number line. For instance, this diagram shows that, to the nearest whole number, 9.25 is rounded to 9.

9.00   **9.25**   9.50   10.00

learning style: visual

You can use front-end estimation when you want to find the sum of several numbers. First add the front numbers. Then estimate the sum of the lesser numbers and adjust the estimate.

EXAMPLE Estimating by Front-End Estimation

2 **Shopping** You have $10 and want to purchase several gift items. You select a kaleidoscope for $4.39, gift wrap for $1.49, and a card for $2.95. Estimate the total cost to determine whether you have enough money.

Step 1 Add the front-end digits.

$$\begin{array}{r} \$4.39 \\ \$1.49 \\ + \ \$2.95 \\ \hline \$7 \end{array}$$

Step 2 Estimate the sum of the cents to the nearest dollar.

$$\begin{array}{r} \$4.39 \\ \$1.49 \end{array}\Big\} \leftarrow \text{about } \$1$$
$$\$2.95 \ \leftarrow \underline{\text{about } \$1}$$
$$\$2 = \$9$$

$+$

The total cost is about $9. You have enough money.

✓ Quick Check

2. Estimate to the nearest dollar the total cost of a dog collar for $5.79, a dog toy for $2.48, and a dog dish for $5.99. **about $14**

Compatible numbers are numbers that are easy to compute mentally. You can use compatible numbers to estimate. Simply adjust the numbers in the problem to ones that are close to make the calculation easier. Compatible numbers are particularly useful for finding quotients.

EXAMPLE Estimating Using Compatible Numbers

3 **Movies** Suppose you have saved $50.25. About how many DVDs can you buy from category D in the table?

$50.25 \div 7.95$ ← Use division.

$48 \div 8$ ← Choose compatible numbers such as 48 and 8.

6 ← Simplify.

DVD Price List	
Category	**Price**
A	$23.95
B	$15.95
C	$12.95
D	$7.95

You can buy about six DVDs from category D.

✓ Quick Check

3. Your friend says you can buy about twice as many DVDs from category D as from category B. Is your friend correct? Explain.

3. Yes; you can buy about 48 ÷ 16, or 3, DVDs from category B. This is half the number of DVDs you can buy from category D.

Advanced Learners L4
Your shopping cart contains food items with prices $1.65, $4.97, $0.79, $2.29, $0.39, and $2.09. Estimate the amount of change you will receive if you give the cashier $20. **about $8**

Pre-AP™

English Language Learners ELL
Ask students to work in pairs. Have one third of the pairs focus on explaining how to estimate by rounding using examples, words, and symbols. The other two thirds should do the same with estimation using compatible numbers and front-end estimation. Have pairs explain their strategies. **learning style: verbal**

Activity Lab

Use before the lesson.

All in One Teaching Resources
Activity Lab 1-1: Using Estimates

Guided Instruction

Example 1
Some students might have difficulty distinguishing the symbol for "is approximately equal to" from the equal sign. Discuss the symbol ≈; ask: *How would you compare this symbol to an equal sign?* Sample: It has two identical segments, like an equal sign, but they are "wavy."

Example 3
Make sure students understand how to identify compatible numbers. Ask: *Why do you use 48 in the division instead of 50?* Sample: It is easy to compute 48 ÷ 8 mentally, so 48 is compatible with 8.

PowerPoint
Additional Examples

1 The length of a Colombian black spider monkey's body is 58.31 cm. The length of its tail is 78.96 cm. To the nearest tenth of a centimeter, estimate the total length of the spider monkey. **about 137.3 cm**

2 You order a taco that costs $3.79, a juice that costs $.89, and a yogurt that costs $1.39. Estimate the total cost of your order. **about $6**

3 Suppose you have saved $61.80. About how many CDs can you buy if each costs $15.95? **about 4 CDs**

All in One Teaching Resources
• Daily Notetaking Guide 1-1 L3
• Adapted Notetaking 1-1 L1

Closure

• Describe three methods for estimating the results of decimal computations.
rounding, front-end estimation, compatible numbers

3. Practice

Assignment Guide

Check Your Understanding
Go over Exercises 1–5 in class before assigning the Homework Exercises.

Homework Exercises
A	Practice by Example	6–24
B	Apply Your Skills	25–32
C	Challenge	33
TEKS ★ TAKS Tune-Up and Mixed Review		34–37

Homework Quick Check
To check students' understanding of key skills and concepts, go over Exercises 14, 22, 27, 31, and 32.

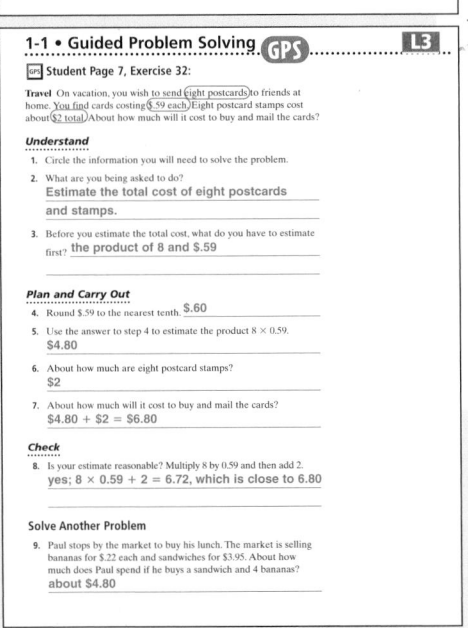

1. Rounded numbers are numbers rounded to the nearest whole number, whereas compatible numbers are chosen because they are easy to compute mentally.

1. **Vocabulary** Explain the difference between rounded numbers and compatible numbers.

2. **Error Analysis** A student estimated the cost of three shirts. What error was made?

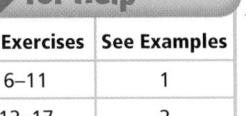
$$\$17.99 + \$23.45 + \$20.15 \approx 18 + 23 + 2 = 43$$

The student rounded 20.15 to 2 instead of 20.

Match each problem with the method you would use to estimate.

3. $22.4 \div 3.21$ C

4. $7.3 + 22.4 + 6.5 + 13.6$ A

5. $21.8 - 17.4$ B

A. front-end estimation
B. rounding
C. compatible numbers

Homework Exercises

For more exercises, see Extra Skills and Word Problems.

GO for Help

For Exercises	See Examples
6–11	1
12–17	2
18–24	3

Estimate. First round to the nearest whole number.

Ⓐ
6. $5.82 - 1.76$ 4
7. $10.13 + 1.46$ 11
8. 6.07×3.29 18

9. 9.86×9.13 90
10. $21.18 - 17.92$ 3
11. $11.53 + 7.23$ 19

Use front-end estimation to estimate each sum.

12. $5.43 + 2.67$ 8
13. $8.09 + 11.24$ 19
14. $7.18 + 5.89$ 13

15. $4.39 + 9.57$ 14
16. $24.21 + 16.03$ 40
17. $3.62 + 2.31$ 6

Use compatible numbers to estimate each quotient.

18. $76.5 \div 8.8$ 9
19. $19.45 \div 4.92$ 4
20. $27.36 \div 3.14$ 9

21. $103.6 \div 9.72$ 10
22. $32.2 \div 7.56$ 4
23. $3.963 \div 1.79$ 2

24. **Trains** The world's fastest train travels about 162 mi/h. Estimate how far the train travels in 4.75 h. about 800 mi

GPS 25. **Guided Problem Solving** A giant burrito required 75.75 lb of cheese. About how many 12-lb boxes of cheese did the cooks use?
   • Which operation will you use to solve the problem?
   • Which numbers will you use to make your estimate?
   about 6 boxes

Ⓑ
26. The first choice; the first choice is less than $3 per magnet, while the second choice is more than $3 per magnet.

26. You can buy 12 magnets for $34.68, or 3 magnets for $9.57. Estimate to decide which is the better buy. Explain your reasoning.
26–27. See left.

27. Answers may vary. Sample: Underestimates ensure you have enough money.

27. **Reasoning** When you estimate to determine if you have enough money, why should you underestimate the amount you have?

Estimate the cost of each group of items.

28. 97¢ per lb   2.35 LB   about $2.30

29. $1.36 per lb   1.48 LB   about $2.10

30. 79¢ per lb   4.16 LB   about $3.20

31. Answers may vary. Sample: Your GPA is an exact answer and is not an estimate.

31. **Writing in Math** When is an estimate *not* as useful as an exact answer? Give an example.

32. **GPS** On vacation, you wish to send eight postcards to friends at home. You find cards costing $.59 each. Eight postcard stamps cost about $2 total. About how much will it cost to buy and mail the cards? about $7

C 33. **Challenge** Your family is going to visit a relative who lives 389.2 mi from your home. The family car gets 29.6 miles per gallon of gasoline. If the price of a gallon of gas is $2.16, about how much will the gasoline for the trip cost? about $26; (390 ÷ 30) × $2

TEKS ★ TAKS Tune-Up and Mixed Review

TAKS Objective 6
TEKS (7.15)(B)

34. The table shows the number of students at Stewart Middle School who belong to several groups. Which conclusion is reasonable? **B**

Stewart Middle School Groups

Group	Number of Students
Pep Club	123
Band	68
Drama Club	32
Student Council	54

(A) Student Council has twice as many members as Drama Club.
(B) Pep Club has about 4 times as many members as Drama Club.
(C) Band has about twice as many members as Pep Club.
(D) Student Council has the fewest members.

TAKS Objective 1
TEKS (7.2)(D)

35. Carrie earned $612 in a year at a part-time job. Which is the best estimate of her weekly earnings? **J**

(F) $18   (G) $16   (H) $14   (J) $12

GO for Help Skills p. 654

Order the numbers from least to greatest.

4.0, 40, 403, 4,004
36. 4.0 4,004 40 403

706.8, 761.8, 768.0, 768.1
37. 761.8 768.1 768.0 706.8

PowerPoint
Lesson Quiz

Use rounding to estimate to the nearest tenth.

1. 5.75 + 1.34 about 7.1
2. 64.54 − 30.19 about 34.3

Use front-end estimation or compatible numbers to estimate.

3. 31.28 + 3.05 about 34
4. 59.63 ÷ 9.84 about 6

Alternative Assessment

Have students work in pairs. Each student writes a decimal problem for each operation: addition, subtraction, multiplication, and division. Then have partners exchange papers and estimate the answers. Have partners discuss the technique they used for each type of problem.

Enrichment 1-1   **L4**

Reteaching 1-1   Using Estimation **L2**

One way to estimate a sum, difference, or product is to round numbers to the nearest whole number. Then add, subtract, multiply or divide.

Round to the nearest whole number		Round to the nearest whole number	
1.6 →	2	17.2 →	20
+ 4.4 →	+ 4	× 7.3 →	× 7
	6 Estimate		140 Estimate

You can get a quick estimate if you use *compatible numbers* to compute mentally.

$24.27 → $24.00
− 8.79   − 9.00
              $15.00 Estimate

Estimate each sum, difference, product or quotient. Sample answers are given.

		Estimate				Estimate
1.	9.265 →	9	2.	12.91 →	13	
	+ 6.840 →	+ 7		− 7.80 →	− 8	
		16			5	
3.	$16.49 →	$16	4.	2.362 →	2.4	
	− 5.25 →	− 5		+ 0.815 →	+ 0.8	
		$11			3.2	
5.	2.4 →	2	6.	6.5 →	7	
	× 5.2 →	× 5		× 0.9 →	× 1	
		10			7	
7.	$12.09 →	$12	8.	6.147 →	6.1	
	− 10.55 →	− 10.5		+ 0.715 →	+ 0.7	
		$1.5			6.8	
9.	65.4 →	65	10.	27.14 →	27	
	− 22.2 →	− 22		× 3.1 →	× 3	
		43			81	
11.	9.21 →	9	12.	110.2 →	110	
	+ 3.95 →	+ 4		+ 10.8 →	+ 11	
		2.25			10	

TEKS ★ TAKS Resources

• TAKS Strategies, p. 59
• TAKS Tune-Up, pp. 63–65

TAKS Tune-Up Kit

• TAKS Daily Review Transparencies
• TAKS Review and Preparation Workbook
• TAKS Strategies with Transparencies
• Texas Progress Monitoring Assessments

TEKS ★ TAKS

(7.2)(B) To use addition and subtraction to solve problems involving decimals **TAKS Obj. 1**

(7.2)(G) To determine the reasonableness of a solution **TAKS Obj. 1**

Dana Center TEKS Toolkit Clarifying Activities (7.2)(B), (7.2)(G)
Visit: PHSchool.com
Web Code: arq-9045

Professional Development

TEKS Math Background

The standard methods for adding and subtracting decimals require that the numbers be matched place for place. That is, tenths must be added to or subtracted from tenths, hundredths must be added to or subtracted from hundredths, and so on. For this reason, the first step in an addition or subtraction is a vertical alignment of the decimal points. Then digits with the same place value are matched and the addition or subtraction can proceed.

More Math Background: p. 2C

Lesson Planning and Resources

See p. 2E for a list of the resources that support this lesson.

PowerPoint

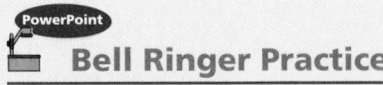 **Bell Ringer Practice**

✓ **Check Skills You'll Need**
Use student page, transparency, or PowerPoint.

TAKS Daily Review 2
Use transparency.

✓ Check Skills You'll Need

1. Vocabulary Review
What is *place value?*
1–5. See below.
Write the value of the digit 8 in each number.
2. 0.385   **3.** 1.879
4. 812.4   **5.** 0.238

GO for Help
Skills Handbook p. 658

nline

Video Tutor Help
Visit: PHSchool.com
Web Code: are-0775

Check Skills You'll Need

1. Place value is the position and value of a digit in a decimal.

2. 8 hundredths

3. 8 tenths

4. 8 hundreds

5. 8 thousandths

1-2 Adding and Subtracting Decimals

TEKS ★ TAKS

- (7.2)(B) To use addition and subtraction to solve problems involving decimals **TAKS Obj. 1**
- (7.2)(G) To determine the reasonableness of a solution **TAKS Obj. 1**
- 🔊 **New Vocabulary** Identity Property of Addition, Commutative Property of Addition, Associative Property of Addition

Why Learn This?

Sometimes an estimate is not good enough. You can add and subtract decimals to find an exact answer.

When you add decimals, you must align the decimal points so that corresponding place values are added. You may need to insert, or "annex," zeros so you have the same number of decimal places in each number.

EXAMPLE   Adding Decimals

1 Music A marching band has 6.5 minutes to perform at a football game. Does the band have enough time to play "America the Beautiful" and "Yankee Doodle Dandy"?

Estimate $3.63 + 2.5 \approx 4 + 3$, or 7

Align the decimal points.

$$\begin{array}{r} 3.63 \\ + 2.50 \\ \hline 6.13 \end{array}$$

Insert a zero so both addends ← have the same number of decimal places.

The band will play for 6.13 minutes. The band will have enough time.

Check for Reasonableness Since 6.13 is close to 7, the answer is reasonable.

✓ Quick Check

1. How long will the band take to play "Stars and Stripes Forever" and "The Star-Spangled Banner"? **8.02 min**

Band Selections

Title	Min
"76 Trombones"	3.12
"Stars and Stripes Forever"	3.52
"Born in the U.S.A."	4.65
"America the Beautiful"	3.63
"Yankee Doodle Dandy"	2.5
"The Star-Spangled Banner"	4.5

---

8   Chapter 1   Decimals and Integers

Differentiated Instruction Solutions for All Learners

Special Needs L1
Review number pairs that add up to multiples of 10. For example, numbers ending in 7 and 3, 6 and 4, or 2 and 8 can always be grouped together to make calculations easier.

learning style: verbal

Below Level L2
Give students simple additions such as the following to focus on the need to line up the decimal points.
0.4 + 0.01 **0.41**   0.12 + 8 **8.12**
0.5 + 16 + 0.03 **16.53**

learning style: visual

When you subtract decimals, you may need to regroup.

EXAMPLE Subtracting Decimals

2 Find 89.9 − 46.78.

Align the decimal points.	Regroup.	Subtract.
$\begin{array}{r} 89.90 \\ -46.78 \end{array}$ ← Insert a zero.	$\begin{array}{r} \overset{8\ 10}{89.\cancel{9}0} \\ -46.78 \end{array}$	$\begin{array}{r} \overset{8\ 10}{89.\cancel{9}0} \\ -46.78 \\ \hline 43.12 \end{array}$

✓ Quick Check

2. Find 26.7 − 14.81. **11.89**

You can use the properties of addition to add mentally.

KEY CONCEPTS Properties of Addition

Identity Property of Addition The sum of 0 and a is a.

Arithmetic $5.6 + 0 = 5.6$ **Algebra** $a + 0 = a$

Commutative Property of Addition Changing the order of the addends does not change the sum.

Arithmetic $1.2 + 3.4 = 3.4 + 1.2$ **Algebra** $a + b = b + a$

Associative Property of Addition Changing the grouping of the addends does not change the sum.

Arithmetic   **Algebra**

$(2.5 + 6) + 4 = 2.5 + (6 + 4)$ $(a + b) + c = a + (b + c)$

EXAMPLE Using Properties of Addition

3 **Mental Math** Find $0.7 + 12.5 + 1.3$.

What You Think

I should look for compatible numbers. The sum of 0.7 and 1.3 is 2. Then I can add 2 and 12.5 for a total of 14.5.

Why It Works

$$0.7 + 12.5 + 1.3 = 0.7 + 1.3 + 12.5 \quad \leftarrow \text{Commutative Property of Addition}$$
$$= (0.7 + 1.3) + 12.5 \quad \leftarrow \text{Associative Property of Addition}$$
$$= 2 + 12.5 = 14.5$$

★ **TAKS Tip**

Look for compatible numbers when you add several numbers.

✓ Quick Check

3. Use mental math to find $4.4 + 5.3 + 0.6$. **10.3**

1-2 Adding and Subtracting Decimals   **9**

2. Teach

Activity Lab

Use before the lesson.

All in One Teaching Resources

Activity Lab 1-2: Adding Decimals on the Road

Guided Instruction

Example 3

Have students write "0.7"; "12.5"; "1.3"; "("; ")"; and two "+" signs on seven small cards, one number or symbol per card. Tell them to use the cards to form 0.7 + 12.5 + 1.3. Students can then change the order and insert the parentheses to act out the properties.

PowerPoint

Additional Examples

1 Find 2.15 + 7.632 + 16.5. **26.282**

2 You have 5.08 min left on a CD. How much time will you have left after you record a 2.5 minute song? **2.58 min**

3 Use mental math to find 0.2 + 15.7 + 3.8. **19.7**

All in One Teaching Resources

• Daily Notetaking Guide 1-2 **L3**
• Adapted Notetaking 1-2 **L1**

Closure

• *How do you add or subtract decimals?* Sample: Align the decimal points; insert zeros so each number has the same number of decimal places; then add or subtract as with whole numbers.

Advanced Learners **L4**

Fill in each box with one of the digits 1, 2, 3, 4, 5 to make a true statement. Each digit is used exactly once.

5.3 − 2.14

□ . □ − □ . □□ = 3.16

Pre-AP™

English Language Learners **ELL**

Make sure students understand the difference between annexing zeros and just writing zeros anywhere in a decimal number. Tell students that the word *annex* means to add on at the end.

learning style: verbal

Assignment Guide

Check Your Understanding
Go over Exercises 1–7 in class before assigning the Homework Exercises.

Homework Exercises
A Practice by Example   8–32
B Apply Your Skills   33–40
C Challenge   41
TEKS ★ TAKS Tune-Up and
Mixed Review   42–47

Homework Quick Check
To check students' understanding of key skills and concepts, go over Exercises 13, 21, 34, 38, and 39.

Differentiated Instruction Resources

✓ Check Your Understanding

1. **Vocabulary** Which property allows you to regroup addends?
   Assoc. Prop. of Add.
2. **Number Sense** Which pair of addends forms compatible numbers in the expression $6.1 + 8.4 + 1.6$? **8.4 and 1.6**

Mental Math Find each sum.

3. $23 + 17$ **40**   4. $0.8 + 1.2$ **2**   5. $16.9 + 2.1$ **19**

Find each missing number.

6. $2.7 + \blacksquare = 1.5 + 2.7$ **1.5**   7. $144.98 + \blacksquare = 144.98$ **0**

Homework Exercises

For more exercises, see Extra Skills and Word Problems.

 for Help

For Exercises	See Examples
8–17	1
18–26	2
27–32	3

Ⓐ **Find each sum.**

8. $4.56 + 2.9$ **7.46**   9. $102.8 + 3$ **105.8**   10. $3.061 + 1.8$ **4.861**

11. $0.582 + 7$ **7.582**   12. $3.29 + 2 + 6.71$ **12**   13. $1.913 + 0.08 + 3$ **4.993**

14. $1.4 + 3.75 + 6$ **11.15**   15. $7.58 + 2.4 + 0.101$ **10.081**   16. $0.005 + 0.5 + 5$ **5.505**

17. The record length of a king cobra is 5.58 m. The average length is 3.7 m. How much longer than average is the record holder? **1.88 m**

Find each difference.

18. $5.3 - 0.12$ **5.18**   19. $12.46 - 7.2$ **5.26**   20. $3.102 - 0.89$ **2.212**

21. $0.1305 - 0.066$ **0.0645**   22. $0.08 - 0.002$ **0.078**   23. $100 - 31.93$ **68.07**

24. $2.101 - 1.22$ **0.881**   25. $46.2 - 38.25$ **7.95**   26. $0.15 - 0.015$ **0.135**

Use mental math to find each sum.

27. $16.2 + 23.5 + 3.8$ **43.5**   28. $24.4 + (5.6 + 11)$ **41.0**   29. $27.4 + 0 + 12.1$ **39.5**

30. $9.2 + 1.8 + 0$ **11.0**   31. $(4.7 + 10.6) + 0.3$ **15.6**   32. $8.5 + 6.3 + 1.5$ **16.3**

Ⓑ **GPS** 33. **Guided Problem Solving** A band can play as much as 8 minutes of music in a competition. If the band plays a 2.33-minute song and a 4.25-minute song, how many minutes does it have left? **1.42 min**
   • **Make a Plan** First find the total number of minutes in the two songs. Then subtract the total from the maximum time allowed.
   • **Carry Out the Plan** The total time is ■. The time remaining is ■.

34. Since $51.23 - 51.23 = 0$, you use the Ident. Prop. of Add. to say $0 + 97.9 = 97.9$.

34. **Writing in Math** How can you use the Identity Property of Addition to find $51.23 - 51.23 + 97.9$? **See left.**

10   **Chapter 1** Decimals and Integers

Use <, =, or > to complete each statement.

35. $3.45 + 2.9$ ▆ $8.9 - 2.75$ `>`

36. $15 - 6.82$ ▆ $32.18 - 24$ `=`

37. **Architecture** Find the difference in the heights of the Empire State Building and the Eiffel Tower. **122.4 m**

320.8 m

443.2 m

38. You decide to save some money. In week 1 you save $4.20, in week 2 you save $3.85, and in week 3 you save $2.50. Estimate your total savings. Then find the exact amount you saved. **about $11; $10.55**

39. **Weather** During a 3-day storm, 8.91 in. of rain fell in Tallahassee and 4.24 in. fell in St. Augustine. How much more rain fell in Tallahassee than in St. Augustine? **4.67 in.**

40. The original price for a jacket is $79.95. How much do you save if you buy the jacket on sale for $62.79? **$17.16**

C 41. **Challenge** The fastest mammal, the cheetah, can run as fast as 67.912 mi/h. The fastest fish, the sailfish, can swim as fast as 1.132 mi/min. Which animal is faster? How much faster is it? **sailfish; 0.008 mi/h**

TEKS ★ **TAKS** **Tune-Up and Mixed Review**

TAKS Objective 1
TEKS (7.2)(F)

42. You receive $50 for your birthday. You buy a book for $14.95 and a baseball cap for $24.95. How much money do you have left? **D**
   - Ⓐ $60.10
   - Ⓑ $39.90
   - Ⓒ $29.90
   - Ⓓ $10.10

TAKS Objective 1
TEKS (7.2)(B)

43. The average rainfall for Houston, Texas, is 4.5 inches in October, 4.2 inches in November, and 3.7 inches in December. Find the total average rainfall for the last three months of the year. **H**
   - Ⓕ 11.4 in.
   - Ⓖ 11.9 in.
   - Ⓗ 12.4 in.
   - Ⓙ 12.9 in.

TAKS Objective 6
TEKS (7.14)(A)

44. Carla bought a CD for $12.99 and a book for $7.29. She also rented a movie for $3.99. Which expression can be used to find the best estimate of the total amount Carla spent, not including tax? **D**
   - Ⓐ $12 + 7 + 3$
   - Ⓒ $13 + 7 + 3$
   - Ⓑ $12 + 7 + 4$
   - Ⓓ $13 + 7 + 4$

GO for Help **Skills p. 656**

Find each product.

45. 17×8 **136**

46. 15×0 **0**

47. 4×56 **224**

Alternative Assessment

Have students write and solve Exercises 8–16 and 18–26 on graph paper using vertical format. Stress that all the decimal points and all digits with the same place value must be aligned.

TEKS ★ **TAKS** **Resources**

- TAKS Strategies, p. 59
- TAKS Tune-Up, pp. 63–65

TAKS **Tune-Up Kit**

- TAKS Daily Review Transparencies
- TAKS Review and Preparation Workbook
- TAKS Strategies with Transparencies
- Texas Progress Monitoring Assessments

---

4. Assess & Reteach

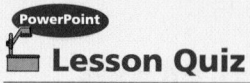

PowerPoint
Lesson Quiz

Find each sum or difference.

1. $15 - 8.72$ **6.28**

2. $3.91 + 11.8$ **15.71**

3. $0.048 + 4.65$ **4.698**

4. $35.9 - 18.33$ **17.57**

11

Using Mental Math

Using Mental Math

Compensation allows you to adjust the numbers and make the expressions easier to calculate mentally. You can use compensation to find sums and differences.

The sum of two numbers remains the same if you add a number to one addend and subtract the same number from the other addend.

The difference between two numbers remains the same if you add (or subtract) the same number from both numbers.

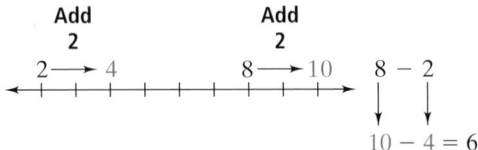

Subtract 3   Add 3

$2 \leftarrow 5 \quad 7 \rightarrow 10$ $7 + 5$

$10 + 2 = 12$

Add 2   Add 2

$2 \rightarrow 4 \quad 8 \rightarrow 10$ $8 - 2$

$10 - 4 = 6$

EXAMPLE   Using Compensation

Find each sum or difference using compensation.

a. $4.96 + $3.79

$$\$4.96 + \$3.79$$
$$\downarrow \qquad \downarrow$$
$$+ 0.04 - 0.04$$
$$\downarrow \qquad \downarrow$$
$$\$5.00 + \$3.75 = \$8.75$$

Add 0.04 to one addend ← and subtract 0.04 from the other addend.

b. $6.1 - 1.3$

$$6.1 - 1.3$$
$$\downarrow \qquad \downarrow$$
$$+ 0.7 + 0.7$$
$$\downarrow \qquad \downarrow$$
$$6.8 - 2 = 4.8$$

Add 0.7 to both numbers ← so that you subtract a whole number.

Exercises

Find each sum or difference using compensation.

1. $\begin{array}{r} 0.95 \\ + 1.45 \end{array}$ 2.4

2. $\begin{array}{r} 2.54 \\ + 8.16 \end{array}$ 10.7

3. $\begin{array}{r} 3.89 \\ + 1.73 \end{array}$ 5.62

4. $\begin{array}{r} 72.2 \\ + 14.9 \end{array}$ 87.1

5. $\begin{array}{r} 38.0 \\ - 11.1 \end{array}$ 26.9

6. $\begin{array}{r} 9.3 \\ - 6.8 \end{array}$ 2.5

7. $\begin{array}{r} 102 \\ - 77 \end{array}$ 25

8. $\begin{array}{r} 41.6 \\ - 0.7 \end{array}$ 40.9

9. $0.4 + 7.8$ 8.2

10. $117 + 96$ 213

11. $74.6 - 35.8$ 38.8

12. $12.4 - 8.3$ 4.1

13. $11.7 - 6.9$ 4.8

14. $2.9 + 10.5$ 13.4

15. $984 - 852$ 132

16. $72.3 + 8.1$ 80.4

17. **Money** You have five items to purchase at the grocery store. The prices are $.98, $3.95, $2.08, $4.99, and $1. Use compensation to determine the amount you owe at the checkout. $13

12   **Extension**   Using Mental Math

Using Mental Math

Students can use the mental math strategy of compensation to find sums and differences without pencil or paper.

Guided Instruction

Sometimes when people go shopping, they have to make a quick estimate, in their heads, of how much they have spent in order to make sure they have enough money for all they intend to buy. Discuss that to do so, they can round some prices up and others down to get a rough estimate. Then point out that when people use this *estimation* strategy, they are using an approach similar to the *mental math* strategy of compensation.

Error Prevention!

Watch for students who confuse compensation with rounding. Compensation provides an exact answer, not an estimate.

Work through the Example parts (a) and (b) with students. Ask: *What aspect of the compensation process is similar in these two examples?* Sample: numbers were added to form a whole number in each case—$5 in one and 2 in the other.

Differentiated Instruction

Special Needs   L1

Elicit from students that forming numbers that are easy to compute with mentally is effective. Provide additional examples, such as $19 + 34 \rightarrow 20 + 33 = 53$.

Resources

• Classroom Aid 7

Modeling Decimal Multiplication

You can use models to multiply decimals. The grid below is divided into 10 columns and 10 rows. Each column or row represents one tenth of the whole, or 0.1. Each square represents one hundredth of the whole, or 0.01.

TEKS **TAKS**

(7.2)(A) To represent multiplication situations involving decimals with models, pictures, words, and numbers **TAKS** Obj. 1

ACTIVITY

You can use three grids to construct a model to find 0.7 × 0.4.

Step 1 Model 0.7 by shading 7 columns in one color. Model 0.4 by shading 4 rows in a different color.

Step 2 Shade 0.7 and 0.4 on the same grid. Count the number of squares that are shaded in both colors.

There are 28 squares shaded in both colors, so 0.7 × 0.4 = 0.28.

Exercises

Draw a model to find each product.   1–3. See margin.

1. 0.2 × 0.9   **2.** 0.5 × 0.3   **3.** 0.4 × 0.4

Write the product represented by each decimal grid.

4. 0.1 × 0.7 = 0.07

5. 0.6 × 0.3 = 0.18

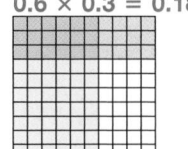

6. 0.9 × 0.5 = 0.45

7. Use Exercises 1–3. Multiply each factor by 10. Find the new products. How do the new products compare to the original products?

The product becomes a whole number.

1.   **2.**   **3.**

Activity Lab

Modeling Decimal Multiplication

Students use grids to model multiplication with decimals.

Guided Instruction

Activity
Be sure students understand that Step 1 shows both factors and Step 2 shows the product in the overlap area.

Exercises
Have students work independently on Exercises 1–3 and with partners on Exercises 4–7. Suggest that they write the factors for each grid in Exercises 4–6.

Alternative Method
Students can also represent decimal multiplication with place-value models. They can use one hundred squares to represent ones, tens squares to represent tenths, and ones squares for hundredths.

Differentiated Instruction

Visual Learners
For Exercise 7, ask students to represent each problem visually as an array.

Advanced Learners   **L4**
Ask students whether the products found in Exercises 1–6 are greater or less than the factors. Have them explain their answer. Less the product of two factors less than 1 is less than either factor.

TEKS ★ TAKS Resources

- Activity Lab 1-3: Taxing Problems
- grid models
- Classroom Aid 2
- Student Manipulatives Kit

Dana Center TEKS Toolkit Clarifying Activities (7.2)(A)
Visit: PHSchool.com
Web Code: arq-9045

TEKS ★ TAKS

(7.2)(A) To represent multiplication situations involving decimals TAKS Obj. 1

(7.2)(B) To use multiplication to solve problems involving decimals TAKS Obj. 1

(7.2)(G) To determine the reasonableness of a solution TAKS Obj. 1

Dana Center TEKS Toolkit Clarifying Activities (7.2)(A), (7.2)(B), (7.2)(G)
Visit: PHSchool.com
Web Code: arq-9045

TEKS Math Background

In mathematics, a *postulate* is a statement that is assumed to be true. An important set of postulates governs the basic arithmetic operations. The properties of multiplication presented in this lesson are among these postulates.

Students sometimes wonder why there are lists of properties for addition and multiplication but no lists of properties for subtraction. The reason is that, algebraically, subtraction is defined in terms of addition. Specifically, for real numbers *a* and *b*:

$$a - b = a + (-b)$$

More Math Background: p. 2C

Lesson Planning and Resources

See p. 2E for a list of the resources that support this lesson.

Bell Ringer Practice

✓ **Check Skills You'll Need**
Use student page, transparency, or PowerPoint.

TAKS **Daily Review 3**
Use transparency.

14

1-3 Multiplying Decimals

✓ Check Skills You'll Need

1. Vocabulary Review
How is estimating different from finding an exact answer?
See below.
Estimate.

2. 2.7×5.3 **15**

3. 4.09×6.8 **28**

4. 1.134×9.76 **10**

 for Help
Lesson 1-1

TEKS ★ TAKS

- **(7.2)(A)** To represent multiplication situations involving decimals TAKS Obj. 1
- **(7.2)(B)** To use multiplication to solve problems involving decimals TAKS Obj. 1
- **(7.2)(G)** To determine the reasonableness of a solution TAKS Obj. 1

◀)) **New Vocabulary** Properties of Multiplication: Identity Property, Zero Property, Commutative Property, Associative Property

Why Learn This?

Multiplying decimals can help you find how much money you will earn working at a part-time job.

To multiply decimals, treat the factors as whole numbers. Then multiply. Count the decimal places in both factors. Use the total to locate the decimal point in the product.

Check Skills You'll Need

1. Estimating gives an approximate answer.

EXAMPLE Multiplying Decimals

1 At your part-time job, you earn $7.30 per hour. You work for two and a half hours. How much money do you earn?

Estimate $7.30 \times 2.5 \approx 7 \times 3 = 21$.

Step 1 Multiply as if the numbers are whole numbers.

$$\begin{array}{r} 730 \\ \times\ 25 \\ \hline 3650 \\ 1460 \\ \hline 18250. \end{array}$$

Step 2 Locate the decimal point in the product by adding the decimal places of the factors.

$$\begin{array}{r} 7.30 \\ \times\ 2.5 \\ \hline 3650 \\ 1460 \\ \hline 18.250 \end{array}$$

7.30 ← two decimal places (hundredths)
× 2.5 ← one decimal place (tenths)

← hundredths × tenths = thousandths
Use three decimal places.

You earn $18.25.

Check for Reasonableness The product 18.25 is close to the estimate of 21. The answer is reasonable.

✓ Quick Check

● **1.** Estimate 14.3×0.81. Then find the product. **11.583**

Differentiated Instruction Solutions for All Learners

Special Needs L1
To show students that in the Associative Property the order of the addends stays the same and only the grouping changes, have them color-code the addends on each side of the equal sign.

learning style: visual

Below Level L2
Review multiplying decimals by 10, 100, and 1,000 by reading aloud exercises like these.

2.7×10 **27** $2.7 \times 1,000$ **2,700**
4.93×100 **493** 49.3×100 **4,930**

learning style: verbal

Four ways to write "3 times 5" using different symbols are shown below.

$$3 \times 5 \qquad 3 \cdot 5 \qquad 3(5) \qquad (3)(5)$$

KEY CONCEPTS Properties of Multiplication

Identity Property of Multiplication The product of 1 and a is a.

Arithmetic	Algebra
$5 \cdot 1 = 5$	$a \cdot 1 = a$
$1 \cdot 5 = 5$	$1 \cdot a = a$

Zero Property The product of 0 and any number is 0.

Arithmetic	Algebra
$5 \cdot 0 = 0$	$a \cdot 0 = 0$
$0 \cdot 5 = 0$	$0 \cdot a = 0$

Commutative Property of Multiplication Changing the order of factors does not change the product.

Arithmetic	Algebra
$5 \cdot 2 = 2 \cdot 5$	$a \cdot 2 = 2 \cdot a$

Associative Property of Multiplication Changing the grouping of factors does not change the product.

Arithmetic	Algebra
$(3 \cdot 2) \cdot 5 = 3 \cdot (2 \cdot 5)$	$(a \cdot b) \cdot c = a \cdot (b : c)$

Vocabulary Tip

To *commute* means "to change places." A commutative property lets numbers change places.

To *associate* means "to gather in groups." An associative property forms groups of numbers.

You can use the properties of multiplication to multiply mentally.

EXAMPLE Using Multiplication Properties

2 Mental Math Use mental math to find $0.25 \cdot 3.58 \cdot 4$.

What you think

I should look for compatible numbers. The product of 0.25 and 4 is 1. Then the product of 1 and 3.58 is 3.58.

Why it works

$$0.25 \cdot 3.58 \cdot 4 = 0.25 \cdot 4 \cdot 3.58 \qquad \leftarrow \text{ Commutative Property of Multiplication}$$
$$= (0.25 \cdot 4) \cdot 3.58 \qquad \leftarrow \text{ Associative Property of Multiplication}$$
$$= 1 \cdot 3.58 \qquad \leftarrow \text{ Simplify.}$$
$$= 3.58 \qquad \leftarrow \text{ Identity Property of Multiplication}$$

✓ Quick Check

2. Use mental math to find $2.5 \cdot 6.3 \cdot 4$. 63

2. Teach

Activity Lab

Use before the lesson.
Student Edition Activity Lab 1-3a, Modeling Decimal Multiplication, p. 13

All in One Teaching Resources
Activity Lab 1-3: Taxing Problems

Guided Instruction

Example 1
Make sure students understand that the term "decimal places" refers to the places to the right of the decimal point—tenths, hundredths, thousandths, and so on.

Example 2
Encourage students to use the complete name of each property. For instance, they should say "the Identity Property of Multiplication" and "the Identity Property of Addition" instead of simply "the Identity Property." The properties of addition and multiplication are related to each other, but distinct.

PowerPoint

Additional Examples

1 Find the product of 11.4 and 3.6. **41.04**

2 Use mental math to find $2 \cdot 4.097 \cdot 0.5$. **4.097**

All in One Teaching Resources
- Daily Notetaking Guide 1-3 **L3**
- Adapted Notetaking 1-3 **L1**

Closure

- *How do you multiply decimals?* First multiply as if the factors were whole numbers. Then add the number of decimal places in both factors to find the number of decimal places in the product.

Advanced Learners **L4**
Show three ways to place the decimal points in the factors so that the product of 543×21 is 114.03.
Samples: 543×0.21; 54.3×2.1; 5.43×21

Pre-AP™

English Language Learners **ELL**
In Example 2, help students to understand why they reordered and regrouped the factors. Explicitly state that they were reordered for compatibility and regrouped to make the multiplication easier.

learning style: verbal

Assignment Guide

Check Your Understanding
Go over Exercises 1–10 in class before assigning the Homework Exercises.

Homework Exercises
A Practice by Example   11–29
B Apply Your Skills   30–40
C Challenge   41
TEKS ★ ⟨TAKS⟩ Tune-Up and
    Mixed Review   42–47

Homework Quick Check
To check students' understanding of key skills and concepts, go over Exercises 13, 27, 37, 39, and 40.

Differentiated Instruction Resources

(Adapted Practice 1-3 — L1)

Practice 1-3   Multiplying   L3

Find each product.
1. 28 × 6   168
2. 7.3 · 0.9   6.57
3. 58 · 2.1   121.8
4. 15(187)   2,805
5. 6.6 × 25   165
6. (1.8)(0.7)   1.26
7. 0.91 · 2.7   2.457
8. 4.6(3.9)   17.94
9. 17.3 × 15.23   263.479
10. 2.33(3.56)   8.2948
11. 12.15 × 19   230.85
12. 481.51 × 623.42   300,182.9642

Rewrite each equation with the decimal point in the correct place in the product.
13. 5.6 × 1.2 = 672   5.6 × 1.2 = 6.72
14. 3.7 × 2.4 = 888   3.7 × 2.4 = 8.88
15. 6.5 × 2.5 = 1625   6.5 × 2.5 = 16.25
16. 1.02 × 6.9 = 7038   1.02 × 6.9 = 7.038
17. 4.4 × 6.51 = 28644   4.4 × 6.51 = 28.644
18. 0.6 × 9.312 = 55872   0.6 × 9.312 = 5.5872

Name the property of multiplication shown.
19. 3 × 4 = 4 × 3   Commutative Property
20. 9 × (6 × 3) = (9 × 6) × 3   Associative Property
21. 2 × 0 = 0   Zero Property
22. 10 × 1 = 10   Identity Property

Solve.
23. Each trip on a ride at the carnival costs $1.25. If Tara goes on 4 rides, how much will it cost her? $5.00
24. Postage stamps cost $0.37 each. How much does a book of 50 stamps cost? $18.50

1-3 • Guided Problem Solving   GPS   L3

Student Page 17, Exercise 39:
In 2003, Texas had about 2.6 times the number of head of cattle as Oklahoma. Oklahoma had 5.2 million. How many head of cattle did Texas have?

Understand
1. Circle the information you will need to solve the problem.
2. What are you being asked to do? Find how many head of cattle Texas had.

Plan and Carry Out
3. How many million head of cattle were in Oklahoma in 2003?   5.2
4. How many times more cattle did Texas have than Oklahoma?   2.6 times more
5. Write an expression for the number of cattle in Texas (in millions).   2.6 × 5.2
6. How many decimal places are in both factors?   2 decimal places
7. Multiply as if the numbers are whole numbers.   1,352
8. Place the decimal in the product using the total number of decimal places from step 6.   13.52 million

Check
9. Estimate the product of 2.6 × 5.2, and compare it to your answer. Is your answer reasonable?   15; yes, the estimate is slightly high, but it is reasonable

Solve Another Problem
10. You buy 6.5 yards of fabric that costs $7.95 per yard. How much money does it cost? $51.68

---

1. **Vocabulary** Which property of multiplication allows you to switch the order of the factors? **Comm. Prop. of Mult.**

2. What product does the model at the left represent? **0.5 × 0.2 = 0.1**

3. **Number Sense** The product of 4 and 25 is 100. What happens to the product when you change one factor from 25 to 2.5? **The product is divided by 10.**

Multiply.

4. 0.5 × 6 **3**
5. 0.25 · 8 **2**
6. 1.5 × 2 **3**

Find the missing numbers. Name the property of multiplication shown.

7. 3.6 · ■ = 0   **0**   **Zero Property**
8. ■ · 1 = 25.5   **25.5**   **Identity Property**
9. ■ · 4 = 4 · 3   **3**   **Commutative Property**
10. (5 · ■) · 2.3 = 5 · (1.4 · 2.3)   **1.4**   **Associative Property**

Homework Exercises

For more exercises, see Extra Skills and Word Problems.

GO for Help

For Exercises	See Examples
11–19	1
20–29	2

A Estimate. Then find each product.

11. 0.2 × 0.7 **0.14**
12. 0.4 × 0.6 **0.24**
13. 0.3 × 0.5 **0.15**
14. 1.02 × 3.6 **3.672**
15. 8.7 × 0.45 **3.915**
16. 1.45 × 2.6 **3.77**
17. 41 × 7.5 **307.5**
18. 1.3 × 0.05 **0.065**
19. 1.1 × 1.1 **1.21**

Mental Math Find each product.

20. 0.2 · 3.41 · 5   **3.41**
21. 1.09 · 23.6 · 0   **0**
22. (2.3 · 0.5) · 4   **4.6**
23. 5 · (4.3 · 1)   **21.5**
24. 0 · 2.78 · 1   **0**
25. 0.4 · 3.29 · 25   **32.9**
26. 0.4 · (0.5 · 0.2)   **0.04**
27. 3.6 · 2.5 · 2   **18**
28. 7.1 · 6.2 · 3.5 · 0   **0**

29. **Biking** If your speed is 3.5 mi/h, how far will you bike in 1.2 h? **4.2 mi**

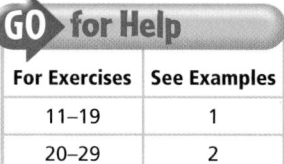

B GPS 30. **Guided Problem Solving** You have 17 pennies, 31 nickels, 22 dimes, and 14 quarters. How much money will you have if you lend $6.50 to a friend? **$.92**
   • How much money do you have in each type of coin?
   • What is the total amount of money you have?

31. **Money** A penny weighs about 0.1 oz. How much is a pound of pennies worth? (1 lb = 16 oz) **$1.60**

32. A cubic foot of water weighs 62.4 lb. A water storage tank can hold 89.5 cubic feet of water. How much will the water in the storage tank weigh when the tank is full? **5,584.8 lb**

37. They both give you the same number you started with, but the identity is zero for addition and one for multiplication.

Find each product.

33. $0.36 \cdot 1.2$
0.432

34. $3.6 \cdot 0.12$
0.432

35. $0.36 \cdot 0.012$
0.00432

36. $0.036 \cdot 0.12$
0.00432

37. <u>Writing in Math</u> How are the identity properties of multiplication and addition similar? How are they different? See margin.

38. New tennis balls must bounce back to no less than 0.53 and no more than 0.58 of the starting height. A ball is dropped from 200 cm. Within what range of heights should it bounce?
between 106 cm and 116 cm

39. One year, Texas had about 2.6 times as many head of cattle as Oklahoma. Oklahoma had 5.2 million. How many head of cattle did Texas have? 13.52 million

40. The product of any two numbers between 0 and 1 will always be less than either of the numbers.

40. **Reasoning** You multiply two decimals that are both less than 1. How does the size of the product compare to each factor? Explain.

C **41.** **Challenge** White flour costs $1.30/kg, and whole wheat flour costs $1.10/kg. Flour is sold in bags of 1.2 kg and 3.4 kg. A chef buys 4 bags of flour. If each bag of flour the chef buys is different, how much must the chef pay? $11.04

TEKS ★ TAKS Tune-Up and Mixed Review

TAKS Objective 1
TEKS (7.2)(A)

42. Which model represents the expression 0.3×0.6? C

 A
 C
 B
 D

TAKS Objective 1
TEKS (7.2)(F)

43. Mr. Porter bought 24 bagels at 6 for $2.49 and 12 cartons of juice at 6 for $1.98. What was the total cost of the bagels and juice Mr. Porter bought, not including tax? J
F $8.84   **G** $9.96   **H** $11.88   **J** $13.92

 for Help **Lesson 1-2**

Find each sum or difference.

44. $8.56 + 3.11$
11.67

45. $9.843 - 8.2$
1.643

46. $9.4 - 7.024$
2.376

47. $17.1 + 3.09$
20.19

Alternative Assessment

Have students work in pairs. Each student writes a decimal for a factor. Partners show their decimals and together determine the number of decimal places in their product before they multiply the decimal factors.

TEKS ★ TAKS Resources

• TAKS Strategies, p. 59
• TAKS Tune-Up, pp. 63–65

TAKS Tune-Up Kit

• TAKS Daily Review Transparencies
• TAKS Review and Preparation Workbook
• TAKS Strategies with Transparencies
• Texas Progress Monitoring Assessments

---

 4. Assess & Reteach

PowerPoint
Lesson Quiz

Find each product.

1. 0.9×4.25 3.825

2. 6.7×8.08 54.136

3. 0.44×2.5 1.1

4. 6.3×0.7 4.41

Exercises

Have students use 10×10 grids or place-value models to help them multiply decimals.

Reteaching 1-3   Multiplying **L2**

Multiply 5.43×1.8.

① Multiply as if the numbers were whole numbers.
5.43
$\times 1.8$ 3 decimal places
4344

② Count the total number of decimal places in the factors.
$+ 543$
9.774 3 decimal places

③ Place the decimal point in the product.

Find each product.

1.	2.	3.	4.
1.42 $\times 7.2$	2.2 $\times 4.1$	5.11 $\times 0.3$	3.68 $\times 5.8$
10.224	9.02	1.533	21.344

5. 2.8×0.05 0.14
6. $1.45 \cdot 0.7$ 1.015
7. $(2.07)(4.9)$ 10.143

8. $9.3(0.56)$ 5.208
9. $0.006(3.75)$ 0.0225
10. 3.8×912 3,465.6

Rewrite each equation with the decimal point in the correct place in the product.

11. $19.2 \times 12.3 = 23616$
$19.2 \times 12.3 = 236.16$

12. $4.35(2.44) = 106140$
$4.35(2.44) = 10.6140$

13. $14 \times 8.66 = 12124$
$14 \times 8.66 = 121.24$

14. $10.821 \times 62.4 = 6752304$
$10.821 \times 62.4 = 675.2304$

15. $1.321 \times 2.23 = 294583$
$1.321 \times 2.23 = 2.94583$

16. $0.233 \times 19.22 = 447826$
$0.233 \times 19.22 = 4.47826$

Enrichment 1-3   Multiplying **L4**
Patterns in Numbers
Find each product.

1.		2.	
26×3	78	26×3	78
26×0.3	7.8	2.6×3	7.8
26×0.03	0.78	0.26×3	0.78
26×0.003	0.078	0.026×3	0.078

3. What pattern do you notice in the products?
Products where the factors have the same number of decimal places are the same.

4. Use the digits 3 and 26 as factors. Find three different pairs of numbers using any combination of decimal places whose product is 0.0000078.
Sample answer: (3)0.0000026; (0.3)0.000026; (0.03)0.00026

Rewrite each equation, adding one or more decimal points to make the equation true. You may also need to add zeros. Each exercise may have more than one correct answer.
Sample answers given.

5. $16 \times 1,175 = 188$
$16 \times 11.75 = 188$
6. $16 \times 1,175 = 18.8$
$16 \times 1.175 = 18.8$
7. $16 \times 1,175 = 1.88$
$16 \times 0.1175 = 1.88$

8. $16 \times 1,175 = 0.188$
$16 \times 0.01175 = 0.188$
9. $16 \times 1,175 = 0.0188$
$16 \times 0.001175 = 0.0188$
10. $16 \times 1,175 = 0.00188$
$16 \times 0.0001175 = 0.00188$

11. $16 \times 1,175 = 0.000188$
$16 \times 0.00001175 = 0.000188$
12. $16 \times 1,175 = 0.000188$
$16 \times 0.000001175 = 0.000188$
13. $16 \times 1,175 = 0.000188$
$0.000000016 \times 1175 = 0.000188$

17

Checkpoint Quiz

Use this Checkpoint Quiz to check students' understanding of the skills and concepts of Lessons 1-1 through 1-3.

Resources

- All in One Teaching Resources Checkpoint Quiz 1
- Texas ExamView CD-ROM
- Success Tracker™ Online Intervention

MATH AT WORK

Detective

Students may not be aware of all the mathematics a detective uses. Some may appreciate that detectives often deal with specific proof that involves mathematics in analyzing crime scenes, working with forensics, and profiling.

Guided Instruction

Have students give examples of how detectives use mathematics from some of their favorite books, television shows, or movies. Then ask questions, such as:

- *For how much time do you think a detective would use mathematics on an ordinary workday? Support your conclusion.* Sample: two hours doing paperwork and figuring out times and distances for a case
- *How would a detective use math to figure out when a crime had been committed?* Sample: checking times with witnesses or recording devices
- *What financial information might be useful to a detective?* Sample: how, where, and when a victim or criminal spent money or used credit cards

---

 Checkpoint Quiz 1 | **Lessons 1-1 through 1-3**

Use each strategy to estimate $3.07 + $3.48 + $4.24.

1. rounding to the nearest dollar first $10

2. front-end estimation $11

Use compatible numbers to estimate each answer.

3–4. Answers may vary. Samples are given.

3. $129.4 \div 23$
about 6

4. $37.6 \div 3.05$
about 13

Find each sum or difference.

5. $2.99 + 3.08 + 18.5$
24.57

6. $9.718 + 4.603$
14.321

7. $11.64 - 8.72$
2.92

8. $22.4 - 0.54$
21.86

Find each product.

9. $1.36 \cdot 8.94$
12.1584

10. 2.4×0.04
0.096

11. 12.16×4.2
51.072

12. $5.45 \cdot 2.04$
11.118

13. Use $<$, $=$, or $>$ to complete $61.25 - 30.17$ ■ 14.8×2.1.
$=$

14. Eduardo can type 65 words per minute. How many words can he type in 7.5 minutes? 487.5 words

15. Crafts A box of supplies contains 0.8 lb of red clay, 1.3 lb of green clay, and 2.1 lb of white clay, as well as three cans of paint that weigh 0.75 lb each. What is the total weight of the supplies? 6.45 lb

---

MATH AT WORK | **Detective**

Most people think of a detective as a person in a trench coat, looking for clues. In reality, detectives dress like anyone else. They can work for lawyers, government agencies, and businesses. Detectives may gather information to trace debtors or conduct background investigations.

Detectives use mathematics to locate stolen funds, develop financial profiles, or monitor expense accounts.

Go Online
PHSchool.com **For:** Information about detectives **Web Code:** arb-2031

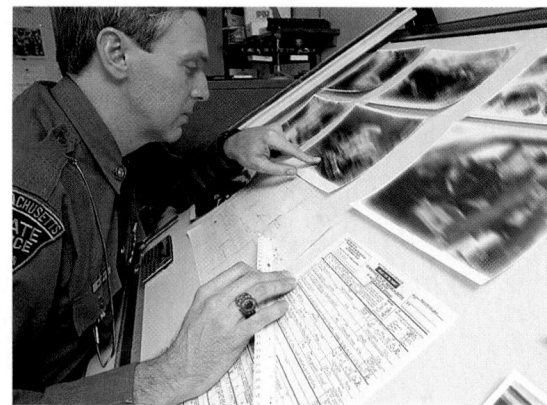

Hands On

TEKS ★ TAKS

(7.2)(A) To represent division situations involving decimals with concrete models, pictures, words, and numbers

TAKS Obj. 1

Modeling Decimal Division

You can use models to divide decimals. Follow the steps in the activity to model the quotient $0.6 \div 0.2$.

ACTIVITY

Step 1 Cut out a rectangular strip of paper that is 10 in. long. This strip represents 1 whole. Mark each inch of the strip. Notice that you now have 10 equal parts, each representing 0.1, or one tenth, of the whole.

1

Step 2 Cut the strip so that you have 2 segments. One segment should represent 0.6 of the whole.

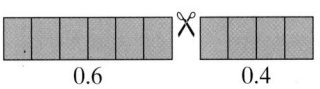

0.6   0.4

Step 3 Use another piece of paper and repeat Step 1.

Step 4 Cut this strip into 5 equal segments, so that each segment represents 0.2 of the whole.

0.2   0.2   0.2   0.2   0.2

Step 5 Align the segments that represent 0.2 under the segment that represents 0.6 of the whole.

0.6

Step 6 Count the number of 0.2 segments needed to equal the length of the 0.6 segment.

0.2   0.2   0.2

● You used 3 segments, each representing 0.2 unit, so $0.6 \div 0.2 = 3$.

Exercises

Use a model to find each quotient. 1–3. See margin.

1. $0.3 \div 0.1$ **2.** $0.4 \div 0.2$ **3.** $0.8 \div 0.4$

Write the quotient represented by each model.

4. $0.8 \div 0.2 = 4$

5. $0.9 \div 0.3 = 3$

6. $0.5 \div 0.1 = 5$
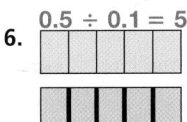

7. Reasoning The quotient of 0.6 and 0.2 is 3. What happens to the quotient when you multiply the dividend and divisor by 10? Explain. See margin.

1. 3;

2. 2;

3. 2;

7. The quotient is the same. You are still dividing the same number of pieces.

Activity Lab

Modeling Decimal Division

Students use paper strips to model dividing decimals.

Guided Instruction

Activity
In Step 2, ask: *What does the second segment represent?* **0.4 of the whole**

Exercises
Have students work in pairs to do Exercises 1–6. Have them discuss their work and share any questions with the class. Use Exercise 7 for class discussion.

Alternative Method
Students can also represent decimal division using 10×10 grids. To model $0.6 \div 0.2$, shade 60 squares and cut the shaded squares into three groups of 20 squares.

Differentiated Instruction

Advanced Learners **L4**
Ask students to explain how the model used in the activity could be used to represent the problem in Exercise 7, $6 \div 2$. **Relabel the segments as 6 and 2.**

TEKS ★ TAKS Resources

• Activity Lab 1-4: Patterns in Numbers
• rectangular paper strips
• Classroom Aids 16, 17
• Student Manipulatives Kit

Dana Center TEKS Toolkit Clarifying Activities (7.2)(A)
Visit: PHSchool.com
Web Code: arq-9045

TEKS ★ TAKS

(7.2)(A) To represent division situations involving decimals with models, pictures, words, and numbers TAKS Obj. 1

Also supports
(7.2)(B) TAKS Obj. 1
(7.2)(F) TAKS Obj. 1

Dana Center TEKS Toolkit Clarifying Activities (7.2)(A), (7.2)(B), (7.2)(F)
Visit: PHSchool.com
Web Code: arq-9045

Professional Development

TEKS Math Background

Students may wonder why there are no lists of properties for division. The reason is similar to that for subtraction. Algebraically, division is defined in terms of multiplication. Specifically, for real numbers a and b:

$$\frac{a}{b} = a \cdot \frac{1}{b}, \text{ where } b \neq 0$$

Since any division problem can be rewritten as a multiplication equivalent, there is no need for a separate set of properties for division.

More Math Background: p. 2C

Lesson Planning and Resources

See p. 2E for a list of the resources that support this lesson.

PowerPoint

Bell Ringer Practice

☑ **Check Skills You'll Need**
Use student page, transparency, or PowerPoint.

TAKS **Daily Review 4**
Use transparency.

1-4 Dividing Decimals

☑ Check Skills You'll Need

1. Vocabulary Review
What are *compatible numbers*?
1–4. See below.
Estimate each quotient using compatible numbers.

2. $103.8 \div 13.2$

3. $128.62 \div 9.86$

4. $41.77 \div 6.07$

GO for Help
Lesson 1-1

Check Skills You'll Need

1. numbers that are easy to compute mentally

2–4. Answers may vary. Samples are given.

2. 8

3. 13

4. 7

TEKS ★ TAKS

- (7.2)(A) To represent division situations involving decimals with models, pictures, words, and numbers TAKS Obj. 1
- (7.2)(B) To use division to solve problems involving decimals TAKS Obj. 1
- (7.2)(F) To select and use appropriate operations to solve problems and justify the selections TAKS Obj. 1

Why Learn This?

You may need to divide decimals to plan how many items you can buy with the money you have.

Suppose you have $1.20 and you want to buy pencils that cost $.30 each. How many pencils can you buy? Three ways to write "1.2 divided by 0.3" appear below.

$$1.2 \div 0.3 \qquad 0.3\overline{)1.2} \qquad \frac{1.2}{0.3}$$

To divide decimals, multiply both the divisor and the dividend by the power of 10 that makes the divisor a whole number. Then divide.

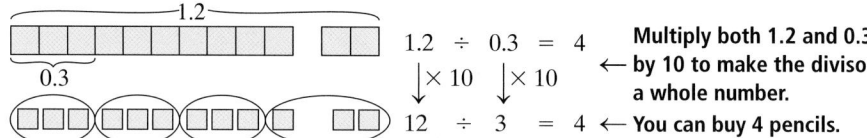

$$1.2 \div 0.3 = 4$$
Multiply both 1.2 and 0.3 by 10 to make the divisor a whole number.
$$\downarrow \times 10 \quad \downarrow \times 10$$
$$12 \div 3 = 4 \leftarrow \text{You can buy 4 pencils.}$$

EXAMPLE Dividing a Decimal by a Decimal

Vocabulary Tip

Recall the names of the parts of a division problem.

divisor → $6\overline{)18}$ ← quotient
↑
dividend

① Find $2.064 \div 0.24$.

$$0.24\overline{)2.064} \rightarrow 24\overline{)206.4}$$

$$\begin{array}{r} 8.6 \\ 24\overline{)206.4} \\ \underline{192} \\ 144 \\ \underline{144} \\ 0 \end{array}$$

Place the decimal point in the ← quotient above the decimal point in the dividend.

↑
Multiply the divisor and the dividend by 100 to make the divisor a whole number.

☑ Quick Check

1. Find each quotient.
  a. $12.42 \div 5.4$ **2.3** **b.** $67.84 \div 0.64$ **106** **c.** $144.06 \div 9.8$ **14.7**

Differentiated Instruction Solutions for All Learners

Special Needs L1
Slowly go over the steps of each example using dollar amounts. For example in Why Learn This?, students may miss why $.30 is written as 0.3 as the divisor.

learning style: visual

Below Level L2
Review dividing decimals by 10, 100, and 1,000 by reading aloud exercises like these.

$35 \div 10$ **3.5**	$3.5 \div 100$ **0.035**
$776 \div 100$ **7.76**	$776 \div 1{,}000$ **0.776**

learning style: verbal

When you divide by a decimal, sometimes you need to annex extra zeros in the dividend.

EXAMPLE Annexing Zeros to Divide

② **TAKS Multiple Choice** According to the American Academy of Pediatrics, the average 2-year-old child drinks about 6.8 ounces of juice per day. Suppose you have 48 ounces of juice. If you pour 6.8 ounces of juice for each child, how many children can you serve?

ⓐ 2   ⓑ 7   ⓒ 8   ⓓ 41

Step 1 Estimate to eliminate unreasonable answers.

$$48 \div 6.8 \approx 49 \div 7 = 7 \quad \leftarrow \text{Use compatible numbers 49 and 7.}$$

Since the estimate is 7, only choices B and C are reasonable. You can eliminate choices A and D.

Step 2 Calculate to decide which answer is correct.

$$6.8\overline{)48.0} \quad \rightarrow \quad 68\overline{)480.}$$
Annex the zero in the dividend.
← Multiply the divisor and dividend by 10 to make the divisor a whole number.

$$68\overline{)480.} \quad \begin{array}{r} 7. \\ \underline{476} \\ 4 \end{array} \quad \rightarrow \quad 68\overline{)480.00} \quad \begin{array}{r} 7.05 \\ \underline{476} \\ 400 \\ \underline{340} \\ 60 \end{array}$$
← Annex two zeros and divide. The quotient is about 7.05, which is only slightly more than 7. Only 7 children can be served.

You can serve 7 children with 48 oz of juice. The answer is B.

To eliminate unreasonable choices, estimate the answer to a multiple-choice question before calculating.

✓ **Quick Check**

2. You use 0.6 lb of bananas in each smoothie. How many smoothies can you make with 3.12 lb of bananas? **5.2 smoothies**

Notice the patterns in the divisors and the quotients at the right. As the divisors decrease by a factor of 10, the quotients increase by a factor of 10.

What happens when you try to divide by zero? Consider these related problems.

$$3 \cdot 2 = 6 \rightarrow 6 \div 3 = 2$$

$$0 \cdot \blacksquare = 12 \rightarrow 12 \div 0 = \blacksquare$$

No value for ■ makes sense! So, division by zero is undefined.

Dividend		Divisor		Quotient
50	÷	100	=	0.5
50	÷	10	=	5
50	÷	1	=	50
50	÷	0.1	=	500
50	÷	0.01	=	5,000
50	÷	0.001	=	50,000
50	÷	0.0001	=	500,000

Advanced Learners L4
Show three ways to place the decimal points in the divisor and dividend of this expression so that the quotient is 8.3.
3 4 8 6 ÷ 4 2
Samples: 34.86 ÷ 4.2; 3.486 ÷ 0.42; 348.6 ÷ 42.0
Pre-AP™

English Language Learners ELL
Help students understand the purpose of making the divisor a whole number when dividing decimals. Stress that students are not simply adding a zero when they multiply by 10, but they are moving the decimal point one place to the right.

learning style: visual

---

2. Teach

Activity Lab
Use before the lesson.
Student Edition Activity Lab, Hands On 1-4a, Modeling Decimal Division, p. 19

All in One Teaching Resources
Activity Lab 1-4: Patterns in Numbers

Guided Instruction

Example 1
Students sometimes have difficulty translating a division from the horizontal form to the "division house" form. Suggest that they make a display like the one below in their notebooks. Have them write each of the words *divisor, dividend,* and *quotient* in a different color, using the same color for the word in each form of the division.

$$\text{dividend} \div \text{divisor} = \text{quotient}$$
$$\text{divisor}\overline{)\text{dividend}}^{\text{quotient}}$$

Example 2
Ask: *How many zeros would you need to annex to divide 48 by 0.68?* **2**

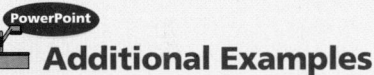

Additional Examples

① Find 40.2616 ÷ 6.824. **5.9**

② In a restaurant, one serving of cole slaw weighs 3.5 oz. The owner buys cole slaw in cans that weigh 98 oz each. How many servings are in each can? **28 servings**

All in One Teaching Resources
• Daily Notetaking Guide 1-4 L3
• Adapted Notetaking 1-4 L1

Closure
• *How do you divide decimals?* Rewrite the divisor as a whole number by multiplying both the divisor and the dividend by 10, 100, or 1,000. Then put the decimal point in the quotient and divide. Annex extra zeros as needed.

21

Assignment Guide

Check Your Understanding
Go over Exercises 1–6 in class before assigning the Homework Exercises.

Homework Exercises

A Practice by Example   7–22
B Apply Your Skills   23–37
C Challenge   38
TEKS ★ TAKS Tune-Up and Mixed Review   39–43

Homework Quick Check
To check students' understanding of key skills and concepts, go over Exercises 11, 18, 33, 35, and 36.

Differentiated Instruction Resources

✓ Check Your Understanding

1. **Vocabulary** The number being divided in a division problem is called the ?. **dividend**

2. **Estimation** Use compatible numbers to estimate $22.54 \div 3.99$. **6**

Find each quotient.

3. $75\overline{)300}$ **4**   4. $7.5\overline{)300}$ **40**   5. $0.75\overline{)300}$ **400**

6. **Patterns** Look at the divisors in Exercises 3–5. Notice that the decimal point moves one place to the left from one exercise to the next. Describe what happens to the quotients.

6. Answers may vary. Sample: The decimal point in the quotient moves one place to the right.

Homework Exercises

For more exercises, see Extra Skills and Word Problems.

GO for Help

For Exercises	See Examples
7–15	1
16–22	2

Ⓐ Find each quotient.

7. $19.2 \div 3.2$ **6**   8. $1.8\overline{)7.74}$ **4.3**   9. $\dfrac{56.4}{4.7}$ **12**

10. $\dfrac{17.8}{8.9}$ **2**   11. $83.7 \div 2.7$ **31**   12. $5.4\overline{)43.2}$ **8**

13. $9\overline{)641.7}$ **71.3**   14. $\dfrac{0.0882}{6}$ **0.0147**   15. $325.28 \div 30.4$ **10.7**

Annex zeros to find each quotient.

16. $0.04\overline{)10}$ **250**   17. $5.4 \div 7.2$ **0.75**   18. $\dfrac{126}{1.2}$ **105**

19. $592 \div 0.8$ **740**   20. $0.21 \div 0.6$ **0.35**   21. $\dfrac{0.003}{0.5}$ **0.006**

22. **Food** Nuts cost \$1.75 per jar. How many jars can you buy with \$14? **8 jars**

Ⓑ GPS 23. **Guided Problem Solving** A store buys 12 pens for \$11.28. The store sells each pen for \$1.99. What is the store's profit per pen? **\$1.05**
- **Make a Plan** Divide to find the cost of one pen. Then subtract the store's cost from the selling price to find the profit.
- **Carry Out the Plan** A single pen costs ■. The profit per pen is ■.

24. You spend \$13.92 for fabric. Each yard costs \$4.35. How many yards of fabric do you buy? **3.2 yd**

25. **Movies** You buy five movie tickets for a total of \$23.75. Your friend gives you \$5 for one ticket. How much change should you give your friend? **\$.25**

GO Online
Homework Help
Visit: PHSchool.com
Web Code: are-0104

26. A car travels 360.25 mi. It uses 13.1 gal of gas. How many miles per gallon of gas does the car travel? **27.5 mi**

Find each quotient.

27. $224.5 \div 0.05$ 4,490 **28.** $1.25\overline{)0.21}$ 0.168 **29.** $4.5\overline{)13.59}$ 3.02

30. $654 \div 0.12$ 5,450 **31.** $1.25\overline{)3.85}$ 3.08 **32.** $5.95\overline{)7.3423}$ 1.234

Careers Landscape architects plan and develop landscape projects.

35. The quotient is greater than the divisor; dividing by a number less than one is the same as multiplying by a number greater than one.

36. No; the quotient will not be the same if you switch the dividend and divisor; $6 \div 2 \neq 2 \div 6$.

33. Landscaping After digging up lilac bushes in a garden, a landscape **GPS** architect uses sod to cover the ground. The sod costs \$2.25/yd. He pays \$31.50. How much sod does he buy? **14 yd**

34. You have a dog-walking business. Last week you worked 7.5 hours and you earned \$41.25. How much do you earn per hour? **\$5.50**

35. Reasoning When you divide a whole number by a decimal divisor less than 1, how does the size of the quotient relate to the divisor? Explain. **See left.**

36. Writing in Math Do you think there is a commutative property of division? Explain why or why not. Give examples. **See left.**

37. You are making a homework planner that is 8.5 in. wide. The first column is 1.25 in. wide and lists the subjects. The next five columns are equally wide and represent the five school days. How many inches wide is the column for Monday? **1.45 in.**

C 38. Challenge You want to cover a square floor that measures 127.2 in. on a side with square tiles. Each tile measures 2.4 in. on a side. How many tiles do you need? **2,809 tiles**

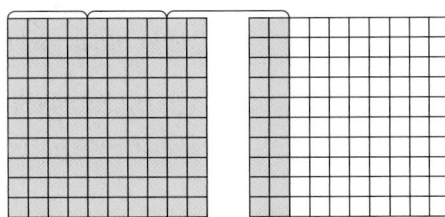

TEKS ★ TAKS Tune-Up and Mixed Review

TAKS Objective 1
TEKS (7.2)(A)

39. Which expression does the model represent? **B**

(A) $1.2 \div 4$ (B) $1.2 \div 3$ (C) $0.2 \div 4$ (D) $0.2 \div 3$

TAKS Objective 1
TEKS (7.2)(B)

40. At Tony's Shoppe, the turkey sandwich contains 5.5 ounces of sliced turkey. Tony has a boneless turkey breast weighing 154 ounces. How many turkey sandwiches can Tony make? **H**

(F) 2   (G) 3   (H) 28   (J) 29

GO for Help **Lesson 1-3** **Mental Math** Find each product.

41. $0.5 \cdot 6.7 \cdot 2$ **6.7**   **42.** $5.3 \cdot 4.9 \cdot 0$ **0**   **43.** $8.2 \cdot 2.5 \cdot 4$ **82**

TEKS ★ TAKS Resources

- TAKS Strategies, p. 59
- TAKS Tune-Up, pp. 63–65

TAKS Tune-Up Kit

- TAKS Daily Review Transparencies
- TAKS Review and Preparation Workbook
- TAKS Strategies with Transparencies
- Texas Progress Monitoring Assessments

PowerPoint
Lesson Quiz

1. $38.164 \div 4.7$ **8.12**

2. $0.7 \div 0.5$ **1.4**

3. $14 \div 0.28$ **50**

4. $336 \div 0.006$ **56,000**

Alternative Assessment

Have students work in pairs. Each student writes a decimal. Partners can then use each decimal as a divisor and dividend. Have partners determine whether they will need to annex zeros to complete each division. Then have partners find both quotients.

Exercises

Have students use 10 × 10 grids or strips of paper to model decimal division for exercises such as Exercise 16.

23

Choosing Operations

In this feature, students first identify what they know and what they want to find out. They show the main idea by drawing a diagram, choosing an operation, estimating the answer, solving the problem, and checking that their answer is reasonable.

Guided Instruction

Discuss with students the need to read the problem carefully. Students need to decide how information is related in the problem.

Have a volunteer read the problem aloud. Ask:

* *How are the two odometer readings related?* The odometer was at 15 when the trip began and at 126.4 when the gas tank was refilled.

* *How can you find the distance the scooter traveled?* Subtract. Find 126.4 − 15.

* *After you find the distance, what do you do next and why?* Divide the distance by 1.2 gallons to find miles traveled per gallon.

Dana Center TEKS Toolkit Clarifying Activities (7.2)(F), (7.13)(C)
Visit: PHSchool.com
Web Code: arq-9045

GPS Guided Problem Solving

Choosing Operations

TEKS ★ TAKS
(7.2)(F) To select and use appropriate operations to solve problems TAKS Obj. 1
(7.13)(C) To select an appropriate problem-solving strategy, including drawing a picture TAKS Obj. 6

Gas Up!   The odometer of a motor scooter with a full tank of gas read 15 miles. It took 1.2 gallons of gas to refill the tank when the odometer read 126.4 miles. How many miles per gallon did the scooter get?

What You Might Think

> What do I know? What do I want to find out?

> How do I show the main idea?

> Can I estimate the answer?

> How do I solve the problem? What is the answer?

> Is the answer reasonable?

What You Might Write

The scooter went 126.4 − 15, or 111.4, miles using 1.2 gallons of gas. I want to find how far the scooter goes on 1 gallon.

Draw a diagram.

```
0 mi                                    111.4 mi
┌─────┬─────┬─────┬─────┬─────┬─────┐
│     │     │     │     │     │     │
└─────┴─────┴─────┴─────┴─────┴─────┘
0 gal    0.4 gal    0.8 gal    1.2 gal
```

Dividing 111.4 miles by a number greater than 1 will give an answer less than 111.4.

Divide 111.4 miles by 1.2 gallons.
$111.4 \div 1.2 \approx 92.8$
The scooter gets 92.8 miles per gallon.

Yes; 92.8 is less than 111.4.

Think It Through

1–3. See right.

1. The diagram above shows the number of gallons used on the same vertical line as the number of miles traveled. Explain why.

2. **Reasoning** Explain how you know that dividing 111.4 by a number greater than 1 will give an answer less than 111.4.

3. **Number Sense** Suppose the scooter had used 0.95 gallons of gas instead of 1.2 gallons to travel the same distance. Would the mileage have been better or worse? Explain.

1. It shows how many gallons of gas were used as the scooter traveled a certain number of miles.

2. Dividing by a number greater than 1 is the same as finding a fraction of that number.

3. The mileage would be better because it used fewer gallons for the same number of miles.

Exercises

Solve each problem. For Exercises 4 and 5, answer the questions first.

4. At an amusement park, Tanya finds a poster for $3.75 and a shirt for $14.95. She has $20. Can she buy both items and still have enough money for a bus ticket home that costs $1.75? Explain.
   a. What do you know? What do you want to find out?
   b. How can you use the diagram below to help find the answer?

$20		
$14.95	$3.75	■

4. No, she would be short $.45.

5. In May, 1860, the longest run in the history of the Pony Express was made using four horses. The table at the right shows the distances run by the horses. What was the average distance? **40.5 mi**
   a. What do you know? What do you want to find out?
   b. How can you use the diagram below to help find the answer?

Horse	Distance (miles)
1	60
2	35
3	37
4	30

60	35	37	30

6. Early settlers often sold their furniture to lighten their wagons. Suppose a settler sold furniture for 0.2 times the amount he paid. If he sold a chair for $3.80, what did he pay for it? **$19**

7. In the 1850s, a wind wagon was invented that was half sailboat and half wagon. The wind wagon took about 133 days to travel 1,968 mi. About how many miles did the wind wagon travel each day? **about 14.8 mi/day**

8. The Mississippi River is 3.2 times longer than the Platte-South Platte River. The Mississippi River is 2,340 mi long. How long is the Platte-South Platte River? **731.25 mi**

TEKS ⭐ **TAKS**

- **(7.2)(B)** To use multiplication to solve problems involving decimals **TAKS** Obj. 1
- **(7.3)(B)** To estimate and find solutions to application problems involving proportional relationships such as related measurement units **TAKS** Obj. 2
- **(7.14)(A)** To communicate mathematical ideas using appropriate units **TAKS** Obj. 6

TEKS ⭐ **TAKS**

(7.2)(B) To use multiplication to solve problems involving decimals **TAKS** Obj. 1

(7.3)(B) To estimate and find solutions to application problems involving proportional relationships such as related measurement units **TAKS** Obj. 1

(7.14)(A) To communicate mathematical ideas using appropriate units **TAKS** Obj. 6

Dana Center TEKS Toolkit Clarifying Activities (7.2)(B), (7.3)(B), (7.14)(A)
Visit: PHSchool.com
Web Code: arq-9045

Check Skills You'll Need

1. Vocabulary Review
$4 \cdot 8 = 8 \cdot 4$ is an example of the __?__ of Multiplication.
Commutative Property

Simplify.

2. $0.25 \cdot 10$ 2.5

3. $4.567 \cdot 1,000$ 4,567

4. $0.03 \cdot 100$ 3

5. $0.07 \cdot 1,000$ 70

GO for Help
Lesson 1-3

TEKS Math Background

The basic units of measurement in the metric system are the *meter* (length), the *gram* (mass), and the *liter* (liquid capacity). All other units of length, mass, and capacity in the system are related to these basic units by powers of ten. So conversions from larger to smaller units can be accomplished by multiplying by 10, 100, 1,000, and so on. Similarly, conversions from smaller to larger units are done by multiplying by 0.1, 0.01, 0.001, and so on.

More Math Background: p. 2C

Lesson Planning and Resources

See p. 2E for a list of the resources that support this lesson.

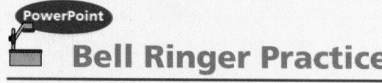
Bell Ringer Practice

✓ **Check Skills You'll Need**
Use student page, transparency, or PowerPoint.

TAKS **Daily Review 5**
Use transparency.

Why Learn This?

Countries around the world use the metric system for measurement. Measurements are easy to convert in the metric system, because it is a decimal system.

The table below is a guide for choosing an appropriate metric unit.

Type	Unit	Reference Example
Length	millimeter (mm)	about the thickness of a dime
	centimeter (cm)	about the width of your little finger
	meter (m)	about the distance from a doorknob to the floor
	kilometer (km)	about the length of 11 football fields
Capacity	milliliter (mL)	a small spoon holds about 5 mL
	liter (L)	a little more than 1 quart
Mass	milligram (mg)	about the mass of a mosquito
	gram (g)	about the mass of a paper clip
	kilogram (kg)	about the mass of a bunch of bananas

EXAMPLE **Choosing a Reasonable Estimate**

① Choose a reasonable estimate. Explain your choice.

a. height of a classroom: 3 cm   3 m   3 km

3 m; a classroom is about 3 times as high as the distance from a doorknob to the floor.

b. mass of a bag of flour: 2.3 mg   2.3 g   2.3 kg

2.3 kg; a bag of flour is much heavier than a few paper clips.

✓ Quick Check

1a. 180 mL

b. 500 mg

1. Choose a reasonable estimate. Explain your choice. See left.

a. capacity of a soup bowl: 180 mL   180 L   180 kL

b. mass of a butterfly: 500 mg   500 g   500 kg

Differentiated Instruction **Solutions for All Learners**

Special Needs L1
Show students a meter stick and the centimeter marks. Have them hold a gram cube in their hands, or something that has a mass of about a gram, so that they can make more informed decisions about what units to use.

learning style: tactile

Below Level L2
Give students several pairs of exercises like these.

$4 \text{ m} = \blacklozenge \text{ cm}$ 400 $9 \text{ g} = \blacklozenge \text{ kg}$ 0.009

$4 \text{ cm} = \blacklozenge \text{ m}$ 0.04 $9 \text{ kg} = \blacklozenge \text{ g}$ 9,000

learning style: visual

The basic unit for length in the metric system is the meter (m). The prefixes *deci-*, *centi-*, and *milli-* describe measures that are less than one basic unit. The prefixes *deca-*, *hecto-*, and *kilo-* describe measures that are greater than one basic unit.

Each unit in the table is 10 times the value of the unit to its right.

Unit	kilo-meter	hecto-meter	deca-meter	meter	deci-meter	centi-meter	milli-meter
Symbol	km	hm	dam	m	dm	cm	mm
Value	1,000 m	100 m	10 m	1 m	0.1 m	0.01 m	0.001 m

The basic unit of mass is the gram. The basic unit of capacity is the liter.

You can change a measurement from one unit to another by finding the relationship between the two units and multiplying.

EXAMPLES Multiplying to Change Units

2 Change 245 milliliters to liters.

$$245 \text{ mL} = \blacksquare \text{ L}$$
$$1 \text{ mL} = 0.001 \text{ L} \quad \leftarrow \text{You are starting with milliliters. Complete the relationship 1 mL} = \blacksquare \text{ L.}$$
$$245 \cdot 0.001 = 0.245 \quad \leftarrow \text{To change milliliters to liters, multiply by 0.001.}$$

245 milliliters equals 0.245 liters.

3 Change 1.4 grams to milligrams.

$$1.4 \text{ g} = \blacksquare \text{ mg}$$
$$1 \text{ g} = 1,000 \text{ mg} \quad \leftarrow \text{You are starting with grams. Complete the relationship 1 g} = \blacksquare \text{ mg.}$$
$$1.4 \cdot 1,000 = 1,400 \quad \leftarrow \text{To change grams to milligrams, multiply by 1,000.}$$

1.4 grams equals 1,400 milligrams.

Check for Reasonableness A gram is greater than a milligram, so the number of grams should be less than the number of milligrams. Since $1.4 < 1,400$, the answer is reasonable.

★ TAKS Tip

Pay attention to the prefixes when you convert metric units.

✓ Quick Check

2. Change 34 liters to milliliters.

3. Change 4,690 grams to kilograms.

1-5 Measuring in Metric Units **27**

---

2. Teach

Activity Lab
Use before the lesson.

All in One Teaching Resources
Activity Lab 1-5: Fractions and Rulers

Guided Instruction

Example 1
Students might wonder about the difference between mass and weight. *Mass* is a measure of the quantity of material that makes up an object. *Weight* is a measure of the force an object experiences due to the pull of gravity.

Example 2
After discussing the solution, ask: *How would the problem be different if you had to change 245 liters to milliliters?* You would multiply 245 L by 1,000. The answer would be 245,000 mL.

PowerPoint
Additional Examples

1 Choose a reasonable estimate. Explain your choice. Accept all reasonable explanations.
- **a.** length of a pencil: **19 cm**
  19 mm   19 cm   19 m
- **b.** mass of a grape: **9.2 g**
  9.2 mg   9.2 g   9.2 kg
- **c.** capacity of a bucket: **12 L**
  12 mL   12 L   12 kL

2 Change 871 centimeters to meters. **8.71 m**

3 **a.** Change 6 m 1 cm to meters. **6.01 m**
b. Change 6 m 1 cm to centimeters. **601 cm**

All in One Teaching Resources
- Daily Notetaking Guide 1-5 L3
- Adapted Notetaking 1-5 L1

- *How do you choose a reasonable metric unit for measuring an object?* Sample: Decide what type of measure is involved: length, mass, or capacity. Then compare the size of the object you are measuring to the size of a reference object for each unit.

- *How do you change a measure from one unit to another?* Find the relationship between the units and multiply.

● More Than One Way

A fruit punch recipe calls for 1 L of orange juice, 400 mL of pineapple juice, 60 mL of lemon juice, 2 L of apple juice, and 840 mL of water. Can you make a batch of this punch in a 5-L punch bowl?

Anna's Method

I can start by subtracting 1 L of orange juice and 2 L of apple juice from the 5 L available. That leaves 2 L of capacity in the punch bowl.

400 mL + 60 mL + 840 mL = 1,300 mL ← Add the ingredients in milliliters.

2 · 1,000 = 2,000; 2 L = 2,000 mL ← Change remaining capacity to milliliters.

Since 1,300 mL is less than 2,000 mL, I can make the punch in the bowl.

Ryan's Method

I can convert all the measures in milliliters to liters by multiplying each measure by 0.001.

400 · 0.001 = 0.4;   400 mL = 0.4 L

60 · 0.001 = 0.06;   60 mL = 0.06 L   ← Change milliliters to liters.

840 · 0.001 = 0.84;   840 mL = 0.84 L

1 L + 0.4 L + 0.06 L + 2 L + 0.84 L = 4.3 L   ← Add all ingredients.

The capacity of the punch bowl is 5 L. I can make a full batch of the punch in the punch bowl.

Answers may vary.
Sample: No; by Ryan's method all measurements are changed to meters. The sum is 10.03 m. You have 10 m of ribbon.

Choose a Method

For a craft project, you need ribbon in lengths of 3 m, 25 cm, 4 m, 58 cm, 1.5 m, and 70 cm. You have 10 m of ribbon. Is that enough? Explain why you chose the method you used. See left.

✓ Check Your Understanding

1. **Vocabulary** In the metric system, the prefix *kilo-* means that the unit is ■ times the basic unit of measure. 1,000

What number should you multiply by to change each unit?

2. grams to kilograms   3. centiliters to liters   4. liters to decaliters
   0.001   0.01   10

Write the number that makes each statement true.
   0.064   0.302   0.00849
5. 64 g = ■ kg   6. ■ L = 302 mL   7. 8,490 mm = ■ km

For more exercises, see Extra Skills and Word Problems.

GO for Help

For Exercises	See Examples
8–10	1
11–17	2–3

A Choose a reasonable estimate.

8. capacity of a small bottle   250 mL   250 L   250 kL
   250 mL

9. height of an oak tree **22 m**   22 cm   22 m   22 km

10. mass of an adult bullfrog **0.5 kg** 0.5 mg   0.5 g   0.5 kg

Complete each statement. You may find a number line helpful.

11. $0.9 \text{ kg} = \blacksquare \text{ g}$
    900

12. $\blacksquare \text{ L} = 90 \text{ mL}$
    0.090

13. $58 \text{ m} = \blacksquare \text{ mm}$
    58,000

14. $7,800 \text{ g} = \blacksquare \text{ kg}$
    7.8

15. $7 \text{ m} = \blacksquare \text{ km}$
    0.007

16. $\blacksquare \text{ L} = 240 \text{ kL}$
    240,000

17. The capacity of a plastic cup is 350 mL. How many cups can you fill from a 2.1-L bottle of juice? **6 cups**

B GPS

18. **Guided Problem Solving** You are making a drawing of a family crest from a book. You have a piece of paper that is 21.5 cm wide and want to leave a 35-mm margin on each side. How wide can you draw the crest? **145 mm or 14.5 cm**
    - What is the width in centimeters of the margin on one side?
    - What is the combined width of the margins on the two sides?
    - How can you find the maximum width of the crest?

19. **Nutrition** You need 1.3 g of calcium per day. You get 290 mg of calcium per glass of milk. If you drink 4 glasses of milk, how much more calcium do you need from other sources? **140 mg**

20. **Geography** Antarctica averages 2,400 meters in elevation. What is the average elevation of Antarctica in kilometers? **2.4 km**

21. The world's tallest man was 272 cm tall. Find his height in meters.
    2.72 m

22. **Choose a Method** A bag of birdseed mix contains 400 g of sunflower seed, 300 g of thistle seed, and 0.5 kg of mixed seeds. You order six bags of birdseed mix. How many grams of birdseed is your order? Explain why you chose the method you used.
    7,200 g; answers will vary.

Match each measurement in the first column with an equivalent measurement in the second column.

23. 25 mL **C**

24. 2.5 km **E**

25. 0.25 L **D**

26. 250 mm **B**

27. 25,000 mg **A**

A. 0.025 kg

B. 25 cm

C. 0.025 L

D. 25 cL

E. 2,500 m

3. Practice

Assignment Guide

Check Your Understanding
Go over Exercises 1–7 in class before assigning the Homework Exercises.

Homework Exercises
A Practice by Example   8–17
B Apply Your Skills   18–36
C Challenge   37
TEKS ★ TAKS Tune-Up and
    Mixed Review   38–43

Homework Quick Check
To check students' understanding of key skills and concepts, go over Exercises 9, 14, 32, 35, and 36.

Differentiated Instruction Resources

Lesson Quiz

Choose a reasonable estimate.

1. length of desk

  0.12 m   1.2 m   12 m   **1.2 m**

Write a number that makes each statement true.

2. 0.8 km = ■ m   **800**

3. 640 mL = ■ L   **0.64**

4. 7 kg 300 g = ■ kg   **7.3**

Alternative Assessment

Provide a balance scale. On one side place objects with known masses, such as a dollar bill with a mass of 1 g. Have small groups work together to record estimates for several classroom objects. Using the balance, have them find and record the actual masses of the objects. Similarly, direct students to estimate, record, and use metric rulers to measure the lengths of classroom objects. Have groups present their estimates to the class.

GO **Online**

Homework Help
Visit: PHSchool.com
Web Code: are-0105

32. You can change a measure from one unit to another by finding the relationship between the two units and multiplying.

Write the metric unit that makes each statement true.

28. 2,034 mg = 2.034 <u>?</u> grams

29. 3.456 cm = 34.56 <u>?</u>
  millimeters

30. 9,023 mL = 90.23 <u>?</u> deciliters

31. 0.1347 m = 134.7 <u>?</u>
  millimeters

32. **Writing in Math** Explain how to change units in the metric system.

33. **Money** A roll of 50 pennies has a mass of 125 g. Find the mass of $5 in pennies. **1,250 g**

34. The mass of a basketball is 620 g. The mass of a soccer ball is 0.45 kg. How much greater is the mass of a basketball in grams?
170 g

35. **Food** The capacity of a coffee mug is 350 mL. How many coffee mugs can you fill from a 2 L container? **5 mugs**

36. **Reasoning** Suppose you want to change 125 kg 84 g to a single unit. Would you choose kilograms or grams? Explain your choice.
Answers may vary. Sample: 125.084 kg

37. **Challenge** A recipe for modeling clay requires 470 mL of baking soda, 240 mL of cornstarch, and 300 mL of water. Can you make a double batch in a 1.9-L pan? Explain. **No; a double batch needs 2.02 L.**

TEKS ★ **TAKS** **Tune-Up and Mixed Review**

TAKS Objective 2
TEKS (7.3)(B)

38. A company is manufacturing a sports water jug that holds 1,350 mL. What is the capacity of the jug in liters? **B**
  Ⓐ 1,350,000 L   Ⓒ 1.305 L
  Ⓑ 1.35 L   Ⓓ 1.035 L

TAKS Objective 2
TEKS (7.3)(B)

39. Tina lives 350 m from school. She walks to school and home again each day. During a 5-day school week, how far does she walk? **H**
  Ⓕ 1750 km   Ⓖ 70 km   Ⓗ 3.5 km   Ⓙ 1.75 km

TAKS Objective 1
TEKS (7.2)(B)

40. A diagram of a bike path is shown below. Shawn biked all the way around the path once. How far did Shawn ride? **C**

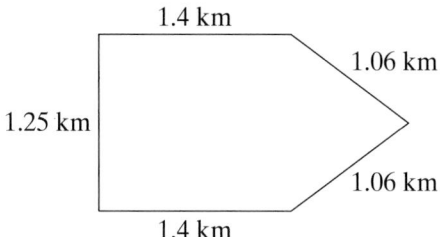

  Ⓐ 3.71 km   Ⓑ 5.6 km   Ⓒ 6.17 km   Ⓓ 6.27 km

GO **for Help**   **Lesson 1-4**   **Find each quotient.**

41. 15.621 ÷ 2.46
  6.35

42. 0.17595 ÷ 1.035
  0.17

43. 5.58 ÷ 9.3
  0.6

TEKS ★ **TAKS** **Resources**

• TAKS Strategies, p. 59
• TAKS Tune-Up, pp. 63–65

TAKS Tune-Up Kit

• TAKS Daily Review Transparencies
• TAKS Review and Preparation Workbook
• TAKS Strategies with Transparencies
• Texas Progress Monitoring Assessments

Comparing and Ordering Integers

TEKS ★ **TAKS**

- **(7.1)(A)** To compare and order integers **TAKS** Obj. 1
- **(7.14)(A)** To communicate mathematical ideas using graphical models **TAKS** Obj. 6

🔊 **New Vocabulary** integers, opposites, absolute value

Why Learn This?

Most shipwrecks lie under water. You can use integers to describe distances above and below sea level.

Integers are the set of positive whole numbers, their opposites, and zero. The wreck of *La Belle*, a ship from the 1600s, lies 12 feet below sea level off the coast of Texas. You can use −12 to describe the wreck's depth.

Two numbers that are the same distance from 0 on a number line, but in opposite directions, are **opposites.** You can use integers to find opposites.

EXAMPLE   Finding an Opposite

1 Find the opposite of −12.

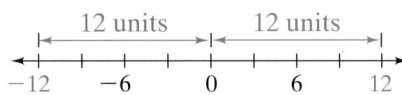

The opposite of −12 is 12, because −12 and +12 are both twelve units from 0, but in opposite directions.

✓ Quick Check

1. Find the opposite of each number.
  a. −8 **8**   **b.** 13 **−13**   **c.** −22 **22**

The **absolute value** of a number is its distance from 0 on a number line. You write "the absolute value of −3" as $|-3|$.

TEKS ★ TAKS

(7.1)(A) To compare and order integers **TAKS** Obj. 1
(7.14)(A) To communicate mathematical ideas using graphical models **TAKS** Obj. 6

Dana Center TEKS Toolkit Clarifying Activities (7.1)(A), (7.14)(A)
Visit: PHSchool.com
Web Code: arq-9045

TEKS Math Background

The *integers* are the numbers . . ., −3, −2, −1, 0, 1, 2, 3, . . . They can be pictured as points on a number line, with 0 as the *origin.* To the right of 0 are the *positive integers* 1, 2, 3, . . . To the left of 0 are −1, −2, −3, . . . called the *negative integers.* Positive and negative numbers are often called *signed numbers.* Zero is neither positive nor negative.

More Math Background: p. 2D

Lesson Planning and Resources

See p. 2E for a list of the resources that support this lesson.

Bell Ringer Practice

✓ **Check Skills You'll Need**
Use student page, transparency, or PowerPoint.

TAKS **Daily Review 6**
Use transparency.

Differentiated Instruction Solutions for All Learners

Special Needs L1	**Below Level** L2
Help students visualize positive and negative integers by showing them both vertical and horizontal number lines. The vertical ones work well to show distance above or below sea level or temperature changes.	Review the proper use of the symbols > (is greater than) and < (is less than). Remind students that the greater number is placed at the larger, or open, side of the symbol.
learning style: visual	learning style: visual

Activity Lab

Use before the lesson.

All in One Teaching Resources

Activity Lab 1-6: Integers and Sports

Guided Instruction

Example 1

To emphasize the distinction between positive and negative integers, have students use the word *positive* when naming integers to the right of 0. They read −7 as "negative seven," and they read 1 as "positive one."

Additional Examples

1 Find the opposite of 2. **−2**

2 Find |−5| and |5|. **5; 5**

3 Compare 3 and −8 using <, >, or =. **3 > −8 or −8 < 3**

4 Arrange the cities by temperature, coldest to warmest.

Low Temperatures for March (°F)

City	Low
Albuquerque, NM	8
Chicago, IL	−8
Cleveland, OH	−5
Columbia, SC	4
Providence, RI	1
Reno, NV	−2

Chicago; Cleveland; Reno; Providence; Columbia; Albuquerque

All in One Teaching Resources

- Daily Notetaking Guide 1-6 **L3**
- Adapted Notetaking 1-6 **L1**

Closure

- Explain how to compare two integers. Locate the integers on a number line. The integer farther to the left is the lesser integer.

32

For: Integers Activity
Use: Interactive Textbook, 1-6

TAKS Tip

Of two integers on a number line, the one farther to the right is greater.

EXAMPLE Finding Absolute Value

2 Find |−3| and |3|.

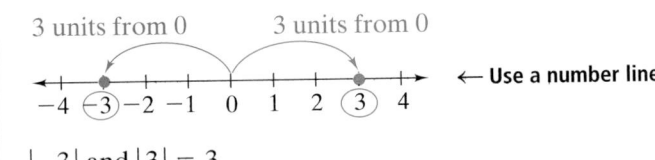

← Use a number line.

|−3| and |3| = 3.

✓ Quick Check

2. Find |−8|. **8**

You can compare and order integers by graphing.

EXAMPLE Comparing Integers

3 Compare −7 and 1 using <, =, or >.

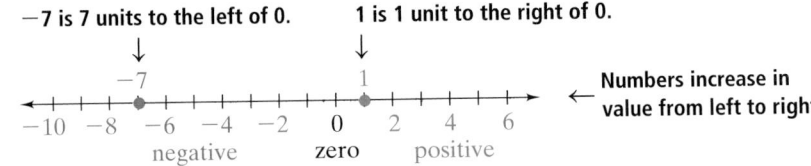

−7 is 7 units to the left of 0.   1 is 1 unit to the right of 0.

Numbers increase in value from left to right

negative   zero   positive

Since −7 is to the left of 1 on the number line, −7 < 1.

✓ Quick Check

3. Compare −8 and −2 using <, =, or >. **−8 < −2**

EXAMPLE Ordering Integers

4 **Climate** Order the cities on the map from coldest to warmest by graphing.

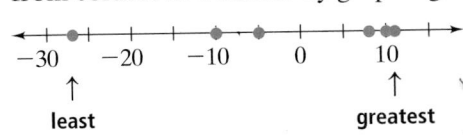

least   greatest

Coldest to warmest: Fairbanks, Nome, Anchorage, Valdez, Kodiak, Juneau.

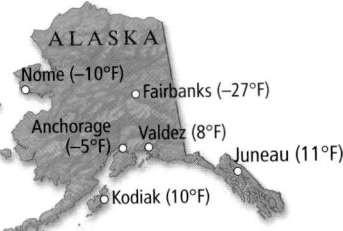

Lowest October Temperatures

ALASKA

Nome (−10°F)   Fairbanks (−27°F)
Anchorage (−5°F)   Valdez (8°F)
Juneau (11°F)
Kodiak (10°F)

Source: National Weather Service

✓ Quick Check

4. Order the numbers 3, −1, −4, and 2 from least to greatest. **−4, −1, 2, 3**

32   Chapter 1   Decimals and Integers

---

1. **Vocabulary** How are integers different from whole numbers?

2. **Number Sense** Which two numbers have an absolute value of 1? −1 and 1

3. **Reasoning** Decide if each of the following is *always true*, *sometimes true*, or *never true* for all integer values of x. See left.

   a. $|x| = x$ b. $|-x| = x$ c. $-|x| = x$ d. $|x| = -x$

Find the opposite of each number.

4. 2 −2   5. 4 −4   6. 3 −3   7. −2 2

Which number in each pair is farther away from zero?

8. 4, −5 −5   9. 2, 5 5   10. −1, −3 −3   11. −12, 11 −12

Homework Exercises

For more exercises, see Extra Skills and Word Problems.

For Exercises	See Examples
12–21	1
22–31	2
32–39	3
40–42	4

A **Find the opposite of each number. You may find a number line helpful.**

12. −1 1   13. −8 8   14. 15 −15   15. 11 −11   16. 90 −90

17. −45 45   18. 20 −20   19. −20 20   20. −123 123   21. 160 −160

Find each absolute value.

22. $|10|$ 10   23. $|-11|$ 11   24. $|-16|$ 16   25. $|-1|$ 1   26. $|4|$ 4

27. $|7|$ 7   28. $|-3|$ 3   29. $|-5|$ 5   30. $|6|$ 6   31. $|-10|$ 10

Compare using $<$, $=$, or $>$.

32. 0 ▨ −2 >   33. −6 ▨ −3 <   34. −14 ▨ 14 <   35. −23 ▨ 0 <

36. −4 ▨ −5 >   37. 17 ▨ −18 >   38. 7 ▨ −12 >   39. 5 ▨ −1 >

Order the numbers from least to greatest.

40. −4, 8, −2, −6, 3   41. −2, 0, 7, −1, −5   42. 2, −3, −7, 1, 10
    −6, −4, −2, 3, 8   −5, −2, −1, 0, 7   −7, −3, 1, 2, 10

43. −12, −7, −3, +2, +4

B **43. Guided Problem Solving** Scores in a golf tournament are reported by the number of strokes each player is above or below par. The scores for five players are −12, +2, −7, +4, and −3. Order the scores from the lowest under par to the greatest over par.
   • Which score is farthest to the left on a number line?
   • Which score is the next-farthest to the left? See left.

44. Start by ordering negative numbers by decreasing absolute value, and then order positive numbers by increasing absolute value. In this case, −5, −4, and 12.

44. **Writing in Math** A friend does not know how to order integers. Explain how to order 12, −4, and −5 from least to greatest. See left.

48. T. Woods, R. Goosen, V. Singh, P. Mickelson, E. Els

49. No; there are no integers between the integers −3 and −4.

3. Practice

Assignment Guide

Check Your Understanding
Go over Exercises 1–11 in class before assigning the Homework Exercises.

Homework Exercises
A Practice by Example   12–42
B Apply Your Skills   43–49
C Challenge   50
TEKS ★ TAKS Tune-Up and
  Mixed Review   51–55

Homework Quick Check
To check students' understanding of key skills and concepts, go over Exercises 24, 36, 44, 48, and 49.

Differentiated Instruction Resources

Lesson Quiz

Compare using <, >, or =.

1. 2 ■ −9 >   **2.** −7 ■ −4 <

3. Find |3| and |−1|. **3; 1**

Order from least to greatest.

4. 0, −4, 7, −5, 2 **−5, −4, 0, 2, 7**

5. 6, 8, −3, −7, 1 **−7, −3, 1, 6, 8**

Alternative Assessment

Distribute number lines to pairs of students. Refer them to Exercises 32–42. Have partners work together to graph the integers on the number lines so they can compare and order them. Have partners explain how the number lines helped them compare integers.

GO **Online**
Homework Help
Visit: PHSchool.com
Web Code: are-0106

45. a. Which city has the highest normal temperature? **Omaha, Nebr.**

b. Which city has the greatest difference between its normal high and normal low temperatures? **Bismarck, N. Dak.**

Order from least to greatest.

46. −14, −15, |−14|, 12, |−16| **−15, −14, 12, |−14|, |−16|**

47. −3551, −3155, −3151, −3515 **−3551, −3515, −3155, −3151**

48. Sports In golf, the person with the lowest score is the winner. Rank the players at the right by ordering their scores from lowest to highest. **See margin.**

49. Reasoning Write three numbers that are between −3 and −4. Are the numbers you wrote integers? Explain. **See margin.**

50. Challenge The number −5 is 5 units away from 0. This means that |−5| = 5. How far away is −3 from 2? What is |−3 − 2|? **5; 5**

City	High	Low
Barrow, Alaska	−8	−20
Bismarck, N. Dak.	21	−1
Caribou, Maine	19	0
Duluth, Minn.	18	−1
Omaha, Nebr.	32	13

Normal Temperatures for January (°F)

Source: National Climatic Data Center.
Go to **PHSchool.com** for a data update.
Web Code: arg-9041

Player	Score
T. Woods	−12
V. Singh	−4
E. Els	+10
P. Mickelson	−3
R. Goosen	−5

TEKS ★ TAKS Tune-Up and Mixed Review

TAKS Objective 1
TEKS (7.1)(A)

51. The table shows the lowest altitudes on four continents. Which continent has the lowest altitude? **B**

Ⓐ Africa
Ⓑ Asia
Ⓒ Europe
Ⓓ North America

Lowest Altitudes

Continent	Altitude (ft below sea level)
Africa	−512
Asia	−1,348
Europe	−92
N. America	−282

TAKS Objective 1
TEKS (7.2)(B)

52. Three friends have a 2.79-liter bottle of water to share. About how much water will each person receive? **F**

Ⓕ 950 mL   Ⓖ 95 mL   Ⓗ 760 mL   Ⓙ 76 mL

GO for Help   **Lesson 1-5**

Write a number that makes each statement true.

53. 45.3 cm = ■ mm **453**   **54.** 26.78 mL = ■ L **0.02678**   **55.** 256 mg = ■ g **0.256**

TEKS ★ TAKS Resources

• TAKS Strategies, p. 59
• TAKS Tune-Up, pp. 63–65

TAKS Tune-Up Kit
• TAKS Daily Review Transparencies
• TAKS Review and Preparation Workbook
• TAKS Strategies with Transparencies
• Texas Progress Monitoring Assessments

Enrichment 1-6 **L4**

Reteaching 1-6 Comparing and Ordering **L2**

The numbers 2 and −2 are opposites. The numbers 7 and −7 are opposites.
Integers are the set of positive whole numbers, their opposites, and zero.

You can use the number line to compare integers.

−2 is less than 0.   7 is greater than 2.
−2 < 0   7 > 2

Numbers to the left are less.	Numbers to the right are greater.
−2 is farther left than 0.	7 is farther to the right than 2.

The **absolute value** of an integer is its distance from zero on the number line. Distance is always positive.

The absolute value of −5 is 5.   The absolute value of 3 is 3.
|−5| = 5 |3| = 3

Compare using <, >, or =.

1. 4 > 2   2. −3 < −2   3. 3 > −4
4. −1 > −2   5. 0 < 5   6. 0 > −4
7. −6 < 4   8. −8 < −1   9. 3 > 0
10. −7 > −10   11. −10 < 10   12. 1 > −1

Find each absolute value.

13. |−6| = 6   14. |3| = 3   15. |−8| = 8
16. |9| = 9   17. |−5| = 5   18. |0| = 0
19. |6| = 6   20. |−10| = 10   21. |−20| = 20

Order the numbers from least to greatest.

22. −4, 5, −2, 0, 1   23. 6, −3, −5, 4, −6
    −4, −2, 0, 1, 5   −6, −5, −3, 4, 6
24. 3, −5, 4, −4, −7, 0   25. 1, 3, −7, −6, 5, −2
    −7, −5, −4, 0, 3, 4   −7, −6, −2, 1, 3, 5

Find each quotient.

1. $4.2 \div 3.5$ **1.2**

2. $6.93 \div 2.2$ **3.15**

3. $3.1\overline{)5.27}$ **1.7**

Write the number that makes each statement true.

4. $5,000 \text{ mL} = \blacksquare \text{ cL}$ **500**

5. $410 \text{ cm} = \blacksquare \text{ m}$ **4.1**

6. $1.7 \text{ kg} = \blacksquare \text{ g}$ **1,700**

Compare using <, =, or >.

7. $-4 \overset{>}{\blacksquare} -5$

8. $-2 \overset{<}{\blacksquare} 0$

9. $|-7| \overset{=}{\blacksquare} |7|$

10. **Baking** A bread recipe calls for 0.24 L of milk. Your measuring cup is marked in milliliters. How many milliliters of milk do you need? **240 mL**

Vocabulary Builder

Learning New Math Terms

Your textbook has many features designed to help you as you read. When you aren't sure what a word means, keep these hints in mind.

- **Look for new vocabulary.** New vocabulary words are listed at the beginning of lessons. The first time vocabulary words are used in a lesson they look like **these words**.
- **Review the key concepts.** Important mathematical terms are explained in Key Concepts boxes.
- **Look for vocabulary tips.** They help you remember what a word means.
- **Use the glossary.** This book contains a glossary, which defines words and refers you to the page where the word is explained.
- **Read carefully.** If necessary, reread a section with new vocabulary until you understand all the information.

Exercises

Look through Lessons 1-1 to 1-3. Write down the page numbers where these items appear.

1. Vocabulary Tip **p. 15**

2. Key Concepts **pp. 9, 15**

3. New Vocabulary
   pp. 4, 8, 14

35

✓ **Checkpoint Quiz**

Use this Checkpoint Quiz to check students' understanding of the skills and concepts of Lessons 1-4 through 1-6.

Resources

- **All in One** Teaching Resources Checkpoint Quiz 2
- Texas ExamView CD-ROM
- Success Tracker™ Online Intervention

Vocabulary Builder

Learning New Math Terms

Students learn strategies for remembering and using new math terms.

Guided Instruction

Call students' attention to the bulleted suggestions. Ask students:
- *What words are new in Lesson 1-6?* **Integers, opposites, absolute value**
- *In Lessons 1-4 to 1-6, are there any Key Concept boxes?* **No**
- *Where is the glossary?* **on pp. 675–710**

Exercises

Have students work in pairs to do Exercises 1–3.

Modeling Integer Addition and Subtraction

Students use chips of different colors to model positive and negative integers and addition and subtraction of integers with the same signs. They make "zero pairs" to model addition and subtraction of integers with different signs.

Guided Instruction

Activity

Students note that all four parts of both activities use integers with the same absolute values: 5 and 2. However, answers differ depending on the signs of the integers.

Before students do Exercises 1–12, you may want them to work through the activities again with a different pair of numbers.

Exercises

Students work independently on Exercises 1–12. Then form three groups to share, evaluate, and adjust their answers. For Exercise 13, have each group write one of the three rules (a), (b), (c). Have groups share their rules.

Differentiated Instruction

Special Needs   L1
Students who have trouble with chips and zero pairs may prefer the number line models in Lesson 1-7.

TEKS ★ TAKS Resources

• Activity Lab 1-7: Integers
• chips of two different colors
• Student Manipulatives Kit

Dana Center TEKS Toolkit Clarifying Activities (7.2)(C)
Visit: PHSchool.com
Web Code: arq-9045

1-7a   Activity Lab

Modeling Integer Addition and Subtraction

TEKS ★ TAKS
(7.2)(C) To use models, such as concrete objects, to add and subtract integers and connect the actions to algorithms TAKS Obj. 1

You can use models to add and subtract integers. Use chips of two different colors. Let one color represent positive integers and the other color represent negative integers.

ACTIVITY

1. Find 5 + 2.   Show 5 "+" chips.   There are 7 "+" chips.
                            Then add 2 "+" chips.   So 5 + 2 = 7.

          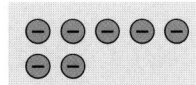

2. Find −5 + (−2).   Show 5 "−" chips.   There are 7 "−" chips.
                                 Then add 2 "−" chips.   So −5 + (−2) = −7.

To add integers with different signs, use zero pairs. These chips ⊕ ⊖ are a *zero pair* because ⊕ ⊖ = 0. Removing a zero pair does not change the sum.

3. Find 5 + (−2).

Show 5 "+" chips.   Pair the "+" and "−" chips.   There are 3 "+" chips left.
Then add 2 "−" chips.   Remove the pairs.   So 5 + (−2) = 3.

4. Find −5 + 2.

Show 5 "−" chips.   Pair the "+" and "−" chips.   There are 3 "−" chips left.
Then add 2 "+" chips.   Remove the pairs.   So −5 + 2 = −3.

ACTIVITY

1. Find 5 − 2.

Show
5 "+" chips.

Take away
2 "+" chips.

There are 3 "+" chips left.
So 5 − 2 = 3.

 → → ⊕ ⊕ ⊕

2. Find −5 − (−2).

Show
5 "−" chips.

Take away
2 "−" chips.

There are 3 "−" chips left.
So −5 − (−2) = −3.

⊖ ⊖ ⊖ ⊖ ⊖ → ⊖ ⊖ ⊖ ⊖ ⊖ → ⊖ ⊖ ⊖

Sometimes you need to insert zero pairs in order to subtract.

3. Find 5 − (−2).

Show
5 "+" chips.

Insert two zero pairs.
Then take away 2 "−" chips.

There are 7 "+" chips left.
So 5 − (−2) = 7.

 → → ⊕ ⊕ ⊕ ⊕ ⊕
⊕ ⊕

4. Find −5 − 2.

Show
5 "−" chips.

Insert two zero pairs.
Then take away 2 "+" chips.

There are 7 "−" chips left.
So −5 − 2 = −7.

 →   →

Exercises

Use chips or mental math to add or subtract the following integers.

1. 4 + 9 **13**

2. 9 + (−3) **6**

3. 13 + (−8) **5**

4. −14 + 6 **−8**

5. −7 + (−12) **−19**

6. 8 + (−11) **−3**

7. 11 − 3 **8**

8. −4 − (−6) **−10**

9. 5 − 12 **−7**

10. −13 − 7 **−20**

11. 5 − (−9) **14**

12. −8 − (−13) **5**

13. Write a rule for adding: (a) two positive integers, (b) two negative integers, and (c) two integers with different signs.
See margin.

13. Answers may vary. Sample:

a. To add two positive integers, add their absolute values. The result is the desired sum.

b. To add two negative integers, add their absolute values. The opposite of the result is the desired sum.

c. To add two integers with different signs, find the difference of the absolute values. Use the sign of the number with the greater absolute value.

1. Plan

TEKS ★ TAKS

(7.2)(C) To use models, such as number lines, to add and subtract integers and connect the actions to algorithms **TAKS** Obj. 1

(7.2)(F) To select and use appropriate operations to solve problems **TAKS** Obj. 1

Dana Center TEKS Toolkit Clarifying Activities (7.2)(C), (7.2)(F)
Visit: PHSchool.com
Web Code: arq-9045

TEKS Math Background

You can model the addition of integers as a series of moves on a number line. Zero is the starting point. Positive numbers are shown as moves to the right. Negative numbers are shown as moves to the left. The ending point of the last move indicates the sum. Subtracting an integer is the same as adding its opposite.

More Math Background: p. 2D

Lesson Planning and Resources

See p. 2E for a list of the resources that support this lesson.

Bell Ringer Practice

✓ **Check Skills You'll Need**
Use student page, transparency, or PowerPoint.

TAKS Daily Review 7
Use transparency.

✓ Check Skills You'll Need

1. Vocabulary Review
On a number line, how far from zero is the opposite of a number?
See below.
Find the opposite of each number.

2. 73 −73   **3.** −49 49

4. 22 −22   **5.** 13 −13

6. −424 424   **7.** −13 13

 for Help
Lesson 1-6

Check Skills You'll Need

1. the same distance from zero as the number

TEKS ★ TAKS

- (7.2)(C) To use models, such as number lines, to add and subtract integers and connect the actions to algorithms **TAKS** Obj. 1
- (7.2)(F) To select and use appropriate operations to solve problems **TAKS** Obj. 1

🔊 **New Vocabulary** additive inverses

Why Learn This?

You can add and subtract integers to keep track of money.

Suppose you start the week with no money. You borrow $10, and then you earn $10 babysitting to pay back the money you borrowed. You can add integers on a number line to see how much money you have.

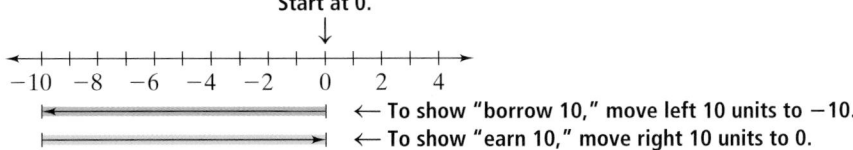

Start at 0.

← To show "borrow 10," move left 10 units to −10.
← To show "earn 10," move right 10 units to 0.

The number line shows that the sum of −10 and 10 is 0. You are back at zero where you started the week. Two numbers whose sum is 0 are **additive inverses.** You can use the following rules to add integers.

KEY CONCEPTS   **Adding Integers**

Same Sign The sum of two positive numbers is positive. The sum of two negative numbers is negative.

Examples $3 + 5 = 8$ $-3 + (-5) = -8$

Different Signs Find the absolute value of each number. Subtract the lesser absolute value from the greater. The sum has the sign of the integer with the greater absolute value.

Examples $-3 + 5 = 2$ $3 + (-5) = -2$

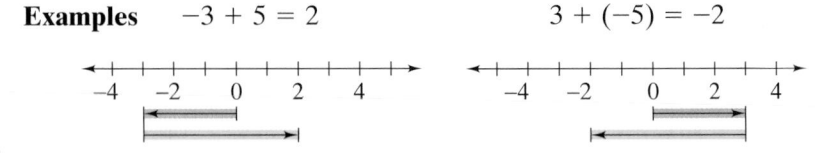

Differentiated Instruction   Solutions for All Learners

Special Needs L1
Students can use several number lines to highlight their sums as they work through addition problems. They can use one color to show a negative movement and a different color to show a positive movement.

learning style: visual

Below Level L2
Have students make number line models for a set of additions like these.

2 + 8 10   −2 + 8 6
−2 + (−8) −10   2 + (−8) −6

learning style: visual

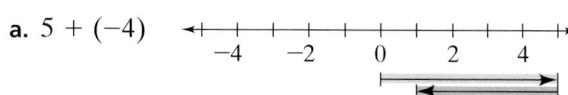 **Adding Integers With a Number Line**

1 Use a number line to find each sum.

a. $5 + (-4)$

The sum is 1.

b. $-5 + (-2)$

The sum is -7.

✓ Quick Check

1. Use a number line to find each sum.
   a. $-8 + 1$ -7 b. $-1 + (-7)$ -8 c. $-6 + 6$ 0

You can also add integers by using the absolute value of an integer.

 Adding Integers

 Tip

Check your answer by sketching a number line.

2 Find each sum.

a. $-18 + (-16) = -34$ ← Both integers are negative. The sum is negative.

b. $-23 + 8$

$|-23| = 23$ and $|8| = 8$ ← Find the absolute value of each integer.

$23 - 8 = 15$ ← Subtract 8 from 23 because $|8| < |-23|$.

$-23 + 8 = -15$ ← The sum has the same sign as -23.

✓ Quick Check

2. Find each sum.
   a. $-97 + (-65)$ -162 b. $21 + (-39)$ -18 c. $22 + (-22)$ 0

You can subtract integers, too. The number line shows that $9 - 5 = 4$ and $9 + (-5) = 4$. Subtracting 5 is the same as adding -5.

Subtract 5.   Add the opposite of 5.
$9 - 5 = 4$ $9 + (-5) = 4$
                ⌐—— The answer is 4. ——⌐

1-7 Adding and Subtracting Integers   **39**

English Language Learners ELL
To enable students to understand the concept of adding integers, continue to provide borrowing and earning money situations for the problems in Key Concepts.

learning style: visual

---

2. Teach

Activity Lab

Use before the lesson.
Student Edition Activity Lab, Hands On 1-7a, Modeling Integer Addition and Subtraction, pp. 36-37

All in One Teaching Resources
Activity Lab 1-7: Integers

Guided Instruction

Example 2
Point out that students can perform any integer addition by drawing a number line and counting units. However, the farther the numbers are from 0, the less practical this method becomes. That is why it is important to learn the rules.

Example 3
Write $4 + (-6)$ directly below $4 - 6$. Use arrows, as shown below, to help students visualize the two important changes: The plus sign is changed to a minus sign, and the 6 is changed to its opposite, which is -6.

$$4 \quad - \quad 6$$
$$\downarrow \quad \downarrow$$
$$4 \quad + \quad (-6)$$

PowerPoint
Additional Examples

1 Use a number line to find each sum.
a. $(-3) + 1$ The sum is -2.

b. $1 + (-3)$ The sum is -2.

2 Find each sum.
a. $24 + (-6)$ 18
b. $-12 + (-19)$ -31

39

This result suggests a rule for subtracting integers.

KEY CONCEPTS **Subtracting Integers**

To subtract an integer, add its opposite.

EXAMPLES **Subtracting Integers**

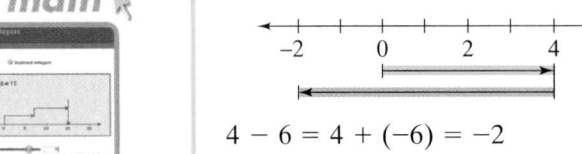

For: Integer Operations Activity
Use: Interactive Textbook, 1-7

3 Find $4 - 6$.

-2 0 2 4

Start at 0. Move 4 units right. Then add the opposite of 6, which is −6.

$$4 - 6 = 4 + (-6) = -2$$

4 Find $-2 - (-5)$.

-2 0 2 4

Start at 0. Move 2 units left. Then add the opposite of −5, which is 5.

$$-2 - (-5) = -2 + 5 = 3$$

✓ Quick Check

3. Find $-6 - 1$. **−7**   **4.** Find $14 - (-7)$. **21**

You can subtract integers to find differences between measurements.

EXAMPLE **Application: Weather**

10°
8°
6°
4°
2°
0°
−2°
−4°
−6°
−8°
−10°

The difference is 12°F.

5 The temperature in Caribou, Maine, was $8°F$ at noon. By 10:00 P.M. the temperature had dropped to $-4°F$. Find the change in the temperatures.

$8 - (-4)$ ← Subtract to find the difference.

$8 + 4$ ← Add the opposite of −4, which is 4.

12

The change in the temperatures is $12°F$.

✓ Quick Check

5. a. During the biggest drop of the Mean Streak roller coaster in Ohio, your altitude changes by -155 ft. The Texas Giant™ in Texas has a -137 ft change. You want to know how much farther you drop on the Mean Streak. Which expression can you use to solve this problem: $-155 - (-137)$, or $-137 - (-155)$? **−137 − (−155)**

b. How much farther do you drop on the Mean Streak? **18 ft**

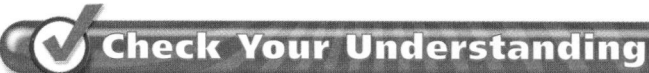

3. Practice

Assignment Guide

Check Your Understanding
Go over Exercises 1–6 in class before assigning the Homework Exercises.

Homework Exercises
A Practice by Example   7–25
B Apply Your Skills   26–37
C Challenge   38
TEKS ★ **TAKS** Tune-Up and Mixed Review   39–43

Homework Quick Check
To check students' understanding of key skills and concepts, go over Exercises 8, 20, 27, 33, and 37.

1. **Vocabulary** The absolute values of two numbers that are additive inverses will __?__ be the same. **A; always**
   Ⓐ always   Ⓑ sometimes   Ⓒ never

2. The sum of a number and −20 is 40. What is the number? **60**

3. **Reasoning** When you add a positive number and a negative number, the positive addend will __?__ be less than the sum. **C; never**
   Ⓐ always   Ⓑ sometimes   Ⓒ never

Find each missing number.

4. $-7 + \blacksquare = -15$ **−8**   5. $7 - \blacksquare = -1$ **8**   6. $-15 - \blacksquare = 15$ **−30**

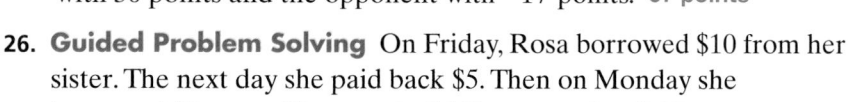**Homework Exercises**

For more exercises, see Extra Skills and Word Problems.

GO for Help

For Exercises	See Examples
7–12	1
13–18	2
19–25	3–5

Ⓐ Use a number line to find each sum.

7. $-5 + 4$ **−1**   8. $2 + (-8)$ **−6**   9. $-6 + 7$ **1**

10. $7 + 3$ **10**   11. $-2 + (-3)$ **−5**   12. $-5 + (-5)$ **−10**

Find each sum.

13. $-99 + 137$ **38**   14. $27 + (-24)$ **3**   15. $-42 + 42$ **0**

16. $-15 + 20$ **5**   17. $-28 + (-32)$ **−60**   18. $126 + (-92)$ **34**

Find each difference. You may find a number line helpful.

19. $29 - 16$ **13**   20. $-3 - (-3)$ **0**   21. $17 - (-8)$ **25**

22. $-14 - 14$ **−28**   23. $12 - (-4)$ **16**   24. $-15 - 2$ **−17**

25. In the game of billiards called 14.1, players lose points if they receive penalties. Find the difference in the scores of the winner with 50 points and the opponent with −17 points. **67 points**

Ⓑ GPS 26. **Guided Problem Solving** On Friday, Rosa borrowed $10 from her sister. The next day she paid back $5. Then on Monday she borrowed $4 more. How much did Rosa owe then? **$9**
   • How much money did Rosa owe before Monday?
   • How much money did Rosa still need to repay?

27. **Temperature** The highest temperature ever recorded in the United
GPS States was 134°F, measured at Death Valley, California. The coldest temperature, −80°F, was recorded at Prospect Creek, Alaska. What is the difference between these temperatures? **214°F**

Differentiated Instruction Resources

Adapted Practice 1-7   **L1**

Practice 1-7   Adding and Subtracting Integers   **L3**

Find each sum.
1. $-2 + (-3)$ -5 2. $8 - 7 + 4$ 5 3. $8 + (-5)$ 3 4. $15 + (-3)$ 12
5. $-16 + 8$ -8 6. $7 + (-10)$ -3 7. $-9 + (-5)$ -14 8. $-12 + 14$ 2

Find each difference.
9. $9 - 26$ -17 10. $-4 - 15$ -19 11. $21 - (-7)$ 28 12. $27 - (-16)$ 43
13. $-16 - (-43)$ 27 14. $47 - 19$ 28 15. $-156 - 98$ -254 16. $-192 - 47$ -239
17. $0 - (-51)$ 51 18. $-63 - 89$ -152 19. $-12 - (-21)$ 9 20. $92 - (-16)$ 108

Find the value of each expression.
21. $3 + 8 + (-4)$ 7 22. $2 + |-3| + (-3)$ 2 23. $9 + 7 - 6$ 10
24. $56 + (-4) + (-58)$ -6 25. $-4 - 3 + (-2)$ -9 26. $|-8| - 15 + (-8)$ -15

Use >, <, or = to complete each statement.
27. $-9 - (-11)$ $>$ 0 28. $-17 + 20$ $>$ 0 29. $11 - (-4)$ $>$ 0
30. $28 - 19$ $>$ 0 31. $52 + (-65)$ $<$ 0 32. $-28 - (-28)$ $=$ 0

Solve.
33. The highest and lowest temperatures ever recorded in Africa are 136°F and −11°F. The highest temperature was recorded in Libya, and the lowest temperature was recorded in Morocco. What is the difference in these temperature extremes?   **147°F**
34. The highest and lowest temperatures ever recorded in South America are 120°F and −27°F. Both the highest and lowest temperatures were recorded in Argentina. What is the difference in these temperature extremes?   **147°F**

1-7 • Guided Problem Solving **GPS**   **L3**

GPS Student Page 39, Exercise 27:

Temperature The highest temperature ever recorded in the United States was 134°F measured at Death Valley, California. The coldest temperature, −80°F, was recorded at Prospect Creek, Alaska. What is the difference between these temperatures?

Understand
1. Circle the information you will need to solve the problem.
2. What are you being asked to do?
   Find the difference between 134°F and −80°F.
3. Which word tells you what operation to perform?
   The word "difference" tells you to subtract.

Plan and Carry Out
4. Write a subtraction expression for the problem.
   $134 - (-80)$
5. Subtracting a negative number is the same as adding what type of number?
   a positive number
6. Write an addition expression that is the same as the expression you wrote in step 4.
   $134 + 80$
7. What is the difference between these temperatures?
   214°F

Check
8. What is 134°F − 214°F?
   −80°F

Solve Another Problem
9. At 6:00 A.M. the temperature was 25°F. At 9:00 P.M. the temperature was −13°F. What was the difference in the temperature?
   38°F

PowerPoint

Lesson Quiz

Find each sum or difference.

1. $7 - (-4)$ **11**

2. $-9 + 3$ **−6**

3. $-8 + (-5)$ **−13**

4. $-5 - 2$ **−7**

Alternative Assessment

Distribute counters in two colors to pairs of students. Have students model Exercises 7–12 and 19–24 using the counters. Assign one color for positive and the second color for negative. For Exercise 7, students would set out 5 negative counters and 4 positive counters. They then pair up 4 negative and 4 positive counters. The remaining 1 negative counter shows the sum of −1. Remind students that to subtract an integer, add its opposite.

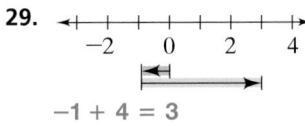

GO **Online**

Homework Help

Visit: PHSchool.com
Web Code: are-0107

Write an addition expression for each model. Then find the sum.

28.
$$-3 + (-1) = -4$$

29.
$$-1 + 4 = 3$$

(Algebra) **Find each value of x.**

30. $-7 + 6 = x$ **−1**   31. $x + 2 = 0$ **−2**   32. $x - 3 = -6$ **−3**

The continental United States has four time zones. Consider time changes as positive when going east and negative when going west. The time is given in your zone. Find the time in the indicated time zone.

33. 6:00 A.M.; 2 time zones east
    8:00 A.M.

34. 9:00 P.M.; 3 time zones west
    6:00 P.M.

35. midnight; 2 time zones west
    10:00 P.M.

36. 12:00 A.M.; 1 time zone east
    1:00 A.M.

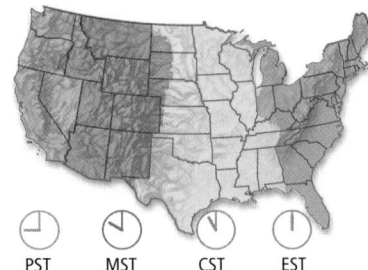

PST   MST   CST   EST

37. Subtracting a number is the same as adding its opposite, so
    $20 - (-38) =$
    $20 + 38 = 58.$

37. **Writing in Math** Your friend has trouble simplifying $20 - (-38)$. Write an explanation to help your friend.

C 38. **Challenge** You earn $5.25 an hour at your job in a restaurant but pay for any food you eat. On Friday, you receive a check for 7 hours of work, minus $8.90 for food. What is the amount on your check? **$27.85**

TEKS ★ (TAKS) Tune-Up and Mixed Review

(TAKS) Objective 1
TEKS (7.2)(C)

39. Which expression is represented by the model below? **C**

(A) $-5 + 0$ (C) $-5 + 3$
(B) $-5 + 2$ (D) $-5 + 5$

(TAKS) Objective 6
TEKS (7.13)(B)

40. The Fred Hartman Bridge in Baytown, Texas, is 381 m long. The Clark Bridge in Alton, Illinois, is 1.408 km. Which method can you use to find the difference in length of the bridges in meters? **H**
    (F) Subtract 140.8 from 0.381.   (H) Subtract 381 from 1,408.
    (G) Divide 381 by 1,408.   (J) Multiply 1,408 by 100.

GO for Help   **Lesson 1-6**

Compare. Use <, =, or >.

41. -4 ▇ -10 **>**   42. $|-3|$ ▇ $|3|$ **=**   43. 16 ▇ $|-23|$ **<**

TEKS ★ (TAKS) Resources

• TAKS Strategies, p. 59
• TAKS Tune-Up, pp. 63–65

(TAKS) Tune-Up Kit

• TAKS Daily Review Transparencies
• TAKS Review and Preparation Workbook
• TAKS Strategies with Transparencies
• Texas Progress Monitoring Assessments

Enrichment 1-7   **L4**

Reteaching 1-7   Adding and Subtracting **L2**

Use these rules to add and subtract integers.

Adding Integers

Same Sign
• The sum of two positive integers is positive.
  Example: $6 + 16 = 22$
• The sum of two negative integers is negative.
  Example: $-9 + (-3) = -12$

Different Signs
• First find the absolute values of each number.
• Then subtract the lesser absolute value from the greater.
• The sum has the sign of the integer with the greater absolute value.
  Example: $-10 + 9 = -1$

Subtracting Integers
• To subtract integers, add the opposite.
• Then following the rules for adding integers.
  Example: $6 - (-3) = 6 + 3 = 9$

Find each sum.
1. $8 + (-2)$ **6**   2. $-9 + 4$ **−5**   3. $3 + (-2)$ **1**
4. $-1 + 11$ **10**   5. $12 + 13$ **25**   6. $-9 + 5$ **−4**
7. $7 + 2$ **9**   8. $-1 + (-7)$ **−8**   9. $-3 + 0$ **−3**
10. $-1 + (-1)$ **−2**   11. $6 + 5$ **11**   12. $3 - (-2)$ **5**

Complete.
13. $-3 - 4$ Change to addition: $-3 + $ **(−4)** $= $ **−7**
14. $5 - 2$ Change to addition: $5 + $ **(−2)** $= $ **3**
15. $-6 - (-10)$ Change to addition: $-6 + $ **10** $= $ **4**

Find each difference.
16. $4 - 5$ **−1**   17. $-5 - 4$ **−9**   18. $-8 - (-7)$ **−1**
19. $19 - (-6)$ **25**   20. $-10 - 12$ **−22**   21. $-12 - 10$ **−22**
22. $-4 - (-5)$ **1**   23. $-2 - (-3)$ **1**   24. $9 - (-7)$ **16**
25. $0 - 3$ **−3**   26. $6 - 8$ **−2**   27. $0 - (-10)$ **10**

Modeling Integer Multiplication

To remember the rules for multiplying integers, you can think of the effects that different operations would have on your bank account. The algebra tiles in the diagrams below show groups of integers added to or taken away from a bank account. Think about whether each action would make you feel positive or negative.

TEKS ★ (TAKS)

(7.2)(C) To use models to multiply integers and connect the actions to algorithms (TAKS) **Obj. 1**

(7.2)(F) To select and use appropriate operations to solve problems (TAKS) **Obj. 1**

ACTIVITY

1. Use algebra tiles to make a "bank account" like the one at the right. Using tiles, add two groups of 3 to your account. Does adding the tiles make you feel positive or negative? Write an equation to represent this operation.

2. Suppose you have to pay two video-rental late fees of $3 each. This is an example of adding negative integers to your account. Would this make you feel positive or negative? Use algebra tiles to model adding two groups of −3 to your account. Use the diagram below to write an equation for the operation.

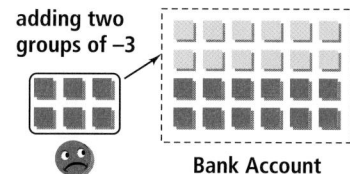

3. Take away two groups of 4 from your account. Use the diagram below to write an equation representing this operation. Describe a situation that this operation might represent.

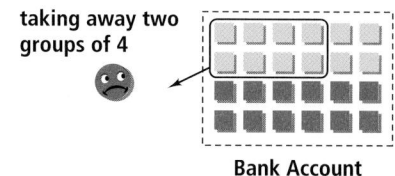

4. Suppose you have two library fines for $4 each. You *owe* this money, so you can use the integer −4 to represent each fine. If the librarian told you that you did not have to pay the fines, how would you feel? Use the diagram at the right to write an equation representing this operation.

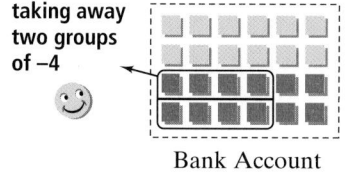

5. Use a table to summarize the rules for multiplying integers. Include all four possibilities. Describe any patterns you notice.

5.

Sign of First Integer	Sign of Second Integer	Sign of Product
positive	positive	positive
positive	negative	negative
negative	positive	negative
negative	negative	positive

When you multiply two integers that have the same sign, the product is positive. When you multiply two integers with different signs, the product is negative.

Modeling Integer Multiplication

Students use algebra tiles to multiply positive and negative integers.

Guided Instruction

Activity

Students should note that the accounts are "balanced" before adding positive or negative integers to the accounts. Be sure students understand that the situation in part 4 is actually a "double negative," or a positive.

Have students work in pairs to make up their own integer multiplication situations to model with algebra tiles.

TEKS ★ (TAKS) Resources

- Activity Lab 1-8: Multiplication Madness
- algebra tiles
- Classroom Aid 37
- Student Manipulatives Kit

Dana Center TEKS Toolkit Clarifying Activities (7.2)(C), (7.2)(F)
Visit: PHSchool.com
Web Code: arq-9045

TEKS ★ TAKS

(7.2)(C) To use models, such as number lines, to multiply and divide integers and connect the actions to algorithms **TAKS** Obj. 1

(7.2)(F) To select and use appropriate operations to solve problems **TAKS** Obj. 1

Dana Center TEKS Toolkit Clarifying Activities (7.2)(C), (7.2)(F)
Visit: PHSchool.com
Web Code: arq-9045

TEKS Math Background

You can view multiplying by a positive integer as repeated addition. So a "positive × positive" product is positive, and a "positive × negative" product is negative. Multiplying by a negative integer is the opposite of multiplying by a positive integer, so the products have opposite signs. A "negative × positive" product is negative, and a "negative × negative" product is positive.

More Math Background: p. 2D

Lesson Planning and Resources

See p. 2E for a list of the resources that support this lesson.

Bell Ringer Practice

✓ **Check Skills You'll Need**
Use student page, transparency, or PowerPoint.

TAKS Daily Review 8
Use transparency.

 Check Skills You'll Need

1. Vocabulary Review
Two numbers that are *additive inverses* always have a sum of __?__. **zero**

Find each sum.

2. $7 + (-3)$ **4**

3. $-4 + 9$ **5**

4. $-22 + (-13)$ **−35**

5. $-17 + 17$ **0**

GO for Help
Lesson 1-7

TEKS ★ TAKS

• (7.2)(C) To use models, such as number lines, to multiply and divide integers and connect the actions to algorithms **TAKS** Obj. 1

• (7.2)(F) To select and use appropriate operations to solve problems **TAKS** Obj. 1

Why Learn This?

Balloonists watch their altitude when they fly. You can multiply integers to find change in altitude.

A balloon descends at a rate of 4 ft/min for 3 min. To multiply integers, think of multiplication as repeated addition.

$$3(-4) = (-4) + (-4) + (-4) = -12 \quad \leftarrow \text{The balloon descends 12 ft.}$$

You can use number lines to multiply integers.

3(2) means three groups of 2.

Begin here.
The sum of 3 groups of +2 is 6.

3(−2) means three groups of −2.

Begin here.
The sum of 3 groups of −2 is −6.

−3(2) is the opposite of three groups of 2.

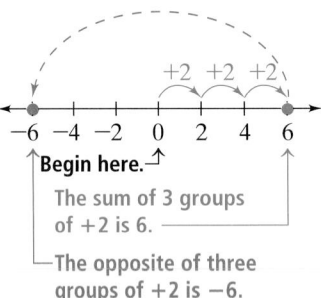

Begin here.
The sum of 3 groups of +2 is 6.
The opposite of three groups of +2 is −6.

−3(−2) is the opposite of three groups of −2.

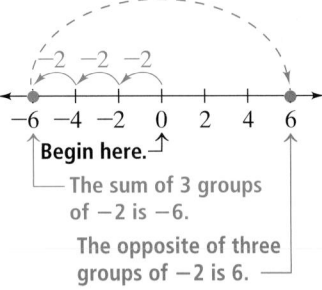

Begin here.
The sum of 3 groups of −2 is −6.
The opposite of three groups of −2 is 6.

This pattern suggests the rules for multiplying integers.

Differentiated Instruction | Solutions for All Learners

Special Needs L1
Have students use number lines to work through Example 1, circling each group on the number line. For example, for 5(–3) they would circle a set of numbers from 0 to –3, another from –3 to –6, another from –6 to –9, and so on, until 5 sets are circled and the product is –15.
Learning style: visual

Below Level L2
Have students name all pairs of integers whose product is 15. **1, 15; 3, 5; −1, −15; −3, −5.** Then have them name all pairs of integers whose product is −15. **−1, 15; 1, −15; −3, 5; 3, −5**
learning style: verbal

KEY CONCEPTS Multiplying Integers

The product of two integers with the same sign is positive. The product of two integers with different signs is negative.

Examples $-3(-2) = 6$ $3(-2) = -6$

EXAMPLE Multiplying Integers

1 Find each product.

a. $5(3) = 15$ ← same signs; positive product →   **b.** $-5(-3) = 15$

c. $5(-3) = -15$ ← different signs; negative product → **d.** $-5(3) = -15$

✓ Quick Check

1. Simplify the expression $-4(-7)$.   28

Since $-2(5) = -10$, you know that $-10 \div (-2) = 5$. The rules for dividing integers are similar to the rules for multiplying.

KEY CONCEPTS Dividing Integers

The quotient of two integers with the same sign is positive. The quotient of two integers with different signs is negative.

Examples $-10 \div (-2) = 5$ $10 \div (-2) = -5$

EXAMPLE Dividing Integers

2 A rock climber is at an elevation of 10,100 feet. Five hours later, she is at 7,340 feet. Use the formula below to find the climber's vertical speed.

$$\text{vertical speed} = \frac{\text{final elevation} - \text{initial elevation}}{\text{time}}$$

$$= \frac{7,340 - 10,100}{5}$$ ← Substitute 7,340 for final elevation, 10,100 for initial elevation, and 5 for time.

$$= \frac{-2,760}{5} = -552$$ ← Simplify. The negative sign means the climber is descending.

The climber's vertical speed is -552 feet per hour.

✓ Quick Check

2. Find the vertical speed of a climber who goes from an elevation of 8,120 feet to an elevation of 6,548 feet in three hours.   −524 ft/h

---

Advanced Learners **L4**

Tell whether each statement is *true* or *false*.

$|2| \cdot |3| = |2 \cdot 3|$ true
$|-2| \cdot |3| = |-2 \cdot 3|$ true
$|-2| \cdot |-3| = |-2 \cdot (-3)|$ true

Pre-AP™

English Language Learners **ELL**

Ask students to work through the Examples in pairs, discussing each. For example, 1a is 5 groups of 3, while 1b is the opposite of 5 groups of negative 3. Asking students to explain aloud will provide them with language to check integer calculations on their own.

learning style: verbal

---

2. Teach

Activity Lab

Use before the lesson.
Student Edition Activity Lab, Hands On 1-8a, Modeling Integer Multiplication, p. 43

All in One Teaching Resources
Activity Lab 1-8: Multiplication Madness

Guided Instruction

Example 2
Students might have difficulty with the terms *vertical speed* and *elevation*. In this problem, *vertical speed* refers to how fast the climber is rising. *Elevation* refers to the height of the mountain and climber.

Alternative Method
Have students use algebra tiles to model integer division. Let one color represent positive integers and a second color represent negative integers.

PowerPoint
Additional Examples

1 Find each product.
a. 3(7) 21   **c.** −3(7) −21
b. 3(−7) −21   **d.** −3(−7) 21

2 You are riding your bicycle at a speed of 12 ft/s. Four seconds later, you come to a complete stop. Find the acceleration of your bicycle by using the formula:

acceleration =

$\frac{\text{final velocity} - \text{initial velocity}}{\text{time}}$ −3 ft/s

All in One Teaching Resources
• Daily Notetaking Guide 1-8 **L3**
• Adapted Notetaking 1-8 **L1**

Closure

• *What are the rules for multiplying and dividing two integers?* Sample: The product or quotient of two integers with the same sign is positive. The product or quotient of two integers with different signs is negative.

45

3. Practice

Assignment Guide

Check Your Understanding
Go over Exercises 1–9 in class before assigning the Homework Exercises.

Homework Exercises
A Practice by Example   10–28
B Apply Your Skills   29–37
C Challenge   38
TEKS ★ TAKS Tune-Up and
      Mixed Review   39–43

Homework Quick Check
To check students' understanding of key skills and concepts, go over Exercises 16, 22, 34, 35, and 37.

Differentiated Instruction **Resources**

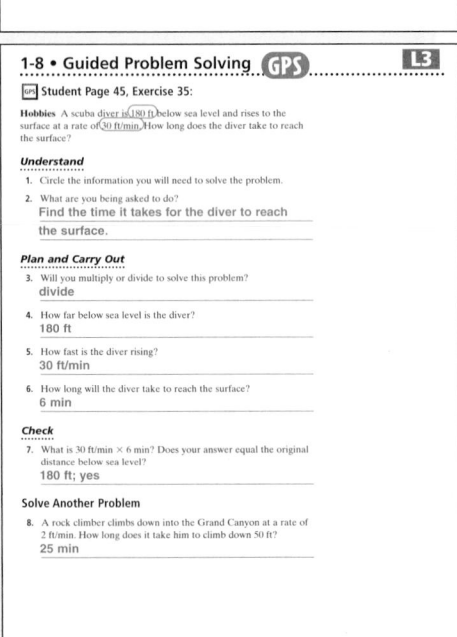

✔ Check Your Understanding

2. At least one integer needs to be zero because of the Zero Prop. of Multiplication.

1. **Number Sense** A cave explorer descends at a rate of 6 m/min. Which expression CANNOT be used to find her depth after 4 min.?   **B**

   Ⓐ $-6 + (-6) + (-6) + (-6)$ Ⓒ $-6(4)$

   Ⓑ $\dfrac{-6}{4}$ Ⓓ $-6 - 6 - 6 - 6$

2. **Reasoning** The product of two integers is zero. What do you know about the value of at least one of the integers? Explain.

Find each missing number.

3. $-7 \times \blacksquare = -28$ 4   4. $-48 \div \blacksquare = 6$ −8   5. $\dfrac{\blacksquare}{-4} = -20$ 80

Find each product or quotient.

6. $-2(-13)$ 26   7. $22 \div (-11)$ −2   8. $-4(9)$ −36   9. $-25 \div 5$ −5

Homework Exercises

For more exercises, see Extra Skills and Word Problems.

Ⓐ **Find each product.**

GO for Help

For Exercises	See Examples
10–18	1
19–28	2

10. -5×4 −20   11. $12(3)$ 36   12. $6(-6)$ −36

13. $-7 \cdot (-3)$ 21   14. $-21 \times (-4)$ 84   15. $3(-33)$ −99

16. $-12(-17)$ 204   17. $-35 \cdot 24$ −840   18. $-102(6)$ −612

Find each quotient.

19. $\dfrac{36}{12}$ 3   20. $\dfrac{14}{-2}$ −7   21. $-42 \div 3$ −14

22. $-80 \div -20$ 4   23. $-8\overline{)64}$ −8   24. $\dfrac{-27}{-9}$ 3

25. $96 \div (-12)$ −8   26. $\dfrac{-195}{13}$ −15   27. $\dfrac{-242}{-1}$ 242

28. **Hiking** In four hours, a hiker in a canyon goes from 892 ft to 256 ft above the canyon floor. Find the hiker's vertical speed. −159 ft/h

Ⓑ **GPS** 29. **Guided Problem Solving** A submarine takes 6 min to dive from a depth of 29 m below the water's surface to 257 m below the surface. Find the submarine's vertical speed. −38 m/min

$$\text{vertical speed} = \frac{\text{final depth} - \text{initial depth}}{\text{time}} = \frac{\blacksquare - (-29)}{\blacksquare}$$

30. **Birds** A hawk soars at an altitude of 1,800 ft. If the hawk descends to the ground in 45 min, what is its vertical speed? −40 ft/min

34. If there is an even number of negative signs, the product is positive. If there is an odd number of negative signs, the product is negative.

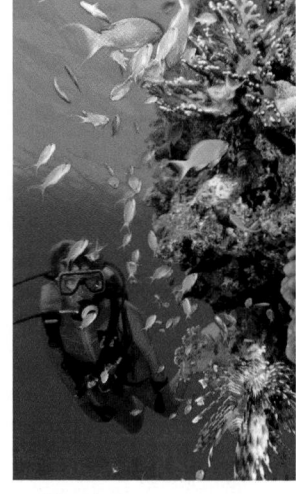

(**Algebra**) **Find each value of x.**

31. $x \cdot 9 = -9$ −1

32. $x \div 3 = -5$ −15

33. $\dfrac{-8}{x} = 4$ −2

34. <u>Writing in Math</u> Explain how you would decide whether the product of three numbers is positive or negative. **See margin.**

35. **Hobbies** A scuba diver is 180 ft below sea level and rises to the surface at a rate of 30 ft/min. How long will the diver take to reach the surface? **6 min**

36. **Open-Ended** Describe a situation that can be represented by the expression $4(-2)$. **Answers may vary. Sample: A person owes four people $2 each.**

37. In July, a sporting goods store offers a bike for $278. Over the next five months, the store reduces the price of the bike $15 each month.
  a. Write an expression for the total change in price after the five months of discounts. **278 − 5(15)**
  b. What is the price of the bike at the end of five months? **$203**

C 38. **Challenge** A bank customer has $172 in a bank account. She withdraws $85 per month for the next 3 months. She also writes 4 checks for $45.75 each. How much money should she deposit to ensure that her balance is at least $25 at the end of the 3 months? **$291**

TEKS ★ TAKS Tune-Up and Mixed Review

39. Which model best represents the expression $2 \times (-4)$? **B**

40. One day in January, five different cities had temperatures of $-12°F$, $5°F$, $-16°F$, $0°F$, and $73°F$. Which list shows the temperatures from least to greatest? **H**
  F $-16°F$, $5°F$, $-12°F$, $0°F$, $73°F$
  G $0°F$, $5°F$, $-12°F$, $-16°F$, $73°F$
  H $-16°F$, $-12°F$, $0°F$, $5°F$, $73°F$
  J $73°F$, $-16°F$, $-12°F$, $0°F$, $5°F$

for Help   Lesson 1-5

Write the number that makes each statement true.

41. $142 \text{ cm} = \blacksquare \text{ m}$ 1.42

42. $0.67 \text{ L} = \blacksquare \text{ mL}$ 670

43. $\blacksquare \text{ kg} = 3{,}400 \text{ g}$ 3.4

TEKS ★ TAKS Resources

- TAKS Strategies, p. 59
- TAKS Tune-Up, pp. 63–65

(TAKS) **Tune-Up Kit**

- TAKS Daily Review Transparencies
- TAKS Review and Preparation Workbook
- TAKS Strategies with Transparencies
- Texas Progress Monitoring Assessments

---

4. Assess & Reteach

PowerPoint
Lesson Quiz

Find each product or quotient.

1. $9 \cdot (-5)$ −45

2. $-63 \div (-7)$ 9

3. $-11 \cdot (-11)$ 121

4. $42 \div (-6)$ −7

Alternative Assessment

Have pairs of students use number lines to illustrate how multiplication is repeated addition. Use four related multiplication problems such as these.

  $3 \cdot 4$
  $3 \cdot (-4)$
  $-3 \cdot 4$
  $-3 \cdot (-4)$

Have students follow the models on page 44 to draw the repeated "jumps" in either the positive or negative direction. Remind students to start at zero.

TEKS Math Background

Without an order of operations, an expression like $3 + 4 \cdot 5$ might have two values. One person might interpret it as the sum $3 + 4$ being multiplied by 5, with a result of 35. Another person might interpret it as the product $4 \cdot 5$ added to 3, with a result of 23. With the order of operations, the second interpretation is universally accepted as the correct one.

In this lesson, students learn the order of operations for expressions involving grouping symbols and the four basic operations. In Lesson 2-1 they will learn the place of exponents in the order of operations.

More Math Background: p. 2D

Lesson Planning and Resources

See p. 2E for a list of the resources that support this lesson.

Bell Ringer Practice

☑️ **Check Skills You'll Need**
Use student page, transparency, or PowerPoint.

TAKS **Daily Review 9**
Use transparency.

48

☑️ Check Skills You'll Need

1. Vocabulary Review
Which property is illustrated by the statement
$1.6 + 4 = 4 + 1.6$?
Comm. Prop. of Add.
Use mental math to simplify.

2. $2.5 + 7.1 + 2.5$ 12.1

3. $6.4 + 6.2 + 5.6$ 18.2

4. $8.1 + 3.8 + 8.1$ 20

 GO for Help
Lesson 1-2

What You'll Learn

To use the order of operations and the Distributive Property

- Prepares for **TEKS (7.2)(E)** To simplify numerical expressions involving order of operations and exponents

🔊 **New Vocabulary** order of operations, Distributive Property

Why Learn This?

Cash registers calculate the total price when a customer buys several items. You can use order of operations to be sure the total is correct.

Suppose you want to find the total price of one shirt and two hats. You can simplify $20 + \$5 \times 2$. If you add first, the price is $50. If you multiply first, then the price is $30.

HATS $5.00 EACH

SHIRTS $20.00 EACH

To avoid confusion, mathematicians have agreed upon a particular **order of operations.**

KEY CONCEPTS Order of Operations

1. Work inside grouping symbols.
2. Multiply and divide in order from left to right.
3. Add and subtract in order from left to right.

EXAMPLE Using the Order of Operations

1 Find the value of each expression.

a. $30 \div 3 + 2 \cdot 6$

$10 + 12$ ← **Divide and multiply.**

22 ← **Add.**

b. $30 \div (3 + 2) \cdot 6$

$30 \div 5 \cdot 6$ ← **Work inside grouping symbols.**

$6 \cdot 6$ ← **Divide.**

36 ← **Multiply.**

Vocabulary Tip

Grouping symbols include parentheses, ( ), brackets, [ ], and fraction bars, $\frac{3+5}{2}$.

☑️ Quick Check

1. Find the value of each expression.

a. $7(-4 + 2) - 1$ −15   **b.** $\frac{-40}{4} + 2 \cdot 5$ 0   **c.** $\frac{8+4}{6} - 11$ −9

48   Chapter 1   Decimals and Integers

Differentiated Instruction Solutions for All Learners

Special Needs **L1**
Have students highlight parts of an expression in different colors according to the order of operations. For example, what you do first, highlight in green; next, highlight in yellow; and last, highlight in pink.

learning style: visual

Below Level **L2**
Discuss this set of exercises with students.

$(6 + 2) \cdot (5 - 3)$ 16 $(6 + 2) \cdot 5 - 3$ 37
$6 + 2 \cdot (5 - 3)$ 10 $6 + 2 \cdot 5 - 3$ 13

learning style: verbal

EXAMPLE **Application: Shopping**

2 You want to buy two magazines and three greeting cards from the rack shown at the left. What is the total cost of the items?

Words   2 magazines plus 3 greeting cards

↓

Expression $2 \cdot 3.99$ + $3 \cdot 1.99$

$2 \cdot 3.99 + 3 \cdot 1.99 = 7.98 + 5.97$ ← First multiply.

$= 13.95$ ← Then add.

The total cost is $13.95.

✓ Quick Check

2. What is the total cost of 5 magazines and 2 greeting cards? $23.93

Note that $3(5 + 4) = 3(9)$, or 27. Note also that $3(5) + 3(4) = 15 + 12$, or 27. This is an example of the Distributive Property.

> **KEY CONCEPTS** **Distributive Property**
>
> | **Arithmetic** | **Algebra** |
> |---|---|
> | $9(4 + 5) = 9(4) + 9(5)$ | $a(b + c) = a(b) + a(c)$ |
> | $5(8 - 2) = 5(8) - 5(2)$ | $a(b - c) = a(b) - a(c)$ |

You can use the Distributive Property to multiply numbers mentally.

EXAMPLE **The Distributive Property in Mental Math**

3 **Mental Math** Use the Distributive Property to find 7(59).

What You Think

If I think of 59 as $(60 - 1)$, then 7(59) is the same as $7(60 - 1)$. I know that $7(60) - 7(1) = 420 - 7 = 413$.

Why It Works $7(59) = 7(60 - 1)$

$= 7(60) - 7(1)$ ← Use the Distributive Property.

$= 420 - 7$ ← Multiply.

$= 413$ ← Subtract.

Look for opportunities for using mental math to make calculations easier.

✓ Quick Check

3. Use the Distributive Property and mental math to find 9(14). 126

1-9 Order of Operations and the Distributive Property   **49**

Advanced Learners **L4**

Find two different ways to make a true statement by inserting $+$, $-$, $\cdot$, or $\div$ into each blank:
$32 \square 8 \square 4 \square 2 = 2$ Samples: $32 \div 8 \div 4 \cdot 2$;
$32 - 8 \cdot 4 + 2$

Pre-AP™

English Language Learners **ELL**

In Example 2, have students make the translation from words to expression. For example, ask them to say *2 magazines for 3.99 each plus 3 greeting cards for 1.99 each.* This makes it easier for them to associate the terms in the expression with the words.

learning style: verbal

Assignment Guide

Check Your Understanding
Go over Exercises 1-7 in class before assigning the Homework Exercises.

Homework Exercises
A Practice by Example   8–25
B Apply Your Skills   26–33
C Challenge   34
TEKS ★ **(TAKS)** Tune-Up and Mixed Review   35–41

Homework Quick Check
To check students' understanding of key skills and concepts, go over Exercises 14, 21, 30, 32, and 33.

Differentiated Instruction **Resources**

Check Your Understanding

2. Yes, by the Comm. Prop. of Mult.

1. **Vocabulary** The Distributive Property combines which operation with addition or subtraction? multiplication

2. **Reasoning** Does $6(50 + 3) = (50 + 3)6$? Explain.

3. **Error Analysis** A classmate used the Distributive Property to find $11(9.2)$. What error did your classmate make?
11(2) should be 11(0.2).

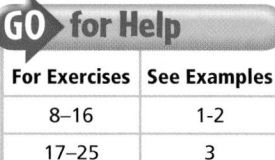
$$11(9.2) = 11(9) + 11(2)$$
$$= 99 + 22$$
$$= 121$$

Use the order of operations to fill in the blanks.

4. $4 \times 5 + 7 = \blacksquare + 7 = \blacksquare$
20; 27

5. $20 - 2 \cdot 8 = \blacksquare - 16 = \blacksquare$
20; 4

Use mental math to find the missing numbers. Then simplify.

6. $\blacksquare(4.8) = 6(5) - 6(\blacksquare)$
6; 0.2; 28.8

7. $5(32) = 5(\blacksquare) + 5(\blacksquare)$
30; 2; 160

Homework Exercises

For more exercises, see Extra Skills and Word Problems.

GO for Help

For Exercises	See Examples
8–16	1-2
17–25	3

Ⓐ **Find the value of each expression.**

8. $6 + 1 \cdot 5$ 11

9. $-4 \div 2 + 9$ 7

10. $5 - 8 \div 4$ 3

11. $3 - 0 \cdot 11$ 3

12. $18 \div 3 \cdot 2$ 12

13. $100 - 7 \cdot 9$ 37

14. $-12 \div 6 - (1 + 4)$ −7

15. $48 \div (-4 \cdot 3) + 2$ −2

16. **Coins** You buy some items at a store and pay with a $5 bill. You receive two quarters, two dimes, and three pennies as change. How much money do you receive? $.73

Use the Distributive Property and mental math to find each product.

17. $5(29)$ 145

18. $6(3.9)$ 23.4

19. $9 \cdot 2.2$ 19.8

20. $5(42)$ 210

21. $7 \cdot 2.6$ 18.2

22. $8(87)$ 696

23. $4 \cdot 10.2$ 40.8

24. $11.6(9)$ 104.4

25. $1.1(22)$ 24.2

Ⓑ **GPS** 26. **Guided Problem Solving** The sheet of plywood at the right has a piece cut from one corner. What is the area of the plywood? 26 ft²
• What are the dimensions of the original piece of plywood?
• What are the dimensions of the missing piece?

33. You could use the Dist. Prop. to rewrite 4(110.5) as 4(110 + 0.5). This gives you 440 + 2, or 442. You could also rewrite 4(110.5) as 4(111 − 0.5). This gives you 444 − 2, or 442.

Copy each statement. Add parentheses to make it true.

27. $4 + 4 \div 4 - 4 = -2$
$(4 + 4) \div 4 - 4 = -2$

28. $4 \cdot 4 \div 4 + 4 = 2$
$(4 \cdot 4) \div (4 + 4) = 2$

29. **Architecture** Use the floor plan at the right. Find the area of the floor. **1,840 ft²**

|← 25 ft →|← 30 ft →|
40 ft
Bedroom
Family Room
Living Room
Bath | Kitchen
Dining Room
28 ft

30. **Business** A florist is buying flowers to use in centerpieces. Each centerpiece has 3 lilies. There are 10 tables in all. Each lily costs \$.98. Use mental math to find the cost of the lilies. **\$29.40**

31. A freight train has 62 cars and a locomotive that is 65 ft long. Each car is 50 ft long. There is 3 ft of space between the locomotive and the first car and between each pair of cars. How long is the train? **3,348 ft**

32. **Geometry** Write two expressions to find the total area of the figure. Then find the area. **See left.**

3 cm
5 cm | 5 cm

33. **Writing in Math** Explain how you can use the Distributive Property in two different ways to calculate 4(110.5). **See margin.**

34. **Challenge** You go with five friends to an amusement park. The tickets originally cost \$36.50 each, but you receive a group discount. The total cost is \$198. What discount does each person receive? **\$3.50**

32. 3(5 + 5) =
3 · 5 + 3 · 5 =
30 cm²
3(5) + 3(5) =
15 + 15 =
30 cm²

 TEKS ★ **TAKS** **Tune-Up and Mixed Review**

TAKS Objective 1
TEKS (7.2)(E)

35. What is the value of the expression $3 \times (-2) + 6 \div (-2) - 5$? **A**
Ⓐ −14   Ⓑ −9   Ⓒ −5   Ⓓ 4

TAKS Objective 1
TEKS (7.2)(C)

36. Which expression does NOT represent the total area of the figure? **H**
Ⓕ 4(7 + 5)   Ⓗ 4(7) + 5
Ⓖ 28 + 20   Ⓙ 4(7) + 4(5)

4 m
7 m | 5 m

TAKS Objective 6
TEKS (7.13)(A)

37. At 8 P.M., the wind-chill temperature was −9°F. One hour later, the wind-chill temperature had fallen to −29°F. Which number sentence shows this change? **A**
Ⓐ −29 − (−9) = −20   Ⓒ −9 − (−29) = 20
Ⓑ 29 + (−9) = 20   Ⓓ 29 + (−9) = −20

GO **for Help**   **Lesson 1-8**

Find each product.

38. −6(8) **−48**   **39.** 12(−5) **−60**   **40.** −7(−9) **63**   **41.** 11(13) **143**

TEKS ★ **TAKS** **Resources**

- TAKS Strategies, p. 59
- TAKS Tune-Up, pp. 63–65

TAKS Tune-Up Kit

- TAKS Daily Review Transparencies
- TAKS Review and Preparation Workbook
- TAKS Strategies with Transparencies
- Texas Progress Monitoring Assessments

4. Assess & Reteach

PowerPoint
Lesson Quiz

Find the value of each expression.

1. $36 + (-2 \cdot 3) - 5$ **25**

2. $(18 - 9) \cdot 8$ **72**

Find each product mentally using the Distributive Property.

3. 3(42) **126**   **4.** 8(3.1) **24.8**

Alternative Assessment

Have students work in pairs. One partner writes an expression similar to those in Exercises 8–15. The other writes an expression similar to those in Exercises 17–25. Students exchange papers and simplify each other's expressions. Have partners check each other's work and work together to resolve any discrepancies. Have students alternate roles as time permits.

Students use number properties to solve algebraic equations.

Guided Instruction

Example 2
Let students add 14.75 + 3.8 and 4.75 + 13.8 to be sure the sums are the same.

Exercises
Have students work in pairs to do Exercises 1–6. For Exercise 7, have each partner make a balance-scale puzzle for his or her partner to solve.

Differentiated Instruction

Tactile Learners
Have students model balance-scale problems on an actual balance using grams, kilograms, and other metric measures.

TEKS ★ TAKS Resources

- Classroom Aid 8
- Student Manipulatives Kit

Dana Center TEKS Toolkit Clarifying Activities (7.15)(B)
Visit: PHSchool.com
Web Code: arq-9045

52

TEKS ★ TAKS
(7.15)(B) To validate conclusions using mathematical properties and relationships *TAKS* Obj. 6

Properties and Equality

Understanding number properties and equality will help you solve algebraic equations.

EXAMPLE Understanding Number Properties

1 Use a number property or number sense to determine whether the equation 8.86 + 12.51 + 1.23 = 1.23 + 8.86 + 12.51 is true or false. Justify your reasoning.

$$8.86 + 12.51 + 1.23 = 8.86 + 1.23 + 12.51 \leftarrow$$ The order of the numbers has changed. This is an example of the Commutative Property of Addition.

● True; the Commutative Property of Addition is being used.

EXAMPLE Understanding Equality

2 Use number properties, mental math, or number sense to determine whether the scales are balanced. Justify your reasoning.

| 4.75 | 13.8 | 14.75 | 3.8 |

14.75 on the right is 10 more than 4.75 on the left. 13.8 on the left is 10 more than 3.8 on the right.

Each side has one block that is 10 more than a block on the other side.
● So the scale is balanced.

Exercises

1–6. See margin.

Determine whether each equation is true or false. Justify your reasoning.

1. 25.97 − (13 − 10) = (25.97 − 13) − 10   **2.** 603 × 9.5 = 603 × 10 − 603 × 0.5

3. 530 ÷ 5 = 500 ÷ 5 + 30 ÷ 5   **4.** 530 ÷ 5 = 530 ÷ 4 + 530 ÷ 1

Determine whether each scale is balanced. Justify your reasoning.

5.

| 3.9 | 4.8 | 4.9 | 3.8 |

6.
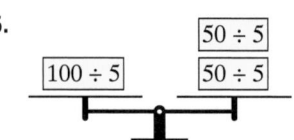

| | 50 ÷ 5 |
| 100 ÷ 5 | 50 ÷ 5 |

7. Make a balance-scale puzzle like those above. Write the solution. Check students' work.

1. False; associative prop. does not apply to subtraction.

2. true; Distributive Property

3. true; Distributive Property

4. False; the Distributive Property does not apply to division.

5. Yes; each side has one block that is 0.1 more than a block on the other side.

6. yes; Distributive Property

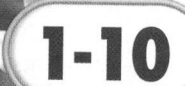

Algebra

Mean, Median, Mode, and Range

1. Plan

 Check Skills You'll Need

1. Vocabulary Review
When you simplify $2 + 6 \div 3$, which operation should you use first?
division

Find the value of each expression.

2. $(7 + 19) \div 2$ 13

3. $\frac{-14 + 6}{2}$ −4

4. $-9 + 4 \cdot 2 - 1$ −2

 for Help
Lesson 1-9

TEKS ★ TAKS

- **(7.12)(A)** To describe a set of data using mean, median, mode, and range
  TAKS **Obj. 5**
- **(7.12)(B)** To choose among mean, median, mode, or range to describe a set of data and justify the choice for a particular situation TAKS **Obj. 5**

🔊 **New Vocabulary** mean, outlier, median, mode, range

Why Learn This?

You can use data to model the past and predict the future.

School officials use averages to predict how many new students will enroll next year. One average is the **mean,** which is the sum of the data divided by the number of data items.

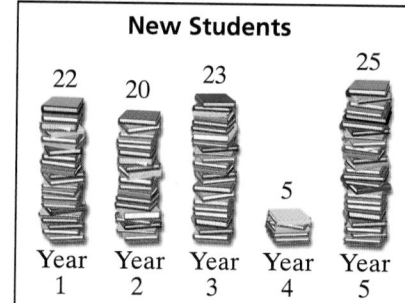

New Students

Year 1: 22
Year 2: 20
Year 3: 23
Year 4: 5
Year 5: 25

EXAMPLE **Finding the Mean**

1 Use the data in the graph above to find the mean number of new students per year.

$$\frac{22 + 20 + 23 + 5 + 25}{5} \quad \leftarrow \text{Divide the sum by the number of items.}$$

$$\frac{95}{5} = 19 \quad \leftarrow \text{Simplify.}$$

The mean is 19 students.

✓ **Quick Check**

1. Find the mean of 216, 230, 198, and 252. 224

An **outlier** is a data item that is much higher or lower than the other items in a set of data. In the data set in Example 1, 5 is an outlier.

Since 5 is far less than the other values, the outlier decreases the mean. When a set of data has outliers, the mean may not be the best measure for describing the data.

 nline

Video Tutor Help
Visit: PHSchool.com
Web Code: are-0775

TEKS ★ TAKS

(7.12)(A) To describe a set of data using mean, median, mode, and range TAKS **Obj. 5**

(7.12)(B) To choose among mean, median, mode, or range to describe a set of data and justify the choice for a particular situation. TAKS **Obj. 5**

Dana Center TEKS Toolkit Clarifying Activities (7.12)(A), (7.12)(B)
Visit: PHSchool.com
Web Code: arq-9045

TEKS Math Background

A number that describes a set of data is a *statistic*. In this lesson, students will study the *mean, median, mode,* and *range*.

The range describes the scope, or extent, of a set of data. In contrast, the mean, median, and mode describe the center of the data. For this reason, the mean, median, and mode are often called *measures of central tendency*.

More Math Background: p. 2D

Lesson Planning and Resources

See p. 2E for a list of the resources that support this lesson.

 Bell Ringer Practice

✓ **Check Skills You'll Need**
Use student page, transparency, or PowerPoint.

TAKS **Daily Review 10**
Use transparency.

Differentiated Instruction **Solutions for All Learners**

Special Needs L1
Students will benefit from finding one measure of central tendency at a time in the practice problems that require all three. Once they find the median, they should review the meaning of mode, and find that. Then they should move on to mean.

learning style: verbal

Below Level L2
Review the process of finding the average of two numbers with exercises like these.

21, 77 49   16, 27 21.5
338, 604 471   6.15, 1.89 4.02

learning style: visual

Guided Instruction

Example 1
Students might use their calculators to find the mean. If they do, remind them to use parentheses to group the sum of the data items.

Error Prevention!

Students might find a median by simply locating the middle item or items in the data set exactly as it is given to them. Stress that the process of finding a median has two steps: first rewriting the data in order from least to greatest and then identifying the middle item or items.

Example 3
Students can remember what the mode is by thinking *mode-most*.

The **median** of a data set is the middle value when the data are arranged in numerical order. The median of a set always separates the data into two groups of equal size. The median for an even number of data items is the mean of the two middle values.

★ TAKS Tip

The median for an odd number of data items is the middle value.

EXAMPLE   Finding the Median

② **TAKS Multiple Choice** The table at the right shows data collected from student responses. What is the median number of times that students drank from the water fountain?

Ⓐ 2   Ⓑ 2.5   Ⓒ 3   Ⓓ 3.5

20 Responses to "How many times a day do you drink from the water fountain?"				
0	1	1	5	2
10	2	3	5	1
5	2	2	3	4
3	5	5	2	2

First write the data in order from least to greatest.

0 1 1 1 2 2 2 2 2 2 2 3 3 3 4 5 5 5 5 5 10

↑↑ The two middle values are 2 and 3.

$\frac{2 + 3}{2} = 2.5$ ← Find the mean of the two middle values.

The median is 2.5. The answer is B.

✓ Quick Check

● **2.** Find the median in the set of data: −5 −1 3 −18 −2 **2. −1.5**

The **mode** of a data set is the item that occurs with the greatest frequency. A set of data may have more than one mode. There is no mode when all the data items occur the same number of times. The mode is a useful measure for data with values that are repetitive or nonnumerical.

EXAMPLE   Finding the Mode

Favorite Flowers of Ten People Surveyed

rose   rose
pansy   peony
pansy   daisy
daisy   rose
daisy   orchid

❸ Find the mode of the data at the left.

Make a table to organize the data.

Rose	Pansy	Peony	Daisy	Orchid
///	//	/	///	/

There are two modes, rose and daisy.

✓ Quick Check

3a. 17

b. no mode

c. pen

3. Find the mode(s). **See left.**
  a. 17 16 18 17 16 17   **b.** 3.2 3.7 3.5 3.7 3.5 3.2
  c. pen, pencil, marker, marker, pen, pen, pen, pencil, marker

---

Differentiated Instruction Solutions for All Learners

Advanced Learners **L4**
Find a set of six whole numbers that satisfies these conditions: The mean is 5. The mode is 4. The median is 4.5. Samples: 4, 4, 4, 5, 6, 7; 2, 4, 4, 5, 6, 9

English Language Learners **ELL**
Ask students to write a data set of numbers, and find the mean, the median, the mode, and the range. Then, in their own words, have them write the meaning of each.

Pre-AP™

learning style: visual

The **range** of a data set is the difference between the greatest and the least values. The range describes the spread of the data. You find the range by subtracting the least value from the greatest value.

EXAMPLE Finding Range

④ **Climate** Temperatures at Verkhoyansk, Russia, have ranged from a low of −90°F to a high of 98°F. Find the temperature range in Verkhoyansk.

$$98 - (-90) = 98 + 90 \quad \leftarrow \text{Add the opposite of } -90, \text{ which is } 90.$$
$$= 188 \quad \leftarrow \text{Simplify.}$$

The temperature range in Verkhoyansk is 188°F.

☑ **Quick Check**

4. Record temperatures in Texas set in the 1930s were a low of −23°F and a high of 120°F. Find the temperature range. **143°F**

☑ **Check Your Understanding**

1. **Vocabulary** A data item that can greatly affect the mean of a set of data is called a(n) **?** . **outlier**

2. If you increase every number in a data set by 2, what will happen to the mean? **increase by 2**

3. **Mental Math** A data set consists of the integers 1 to 9. What is the median of this data set? **5**

4. **5; the mode is always an item in the data set.**

4. A data set has a mean of 3, a median of 4, and a mode of 5. Which number *must be* in the data set—3, 4, or 5? Explain.

5. **Choose a Method** Is mean or median the better way to describe the data below? Explain your choice.

8. **Your teammate did not divide by 5.**

2 4 5 5 5 6 8 10 45 **Median; the outlier 45 greatly affects the mean.**

Find the mean, median, mode, and range of each set of data.

6. 1 2 3 5 5
   3.2; 3; 5; 4

7. 3 3 3 4 4 4
   3.5; 3.5; no mode; 1

8. **Error Analysis** Each day your tennis team practices for at least one hour and for at most five hours. Your teammate does the calculation shown. What mistake does your teammate make? **See above left.**

Times (hours): 1, 3, 4, 5, 3
Mean: 1 + 3 + 4 + 5 + 3
Mean = 16 hours

PowerPoint
Additional Examples

① Find the mean of 502, 477, 593, 481, 735, and 614. **567**

Use the chart below for Exercises 2 and 3.
15 Responses to "How many pets do you have?"

2	0	1	2	4
1	0	3	2	0
0	1	2	3	0

② Find the median of the data in the chart. **1**

③ Find the mode of the data in the chart. **0**

④ Temperatures one day in January ranged from −7°F to 11°F. What was the temperature range? **18°F**

All in One Teaching Resources
• Daily Notetaking Guide 1-9 **L3**
• Adapted Notetaking 1-9 **L1**

Closure

• *What is the mean of a set of data?* the sum of the data divided by the number of data items
• *What is the median of a set of data?* the middle item in a set of data that has been written in order
• *What is the mode of a set of data?* the data item that occurs most often
• *What is the range of a set of data?* the difference between the greatest and least values

Assignment Guide

Check Your Understanding
Go over Exercises 1–8 in class before assigning the Homework Exercises.

Homework Exercises
A Practice by Example   9–23
B Apply Your Skills   24–32
C Challenge   33
TEKS ★ TAKS Tune-Up and
Mixed Review   34–37

Homework Quick Check
To check students' understanding of key skills and concepts, go over Exercises 11, 15, 26, 31, and 32.

Differentiated Instruction Resources

Adapted Practice 1-10   L1

Practice 1-10   Mean, Median, Mode, a   L3

The sum of the heights of all the students in a class is 1,472 in.

1. The mean height is 5 ft 4 in. How many students are in the class?
(1 ft = 12 in.)
23 students

2. a. The median height is 5 ft 2 in. How many students are 5 ft 2 in. or taller?
12 students

b. How many students are shorter than 5 ft 2 in.?
11 students

The number of pages read (to the nearest multiple of 50) by the students in history class last week are shown in the tally table at the right.

Pages	Tally
50	I
100	
150	II
200	ℍℍ I
250	I
300	ℍℍ
350	III
400	IIII
450	
500	I

3. Find the mean, median, mode, and range of the data.
mean: 287.5; median: 300; mode: 200

4. What is the outlier in this set of data? **50**

5. Does the outlier raise or lower the mean? **lower**

A student hopes to have a 9-point average on his math quizzes. His quiz scores are 7, 6, 10, 8, and 9. Each quiz is worth 12 points.

6. What is his average quiz score?
8 points

7. There are two more quizzes. How many more points will be needed to give a 9-point quiz average?
23 points

Find the mean, median, mode, and range for each situation.

8. number of miles biked in one week
21, 17, 15, 18, 22, 16, 20 **18.4; 18; no mode; 7**

9. number of strikeouts per inning
3, 2, 0, 0, 1, 2, 3, 0, 2 **1.4; 2; 2 and 0; 3**

1-10 • Guided Problem Solving GPS   L3

GPS **Student Page 54, Exercise 26:**

Find the mean, median, and mode for the hours of practice before a concert:
2 1 0 1 5 3 4 2 0 3 1 2

Understand

1. What does this data set refer to?
the number of hours of practice before a concert

2. What are you being asked to do?
Find the mean, median, and mode of the data.

3. How many numbers are in the data set? **12**

Plan and Carry Out

4. Find the sum of the numbers in the data set. **24**

5. Find the mean by dividing the sum of the numbers by the total number of numbers. **2**

6. Order the numbers in the data set in increasing order.
0 0 1 1 1 2 2 2 3 3 4 5

7. What are the two middle numbers? **2 and 2**

8. Find the median of the data by finding the mean of the two middle numbers. **2**

9. Find the mode by finding which number is listed most often. **1 and 2**

10. How many modes are there? **2**

Check

11. What do you notice about the mean, median, and mode of this data?
2 is the mean, median, and mode of the data.

Solve Another Problem

12. Millie has 3 siblings, Peggy has one sister, Larry has 5 brothers, Joey is an only child, and Marie has 6 siblings. What is the mean number of siblings for this group of people? **3 siblings**

Homework Exercises

For more exercises, see Extra Skills and Word Problems.

GO for Help

For Exercises	See Examples
9–12	1
13–16	2
17–19	3
20–23	4

Ⓐ **Find the mean of each set of data.**

9. 8   12   6   9   5   **8**

10. 3.4   0.53   1.3   2.9   1.47   0.24   **1.64**

11. −6   3   −2   6   7   −3   −5   **8 1**

12. −17   32   −9   0   52   12   −14   **8**

Find the median of each set of data.

13. 5   10   18   3   6   2   9   1   8   15   10   **8**

14. 23   18   67   32   54   41   70   11   56   33   41   58   **41**

15. −4   −1   −8   −5   −6   −2   7   2   0   −1   −7   2   **−1.5**

16. 2.1   −41.2   0.13   −7.1   −1.68   8.32   2.45   7.89   3.19   **2.1**

Find the mode(s).

17. 51   58   54   58   51   57   55   58   51   54   **51 and 58**

18. 1   12   2   21   22   1   13   31   32   31   12   **1, 12, and 31**

19. red, blue, white, white, red, red, red, blue, white, blue   **red**

Find the range.

20. from 24 to −2 **26**   21. from −3 to 7 **10**   22. from −145 to 234
379

23. Video game scores vary from 6 to −6. What is the range? **12**

Ⓑ **GPS**

24. **Guided Problem Solving** A city has kept records on cloud cover for 47 years. The mean number of cloudless days in October is 13. How many cloudless days occurred in October during that time?
611 days

mean number of cloudless days in October   ■
number of years of records   × ■
total number of cloudless days   ■

25. There are eight dogs in a kennel. Each of the two small dogs needs 1 cup of dry food per day. Each of the three medium-sized dogs needs 2 cups per day. Each of the remaining three large dogs needs 4 cups per day. What is the mean number of cups of food required per dog each day? **2.5 cups**

26. Find the mean, median, and mode for the hours of practice before a
GPS concert: 2   1   0   1   5   3   4   2   0   3   1   2. **2 h; 2 h; 1 h and 2 h**

27. Answers may vary.
Sample: $1,500,000

27. **Estimation** A company's mean weekly profit is $30,021. Estimate how much profit the company will make in a year.

28. The table at the right shows the average life expectancy for several animals.
   a. Find the mean, median, mode, and range of the data. **12.7 yr; 12 yr; 12 and 15 yr; 12 yr**
   b. **Choose a Method** Which measure best describes the data? Explain.
      Median; 20 may be considered an outlier.

29–30. Answers may vary. Samples are given.

Make a data set for each condition.

29. mode > median
    1, 2, 3, 5, 5

30. median = mean
    5, 5, 5, 5, 5

31. Answers may vary. Sample: Data set 2, 4, 6, 6, 12, 18 has a mean of 8, and a median and mode of 6. Data set 4, 6, 6, 6, 18 has a mean of 8, and a median and mode of 6.

31. <u>Writing in Math</u> Explain how it is possible for two sets of data to consist of different numbers but have the same mean, the same median, and the same mode. Give an example.

32. **Music** When you join a music club, you get six CDs for 1 cent each. You buy eight more CDs at $7.99 each. What is the mean price you pay for a CD? **$4.57**

C 33. **Challenge** According to the U.S. Department of Agriculture, the mean annual egg consumption in the United States is 258.2 eggs per person. Find the number of cartons of eggs needed in a year for an average family of four. Each carton holds one dozen eggs. **87 cartons**

Average Life Expectancy

Animal	Years
Bison	15
Cow	15
Deer	8
Donkey	12
Elk	15
Goat	8
Horse	20
Moose	12
Pig	10
Sheep	12

SOURCE: *The World Almanac*

TEKS ★ TAKS Tune-Up and Mixed Review

TAKS Objective 5
TEKS (7.12)(A)

34. The table shows Tammy's times in the 100-meter dash. Which number could be added to make the median and mode of the set equal? **D**
   (A) 11.6   (C) 12
   (B) 11.8   (D) 12.25

TAKS Objective 1
TEKS (7.2)(C)

35. In a golf tournament, five players had scores of −6, +5, +1, −2, and −8. Which expression can be used to find the average score? **H**
   (F) $(6 + 5 + 1 + 2 + 8) \div 5$
   (G) $6 + 5 + 1 + 2 + 8 \div 5$
   (H) $[-6 + 5 + 1 + (-2) + (-8)] \div 5$
   (J) $-6 + 5 + 1 + (-2) + (-8) \div 5$

Tammy's Times in the 100-meter Dash

Trial	Time (seconds)
1	12.8
2	11.96
3	12.4
4	11.6
5	12.25
6	▪

GO for Help

Lesson 1-2   **Order each set of numbers from least to greatest.**

36. 32   35   −21   −42   29
    −42, −21, 29, 32, 35

37. 213   231   312   123   321
    123, 213, 231, 312, 321

TEKS ★ TAKS Resources

- TAKS Strategies, p. 59
- TAKS Tune-Up, pp. 63–65

TAKS Tune-Up Kit
- TAKS Daily Review Transparencies
- TAKS Review and Preparation Workbook
- TAKS Strategies with Transparencies
- Texas Progress Monitoring Assessments

---

4. Assess & Reteach

PowerPoint
Lesson Quiz

Find the mean, median, mode, and range of each set of data.

1. 25 27 21 27 20   **mean, 24; median, 25; mode, 27; range, 7**

2. −8 −4 2 10 −10   **mean, −2; median, −4; mode, no mode; range, 20**

3. 7.5 3.6 15.4 3.6 15.4   **mean, 9.1; median, 7.5; mode, 3.6 and 15.4; range, 11.8**

Alternative Assessment

Have students work in groups of four. Refer them to Exercises 13–16. For each set of data, have one student find the mean to the nearest hundredth, another find the median, the third find the mode, and the fourth find the range. Have students check each other's work.

Enrichment 1-10   L4

Reteaching 1-10   Mean, Median, Mode, an   L2

Alexis, Rita, Ming, Mario, and Jewel are in the Library Club. During the summer they read the following numbers of books.

11, 6, 11, 8, 3

To find the **mean**, or average, number of books read by the Library Club members:
① Find the sum of the numbers of books read.   11 + 6 + 11 + 8 + 3 = 39
② Divide the sum by the number of readers, 5.   39 ÷ 5 = 7.8
The mean is 7.8 books.

To find the **median**, or middle value, of the data set:
① Arrange the numbers in order.   3, 6, 8, 11, 11
② Find the middle number.
8 is the middle number.
The median is 8 books.

The **mode** is the number that occurs most often.   3, 6, 8, **11, 11**
In this data set, 11 occurs twice. The mode is 11.
The **range** is the difference between the greatest and the least values. The range is 8.   11 − 3 = **8**

Use the table to complete Exercises 1–4.

1. Jerry plays basketball. What number would you divide by to find the mean number of points Jerry scored per game? 9
2. What is the mean number of points Jerry scored? **12.3 points**
3. Write the data in order. Then find the median number of points Jerry scored.
   9, 10, 10, 11, 12, 15, 16, 18; 11 points
4. What is the mode of the data? 10 points
5. What is the range between Jerry's highest- and lowest-scoring games? 9 points

Points Scored by Jerry per Game		
10	11	15
18	9	16
10	12	10

Find the mean, median, mode, and range for the following situation.

6. the miniature golf scores for 7 friends:
   23, 30, 39, 32, 35, 14, 23
   mean 28   median 30   mode 23   range 25

57

Box-and-Whisker Plots

Students use box-and-whisker plots to show data along a number line.

Guided Instruction

Activity
In Step 2, point out that the median is the middle number so that the middle of the lower half is the lower quartile. Relate this to $\frac{1}{2}$ and $\frac{1}{4}$.

Exercises
Have students make up data for Team C and make a box-and-whisker plot. Be sure students keep data within a reasonable range for a team.

Differentiated Instruction

Visual Learners
Box-and-whisker plots are visual ways of displaying data. Have a visual learner explain what the box shows and what the whiskers show using the example on p. 58 or a box-and-whisker plot he or she has made. Encourage the use of vocabulary such as *median, upper quartile,* and *lower quartile.*

TEKS ★ **TAKS** **Resources**

• Classroom Aid 31, 32, 33

Box-and-Whisker Plots

A **box-and-whisker plot** is a graph that summarizes a data set along a number line.

TEKS ★ **TAKS**
Prepares for **TEKS** (8.12)(C)
To use an appropriate representation for presenting and displaying data, including box-and-whisker plots

ACTIVITY

Points Scored per Player

Team A	Team B
6	5
2	9
8	7
10	9
3	13
15	11
4	13
20	15
7	14
4	10

Step 1 Arrange the data for Team A from least to greatest. Find the median. This value is called the middle quartile.

2   3   4   4   6   7   8   10   15   20

The median is 6.5.

Step 2 Find the median of the lower half of the data. This value is the lower quartile.

2   3   4   4   6

The median is 4.

Step 3 Find the median of the upper half of the data. This value is the upper quartile.

7   8   10   15   20

The median is 10.

Step 4 Identify the least and greatest values of the full data set.

least value = 2   greatest value = 20

Step 5 Draw a number line. Plot the points of the 5 values you found in Steps 1–4 above the number line.

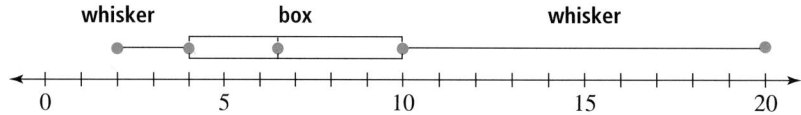

Step 6 Draw a box using the lower and upper quartile points as the ends of the box. Then draw lines, or whiskers, from the ends of the box to the least and greatest values.

Exercises

1. Make a box-and-whisker plot using the data for Team B.
   See margin.
2. Compare your graph to the one in the activity. What do the two graphs tell you about how the players on each team score? See right.

2. The range is greater in the upper half of the data for Team A. Team A has low and high points, whereas Team B has a smaller range.

1.

TAKS Strategies

Writing Griddable Responses

Some tests call for griddable responses. You find a numerical answer. Then you write the answer at the top of the grid and fill in the corresponding bubbles below. You must use the grid correctly.

EXAMPLES

1 The mean of 0.2, 0.4, 0.6, and 0.8 is 0.5. Record this answer.

You can write the answer as 0.5 or .5. Here are the two ways to enter these answers.

2 Cindy had $19.25 before she went shopping. She spent $18.50 on purchases that day. How much money, in dollars, did she have left?

$$\begin{array}{r} 19.25 \\ -\ 18.50 \\ \hline 0.75 \end{array}$$

The answer is 0.75. You grid this as 0.75 or .75.

Exercises

TAKS Objective 1
TEKS (7.2)(B)

Write the number you would grid for each answer. If you have a grid, complete it.

1. A bottle of apple juice holds 3.79 L. A bottle of orange juice holds 1.89 L. How many more liters does the bottle of apple juice hold?
1.9

TAKS Objective 1
TEKS (7.2)(F)

2. You are organizing a pet show. On the first morning, 40 dogs will be shown. For each dog, you will allow one minute to set up and four minutes for showing. How many minutes will the morning session last? 200

TAKS Objective 5
TEKS (7.12)(A)

3. A student scores 88, 93, 79, and 68 on four quizzes. What is the mean of the scores? 82

TAKS Strategies Writing Griddable Responses **59**

Writing Griddable Responses

Students learn to correctly use griddable response sheets to answer test questions.

Guided Instruction

Exercises

Ask: *Do any of Exercises 1–3 have two possibilities for gridding responses?* Yes, Exercise 1: 1.9 or 1.90; Exercise 3: 82 or 82.0

TEKS ★ TAKS Resources

TAKS Strategies with Transparencies
• Transparency 2
• Practice Sheet, p. 13

Chapter 1 Review

TEKS ★ TAKS Resources

Student Edition
Extra Skills and Word Problems
  Practice, Ch. 1, p. 630
English/Spanish Glossary, p. 675
Formulas and Properties, p. 673
Tables, p. 670
All in One Teaching Resources
• Vocabulary and Study
  Skills 1F   L3

TAKS Tune-Up Kit
• TAKS Daily Review
  Transparencies
• TAKS Review and Preparation
  Workbook
• TAKS Strategies with
  Transparencies
• Texas Progress Monitoring
  Assessments
• Texas ExamView CD-ROM
• MindPoint Quiz Show CD-ROM

Differentiated Instruction
Spanish Vocabulary Workbook
  with Study Skills   ELL
Texas Interactive Textbook
• Audio Glossary
Online Vocabulary Quiz

Success Tracker™
Online at PHSchool.com

Spanish Vocabulary/Study Skills ELL

Vocabulary/Study Skills L3

1F: Vocabulary Review Puzzle For use with the Chapter Review

Study Skill Vocabulary is an important part of every subject you learn.
Review new words and their definitions using flashcards.

Find each of the following words in the word search. Circle the word
and then cross it off the word list. Words can be displayed forwards,
backwards, up, down, or diagonally.

absolute value	integers	order
median	mode	mean
opposites	outlier	range
compatible	distributive	multiplication

```
C Q E D E T A J P K A Z L H N
F K E E R E D R O N D A H U N
M Z D W I T E P I E B B I P O
R N O U R O L C C V E S E F I
A O M B A P B M E I T O V X T
N P R J N P I E P T I L A S A
G F I R L O T T E U F U T E C
E I N P M S A R T B E T K T I
Y O T H G I P A A I I E O R L
I D E O O T M N R R N V U O P
W A G R F E O V O T K A T I I
P D E F N S C O O S E L L J T
G K R N N A W S O I G U I R L
N M S D K A E V N D S E E U U
M E D I A N F M A R O M R L M
```

60

Chapter 1 Review

Vocabulary Review

 absolute value (p. 31)
additive inverse (p. 38)
Associative Property of
  Addition (p. 9)
Associative Property of
  Multiplication (p. 15)
Commutative Property of
  Addition (p. 9)

Commutative Property of
  Multiplication (p. 15)
compatible numbers (p. 5)
Distributive Property (p. 49)
Identity Property of Addition
  (p. 9)
Identity Property of
  Multiplication (p. 15)
integers (p. 31)

mean (p. 53)
median (p. 54)
mode (p. 54)
opposites (p. 31)
order of operations (p. 48)
outlier (p. 53)
range (p. 55)
Zero Property (p. 15)

Go Online
PHSchool.com
For: Online vocabulary quiz
Web Code: arj-0151

Choose the correct term to complete each sentence.

1. The __?__ combines multiplication with sums and differences.
   Distr. Prop.
2. The statement $3 + (5 + 7) = (3 + 5) + 7$ demonstrates the __?__.
   Assoc. Prop. of Add.
3. The __?__ of a number is its distance from 0 on a number line.
   absolute value
4. To find the __?__, take the data item that occurs most often.
   mode
5. By the __?__, you know that $4 + 7 \cdot 3$ equals 25 and not 33.
   order of operations

Skills and Concepts   TEKS ★ TAKS

Lesson 1-1

(7.13)(A) To apply
mathematics to everyday
experiences **TAKS** Obj. 6

(7.13)(D) To select
estimation to solve
problems

You can estimate decimals using rounding, front-end estimation, or
compatible numbers. 6–9. See margin.

Use any estimation strategy to calculate. Name the strategy you used.

6. $50.3 \div 6.9$ 7. $98.52 - 46.91$ 8. 6.9×8.92 9. $1.46 + 4.38$

Lessons 1-2, 1-3, 1-4

(7.2)(A) To represent
multiplication and division
situations involving decimals
TAKS Obj. 1

(7.2)(B) To use addition,
subtraction, multiplication,
and division to solve
problems involving decimals
TAKS Obj. 1

(7.2)(G) To determine the
reasonableness of a solution
TAKS Obj. 1

(7.2)(F) To select and use
appropriate operations to
solve problems **TAKS** Obj. 1

To add or subtract decimals, align the decimal points. To multiply
decimals, use the sum of the number of decimal places in the factors. To
divide decimals, rewrite the problem so the divisor is a whole number.

Use the **commutative properties** to change the order in an expression.
Use the **associative properties** to change the grouping.

Simplify.

10. $23.68 \div 6.4$ 11. $0.54 + 0.027$ 12. $4.6 - 3.87$ 13. 2.7×6.25
    3.7   0.567   0.73   16.875

14. **Shopping** At a grocery store, you buy hamburger weighing 1.42 lb,
    sausage weighing 2.16 lb, and chicken weighing 3.73 lb. How many
    pounds of meat do you buy? **7.31 lb**

60 Chapter 1 Chapter Review

Exercises 6–9. Answers may vary. Samples
are given.

6. 7; compatible numbers

7. 52, rounding

8. 63, rounding

9. 6; front-end estimation

Lesson 1-5

(7.2)(B) To use multiplication to solve problems involving decimals ⒜ **Obj. 1**

(7.3)(B) To estimate and find solutions to application problems involving related measurement units ⒜ **Obj. 2**

To change a measure from one unit to another, find a relationship between the two units and then multiply.

Write the number that makes each statement true.

15. 4.56 mm = ▪ cm
0.456

16. 14.2 L = ▪ mL
14,200

17. 0.34 kg = ▪ g
340

18. You have three lengths of kite string measuring 18.2 m, 927 cm, and 0.044 km. What is the total length of kite string in meters? **71.47 m**

Lesson 1-6

(7.1)(A) To compare and order integers ⒜ **Obj. 1**

(7.14)(A) To communicate mathematical ideas using graphical models ⒜ **Obj. 6**

Opposites are two numbers that are the same distance from 0 on a number line, but in opposite directions. **Integers** are the set of positive whole numbers, their opposites, and zero. The **absolute value** of an integer is its distance from 0 on a number line.

Compare. Use <, =, or >.

19. -7 ▪ 7 `<`

20. $|-3|$ ▪ $|3|$ `=`

21. 9 ▪ $|-4|$ `>`

22. $|8|$ ▪ -15 `>`

Lessons 1-7, 1-8

(7.2)(C) To use models, such as number lines, to add, subtract, multiply, and divide integers and connect the actions to algorithms ⒜ **Obj. 1**

(7.2)(F) To select and use appropriate operations to solve problems ⒜ **Obj. 1**

The sum of two positive integers is positive. The sum of two negative integers is negative. To find the sum of two integers with different signs, find the absolute value of each integer. Subtract the lesser absolute value from the greater. The sum has the sign of the integer with the greater absolute value. To subtract an integer, add its opposite.

The product or quotient of two integers with the same sign is positive. The product or quotient of two integers with different signs is negative.

Simplify.

23. $14 + (-8)$
6

24. $17 - (-12)$
29

25. $-5 \cdot 6$
-30

26. $125 \div (-5)$
-25

Lessons 1-9, 1-10

Prepares for **TEKS (7.2)(E)** To simplify numerical expressions involving order of operations and exponents

(7.12)(A) To describe a set of data using mean, median, mode, and range ⒜ **Obj. 5**

(7.12)(B) To choose among mean, median, mode, or range to describe a set of data and justify the choice for a particular situation ⒜ **Obj. 5**

Use the **order of operations** to simplify an expression. The **Distributive Property** combines multiplication with addition or subtraction. The **mean, median, mode,** and **range** of a set of data, along with any **outliers,** reflect the characteristics of the data.

Find the value of each expression.

27. $(7.3 + 4) \div 4 + 0.3 \cdot 2$ 3.425

28. $8 - 6.2 \div 5 + 7(0.91)$ 13.13

29. $20 + 24 \div 2 - (8 + 5)$ 19

30. $8(20.3)$ 162.4

31. Pets The data set below gives the weights, in ounces, of one-month-old hamsters. Find the mean, median, mode, and range of the data set.
4, 1, 3, 2, 2, 2, 1, 1, 2, 1, 2, 3 2; 2; 2; 3

Chapter 1 Test

TEKS ★ TAKS Resources

- Texas ExamView CD-ROM
  - Ch. 1 Ready-Made Test
  - Make your own Ch. 1 test
- MindPoint Quiz Show CD-ROM
  - Chapter 1 Review

Differentiated Instruction

All in One Teaching Resources
- Chapter 1 Test — **L2**
- Chapter 1 Test — **L3**
- Chapter 1 Alternative Assessment — **L4**

Spanish Assessment Resources — **ELL**
- Chapter 1 Test — **L2**
- Chapter 1 Test — **L3**
- Chapter 1 Alternative Assessment — **L4**

Texas ExamView CD-ROM
- Special Needs Test — **L1**
- Special Needs Practice Bank — **L1**

Online Chapter 1 Test at www.PHSchool.com — **L3**

Estimate using any estimation strategy.

1. 289.76 − 52 about 240

2. 7.532 + 2.19 about 10

3. 97.6 · 3.4 about 350

4. 68.5 ÷ 7.02 about 10

5. Use front-end estimation to estimate the sum of the following grocery items to the nearest dollar: $7.99, $2.79, $4.15, $2.09. about $17

Simplify.

6. 9.53 + 3.29 12.82

7. 8 − 6.17 1.83

8. 10.5 − 9.67 0.83

9. 0.57 + 1.825 2.395

10. **Money** You have a balance of $213.15 in a savings account. You make withdrawals of $68.94 and $128.36. Find your new balance. $15.85

11. **Decorations** For a class party, the student council purchases 42 balloons at $1.85 each. Estimate the total cost of the balloons. about $78

Identify each property shown.

12. 9.5 + 6.1 + 2.3 = 9.5 + 2.3 + 6.1 Comm. Prop. of Add.

13. 7.2 × (1.6 × 3.9) = (7.2 × 1.6) × 3.9 Assoc. Prop. of Mult.

14. 5.1(7.4 − 3.1) = 5.1(7.4) − 5.1(3.1) Distr. Prop.

Find each quotient. Round to the nearest tenth.

15. 1.2 ÷ 0.3 4.0

16. 1.58 ÷ 1.1 1.4

Find the value of each expression.

17. 9.5 − 7.1 + 2.4 · 0.5 − 1.3 2.3

18. $\frac{8.25}{4} \cdot (0.6 - 0.54) + 8.3$ 8.42375

Change each measurement to the given unit.

19. 4.2 cm = ▇ m 0.042

20. 5.17 kL = ▇ L 5,170

21. 6 kg 14 g = ▇ g 6,014

22. 2 km 7 m = ▇ km 2.007

Compare. Use <, =, or >.

23. −12 ▇ 12 <

24. −9 ▇ −5 <

25. |−7| ▇ −8 >

26. |−6| ▇ 6 =

Mental Math Find each product mentally using the Distributive Property.

27. 6(10.5) 63

28. 3(98) 294

Write an expression for each model. Then find the sum.

29.   3 + (−4) = −1

30.   −1 + (−4) = −5

31. Write these integers in order from least to greatest: 2 5 0 −7 −3. −7, −3, 0, 2, 5

Simplify.

32. −3 + 5 2

33. −2 + (−2) −4

34. −4 − 9 −13

35. −8 · (−9) 72

36. 48 ÷ (−3) −16

37. −6(11) −66

38. **Produce** The weights of four bags of apples are 3.5 lb, 3.8 lb, 4.2 lb, and 3.5 lb. What is the median weight? 3.65 lb

39. **Fitness** Suppose you plan to ride your bicycle a total of 257.5 mi in a benefit ride. How many miles must you average each day to finish the ride in 4.5 days? about 57.2 mi

40. **Writing in Math** When you calculate a mean, the sign of the quotient always depends on the sign of the dividend. Why? See margin.

41. **Sports** On successive plays, the home football team gains 12 yd, loses 3 yd, loses 5 yd, gains 15 yd, and runs 16 yd for a touchdown. What is the average gain or loss in yards per play? 7 yd gain

42. Find the mean, median, and mode for the following junior league bowling scores: 45, 56, 134, 55, 78, 121, 38, 66, 56, 41. 69; 56; 56

Chapter Test — **L2**

Chapter Test — **L3**

Chapter Test

Chapter 1

1. Use rounding to estimate the product to the nearest whole number. 110.5 × 10.2
1110

2. Use front-end estimation to estimate the sum to the nearest whole number. 5.312 + 3.726
9

Find each sum or difference.

3. 8.27 + 6.9 + 5
20.17

4. 19 − 12.735
6.265

5. 21.6 − 9.24
12.36

6. 0.68 + 5.681
6.361

7. 52.1 − 51.06
1.04

8. 74.5 + 0 + 17.3
91.8

Find each product or quotient.

9. $\frac{57.96}{2.8}$
20.7

10. $\frac{408.48}{8}$
51.06

11. 5.9 · 0.32
1.888

12. 6.73 · 0.04
0.2692

13. 3.2 ÷ 0.128
25

14. (2.6)(0.02)
0.052

Change each measurement to the given unit.

15. 24 m 5 cm to centimeters 2405 cm

16. 5 kg 240 g to kilograms 5.24 kg

17. 11 L 17 mL to liters 11.017 L

Write the metric unit that makes each statement true.

18. 12.451 dL = 1,245.1 **m**

19. 2.48 cm = 24.8 **mm**

20. In last Saturday's parade, Tom counted all of the bicycles and tricycles, for a total of 227 wheels. His count included 76 bicycles. How many tricycles were in the parade?
25 tricycles

40. The divisor will always be a positive number.

TAKS Tune-Up

★ TAKS Tips

Some TAKS tests ask you questions about mean, median, and mode. The question at the right asks you to study a table and determine the median. Read the question and review the answer choices. Then follow the tips to answer the sample question.

The table below shows the ages in years of 10 children on a playground.

Tip
Order the data from least to greatest.

Name	Age
Audra	8
Bonnie	10
Chandra	7
Dwayne	7
Giorgio	7
Juan	6
Kendra	6
Maxine	9
Shari	8
Theo	10

Tip
When there is an even number of data items, take the average of the middle two numbers.

What is the median age of the children?
- **A** 6.5
- **B** 7
- **C** 7.5
- **D** 8

Think It Through
Keep in mind that the *median* is the middle number. Once the list of ages is put in order, you can see that the middle two numbers are 7 and 8. The average of 7 and 8 is 7.5. The answer is C.

TEKS ★ TAKS Resources

TAKS Review and Preparation Workbook
Texas ExamView CD-ROM
- Instant TAKS Practice Test
- TAKS Test Items

Differentiated Instruction

Spanish Assessment Resources
- Spanish Cumulative Review   **ELL**

Texas ExamView CD-ROM
- Special Needs Practice Bank   **L1**

Vocabulary Builder

As you solve test items, you must understand the meanings of mathematical terms. Select the correct term from the pair in each sentence.

A. A statement with two expressions that do not have the same value is an (equality, inequality). **inequality**

B. A phrase that uses operations with numbers is (a statement, an expression). **an expression**

C. You (reorder, simplify) when you replace an expression with its simplest name. **simplify**

D. (Order of operations, Simplification steps) are the rules that tell you which operation comes next. **order of operations**

Multiple Choice

Read each question. Then write the letter of the correct answer on your paper.

1. Last week, Mary ran between 1.8 and 3.2 kilometers each day. Which of the following is a reasonable assumption about the total distance Mary ran in 6 days? **B**
- **A** Mary ran between 6 and 12 km.
- **B** Mary ran between 12 and 19 km.
- **C** Mary ran between 19 and 21 km.
- **D** Mary ran between 21 and 24 km.

2. Trent rode his bicycle for 2.4 hours at an average speed of 10.8 miles per hour. About how far did he ride? **J**
- **F** 5 mi
- **G** 8 mi
- **H** 13 mi
- **J** 26 mi

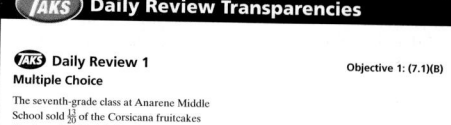 **TAKS** **Daily Review Transparencies**

TAKS **Daily Review 1**
Multiple Choice
Objective 1: (7.1)(B)

The seventh-grade class at Anarene Middle School sold $\frac{13}{20}$ of the Corsicana fruitcakes they bought. Which decimal is equivalent to the fraction sold?
A 65
B 0.65
C 6.5
D 650

Answer: B

TAKS **Daily Review 2**
Multiple Choice
Objective 5: (7.12)(A)

Shey has been practicing running the 200-meter foot race. Her last 6 times are shown.
23.60 24.15 24.68 28.62 24.25 23.92
What is her mean time?
F 5.02
G 23.92
H 24.21
J 24.87

63

3. The table shows selected ticket prices for a professional basketball game.

Selected Basketball Ticket Prices

Price Code	Price
A	$240
C	$130
D	$109
G	$67
I	$39

Based on the information in the table, which of the following is a reasonable assumption? **C**

  Ⓐ The A tickets cost about 3 times as much as the G tickets.

  Ⓑ The D tickets are twice as expensive as the I tickets.

  Ⓒ The C tickets cost about twice as much as the G tickets.

  Ⓓ The most expensive tickets are the C tickets.

4. A bookstore receives a carton that contains 12 copies of a dictionary. Each dictionary weighs 2.3 kilograms, and the carton weighs 1.3 kilograms. How would you find the total weight? **G**

  Ⓕ Multiply the number of dictionaries by the weight of each one.

  Ⓖ Multiply the number of dictionaries by the weight of each one, and then add the weight of the carton.

  Ⓗ Add the weight of the dictionary and the weight of the carton.

  Ⓙ Add the weight of the dictionary and the weight of the carton, and then multiply the sum by the number of dictionaries.

5. Sue received $10 for her birthday. She wants to buy goldfish that cost $1.40 each. How many goldfish can she buy? **D**

  Ⓐ 14   Ⓑ 8   Ⓒ 7.14   Ⓓ 7

6. Which expression is represented by the model below? **J**

  Ⓕ 0.4×0.7 Ⓗ 0.5×0.7

  Ⓖ 0.4×0.8 Ⓙ 0.5×0.8

7. Which model represents the expression $0.8 \div 0.2$? **A**

  Ⓐ   Ⓒ

  Ⓑ   Ⓓ

8. Which expression can be used to find the maximum number of 0.15-kilogram hamburgers than can be made from 4.5 kilograms of ground beef? **F**

  Ⓕ $4.5 \div 0.15$ Ⓗ $4.5 + 0.15$

  Ⓖ $0.15 \div 0.45$ Ⓙ 0.15×0.45

9. Use the order of operations to find the value of $60 - 5 \times 7 + 2$. **C**

  Ⓐ 495   Ⓑ 387   Ⓒ 27   Ⓓ 15

10. Use the order of operations to find the value of $4 + 5 \times (11 - 8)$. **G**

  Ⓕ 7   Ⓖ 19   Ⓗ 27   Ⓙ 91

11. The five children in the LeBlanc family keep "accounts" with their parents. The balances in the accounts at the end of February were $23, −$15, $8, −$12, and −$4. Which shows these balances from least to greatest? **B**

   Ⓐ $23, −$15, $8, −$12, −$4
   Ⓑ −$15, −$12, −$4, $8, $23
   Ⓒ −$12, −$15, −$4, $8, $23
   Ⓓ −$4, −$12, −$15, $8, $23

12. Which expression is represented by the model below? **H**

   Ⓕ −6 + 0   Ⓗ −6 + (−3)
   Ⓖ −6 + (−9)   Ⓙ −6 + 3

13. Which expression is represented by the model below? **A**

   Ⓐ 4 × (−3)   Ⓒ 3 × (−4)
   Ⓑ 2 × (−6)   Ⓓ 3 × (−3)

14. In which data set are the mean, median, mode, and range all the same number? **F**

   Ⓕ {2, 5, 7, 4, 5, 7, 5}
   Ⓖ {3, 2, 5, 7, 5, 7, 5}
   Ⓗ {6, 4, 7, 6, 2, 3, 5}
   Ⓙ {5, 8, 2, 5, 5, 6, 3}

15. The table shows the diameters of four impact craters on Earth.

Impact Craters

Crater and Location	Diameter in Miles
Gosses Bluff, Australia	14
Kara-Kul, Tajikistan	28
Manicouagan, Canada	40
Vredefort, South Africa	87

   What is the median of the data? **B**
   Ⓐ 28   Ⓒ 41
   Ⓑ 34   Ⓓ 42.5

16. Troy bought 2,450 grams of oranges and 1 kilogram 25 grams of grapes. How many kilograms of fruit did Troy buy in all? **H**
   Ⓕ 1.495 kg   Ⓗ 3.475 kg
   Ⓖ 3.375 kg   Ⓙ 3.70 kg

Griddable Items
Record your answer in a grid.

17. A carpenter cut a 3-meter board into four pieces of equal length. How many centimeters long was each piece? **75**

18. Trista can buy a 2-liter bottle of juice or a pack of six bottles. Each bottle holds 330 milliliters. How many liters of juice are in the six-pack? **1.98**

TAKS GO for Help Guide

TAKS Objective	Item Number	GO To	TAKS Objective	Item Number	GO To
Obj. 6: (7.13)(A)	1–3	Lesson 1-1	Obj. 1: (7.1)(A)	11	Lesson 1-6
Obj. 1: (7.2)(B)	4	Lesson 1-3	Obj. 1: (7.2)(C)	12	Lesson 1-7
	5	Lesson 1-4		13	Lesson 1-8
Obj. 1: (7.2)(A)	6	Lesson 1-3	Obj. 5: (7.12)(A)	14–15	Lesson 1-10
	7–8	Lesson 1-4	Obj. 2: (7.3)(B)	16–18	Lesson 1-5
Obj. 1: (7.2)(E)	9–10	Lesson 1-9			

For additional TAKS practice, see the *TAKS Review and Preparation Workbook.*

2 Exponents, Factors, and Fractions

Chapter at a Glance

Lesson Titles, Objectives, and Features	Assessment	NCTM Standards	TEKS ⭐ TAKS
2-1 Exponents and Order of Operations • To write and simplify expressions with exponents 2-1b Activity Lab, Technology: Using a Scientific Calculator	Lesson Quiz	1, 2, 6, 7, 8, 9, 10	**TEKS** (7.1)(C), (7.2)(E) **TAKS** Obj. 1 **TEKS** (7.13)(D)
2-2a Activity Lab, Hands On: Divisibility Tests **2-2 Prime Factorization** • To find multiples and factors and to use prime factorization Guided Problem Solving: Using LCM and GCF	Lesson Quiz Checkpoint Quiz 1	1, 3, 6, 7, 8, 9, 10	**TEKS** (7.13)(A), (7.13)(C) **TAKS** Obj. 6; Prepares for **TEKS** (7.2)(B)
2-3 Simplifying Fractions • To write equivalent fractions and to simplify fractions	Lesson Quiz	1, 2, 3, 6, 7, 8, 9, 10	Prepares for **TEKS** (7.2)(B)
2-4a Activity Lab, Hands On: Comparing Fractions **2-4 Comparing and Ordering Fractions** • To compare and order fractions	Lesson Quiz	1, 2, 3, 6, 7, 8, 9, 10	**TEKS** (7.1)(A) **TAKS** Obj. 1
2-5 Mixed Numbers and Improper Fractions • To write mixed numbers and improper fractions	Lesson Quiz	1, 2, 3, 6, 7, 8, 9, 10	Prepares for **TEKS** (7.1)(A)
2-6a Activity Lab: Comparing Fractions and Decimals **2-6 Fractions and Decimals** • To convert between fractions and decimals 2-6b Activity Lab, Data Analysis: Using Tables to Compare Data	Lesson Quiz Checkpoint Quiz 2	1, 2, 6, 7, 8, 9, 10	**TEKS** (7.1)(A), (7.1)(B) **TAKS** Obj. 1
2-7 Rational Numbers • To compare and order rational numbers	Lesson Quiz	1, 2, 3, 6, 7, 8, 9, 10	**TEKS** (7.1)(A), (7.1)(B) **TAKS** Obj. 1
2-8 Scientific Notation • To write numbers in both scientific notation and standard form Extension: Negative Exponents	Lesson Quiz	1, 4, 6, 7, 8, 9, 10	
TAKS Tune-Up: Cumulative Practice			

NCTM Standards 2000
1 Number and Operations
6 Problem Solving
2 Algebra
7 Reasoning and Proof
3 Geometry
8 Communication
4 Measurement
9 Connections
5 Data Analysis and Probability
10 Representation

Correlations to Standardized Tests

All content for these tests is contained in *Prentice Hall Math,* Course 2. This chart reflects coverage in this chapter only.

	2-1	2-2	2-3	2-4	2-5	2-6	2-7	2-8
Terra Nova CAT6 (Level 17)								
Number and Number Relations	✔	✔	✔	✔	✔	✔	✔	✔
Computation and Numerical Estimation	✔	✔	✔	✔	✔	✔	✔	✔
Operation Concepts	✔	✔	✔	✔	✔	✔	✔	✔
Measurement								
Geometry and Spatial Sense								
Data Analysis, Statistics, and Probability								
Patterns, Functions, Algebra	✔	✔	✔	✔	✔	✔	✔	✔
Problem Solving and Reasoning	✔	✔	✔	✔	✔	✔	✔	✔
Communication	✔	✔	✔	✔	✔	✔	✔	✔
Decimals, Fractions, Integers, and Percent	✔	✔	✔	✔	✔	✔	✔	✔
Order of Operations	✔							
Terra Nova CTBS (Level 17)								
Decimals, Fractions, Integers, Percents	✔	✔	✔	✔	✔	✔	✔	✔
Order of Operations, Numeration, Number Theory	✔	✔	✔	✔	✔	✔	✔	✔
Data Interpretation								
Pre-algebra	✔		✔	✔	✔	✔	✔	
Measurement								
Geometry								
ITBS (Level 13)								
Number Properties and Operations	✔	✔	✔	✔	✔	✔	✔	✔
Algebra	✔	✔	✔	✔	✔	✔	✔	✔
Geometry								
Measurement								
Probability and Statistics								
Estimation								
SAT10 (Int 3 Level)								
Number Sense and Operations	✔	✔	✔	✔	✔	✔	✔	✔
Patterns, Relationships, and Algebra	✔	✔	✔	✔	✔	✔	✔	✔
Data, Statistics, and Probability								
Geometry and Measurement								
NAEP								
Number Sense, Properties, and Operations	✔	✔	✔	✔	✔	✔	✔	✔
Measurement								
Geometry and Spatial Sense								
Data Analysis, Statistics, and Probability								
Algebra and Functions								

CAT6 California Achievement Test, 6th Ed.   **CTBS** Comprehensive Test of Basic Skills   **ITBS** Iowa Test of Basic Skills, Form M
SAT10 Stanford Achievement Test, 10th Ed.   **NAEP** National Assessment of Educational Progress 2005 Mathematics Objectives

TEKS Math Background

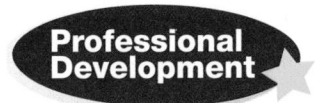

Focus on the TEKS

- At Grade 7, students convert between fractions, decimals, and whole numbers (7.1)(B). Analysis of TAKS results shows that students struggle with this student expectation.

  In Lesson 2-6, students write fractions as decimals and decimals as fractions. Students make conversions involving mixed numbers and repeating decimals. Place special emphasis on this lesson because it focuses on (7.1)(B).

- New at Grade 7 is simplifying numerical expressions involving order of operations and exponents (7.2)(E). Students apply Grade 6 skills to use the order of operations with whole numbers after being introduced to exponents in Lesson 2-1 (7.2)(E). Later, in Lesson 2-8, students use exponents to write scientific notation.

2-1 Exponents and Order of Operations

TEKS ★ TAKS (7.1)(C), (7.2)(E) Obj. 1

Math Understandings

- Exponentiation is a mathematical operation that indicates repeated multiplication.

An exponent shows how many times the base is used as a factor. A number that can be written using an exponent is a **power**. 81 is a power of 3 because 81 can be written as 3^4.

Example: 5^3 is $5 \cdot 5 \cdot 5$, or 125.

Example: $(-2)^4$ is $(-2) \cdot (-2) \cdot (-2) \cdot (-2)$, or 16.

The Order of Operations

1. Do all operations within groupings first.
2. Evaluate any term(s) with exponents.
3. Multiply and divide in order from left to right.
4. Add and subtract in order from left to right.

Example: Simplify $4^3 + (8 - 3)^2$

$$4^3 + (8 - 3)^2 = 4^3 + 5^2 \quad \leftarrow \textbf{Do operation in parentheses.}$$
$$= 64 + 25 \quad \leftarrow \textbf{Find the values of the powers.}$$
$$= 89 \quad \leftarrow \textbf{Add.}$$

2-2 Prime Factorization

TEKS ★ TAKS Prepares for TEKS (7.2)(B)

Math Understandings

- Any number is always divisible by all of its factors.
- Every composite number has a unique prime factorization.
- The number 1 is neither prime nor composite.

One whole number is **divisible** by a second whole number if the remainder is 0 when you divide the first number by the second. A **factor** is a whole number that divides another whole number with a remainder of 0. A **multiple** of a number is the product of that number and any nonzero whole number. The **least common multiple (LCM)** of two or more numbers is the least multiple that is common to all of the numbers. A **composite number** is a whole number greater than 1 that has more than two factors. A **prime number** is a whole number with exactly two factors, 1 and the number itself. The **greatest common factor (GCF)** of two or more numbers is the greatest number that is a factor of all the numbers.

2-3 2-4 Simplifying, Comparing, and Ordering Fractions

TEKS ★ TAKS (7.1)(A) TAKS Obj. 1; Prepares for TEKS (7.2)(B)

Math Understandings

- One number can be written in many different forms, all of which are equivalent.
- A fraction has a unique simplest form, which may be an improper fraction, such as $\frac{3}{2}$.

Fractions that name the same amount are equivalent fractions. Fractions obtained by multiplying (or dividing) both numerator and denominator by the same nonzero number are equivalent to each other. A fraction is written in **simplest form** when the numerator and the denominator have no common factors other than 1.

With two fractions, if the denominators are the same, the numerators tell which is greater.

Example: $\frac{5}{5} < \frac{8}{5}$ because $5 < 8$

With two fractions, if the numerators are the same, the fraction with the lesser denominator has the greater value.

Example: $\frac{3}{4} > \frac{3}{12}$ because $4 > 12$

The **least common denominator (LCD)** of two or more fractions is the least common multiple (LCM) of their denominators.

Example: Find the LCD for the fractions $\frac{2}{3}$ and $\frac{1}{4}$. The LCM of 3 and 4 is 12. So, 12 is the LCD for the denominators 3 and 4.

2-5 Mixed Numbers and Improper Fractions

TEKS ★ (TAKS) Prepares for TEKS (7.1)(A)

Math Understandings

- A quantity greater than 1 may be written as an improper fraction or as a mixed number.
- A mixed number, such as $3\frac{1}{2}$, can be written as the equivalent sum, for example, $3 + \frac{1}{2}$.

An **improper fraction** has a numerator that is greater than or equal to its denominator.

Examples: $\frac{5}{5}$, $\frac{8}{5}$, $\frac{3}{2}$, and $\frac{25}{3}$ are all improper fractions.

A **mixed number** is the sum of a whole number and a fraction.

Examples: $1\frac{1}{3}$, $2\frac{3}{4}$, and $7\frac{2}{3}$ are mixed numbers.

2-6 Fractions, Decimals, and 2-7 Rational Numbers

TEKS ★ (TAKS) (7.1)(A), (7.1)(B) Obj. 1

Math Understandings

- The number π (pi) can be represented by a nonterminating and nonrepeating decimal. Pi is an *irrational number*. It is only approximately equal to $\frac{22}{7}$ or 3.14.

A decimal that stops, or terminates, is a **terminating decimal**. If the same block of digits in a decimal repeats without end, the decimal is a **repeating decimal**. Both repeating and terminating decimals are rational numbers. A **rational number** is a number that can be written as a quotient of two integers, where the divisor is not zero.

Examples of rational numbers:
$\frac{17}{23}$, $\frac{1}{3}$, $0.\overline{6}$, $\frac{2}{9}$, $1.789\overline{789}$, -3, $-0.\overline{8}$, $-\frac{2}{3}$, -7.5079

Examples of irrational numbers:
π, $0.121221222\ldots$, $-530.53005300053\ldots$

2-8 Scientific Notation

Math Understandings

- Scientific notation is a shorthand way to write very large and very small numbers.
- Very large and very small numbers can be compared and combined more easily when written in scientific notation.

A number in **scientific notation** is written as the product of two factors, one greater than or equal to 1 and less than 10, and the other a power of 10. For example, 3.25×10^8 is 325,000,000.

Example: 341,500,000 in scientific notation is 3.415×10^8.

Additional Professional Development Opportunities

Math Background Notes for Chapter 2: Every lesson has a Math Background in the PLAN section.

Research Overview, Mathematics Strands
Additional support for these topics and more is in the front of the Teacher's Edition.

LessonLab
LessonLab, a Pearson Education company, offers comprehensive, facilitated professional development designed to help teachers to improve student achievement. To learn more, please visit lessonlab.com.

Texas Chapter 2 Resources

	2-1	2-2	2-3	2-4	2-5	2-6	2-7	2-8	For the Chapter
Print Resources									
L3 Practice	●	●	●	●	●	●	●	●	
L1 Adapted Practice	●	●	●	●	●	●	●	●	
L3 Guided Problem Solving	●	●	●	●	●	●	●	●	
L2 Reteaching	●	●	●	●	●	●	●	●	
L4 Enrichment	●	●	●	●	●	●	●	●	
L3 Daily Notetaking Guide	●	●	●	●	●	●	●	●	
L1 Adapted Daily Notetaking Guide	●	●	●	●	●	●	●	●	
L3 Vocabulary and Study Skills Worksheets	●		●	●		●		●	●
L3 Daily Puzzles	●	●	●	●	●	●	●	●	
L3 Activity Labs	●	●	●	●	●				
L3 Checkpoint Quiz		●				●			
L3 Chapter Project									●
L2 Chapter Test									●
L3 Chapter Test									●
L4 Alternative Assessment									●
L3 Cumulative Review									●
Spanish Resources ELL									
L3 Practice	●	●	●	●	●	●	●		
L3 Vocabulary and Study Skills Worksheets	●		●	●		●		●	●
L3 Checkpoint Quiz		●				●			
L2 Chapter Test									●
L3 Chapter Test									●
L4 Alternative Assessment									●
L3 Cumulative Review									●
Transparencies									
Check Skills You'll Need	●	●	●	●	●	●	●	●	
Additional Examples	●	●	●	●	●	●	●	●	
Problem of the Day	●	●	●	●	●	●	●	●	
TAKS Daily Review	●	●	●	●	●	●	●	●	
Classroom Aid									
Student Edition Answers	●	●	●	●	●	●	●	●	●
Lesson Quiz	●	●	●	●	●	●	●	●	
TAKS Strategies									●
Technology									
Texas Interactive Textbook Online	●	●	●	●	●	●	●	●	●
Texas StudentExpress CD-ROM	●	●	●	●	●	●	●	●	●
Success Tracker™ Online Intervention	●	●	●	●	●	●	●	●	●
TeacherExpress CD-ROM	●	●	●	●	●	●	●	●	●
PresentationExpress CD-ROM	●	●	●	●	●	●	●	●	●
Texas ExamView CD-ROM with QuickTake	●	●	●	●	●	●	●	●	●
MindPoint Quiz Show CD-ROM	●	●	●	●	●	●	●	●	●
Prentice Hall Web Site: PHSchool.com	●	●	●	●	●	●	●	●	●

Also available: TAKS Tune-Up Kit
- TAKS Daily Review Transparencies
- TAKS Review and Preparation Workbook
- TAKS Strategies with Transparencies
- Texas Progress Monitoring Assessments
- Texas ExamView CD-ROM
- MindPoint Quiz Show CD-ROM

Other Resources
Algebra Readiness Tests
All-in-One Student Workbook
All-in-One Student Workbook, Adapted Version
Multilingual Handbook

Solution Key
Math Notes Study Folder
Spanish Cumulative Assessment

Where You Can Use the Lesson Resources

Here is a suggestion, following the four-step teaching plan, for how you can incorporate Differentiated Instruction Resources into your teaching.

	Instructional Resources L3	Differentiated Instruction Resources
1. Plan		
Preparation Read the Math Background in the Teacher's Edition to connect this lesson with students' previous experience. **Starting Class** **Check Skills You'll Need** Assign these exercises to review prerequisite skills. **TEKS ★ TAKS** Review the full text of the TEKS student expectations and TAKS objectives covered in this lesson. **New Vocabulary** Help students pre-read the lesson by pointing out the new terms introduced in the lesson.	**TEKS Math Background** **Math Understandings** **Transparencies & PresentationExpress CD-ROM** Check Skills You'll Need Problem of the Day TAKS Daily Review **Resources** Vocabulary and Study Skills	**Spanish Support** ELL Vocabulary and Study Skills
2. Teach		
L3 Guided Instruction Use the Activity Labs to build conceptual understanding. Teach each Example. Use the Teacher's Edition side column notes for specific teaching tips, including Error Prevention notes. Use the Additional Examples found in the side column (and on transparency and PowerPoint) as an alternative presentation for the content. After each Example, assign the Quick Check exercise for that Example to get an immediate assessment of student understanding. Use the Closure activity in the Teacher's Edition to help students attain mastery of lesson content.	**Student Edition** Activity Lab **Resources** Daily Notetaking Guide Activity Lab **Transparencies & PresentationExpress CD-ROM** Additional Examples Classroom Aids **Texas ExamView CD-ROM with QuickTake**	**Teacher's Edition** Every lesson includes suggestions for working with students who need special attention. L1 Special Needs L2 Below Level L4 Advanced Learners ELL English Language Learners **Resources** L1 Adapted Daily Notetaking Guide **Multilingual Handbook**
3. Practice		
Assignment Guide **Check Your Understanding** Use these questions to check students' understanding before you assign homework. **Homework Exercises** Assign homework from these leveled exercises in the Assignment Guide. 　A Practice by Example 　B Apply Your Skills 　C Challenge 　TAKS Tune-Up and Mixed Review **Homework Quick Check** Use these key exercises to quickly check students' homework.	**Transparencies & PresentationExpress CD-ROM** Student Answers **Resources** Practice Guided Problem Solving Vocabulary and Study Skills Activity Lab Daily Puzzles **Texas ExamView CD-ROM with QuickTake**	**Spanish Support** ELL Practice ELL Vocabulary and Study Skills **Resources** L1 Adapted Practice L4 Enrichment
4. Assess & Reteach		
Lesson Quiz Assign the Lesson Quiz to assess students' mastery of the lesson content. **Checkpoint Quiz** Use the Checkpoint Quiz to assess student progress over several lessons.	**Transparencies & PresentationExpress CD-ROM** Lesson Quiz **Resources** Checkpoint Quiz	**Resources** L2 Reteaching ELL Checkpoint Quiz Success Tracker™ Online Intervention **Texas ExamView CD-ROM with QuickTake**

KEY　L1 Special Needs　L2 Below Level　L3 For All Students　L4 Advanced, Gifted　ELL English Language Learners

Exponents, Factors, and Fractions

 Check Your Readiness

Answers are in the back of the textbook.

For intervention, direct students to:

Adding and Subtracting Decimals
Lesson 1-2
Extra Skills and Word
  Problems Practice, Ch. 1

Comparing Integers
Lesson 1-6
Extra Skills and Word
  Problems Practice, Ch. 1

Multiplying and Dividing Integers
Lesson 1-8
Extra Skills and Word
  Problems Practice, Ch. 1

Order of Operations and the Distributive Property
Lesson 1-9
Extra Skills and Word
  Problems Practice, Ch. 1

 ## What You've Learned
TEKS ★ **TAKS**

- **(6.1)(E)** In a previous course, you learned to identify factors of a positive integer. **TAKS Obj. 1**
- **(7.2)(C)** In Chapter 1, you used models to add, subtract, multiply, and divide integers and to connect the actions to algorithms. **TAKS Obj. 1**
- **(7.1)(A)** You compared and ordered integers. **TAKS Obj. 1**

 ### Check Your Readiness

For Exercises	See Lesson
1–4	1-2
5–10	1-6
11–14	1-8
15–17	1-9

Adding and Subtracting Decimals

Find each sum or difference.

1. $2.1 + 3.4$ **5.5**
2. $6.02 - 4.597$ **1.423**
3. $7.0 - 3.11$ **3.89**
4. $671.02 + 6.427$ **677.447**

Comparing Integers

Compare. Use $<$, $=$, or $>$.

5. $|-2| \blacksquare |-5|$ $<$
6. $|11| \blacksquare |-13|$ $<$
7. $10 \blacksquare |-10|$ $=$
8. $-8 \blacksquare |-8|$ $<$
9. $|9| \blacksquare |-14|$ $<$
10. $|-1| \blacksquare 0$ $>$

Multiplying and Dividing Integers

Find each product or quotient.

11. $-9 \cdot 3$ **−27**
12. $-3 \cdot (-3)$ **9**
13. $27 \div -3$ **−9**
14. $-16 \div (-4)$
    4

Order of Operations and the Distributive Property

Find the value of each expression.

15. $12 + 4(16 \div 4)$
    28
16. $30 \div 3 - 4 \cdot 2$
    2
17. $(8 + 4) \div 4 - 2$
    1

Number, Operation, and Quantitative Reasoning
TEKS (7.1)(A), (7.1)(B), (7.1)(C), (7.2)(E)
TAKS Obj. 1

Patterns, Relationships, and Algebraic Thinking
TEKS (7.13)(A), (7.13)(C)
TAKS Obj. 6;
TEKS (7.13)(D)

Chapter 2 Overview

In this chapter, students extend the order of operations to include exponents. Students then simplify fractions, compare and order fractions and mixed numbers, and express fractions as decimals and decimals as fractions. They learn why fractions and decimals are rational numbers. Lastly, they express numbers in scientific notation.

Activating Prior Knowledge

In this chapter, students will build on their knowledge of basic division facts and prior work with fractions and decimals. They learn about scientific notation and develop their understanding of fraction concepts and properties. They also draw upon their understanding of the order of operations to include expressions involving exponents. Ask questions such as: *When is a fraction expressed in simplest form?* when the only number that can divide both terms of the fraction without a remainder is 1

What You'll Learn Next

TEKS ★ TAKS

- **(7.1)(A)** In this chapter, you will compare and order positive rational numbers. **TAKS** Obj. 1

- **(7.1)(B)** You will convert between fractions and decimals mentally, on paper, or with a calculator. **TAKS** Obj. 1

- **(7.2)(E)** You will simplify numerical expressions involving order of operations and exponents. **TAKS** Obj. 1

TAKS Tune-Up On pages 115–117, you will review and practice the vocabulary and *TAKS* objectives you have learned.

🔊 Key Vocabulary

- base (p. 68)
- composite number (p. 75)
- equivalent fraction (p. 82)
- exponent (p. 68)
- greatest common factor (GCF) (p. 75)
- improper fraction (p. 91)
- least common denominator (LCD) (p. 87)
- least common multiple (LCM) (p. 74)
- mixed number (p. 91)
- prime number (p. 75)
- rational number (p. 102)

Chapter 2 **67**

TEKS ★ TAKS

(7.2)(E) To simplify numerical expressions involving order of operations and exponents TAKS Obj. 1

(7.1)(C) To represent squares using geometric models TAKS Obj. 1

Dana Center TEKS Toolkit Clarifying Activities (7.2)(E), (7.1)(C)
Visit: PHSchool.com
Web Code: arq-9045

Professional Development

TEKS Math Background

Raising a number to a power is a mathematical operation. Because this operation is an extension of a basic operation, namely multiplication, it is considered a *higher order* operation. The formal name of the operation is *exponentiation*, but it is also referred to as *powering*.

More Math Background: p. 66C

Lesson Planning and Resources

See p. 66E for a list of the resources that support this lesson.

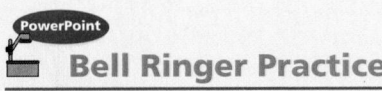

PowerPoint

Bell Ringer Practice

✓ **Check Skills You'll Need**
Use student page, transparency, or PowerPoint.

TAKS **Daily Review 11**
Use transparency.

✓ Check Skills You'll Need

1. Vocabulary Review
Using the *order of operations,* do you multiply factors before or after you add? **before**

Find the value of each expression.

2. 5 − 1 · 3   **2**

3. (5 − 1) · 3   **12**

4. 10 ÷ 2 − 3 · 5   **−10**

5. (1 + 99) ÷ 10 − 9   **1**

GO for Help
Lesson 1-9

GO Online

Video Tutor Help
Visit: PHSchool.com
Web Code: are-0775

2-1 Exponents and Order of Operations

TEKS ★ TAKS

- (7.2)(E) To simplify numerical expressions involving order of operations and exponents TAKS **Obj. 1**
- (7.1)(C) To represent squares using geometric models TAKS **Obj. 1**

🔊 **New Vocabulary** exponent, base, power

Why Learn This?

Googol is a large number written as the digit one followed by 100 zeros. Writing out the number takes a long time. You can use exponents to write googol and other large numbers in a easier way. For example, you can write googol as 10^{100}.

An **exponent** tells you how many times a number, or **base,** is used as a factor.

$$\underset{\text{base}}{\overset{\text{exponent}}{5^3}} = \underbrace{5 \cdot 5 \cdot 5}_{\text{The base is used as a factor three times.}} = \overset{\text{value of the expression}}{125}$$

A number that can be expressed using an exponent is called a **power.** The number 125 is a power of 5 because it can be written as 5^3.

EXAMPLE   Writing Expressions Using Exponents

❶ Write 3 · 3 · 3 · 3 · 3 using an exponent.

$3 \cdot 3 \cdot 3 \cdot 3 \cdot 3 = 3^5$ ← 3 is the base. 5 is the exponent.

✓ Quick Check

1. Write each product using exponents.
  a. 44 · 44 · 44 · 44 44^4 **b.** (−2) · (−2) $(-2)^2$

You can find the value of an expression with exponents by writing it as the product of repeated factors. You can also use a scientific calculator.

68   Chapter 2   Exponents, Factors, and Fractions

EXAMPLE Application: Geography

② Gibraltar is at the mouth of the Mediterranean Sea. Its area is about the same as the area of a square 1.5 mi on a side. Find Gibraltar's area.

Method 1 Since $A = s^2$, compute to find 1.5^2.

$1.5^2 = (1.5)(1.5)$ ← **Write as a product of repeated factors.**

$= 2.25$ ← **Multiply.**

Method 2 Use a geometric model. In the model, each side of the blue square has a length of 1.5. The total area in blue equals one whole square plus two half squares plus one quarter square. The total is 2.25 squares. The area of Gibraltar is about 2.25 mi^2.

Calculator Tip

You can use the ⌃ or y^x key to find a power.

To find 1.5^2, use 1.5 ⌃ 2 ▤ 2.25 or 1.5 y^x 2 ▤ 2.25.

If your calculator does not have an exponent key, use 1.5 ✕ 1.5 ▤ 2.25.

✓ Quick Check

2. Simplify. Use paper and pencil, a model, or a calculator.
   a. 3^5 243   **b.** 10^9 1,000,000,000   **c.** 3.1^2 9.61

The order of operations includes expressions with exponents.

KEY CONCEPTS Order of Operations

1. Do all operations within grouping symbols first.
2. Evaluate any term(s) with exponents.
3. Multiply and divide in order from left to right.
4. Add and subtract in order from left to right.

Vocabulary Tip

The phrase *Please Excuse My Dear Aunt Sally* can help you remember the order of operations. The first letter of each word in the phrase stands for *Parentheses, Exponents, Multiplication, Division, Addition,* and *Subtraction.*

The expressions -2^4 and $(-2)^4$ are not equivalent. The expression -2^4 means the opposite, or the negative, of 2^4. The base of -2^4 is 2, not -2.

EXAMPLE Simplifying Using Order of Operations

③ Simplify $-2^4 + (3 - 5)^4$.

$-2^4 \cdot (3 - 5)^4 = -2^4 + (-2)^4$ ← **Do operations in parentheses.**

$= -16 + 16$ ← **Find the values of the powers.**

$= 0$ ← **Add.**

✓ Quick Check

3. Simplify.
   a. $(-3)^3$ −27   **b.** -3^3 −27   **c.** $(3 + 5)^2 - 2$ 62

Activity Lab

Use before the lesson.

All in One Teaching Resources

Activity Lab 2-1: Exploring Exponents

Guided Instruction

Example 3
The expression $(7 - 2)^3$ should be read as "the quantity seven minus two, raised to the third power." If it is read as "seven minus two to the third power," students with visual impairments might have difficulty distinguishing it from the expression $7 - 2^3$.

PowerPoint

Additional Examples

① Write using exponents.
   a. $7 \cdot 7 \cdot 7 \cdot 7$ 7^4
   b. $2 \cdot 2 \cdot 2 \cdot 2 \cdot 2 \cdot 2$ 2^6

② A seaside village has an area of 1.3^2 km^2. Find the value of 1.3^2. **1.69**

③ Simplify $2^3 \cdot (9 - 3)^2$. **288**

All in One Teaching Resources

- Daily Notetaking Guide 2-1 **L3**
- Adapted Notetaking 2-1 **L1**

Closure

- *How do you find the value of a number raised to a power?* Perform a multiplication in which the number is used as a factor the number of times indicated by the exponent.
- *What is the order of operations when exponents are involved?* Do operations within grouping symbols. Evaluate terms with exponents. Multiply and divide in order from left to right. Add and subtract in order from left to right.

Advanced Learners **L4**
Use four 4's and any operations to make an expression that is equal to 68. **Samples:**
$4^4 \div 4 + 4$; $4 \cdot 4 \cdot 4 + 4$

English Language Learners **ELL**
Make sure students understand that the word *groupings* in the order of operations frequently refers to *parentheses.*

Pre-AP™

learning style: verbal

69

3. Practice

Assignment Guide

Check Your Understanding
Go over Exercises 1–8 in class before assigning the Homework Exercises.

Homework Exercises
A Practice by Example   9–29
B Apply Your Skills   30–40
C Challenge   41
TEKS ★ *TAKS* Tune-Up and Mixed Review   42–47

Homework Quick Check
To check students' understanding of key skills and concepts, go over Exercises 10, 22, 35, 36, and 39.

Differentiated Instruction **Resources**

Adapted Practice 2-1   L1

Practice 2-1   Exponents and Order of O   L3

Write using exponents.
1. $3 \times 3 \times 3 \times 3 \times 3$ 3^5 2. $2.7 \times 2.7 \times 2.7$ 2.7^3
3. $11.6 \times 11.6 \times 11.6 \times 11.6$ 11.6^4 4. $2 \times 2 \times 2 \times 2 \times 2 \times 2$ 2^6
5. $8.3 \times 8.3 \times 8.3 \times 8.3 \times 8.3$ 8.3^5 6. $4 \times 4 \times 4 \times 4 \times 4 \times 4 \times 4 \times 4$ 4^8

Write as the product of repeated factors. Then simplify.
7. $(0.5)^3$ $0.5 \times 0.5 \times 0.5; 0.125$
8. $(-4)^5$ $(-4) \times (-4) \times (-4) \times (-4) \times (-4); -1,024$
9. $(2.7)^2$ $2.7 \times 2.7; 7.29$
10. 2^3 $2 \times 2 \times 2; 8$
11. $(-5)^6$ $(-5) \times (-5) \times (-5) \times (-5) \times (-5) \times (-5); 15,625$
12. $(8.1)^3$ $8.1 \times 8.1 \times 8.1; 531.441$

Simplify. Use a calculator, paper and pencil, or mental math.
13. -4^3 -64 14. $11 + (-6^3)$ 205 15. $14 + 16^2$ 270
16. $8 + 6^4$ $1,304$ 17. $3^2 \cdot 5^4$ $5,625$ 18. $6^2 - 2^4$ 20
19. $4(0.9 + 1.3)^3$ 42.592 20. $35 - (4^2 + 5)$ 14 21. $(3^3 + 6) - 7$ 26
22. $5(0.3 \cdot 1.2)^2$ 0.648 23. $5(4 + 2)^2$ 180 24. $(8 - 6.7)^3$ 2.197

25. A cubic aquarium has edges measuring 4.3 ft each. Find the volume of the aquarium in cubic feet. 79.507 ft^3

26. Lana is 2^3 in. taller than her little sister. How many inches taller is Lana than her sister?   8 in.

2-1 • Guided Problem Solving GPS   L3

Student Page 71, Exercise 37:

Technology A Scanning Electron Microscope (SEM) can magnify an image up to 10^5 times its size. How many times is this?

Understand
1. What are you being asked to do?
Determine what number 10^5 is.

2. What do you call the 5 in 10^5?
the exponent

3. What do you call the 10 in 10^5?
the base

Plan and Carry Out
4. The number 10^5 is what number?   100,000
5. How many zeros are in the number 10^5?   5
6. How many times does the SEM magnify?   100,000

Check
7. Does your answer follow the pattern of powers of 10? Explain.
Yes, because 10^2 has 2 zeros and magnifies 100 times; 10^3 has 3 zeros and magnifies 1,000 times.

Solve Another Problem
8. Lucy has a microscope that magnifies an image up to 10^3 times its size. Aaron has a microscope that magnifies an image up to 10^4 times its size. What is the difference in these two numbers?
9,000

70

Check Your Understanding

●nline
active math*

Simplify the expression show below.
Click on the parts of the expression to perform the associated operation.

$(2^2 \cdot 20 - 16) + 16$

For: Order of Operations Activity
Use: Interactive Textbook, 2-1

1. **Vocabulary** How is an exponent different from a base? The exponent tells you how many times the base is used as a factor.
2. Write an expression for *the opposite of the fourth power of 2.* -2^4

Simplify each expression.

3. $-1 \cdot 5^4$ -625 4. $(-5)^4$ 625   5. $2^4 \cdot (7 - 6)^3$ 16

Science **Match each fact with the appropriate power.**

6. number of moons orbiting Earth   C   **A.** 2^5
7. planets in the solar system   B   **B.** 3^2
8. freezing point of water in degrees Fahrenheit   A   **C.** 1^1

Homework Exercises

For more exercises, see Extra Skills and Word Problems.

GO for Help

For Exercises	See Examples
9–14	1
15–23	2
24–29	3

9. 2^6

31. $60 \cdot 60 \cdot 60; 6^3$

33.

Ⓐ **Write using an exponent.**

9. $2 \cdot 2 \cdot 2 \cdot 2 \cdot 2 \cdot 2$ See left.   10. $7 \cdot 7 \cdot 7 \cdot 7 \cdot 7$ 7^5 11. $6 \cdot 6 \cdot 6$ 6^3
12. $-5 \cdot -5 \cdot -5 \cdot -5$ $(-5)^4$ 13. $9 \cdot 9 \cdot 9 \cdot 9 \cdot 9 \cdot 9$ 9^6 14. $12 \cdot 12 \cdot 12 \cdot 12$ 12^4

Simplify. Use paper and pencil, a model, or a calculator.

15. 9^2 81   16. 10^8 100,000,000   17. 0.2^6 0.000064   18. 1.7^3 4.913
19. -3^4 -81 20. $(-3)^4$ 81   21. $(-2)^3$ -8 22. $(-4)^3$ -64

23. Each side of a sugar cube is 0.6 in. long. Find the volume of the sugar cube. 0.216 in.^3

Simplify using the order of operations.

24. $2^3 \cdot (6 - 3)^2$ 72   25. $(2^3 \cdot 6) - 3^2$ 39   26. $2^3 \cdot 6 - 3^2$ 39
27. $-3^2 + 2^3 \cdot 6$ 39   28. $3^2 - 2^3$ 1   29. $(2 + 1)^3 \div 3^2$ 3

Ⓑ **GPS** 30. **Guided Problem Solving** Suppose you have a part-time job. Your boss offers to pay you $2 the first day, with the amount to double each day. How much will you be paid for the tenth day? $1,024
- **Make a Plan** Find the amounts you will be paid on the second, third, and fourth days. Write each amount using exponents.
- **Carry Out the Plan** On each day, you will earn ■ dollars, which can be written using exponents as $2^{■}$. Identify the pattern.

31. Write two equivalent expressions for the number of seconds in 60 hours. Use exponents in only one of the expressions. See left.

33.

Power of 10	Value	Number of Zeros
10^1	10	1
10^2	100	2
10^3	1,000	3
10^4	10,000	4
10^5	100,000	5

32. (**Algebra**) Suppose a is a nonzero number. How would you write $a \cdot a \cdot a$ using an exponent? a^3

For Exercises 33–35, refer to the table.

33. Copy the table. Fill in the missing values. See margin.

34. The exponent is equal to the number of zeros.

34. **Patterns** What patterns do you notice? See left.

35. **Reasoning** Predict the number of zeros in 10^{12}. 12

Power of 10	Value	Number of Zeros
10^1	▓	1
10^2	▓	▓
10^3	▓	▓
10^4	▓	▓
10^5	▓	▓

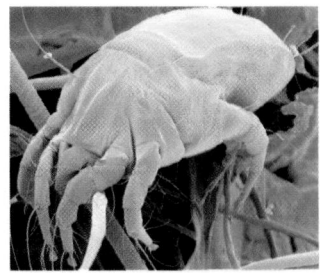

This dust mite has been magnified 1.5×10^5 times.

36. A scanning electron microscope (SEM) **GPS** can magnify an image to as much as 10^5 times the actual size. How many times is this? 100,000 times

37. Without calculating, decide whether the value of $(-672)^2 - 192$ is positive or negative. Explain your reasoning. Positive; $(-672)^2$ is positive and larger than 192.

38. What exponent completes the table below? Use your answer to find $2^0, 3^0, 4^0, 5^0,$ and 10^0. 0; 1, 1, 1, 1, 1

Value	16	8	4	2	1
Power of 2	2^4	2^3	2^2	2^1	$2^{▓}$

39. **Writing in Math** Write a general rule to find the value of a nonzero expression with an exponent of 0. If $x \neq 0$, then $x^0 = 1$.

40a. 5

b. 25

c. Answers may vary. Sample: "5 squared" is the number of units of area if 5 is the length of a side.

40. **a. Geometry** How many small squares line up on one edge of the larger square? 40a–c. See left.
b. How many small squares fit in the large square?
c. Explain why 5^2 is read as "5 squared."

C 41. **Challenge** Evaluate $g^2(f + h)$ for $f = -2, g = -3,$ and $h = -4$. -54

TEKS ★ TAKS Tune-Up and Mixed Review

TAKS Objective 1
TEKS (7.2)(E)

42. What is the value of the expression $(4 - 1)^3 - 3 \times 8 \div 6$? **D**
Ⓐ 0.5　Ⓑ 5　Ⓒ 21　Ⓓ 23

TAKS Objective 1
TEKS (7.2)(B)

43. The table shows a plant's growth each week for four weeks. If the plant grew 4.75 cm in all, how much did it grow in week 4? **H**
Ⓕ 0.65 cm　Ⓗ 1.65 cm
Ⓖ 1.35 cm　Ⓙ 4.75 cm

Week	Growth (cm)
1	0.25
2	1.5
3	1.35
4	

GO for Help **Lesson 1-8**

Find the value of each expression.

44. $12(-2)$ -24　**45.** $-4(-10)$ 40　**46.** $-8 \div (-4)$ 2　**47.** $49 \div (-7)$ -7

Lesson Quiz

Simplify.

1. 6^3 216

2. $2(3^2 + 12)$ 42

3. -7^4 $-2,401$

4. $4(10 - 8)^5$ 128

Alternative Assessment

Turn to the order of operations on page 69. For Exercises 24–29 on page 70, have students tell what operation they must perform first, second, and so on to complete each Exercise. Have them show each step of their simplification process.

TEKS ★ TAKS Resources
• TAKS Strategies, p. 111
• TAKS Tune-Up, pp. 115–117
TAKS Tune-Up Kit
• TAKS Daily Review Transparencies
• TAKS Review and Preparation Workbook
• TAKS Strategies with Transparencies
• Texas Progress Monitoring Assessments

71

Using a Scientific Calculator

Students use a scientific calculator to simplify expressions. This will help them extend their use of the order of operations in Lesson 2-1.

Guided Instruction

Explain that, to simplify expressions with multiple steps, they must enter the information into the calculator in a specific way to get the correct solution. Ask:

- *What happens after you press the first three keys in the problem in Example 1?* **The calculator displays the total.**
- *Is it necessary to insert the parentheses in Example 2? Why?* **No, the total is the same with or without parentheses.**
- *What happens if you don't enter the parentheses in Example 3?* **The calculator divides (−7 − 5) by −6 and then adds 3 to that total.**

Exercises

Have students work on the Exercises. Review the answers and the calculator keystrokes as a class.

Differentiated Instruction

Below Level   L2

Have student solve the problems in the Exercises by hand and by calculator. Help them compare the steps in their calculations with what the calculator does.

TEKS ★ **TAKS Resources**

- scientific calculator

Dana Center TEKS Toolkit Clarifying Activities (7.2)(E), (7.13)(D)
Visit: PHSchool.com
Web Code: arq-9045

TEKS ★ **TAKS**

(7.2)(E) To simplify numerical expressions involving order of operations **TAKS Obj. 1**

(7.13)(D) To select tools such as technology to solve problems

Using a Scientific Calculator

Many calculators use the order of operations. To test your calculator, try to compute $3 + 5 \cdot 2$. If the answer is 13, your calculator uses the order of operations.

You can use a scientific calculator to simplify expressions that contain more than one operation.

EXAMPLE Simplifying Expressions

1 Find $6 + 18 \div 2$.

6 ➕ 18 ➗ 2 ＝ 15

The expression $6 + 18 \div 2$ simplifies to 15.

You can use a scientific calculator to simplify expressions that have grouping symbols.

EXAMPLE Using Grouping Symbols

2 Find $(5.5 - 9) \div 2$.

❨ 5 ・ 5 ➖ 9 ❩ ➗ 2 ＝ −1.75

The expression simplifies to −1.75.

You can simplify expressions by inserting grouping symbols.

EXAMPLE Inserting Parentheses

3 Find $\frac{-7 - 5}{-6 + 3}$.

❨ (−) 7 ➖ 5 ❩ ➗ ❨ (−) 6 ➕ 3 ❩ ＝ 4   ← Use the (−) key for negative numbers.

The quotient is 4.

Exercises

Use a calculator to find the value of each expression.

1. $9 + 4 \cdot 2$ **17**

2. $5.6 - 9 \div 2.5$ **2**

3. $(5 - 14.9) \div 3$ **−3.3**

4. $\frac{8.2 - 16.3}{4.5}$ **−1.8**

5. $7.2 \div (4.3 - 3.7)$ **12**

6. $\frac{-9 - 6.2}{2.1 + 2.9}$ **−3.04**

Divisibility Tests

One whole number is **divisible** by a second whole number if the remainder is 0 when you divide the first number by the second number. The table below shows tests to determine if a number is divisible by 2, 3, 4, 5, 8, 9, or 10.

TEKS ★ *TAKS*

Prepares for **TEKS** (7.2)(B)
To use division to solve problems involving fractions

EXAMPLES

1 Is 567 divisible by 3?

Yes, $5 + 6 + 7 = 18$; 18 is divisible by 3.

2 Is 934 divisible by 4?

No it is not, since 34 is not divisible by 4.

3 Is 29,640 divisible by 8?

Yes it is, because 640 is divisible by 8.

4 Is 3,016 divisible by 9?

No, $3 + 0 + 1 + 6 = 10$; 10 is not divisible by 9.

Number	Test for Divisibility
2	Number ends in 0, 2, 4, 6, or 8.
3	Sum of the digits is divisible by 3.
4	The number formed by the last two digits is divisible by 4.
5	Number ends in 0 or 5.
8	The number formed by the last three digits is divisible by 8.
9	Sum of the digits is divisible by 9.
10	Number ends in 0.

Exercises

Tell whether each number is divisible by 2, 3, 4, 5, 8, 9, or 10. Some numbers may be divisible by more than one number.

1. 324 2, 3, 4, 9
2. 840 2, 3, 4, 5, 8, 10
3. 2,724 2, 3, 4
4. 81,816 2, 3, 4, 8
5. 7,848 2, 3, 4, 8, 9

6. **Games** In an adventure game, you can open the door to a treasure room if you have the correct key. The number of the correct key is divisible by 3 and 4, but not 5. Which color key will open the door? orange

413,270   267,528   326,340   135,480   640,905

7. A *conjecture* is a prediction that suggests what can be expected to happen. Make a conjecture for the divisibility tests of 12 and 15.
Answers may vary. Sample: A number is divisible by 12 if it is divisible by 3 and 4. A number is divisible by 15 if it is divisible by 3 and 5.

Activity Lab Divisibility Tests   **73**

Activity Lab

Divisibility Tests

Students use rules for divisibility on a large number. This will help them work with prime factorization in Lesson 2-2.

Guided Instruction

Have students study the table. Give the example that all even numbers are divisible by 2 because there is no remainder, but odd numbers are not divisible by 2 because there will always be a remainder of 1.
Ask:
- *Are numbers divisible by 9 also divisible by 3? Why?* Yes, 9 is divisible by 3 so numbers that divide into 9 parts can also divide into 3 parts.
- *Are all numbers divisible by 2 also divisible by 4? Why?* No, some even numbers like 10 are not divisible by 4.
- *What is a good rule for divisibility by doubles? For perfect squares?* Sample: A number divisible by an even number is also divisible by half that number. A number divisible by a perfect square is also divisible by that number's square root.

Exercises

Have students work on the Exercises. Then have them form small groups and compare lists of numbers that each number is divisible by.

Alternative Method

Provide students with base ten manipulatives to model divisibility and help make the connection with the rules of divisibility.

Resources

- Activity Lab 2-2: Factors
- Student Manipulatives Kit

Prepares for **TEKS (7.2)(B)** To solve problems involving fractions

TEKS Math Background

Every integer greater than 1 has exactly one prime factorization. This idea is so important to the study of mathematics that it is sometimes called the *Fundamental Theorem of Arithmetic*. In this lesson, students learn to recognize prime numbers and to find the prime factorization of an integer.

More Math Background: p. 66C

Lesson Planning and Resources

See p. 66E for a list of the resources that support this lesson.

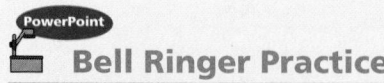

Bell Ringer Practice

✓ **Check Skills You'll Need**
Use student page, transparency, or PowerPoint.

TAKS Daily Review 12
Use transparency.

2-2

Prime Factorization

✓ **Check Skills You'll Need**

1. Vocabulary Review
A whole number is divisible by a second whole number if the remainder after division is ■.
0

Use mental math to find the quotient.

2. 48 ÷ 2 24

3. 63 ÷ 3 21

4. 72 ÷ 6 12

 for Help

Skills Handbook, page 657

What You'll Learn

To find multiples and factors and to use prime factorization
• Prepares for **TEKS (7.2)(B)** To solve problems involving fractions
🔊 **New Vocabulary** multiple, least common multiple, factor, composite, prime, prime factorization, greatest common factor

Why Learn This?

You can use factors and multiples to solve problems involving scheduling.

Suppose you volunteer every third day at an animal shelter, and your friend volunteers every fourth day. You can use multiples to find the next day when you both will be at the shelter.

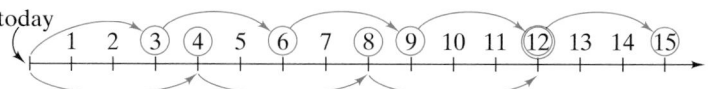

A **multiple** of a number is the product of that number and any nonzero whole number. The diagram above shows multiples of 3 and 4. The **least common multiple (LCM)** of two or more numbers is the least multiple that is common to all of the numbers.

EXAMPLE **Finding the LCM**

1 **Scheduling** A fish sandwich is on a school's lunch menu every 6 school days. Spaghetti with meat sauce is on the menu every 9 school days. If both items are on the menu today, when will both be served again?

Find the least common multiple of 6 and 9.

Multiples of 6: 6, 12, 18, 24, 30, 36, . . . ⎱ ← **List the first several**
Multiples of 9: 9, 18, 27, 36, . . .   ⎰   **multiples of 6 and 9.**

The LCM of 6 and 9 is 18. Both will be served again in 18 school days.

✓ **Quick Check**

1. Find the LCM of each pair of numbers.
    a. 4, 10 20   **b.** 5, 7 35   **c.** 12, 15 60

Differentiated Instruction **Solutions for All Learners**

Special Needs **L1**
Provide students with a multiplication grid or a table of the multiplication facts. This will help them list the multiples, and figure out the factors, or at least check once they have listed them.

learning style: visual

Below Level **L2**
Give students several missing-factor exercises like these.

1 • ☐ = 54 54   2 • ☐ = 54 27
3 • ☐ = 54 18   6 • ☐ = 54 9

learning style: visual

A **factor** is a whole number that divides another whole number with a remainder of 0. Any number is always divisible by all of its factors.

A **composite number** is a whole number that has more than two factors. A **prime number** is a whole number with exactly two factors, 1 and the number itself. The number 1 is neither prime nor composite.

EXAMPLE Prime Numbers and Composite Numbers

2 Determine whether each number is prime or composite.

a. 12

Look for pairs of numbers with a product of 12:

$$1 \cdot 12 \quad 2 \cdot 6 \quad 3 \cdot 4$$

Then list the factors in order: 1, 2, 3, 4, 6, 12.

Since 12 has factors other than 1 and itself, 12 is a composite number.

b. 13

Look for pairs of numbers with a product of 13: $1 \cdot 13$.

Since 13 has no factors other than 1 and itself, 13 is a prime number.

✓ Quick Check

2. Is 15 prime or composite? Explain. composite; the factors of 15 are 1, 3, 5 and 15. Since 15 has more than two factors, 15 is composite.

Writing a composite number as the product of its prime factors shows its **prime factorization.** This product is unique except for the order of the factors. You can use a factor tree to find prime factors.

EXAMPLE Writing Prime Factorization

GO for Help

For help with writing expressions involving exponents, go to Lesson 2-1, Example 1.

3 Use a factor tree to write the prime factorization of 60.

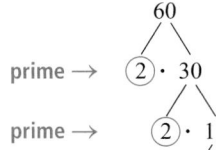

prime → ② · 30 ← **Write 60 as the product of any two of its factors.**

prime → ② · 15 ← **Write 30 as the product of two factors.**

prime → ③ · ⑤ ← **Write 15 as the product of two factors.**

$60 = 2 \cdot 2 \cdot 3 \cdot 5$. Using exponents, you can write $60 = 2^2 \cdot 3 \cdot 5$.

✓ Quick Check

3. Write the prime factorization of 72. Use exponents where possible.
$72 = 2^3 \cdot 3^2$

The **greatest common factor (GCF)** of two or more numbers is the greatest number that is a factor of all the numbers.

Activity Lab

Use before the lesson.
Student Edition Activity Lab 2-2a, Divisibility Tests, p. 73

All in One Teaching Resources
Activity Lab 2-2: Factors

Guided Instruction

Example 1
Point out to students that they are already familiar with one special set of multiples: The *even numbers* are all the multiples of 2.

Example 2
Point out that 2 is the only prime number that is an even number. All other even numbers can be written as the product of 2 and some positive integer greater than 1.

Error Prevention!

Students might end their factor trees with one or more composite numbers. For instance, in Quick Check 3, they might write $2^3 \cdot 9$. Remind them that the purpose of the tree is finding a *prime* factorization, so all the ending numbers must be prime.

Advanced Learners **L4**
Find the GCF and the LCM of each set of numbers.

12, 24, 32 4; 96   24, 36, 48 12; 144
12, 15, 36 3; 180   9, 16, 25 1; 3,600

Pre-AP™

English Language Learners **ELL**
Help students restate or rephrase the meaning of *least common multiple.* For example, for *least*, use the words *lowest* or *least value.* For *common*, use the words *the same.* An alternate definition might be: *The multiple with the lowest value that is the same for both numbers.*

learning style: verbal

75

1 Dan goes to the health club every 4 days. His sister Neesa goes there every 6 days. Dan and Neesa both went to the health club today. When will they both go there on the same day again? **12 days**

2 Tell whether each number is prime or composite.

a. 17 **prime**

b. 22 **composite**

3 Use a factor tree to write the prime factorization of 90.

```
        90
       /  \
      45   (2)
     /  \
    9   (5)
   / \
  (3) (3)
```

90 = 2 · 3 · 3 · 5, or 2 · 3² · 5

4 Find the GCF of 32 and 48. **16**

All in One Teaching Resources

• Daily Notetaking Guide 2-2 **L3**
• Adapted Notetaking 2-2 **L1**

Closure

• Refer students to the *New Vocabulary* list on page 74. Ask them to illustrate as many of the vocabulary words as they can using the numbers 8 and 10. **Samples: The multiples of 8 are 8, 16, 24, . . . The multiples of 10 are 10, 20, 30, . . . The LCM of 8 and 10 is 40. The factors of 8 are 1, 2, 4, and 8. The factors of 10 are 1, 2, 5, and 10. Both 8 and 10 are composite numbers.**

EXAMPLE Finding the GCF

4 Find the GCF of 24 and 36.

$24 = 2 \cdot 2 \cdot 2 \cdot 3$ $36 = 2 \cdot 2 \cdot 3 \cdot 3$ ← Write the prime factorizations.

$GCF = 2 \cdot 2 \cdot 3 = 12$ ← Find the product of the common factors.

The GCF of 24 and 36 is 12.

Quick Check

4. Find the GCF of 16 and 24. **8**

More Than One Way

Two different teams are marching in rows that all contain the same number of people. One team has 32 members and the other has 40. If the rows are as long as possible, how many people are in each row?

Carlos's Method

I'll write the prime factorizations of 40 and 32. Then I'll find the GCF.

```
       40              32
      /  \            /  \
     4 · 10          4 · 8          ← Write as products of two factors.
    /|   |\         /|   |\
  (2)(2)(2)(5)    (2)(2)(2) 4       ← Write as products of two factors.
                          / \
                        (2)·(2)     ← Write as a product of two factors.
```

$40 = 2 \cdot 2 \cdot 2 \cdot 5$
$32 = 2 \cdot 2 \cdot 2 \cdot 2 \cdot 2$ ← Write the prime factorizations.

$GCF = 2 \cdot 2 \cdot 2 = 8$ ← Multiply the common factors.

There are 8 people in each row.

Anna's Method

First I'll list the possible sizes of rows. Then I'll choose the greatest number in both lists.

The factors of 32 are 1, 2, 4, 8, 16, and 32.
The factors of 40 are 1, 2, 4, 5, 8, 10, 20, and 40.

The greatest common factor is 8. There are 8 people in each row.

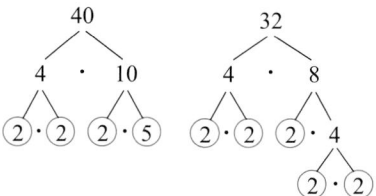

Choose a Method

Teams of 36 and 60 will march in rows of equal length. How many marchers will be in the longest row possible? **12**

76 **Chapter 2** Exponents, Factors, and Fractions

Check Your Understanding

1. A factor is a whole number that divides another whole number with a remainder of 0. A multiple of a number is the product of the number and another whole number.

1. **Vocabulary** How is a factor different from a multiple? See left.

2. **Number Sense** Which numbers are factors of all even numbers? 1, 2

3. What is the only even prime number? 2

Is the number prime or composite? Explain. 4–7. See margin.

4. 29   5. 28   6. 27   7. 26

Homework Exercises

For more exercises, see Extra Skills and Word Problems.

GO for Help	
For Exercises	**See Examples**
8–16	1
17–24	2
25–32	3
33–40	4

(A) Find the LCM of each pair of numbers.

8. 4, 6 12   9. 9, 12 36   10. 8, 5 40   11. 2, 5 10

12. 6, 7 42   13. 5, 10 10   14. 10, 6 30   15. 24, 8 24

16. **Fitness** You have aerobics classes every 3 days and soccer practice every 7 days. Today you had both aerobics and soccer. When will you next have both activities on the same day? in 21 days

Find the factors of each number.

17. 20   18. 23 1, 23   19. 32   20. 62
1, 2, 4, 5, 10, 20   1, 2, 4, 8, 16, 32   1, 2, 31, 62

Determine whether each number is prime or composite.

21. 37 prime   22. 50 composite   23. 1 neither   24. 63 composite

Write the prime factorization of each number. Use exponents.

25. 45 $3^2 \cdot 5$ 26. 64 2^6 27. 84 $2^2 \cdot 3 \cdot 7$ 28. 111 $3 \cdot 37$

29. 52 $2^2 \cdot 13$ 30. 75 $3 \cdot 5^2$ 31. 60   32. 132
$2^2 \cdot 3 \cdot 5$ $2^2 \cdot 3 \cdot 11$

Find the GCF of each pair of numbers.

33. 18, 32 2   34. 12, 15 3   35. 16, 80 16   36. 10, 85 5

37. 38, 76 38   38. 75, 90 15   39. 54, 80 2   40. 52, 26 26

(B) 41. **Guided Problem Solving** In his art class, Raul made two rectangular mosaics with 1-cm tiles. He used 48 tiles for one mosaic and 56 tiles for the other. Both mosaics have the same length, measured in whole centimeters. What is the greatest possible length of each mosaic? 8 cm
- What are the possible lengths of each mosaic?
- What are the corresponding widths for each mosaic?

4. Prime; 1 and 29 are the only factors.

5. Composite; the factors are 1, 2, 4, 7, 14 and 28.

6. Composite; the factors are 1, 3, 9 and 27.

7. Composite; the factors are 1, 2, 13 and 26.

Assignment Guide

Check Your Understanding
Go over Exercises 1–7 in class before assigning the Homework Exercises.

Homework Exercises
A Practice by Example 8–40
B Apply Your Skills 41–51
C Challenge 52
TEKS ★ TAKS Tune-Up and Mixed Review 53–57

Homework Quick Check
To check students' understanding of key skills and concepts, go over Exercises 19, 35, 43, 48, and 51.

Differentiated Instruction Resources

Lesson Quiz

Write the prime factorization. Use exponents.

1. 24 $2^3 \cdot 3$ **2.** 20 $2^2 \cdot 5$

3. 63 $3^2 \cdot 7$ **4.** 84 $2^2 \cdot 3 \cdot 7$

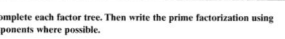

Reteaching 2-2 Prime Fact **L2**

A **prime number** has exactly two factors, 1 and itself. 2 and 7 are prime numbers. 2 is the smallest prime number.

$2 \times 1 = 2$ $7 \times 1 = 7$

Every **composite number** can be written as a product of two or more prime numbers. This is called the **prime factorization** of the number.

$60 = 2 \cdot 2 \cdot 3 \cdot 5 = 2^2 \cdot 3 \cdot 5$
$40 = 2 \cdot 2 \cdot 2 \cdot 5 = 2^3 \cdot 5$

You can use a *factor tree* and division to find the prime factorization of a number.

① Divide by a factor other than 1 and the number itself. Record the divisor and the quotient in the factor tree.

② Continue dividing until all the factors are prime numbers.

③ Use exponents to write the prime factorization.

$36 \div 2 = 18$ $2 \cdot 18$
$18 \div 2 = 9$ $2 \cdot 9$
$9 \div 3 = 3$ $3 \cdot 3$

$36 = 2^2 \cdot 3^2$

Complete each factor tree. Then write the prime factorization using exponents where possible.

1. 24 → 2 · 12 → 2 · 6 → 2 · 3 $2^3 \cdot 3$
2. 30 → 3 · 10 → 2 · 5 $2 \cdot 3 \cdot 5$
3. 27 → 3 · 9 → 3 · 3 3^3

Write the prime factorization of each number. Use exponents where possible.

4. 20 = $2^2 \times 5$
5. 54 = 2×3^3
6. 40 = $2^3 \times 5$
7. 48 = $2^4 \times 3$
8. 56 = $2^3 \times 7$
9. 150 = $2 \times 3 \times 5^2$

Enrichment 2-2 Prime Fact **L4**
Decision Making

Mr. Jones wants to arrange 24 desks into groups so that students can work together. He wants each group to be the same size.

1. What different sizes of groups can Mr. Jones use?
   2 groups of 12, 3 of 8, 4 of 6, 6 of 4, 8 of 3, 12 of 2

2. What does Mr. Jones need to consider when he moves the desks into the groups?
   Sample answer: whether or not all students can see the chalkboard; whether or not all group members can communicate; whether or not there is enough aisle space

3. The current project is a class debate. There will be four teams. In the space below, show two ways that Mr. Jones can arrange the desks so that students on each team will be sitting together. Sample answers:

4. For the next project, each group will perform a skit showing a typical day in the life of a teenager in another country. What would be the best group size for this project? Explain.
   Sample answer: groups of eight, so that there will be sufficient people to research the topic and write and act in the skit

5. How can Mr. Jones arrange the desks for students to work on the skit? Use the space to the right to show the arrangement. Why is this the best seating arrangement?
   Sample answer: It keeps the groups far enough apart. However, some students will have to move to see the chalkboard.

78

Mental Math **Find the GCF of each pair of numbers.**

42. 3, 10 1 **43.** 7, 12 1 **44.** 4, 20 4 **45.** 50, 1000 50

46. Find two composite numbers with a GCF of 1. **Answers may vary. Sample: 21 and 22**

47. Choose a Method You can buy juice boxes in packs of 12 or 30. Both packs contain the same number of boxes in each row. What is the greatest possible number of boxes per row? Describe your method and explain why you chose it. **6 boxes**

48. A movie theater just added two rooms. One room is large enough for 125 people, and the other can seat up to 350 people. In each room, the seating is arranged in horizontal rows with the same number of seats in each row. What is the greatest number of seats that can make up each row? **25 seats**

49. Error Analysis Two students made factor trees of the prime factors of 24. Are both correct? Explain. **See left.**

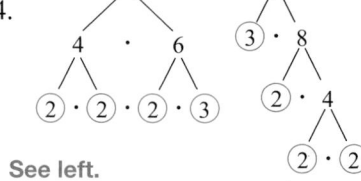

50. You can express 100 as 10^2 using exponents. Is 10^2 the same as the prime factorization of 100? Explain. **See left.**

49. Yes; both can be written as $2^3 \cdot 3$.

50. No; 10 is not a prime. The prime factorization of 100 is $2^2 \cdot 5^2$.

51. Writing in Math Describe the relationships among 3, 5, and 15 using the words *factor* and *multiple*. **Answers may vary. Sample: 15 is the LCM of 3 and 5, and 3 and 5 are factors of 15.**

C **52. Challenge** Let *n* be any prime number. Tell whether the statement "$2n + 1$ is prime" is *sometimes*, *always*, or *never* true. **sometimes**

TEKS ★ TAKS Tune-Up and Mixed Review

TAKS Objective 6
TEKS (7.13)(A)

53. The Stillwater High School library is arranging 108 books. Each shelf can hold as many as 10 books, and the librarian wants to place the same number of books on each shelf. What is the greatest number of books that can be placed on each shelf? **B**
Ⓐ 2 Ⓑ 9 Ⓒ 10 Ⓓ 12

TAKS Objective 1
TEKS (7.2)(B)

54. The table shows how far model cars traveled after rolling down an incline. How many centimeters farther did car 2 travel than car 4 and car 5 combined? **G**
Ⓕ 16.71 Ⓗ 42.19
Ⓖ 17.88 Ⓙ 58.9

Car	Distance (cm)
1	52.64
2	83.21
3	66.86
4	24.31
5	41.02

GO for Help **Lesson 1-6** **Order from least to greatest.**

55. 3, −4, −5, 6 **56.** −7, −10, −13 **57.** 20, −21, 21, 0
−5, −4, 3, 6 −13, −10, −7 −21, 0, 20, 21

78 Chapter 2 Exponents, Factors, and Fractions

TEKS ★ TAKS Resources

• TAKS Strategies, p. 111
• TAKS Tune-Up, pp. 115–117

TAKS Tune-Up Kit

• TAKS Daily Review Transparencies
• TAKS Review and Preparation Workbook
• TAKS Strategies with Transparencies
• Texas Progress Monitoring Assessments

Alternative Assessment

Have students draw factor trees to find the prime factorization of composite numbers such as 32, 450, 396, and 384. When assisting students, ask: *What two numbers multiplied have a product of 32?* **1, 32; 2, 16; 4, 8** Make sure students arrive at a prime factorization. 2^5 Remind them to use exponents in their final answer.

Simplify each expression.

1. $8^2 + 11$ 75

2. $(-1)^4$ 1

3. $5 + (3^2 - 2)^2$ 54

Find the LCM of each pair of numbers.

4. 3, 4 12

5. 7, 10 70

6. 5, 12 60

Find the factors of each number.

7. 39 1, 3, 13, 39

8. 52 1, 2, 4, 13, 26, 52

9. 110 1, 2, 5, 10, 11, 22, 55, 110

10. 200 See margin.

Write the prime factorization of each number. Use exponents where possible.

11. 96 $2^5 \cdot 3$

12. 150 $2 \cdot 3 \cdot 5^2$

13. 225 $3^2 \cdot 5^2$

14. 333 $3^2 \cdot 37$

15. Two pieces of rope have lengths 72 ft and 96 ft. A woodcutter needs to cut the two pieces into smaller pieces all of equal lengths. What is the greatest possible length of each smaller piece? 12 ft

---

✓ Checkpoint Quiz

Use this Checkpoint Quiz to check students' understanding of the skills and concepts of Lessons 2-1 through 2-2.

Resources

- All-in-One Teaching Resources Checkpoint Quiz 1
- Texas ExamView CD-ROM
- Success Tracker™ Online Intervention

MATH GAMES

Factor Cards

In this game, students practice finding the factors of numbers. One team chooses a number from 1–40 and the other team must find all the factors of that number. The game continues until all numbers from 1–40 are used.

Guided Instruction

Before they play the game, remind students of the meaning of factors. Have a volunteer read the rules. Explain that if factor-finding teams must find the factors that remain in the deck, some factors may already have been taken by the other team on a previous turn.

Resources

- 40 index cards, numbered 1–40

MATH GAMES

Factor Cards

What You'll Need

- 40 index cards, numbered from 1 to 40

How To Play

- Form two teams.
- Team A chooses a card at random.
- Team B removes the cards from the deck that are factors of Team A's card. For example, if Team A picks 10, Team B takes cards 1, 2, and 5.
- Teams switch places until all of the cards are taken. No points are given for cards that have already been chosen. The team whose cards have the highest sum wins.

10. 1, 2, 4, 5, 8, 10, 20, 25, 40, 50, 100, 200

Using LCM and GCF

TEKS ★ **TAKS**

(7.13)(C) To select an appropriate problem-solving strategy, including drawing a picture **TAKS** Obj. 6

(7.13)(A) To identify and apply mathematics to activities in and outside of school **TAKS** Obj. 6

Using LCM and GCF

In this feature, students practice solving problems involving the least common multiple and the greatest common factor.

Guided Instruction

Remind students of the meanings of LCM and GCF. Have a volunteer read the question aloud.
Ask:

- *Why do we need to find the LCM of 6 and 8?* Multiples of 6 will get the free popcorn, multiples of 8 will get the free rental, the LCM of 6 and 8 will be the first to get both.
- *How would you find the next person to get both free items?* Find the next common multiple of 6 and 8.
- *How can you check the reasonableness of your answer?* Check to see if 24 is divisible by 6 and 8.

Using LCM and GCF

Movie Rentals   To boost sales, a video rental store offered a free bag of microwave popcorn to every sixth customer and a free movie rental to every eighth customer. What customer was the first to win both popcorn *and* a free movie rental?

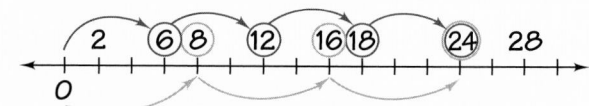

What You Might Think

What do I know?

What am I trying to find out?

How do I show the main idea?

How do I solve the problem?

What is the answer?

What You Might Write

Every sixth person in line won popcorn and every eighth person won a free movie rental.

I want to know which person was the first to win both popcorn and a free movie rental.

Draw a diagram.

Find the least common multiple (LCM) of 6 and 8. This means I need to find the smallest number that is a multiple of both 6 and 8.

The multiples of 8 are 8, 16, 24, 32, 40, . . .

The smallest number that is also a multiple of 6 is 24.

The 24th person in line was the first to win both the popcorn and a free movie rental.

Think It Through

1. Explain how the diagram shows multiples of 6 *and* multiples of 8.

2. Explain why it makes sense to look first at the multiples of the larger number when finding the LCM. **By looking at the multiples of the larger number, you don't have to check as many multiples.**

3. What is the number of the second person in line to win both prizes? The third person in line to win both prizes?   **48; 72**

The arrows on top point to multiples of 6, and the arrows below the line point to multiples of 8.

TEKS ★ **TAKS** **Resources**

Dana Center TEKS Toolkit Clarifying Activities (7.13)(C), (7.13)(A)
Visit: PHSchool.com
Web Code: arq-9045

Exercises

Have students work independently on the Exercises. Circulate and help students figure out what they need to know and how they can find it. Compare answers as a class and discuss reasoning.

Differentiated Instruction

Below Level L2

If students have difficulty identifying the LCM or GCF, allow them to list multiples and factors.

Exercises

For Exercises 4 and 5, answer the questions first. Then solve the problem.

4. As a promotion, a "hot wings" restaurant gave away free boxes according to the sign below.

HOT WING BOXES   FREE to this customer
6 wings   every 6th in line
10 wings   every 10th in line
15 wings   every 15th in line

   Which person in line was the first to get boxes of all three sizes? the 30th person
   a. What do you know?
   b. What do you want to find out?
   c. Draw a diagram that shows people winning different boxes.
   d. How will finding the LCM of three numbers help you?

5. Southside Middle School held a tug-of-war contest. Seventy-eight seventh graders and seventy-two eighth graders signed up. Each grade was divided into several teams. If both grades had the same number of people on each team, what was the greatest possible number of people on a team? 6 people
   a. What do you know?
   b. What do you want to find out?
   c. How will finding the GCF of 72 and 78 help you?

6. Jeremiah wants to make a square pattern for an art project using tiles 8 cm by 12 cm. What is the smallest square he can design using whole tiles? 24 cm by 24 cm

7. There are 252 beats in one passage of a musical composition. In this passage, the triangle player plays once every 12 beats. The timpani player plays once every 9 beats. How many times will they play at the same time during this passage? 7 times

8. All the school lockers are closed at the beginning of the school day. Wayne is the first person to come into school, and he opens every tenth locker. Jake comes in after Wayne and switches every eighth locker from open to closed, or vice versa. Which locker is the first to be opened and then closed? the 40th locker

Guided Problem Solving Using LCM and GCF   **81**

TEKS ★ **TAKS**

Prepares for **TEKS (7.2)(B)** To use addition, subtraction, multiplication, and division to solve problems involving fractions.

TEKS Math Background

A *fraction* represents part of a whole. The whole could be a single object or region, as in "one fourth of a pizza." The whole might also be a group of objects, as in "half of a dozen eggs." Two fractions that represent the same part of a whole, such as $\frac{3}{4}$ and $\frac{6}{8}$, are called *equivalent fractions*.

More Math Background: p. 66C

Lesson Planning and Resources

See p. 66E for a list of the resources that support this lesson.

Bell Ringer Practice

✓ **Check Skills You'll Need**
Use student page, transparency, or PowerPoint.

TAKS Daily Review 13
Use transparency.

✓ Check Skills You'll Need

1. Vocabulary Review
What is special about the GCF of a pair of numbers?
See below.
Find the GCF of each pair of numbers.

2. 6, 10   2

3. 12, 24   12

4. 45, 50   5

5. 17, 23   1

GO for Help
Lesson 2-2

Check Skills You'll Need

1. It is the greatest factor that divides both numbers.

What You'll Learn

To write equivalent fractions and to simplify fractions

• Prepares for **TEKS (7.2)(B)** To use addition, subtraction, multiplication, and division to solve problems involving fractions

🔊 **New Vocabulary** equivalent fractions, simplest form

Why Learn This?

Suppose you have three identical chocolate bars. You break one bar into 4 pieces and give away 3 of them. You break the second bar into 8 pieces and give away 6. You break the third bar into 12 pieces and give away 9. The model below shows that you give away the same fraction of each bar.

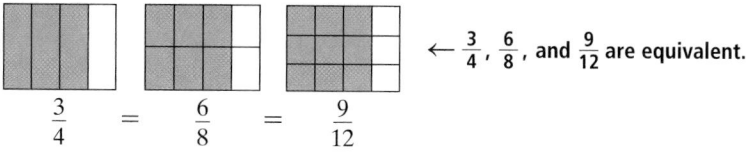

← $\frac{3}{4}$, $\frac{6}{8}$, and $\frac{9}{12}$ are equivalent.

$$\frac{3}{4} = \frac{6}{8} = \frac{9}{12}$$

Fractions that name the same amount are **equivalent fractions**. You can write equivalent fractions by multiplying or dividing the numerator and the denominator by the same nonzero number.

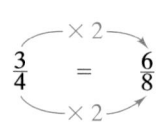

EXAMPLE   Using Multiples

❶ Use a table of multiples to write three fractions equivalent to $\frac{7}{8}$.

	×2	×3	×4
7	14	21	28
8	16	24	32

← Multiples in the same column form fractions equivalent to $\frac{7}{8}$.

Three fractions equivalent to $\frac{7}{8}$ are $\frac{14}{16}$, $\frac{21}{24}$, and $\frac{28}{32}$.

✓ Quick Check

1. Use multiples to write two fractions equivalent to $\frac{4}{5}$.   Answers may vary.
Sample: $\frac{8}{10}$, $\frac{12}{15}$

A fraction is written in **simplest form** when the numerator and the denominator have no common factors other than 1. For example, $\frac{1}{3}$ and $\frac{3}{9}$ are equivalent, but only $\frac{1}{3}$ is written in simplest form.

Differentiated Instruction   Solutions for All Learners

Special Needs   **L1**
Students can temporarily use a multiplication grid or table of multiples to find the Greatest Common Factor. This will enable them to work the process of simplifying a fraction without getting bogged down in figuring out the GCF. Eventually take the table or grid away.
learning style: visual

Below Level   **L2**
Have students use fraction bars to model several sets of equivalent fractions, such as $\frac{1}{2}$, $\frac{2}{4}$, $\frac{5}{10}$.
learning style: tactile

EXAMPLE **Using Factors**

2️⃣ Write three fractions equivalent to $\frac{24}{30}$.

Factors of 24: 1, 2, 3, 4, 6, 8, 12, 24, ...   **List the factors of each number.**
Factors of 30: 1, 2, 3, 5, 6, 10, 15, 30, ...   **Look for common factors.**

$$\overset{\div 2}{\overbrace{\frac{24}{30}}} = \underset{\div 2}{\underbrace{\frac{12}{15}}} \qquad \overset{\div 3}{\overbrace{\frac{24}{30}}} = \underset{\div 3}{\underbrace{\frac{8}{10}}} \qquad \overset{\div 6}{\overbrace{\frac{24}{30}}} = \underset{\div 6}{\underbrace{\frac{4}{5}}}$$

Three fractions equivalent to $\frac{24}{30}$ are $\frac{12}{15}$, $\frac{8}{10}$, and $\frac{4}{5}$.

✓ **Quick Check**

2. Use common factors to write two fractions equivalent to $\frac{18}{30}$.
   Answers may vary. Sample: $\frac{9}{15}$, $\frac{3}{5}$

EXAMPLE **Simplifying by Dividing**

Vocabulary Tip

Another term for *simplest form* is *lowest terms*.

3️⃣ Simplify $\frac{12}{24}$.

$$\frac{12 \div 2}{24 \div 2} = \frac{6}{12}$$ ← **Divide the numerator and denominator by a common factor.**

$$\frac{6 \div 6}{12 \div 6} = \frac{1}{2}$$ ← **If necessary, divide again by another common factor.**

In simplest form, $\frac{12}{24}$ is $\frac{1}{2}$.

✓ **Quick Check**

3. Write $\frac{8}{12}$ in simplest form. $\frac{2}{3}$

EXAMPLE **Using the GCF to Simplify a Fraction**

4️⃣ In the United States, there are 48 types of road signs. Of these, 16 are instructional, such as speed limit or stop signs. What fraction of road signs are instructional? Write your answer in simplest form.

$$\frac{16}{48} = \frac{16 \div 16}{48 \div 16} = \frac{1}{3}$$ ← **Divide both numerator and denominator by the GCF, 16.**

The fraction of road signs that are instructional is $\frac{1}{3}$.

✓ **Quick Check**

4. Your class ordered 45 calculators. Of these, 18 were solar powered. What fraction of the calculators were solar powered? $\frac{2}{5}$

2-3 Simplifying Fractions   **83**

2. Teach

Activity Lab

Use before the lesson.

All in One Teaching Resources

Activity Lab 2-3: Fractions and Surveys

Guided Instruction

Example 1

Give students a sheet with four congruent circles that are divided respectively into 8, 16, 24, and 32 equal parts. Tell students to shade 7 of the 8 equal parts in the first circle. Then instruct them to shade the same area in each of the other three circles. Have them label each circle with the appropriate fraction equivalent to $\frac{7}{8}$. $\frac{7}{8}$, $\frac{14}{16}$, $\frac{21}{24}$, $\frac{28}{32}$

PowerPoint

Additional Examples

1️⃣ Use a table of multiples to write three fractions equivalent to $\frac{4}{5}$. Samples: $\frac{8}{10}$, $\frac{12}{15}$, $\frac{16}{20}$

2️⃣ Find three fractions equivalent to $\frac{16}{24}$. Samples: $\frac{8}{12}$, $\frac{4}{6}$, $\frac{2}{3}$

3️⃣ Write $\frac{18}{30}$ in simplest form. $\frac{3}{5}$

4️⃣ There are 28 students in Mai's homeroom. Of these, 20 students have a pet. What fraction of the students have a pet? Write your answer in simplest form. $\frac{5}{7}$

All in One Teaching Resources

- Daily Notetaking Guide 2-3 **L3**
- Adapted Notetaking 2-3 **L1**

Closure

- *What are equivalent fractions?* fractions that name the same amount
- *When is a fraction in simplest form?* when the numerator and denominator have no common factors other than 1

Advanced Learners **L4**
Separate these into two groups of equivalent fractions.
a. $\frac{48}{108}$ b. $\frac{54}{126}$ c. $\frac{64}{144}$ d. $\frac{72}{168}$ e. $\frac{144}{336}$
a and c; b, d, and e

Pre-AP™

English Language Learners **ELL**
Connect the words *simplest form* to the idea of simplifying a fraction. Remind students that when they simplify a fraction they are reducing it to its simplest form.

learning style: verbal

3. Practice

Assignment Guide

Check Your Understanding
Go over Exercises 1–6 in class before assigning the Homework Exercises.

Homework Exercises
A Practice by Example   7–28
B Apply Your Skills   29–36
C Challenge   37
TEKS ★ TAKS Tune-Up and
Mixed Review   38–42

Homework Quick Check
To check students' understanding of key skills and concepts, go over Exercises 17, 25, 28, 34, and 36.

Differentiated Instruction Resources

Adapted Practice 2-3   L1

Practice 2-3   Simplifying L3

Write each fraction in simplest form.
1. $\frac{8}{12}$ $\frac{2}{3}$ 2. $\frac{9}{15}$ $\frac{3}{5}$ 3. $\frac{16}{20}$ $\frac{4}{5}$ 4. $\frac{20}{25}$ $\frac{4}{5}$
5. $\frac{15}{18}$ $\frac{5}{6}$ 6. $\frac{14}{10}$ $\frac{7}{5}$ 7. $\frac{11}{44}$ $\frac{1}{4}$ 8. $\frac{24}{36}$ $\frac{2}{3}$

Write each fraction in simplest form. Give the GCF of the numerator and denominator.
9. $\frac{125}{200}$ $\frac{5}{8}$ GCF = 25   10. $\frac{9}{16}$ $\frac{9}{16}$ GCF = 4   11. $\frac{65}{8}$ $\frac{13}{8}$ GCF = 5
12. $\frac{45}{72}$ $\frac{5}{8}$ GCF = 9   13. $\frac{35}{17}$ $\frac{7}{17}$ GCF = 5   14. $\frac{30}{42}$ $\frac{5}{7}$ GCF = 6

Solve.
15. Emily exercised from 4:05 P.M. to 4:32 P.M. For what part of an hour did Emily exercise? Write the fraction in simplest form.
$\frac{9}{20}$ h

16. Luis rode his bike after school for 48 min. For what part of an hour did he ride his bike? Write the fraction in simplest form.
$\frac{4}{5}$ h

17. Philip played video games for 55 min before dinner. For what part of an hour did he play?
$\frac{11}{12}$ h

18. What part of an hour is your school lunch time?
Check students' answers

19. Survey 12 people to find their favorite kind of pizza from the following choices. Write the results in fraction form. Then shade the pizza shapes using different colors to indicate their choices.

Pizza Favorites
Cheese _____ Check students' answers
Green Pepper _____
Olive _____
Mushroom _____

2-3 • Guided Problem Solving GPS   L3
Student Page 84, Exercise 28:

Weather The city of Houston, Texas, typically has 90 clear days out of the 365 days in a year. Houston's clear days represent what fraction of a year? Write your answer in simplest form.

Understand
1. Circle the information you will need to solve.
2. What are you being asked to do?
Write the number of clear days out of a year in Houston as a fraction in simplest form.

Plan and Carry Out
3. Write the fraction for the expression 75 out of 365.
$\frac{75}{365}$
4. List the prime factors of 75.
$5 \cdot 5 \cdot 3$
5. List the prime factors of 365.
$5 \cdot 73$
6. List the factors that 75 and 365 have in common.
5
7. Divide both 75 and 365 by the common factors.
15; 73
8. Write the fraction in simplest form. $\frac{15}{73}$

Check
9. Is $365 \div 75$ the same as $73 \div 15$? Explain.
yes; $365 \div 75 = (73 \times 5) \div (15 \times 5) = 73 \div 15$

Solve Another Problem
10. Gerald received a score of 66 out of 72 on his vocabulary test. Write his score as a fraction in simplest form.
$\frac{11}{12}$

84

✓ Check Your Understanding

1. No; the GCF of the numerator and denominator of a fraction in simplest form is 1.

1. **Vocabulary** Can two equivalent fractions both be fractions written in simplest form? Explain. See left.

2. Are $\frac{2}{4}$ and $\frac{8}{8}$ equivalent? Explain. No; $\frac{2}{4} = \frac{1}{2}$ and $\frac{8}{8} = \frac{1}{1}$.

3. **Error Analysis** A teacher asked students to find a fraction equivalent to $\frac{5}{6}$. One answer is below. Is it correct? Explain.
$\frac{5}{6} = \frac{5+4}{6+4} = \frac{9}{10}$ No; the student added 4 instead of multiplying by 4.

For each term, write three equivalent fractions, one in simplest form.

4. $\frac{3}{9}$ $\frac{1}{3}, \frac{6}{18}, \frac{9}{27}$
5. $\frac{36}{48}$ $\frac{3}{4}, \frac{12}{16}, \frac{9}{12}$
6. $\frac{16}{36}$ $\frac{4}{9}, \frac{8}{18}, \frac{32}{72}$

4–22. Answers may vary. Samples are given.

Homework Exercises

For more exercises, see Extra Skills and Word Problems.

GO for Help

For Exercises	See Examples
7–14	1
15–22	2
23–28	3–4

A Use multiples to write two fractions equivalent to each fraction.

7. $\frac{5}{6}$ $\frac{10}{12}, \frac{15}{18}$
8. $\frac{3}{8}$ $\frac{6}{16}, \frac{9}{24}$
9. $\frac{2}{9}$ $\frac{4}{18}, \frac{6}{27}$
10. $\frac{7}{10}$ $\frac{14}{20}, \frac{21}{30}$

11. $\frac{4}{7}$ $\frac{8}{14}, \frac{12}{21}$
12. $\frac{3}{5}$ $\frac{6}{10}, \frac{9}{15}$
13. $\frac{6}{11}$ $\frac{12}{22}, \frac{18}{33}$
14. $\frac{1}{5}$ $\frac{2}{10}, \frac{3}{15}$

Use common factors to write two fractions equivalent to each fraction.

15. $\frac{8}{24}$ $\frac{4}{12}, \frac{1}{3}$
16. $\frac{18}{36}$ $\frac{9}{18}, \frac{1}{2}$
17. $\frac{27}{81}$ $\frac{9}{27}, \frac{1}{3}$
18. $\frac{60}{140}$ $\frac{30}{70}, \frac{3}{7}$

19. $\frac{30}{42}$ $\frac{15}{21}, \frac{5}{7}$
20. $\frac{45}{90}$ $\frac{9}{18}, \frac{1}{2}$
21. $\frac{24}{84}$ $\frac{12}{42}, \frac{2}{7}$
22. $\frac{36}{80}$ $\frac{18}{40}, \frac{9}{20}$

Write each fraction in simplest form.

23. $\frac{24}{32}$ $\frac{3}{4}$
24. $\frac{18}{27}$ $\frac{2}{3}$
25. $\frac{33}{39}$ $\frac{11}{13}$
26. $\frac{8}{18}$ $\frac{4}{9}$

27. **Biology** An adult's body has 206 bones. Of these, 106 are in the feet, ankles, wrist, and hands. What fraction of an adult's bones are in the feet, ankles, wrists, and hands? $\frac{53}{103}$

28. **Weather** The city of Houston, Texas, typically has 90 clear days out
GPS of the 365 days in a year. Houston's clear days represent what fraction of a year? Write your answer in simplest form. $\frac{18}{73}$

B **GPS** 29. **Guided Problem Solving** A school offers two summer sports: lacrosse and tennis. There are 438 students in all. Of this number, 52 participate in lacrosse and 94 participate in tennis. Nobody does both. What fraction of the students participate in a sport? $\frac{1}{3}$
• The number of students who participate in a summer sport is ▦.
• The total number of students at the school is ▦.

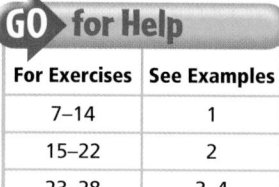

84   Chapter 2   Exponents, Factors, and Fractions

34. Use divisibility rules to tell if the numerators and denominators are divisible by the same number(s). For the fractions $\frac{9}{16}$, $\frac{10}{24}$, and $\frac{15}{35}$, 9 and 16 have no common factors, 10 and 24 are both divisible by 2, and 15 and 35 are both divisible by 5. So $\frac{9}{16}$ is in simplest form, but $\frac{10}{24}$ and $\frac{15}{35}$ are not.

36. Answers may vary. Sample:

Write two equivalent fractions for each model.
30–32. Answers may vary. Samples are given.

30.

$\frac{4}{6}$, $\frac{2}{3}$

31.

$\frac{5}{8}$, $\frac{10}{16}$

32.

$\frac{1}{2}$, $\frac{2}{4}$

33. Which square does *not* have the same fraction shaded as the others? D

A.   **B.**   **C.**   **D.**

34. **Writing in Math** Are the fractions $\frac{9}{16}$, $\frac{10}{24}$, and $\frac{15}{35}$ in simplest form? Explain. **See margin.**

35. School $\frac{7}{24}$, Sleeping $\frac{1}{3}$, Job/Homework $\frac{1}{6}$, TV/Activity $\frac{1}{8}$, Eating $\frac{1}{12}$

35. The circle graph shows a student's daily activities. Write a fraction in simplest form to represent the time spent on each activity. **See left.**

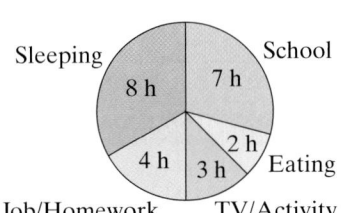

36. Draw models to show that the fractions $\frac{2}{3}$ and $\frac{10}{15}$ are equivalent.
See margin.

C **37.** **Challenge** The variables *a* and *b* represent positive integers. Name two fractions equivalent to $\frac{a}{b}$. **Answers may vary. Sample:** $\frac{2a}{2b}$, $\frac{3a}{3b}$

TEKS ★ TAKS Tune-Up and Mixed Review

TAKS Objective 1
TEKS (7.2)(B)

38. If only one thousand people lived on Earth, the population would be distributed according to the table below. What fraction of the people live in Africa? B

Asia	Africa	Europe	South America	Australia	North America
607	132	120	57	5	79

Ⓐ $\frac{3}{25}$ Ⓑ $\frac{33}{250}$ Ⓒ $\frac{7}{50}$ Ⓓ $\frac{4}{25}$

TAKS Objective 6
TEKS (7.13)(C)

39. Pablo spent half of his birthday money on concert tickets and one third of the remaining amount on food. After he used $12.35 on a train ticket, he had $8.25 left. How much money did Pablo begin with? H

Ⓕ $20.60   Ⓖ $41.20   Ⓗ $61.80   Ⓙ $123.60

 for Help   **Lesson 1-2**

Find each sum or difference.

3.432

40. $14.02 + 3.06$ **17.08**   **41.** $25.98 - 8.89$ **17.09**   **42.** $10.132 - 6.7$

---

4. Assess & Reteach

Lesson Quiz

Simplify.

1. $\frac{20}{35}$ $\frac{4}{7}$ **2.** $\frac{18}{42}$ $\frac{3}{7}$

3. $\frac{20}{75}$ $\frac{4}{15}$ **4.** $\frac{30}{48}$ $\frac{5}{8}$

Reteaching 2-3   Simplifying **L2**

Enrichment 2-3   Simplifying **L4**

Alternative Assessment

Provide pairs of students with a list of fractions, such as $\frac{21}{35}$, $\frac{18}{48}$, $\frac{19}{27}$, including some in simplest form. Have pairs circle the fractions already in simplest form. $\frac{19}{27}$ Then have them work together to rewrite the others in simplest form.

TEKS ★ TAKS Resources

• TAKS Strategies, p. 111
• TAKS Tune-Up, pp. 115–117

TAKS Tune-Up Kit

• TAKS Daily Review Transparencies
• TAKS Review and Preparation Workbook
• TAKS Strategies with Transparencies
• Texas Progress Monitoring Assessments

85

Comparing Fractions

Students use models to compare fractions. This will prepare them to compare and order fractions mentally in Lesson 2-4.

Guided Instruction

Explain to students that they can use a number line to compare numbers that are less than 1, just as they would use it to compare whole numbers.
Ask questions, such as:

• *Why is 10 cm a good length for the number line?* **5 is a factor of 10 so it is easy to make both fraction models for $\frac{3}{5}$ and $\frac{7}{10}$ to this scale.**

• *What is another way to determine which fraction is greater?* **Use the GCF to simplify and compare the numerators.**

• *How long would your model of $\frac{3}{4}$ be?* **7.5 cm**

Activity

Have students work in small groups on the Activity. Have each choose a representative to share their answers when you review the Activity as a class.

Alternative Method

Allow students to make models by shading graph paper. Point out that shading two squares in a ten square section makes one fifth. Have them shade three fifths of one ten square section and 7 squares of another ten square section and compare the two shaded areas.

TEKS ★ (TAKS) Resources

• Activity Lab 2-4: Critical Thinking
• 10 cm strips of paper
• graph paper

Dana Center TEKS Toolkit Clarifying Activities (7.1)(A)
Visit: PHSchool.com
Web Code: arq-9045

Comparing Fractions

TEKS ★ (TAKS)
(7.1)(A) To compare and order integers and positive rational numbers
(TAKS) **Obj. 1**

You can use a number line to compare two integers such as 3 and −5. You know 3 is greater because it lies to the right of −5. In this activity, you will use paper strips and a number line to compare two fractions.

You can compare $\frac{3}{5}$ and $\frac{7}{10}$ using two strips of paper, each 10 cm long, and a number line that is 10 cm long. On your number line, mark the points 0, $\frac{1}{2}$, and 1.

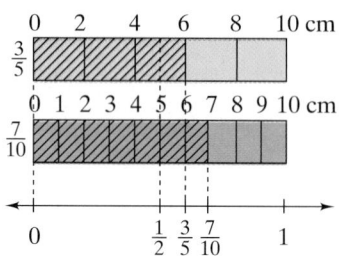

← **Divide one strip into 5 equal parts. Shade in 3 parts to represent $\frac{3}{5}$.**

← **Divide the other strip into 10 equal parts. Shade in 7 parts to represent $\frac{7}{10}$.**

← **Use the strips to mark the two fractions on a number line.**

Since $\frac{7}{10}$ is to the right of $\frac{3}{5}$ on the number line, you know that $\frac{7}{10} > \frac{3}{5}$.

ACTIVITY

$\frac{7}{12} < \frac{3}{4}, \frac{1}{4} < \frac{2}{5}, \frac{2}{3} < \frac{6}{8},$
$\frac{5}{7} < \frac{3}{4}, \frac{3}{10} < \frac{2}{6}$

Step 1 Using paper strips, compare the five pairs of fractions listed in the table at the right. For each pair, cut two strips of paper to the given length. Then use a number line and an inequality to show your comparison.

Step 2 Use 15-cm strips of paper to compare $\frac{7}{10}$ and $\frac{6}{9}$. Explain why this comparison is more difficult than the others. What would be a better length for the paper strips? Explain. **See margin.**

Step 3 Explain how the paper lengths shown in the table relate to the fractions being compared. Why do you think those lengths were chosen? **They are the LCM of the denominators, so it is easy to divide them into equal parts.**

Step 4 List several fraction pairs that could be compared using paper strips that are 32 cm long.

Step 5 How long would you make the paper strips to compare $\frac{6}{8}, \frac{4}{5},$ and $\frac{7}{10}$? Explain. **40 cm; 40 is divisible by 8, 5, and 10.**

Step 6 Use what you have learned to compare $\frac{7}{9}$ and $\frac{4}{5}$ without making paper strips. Explain your reasoning. $\frac{7}{9} < \frac{4}{5}$ since $\frac{35}{45} < \frac{36}{45}$.

Fractions	Paper Length
$\frac{3}{4}$ and $\frac{7}{12}$	12 cm
$\frac{2}{5}$ and $\frac{1}{4}$	20 cm
$\frac{6}{8}$ and $\frac{2}{3}$	24 cm
$\frac{3}{4}$ and $\frac{5}{7}$	28 cm
$\frac{3}{10}$ and $\frac{2}{6}$	30 cm

4. **Answers may vary. Samples are given.** $\frac{3}{32}$ and $\frac{5}{8}$; $\frac{9}{32}$ and $\frac{1}{2}$; $\frac{1}{32}$ and $\frac{7}{4}$

2. **This is difficult, since 15 is not the LCM of the denominators. It would be easier to use a length of 90 cm.**

Check Skills You'll Need

1. Vocabulary Review What is the name for the smallest multiple common to two numbers?
least common multiple
Find the LCM of each pair of numbers.

2. 3, 4 **12**

3. 4, 10 **20**

4. 2, 8 **8**

5. 9, 15 **45**

for Help
Lesson 2-2

TEKS ★ **TAKS**

• (7.1)(A) To compare and order positive rational numbers **TAKS** Obj. 1

◄)) **New Vocabulary** least common denominator (LCD)

Why Learn This?

Camera exposure times are given as fractions of a second. Knowing how to compare fractions can help you choose the correct exposure times and take better pictures.

The exposure times below are listed in order of greatest to least. If the numerators of two fractions are the same, the fraction with the lesser denominator has the greater value. For example, $\frac{1}{125} > \frac{1}{500}$, because 1 divided into 125 parts is greater than 1 divided into 500 parts.

Camera Exposure Times

$$\frac{1}{4} \quad \frac{1}{30} \quad \frac{1}{60} \quad \frac{1}{125} \quad \frac{1}{250} \quad \frac{1}{500} \quad \frac{1}{1000}$$

Longer time—lets in more light

Shorter time—lets in less light

If the denominators are the same, the numerators show which fraction is greater. Use the "is greater than" (>) or the "is less than" (<) symbol.

You can use a number line to compare fractions. Any number to the right of any other number on a number line is the greater of the two.

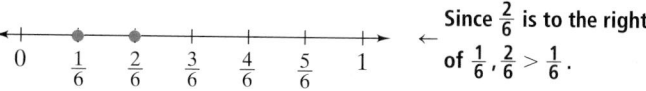

Since $\frac{2}{6}$ is to the right of $\frac{1}{6}$, $\frac{2}{6} > \frac{1}{6}$.

You can also use models to compare fractions. The fraction models show that $\frac{7}{12} > \frac{3}{8}$. To compare fractions with different denominators, rewrite each with a common denominator.

The **least common denominator (LCD)** of two or more fractions is the least common multiple (LCM) of their denominators.

Dana Center TEKS Toolkit Clarifying Activities (7.1)(A)
Visit: PHSchool.com
Web Code: arq-9045

TEKS Math Background

There are two common methods for comparing fractions visually: If two fractions are represented by points on a number line, the fraction to the right is greater. If two fractions are represented as parts of a whole region, the fraction that represents the larger part is greater. This lesson develops a method for comparing fractions arithmetically, using common denominators.

More Math Background: p. 66C

Lesson Planning and Resources

See p. 66E for a list of the resources that support this lesson.

PowerPoint
Bell Ringer Practice

✓ **Check Skills You'll Need**
Use student page, transparency, or PowerPoint.

TAKS **Daily Review 14**
Use transparency.

GO Online

Video Tutor Help
Visit: PHSchool.com
Web Code: are-0775

Differentiated Instruction Solutions for All Learners

Special Needs L1
Provide students with paper fraction pieces, or pre-made kits. Have them compare the relative sizes of denominators such as halves, thirds, fourths, and eighths. They may need this reminder that the larger the denominator, the smaller the "piece."

learning style: tactile

Below Level L2
Review the use of a number line for comparing and ordering integers. Check that students recall the meaning of the symbols > (greater than) and < (less than).

learning style: visual

87

Activity Lab

Use before the lesson.
Student Edition Activity Lab
Hands On 2-4a, Comparing
Fractions, p. 86

All in One Teaching Resources
Activity Lab 2-4: Critical Thinking

Guided Instruction

Example 1
Students can use calculators to
check the comparison.

$\frac{3}{4} \rightarrow 3 \div 4 = 0.75$

$\frac{7}{10} \rightarrow 7 \div 10 = 0.7$

Since $0.75 > 0.7$, $\frac{3}{4} > \frac{7}{10}$

Example 2
Have student first use fraction
bars to order the fractions. They
should keep the fraction bars in
sight as you show them how to
order by using common
denominators.

PowerPoint

Additional Examples

1 Compare $\frac{7}{12}$ and $\frac{5}{9}$. $\frac{7}{12} > \frac{5}{9}$

2 Giselda wants to paint her
room. She found $\frac{3}{5}$ gal of
yellow paint, $\frac{2}{3}$ gal of blue
paint, and $\frac{1}{2}$ gal of green
paint.

a. Order these amounts from
least to greatest.
$\frac{1}{2}$ gal $< \frac{3}{5}$ gal $< \frac{2}{3}$ gal

b. Of which color is there the
least amount? green

c. Of which color is there the
greatest amount? blue

All in One Teaching Resources
• Daily Notetaking Guide 2-4 **L3**
• Adapted Notetaking 2-4 **L1**

Closure

• Explain how to compare
fractions with different
denominators. Rewrite them as
equivalent fractions with a
common denominator, then
compare the numerators.

★ TAKS Tip

Draw a number line to help
you visualize the order of
the fractions.

EXAMPLE Comparing Fractions

1 Compare $\frac{3}{4}$ and $\frac{7}{10}$.

The denominators are 4 and 10. Their LCM is 20. So 20 is the LCD.

$\frac{3}{4} = \frac{3 \times 5}{4 \times 5} = \frac{15}{20}$

$\frac{7}{10} = \frac{7 \times 2}{10 \times 2} = \frac{14}{20}$ Write the equivalent fractions with a denominator of 20.

$\frac{14}{20} < \frac{15}{20}$ ← Compare the numerators.

So $\frac{7}{10} < \frac{3}{4}$.

✓ Quick Check

1. Compare each pair of fractions. Use $<, =,$ or $>$.

a. $\frac{3}{4} \boxed{} \frac{5}{6}$ $<$

b. $\frac{1}{6} \boxed{} \frac{2}{9}$ $<$

c. $\frac{4}{10} \boxed{} \frac{3}{8}$ $>$

You can use the LCD to order more than two fractions.

EXAMPLE Application: Construction

2 **TAKS Multiple Choice** A construction company uses plywood sheets in
the following thicknesses: $\frac{3}{8}$ in. for roofing, $\frac{1}{2}$ in. for flooring, $\frac{1}{4}$ in. for
countertop surfaces, and $\frac{1}{8}$ in. for filling gaps. Which list shows the
fractions in order from least to greatest?

Ⓐ $\frac{1}{4}, \frac{3}{8}, \frac{1}{2}, \frac{1}{8}$ Ⓑ $\frac{1}{2}, \frac{1}{4}, \frac{1}{8}, \frac{3}{8}$ Ⓒ $\frac{1}{8}, \frac{1}{4}, \frac{1}{2}, \frac{3}{8}$ Ⓓ $\frac{1}{8}, \frac{1}{4}, \frac{3}{8}, \frac{1}{2}$

Order $\frac{3}{8}, \frac{1}{2}, \frac{1}{4}$, and $\frac{1}{8}$. The LCM of 8, 2, and 4 is 8. So 8 is the LCD.

Roofing: $\frac{3}{8}$

Flooring: $\frac{1}{2} = \frac{1 \times 4}{2 \times 4} = \frac{4}{8}$

Countertop: $\frac{1}{4} = \frac{1 \times 2}{4 \times 2} = \frac{2}{8}$ ← Use the LCD to write equivalent fractions.

Filling: $\frac{1}{8}$

$\frac{1}{8} < \frac{2}{8} < \frac{3}{8} < \frac{4}{8}$. So $\frac{1}{8} < \frac{1}{4} < \frac{3}{8} < \frac{1}{2}$.   ← Compare the numerators.

The order is $\frac{1}{8}, \frac{1}{4}, \frac{3}{8}$, and $\frac{1}{2}$. The correct answer is choice D.

✓ Quick Check

2. A carpenter uses four screws with diameters of $\frac{1}{4}$ in., $\frac{3}{8}$ in., $\frac{5}{16}$ in., and
$\frac{5}{32}$ in. Order the diameters from least to greatest.

$\frac{5}{32}$ in., $\frac{1}{4}$ in., $\frac{5}{16}$ in., $\frac{3}{8}$ in.

Advanced Learners **L4**
Have students devise a rule for comparing fractions
with the same numerator. The fraction with the
lesser denominator is the greater fraction.

Pre-AP™

English Language Learners **ELL**
It is a good idea for students to read and say LCM as
least common multiple and LCD as *least common
denominator.* Otherwise, it is easy for them to lose
track of the meaning of the abbreviations, especially
since they have words in common.

learning style: verbal

1. Vocabulary How are the least common multiple (LCM) and least common denominator (LCD) related? The LCM of the denominators of two or more fractions is the LCD.

2. All of the fractions have a common denominator of 5 when in simplest form.

2. Reasoning To order $\frac{4}{10}$, $\frac{3}{5}$, and $\frac{5}{25}$, it is helpful to write each fraction in simplest form first, before finding the LCD. Explain why. See left.

Find the LCD of each pair of fractions.

3. $\frac{5}{7}$, $\frac{2}{9}$ 63

4. $\frac{3}{11}$, $\frac{2}{5}$ 55

5. $\frac{7}{8}$, $\frac{1}{3}$ 24

Compare each pair of fractions. Use <, =, or >.

6. $\frac{1}{7}$ ▨ $\frac{3}{8}$
<

7. $\frac{3}{12}$ ▨ $\frac{1}{6}$
>

8. $\frac{2}{10}$ ▨ $\frac{3}{5}$
<

Homework Exercises

For more exercises, see Extra Skills and Word Problems.

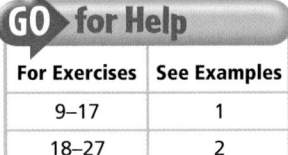

GO for Help

For Exercises	See Examples
9–17	1
18–27	2

Ⓐ **Compare each pair of fractions. Use <, =, or >.**

9. $\frac{5}{12}$ ▨ $\frac{7}{12}$ <

10. $\frac{5}{6}$ ▨ $\frac{3}{6}$ >

11. $\frac{1}{3}$ ▨ $\frac{3}{4}$ <

12. $\frac{5}{6}$ ▨ $\frac{3}{5}$ >

13. $\frac{3}{8}$ ▨ $\frac{2}{3}$ <

14. $\frac{4}{7}$ ▨ $\frac{4}{5}$ <

15. $\frac{2}{3}$ ▨ $\frac{5}{8}$ >

16. $\frac{5}{6}$ ▨ $\frac{5}{10}$ >

17. $\frac{1}{8}$ ▨ $\frac{3}{16}$ <

Order from least to greatest.

18. $\frac{1}{3}$, $\frac{5}{6}$, $\frac{3}{8}$ $\frac{1}{3}$, $\frac{3}{8}$, $\frac{5}{6}$

19. $\frac{1}{8}$, $\frac{1}{6}$, $\frac{1}{9}$ $\frac{1}{9}$, $\frac{1}{8}$, $\frac{1}{6}$

20. $\frac{3}{15}$, $\frac{3}{10}$, $\frac{3}{5}$ $\frac{3}{15}$, $\frac{3}{10}$, $\frac{3}{5}$

21. $\frac{5}{8}$, $\frac{7}{9}$, $\frac{2}{1}$ $\frac{5}{8}$, $\frac{7}{9}$, $\frac{2}{1}$

22. $\frac{6}{10}$, $\frac{7}{12}$, $\frac{5}{8}$ $\frac{7}{12}$, $\frac{6}{10}$, $\frac{5}{8}$

23. $\frac{2}{5}$, $\frac{3}{20}$, $\frac{4}{5}$ $\frac{3}{20}$, $\frac{2}{5}$, $\frac{4}{5}$

24. 1, $\frac{4}{6}$, $\frac{1}{3}$ $\frac{1}{3}$, $\frac{4}{6}$, 1

25. $\frac{10}{15}$, $\frac{6}{10}$, $\frac{1}{3}$ $\frac{1}{3}$, $\frac{6}{10}$, $\frac{10}{15}$

26. $\frac{1}{8}$, $\frac{3}{12}$, $\frac{4}{10}$ $\frac{1}{8}$, $\frac{3}{12}$, $\frac{4}{10}$

27. Languages At an international school, $\frac{1}{3}$ of the languages spoken are Romance languages, $\frac{2}{15}$ are Germanic, and $\frac{8}{15}$ are Balto-Slavic. Order the language categories from least to greatest. Germanic, Romance, Balto-Slavic

Ⓑ **GPS** **28. Guided Problem Solving** A bank offers three types of interest-bearing accounts. One account increases by $\frac{1}{2}$ percent annually, another increases by $\frac{3}{5}$ percent, and a third increases by $\frac{7}{12}$ percent. In which account would you prefer to invest your money? Explain.
- What is the least common denominator of the three fractions?
- Is it better to earn more interest or less interest? $\frac{3}{5}$; it is the highest increase.

29. $\frac{3}{4}$ in.; the $\frac{3}{8}$-in. nail is not long enough to go all the way through the board.

29. Carpentry You want to nail a board that is $\frac{1}{2}$ in. thick onto a wall. **GPS** You can choose between nails that are $\frac{3}{8}$ in. long and $\frac{3}{4}$ in. long. Which size nail is the better choice? Explain. See left.

Assignment Guide

Check Your Understanding
Go over Exercises 1–8 in class before assigning the Homework Exercises.

Homework Exercises
A	Practice by Example	9–27
B	Apply Your Skills	28–39
C	Challenge	40

TEKS ★ ⓉⒶⓀⓈ Tune-Up and Mixed Review   41–46

Homework Quick Check
To check students' understanding of key skills and concepts, go over Exercises 14, 21, 29, 36, and 39.

Differentiated Instruction Resources

Lesson Quiz

Order from least to greatest.

1. $\frac{3}{4}$, $\frac{5}{6}$, $\frac{1}{3}$ $\frac{1}{3} < \frac{3}{4} < \frac{5}{6}$

2. $\frac{2}{3}$, $\frac{5}{8}$, $\frac{5}{12}$ $\frac{5}{12} < \frac{5}{8} < \frac{2}{3}$

3. $\frac{7}{10}$, $\frac{4}{5}$, $\frac{1}{2}$ $\frac{1}{2} < \frac{7}{10} < \frac{4}{5}$

4. $\frac{1}{5}$, $\frac{6}{7}$, $\frac{6}{10}$ $\frac{1}{5} < \frac{6}{10} < \frac{6}{7}$

39. If two fractions have the same numerator, then the fraction with the smaller denominator is greater, because the numerator makes up a larger part of the whole.

Reteaching 2-4   Comparing and Ordering **L2**

Follow these steps to *compare* $\frac{2}{5}$ and $\frac{3}{10}$ (unlike denominators).

① Find the **least common denominator (LCD).**

The denominators are 5 and 10. The LCD of 5 and 10 is their least common multiple.

② Write the equivalent fractions using the LCD. $\frac{2}{5} = \frac{4}{10}$ and $\frac{3}{10} = \frac{3}{10}$

③ Compare the numerators. $4 > 3$

So, $\frac{4}{10} > \frac{3}{10}$ and $\frac{2}{5} > \frac{3}{10}$.

Follow these steps to *order* the fractions $\frac{1}{2}$, $\frac{3}{5}$, and $\frac{2}{3}$.

① Find the LCD.   The LCD of 2, 5, and 3 is 30.

② Write equivalent fractions using the LCD.
$\frac{1}{2} = \frac{1 \cdot 15}{2 \cdot 15} = \frac{15}{30}$
$\frac{3}{5} = \frac{3 \cdot 6}{5 \cdot 6} = \frac{18}{30}$
$\frac{2}{3} = \frac{2 \cdot 10}{3 \cdot 10} = \frac{20}{30}$

③ Order the fractions using their numerators.
$\frac{15}{30} < \frac{18}{30} < \frac{20}{30}$
So, $\frac{1}{2} < \frac{3}{5} < \frac{2}{3}$.

Find each missing number. Then compare the fractions. Use <, >, or =.

1. $\frac{2}{3}$ and $\frac{3}{5}$
   2. $\frac{1}{2}$ and $\frac{5}{8}$
   3. $\frac{3}{4}$ and $\frac{9}{12}$

a. $\frac{2}{3} = \frac{10}{15}$, $\frac{3}{5} = \frac{9}{15}$ a. $\frac{1}{2} = \frac{4}{8}$, $\frac{5}{8} = \frac{5}{8}$ a. $\frac{3}{4} = \frac{9}{12}$, $\frac{9}{12} = \frac{9}{12}$

b. $\frac{2}{3} > \frac{3}{5}$ b. $\frac{1}{2} < \frac{5}{8}$ b. $\frac{3}{4} = \frac{9}{12}$

Compare each pair of fractions. Use <, >, or =.

4. $\frac{3}{5} < \frac{2}{3}$ 5. $\frac{3}{4} > \frac{2}{7}$ 6. $\frac{1}{8} = \frac{2}{16}$ 7. $\frac{1}{4} < \frac{9}{16}$

8. $\frac{2}{3} > \frac{1}{4}$ 9. $\frac{3}{6} = \frac{5}{10}$ 10. $\frac{9}{12} > \frac{2}{6}$ 11. $\frac{3}{8} < \frac{4}{5}$

Order from least to greatest.

12. $\frac{1}{3}, \frac{4}{4}, \frac{1}{4}$ 13. $\frac{3}{9}, \frac{3}{4}, \frac{1}{8}$ 14. $\frac{5}{6}, \frac{7}{8}, \frac{5}{6}$

15. $\frac{1}{8}, \frac{5}{5}, \frac{5}{6}$ 16. $\frac{1}{10}, \frac{3}{5}, \frac{7}{10}$ 17. $\frac{3}{4}, \frac{4}{12}, \frac{11}{12}$

Enrichment 2-4   Comparing and Ordering **L4**

Critical Thinking

You can compare fractions using *cross products*.

Compare $\frac{3}{7}$ and $\frac{4}{9}$. $\frac{3}{7} ? \frac{4}{9}$

① Write the cross products. $27 = 3 \times 9$, $7 \times 4 = 28$

② Compare the cross products. $27 < 28$

③ Compare the fractions.   so $\frac{3}{7} < \frac{4}{9}$

Use the cross-product method to order the five fractions below from least to greatest.

$$\frac{7}{9}, \quad \frac{8}{11}, \quad \frac{4}{7}, \quad \frac{13}{19}, \quad \frac{3}{4}$$

1. Compare the first two fractions on the left. List them in order with the smaller fraction first. $\frac{8}{11}, \frac{7}{9}$

2. Compare the middle fraction with the smaller fraction you found in exercise 1. Is it smaller or larger?   smaller

3. Starting from the left, list the first three fractions in order. $\frac{4}{7}, \frac{8}{11}, \frac{7}{9}$

4. How will you determine the position of the fraction $\frac{13}{19}$? Show your work.
Sample answer: $\frac{13}{19} > \frac{4}{7}$; $\frac{13}{19} < \frac{8}{11}$. So $\frac{13}{19}$ falls between these two fractions.

5. List all five of the fractions in order from least to greatest.
$\frac{4}{7}, \frac{13}{19}, \frac{8}{11}, \frac{3}{4}, \frac{7}{9}$

6. When would it be easier to use cross products to compare fractions than to find equivalent fractions with a common denominator?
Sample answer: If two fractions have large unlike denominators, use cross products.

7. Would you ever use both methods to order a list of fractions? Explain.
Sample answer: Yes; list common denominators for some common fractions. Cross products can be used to determine the rest.

GO Online
Homework Help
Visit: PHSchool.com
Web Code: are-0204

Compare each pair of fractions. Use <, =, or >.

30. $\frac{7}{12} \blacksquare \frac{5}{9}$ **>**

31. $\frac{10}{15} \blacksquare \frac{16}{24}$ **=**

32. $\frac{8}{16} \blacksquare \frac{15}{32}$ **>**

33. $\frac{22}{26} \blacksquare \frac{10}{13}$ **>**

Use the table at the right.

34. Do people remember more of what they say or what they do?   **what they do**

35. Do people remember more of what they hear or what they say?   **what they say**

Memory Facts	
People remember …	**of …**
three fourths	what they say.
one tenth	what they hear.
nine tenths	what they do.

Write two fractions for the models and compare them. Use <, =, or >.

36. $\frac{3}{5} < \frac{4}{5}$

37. $\frac{3}{4} > \frac{7}{10}$

38. **Patterns** Copy the table. Compare the fractions and fill in your answers. Use <, =, or >.   **See left.**

$\frac{1}{2} > \frac{1}{3}$
$\frac{1}{3} > \frac{1}{4}$
$\frac{1}{4} > \frac{1}{5}$
$\frac{1}{5} > \frac{1}{6}$

$\frac{1}{2}$ $\blacksquare$	$\frac{1}{3}$
$\frac{1}{3}$ $\blacksquare$	$\frac{1}{4}$
$\frac{1}{4}$ $\blacksquare$	$\frac{1}{5}$
$\frac{1}{5}$ $\blacksquare$	$\frac{1}{6}$

39. **Writing in Math** Describe an easy way to compare fractions that have the same numerator, such as $\frac{4}{5}$ and $\frac{4}{7}$. Explain why your method works.   **See margin.**

C 40. **Challenge** The variable n represents a positive integer. Which is greater, $\frac{1}{n}$ or $\frac{1}{n+1}$? $\frac{1}{n}$

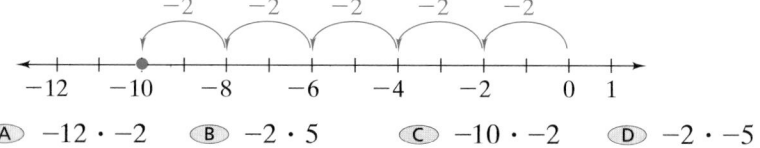

TEKS ★ TAKS Tune-Up and Mixed Review

TAKS Objective 1
TEKS (7.1)(A)

41. Which fraction is found between $\frac{7}{12}$ and $\frac{5}{6}$ on a number line?   **D**

Ⓐ $\frac{13}{24}$ Ⓑ $\frac{11}{12}$ Ⓒ $\frac{5}{12}$ Ⓓ $\frac{17}{24}$

TAKS Objective 1
TEKS (7.2)(G)

42. Eddie bought 12.9 gallons of gas that cost $2.89 per gallon. About how much did he pay for the gas?   **J**

Ⓕ Less than $23   Ⓗ Between $30 and $36
Ⓖ Between $23 and $30   Ⓙ More than $36

TAKS Objective 1
TEKS (7.2)(C)

43. Which expression is represented by the model below?   **B**

$-2 \quad -2 \quad -2 \quad -2 \quad -2$

$-12 \quad -10 \quad -8 \quad -6 \quad -4 \quad -2 \quad 0 \quad 1$

Ⓐ $-12 \cdot -2$ Ⓑ $-2 \cdot 5$ Ⓒ $-10 \cdot -2$ Ⓓ $-2 \cdot -5$

GO for Help   **Lesson 2-1**   **Simplify.**   1,936

44. $4^2 + 2^3 \cdot 3$ 40   45. $(4^2 + 2^3) \cdot 3$ 72   46. $4^2 \cdot (2^3 + 3)^2$

TEKS ★ TAKS Resources

- TAKS Strategies, p. 111
- TAKS Tune-Up, pp. 115–117

TAKS Tune-Up Kit

- TAKS Daily Review Transparencies
- TAKS Review and Preparation Workbook
- TAKS Strategies with Transparencies
- Texas Progress Monitoring Assessments

Alternative Assessment

Provide pairs of students with several sets of three different fractions, such as $\frac{2}{3}$, $\frac{3}{5}$, $\frac{3}{4}$. Provide fraction manipulatives such as fraction bars. Have pairs model each fraction in a set, arrange the models from least to greatest, and then record the correct order of the fractions.

2-5

Mixed Numbers and Improper Fractions

Check Skills You'll Need

1. Vocabulary Review
What does it mean when a fraction is in *simplest form*?
See below.
Write each fraction in simplest form.

2. $\frac{12}{20}$ $\frac{3}{5}$ **3.** $\frac{15}{18}$ $\frac{5}{6}$

4. $\frac{45}{60}$ $\frac{3}{4}$ **5.** $\frac{20}{48}$ $\frac{5}{12}$

GO for Help
Lesson 2-3

Check Skills You'll Need

1. The numerator and denominator have no common factors other than 1.

What You'll Learn

To write mixed numbers and improper fractions

• Prepares for **TEKS (7.1)(A)** To compare and order positive rational numbers

🔊 **New Vocabulary** improper fraction, mixed number

Why Learn This?

Suppose you are trying to share the extra pies left over from a pie eating contest. You can use improper fractions to find the number of equal-sized parts you can make from the leftovers.

The models below show that $1\frac{2}{3} = \frac{5}{3}$.

 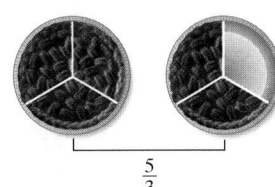

$1\frac{2}{3}$ $\frac{5}{3}$

The fraction $\frac{5}{3}$ is an improper fraction. An **improper fraction** is a fraction that has a numerator that is greater than or equal to its denominator.

The number $1\frac{2}{3}$ is a mixed number. A **mixed number** is the sum of a whole number and a fraction.

A number line can also help you understand improper fractions and mixed numbers.

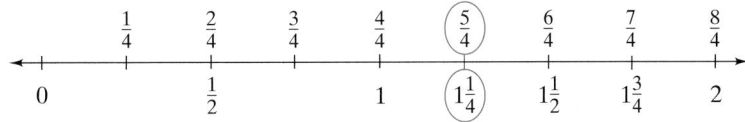

The number line shows that $1\frac{1}{4} = \frac{5}{4}$.

One way to write a mixed number as an improper fraction is to write the mixed number as a sum. Write a fraction that is equivalent to the whole number and then find the sum of the fractions.

TEKS Math Background

A *mixed number* consists of two parts: a whole number and a fraction. It represents one or more identical whole quantities, plus some fractional part of the whole. It is possible to rewrite any mixed number as a single fraction, which is called an *improper fraction*.

More Math Background: p. 66D

Lesson Planning and Resources

See p. 66E for a list of the resources that support this lesson.

PowerPoint
Bell Ringer Practice

✓ **Check Skills You'll Need**
Use student page, transparency, or PowerPoint.

TAKS **Daily Review 15**
Use transparency.

Differentiated Instruction Solutions for All Learners

Special Needs L1
Provide students with fraction models or kits. Alternatively, allow them to draw models to help them when rewriting numbers as improper fractions or mixed numbers.

learning style: tactile

Below Level L2
Give students several exercises like the following.

$2 = \frac{\square}{2}$ 4 $5 = \frac{\square}{3}$ 15

learning style: visual

2. Teach

Activity Lab

Use before the lesson.

All in One Teaching Resources

Activity Lab 2-5: Mixed Numbers and Improper Fractions

Guided Instruction

Example 1

Have students listen as you read "four and two thirds" aloud. Tell them to listen for the word "and," which signals an addition.

Error Prevention!

Using Method 2, students might multiply the numerator by the whole number, then add the denominator. For instance, they might write $3\frac{4}{5}$ as $\frac{(3 \times 4) + 5}{5}$, or $\frac{17}{5}$. Remind them that their goal is to write an improper fraction with the same denominator as the denominator in the mixed number.

PowerPoint
Additional Examples

❶ Write $3\frac{2}{5}$ as an improper fraction. $\frac{17}{5}$

❷ Karl needs $\frac{18}{4}$ cups of milk to make several loaves of bread. Express the amount of milk as a mixed number in simplest form. $4\frac{1}{2}$ cups of milk

All in One Teaching Resources

- Daily Notetaking Guide 2-5 **L3**
- Adapted Notetaking 2-5 **L1**

Closure

- Explain how to write a mixed number as an improper fraction. Write the mixed number as a sum of the whole number and the fraction. Write an equivalent fraction for the whole number using the same denominator as the fraction. Find the sum of both fractions by adding numerators. Simplify the sum.

Online active math

For: Fractions Activity
Use: Interactive Textbook, 2-5

EXAMPLE **Writing an Improper Fraction**

❶ Write $4\frac{2}{3}$ as an improper fraction.

Method 1 Using addition

$$4\frac{2}{3} = 4 + \frac{2}{3}$$ ← Write the mixed number as a sum.

$$= \frac{12}{3} + \frac{2}{3}$$ ← Change 4 to a fraction with the same denominator as $\frac{2}{3}$. Substitute. $4 = 4 \times \frac{3}{3} = \frac{12}{3}$

$$= \frac{12 + 2}{3} = \frac{14}{3}$$ ← Add the numerators.

Method 2 Using multiplication

Multiply the denominator by the whole number. → ↓   Add the numerator. → ↓

$$4\frac{2}{3} = 4 \underset{\times}{\overset{+}{\frown}} \frac{2}{3} = \frac{(3 \quad \times \quad 4) \quad + \quad 2}{3} = \frac{14}{3}$$

↑ The denominator stays the same.

✓ Quick Check

● **1. Choose a Method** Write $2\frac{5}{8}$ as an improper fraction. $\frac{21}{8}$

To write an improper fraction as a mixed number, divide and write the remainder as a fraction of the denominator. Then simplify the fraction.

EXAMPLE **Writing a Mixed Number**

❷ You are planning a party and estimate that you will need 30 slices of pie for your guest. If each pie contains 8 slices, how many pies should you buy?

To find the number of pies, write $\frac{30}{8}$ as a mixed number.

denominator → $8\overline{)30}$ $\begin{array}{r}3 \\ \end{array}$ ← whole number
$\underline{-24}$
6 ← remainder

$$3\frac{6}{8} = 3\frac{3}{4}$$ ← Write the remainder as a fraction, $\frac{\text{remainder}}{\text{denominator}}$. Simplify.

Since you cannot buy $3\frac{3}{4}$ pies, you should buy 4 pies.

✓ Quick Check

● **2.** A bakery sells a jumbo pie with 12 slices. If you need 30 slices, how many jumbo pies should you buy? **3**

92 Chapter 2 Exponents, Factors, and Fractions

Advanced Learners **L4**	**English Language Learners** **ELL**
Have students list ways that they use mixed numbers in their everyday activities. Sample: measuring ingredients for a recipe	Allow students time to change whole numbers to fractions with given denominators. Have them work in pairs. One student names a whole number, such as 5, and a denominator, such as thirds. The other students must rename 5 as the fraction $\frac{15}{3}$. They can then switch and repeat the process. **learning style: verbal**

Pre-AP™

Check Your Understanding

1. **Vocabulary** How are mixed numbers and improper fractions related? **Both are larger than 1.**

2. Write 7 as an improper fraction. **Answers may vary. Sample: $\frac{14}{2}$**

Label each as an *improper fraction, mixed number,* or *proper fraction*.

3. $\frac{7}{11}$ **proper fraction**   4. $4\frac{1}{2}$ **mixed number**   5. $\frac{15}{6}$ **improper fraction**

Fill in the blank.

6. $7 = \frac{\blacksquare}{2}$ **14**   7. $2\frac{2}{3} = \frac{\blacksquare}{3}$ **8**   8. $\blacksquare = \frac{18}{3}$ **6**

9. **Mental Math** Without calculating, decide whether the value of $\frac{72}{12}$ is a whole number or a mixed number. Explain your reasoning.
It is a whole number because 72 is divisible by 12.

Homework Exercises

For more exercises, see Extra Skills and Word Problems.

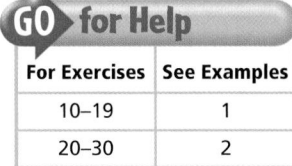

For Exercises	See Examples
10–19	1
20–30	2

Ⓐ Write each mixed number as an improper fraction. You may find a model helpful.

10. $2\frac{3}{8}$ $\frac{19}{8}$ 11. $5\frac{3}{4}$ $\frac{23}{4}$ 12. $1\frac{1}{12}$ $\frac{13}{12}$ 13. $4\frac{3}{5}$ $\frac{23}{5}$ 14. $1\frac{3}{7}$ $\frac{10}{7}$

15. $4\frac{5}{8}$ $\frac{37}{8}$ 16. $3\frac{2}{5}$ $\frac{17}{5}$ 17. $2\frac{11}{12}$ $\frac{35}{12}$ 18. $5\frac{2}{3}$ $\frac{17}{3}$ 19. $9\frac{1}{4}$ $\frac{37}{4}$

Write each improper fraction as a mixed number in simplest form. You may find a model helpful.

20. $\frac{16}{3}$ $5\frac{1}{3}$ 21. $\frac{25}{3}$ $8\frac{1}{3}$ 22. $\frac{42}{4}$ $10\frac{1}{2}$ 23. $\frac{31}{12}$ $2\frac{7}{12}$ 24. $\frac{28}{6}$ $4\frac{2}{3}$

25. $\frac{49}{6}$ $8\frac{1}{6}$ 26. $\frac{40}{6}$ $6\frac{2}{3}$ 27. $\frac{45}{10}$ $4\frac{1}{2}$ 28. $\frac{48}{11}$ $4\frac{4}{11}$ 29. $\frac{15}{8}$ $1\frac{7}{8}$

30. A recipe calls for $\frac{1}{4}$ c of flour. You need $\frac{11}{4}$ c to make 11 servings. Write $\frac{11}{4}$ as a mixed number. $2\frac{3}{4}$

Ⓑ 31. **Guided Problem Solving** 101 faculty members attended a breakfast, and each member was served $\frac{1}{4}$ loaf of banana bread. If each loaf contains eight slices, about how many slices of bread were served? About how many loaves were baked? **about 202 slices, about 26 loaves**
   - *Draw a diagram.* If eight slices make one loaf, how many slices are in $\frac{1}{4}$ loaf?
   - 101 people were served $\frac{1}{4}$ loaf. How many whole loaves is that?

32. Marisa is sewing an outfit. She uses $2\frac{5}{6}$ yards of fabric for her blouse, 3 yards of fabric for her skirt, and $\frac{20}{3}$ yards of fabric for her jacket. Write these values in order from least to greatest. $2\frac{5}{6}, 3, \frac{20}{3}$

Assignment Guide

Check Your Understanding
Go over Exercises 1–9 in class before assigning the Homework Exercises.

Homework Exercises
A Practice by Example 10–30
B Apply Your Skills 31–41
C Challenge 42
TEKS ⭐ **TAKS** Tune-Up and Mixed Review 43–47

Homework Quick Check
To check students' understanding of key skills and concepts, go over Exercises 12, 27, 34, 38, and 40.

Differentiated Instruction **Resources**

Lesson Quiz

Write as an improper fraction.

1. $5\frac{3}{8}$ $\frac{43}{8}$ **2.** $6\frac{2}{3}$ $\frac{20}{3}$

Write as a mixed number in simplest form.

3. $\frac{34}{8}$ $4\frac{1}{4}$ **4.** $\frac{40}{6}$ $6\frac{2}{3}$

Reteaching 2-5   Mixed Numbers and Improper **L2**

An *improper fraction* is greater than or equal to 1. Its numerator is greater than or equal to its denominator.

Improper fractions $\frac{9}{4}$ $\frac{8}{8}$ $\frac{10}{3}$ $\frac{7}{2}$

A *mixed number* is the sum of a whole number and a fraction.

Mixed numbers $1\frac{1}{3}$ $5\frac{2}{5}$ $3\frac{1}{4}$

To write a mixed number as an improper fraction:

① Write the mixed number as a sum. $3\frac{1}{2} = 3 + \frac{1}{2}$

② Write both numbers as fractions. $= \frac{6}{2} + \frac{1}{2}$

③ Add the fractions. $= \frac{7}{2}$

To write an improper fraction as a mixed number:

① Divide the numerator by the denominator. $\frac{7}{2}$ Think: $7 \div 2$ $2\overline{)7}$ $\frac{-6}{1}$

② Write the whole number, then the remainder over the divisor. $\frac{7}{2} = 3\frac{1}{2}$

Write each mixed number as an improper fraction.

1. $3\frac{1}{4}$ $\frac{13}{4}$ 2. $2\frac{2}{3}$ $\frac{8}{3}$ 3. $1\frac{3}{8}$ $\frac{11}{8}$
4. $5\frac{1}{3}$ $\frac{16}{3}$ 5. $6\frac{3}{4}$ $\frac{27}{4}$ 6. $1\frac{1}{9}$ $\frac{10}{9}$
7. $4\frac{1}{2}$ $\frac{9}{2}$ 8. $3\frac{4}{5}$ $\frac{19}{5}$ 9. $5\frac{1}{6}$ $\frac{31}{6}$
10. $3\frac{1}{3}$ $\frac{10}{3}$ 11. $5\frac{7}{8}$ $\frac{47}{8}$ 12. $4\frac{1}{8}$ $\frac{33}{8}$

Write each improper fraction as a mixed number in simplest form.

13. $\frac{14}{4}$ $3\frac{1}{2}$ 14. $\frac{12}{2}$ 6 15. $\frac{22}{5}$ $4\frac{2}{5}$
16. $\frac{16}{3}$ $5\frac{1}{3}$ 17. $\frac{47}{8}$ $5\frac{7}{8}$ 18. $\frac{56}{7}$ 8
19. $\frac{17}{4}$ $4\frac{1}{4}$ 20. $\frac{21}{6}$ $3\frac{1}{2}$ 21. $\frac{13}{5}$ $2\frac{3}{5}$
22. $\frac{21}{4}$ $5\frac{1}{4}$ 23. $\frac{13}{9}$ $1\frac{4}{9}$ 24. $\frac{14}{2}$ 7

Enrichment 2-5   Mixed Numbers and Improper **L4**

Patterns in Numbers

The fractions shown below are called *continued fractions*. A continued fraction is the sum of a number and a fraction whose numerator is 1 and whose denominator is the sum of a number and a fraction, and so on as shown in this model.

Number Fraction $1 + \frac{1}{1 + \frac{1}{1}} = 1 + \frac{1}{1 + \frac{1}{2}} = 1 + \frac{1}{1\frac{1}{2}} = 1\frac{1}{2} = \frac{3}{2}$

$1 + \frac{1}{1 + \frac{1}{1}}$ is a continued fraction.

Number → $1 + \frac{1}{1 + \frac{1}{1}}$ ← Numerator
← Fraction

Write each continued fraction as a mixed number and as an improper fraction. To evaluate a continued fraction, find the denominator of the last fraction written and work backward.

	Mixed	Improper
1. $1 + \frac{1}{1 + \frac{1}{1 + \frac{1}{1}}}$	$1\frac{2}{3}$	$\frac{5}{3}$
2. $1 + \frac{1}{1 + \frac{1}{1 + \frac{1}{1 + \frac{1}{1}}}}$	$1\frac{3}{5}$	$\frac{8}{5}$
3. $1 + \frac{1}{1 + \frac{1}{1 + \frac{1}{1 + \frac{1}{1 + \frac{1}{1}}}}}$	$1\frac{5}{8}$	$\frac{13}{8}$

4. Write the next fraction as a mixed number and an improper fraction. $1\frac{13}{21}$ $\frac{34}{21}$

5. What pattern do you see in the improper fractions?
Sample answer: The numerator is the sum of numerators of two prior fractions; the denominator is the sum of two prior denominators.

6. What would be the value of the tenth continued fraction? $\frac{233}{144}$

---

40. $\frac{9}{4}$ mi; $1\frac{1}{2}$ mi $= \frac{6}{4}$ mi, which is less than $\frac{9}{4}$.

(**Algebra**) In Exercises 33–35, evaluate each expression for $a = 6$, $b = 3, c = 2,$ and $d = 5$. Write your answer in simplest form.

33. $\frac{b}{a^2}$ $\frac{1}{12}$ **34.** $\frac{a^2 + b}{c}$ $19\frac{1}{2}$ **35.** $\frac{a + c}{b + d}$ 1

Write each length as a mixed number and as an improper fraction.

36.

inches

$1\frac{3}{4}$, $\frac{7}{4}$

37.

inches

$1\frac{5}{8}$, $\frac{13}{8}$

38. A tailor designs a skirt that is $25\frac{1}{4}$ in. long. What is the length in
GPS eighths of an inch? Write your answer as an improper fraction. 202 eighths; $\frac{202}{8}$

39. The distance around a track is $\frac{1}{8}$ mi. A wheelchair racer completes 35 laps around the track. Write the distance he travels in miles as a mixed number. $4\frac{3}{8}$ mi

40. **Writing in Math** Which is longer, $\frac{9}{4}$ miles or $1\frac{1}{2}$ miles? Explain. See left.

41. Write two mixed numbers and an improper fraction for the model.

$3\frac{2}{8}$, $3\frac{1}{4}$, $\frac{26}{8}$

C **42.** **Challenge** Using each of the digits 2, 5, and 9 exactly once, write a fraction with the greatest possible value. Then write the fraction as a mixed number. $\frac{95}{2}$; $47\frac{1}{2}$

TEKS ★ (TAKS) Tune-Up and Mixed Review

(**TAKS**) **Objective 1**
TEKS (7.1)(A)

43. The table below shows the distances a football team ran each day last week. On which day did the team run the least? **B**

Football Practice

Day	Monday	Tuesday	Wednesday	Thursday
Distance Run	$\frac{7}{10}$ mile	$\frac{5}{8}$ mile	$\frac{3}{4}$ mile	$\frac{2}{3}$ mile

Ⓐ Monday   Ⓑ Tuesday   Ⓒ Wednesday   Ⓓ Thursday

(**TAKS**) **Objective 2**
TEKS (7.3)(B)

44. A 1-cup serving of mashed potatoes with whole milk and butter has 634 milligrams of sodium. How many grams of sodium are in 3 cups of mashed potatoes? **G**

Ⓕ 0.1902 g   Ⓖ 1.902 g   Ⓗ 190.2 g   Ⓙ 1,902 g

 GO **for Help**

Lesson 1-7   Find each difference.

45. $-3 - 9$ -12 **46.** $(-10) - (-18)$ 8 **47.** $21 - (-7)$ 28

TEKS ★ (TAKS) Resources

• TAKS Strategies, p. 111
• TAKS Tune-Up, pp. 115–117

(**TAKS**) **Tune-Up Kit**

• TAKS Daily Review Transparencies
• TAKS Review and Preparation Workbook
• TAKS Strategies with Transparencies
• Texas Progress Monitoring Assessments

Alternative Assessment

Have students work in pairs. Each student writes two improper fractions and two mixed numbers. Students exchange papers. They write each improper fraction as a mixed number in simplest form and each mixed number as an improper fraction. Have students explain to their partners the steps they took to complete each procedure.

Comparing Fractions and Decimals

TEKS ★ **TAKS**

(7.1)(A) To compare and order integers and positive rational numbers **TAKS** Obj. 1

(7.1)(B) To convert between fractions and decimals with a calculator **TAKS** Obj. 1

A baseball player's batting average is the number of hits divided by the number of times at bat. You can tell which player has the best record by comparing batting averages.

ACTIVITY

1. Copy the table below.

Name of Player	Number of Hits	Times at Bat	Batting Average	
			Fraction	Decimal
Allan	43	195	■	■
Belinda	8	127	■	■
Char	43	183	■	■
Denise	47	183	■	■
Emil	29	174	■	■
Farik	45	135	■	■

2. Write each batting average as a fraction.

3. Use a calculator to write each batting average as a decimal. Round to the nearest thousandth.

1–3.

Name of Player	Batting Average	
	Fraction	Decimal
Allan	$\frac{43}{195}$	.221
Belinda	$\frac{8}{127}$	.063
Char	$\frac{43}{183}$	.235
Denise	$\frac{47}{183}$	.257
Emil	$\frac{29}{174}$	.167
Farik	$\frac{45}{135}$	.333

Exercises

1. a. Which players had averages that are decimals with a repeating block of digits? **Emil, Farik**

 b. List the players in order, from highest to lowest batting averages.
 Farik, Denise, Char, Allan, Emil, Belinda

2. Is it easier to compare and order batting averages using fractions or decimals? Explain. **Decimals; the fractions do not have common denominators.**

3. A student thought that Belinda's average was 0.630. What error do you think she made? **Answers may vary. Sample: She used 80 instead of 8.**

4. How can you tell, without using decimals, that Denise has a higher average than Char? **They both batted the same number of times, but Denise had more hits.**

5. Can a player get 132 hits in 125 times at bat? How is your answer related to the highest possible batting average of 1.000? **No; a player cannot get more hits than times at bat.**

Activity Lab

Comparing Fractions and Decimals

Students practice ordering fractions and converting fractions to decimals. This will prepare them to compare and order fractions and decimals in Lesson 2-6.

Guided Instruction

Explain a *batting average* and that it can be expressed as a fraction or a decimal. Provide examples of record batting averages from a sports record book.
Ask:
- *Would a batting average ever be expressed as a mixed number? Why?* No, a person cannot have more hits than number of times at bat.
- *Batting averages are usually expressed to the thousandths place. How would you convert a fraction to make a conventional batting average?* Convert the fraction to a decimal, round to the thousandths place or annex zeros to get to the thousandths place.

Exercises

Have students work on the Exercises. Then have them trade papers with a partner and compare answers.

Alternative Method

Allow students to use graph paper and shade sections to model the given fractions.

TEKS ★ TAKS Resources

- Activity Lab 2-6: Fractions and Decimals
- graph paper

Dana Center TEKS Toolkit Clarifying Activities (7.1)(A), (7.1)(B)
Visit: PHSchool.com
Web Code: arq-9045

TEKS ⭐ *TAKS*

(7.1)(A) To compare and order positive rational numbers *TAKS* Obj. 1

(7.1)(B) To convert between fractions, decimals, and whole numbers mentally, on paper, or with a calculator *TAKS* Obj. 1

Dana Center TEKS Toolkit Clarifying Activities (7.1)(A), (7.1)(B)
Visit: PHSchool.com
Web Code: arq-9045

TEKS Math Background

For denominators whose only prime factors are 2 or 5—denominators such as 2, 4, 5, 8, 10, 16, 20, 25, 32, 40, 50, and so on—the quotient will be a *terminating decimal*. That is, the division $a \div b$ will end, or *terminate*, with a remainder of zero. Otherwise, a block of digits in the quotient will repeat without end, resulting in a *repeating decimal*.

More Math Background: p. 66D

Lesson Planning and Resources

See p. 66E for a list of the resources that support this lesson.

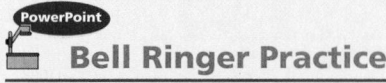

Bell Ringer Practice

✓ **Check Skills You'll Need**
Use student page, transparency, or PowerPoint.

TAKS **Daily Review 16**
Use transparency.

✓ **Check Skills You'll Need**

1. Vocabulary Review
How can you tell whether fractions are *equivalent fractions*?
1–5. See below.
Write two fractions equivalent to each fraction.

2. $\frac{16}{20}$ 3. $\frac{15}{20}$

4. $\frac{6}{9}$ 5. $\frac{10}{50}$

  for Help
Lesson 2-3

 Tip

You may shade in either .16 or 0.16 on your grid. Both answers are correct.

Check Skills You'll Need

1. In simplest form, they are the same.

2–5. Answers may vary. Samples are given.

2. $\frac{4}{5}$, $\frac{8}{10}$

3. $\frac{3}{4}$, $\frac{6}{8}$

4. $\frac{2}{3}$, $\frac{8}{12}$

5. $\frac{1}{5}$, $\frac{2}{10}$

TEKS ⭐ *TAKS*

- (7.1)(A) To compare and order positive rational numbers *TAKS* Obj. 1
- (7.1)(B) To convert between fractions, decimals, and whole numbers mentally, on paper, or with a calculator *TAKS* Obj. 1

🔊 **New Vocabulary** terminating decimal, repeating decimal

Why Learn This?

When you order sandwich meat at a delicatessen, you may ask for half a pound. The scales at a deli often use decimal measures. You can convert between fractions and decimals to make sure you are receiving the correct amount.

You write a fraction as a decimal by dividing the numerator by the denominator. A decimal that stops, or terminates, is a **terminating decimal.**

EXAMPLE Writing a Terminating Decimal

1 *TAKS* **Griddable Item** The pull of gravity is weaker on the moon than on Earth. The fraction $\frac{4}{25}$ represents the ratio of the moon's gravity to Earth's gravity. Write this fraction as a decimal.

$$\frac{4}{25} \text{ or } 4 \div 25 = 25 \overline{)4.00} \quad \leftarrow \text{quotient} \atop 0.16$$

$$\begin{array}{r} 0.16 \\ 25\overline{)4.00} \\ -25 \\ \hline 150 \\ -150 \\ \hline 0 \quad \leftarrow \text{The remainder is 0.} \end{array}$$

The ratio of the moon's gravity to Earth's gravity as a decimal is 0.16. This is a terminating decimal because the division process stops when the remainder is 0.

✓ **Quick Check**

1. The fraction of nitrogen in a chemical sample is $\frac{5}{8}$. Write the fraction as a decimal. **0.625**

Differentiated Instruction Solutions for All Learners

Special Needs L1
To help students with decimal and fraction relationships, draw a rectangular model for the fraction $\frac{2}{5}$, with 2 of the 5 bars shaded. Then have them superimpose a same-sized rectangle divided into tenths to name the decimal equivalent (4 tenths or 0.4).
learning style: tactile

Below Level L2
Review divisions in which zeros must be annexed to the dividend, such as $1.2 \div 5$.

$$5\overline{)1.2} \rightarrow 5\overline{)1.20} \rightarrow 5\overline{)1.20} \atop 0.24$$

learning style: visual

Vocabulary Tip

The symbol for a repeating decimal is a bar over the repeated digit(s), for example, $0.\overline{17}$.

If the same block of digits in a decimal repeats without end, the decimal is a **repeating decimal.** The repeating block can include one or more digits.

$$5.355555555555\ldots = 5.3\overline{5} \quad \leftarrow \text{The digit 5 repeats.}$$
$$0.171717171717\ldots = 0.\overline{17} \quad \leftarrow \text{The digits 17 repeat.}$$

EXAMPLE **Writing a Repeating Decimal**

② Write $\frac{3}{11}$ as a decimal.

Method 1 Paper and Pencil

$$\frac{3}{11} \text{ or } 3 \div 11 = 11\overline{)3.00000} \quad \begin{array}{l} 0.27272 \quad \leftarrow \text{The digits 27 repeat.} \end{array}$$

$$\begin{array}{r} -22 \\ \hline 80 \\ -77 \\ \hline 30 \\ -22 \\ \hline 80 \\ -77 \\ \hline 30 \end{array} \quad \leftarrow \begin{array}{l} \text{There will always be a remainder} \\ \text{of 30 or 80.} \end{array}$$

Calculator Tip

Most calculators display as many digits as possible of a repeating decimal and round off the final digit. For example, $0.\overline{27}$ might be shown as 0.272727273.

Method 2 Calculator

$$3 \boxed{\div} 11 \boxed{=} 0.27272727273$$

So $\frac{3}{11} = 0.\overline{27}$.

✓ Quick Check

● 2. Write $\frac{5}{9}$ as a decimal. $0.\overline{5}$

You can write a terminating decimal as a fraction or a mixed number by writing the digits to the right of the decimal point as a fraction.

EXAMPLE **Writing a Decimal as a Fraction**

③ Write 1.325 as a mixed number with a fraction in simplest form.

Since $0.325 = \frac{325}{1,000}$, $1.325 = 1\frac{325}{1,000}$.

$$1\frac{325}{1,000} = 1\frac{325 \div 25}{1,000 \div 25} \quad \leftarrow \text{Use the GCF to write the fraction in simplest form.}$$

$$= 1\frac{13}{40}$$

✓ Quick Check

● 3. Write each decimal as a mixed number in simplest form.

    a. 1.364 $1\frac{91}{250}$ **b.** 2.48 $2\frac{12}{25}$ **c.** 3.6 $3\frac{3}{5}$

Activity Lab

Use before the lesson.
Student Edition Activity Lab 2-6a, Comparing Fractions and Decimals, p. 95

All in One Teaching Resources
Activity Lab 2-6: Fractions and Decimals

Guided Instruction

Example 3
Some students might not recognize 25 as the GCF of 325 and 1,000. It might be easier for them to perform two successive divisions by 5.

$$1\frac{325}{1,000} = 1\frac{325 \div 5}{1,000 \div 5} = 1\frac{65}{200}$$
$$1\frac{65}{200} = 1\frac{65 \div 5}{200 \div 5} = 1\frac{13}{40}$$

Error Prevention!

In writing repeating decimals, students might place the bar over too few or too many digits. Be sure they understand that the bar must be placed over all the digits that repeat, and only those digits that repeat.

PowerPoint
Additional Examples

❶ The total amount of rainfall yesterday was reported as $\frac{1}{4}$ in. Express the amount of rainfall as a decimal. 0.25 in.

❷ Write $\frac{7}{15}$ as a decimal. $0.4\overline{6}$

❸ Write 4.105 as a fraction in simplest form. $4\frac{21}{200}$

❹ Order from least to greatest: $3\frac{3}{4}$, 2.897, $3\frac{7}{10}$. 2.897, $3\frac{7}{10}$, $3\frac{3}{4}$

❺ In a survey of next year's seventh-grade students, 0.25 said they will come to school by bus, $\frac{5}{24}$ said they will walk, 0.375 said they will come in a car, and $\frac{1}{16}$ said they will ride their bicycles. Order the means of transportation from most used to least used. car, bus, walk, bicycle

Advanced Learners **L4**
Write each fraction as a decimal.
$\frac{1}{7}$ $0.\overline{142857}$ $\frac{1}{13}$ $0.\overline{076923}$

Pre-AP™

English Language Learners **ELL**
Make sure students are reading the decimal numbers correctly, in tenths, hundredths, and thousandths. Discourage the use of language like *0 point 2* for two-tenths. Remind students that decimals always have denominators that are multiples of ten.

learning style: verbal

Closure

- *What is a terminating decimal?*
  the decimal that results when the numerator divided by the denominator has a remainder of zero
- *What is a repeating decimal?*
  the decimal that results when the numerator divided by the denominator has a block of digits that repeats without end

To compare fractions and decimals, you can write the decimals as fractions or the fractions as decimals. You can decide which is easier for different numbers.

GO▶for Help

For help with place value and decimals, go to Skills Handbook p. 658

EXAMPLE Ordering Fractions and Decimals

④ Order from greatest to least: $2, 2.55, 2\frac{6}{18}$.

$$2\frac{6}{18} = 2\frac{1}{3} = 2.\overline{3} \quad \longleftarrow \quad \text{Use a calculator to change the mixed number to a decimal.}$$

Use a number line to find each decimal number's relative position.

```
                              2      2.3   2.55
  ◄──┼──┼──┼──┼──┼──┼──┼──●──┼──┼──●──┼──●──┼──┼──►
    1.0  1.2  1.4  1.6  1.8  2.0  2.2  2.4  2.6  2.8
```

So the order of the numbers from greatest to least is $2.55, 2\frac{6}{18},$ and 2.

✓ Quick Check

● **4.** Order from greatest to least: $1\frac{3}{8}, 1\frac{7}{15}, 1.862$. $1.862, 1\frac{7}{15}, 1\frac{3}{8}$

You can order rational numbers to analyze data results.

EXAMPLE Application: Surveys

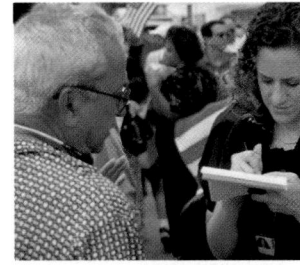

Careers Journalists gather information, analyze data, and write reports.

⑤ For a survey naming four animals, adults were asked to choose the animal they thought was the most endangered species. Of the adults surveyed, 0.25 chose black rhinoceros, $\frac{10}{48}$ chose tiger, $\frac{5}{12}$ chose giant panda, and 0.125 chose mako shark. List their choices in order of frequency.

First write all 4 ratios as decimals.

black rhinoceros: 0.25

tiger: $\frac{10}{48} = \frac{5}{24} = 0.208\overline{3}$ ⎫
                                                          ⎬ ← Use a calculator to change the fractions to decimals.
giant panda: $\frac{5}{12} = 0.41\overline{6}$ ⎭

mako shark: 0.125

Since $0.41\overline{6} > 0.25 > 0.208\overline{3} > 0.125$, the order of frequency was giant panda, black rhinoceros, tiger, and mako shark.

✓ Quick Check

5. In a survey about pets, $\frac{2}{5}$ of students prefer cats, 0.33 prefer dogs, $\frac{3}{25}$ prefer birds, and 0.15 prefer fish. List the choices in order of preference. **cats, dogs, fish, birds**

Check Your Understanding

1. **Vocabulary** What is the difference between a terminating decimal and a repeating decimal? A terminating decimal stops, whereas a repeating decimal has a block of digits that repeat without end.

2. **Reasoning** Is a remainder of 0 the same as no remainder? Explain. Yes; in each case a number is divisible by the other.

Write each decimal as a mixed number or a fraction in simplest form.

3. 1.375 $1\frac{3}{8}$

4. 0.44 $\frac{11}{25}$

5. 3.99 $3\frac{99}{100}$

6. **Reasoning** Is 3.03003000300003 . . . a repeating decimal? Explain. No; the same block of digits is not repeating.

7. Order the following numbers from least to greatest: $1.\overline{9}$, $1\frac{1}{3}$, 2, 0.5. 0.5, $1\frac{1}{3}$, $1.\overline{9}$, 2

Homework Exercises

For more exercises, see Extra Skills and Word Problems.

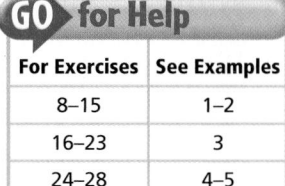

For Exercises	See Examples
8–15	1–2
16–23	3
24–28	4–5

Ⓐ **Write each fraction as a decimal.**

8. $\frac{2}{5}$ 0.4

9. $\frac{4}{5}$ 0.8

10. $\frac{3}{8}$ 0.375

11. $\frac{2}{3}$ $0.\overline{6}$

12. $\frac{3}{4}$ 0.75

13. $\frac{1}{8}$ 0.125

14. $\frac{7}{11}$ $0.\overline{63}$

15. $\frac{3}{16}$ 0.1875

Write each decimal as a mixed number or a fraction in simplest form.

16. 0.125 $\frac{1}{8}$

17. 0.66 $\frac{33}{50}$

18. 2.5 $2\frac{1}{2}$

19. 3.75 $3\frac{3}{4}$

20. 0.32 $\frac{8}{25}$

21. 0.19 $\frac{19}{100}$

22. 0.8 $\frac{4}{5}$

23. 0.965 $\frac{193}{200}$

Order from greatest to least. 24–27. See left.

24. $\frac{44}{44}$, $\frac{7}{8}$, 0.83, $\frac{9}{22}$, 0.4

25. 3.84, $3\frac{41}{50}$, 3.789, 3

26. 0.67, $\frac{2}{3}$, $\frac{7}{12}$, 0.58, $\frac{5}{9}$

27. 0.1225, $0.1\overline{2}$, $\frac{3}{25}$, $\frac{7}{125}$

24. $\frac{9}{22}$, 0.83, $\frac{7}{8}$, 0.4, $\frac{44}{44}$

25. 3.84, 3.789, 3, $3\frac{41}{50}$

26. $\frac{2}{3}$, 0.67, $\frac{5}{9}$, 0.58, $\frac{7}{12}$

27. $0.1\overline{2}$, 0.1225, $\frac{3}{25}$, $\frac{7}{125}$

28. **Biology** DNA content in a cell is measured in picograms (pg). A sea star cell has $\frac{17}{20}$ pg of DNA, a scallop cell has $\frac{19}{20}$ pg, a red water mite cell has 0.19 pg, and a mosquito cell has 0.24 pg. Order the DNA contents from greatest to least. $\frac{19}{20}$ pg, $\frac{17}{20}$ pg, 0.24 pg, 0.19 pg

Ⓑ 29. **Guided Problem Solving** On an adventure trail, you biked 12 mi, walked 4 mi, ran 6 mi, and swam 2 mi. What fraction of the total distance did you bike? Write this number as a decimal. $\frac{1}{2}$; 0.5
   • The total distance of the adventure trail is ▪ mi.
   • You biked ▪ mi. As a fraction, this is ▪ of the total distance.

30. **Music** To compose music on a computer, you can write notes as decimals. What decimals should you enter for a half note, a quarter note, an eighth note, and a sixteenth note? 0.5, 0.25, 0.125, 0.0625

3. Practice

Assignment Guide

Check Your Understanding
Go over Exercises 1–7 in class before assigning the Homework Exercises.

Homework Exercises

A	Practice by Example	8–28
B	Apply Your Skills	29–40
C	Challenge	41

TEKS ★ TAKS Tune-Up and Mixed Review   42–48

Homework Quick Check
To check students' understanding of key skills and concepts, go over Exercises 13, 21, 28, 36, and 40.

Differentiated Instruction Resources

Lesson Quiz

Write each fraction as a decimal.

1. $\frac{7}{8}$ 0.875   **2.** $\frac{4}{9}$ $0.\overline{4}$

3. $\frac{3}{5}$ 0.6   **4.** $\frac{5}{16}$ 0.3125

Alternative Assessment

Have students work in pairs. Each student writes a decimal and a fraction. Students exchange papers and rewrite the decimal as a fraction and the fraction as a decimal. Then pairs work together to arrange the original decimals and fractions in order from least to greatest.

Reteaching 2-6
Fractions and **L2**

To change a fraction to a decimal, divide the numerator by the denominator.

To change a decimal to a fraction:
① Read the decimal to find the denominator. Write the decimal digits over 10, 100, or 1,000.
② Use the GCF to write the fraction in simplest form.

Write each fraction as a decimal.

1. $\frac{4}{5}$ = 0.8   **2.** $\frac{3}{4}$ = 0.75   **3.** $\frac{1}{6}$ = $0.1\overline{6}$
4. $\frac{1}{4}$ = 0.25   **5.** $\frac{2}{3}$ = $0.\overline{6}$ **6.** $\frac{7}{10}$ = 0.7
7. $\frac{5}{9}$ = $0.\overline{5}$ **8.** $\frac{1}{5}$ = 0.2   **9.** $\frac{3}{8}$ = 0.375

Write each decimal as a mixed number or fraction in simplest form.

10. 0.4 = $\frac{2}{5}$ **11.** 0.75 = $\frac{3}{4}$ **12.** 1.5 = $1\frac{1}{2}$
13. 0.35 = $\frac{7}{20}$ **14.** 2.7 = $2\frac{7}{10}$ **15.** 1.8 = $1\frac{4}{5}$
16. 0.625 = $\frac{5}{8}$ **17.** 0.78 = $\frac{39}{50}$ **18.** 0.88 = $\frac{22}{25}$

Order from least to greatest.

19. $2.6, \frac{13}{6}, 2\frac{5}{6}$ **20.** $2.\overline{02}, 2.\overline{200}, 2.0202$ **21.** $\frac{5}{4}, 1\frac{3}{5}, 1.\overline{4}$
$\frac{13}{6}, 2.6, 2\frac{5}{6}$ $2.\frac{1}{200}, 2.0202, 2.\overline{02}$ $\frac{5}{4}, 1.\overline{4}, 1\frac{3}{5}$

Enrichment 2-6
Fractions and **L4**
Patterns in Numbers

Find a decimal for each fraction. Use your calculator to check your work.

1. $\frac{3}{8}$ 0.375   **2.** $\frac{5}{6}$ $0.8\overline{3}$
3. $\frac{7}{12}$ $0.58\overline{3}$ **4.** $\frac{4}{5}$ 0.8
5. $\frac{8}{9}$ $0.\overline{8}$ **6.** $\frac{3}{10}$ 0.3

7. List the denominators for the fractions that produced terminating decimals.
5, 8, 10

8. Find the prime factors of the denominators in exercise 7.
2, 5

9. List the denominators for the fractions that produced repeating decimals.
6, 9, 12

10. Find the prime factors of the denominators in exercise 9.
2, 3, 5, 11

11. What pattern do you notice?
Possible answer: Denominators for terminating decimals have only 2, only 5, or 2 and 5 as prime factors.

12. Without dividing, tell whether each of the following fractions will produce a terminating or a repeating decimal.
a. $\frac{7}{24}$ repeating   b. $\frac{35}{64}$ terminating
c. $\frac{17}{111}$ repeating   d. $\frac{14}{15}$ repeating

13. Write a fraction that, as a decimal, will terminate. Use a 2-digit or a 3-digit number as the denominator.
Sample answer: $\frac{102}{160}$

14. Write a fraction that, as a decimal, will repeat. Use a 2-digit or a 3-digit number as the denominator.
Sample answer: $\frac{36}{101}$

100

Greenland is the world's largest island.

41. The quotients are 0.5, 5, 50, 500, 5,000, and 50,000. As the divisor gets smaller, the quotient gets larger because divisor × quotient = dividend.

Algebra Compare. Use $<$, $=$, or $>$. (*Note:* n is a value greater than 1.)

31. $\frac{1}{n}$ ▇ $\frac{n}{n}$ $<$ **32.** 1 ▇ $\frac{n}{1}$ $<$ **33.** n ▇ $\frac{1}{n}$ $>$ **34.** $\frac{n}{n^2}$ ▇ $\frac{1}{n}$ $=$

35. Number Sense Examine the fractions $\frac{2}{3}$, $\frac{3}{3}$, $\frac{4}{3}$, $\frac{5}{3}$, and $\frac{6}{3}$. Explain when a denominator of 3 will result in a repeating decimal.
when the numerator is not a multiple of 3

36. Geography About 12,500 icebergs break away from Greenland each year. Of these, about 375 float into the Atlantic Ocean.
a. What fraction of the icebergs float into the Atlantic Ocean? $\frac{3}{100}$
b. Write your answer for part (a) as a decimal. 0.03
c. What fraction of the icebergs do *not* float into the Atlantic? $\frac{97}{100}$

For Exercises 37–39, use the table at the right.
37. See margin.
37. For each state, write a fraction that shows the ratio $\frac{\text{number of people under age 18}}{\text{total population}}$.

38. For most of the states, would $\frac{1}{2}$, $\frac{1}{3}$, or $\frac{1}{4}$ best describe the fraction of the population that is under age 18? $\frac{1}{4}$

39. Calculator Order the states from least to greatest fraction under age 18.
Fla., N.Y., Ohio, Tex., Calif.

40. Writing in Math Describe some everyday situations in which you need to change fractions to decimals.
Answers may vary. Sample: finding the cost per ounce of cereal that costs $1.59 for $4\frac{3}{4}$

C 41. Challenge Divide 50 by these numbers: 100, 10, 1, 0.1, 0.01, 0.001. Explain how the quotient changes as the divisor approaches 0.
See left.

Population (thousands)

State	Total	Under Age 18
N.Y.	19,227	4,572
Texas	22,490	6,267
Calif.	33,893	9,596
Fla.	17,397	4,003
Ohio	11,459	2,779

Source: U.S. Census Bureau. Go to PHSchool.com for a data update.

TEKS ★ TAKS Tune-Up and Mixed Review

GRIDDABLE ITEMS

TAKS Objective 1
TEKS (7.2)(B)

42. Bennie's teacher gave him a score of $\frac{34}{40}$ on his quiz. What decimal is equivalent to the score Bennie received? 0.85

TAKS Objective 1
TEKS (7.1)(B)

43. When Rahmi was 11 years old, he was 150.25 centimeters tall. For the next 4 years, he grew 6.5 centimeters a year. To the nearest centimeter, how tall was Rahmi when he was 15 years old? 176

TAKS Objective 5
TEKS (7.12)(A)

44. Serena has a part-time job at a supermarket. Her boss tells her to find last week's average number of smoothies sold per day. He gives her the printout of sales in the past seven days: 14, 23, 42, 22, 15, 28, and 31. Serena correctly finds the average number of smoothies sold per day. What is the number? 25

GO for Help Lesson 1-3   **Find each product.**

45. $0.4 \cdot 0.9$ 0.36   **46.** $1.7 \cdot 0.5$ 0.85   **47.** $3.06 \cdot 0.3$ 0.918   **48.** $9.013 \cdot 1.0$ 9.013

100   **Chapter 2** Exponents, Factors, and Fractions

TEKS ★ TAKS Resources

• TAKS Strategies, p. 111
• TAKS Tune Up, pp. 115–117

TAKS Tune-Up Kit

• TAKS Daily Review Transparencies
• TAKS Review and Preparation Workbook
• TAKS Strategies with Transparencies
• Texas Progress Monitoring Assessments

37. N.Y.: $\frac{4,572}{19,227}$

Tex.: $\frac{6,267}{22,490}$

Calif.: $\frac{9,596}{33,893}$

Fla.: $\frac{4,003}{17,397}$

Ohio: $\frac{2,779}{11,459}$

TEKS ★ TAKS

(7.1)(A) To compare and order positive rational numbers TAKS Obj. 1

Using Tables to Compare Data

Analyzing data is easier if the data are organized. You can rearrange a table to organize and display data.

An experiment with seeds resulted in the data recorded in the table. Analyze the data and redraw the table to show which seed types sprouted most frequently.

Seed Type	A	B	C	D	E	F	G	H	I
Number Sprouted	15	5	22	17	18	21	14	18	8
Number Planted	48	20	44	35	52	63	55	35	15

1. For each seed type, find the fraction $\dfrac{\text{number sprouted}}{\text{number planted}}$. **See margin.**

2. Compare the fractions. Order the seed types from most frequently sprouted to least frequently sprouted. (*Hint:* Convert to decimals.) **I, H, C, D, E, F, A, G, B**

3. Redraw the table showing the seed types in order from most frequently sprouted to least frequently sprouted. **See margin.**

✓ Checkpoint Quiz 2

Lessons 2-3 through 2-6

Simplify each fraction.

1. $\dfrac{18}{36}$ $\frac{1}{2}$

2. $\dfrac{42}{60}$ $\frac{7}{10}$

3. $\dfrac{35}{56}$ $\frac{5}{8}$

Compare. Use <, =, or >.

4. $\dfrac{1}{8}$ ■ $\dfrac{2}{100}$
   >

5. $\dfrac{5}{12}$ ■ $\dfrac{7}{9}$
   <

6. $\dfrac{12}{20}$ ■ $\dfrac{3}{5}$
   =

Write each improper fraction as a mixed number and each mixed number as an improper fraction.

7. $\dfrac{29}{6}$ $4\frac{5}{6}$

8. $4\frac{1}{9}$ $\frac{37}{9}$

9. $\dfrac{82}{5}$ $16\frac{2}{5}$

10. Twins are born once in every 89 births. Identical twins are born 4 times in every 1,000 births. Triplets are born once in every 6,900 births. Write each birth frequency as a decimal and order the decimals from least to greatest frequency. **0.00015, 0.004, 0.0112**

101

1. See back of book.
3. See back of book.

TEKS ★

(7.1)(A) To compare and order positive rational numbers **TAKS** Obj. 1

(7.1)(B) To convert between fractions and decimals **TAKS** Obj. 1

Dana Center TEKS Toolkit Clarifying Activities (7.1)(A), (7.1)(B)
Visit: PHSchool.com
Web Code: arq-9045

TEKS Math Background

A *rational number* is a number that can be expressed in the form $\frac{a}{b}$, where *a* and *b* are integers and *b* is not zero. Students learn to compare rational numbers using both fraction and decimal forms.

More Math Background: p. 66D

Lesson Planning and Resources

See p. 66E for a list of the resources that support this lesson.

Bell Ringer Practice

✓ **Check Skills You'll Need**
Use student page, transparency, or PowerPoint.

TAKS Daily Review 17
Use transparency.

✓ Check Skills You'll Need

1. Vocabulary Review
Is 1.234 a repeating decimal or a terminating decimal? Explain.
See below.
Write each fraction as a decimal.

2. $\frac{3}{4}$ 0.75   3. $-\frac{7}{9}$ $-0.\overline{7}$

4. $1\frac{1}{3}$ $1.\overline{3}$ 5. $\frac{12}{48}$ 0.25

GO for Help
Lesson 2-6

Check Skills You'll Need

1. Terminating decimal; the decimal stops.

GO for Help

For help with writing equivalent fractions, go to Lesson 2-3, Example 1.

TEKS ★ **TAKS**

• (7.1)(A) To compare and order positive rational numbers **TAKS** Obj. 1
• (7.1)(B) To convert between fractions and decimals **TAKS** Obj. 1

🔊 **New Vocabulary** rational number

Why Learn This?

Rational numbers are part of everyday life. You see them on price tags, highway signs, and charts. Rational numbers can be written in different forms. To compare rational numbers, it is easier to convert them into the same form.

A **rational number** is a number that can be written as a quotient of two integers, where the divisor is not 0. Examples are $\frac{2}{5}$, $0.\overline{3}$, -6, and $3\frac{1}{2}$.

EXAMPLE Comparing Rational Numbers

① Compare $-\frac{1}{2}$ and $-\frac{3}{4}$.

Method 1

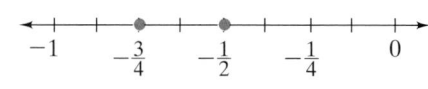

← Since $-\frac{3}{4}$ is farther to the left on the number line, it is the lesser number.

So $-\frac{3}{4} < -\frac{1}{2}$.

Method 2

$$-\frac{1}{2} = \frac{-1}{2}$$ ← Rewrite $-\frac{1}{2}$ with -1 in the numerator.

$$= \frac{-1 \times 2}{2 \times 2}$$ ← The LCD is 4. Write an equivalent fraction.

$$= \frac{-2}{4} = -\frac{2}{4}$$ ← The fraction $-\frac{2}{4}$ is equivalent to $\frac{-2}{4}$.

Since $-\frac{3}{4} < -\frac{2}{4}$, $-\frac{3}{4} < -\frac{1}{2}$.

✓ Quick Check

● **1.** Compare $-\frac{2}{3}$ and $-\frac{1}{6}$. Use $<, =,$ or $>$. $-\frac{2}{3} < -\frac{1}{6}$

---

102   **Chapter 2** Exponents, Factors, and Fractions

Differentiated Instruction Solutions for All Learners

Special Needs L1	**Below Level** L2
For Example 1, have students draw a number line from −1 to 1 with intervals of halves and fourths. Have them trace the distance between 0 and $-\frac{1}{2}$ and then from 0 and $-\frac{3}{4}$ with their finger. Note that the number that is the greater distance in the negative direction is smaller. **learning style: tactile**	Review the procedure for writing two fractions as equivalent fractions with a common denominator. **learning style: verbal**

EXAMPLE **Comparing Decimals**

2 **a.** Compare −4.4 and 4.7.

$$-4.4 < 4.7 \quad \leftarrow \text{Any negative number is less than a positive number.}$$

b. Compare −4.4 and −4.7.

← Place the decimals on a number line and compare their locations.

$-4.4 > -4.7$ since -4.4 is to the right of -4.7.

✓ Quick Check

2. Compare −4.2 and −4.9. Use <, =, or >. **−4.2 > −4.9**

When you compare and order decimals and fractions, it is often helpful to write the fractions as decimals.

EXAMPLE **Ordering Rational Numbers**

3 **TAKS** **Multiple Choice** The peaks of four mountains or seamounts are located either below or above sea level as follows: $\frac{1}{4}$ mi, −0.2 mi, $-\frac{2}{9}$ mi, 1.1 mi. Which list shows the order of numbers from least to greatest?

Ⓐ $\frac{1}{4}, -0.2, -\frac{2}{9}, 1.1$

Ⓑ $\frac{1}{4}, -\frac{2}{9}, 1.1, -0.2$

Ⓒ $-\frac{2}{9}, -0.2, \frac{1}{4}, 1.1$

Ⓓ $-0.2, -\frac{2}{9}, 1.1, \frac{1}{4}$

Order these numbers from least to greatest: $\frac{1}{4}, -0.2, -\frac{2}{9}, 1.1$.

$$\frac{1}{4} = 1 \div 4 = 0.250 \quad \leftarrow \text{Write as a decimal.}$$

$$-\frac{2}{9} = -2 \div 9 = -0.22222\ldots = -0.\overline{2} \quad \leftarrow \text{Write as a repeating decimal.}$$

You can use a number line to order the numbers.

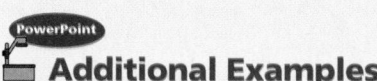

$-0.\overline{2} < -0.2 < 0.25 < 1.1 \quad \leftarrow \text{Compare the decimals.}$

In order, the numbers are $-\frac{2}{9}, -0.2, \frac{1}{4}$, and 1.1. The answer is C.

✓ Quick Check

3. The following temperatures were recorded during a science project: $12\frac{1}{2}°C, -4°C, 6.55°C,$ and $-6\frac{1}{4}°C$. Order the temperatures from least to greatest. **$-6\frac{1}{4}, -4, 6.55, 12\frac{1}{2}$**

★ TAKS Tip

Sometimes it is easier to order rational numbers when they are all written as decimals.

Advanced Learners **L4**

Find four rational numbers that are between −0.3 and $-\frac{1}{3}$. Samples: −0.31, −0.32, −0.315, −0.325

English Language Learners **ELL**

For Example 3, have students draw a vertical number line, with zero as *sea level*. On the left side, have them write intervals from 2 to −2 in tenths. On the right, have them write the intervals using fractions. This will give them a sense of the relative sizes of the numbers.

Pre-AP™

learning style: visual

---

2. Teach

Activity Lab

Use before the lesson.

All in One Teaching Resources

Activity Lab 2-7: Rational Number Shuffle

Guided Instruction

Error Prevention!

When using common denominators to compare, students might focus so intently on rewriting the fractions that they forget whether the original numbers were positive or negative. Encourage them to use a number line to check their work.

Example 3

Divide the work into smaller tasks. Order the negative numbers first, then order the positive numbers:

$-\frac{2}{9} < -0.2 \qquad \frac{1}{4} < 1.1$

Negative numbers are all less than positive numbers, so the four numbers are ordered.

PowerPoint

Additional Examples

1 Compare $-\frac{1}{4}$ and $-\frac{3}{8}$.

$-\frac{1}{4} > -\frac{3}{8}$

2 Compare. Use <, >, or =.

a. 8.7 ■ 8.1 **8.7 > 8.1**

b. −8.7 ■ 8.1 **−8.7 < 8.1**

c. −8.7 ■ 28.1 **−8.7 < −8.1**

3 Order these numbers from least to greatest:

$-\frac{3}{5}, 0.625, \frac{2}{3}, -0.5$

$-\frac{3}{5}, -0.5, 0.625, \frac{2}{3}$

All in One Teaching Resources

• Daily Notetaking Guide 2-7 **L3**
• Adapted Notetaking 2-7 **L1**

Closure

• *How do you compare rational numbers?* Use a number line; express them as fractions with a common denominator and compare the numerators; or express them as decimals and compare them place-by-place.

3. Practice

Assignment Guide

Check Your Understanding
Go over Exercises 1–6 in class before assigning the Homework Exercises.

Homework Exercises
A Practice by Example 7–22
B Apply Your Skills 23–30
C Challenge 31
TEKS ★ **TAKS** Tune-Up and Mixed Review 32–37

Homework Quick Check
To check students' understanding of key skills and concepts, go over Exercises 12, 21, 24, 28, and 29.

Differentiated Instruction Resources

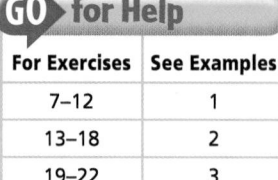

Adapted Practice 2-7 **L1**

Practice 2-7 Rational **L3**

Compare. Use <, >, or =.

2-7 • Guided Problem Solving **GPS** **L3**

Check Your Understanding

1. Answers may vary. Sample: A rational number is a number that can be written as a quotient of two integers.

1. **Vocabulary** In your own words, define *rational number*.

Compare. Use <, =, or >.

2. $2\frac{1}{5}$ ▨ $3\frac{1}{3}$ <

3. $-3\frac{1}{2}$ ▨ $-3\frac{3}{4}$ >

4. -6.1 ▨ -6 <

Order from least to greatest.

5. $-236, -7\frac{1}{7}, 0, \frac{41}{99}, -3.\overline{3}$

$-236, -7\frac{1}{7}, -3.\overline{3}, 0, \frac{41}{99}$

6. $-8, -5\frac{1}{3}, -8.22, -8\frac{1}{3}, \frac{16}{42}$

$-8\frac{1}{3}, -8.22, -8, -5\frac{1}{3}, \frac{16}{42}$

Homework Exercises

For more exercises, see Extra Skills and Word Problems.

GO for Help

For Exercises	See Examples
7–12	1
13–18	2
19–22	3

A **Compare. Use <, =, or >.**

7. $-\frac{1}{7}$ ▨ $-\frac{6}{7}$ >

8. $-\frac{3}{4}$ ▨ -3 >

9. $-\frac{1}{2}$ ▨ $-\frac{2}{10}$ <

10. $-\frac{3}{4}$ ▨ -1 >

11. $-\frac{1}{2}$ ▨ $-\frac{5}{6}$ >

12. $-\frac{4}{5}$ ▨ $-\frac{1}{3}$ <

13. 5.2 ▨ -8.3 >

14. -6.5 ▨ 6.2 <

15. -4.9 ▨ -4.3 <

16. 1.09 ▨ -1.90 >

17. -1.22 ▨ -6.5 >

18. -10.2 ▨ -10.23 >

Order from least to greatest. 19–21. See left.

19. $-1.0, -\frac{3}{4}, 0.25, \frac{3}{2}$

20. $-1.34, -\frac{6}{25}, \frac{7}{3}, 2.4$

21. $-1.5, \frac{1}{2}, 0.545, \frac{6}{11}$

19. $\frac{3}{2}, 0.25, -\frac{3}{4}, -1.0$

20. $\frac{7}{3}, 2.4, -\frac{6}{25}, -1.34$

21. $\frac{6}{11}, -1.5, 0.545, \frac{1}{2}$

22. $\frac{7}{6}, \frac{11}{12}, \frac{14}{24}, 1\frac{14}{24}, \frac{11}{12}, 1, \frac{7}{6}$

B **GPS** 23. **Guided Problem Solving** You are skier A, the first skier in a skiing event with three other skiers. Compared to your time, skier B is slower, by a time of +00:28. Skier C has a time of +02:13, and skier D has a time of −01:24. Who is the fastest skier? **skier D**
- Since all times are compared to yours, what is your time?
- What is the order of times, from fastest to slowest?

24. The table below shows melting points of four elements. Which element has the highest melting point? **xenon**

Melting Points

Chemical Solid	Krypton	Argon	Xenon	Helium
Melting Point (°C)	−157.36	−189.35	−111.79	−272.2

SOURCE: Encyclopædia Brittanica

28. Explanations may vary. Sample:
$-\frac{5}{8} > -\frac{3}{4}$. Common denominators would be easier, since 4 is a factor of 8.

GO Online

Homework Help
Visit: PHSchool.com
Web Code: are-0207

Compare. Use <, =, or >.

25. $-5.8 \ \blacksquare \ -5\frac{9}{10}$
    >

26. $-6\frac{11}{50} \ \blacksquare \ -6.21$
    <

27. $-10.42 \ \blacksquare \ -10.4\overline{2}$
    >

28. **Writing in Math** Compare $-\frac{5}{8}$ and $-\frac{3}{4}$. Is it easier to find common denominators or to write decimal equivalents? Explain. See margin.

29. **Animals** About $\frac{1}{25}$ of a toad's eggs survive to adulthood. About 0.25 of a frog's eggs and $\frac{1}{5}$ of a green turtle's eggs survive to adulthood. Which animal's eggs have the highest survival rate? **GPS** frog

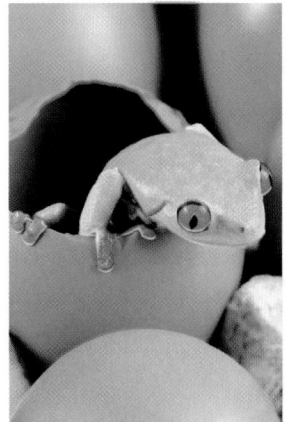

30. **Money** Here is part of Mr. Lostcash's checkbook register. Order his balances from greatest to least. See below left.

Description	Debits (−)	Credits (+)	Balance
Paycheck		122.18	122.18
Sneakers	95.00		27.18
Two outfits	68.09		−40.91
Paycheck		122.18	81.27
Insufficient funds fee	25.00		56.27
Three CDs	59.97		−3.70

30. $122.18, $81.27, $56.27, $27.18, −$3.70, −$40.91

31. **Challenge** Evaluate $\frac{m-n}{-12}$ for $m = -3$ and $n = 6$. $\frac{3}{4}$

TEKS ★ TAKS Tune-Up and Mixed Review

TAKS Objective 6
TEKS (7.13)(B)

32. Harry's class wants to buy one slice of pie for each person in the class. The table below shows prices from a local bakery. What additional information is needed to estimate the total cost? B

Rainbow Bakery Pies

Pie Size	Price	Number of Pieces
Small	$8	2
Medium	$10	3

  Ⓐ The cost of each piece for each pie size
  Ⓑ The number of students in Harry's class
  Ⓒ The number of pieces in each pie
  Ⓓ The flavors of the pies

TAKS Objective 1
TEKS (7.2)(B)

33. Eight photo albums contain equal numbers of photos. Which of the following could be the total number of photos in all the albums? J
  Ⓕ 1,821   Ⓖ 1,218   Ⓗ 1,182   Ⓙ 1,128

GO for Help

Lesson 2-3

Write each fraction in simplest form.

34. $\frac{36}{38}$ $\frac{18}{19}$

35. $\frac{14}{28}$ $\frac{1}{2}$

36. $\frac{12}{56}$ $\frac{3}{14}$

37. $\frac{18}{48}$ $\frac{3}{8}$

 Online lesson quiz, PHSchool.com, Web Code: ara-0207   2-7 Rational Numbers **105**

---

4. Assess & Reteach

Lesson Quiz

Compare. Use <, >, or =.

1. $-\frac{3}{4} \ \blacksquare \ -\frac{4}{7}$ <

2. $-\frac{1}{8} \ \blacksquare \ -\frac{3}{8}$ >

3. $3.4 \ \blacksquare \ -3.4$ >

4. $-8.9 \ \blacksquare \ -8.6$ <

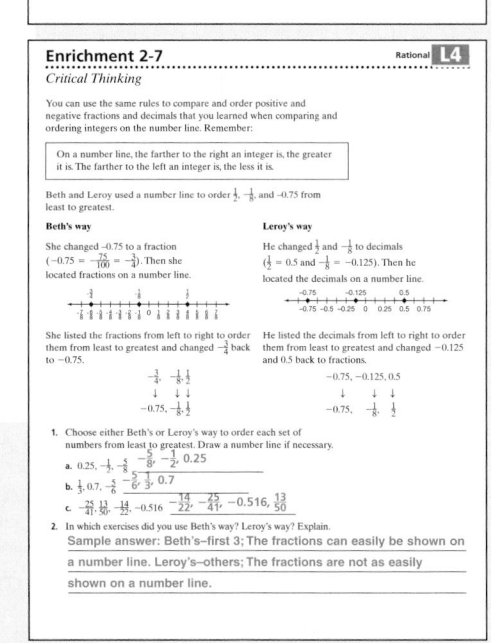

Alternative Assessment

Provide pairs of students with examples such as those in Exercises 7–22. Have partners work together to use number lines to compare the rational numbers.

TEKS ★ TAKS Resources

- TAKS Strategies, p. 111
- TAKS Tune-Up, pp. 115–117

TAKS Tune-Up Kit

- TAKS Daily Review Transparencies
- TAKS Review and Preparation Workbook
- TAKS Strategies with Transparencies
- Texas Progress Monitoring Assessments

105

Objectives

To write numbers in both scientific notation and standard form

Examples

1 Writing in Scientific Notation
2 Writing in Standard Form

✓ Check Skills You'll Need

1. Vocabulary Review
An exponent tells you how many times a number, or base, is used as a __?__.

factor

Simplify.

2. 3^3 27   **3.** 4^2 16

4. 10^5 **5.** 2^4 16
100,000

GO for Help
Lesson 2-1

What You'll Learn

To write numbers in both scientific notation and standard form

◀)) **New Vocabulary** scientific notation

Why Learn This?

Some numbers are so large that they are difficult to write. You can use scientific notation to express large numbers, such as distances and speeds in space. Scientists use scientific notation to calculate with large numbers.

In Lesson 2-1, you learned about exponents. When the base is 10, the exponent tells you the number of zeros the number will have in standard form.

Powers of 10

Exponential Form	10^1	10^2	10^3	10^4	10^5	10^6
Number of Zeros in Standard Form	1	2	3	4	5	6
Standard Form	10	100	1,000	10,000	100,000	1,000,000

When you multiply a factor by a power of 10, you can find the product by moving the decimal point in the factor to the right. The exponent tells you how many places to move the decimal point. When you divide by a power of 10, you move the decimal point to the left.

Multiplying and Dividing by Powers of 10

Standard Form	$3.5 \div 100$	$3.5 \div 10$	3.5×10	3.5×100	$3.5 \times 1,000$
Exponential Form	$3.5 \div 10^2$	$3.5 \div 10^1$	3.5×10^1	3.5×10^2	3.5×10^3
Number	0.035	0.35	35	350	3,500

Scientific notation is a shorter way to write numbers using powers of 10.

Math Background

Scientific notation is a practical way to record the very large and very small measurements that arise in scientific endeavors. This lesson focuses on the scientific notation for numbers greater than 1, which involves positive powers of 10.

More Math Background: p. 66D

Lesson Planning and Resources

See p. 66E for a list of the resources that support this lesson.

Bell Ringer Practice

✓ **Check Skills You'll Need**
Use student page, transparency, or PowerPoint.

TAKS Daily Review 18
Use transparency.

Differentiated Instruction Solutions for All Learners

Special Needs L1
Show students that 10 x 10 x 10 is equal to 1,000, which is written as 10^3. Have them test this out with other powers of ten.

learning style: visual

Below Level L2
Review the process of multiplying and dividing decimals by 10, 100, and 1,000.

learning style: verbal

A number in **scientific notation** is written as the product of two factors, one greater than or equal to 1 and less than 10, and the other a power of 10.

$$7,500,000,000,000 = 7.5 \times 10^{12}$$

EXAMPLE Writing in Scientific Notation

1 **Science** The moon orbits Earth at a distance of 384,000 km. Write this number in scientific notation.

$3.84000.$ ← Move the decimal point to get a factor greater than 1 but less than 10.

$384,000 = 3.84 \times 100,000$ ← Write as a product of 2 factors.

$\qquad\quad = 3.84 \times 10^5$ ← Write 100,000 as a power of 10.

The moon orbits Earth at a distance of 3.84×10^5 km.

Quick Check

1. NASA's Hubble Telescope took pictures of a supernova that is 169,000 light years away. Write this number in scientific notation.

1.69×10^5

You can change expressions from scientific notation to standard form by simplifying the product of the two factors.

EXAMPLE Writing in Standard Form

2 **Science** The mean distance from the sun to Mars is approximately 2.3×10^8 km. Write this number in standard form.

Method 1

$2.3 \times 10^8 = 2.3 \times 100,000,000$ ← Write as a product of 2 factors.

$\qquad\quad = 230,000,000$ ← Multiply the factors.

Method 2

$2.3 \times 10^8 = 2.30000000$ ← The exponent is 8. Move the decimal 8 places to the right.

$\qquad\quad = 230,000,000$

The mean distance is approximately 230,000,000 km.

Quick Check

2. A large telescope gathers about 6.4×10^5 times the amount of light your eye receives. Write this number in standard form. **640,000**

Advanced Learners **L4**

Write each product in scientific notation.

$(4 \times 10^3) \times (2 \times 10^6)$ **8 $\times 10^9$**

$(5 \times 10^4) \times (7 \times 10^8)$ **3.5 $\times 10^{13}$**

Pre-AP™

English Language Learners **ELL**

Have students work in pairs to make a table for multiplying and dividing by powers of 10 similar to the one on page 106. Have students start with standard form for $0.27 \div 100$ and go to $0.27 \div 1,000$. They should give exponential form and the actual number for each product.

learning style: visual

---

2. Teach

Activity Lab

Use before the lesson.

All in One Teaching Resources

Activity Lab 2-8: Scientific Notation

Guided Instruction

Example 1

Students might find it helpful to quietly count the places aloud as they move the decimal point.

Error Prevention!

When changing a number from standard form to scientific notation, students might determine the exponent of 10 by counting all the digits or by counting just the zeros. Suggest that they cover the first digit with one finger and count the remaining digits.

PowerPoint

Additional Examples

1 The mean distance from Mars to the sun is about 141,750,000 mi. Write this number in scientific notation. **1.4175 $\times 10^8$ mi**

2 Light from the sun reaches Earth in about 4.99012×10^2 seconds. Write this time in standard form. **499.012 s**

All in One Teaching Resources

- Daily Notetaking Guide 2-8 **L3**
- Adapted Notetaking 2-8 **L1**

Closure

- *How do you change a number from standard form to scientific notation?* Move the decimal point to obtain a factor that is greater than or equal to 1, but less than 10. Write the second factor as a power of 10 whose exponent is the number of places that you moved the decimal point.

Assignment Guide

Check Your Understanding
Go over Exercises 1–7 in class before assigning the Homework Exercises.

Homework Exercises
A Practice by Example   8–25
B Apply Your Skills   26–33
C Challenge   34
TEKS ★ TAKS Tune-Up and Mixed Review   35–39

Homework Quick Check
To check students' understanding of key skills and concepts, go over Exercises 8, 19, 28, 29, and 31.

Differentiated Instruction Resources

Check Your Understanding

1. It is written as the product of two factors, one greater than or equal to 1 and less than 10, and the other a power of 10.

1. **Vocabulary** Describe how to write a number in scientific notation.

2. **Reasoning** Is 107×10^4 written in scientific notation? Explain.
   No; 107 is not less than 10.

Fill in the blank.

3. $1,700 = 1.7 \times 10^{\blacksquare}$ 3

4. $2,850,000 = \blacksquare \times 10^6$ 2.85

Match the equivalent numbers.

5. 3.96×10^6 B

6. 3.96×10^7 C

7. 3.96×10^5 A

A. 396,000
B. 3,960,000
C. 39,600,000

Homework Exercises

For more exercises, see Extra Skills and Word Problems.

GO for Help

For Exercises	See Examples
8–16	1
17–25	2

A **Write in scientific notation.**

8. 7,500
   7.5×10^3

9. 75,000,000
   7.5×10^7

10. 1,250
    1.25×10^3

11. 44,000
    4.4×10^4

12. 149,000,000
    1.49×10^8

13. 34,025
    3.4025×10^4

14. 11,020
    1.102×10^4

15. 120,000
    1.2×10^5

16. One light year is 5,880,000,000,000 mi. Write in scientific notation.
    5.88×10^{12}

Write in standard form.

17. 3.4×10^3
    3,400

18. 5.9×10^2
    590

19. 8.21×10^3
    8,210

20. 6.678×10^2
    667.8

21. 7.45×10^4
    74,500

22. 9.9673×10^2
    996.73

23. 5×10^{11}
    500,000,000,000

24. 7.02×10^1
    70.2

25. The normal red blood cell count for adult males is about 4.5×10^{12} per liter. Write this number in standard form. 4,500,000,000,000

B **GPS** 26. **Guided Problem Solving** The Folsom Dam in California holds back 319 billion gallons of water. Write this in scientific notation.
   - How can you rewrite 319 billion in standard form? 3.19×10^{11}
   - How do you write 319 billion in scientific notation?

27. **Ballooning** The first balloon to carry passengers weighed 1.6×10^3 lb. Write the number of pounds in standard form.
    1,600 lb

28. The first colony is growing faster, because $2.2 \times 10^6 > 6.3 \times 10^5$.

28. A scientist observes two colonies of bacteria. The first grows at a rate of 2.2×10^6 bacteria per hour. The other grows at a rate of 6.3×10^5 bacteria per hour. Which grows faster? How do you know? See left.

GO Online
Homework Help
Visit: PHSchool.com
Web Code: are-0208

29. **Writing in Math** Explain how you would find the power of 10 needed to write 725,000,000 in scientific notation. See margin.

29. Answers may vary. Sample: The decimal point moves 8 places to the left in 725,000,000 to get 7.25, so the exponent is 8; $725,000,000 = 7.25 \times 10^8$.

30. 1.290×10^{22}, 3.303×10^{23}, 6.421×10^{23}, 4.869×10^{24}, 5.976×10^{24}, 8.686×10^{25}, 1.024×10^{26}, 5.688×10^{26}, 1.900×10^{27}

Planet	Mass (kg)
Mercury	3.303×10^{23}
Venus	4.869×10^{24}
Earth	5.976×10^{24}
Mars	6.421×10^{23}
Jupiter	1.900×10^{27}
Saturn	5.688×10^{26}
Uranus	8.686×10^{25}
Neptune	1.024×10^{26}
Pluto	1.290×10^{22}

30. **Science** The table at the left shows the planets in the solar system and their masses. List the masses in order from least to greatest.
See margin.

31. **Plants** There are about 350,000 species of plants on Earth. Write this number in scientific notation. 3.5×10^5

Math in the Media Use the cartoon below for Exercises 32 and 33.

FOX TROT   by Bill Amend

32. How many minutes was the warning? Write in standard form.
20,000 min

33. Convert the time to hours. Write in scientific notation.
about 3.3×10^2 h

C 34. **Challenge** An astronomical unit (AU) is approximately 9.3×10^7 mi. Pluto is about 39 AU from the sun. Write the distance in miles using both scientific notation and standard form.
3.627×10^9, 3,627,000,000

TEKS ★ TAKS Tune-Up and Mixed Review

TAKS Objective 5
TEKS (7.11)(B)

35. Population density is a measure of how crowded a place is. The table below shows the population density of several states in 1990 and in 2000. Based on the information in the table, which of the following is NOT a reasonable assumption? A

A Texas had the same population density in 1990 that Alabama had in 2000.

B Alabama was more crowded in 1990 than West Virginia was in 2000.

C In 1990, West Virginia was more crowded than Texas.

D All of the states had a greater population density in 2000 than they did in 1990.

Population Density

State	Persons per Square Mile	
	1990	2000
Alabama	$79\frac{3}{5}$	87.6
Missouri	$74\frac{3}{10}$	81.2
Texas	$64\frac{9}{10}$	79.6
W. Virginia	$74\frac{1}{2}$	75.1

 for Help **Lesson 2-2**

Find the LCM of each pair of numbers.

36. 7, 8 56   37. 6, 20 60   38. 11, 3 33   39. 9, 15 45

2-8 Scientific Notation **109**

Lesson Quiz

Write in scientific notation.

1. 45,300 4.53×10^4

2. 714,900,000 7.149×10^8

Write in standard form.

3. 5.7×10^3 5,700

4. 6.034×10^6 6,034,000

Alternative Assessment

Provide 8 index cards to pairs of students. One student writes a decimal greater than or equal to 1 but less than 10 on each of four cards. The other writes a different power of 10 on each of the four other cards. Have students place the cards facedown in two stacks. Pairs draw a card from each stack to make a number written in scientific notation. They then work together to write the number in standard form.

TEKS ★ TAKS Resources

• TAKS Strategies, p. 111
• TAKS Tune-Up, pp. 115–117

TAKS Tune-Up Kit
• TAKS Daily Review Transparencies
• TAKS Review and Preparation Workbook
• TAKS Strategies with Transparencies
• Texas Progress Monitoring Assessments

109

Negative Exponents

This Extension shows how to use scientific notation and negative exponents to represent very small numbers. Students learn to rewrite numbers between 0 and 1 using scientific notation and, conversely, to rewrite in standard form numbers between 0 and 1 that are expressed in scientific notation.

Guided Instruction

Alternative Method
To help students grasp the meaning of negative exponents, discuss the following pattern.

$3^3 = 3 \times 3 \times 3 = 27$

$3^2 = 3 \times 3 = 9$

$3^1 = 3$

$3^0 = 1$

$3^{-1} = \frac{1}{3} = \frac{1}{3^1}$

$3^{-2} = \frac{1}{3} \times \frac{1}{3} = \frac{1}{3^2} = \frac{1}{9}$

$3^{-3} = \frac{1}{3} \times \frac{1}{3} \times \frac{1}{3} = \frac{1}{3^3} = \frac{1}{27}$

The pattern leads to: $a^{-n} = \frac{1}{a^n}$.

Exercises
Have students work on the Exercises and trade papers with a partner to correct each other's work.

Differentiated Instruction

Advanced Learners   **L4**
Have students write several numbers that are less than some in standard form and in scientific notation. Have pairs trade papers and convert numbers to the appropriate form.

Negative Exponents

To write a number between 0 and 1 in scientific notation, you use a negative exponent.

EXAMPLE   **Writing in Scientific Notation**

① Write 0.0084 in scientific notation.

$0.008.4$ ← **Move the decimal point to obtain a factor greater than 1 but less than 10.**

$0.0084 = 8.4 \times 0.001$ ← **Write as the product of 2 factors.**

$= 8.4 \times 10^{-3}$ ← **The decimal point was moved 3 places to the right. Use −3 as the exponent.**

In scientific notation, 0.0084 is written as 8.4×10^{-3}.

EXAMPLE   **Writing in Standard Form**

② Write 3.52×10^{-5} in standard form.

Method 1

$3.52 \times 10^{-5} = 3.52 \times 0.00001$ ← **Write as the product of 2 factors.**

$= 0.0000352$ ← **Multiply the factors.**

Method 2

$3.52 \times 10^{-5} = 0.00003.52$ ← **The exponent of 10 is −5.**
Move the decimal 5 places to the left.

$= 0.0000352$

The value of 3.52×10^{-5} is 0.0000352.

Exercises

Write each number in scientific notation.

1. 0.0008 8.0×10^{-4}

2. 0.00000691
   6.91×10^{-6}

3. 0.5 5.0×10^{-1}

4. 0.049562
   4.9562×10^{-2}

Write each number in standard form.

5. 8.55×10^{-1} 0.855

6. 2.005×10^{-2} 0.02005

7. 6.079×10^{-5} 0.00006079

8. The width of a hair is about 3×10^{-7} meters. 0.0000003

9. A flea weighs 4.9×10^{-3} grams. 0.0049

Finding Needed Information

Some test questions will ask you to find information that is needed to solve a problem.

Brian bought 3 sponges at $1.09 each, 2 bottles of soap at $3.49 each, and a mop for $8.99. He paid sales tax on his purchase and paid with a $20 bill. What other information is necessary to find Brian's total cost?

- Ⓐ Cost of the 3 sponges, 2 soaps, and mop
- Ⓑ Amount of tax he paid on his purchase
- Ⓒ Amount of time he spent cleaning his house
- Ⓓ Brand of soap he bought

You need to find Brian's total cost. Since choices C and D are unrelated to the total cost, eliminate them.

You need to know the amount of tax he paid to find the total cost. The correct answer is choice B.

Objective 6
TEKS (7.13)(B)

1. Minnie bought decorations for her friend's birthday party. She bought one package of 12 candles for $2.99, 15 balloons for $0.49 each, and one birthday cake. She paid 8.25% tax on her purchase and paid with a $50 bill. What other information is necessary to find the change Minnie received? **A**
   - Ⓐ Cost of the birthday cake
   - Ⓑ Color of the candles
   - Ⓒ Cost of 15 balloons
   - Ⓓ Minnie's friend's name

Objective 6
TEKS (7.14)(A)

2. Hans bought mugs for $2 each. He decorated the mugs and sold them for $4.99 each. He sold 13 mugs on Saturday and even more on Sunday. What additional piece of information is needed to find the amount of profit he made from the sale of mugs on Saturday and Sunday? **G**
   - Ⓕ Number of mugs sold on Friday
   - Ⓖ Number of mugs sold on Sunday
   - Ⓗ Total profit Hans makes on each mug
   - Ⓙ Where Hans buys the mugs

 Strategies

Finding Needed Information

Some test questions ask students what information is needed to solve a problem without asking students to solve the problem. In this feature, students learn to determine what information is missing and necessary to solve a problem.

Guided Instruction

List all the information given in the problem. Then write a word equation with this information. Review and determine what information is still needed.

Exercises

Have students work on the Exercises. Then have a volunteer explain to the class how he or she arrived at their answers.

TEKS   Resources

Strategies with Transparencies
- Transparency 4
- Practice sheet, p. 14

Strategies with Transparencies

Test-Taking Strategies: Finding Needed Information

Some test questions ask you to find missing information needed to solve a problem. First, figure out how you would solve the problem. Then decide what information you still need.

> *Example* Molly bought toys for her sister's sandbox. She bought 4 shovels for $1.29 each, 2 buckets for $1.89 each and a set of toy trucks. The tax on her purchase was 8.25% and she paid with a $20 bill. What other information is necessary to find the change Molly received?
>
> A. Cost of the set of trucks
> B. The color of the shovels
> C. The cost of the 2 buckets
> D. The number of children playing in the sandbox

- The color of the shovels does not affect the price. Eliminate choice B.
- The cost of 2 buckets is given. Eliminate choice C.
- The number of children playing in the sandbox does not change the purchase price. Eliminate choice D.
- You need to know the cost of the set of trucks in order to find the total cost of the toys, so the correct answer is A.

Apples cost $0.75 each and bananas cost $0.15 each. Trinity bought 5 apples and 6 bananas. What other information is necessary to find the amount of change Trinity will receive from the cashier?

A. the weight of each apple
B. the amount given to the cashier
C. the number of pieces of fruit purchased
D. the weight of each banana

Chapter 2 Review

Vocabulary Review

 base (p. 68)
composite number (p. 75)
equivalent fractions (p. 82)
exponent (p. 68)
factor (p. 75)
greatest common factor (GCF)
  (p. 75)

improper fraction (p. 91)
least common denominator
  (LCD) (p. 87)
least common multiple (p. 74)
mixed number (p. 91)
multiple (p. 74)
power (p. 68)

prime factorization (p. 75)
prime number (p. 75)
rational number (p. 102)
repeating decimal (p. 97)
scientific notation (p. 107)
simplest form (p. 82)
terminating decimal (p. 96)

Go Online
PHSchool.com
For: Online vocabulary quiz
Web Code: arj-0251

Choose the correct term to complete each sentence.

1. In the expression 6^3, 3 represents the (power, exponent). **exponent**

2. A (composite, prime) number has exactly two factors, 1 and itself. **prime**

3. (Multiples, Factors) of 28 are 1, 2, 4, 7, 14, and 28. **factors**

4. At a class party, you and two friends eat $\frac{6}{8}$ of a pizza. This can also be written as the (improper fraction, equivalent fraction) $\frac{3}{4}$. **equivalent fraction**

5. The (GCF, LCM) of 24 and 36 is 12. **GCF**

Skills and Concepts   **TEKS** ★ **TAKS**

Lesson 2-1
(7.2)(E) To simplify
expressions involving
order of operations
and exponents **TAKS** Obj. 1
(7.1)(C) To represent
squares using geometric
models **TAKS** Obj. 1

An **exponent** tells you how many times a number, or base, is used as a factor. A number expressed with an exponent is a **power**.

Simplify.

6. -2^4 −16   7. $(-4)^3$ −64   8. $5^2 + 10^2$ 125   9. $4(5^2 - 10)$
                                                                         60

Lesson 2-2
• To find multiples and
  factors and to use prime
  factorization
• Prepares for **TEKS**
  (7.2)(B) To solve problems
  involving fractions

A **multiple** is the product of a number and any nonzero whole number. A **factor** is a whole number that divides another whole number with a remainder of 0. A whole number greater than 1 is **composite** if it has more than two factors and is **prime** if its only factors are 1 and itself.

Write the prime factorization. Use exponents where possible.

10. 84   11. 78   12. 90   13. 92   14. 125
$2^2 \cdot 3 \cdot 7$ $2 \cdot 3 \cdot 13$ $2 \cdot 3^2 \cdot 5$ $2^2 \cdot 23$ 5^3

15. A grocer buys food from three suppliers. The suppliers deliver every 5 days, 6 days, and 7 days. All three came today. In how many days will they all deliver on the same day again? **210 days from now**

112

Lessons 2-3, 2-4

(7.1)(A) To compare and order positive rational numbers ⟨TAKS⟩ Obj. 1

Prepares for **TEKS** (7.2)(B) To use addition, subtraction, multiplication, and division to solve problems involving fractions

A fraction is in **simplest form** when the numerator and denominator have no common factors other than 1. To compare and order fractions, you can use the **least common denominator (LCD),** which is the least common multiple of the fractions' denominators.

Order from least to greatest. $\frac{5}{9}, \frac{7}{12}, \frac{2}{3}$

16. $\frac{1}{4}, \frac{1}{3}, \frac{1}{6}$ $\frac{1}{6}, \frac{1}{4}, \frac{1}{3}$ **17.** $\frac{1}{4}, \frac{2}{5}, \frac{3}{8}$ $\frac{1}{4}, \frac{3}{8}, \frac{2}{5}$ **18.** $\frac{3}{8}, \frac{5}{6}, \frac{1}{2}$ $\frac{3}{8}, \frac{1}{2}, \frac{5}{6}$ **19.** $\frac{5}{9}, \frac{2}{3}, \frac{7}{12}$

20. Martha saw the same item on sale at two stores. Store A's sign read "Sale! $\frac{1}{3}$ off!" Store B's sign read "Sale! $\frac{2}{5}$ off!" Which store offered a greater discount?   store B

Lesson 2-5

• To write mixed numbers and improper fractions

• Prepares for **TEKS** (7.1)(A) To compare and order positive rational numbers

An **improper fraction** has a numerator that is greater than or equal to its denominator. A **mixed number** is the sum of a whole number and a fraction.

21. Tracey worked a total of 345 min. on a project. Use mixed numbers to write the time in hours. $5\frac{3}{4}$ h

Write each improper fraction as a whole or mixed number. Simplify.

22. $\frac{42}{7}$ 6   **23.** $\frac{27}{12}$ $2\frac{1}{4}$ **24.** $\frac{20}{3}$ $6\frac{2}{3}$ **25.** $\frac{125}{5}$ 25   **26.** $\frac{84}{12}$ 7

Lessons 2-6, 2-7

(7.1)(A) To compare and order positive rational numbers ⟨TAKS⟩ Obj. 1

(7.1)(B) To convert between fractions, decimals, and whole numbers mentally, on paper, or with a calculator ⟨TAKS⟩ Obj. 1

To write a fraction as a decimal, you divide the numerator by the denominator. When the division ends with a remainder of 0, the quotient is a **terminating decimal.** When the same block of digits in a decimal repeats without end, the quotient is a **repeating decimal.** A **rational number** can be written as the quotient of two integers, where the denominator is not zero.

Write each fraction as a decimal.

27. $\frac{1}{3}$ $0.\overline{3}$ **28.** $\frac{5}{9}$ $0.\overline{5}$ **29.** $\frac{5}{2}$ 2.5   **30.** $\frac{16}{20}$ 0.8   **31.** $\frac{4}{50}$ 0.08

Order from least to greatest.   32–34. See margin.

32. $\frac{3}{4}, 0.\overline{3}, -\frac{7}{8}$ **33.** $2.7, -0.3, -\frac{4}{11}$ **34.** $-\frac{5}{6}, 2.2, -0.5$

Lesson 2-8

• To write numbers in scientific notation and in standard form

A number in **scientific notation** is written as a product of a factor greater than or equal to 1 but less than 10, and another factor that is a power of 10.

Write in scientific notation or in standard form.   35–38. See margin.

35. 7,123,000   **36.** 9.06×10^5 **37.** 81,900   **38.** 6.015×10^8

Chapter 2   Chapter Review   **113**

32. $-\frac{7}{8}, 0.\overline{3}, \frac{3}{4}$

33. $-\frac{4}{11}, -0.3, 2.7$

34. $-\frac{5}{6}, -0.5, 2.2$

35. 7.123×10^6

36. 906,000

37. 8.19×10^4

38. 601,500,000

Chapter 2 Test

Go Online For: Online chapter test
PHSchool.com **Web Code:** ara-0252

Find the value of each expression.

1. $(3^2 - 4) + 5$ 10
2. $5^2 - 7^2$ −24
3. $(6 - 9)^3$ −27
4. $54 + 3^2$ 63

Write using an exponent.

5. $3 \cdot 3 \cdot 3 \cdot 3$ 3^4
6. $11 \cdot 11 \cdot 11$ 11^3

Write the prime factorization. Use exponents where possible.

7. 48 $2^4 \cdot 3$
8. 60 $2^2 \cdot 3 \cdot 5$
9. 121 11^2

List 3 factors and 3 multiples of each number.
10–13. See margin.
10. 27   **11.** 36   **12.** 100   **13.** 25

Find the GCF of each pair of numbers.

14. 32, 40   8
15. 55, 15   5
16. 36, 57   3
17. 24, 68   4

18. Reasoning Tell whether each statement is true or false. 18a. false   b. false
a. 2 is a composite number.
b. Any factor of a whole number is greater than any multiple of a whole number.
c. A number is divisible by 3 if its last digit is divisible by 3.   false
d. 1 is neither composite nor prime.   true

19. Use a factor tree to write the prime factorization of 42.   See margin.

Write two fractions equivalent to each fraction.

20. $\frac{1}{3}$ **21.** $-\frac{15}{24}$ **22.** $-\frac{4}{5}$ **23.** $\frac{16}{28}$
20–23. See margin.

Write each fraction in simplest form.

24. $\frac{12}{18}$ $\frac{2}{3}$
25. $\frac{27}{54}$ $\frac{1}{2}$
26. $\frac{36}{96}$ $\frac{3}{8}$
27. $\frac{7}{42}$ $\frac{1}{6}$

28. Writing in Math Explain how you can use prime factorization to write a fraction in simplest form.   See margin.

29. Modeling Draw models to represent $\frac{3}{4}$ and $2\frac{3}{5}$.   See margin.

30. What fraction does the shaded part of the model represent? $\frac{3}{8}$

Compare. Use <, =, or >.

31. $\frac{2}{9}$ ■ $\frac{8}{9}$ <
32. $\frac{5}{16}$ ■ $\frac{3}{8}$ <
33. $\frac{7}{18}$ ■ $\frac{2}{5}$ <

34. Ships A crew finds a treasure chest with 168 gold coins and 200 silver coins. Each crew member gets the same share of gold coins and of silver coins, with none left over.
a. What is the greatest possible number of crew members?   8 crew members
b. How many of each type of coin does each crew member get?   21 gold, 25 silver

Write as an improper fraction.

35. $5\frac{2}{3}$ $\frac{17}{3}$
36. $4\frac{5}{6}$ $\frac{29}{6}$
37. $8\frac{7}{10}$ $\frac{87}{10}$
38. $3\frac{2}{5}$ $\frac{17}{5}$

Write as a whole number or a mixed number.

39. $\frac{12}{5}$ $2\frac{2}{5}$
40. $\frac{30}{9}$ $3\frac{1}{3}$
41. $\frac{48}{12}$ 4
42. $\frac{42}{30}$ $1\frac{2}{5}$

Write each fraction as a decimal.

43. $\frac{2}{16}$ 0.125
44. $\frac{6}{15}$ 0.4
45. $\frac{5}{4}$ 1.25
46. $\frac{8}{25}$ 0.32

Write each decimal as a mixed number or fraction in simplest form.

47. 0.2 $\frac{1}{5}$
48. 1.3 $1\frac{3}{10}$
49. 0.35 $\frac{7}{20}$
50. 3.62 $3\frac{31}{50}$

Write using scientific notation.

51. 12,300,000 1.23×10^7
52. 75,462 7.5462×10^4

Write in standard form.

53. 2.1×10^4 21,000
54. 8×10^9 8,000,000,000

55. Order from least to greatest:
$$2.56, -2.\overline{5}, -2\frac{1}{5}, \frac{24}{10}, -2.4$$
$-2.\overline{5}, -2.4, -2\frac{1}{5}, \frac{24}{10}, 2.56$

Exercises 10–13. Answers may vary. Samples are given.

10. 1, 3, 9; 54, 81, 108
11. 1, 2, 3; 72, 108, 144
12. 1, 2, 4; 200, 300, 400
13. 1, 5, 25; 50, 75, 100

19.

42
6   7
3   2

Exercises 20–23. Answers may vary. Samples are given.

20. $\frac{2}{6}, \frac{3}{9}$
21. $-\frac{5}{8}, -\frac{10}{16}$
22. $-\frac{8}{10}, -\frac{12}{15}$
23. $\frac{4}{7}, \frac{8}{14}$

28–29. See back of book.

★ TAKS Tips

Some TAKS test questions ask you to use data from a table to find the correct answer. Read the question and review the answer choices. Then follow the tips to answer the sample question.

The table below shows prices per pound of different vegetables sold at a market.

Vegetable	Price per lb.
Potatoes	$0.99
Onions	$1.49
Carrots	$2.19
Zucchini	$1.75

What is the median price per pound for these vegetables?

- (A) $1.49
- (B) $1.62
- (C) $1.75
- (D) $1.84

Tip 1
You are asked to find the *median* of this set of data. Rewrite the prices in order, from least to greatest.

Think It Through
You know the answer will be between $1.49 and $1.75, so you can eliminate choices A and C. You can also eliminate D since it is too great. The correct answer is B.

Tip 2
Since there are an even number of items, you will need to average the middle 2 items, which are $1.49 and $1.75.

TEKS ★ TAKS Resources

TAKS Review and Preparation Workbook

Texas ExamView CD-ROM
- Instant TAKS Practice Test
- TAKS Practice Items

Differentiated Instruction

Texas Progress Monitoring Assessments
- Benchmark Test 1 **L3**

Spanish Assessment Resources
- Spanish Cumulative Review **ELL**

Texas ExamView CD-ROM
- Special Needs Practice Bank **L1**

Vocabulary Builder

As you solve test items, you must understand the meanings of mathematical terms. Match each term with its mathematical meaning.

A. expression II

B. median I

C. range III

D. equivalent IV
fraction

I. the middle value when data are arranged in numerical order

II. a mathematical phrase made up of numbers and operations

III. the difference between the greatest and least values in a set of data

IV. a fraction that names the same amount as another fraction

---

Multiple Choice

Read each question. Then write the letter of the correct answer on your paper.

1. The table shows the typical temperatures in Fairbanks, Alaska, for selected months of the year.

Typical Temperatures in Fairbanks, Alaska

Month	Temperature
January	−10°F
February	−4°F
March	11°F
October	24°F
November	2°F
December	−6°F

Which month has the lowest typical temperature? **A**

- (A) January
- (B) February
- (C) November
- (D) December

TAKS Daily Review Transparencies

TAKS Daily Review 1 Objective 1: (7.1)(B)
Multiple Choice

The seventh-grade class at Anarene Middle School sold 13/20 of the Corsicana fruitcakes they bought. Which decimal is equivalent to the fraction sold?

A 65
B 0.65
C 6.5
D 650

Answer: B

TAKS Daily Review 2 Objective 5: (7.12)(A)
Multiple Choice

Shey has been practicing running the 200-meter foot race. Her last 6 times are shown.

23.60 24.15 24.68 28.62 24.25 23.92

What is her mean time?

F 5.02
G 23.92
H 24.21
J 24.87

Answer: J

---

2. Misty's four puppies weigh $\frac{7}{16}$, $\frac{5}{16}$, $\frac{5}{8}$, and $\frac{3}{8}$ pound. Which weight is greater than one half pound? **H**

   F $\frac{7}{16}$ lb   H $\frac{5}{8}$ lb

   G $\frac{5}{16}$ lb   J $\frac{3}{8}$ lb

3. A scientist found the following weights in tons for four whales: $\frac{1}{2}$, $\frac{3}{5}$, $\frac{11}{20}$, and $\frac{7}{10}$. Which weight is the greatest? **D**

   A $\frac{1}{2}$ B $\frac{3}{5}$ C $\frac{11}{20}$ D $\frac{7}{10}$

4. Which expression is represented by the model below? **G**

   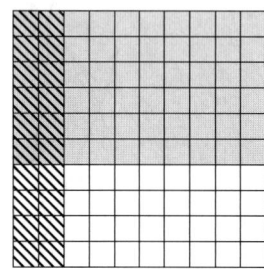

   F 0.5 × 0.2   H 0.6 × 0.3

   G 0.6 × 0.2   J 0.5 × 0.3

5. Joe bought 4.5 meters of cotton cloth for $2.85 per meter. Which expression can be used to find the total cost of the cloth, before tax? **A**

   A 4.5 × 2.85   C 4.5 + 2.85

   B 4.5 ÷ 2.85   D 4.5 − 2.85

6. A farmer had a 20-acre tract of land with $\frac{4}{5}$ of the acres planted in wheat, as shown below.

   Which decimal is equivalent to the part of the farmer's land planted in wheat? **H**

   F 0.08   G 0.45   H 0.80   J 80.0

7. Carly made 21 pints, or $\frac{21}{8}$ gallons, of fruit punch. What is $\frac{21}{8}$ as a mixed number? **C**

   A $3\frac{5}{8}$ B $2\frac{3}{4}$ C $2\frac{5}{8}$ D $2\frac{3}{8}$

8. Jamie had four automobiles between 2000 and 2006. The following table shows the miles per gallon (mpg) each car got on the highway and in the city. **J**

Cars	Highway (mpg)	City (mpg)
2000	19	15
2002	42	38
2004	26	25
2006	28	21

   Which year shows the greatest range between highway and city miles per gallon?

   F 2000   G 2002   H 2004   J 2006

9. On Saturday, McGuire's Tree Lot sold 19 pine trees for $30 each and 1 fir tree for $50. What was the mean amount of money the tree lot made per tree on Saturday? **B**

   A $4.00   C $32.78

   B $31.00   D $40.00

10. The table at the right shows the costs of different types of flowers at Sue's Flower Shop. What is the median price per flower? **G**

Flower	Cost
Rose	$2.25
Baby's breath	$0.75
Carnation	$1.35
Lily	$1.75
Iris	$1.80

    F $1.80   G $1.75   H $1.58   J $1.35

11. Krista is driving 1,500 miles to see her aunt. Her car can travel 25 miles per gallon of gas. What additional information does she need to estimate the total cost of gas for the trip? **D**

    A The time it will take to drive

    B The amount of gas her car will hold

    C The kind of car she has

    D The cost of each gallon of gas

---

12. Which is NOT a step you would use to find how many hours there are between 10:00 A.M. and 2:55 P.M. as a mixed number in simplest form? **H**

Ⓕ Simplify $4\frac{55}{60}$ to $4\frac{11}{12}$.

Ⓖ Count 4 h from 10:00 A.M. to 2:00 P.M.

Ⓗ Simplify $\frac{455}{60}$.

Ⓙ Write the minutes as $\frac{55}{60}$ hour.

13. In a survey, 150 students were asked to name their dream car. The results are in the table.

Dream Car	Number of Students
Porsche 900	20
Ferrari F355	32
Mustang	48
Mazda Miata	4
Firebird	10
Other	36

Which of the following statements is supported by the information in the table?

Ⓐ About $\frac{1}{4}$ of the students chose the Firebird.

Ⓑ About $\frac{1}{2}$ of the students chose either the Ferrari or the Porsche 900.

Ⓒ About $\frac{1}{3}$ of the students chose the Mustang.

Ⓓ The least number of students chose the Mazda because of the price of the car.

C

14. The table shows the number of animals a veterinarian saw each month for 6 months. Based on the information in the table, which of the following is NOT a reasonable assumption? **H**

Month	Number of Animals
January	63
February	76
March	122
April	188
May	243
June	164

Ⓕ The veterinarian saw about half as many animals in January as in March.

Ⓖ The veterinarian saw almost 3 times as many animals in April as in January.

Ⓗ The total number of animals seen in the first 3 months is the same as the total number seen in the last 3 months.

Ⓙ The total number of animals seen in the first 6 months is about 900.

Griddable Items
Record your answers in a grid.

15. One lap around a track is 0.94 kilometers. Jessie ran 4.5 laps. How many kilometers did Jessie run? **4.23**

16. Bo takes 0.625 milligrams of an antibiotic, 4 times a day. How many milligrams of antibiotic does Bo take each day? **2.5**

(TAKS) GO for Help Guide

TAKS Objective	Item Numbers	GO To	TAKS Objective	Item Numbers	GO To
Obj. 1: (7.1)(A)	1	Lesson 1-6	Obj. 5: (7.12)(A)	8–10	Lesson 1-10
	2–3	Lesson 2-4	Obj. 6: (7.13)(B)	11	Lesson 1-8
Obj. 1: (7.2)(A)	4–5	Lesson 1-3		12	Lesson 2-5
Obj. 1: (7.1)(B)	6	Lesson 2-6	Obj. 5: (7.11)(B)	13–14	Lesson 2-3
	7	Lesson 2-5	Obj. 1: (7.2)(B)	15–16	Lesson 1-3

For additional TAKS practice, see the *TAKS Review and Preparation Workbook*.

3 Operations With Fractions

Chapter at a Glance

Lesson Titles, Objectives, and Features	Assessment	NCTM Standards	TEKS ★ TAKS
3-1 Estimating With Fractions and Mixed Numbers • To estimate sums, differences, products, and quotients of fractions **Vocabulary Builder:** High-Use Academic Words	Lesson Quiz	1, 2, 6, 7, 8, 9, 10	**TEKS** (7.14)(A) **TAKS** Obj. 6; Prepares for **TEKS** (7.2)(B)
3-2a Activity Lab, Hands On: Using Fraction Models **3-2 Adding and Subtracting Fractions** • To add and subtract fractions and to solve problems involving fractions	Lesson Quiz	1, 2, 6, 7, 8, 9, 10	**TEKS** (7.2)(B), (7.2)(F), (7.2)(G) **TAKS** Obj. 1 **TEKS** (7.13)(D)
3-3 Adding and Subtracting Mixed Numbers • To add and subtract mixed numbers and to solve problems involving mixed numbers	Lesson Quiz Checkpoint Quiz 1	1, 2, 6, 7, 8, 9, 10	**TEKS** (7.2)(B), (7.2)(F), (7.2)(G) **TAKS** Obj. 1
3-4a Activity Lab, Hands On: Modeling Fraction Multiplication **3-4 Multiplying Fractions and Mixed Numbers** • To multiply fractions and mixed numbers and to solve problems by multiplying	Lesson Quiz	1, 2, 6, 7, 8, 9, 10	**TEKS** (7.2)(A), (7.2)(B), (7.2)(F), (7.14)(A) **TAKS** Obj. 1, 6
3-5a Activity Lab, Hands On: Modeling Fraction Division **3-5 Dividing Fractions and Mixed Numbers** • To divide fractions and mixed numbers and to solve problems by dividing **Guided Problem Solving:** Practice Solving Problems	Lesson Quiz	1, 2, 6, 7, 8, 9, 10	**TEKS** (7.2)(A), (7.3)(B), (7.2)(G) **TAKS** Obj. 1 **TEKS** (7.13)(D)
3-6 Changing Units in the Customary System • To change units of length, capacity, and weight in the customary system **3-6b Activity Lab, Algebra Thinking:** Solving Puzzles	Lesson Quiz Checkpoint Quiz 2	1, 2, 4, 6, 7, 8, 9, 10	**TEKS** (7.2)(B), (7.2)(F), (7.3)(B), (7.14)(A) **TAKS** Obj. 1, 2, 6
3-7a Activity Lab: Choosing Appropriate Units **3-7 Precision** • To find and compare the precision of measurement **3-7b Activity Lab:** Estimating in Diffent Systems	Lesson Quiz	1, 2, 4, 6, 7, 8, 9, 10	**TEKS** (7.2)(B), (7.3)(B), (7.14)(A) **TAKS** Obj. 1, 2, 6
TAKS Tune-Up: Cumulative Practice			

NCTM Standards 2000

1 Number and Operations	2 Algebra	3 Geometry	4 Measurement	5 Data Analysis and Probability
6 Problem Solving	7 Reasoning and Proof	8 Communication	9 Connections	10 Representation

Correlations to Standardized Tests

All content for these tests is contained in *Prentice Hall Math*, Course 2. This chart reflects coverage in this chapter only.

	3-1	3-2	3-3	3-4	3-5	3-6	3-7
Terra Nova CAT6 (Level 17)							
Number and Number Relations	✔	✔	✔	✔	✔	✔	✔
Computation and Numerical Estimation	✔	✔	✔	✔	✔	✔	✔
Operation Concepts	✔	✔	✔	✔	✔	✔	✔
Measurement						✔	✔
Geometry and Spatial Sense							
Data Analysis, Statistics, and Probability							
Patterns, Functions, Algebra	✔	✔	✔	✔	✔	✔	✔
Problem Solving and Reasoning	✔	✔	✔	✔	✔	✔	✔
Communication	✔	✔	✔	✔	✔	✔	✔
Decimals, Fractions, Integers, and Percent	✔	✔	✔	✔	✔	✔	✔
Order of Operations							
Terra Nova CTBS (Level 17)							
Decimals, Fractions, Integers, Percents	✔	✔	✔	✔	✔	✔	✔
Order of Operations, Numeration, Number Theory	✔	✔	✔	✔	✔	✔	✔
Data Interpretation							
Pre-Algebra	✔	✔	✔	✔	✔	✔	✔
Measurement						✔	✔
Geometry							
ITBS (Level 13)							
Number Properties and Operations	✔	✔	✔	✔	✔	✔	✔
Algebra	✔	✔	✔	✔	✔	✔	✔
Geometry							
Measurement						✔	✔
Probability and Statistics							
Estimation	✔						
SAT10 (Int 3 Level)							
Number Sense and Operations	✔	✔	✔	✔	✔	✔	✔
Patterns, Relationships, and Algebra	✔	✔	✔	✔	✔	✔	✔
Data, Statistics, and Probability							
Geometry and Measurement						✔	✔
NAEP							
Number Sense, Properties, and Operations	✔	✔	✔	✔	✔		
Measurement						✔	✔
Geometry and Spatial Sense							
Data Analysis, Statistics, and Probability							
Algebra and Functions							

CAT6 California Achievement Test, 6th Ed. **CTBS** Comprehensive Test of Basic Skills **ITBS** Iowa Test of Basic Skills, Form M
SAT10 Stanford Achievement Test, 10th Ed. **NAEP** National Assessment of Educational Progress 2005 Mathematics Objectives

TEKS Math Background

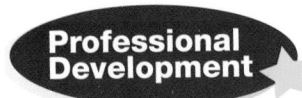

Focus on the TEKS

- At Grade 7, students represent multiplication and division situations involving fractions with models (7.2)(A). Analysis of TAKS results shows that students struggle with this new student expectation.

  In Lessons 3-4 and 3-5, students use models and pictures to gain an understanding of multiplication and division with fractions and mixed numbers. Place special emphasis on these lessons because they all focus on (7.2)(A).

- Also new at Grade 7, students estimate and find solutions involving proportional relationships (7.3)(B). In Lesson 3-6, students apply concepts of proportional relationships to solve problems involving related measurement units.

3-1 Estimating With Fractions and Mixed Numbers

TEKS ★ TAKS Prepares for TEKS (7.2)(B)

Math Understandings

- You can find approximate answers by using estimation.
- You can estimate the value of fractions between 0 and 1 by comparing the size of the numerator and the denominator.
- You can estimate the value of mixed numbers by rounding to the nearest whole number.

A **benchmark** is a value that can be used as a reference point. Round to the benchmark 0 when the numerator of a fraction is very small compared to the denominator; use $\frac{1}{2}$ when the numerator is about half the denominator; and use 1 when the numerator and denominator are nearly equal.

| Estimate as 0 when the numerator is very small compared to the denominator. | Estimate as $\frac{1}{2}$ when the numerator is about half the denominator. | Estimate as 1 when the numerator and denominator are nearly equal. |

3-2 3-3 Adding and Subtracting Fractions and Mixed Numbers

TEKS ★ TAKS (7.2)(B), (7.2)(F), (7.2)(G) Obj. 1

Math Understandings

- The idea of changing something to something simpler is a powerful idea in math.
- The product of the denominators will always give a common denominator, but it may not be the Least Common Denominator.
- Any common denominator can be used, but using the Least Common Denominator may save steps.
- In order to subtract from a mixed number, it may be necessary to rename the mixed number.

Usually, to add or subtract two mixed numbers, combine the fraction parts and then combine the whole numbers. An alternative method is to write the mixed numbers as improper fractions and combine them.

3-4 3-5 Multiplying and Dividing Fractions and Mixed Numbers

TEKS ★ TAKS (7.2)(A), (7.2)(B), (7.2)(F), (7.2)(G) Obj. 1

Math Understandings

- Multiplying fractions and mixed numbers does not necessarily give a product less than both factors.
- Finding half of a number is the same as multiplying that number by $\frac{1}{2}$ and as dividing that number by 2.
- A number and its reciprocal multiply to a product of 1.
- You can rewrite dividing by a number as multiplying by the reciprocal of that number.

Multiplying Fractions	
Arithmetic	**Algebra**
$\frac{3}{4} \cdot \frac{1}{2} = \frac{3 \cdot 1}{4 \cdot 2} = \frac{3}{8}$	$\frac{a}{b} \cdot \frac{c}{d} = \frac{ac}{bd}$, b and $d \neq 0$
Dividing Fractions	
Arithmetic	**Algebra**
$\frac{5}{8} \div \frac{1}{8} = \frac{5}{8} \cdot \frac{8}{1}$	$\frac{a}{b} \div \frac{c}{d} = \frac{a}{b} \cdot \frac{d}{c}$, b, c and $d \neq 0$

To multiply a fraction by a whole number, rewrite the whole number as a fraction with a denominator of 1, for example, 7 becomes $\frac{7}{1}$. To multiply mixed numbers, rewrite them as improper fractions and then multiply.

Two numbers are **reciprocals** if their product is 1. The reciprocal of a fraction is the fraction with the numerator and denominator interchanged, for example, 5 and $\frac{1}{5}$, $\frac{2}{3}$ and $\frac{3}{2}$.

3-6 Changing Units in the Customary System

TEKS ★ TAKS (7.2)(B), (7.2)(F), (7.3)(B), (7.14)(A) Obj. 1, 2, 6

Math Understandings
- To change between customary units, use multiplication or division of equivalent units.

You can use the customary unit equivalents to change from smaller units to larger units and from larger units to smaller units.

Customary Units of Measure			
Type	**Length**	**Capacity**	**Weight**
Unit	inch (in.)	fluid ounce (fl oz)	ounce (oz)
			pound (lb)
	foot (ft)	cup (c)	ton (t)
	yard (yd)	pint (pt)	
	mile (mi)	quart (qt)	
		gallon (gal)	
Equivalents	1 ft = 12 in.	1 c = 8 fl oz	1 lb = 16 oz
	1 yd = 3 ft	1 pt = 2 c	1 t = 2,000 lb
	1 mi = 5,280 ft	1 qt = 2 pt	
		1 gal = 4 qt	

3-7 Precision

TEKS ★ TAKS (7.2)(B) Obj. 1

Math Understandings
- Every measurement is an approximation that is only as accurate as the method and the instruments used.
- The precision of a measurement tells you how finely the measurement is made.
- When you compare measurements, the more precise measurement is the one with the smaller unit of measure.

The **precision** of a measurement is its degree of exactness, which you can determine from the smallest marks on the measuring instrument used.

Example: Choose the more precise measurement.

16 cm, 15.5 cm

Tenths of a cm are smaller than the units digit, so 15.5 cm is more precise.

Additional Professional Development Opportunities

Math Background Notes for Chapter 3: Every lesson has a Math Background in the PLAN section.

Research Overview, Mathematics Strands
Additional support for these topics and more is in the front of the Teacher's Edition.

LessonLab
LessonLab, a Pearson Education company, offers comprehensive, facilitated professional development designed to help teachers to improve student achievement. To learn more, please visit lessonlab.com.

Texas Chapter 3 Resources

Print Resources

	3-1	3-2	3-3	3-4	3-5	3-6	3-7	For the Chapter
L3 Practice	●	●	●	●	●	●	●	
L1 Adapted Practice	●	●	●	●	●	●	●	
L3 Guided Problem Solving	●	●	●	●	●	●	●	
L2 Reteaching	●	●	●	●	●	●	●	
L4 Enrichment	●	●	●	●	●	●	●	
L3 Daily Notetaking Guide	●	●	●	●	●	●	●	
L1 Adapted Daily Notetaking Guide	●	●	●	●	●	●	●	
L3 Vocabulary and Study Skills Worksheets	●					●	●	●
L3 Daily Puzzles	●	●	●	●	●	●	●	
L3 Activity Labs	●	●	●	●	●	●	●	
L3 Checkpoint Quiz			●			●		
L3 Chapter Project								●
L2 Chapter Test								●
L3 Chapter Test								●
L4 Alternative Assessment								●
L3 Cumulative Review								●

Spanish Resources ELL

	3-1	3-2	3-3	3-4	3-5	3-6	3-7	For the Chapter
L3 Practice	●	●	●	●	●	●	●	●
L3 Vocabulary and Study Skills Worksheets	●		●	●		●	●	●
L3 Checkpoint Quiz			●			●		
L2 Chapter Test								●
L3 Chapter Test								●
L4 Alternative Assessment								●
L3 Cumulative Review								●

Transparencies

	3-1	3-2	3-3	3-4	3-5	3-6	3-7	For the Chapter
Check Skills You'll Need	●	●	●	●	●	●	●	
Additional Examples	●	●	●	●	●	●	●	
Problem of the Day	●	●	●	●	●	●	●	
TAKS Daily Review	●	●	●	●	●	●	●	
Classroom Aid	●							
Student Edition Answers	●	●	●	●	●	●	●	●
Lesson Quiz	●	●	●	●	●	●	●	
TAKS Strategies								●

Technology

	3-1	3-2	3-3	3-4	3-5	3-6	3-7	For the Chapter
Texas Interactive Textbook Online	●	●	●	●	●	●	●	●
Texas StudentExpress CD-ROM	●	●	●	●	●	●	●	●
Success Tracker™ Online Intervention	●	●	●	●	●	●	●	●
TeacherExpress CD-ROM	●	●	●	●	●	●	●	●
PresentationExpress CD-ROM	●	●	●	●	●	●	●	●
Texas ExamView CD-ROM with QuickTake	●	●	●	●	●	●	●	●
MindPoint Quiz Show CD-ROM	●	●	●	●	●	●	●	●
Prentice Hall Web Site: PHSchool.com	●	●	●	●	●	●	●	●

Also available: **TAKS Tune-Up Kit**
- TAKS Daily Review Transparencies
- TAKS Review and Preparation Workbook
- TAKS Strategies with Transparencies
- Texas Progress Monitoring Assessments
- Texas ExamView CD-ROM
- MindPoint Quiz Show CD-ROM

Other Resources
Algebra Readiness Tests
All-in-One Student Workbook
All-in-One Student Workbook, Adapted Version
Multilingual Handbook

Solution Key
Math Notes Study Folder
Spanish Cumulative Assessment

Where You Can Use the Lesson Resources

Here is a suggestion, following the four-step teaching plan, for how you can incorporate Differentiated Instruction Resources into your teaching.

	Instructional Resources L3	**Differentiated Instruction Resources**
1. Plan		
Preparation Read the Math Background in the Teacher's Edition to connect this lesson with students' previous experience. **Starting Class** **Check Skills You'll Need** Assign these exercises to review prerequisite skills. **TEKS ★ TAKS** Review the full text of the TEKS student expectations and TAKS objectives covered in this lesson. **New Vocabulary** Help students pre-read the lesson by pointing out the new terms introduced in the lesson.	**TEKS Math Background** **Math Understandings** **Transparencies & PresentationExpress CD-ROM** Check Skills You'll Need Problem of the Day TAKS Daily Review **Resources** Vocabulary and Study Skills	**Spanish Support** ELL Vocabulary and Study Skills
2. Teach		
L3 Guided Instruction Use the Activity Labs to build conceptual understanding. Teach each Example. Use the Teacher's Edition side column notes for specific teaching tips, including Error Prevention notes. Use the Additional Examples found in the side column (and on transparency and PowerPoint) as an alternative presentation for the content. After each Example, assign the Quick Check exercise for that Example to get an immediate assessment of student understanding. Use the Closure activity in the Teacher's Edition to help students attain mastery of lesson content.	**Student Edition** Activity Lab **Resources** Daily Notetaking Guide Activity Lab **Transparencies & PresentationExpress CD-ROM** Additional Examples Classroom Aids **Texas ExamView CD-ROM with QuickTake**	**Teacher's Edition** Every lesson includes suggestions for working with students who need special attention. L1 Special Needs L2 Below Level L4 Advanced Learners ELL English Language Learners **Resources** L1 Adapted Daily Notetaking Guide **Multilingual Handbook**
3. Practice		

Assignment Guide
Check Your Understanding
Use these questions to check students' understanding before you assign homework.
Homework Exercises
Assign homework from these leveled exercises in the Assignment Guide.
  A Practice by Example
  B Apply Your Skills
  C Challenge
  TAKS Tune-Up and Mixed Review
Homework Quick Check
Use these key exercises to quickly check students' homework.
	Transparencies & PresentationExpress CD-ROM
	Student Answers
	Resources
	Practice
	Guided Problem Solving
	Vocabulary and Study Skills
	Activity Lab
	Daily Puzzles
	Texas ExamView CD-ROM with QuickTake
		Spanish Support
		ELL Practice
		ELL Vocabulary and Study Skills
		Resources
		L1 Adapted Practice
		L4 Enrichment

4. Assess & Reteach		
Lesson Quiz Assign the Lesson Quiz to assess students' mastery of the lesson content. **Checkpoint Quiz** Use the Checkpoint Quiz to assess student progress over several lessons.	**Transparencies & PresentationExpress CD-ROM** Lesson Quiz **Resources** Checkpoint Quiz	**Resources** L2 Reteaching ELL Checkpoint Quiz Success Tracker™ Online Intervention **Texas ExamView CD-ROM with QuickTake**

KEY   L1 Special Needs   L2 Below Level   L3 For All Students   L4 Advanced, Gifted   ELL English Language Learners

Operations With Fractions

What You've Learned
TEKS ★ TAKS

- **(7.2)(C)** In Chapter 1, you used models, such as concrete objects, and number lines, to add, subtract, multiply, and divide integers and connected the actions to algorithms. **TAKS Obj. 1**

- **(7.1)(B)** In Chapter 2, you converted between fractions and decimals. **TAKS Obj. 1**

 Check Your Readiness

Adding and Subtracting Integers

Find each sum or difference.

1. $-55 + 15$ -40 **2.** $-3 + (-21)$ -24

3. $58 - (-42)$ 100 **4.** $-7 - (-25)$ 18

Multiplying and Dividing Integers

Find each product or quotient.

5. $-3 \cdot 15$ -45 **6.** $-12 \cdot (-5)$ 60 **7.** $39 \div (-13)$ -3 **8.** $-60 \div (-3)$ 20

Finding the Greatest Common Factor

Use prime factorization to find the GCF of each pair of numbers.

9. $18, 27$ 9 **10.** $21, 42$ 21 **11.** $24, 36$ 12 **12.** $45, 36$ 9

Simplifying Fractions

Write each fraction in simplest form.

13. $\dfrac{12}{16}$ $\dfrac{3}{4}$ **14.** $\dfrac{15}{30}$ $\dfrac{1}{2}$ **15.** $\dfrac{42}{48}$ $\dfrac{7}{8}$ **16.** $\dfrac{27}{72}$ $\dfrac{3}{8}$

17. $\dfrac{19}{57}$ $\dfrac{1}{3}$ **18.** $\dfrac{25}{45}$ $\dfrac{5}{9}$ **19.** $\dfrac{34}{51}$ $\dfrac{2}{3}$ **20.** $\dfrac{16}{56}$ $\dfrac{2}{7}$

For Exercises	See Lesson
1–4	1-7
5–8	1-8
9–12	2-4
13–20	2-5

GO for Help

118   Chapter 3

Number, Operation, and Quantitative Reasoning
TEKS (7.2)(A), (7.2)(B), (7.2)(F), (7.2)(G)
TAKS Obj. 1

Patterns, Relationships, and Algebraic Thinking
TEKS (7.3)(B) *TAKS* Obj. 2

Underlying Processes and Mathematical Tools
TEKS (7.14)(A) *TAKS* Obj. 6;
TEKS (7.13)(D)

Chapter 3 Overview

In this chapter, students build on fraction concepts to estimate and compute with fractions and mixed numbers. They change units within the customary measurement system. Then they learn about the concept of precision.

Activating Prior Knowledge

In this chapter, students will build on their knowledge of fraction concepts to add, subtract, multiply, and divide fractions. Ask questions such as:

- *What is the greatest common factor of two numbers?* the greatest number that divides each number without a remainder
- *What is the greatest common factor of 9 and 12?* 3
- *What is the least common multiple of two numbers?* the least number that is a multiple of both numbers
- *What is the least common multiple of 6 and 8?* 24

What You'll Learn Next
TEKS ★ *TAKS*

- **(7.2)(B)** In this chapter, you will use addition, subtraction, multiplication, and division to solve problems involving fractions. *TAKS* **Obj. 1**

- **(7.2)(A)** You will represent multiplication and division situations involving fractions with models including concrete objects, pictures, words, and numbers. *TAKS* **Obj. 1**

- **(7.14)(A)** You will communicate mathematical ideas using appropriate units. *TAKS* **Obj. 6**

 Key Vocabulary

- benchmark (p. 120)
- precision (p. 154)
- reciprocal (p. 141)

> **(*TAKS* Tune-Up)** On pages 163–165, you will review and practice the vocabulary and *TAKS* objectives you have learned.

Chapter 3   **119**

Estimating With Fractions and Mixed Numbers

Prepares for **TEKS (7.2)(B)** To use addition, subtraction, multiplication, and division to solve problems involving fractions

TEKS Math Background

A benchmark is a value that can be used as a reference point. Using benchmarks to estimate, will help students later when they evaluate the reasonableness of their answers. Students can use the benchmark values of 0, $\frac{1}{2}$, and 1 to estimate sums and differences for fractions between 0 and 1.

More Math Background: p. 118C

Lesson Planning and Resources

See p. 118E for a list of the resources that support this lesson.

PowerPoint

Bell Ringer Practice

☑ **Check Skills You'll Need**
Use student page, transparency, or PowerPoint.

TAKS Daily Review 19
Use transparency.

☑ **Check Skills You'll Need**

1. Vocabulary Review
How is estimating with *compatible numbers* different from estimating by *rounding*?
See below.
Use compatible numbers to estimate each quotient.

2. 49.8 ÷ 6.8 **7**

3. 21.05 ÷ 5.29 **4**

4. 25.27 ÷ 2.99 **8**

5. 52.6 ÷ 8.8 **6**

6. 19.4 ÷ 10.1 **2**

 for Help
Lesson 1-1

Check Skills You'll Need

1. When you estimate by rounding, you round a number to the nearest unit. When you use compatible numbers, you look for numbers that are easy to compute mentally.

What You'll Learn

To estimate sums, differences, products, and quotients involving fractions

- Prepares for **TEKS (7.2)(B)** To use addition, subtraction, multiplication, and division to solve problems involving fractions

🔊 **New Vocabulary** benchmark

Why Learn This?

Estimation can help you find amounts that are not whole numbers.

At the right, $\frac{7}{12}$ of one pie and $\frac{3}{8}$ of the other pie remain. You can estimate that a total of about one full pie remains.

A **benchmark** is a convenient number used to replace fractions less than 1. You can use the benchmarks 0, $\frac{1}{2}$, and 1 to estimate fractions.

Estimate as 0 when the numerator is very small compared to the denominator.

Estimate as $\frac{1}{2}$ when the numerator is about half the denominator.

Estimate as 1 when the numerator and denominator are nearly equal.

EXAMPLE Using Benchmarks With Fractions

① A family bought a plot of land last year that was $\frac{4}{9}$ acre. They plan to buy an adjoining plot this year that is $\frac{7}{8}$ acre. Estimate the total amount of land the family will have.

$$\frac{4}{9} + \frac{7}{8} \approx \frac{1}{2} + 1 = 1\frac{1}{2} \quad \leftarrow \text{Use benchmarks to estimate each fraction. Then add.}$$

The family will have about $1\frac{1}{2}$ acres of land.

☑ Quick Check

1. Use benchmarks to estimate $\frac{3}{5} - \frac{1}{8}$. about $\frac{1}{2}$

Differentiated Instruction Solutions for All Learners

Special Needs **L1**
Give students number lines and rectangles. Have them shade in about $\frac{1}{8}$ on one rectangle, about $\frac{4}{5}$ on another and about $\frac{2}{5}$ on another. Then have them place a point for each fraction on the number line closest to the benchmark number to which it corresponds.   **learning style: visual**

Below Level **L2**
Have students make lists of fractions whose benchmark values are 0, $\frac{1}{2}$, and 1.
Sample: 0: $\frac{1}{9}, \frac{3}{16}, \frac{2}{7}, \ldots$;
$\frac{1}{2}: \frac{5}{10}, \frac{2}{5}, \frac{3}{8}, \frac{4}{9}, \ldots$; 1: $\frac{4}{5}, \frac{7}{9}, \frac{10}{13}, \frac{15}{18} \ldots$
learning style: visual

To estimate a sum, difference, or product of mixed numbers, you can first round each mixed number to the nearest whole number. Then compute.

EXAMPLES **Estimating With Mixed Numbers**

2 A skysurfer falls 500 feet in about $2\frac{4}{5}$ seconds. A skydiver wearing a wing suit falls 500 feet in about $4\frac{1}{6}$ seconds. Approximately how many more seconds than the skysurfer does the skydiver take to fall 500 feet?

$$4\frac{1}{6} - 2\frac{4}{5} \qquad \leftarrow \text{Use subtraction.}$$
$$\downarrow \qquad \downarrow$$
$$4 \ - \ 3 \ = \ 1 \qquad \leftarrow \text{Round each mixed number. Then subtract.}$$

The skydiver takes about 1 more second than the skysurfer to fall 500 ft.

3 Estimate the product $2\frac{2}{5} \cdot 6\frac{1}{10}$.

$$2\frac{2}{5} \ \cdot \ 6\frac{1}{10}$$
$$\downarrow \qquad \downarrow$$
$$2 \ \cdot \ 6 \ = \ 12 \qquad \leftarrow \text{Round each mixed number. Then multiply.}$$

✓ Quick Check

2. Science For an experiment on plant growth, you recorded the height of a plant every day. On Monday, the plant was $5\frac{1}{4}$ in. tall. A week later, it was $10\frac{7}{8}$ in. tall. About how many inches did the plant grow?
about 6 in.

3. Use rounding to estimate each product.

   a. $3\frac{5}{6} \cdot 5\frac{1}{8}$ about 20   **b.** $8\frac{1}{8} \cdot 5\frac{11}{12}$ about 48   **c.** $7\frac{1}{3} \cdot 1\frac{13}{16}$
                                                                       about 14

To estimate a quotient of mixed numbers, you can use compatible numbers. Choose numbers that are easy to divide.

EXAMPLE **Estimating With Compatible Numbers**

Vocabulary Tip

Compatible numbers are numbers that are easy to compute mentally.

4 Estimate the quotient $43\frac{1}{4} \div 5\frac{7}{8}$.

$$43\frac{1}{4} \div 5\frac{7}{8}$$
$$\downarrow \qquad \downarrow$$
$$42 \div 6 = 7 \quad \leftarrow \begin{array}{l}\text{Use compatible numbers.}\\ \text{Use 42 for } 43\frac{1}{4} \text{ and use 6 for } 5\frac{7}{8}.\end{array}$$

✓ Quick Check

4. Use compatible numbers to estimate each quotient.

   a. $35\frac{3}{4} \div 5\frac{11}{12}$ **b.** $22\frac{7}{8} \div 3\frac{5}{6}$ **c.** $46\frac{2}{5} \div 5\frac{1}{10}$
     about 6   about 6   about 9

3-1 Estimating With Fractions and Mixed Numbers   **121**

Advanced Learners **L4**

Estimate.

$2\frac{1}{2} + 3\frac{1}{5} + 1\frac{5}{20}$ 7

$2\frac{1}{2} \cdot 3\frac{1}{5} \cdot 1\frac{5}{20}$ 9

Pre-AP™

English Language Learners **ELL**

Provide examples of fractions such as $\frac{1}{8}, \frac{4}{5}, \frac{2}{5}$. Have students decide on the benchmark number to which each is closest and answers in complete sentences. Ask: *Is $\frac{1}{8}$ closer to 0, $\frac{1}{2}$, or 1? How do you know?* Sample: $\frac{1}{8}$ is closest to the benchmark value of 0.

learning style: verbal

---

2. Teach

Activity Lab

Use before the lesson.

All in One Teaching Resources

Activity Lab 3-1: Estimating With Fractions

Guided Instruction

Example 2

Ask students how long it would take them to clean their desks or lockers in hours and fractions of an hour. Use those mixed numbers to create comparison problems.

Example 4

If students are unable to recognize compatible numbers, include the intermediate step of rounding to the nearest whole number. Then ask: *What division fact is closest to this problem?*
$42 \div 6 = 7$

PowerPoint

Additional Examples

1 Use benchmarks to estimate $\frac{4}{7} + \frac{4}{5} \cdot \frac{1}{2} + 1 = 1\frac{1}{2}$

2 Estimate $5\frac{1}{9} - 2\frac{5}{6}$. $5 - 3 = 2$

3 Estimate $6\frac{1}{8} \cdot 6\frac{5}{8}$. $6 \cdot 7 = 42$

4 Estimate $26\frac{1}{4} \div 8\frac{2}{3}$.
$27 \div 9 = 3$

All in One Teaching Resources

• Daily Notetaking Guide 3-1 **L3**
• Adapted Notetaking 3-1 **L1**

Closure

• *Which fractions have a benchmark estimate of 0?* those where the numerator is much smaller than the denominator
• *What are the two steps in estimating a product of mixed numbers?* Round each mixed number to the nearest whole number. Multiply.

Assignment Guide

Check Your Understanding
Go over Exercises 1–10 in class before assigning the Homework Exercises.

Homework Exercises
A Practice by Example 11–32
B Apply Your Skills 33–43
C Challenge 44
TEKS ★ TAKS Tune-Up and Mixed Review 45–51

Homework Quick Check
To check students' understanding of key skills and concepts, go over Exercises 17, 25, 34, 37, and 43.

Differentiated Instruction Resources

Adapted Practice 3-1 · Practice 3-1 · 3-1 Guided Problem Solving worksheets

Check Your Understanding

1. Answers may vary. Sample: A benchmark is a convenient number used to replace a fraction. Examples are 0, $\frac{1}{2}$, and 1 for fractions between 0 and 1.

1. **Vocabulary** What is a benchmark? See left.

2. **Reasoning** How can you tell whether a fraction is greater than, less than, or equal to $\frac{1}{2}$? Explain. See margin.

Choose a benchmark for each fraction. Use 0, $\frac{1}{2}$, or 1.

3. $\frac{15}{16}$ 1   4. $\frac{1}{10}$ 0   5. $\frac{5}{8}$ $\frac{1}{2}$ 6. $\frac{2}{9}$ 0

Round each mixed number to the nearest whole number.

7. $1\frac{1}{3}$ 1   8. $10\frac{3}{4}$ 11   9. $6\frac{7}{12}$ 7   10. $8\frac{2}{5}$ 8

Homework Exercises

For more exercises, see Extra Skills and Word Problems.

GO for Help

For Exercises	See Examples
11–19	1
20–28	2–3
29–32	4

Ⓐ **Use benchmarks to estimate each sum or difference.**

11. $\frac{1}{7} + \frac{3}{8}$ about $\frac{1}{2}$ 12. $\frac{3}{5} - \frac{1}{2}$ about 0   13. $\frac{5}{11} - \frac{1}{5}$ about $\frac{1}{2}$ 14. $\frac{8}{9} - \frac{5}{6}$ about 0

15. $\frac{1}{6} + \frac{5}{8}$ about $\frac{1}{2}$ 16. $\frac{3}{4} + \frac{1}{5}$ about 1   17. $\frac{3}{4} - \frac{5}{6}$ about 0   18. $\frac{9}{10} + \frac{7}{16}$ about $1\frac{1}{2}$

19. Suppose it rains $\frac{4}{5}$ inch in the morning and $\frac{6}{7}$ inch in the afternoon. About how many inches of rain fall during the day? about 2 in.

Use rounding to estimate.

20. $9\frac{1}{11} - 3\frac{7}{9}$ about 5   21. $5\frac{3}{5} + 3\frac{2}{3}$ about 10   22. $4\frac{1}{2} - \frac{24}{25}$ about 4   23. $7\frac{2}{3} - 2\frac{11}{12}$ about 5

24. $2\frac{1}{8} \cdot 3\frac{6}{7}$ about 8   25. $5\frac{2}{9} \cdot 4\frac{9}{10}$ about 25   26. $3\frac{3}{8} \cdot 5\frac{1}{6}$ about 15   27. $1\frac{7}{10} \cdot 8\frac{1}{12}$ about 16

28. Marsha bought $1\frac{3}{8}$ lb of snow peas and $3\frac{1}{10}$ lb of carrots at the market. About how many more pounds of carrots did she buy? 2 lb

Use compatible numbers to estimate each quotient.

29. $10\frac{7}{8} \div 3\frac{1}{9}$ about 4   30. $36\frac{1}{3} \div 4\frac{2}{5}$ about 9   31. $7\frac{3}{5} \div 1\frac{1}{2}$ about 4   32. $8\frac{2}{12} \div 8\frac{2}{7}$ about 1

Ⓑ **GPS** 33. **Guided Problem Solving** You want to make three kinds of pasta salad. The recipes call for $\frac{2}{3}$ c, $\frac{3}{4}$ c, and $1\frac{2}{3}$ c of pasta. You have 4 c of pasta. Do you have enough? Explain.
- About how many cups of pasta do you need for each recipe?
- About how many cups of pasta do you need for all 3 recipes?

34. **Number Sense** $30\frac{1}{7} \div 1\frac{4}{5}$ is about $30 \div 2 = 15$. Is the estimate of 15 for the quotient high or low? Explain. See above left.

34. Low; the dividend, $30\frac{1}{7}$, becomes smaller when estimating, and the divisor, $1\frac{4}{5}$, becomes larger. When you divide by a larger number, the quotient is smaller.

33. Yes; $\frac{2}{3} + \frac{3}{4} + 1\frac{2}{3} = 3\frac{1}{12}$, which is less than 4.

2. Compare the fraction's numerator and denominator. If the numerator is less than half the denominator, the fraction is less than $\frac{1}{2}$. If the numerator is greater than half the denominator, the fraction is greater than $\frac{1}{2}$. If the numerator is the same as half the denominator, the fraction is equal to $\frac{1}{2}$.

39. about $\frac{1}{2}$ t

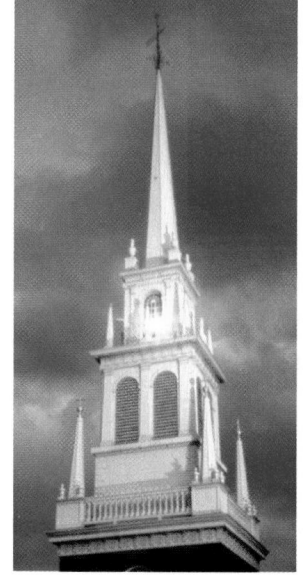

Use benchmarks to estimate each sum or difference.

35. $6\frac{5}{6} + 8\frac{2}{12} + 14\frac{1}{7}$ about 29

36. $19\frac{9}{11} - 4\frac{5}{14} - 3\frac{7}{8}$ about 12

37. A teacher's school day is $8\frac{1}{4}$ h long. The teacher has six classes every day. Each class is $\frac{5}{6}$ h long. About how many hours of the school day is the teacher not in class? **2 h**

Music The table below shows the weight of the bells of Boston's Old North Church. Use the table for Exercises 38–42.

Tone	F	E	D	C	B-flat	A	G	Low F
Weight in Tons	$\frac{3}{10}$	$\frac{3}{10}$	$\frac{7}{20}$	$\frac{2}{5}$	$\frac{11}{25}$	$\frac{19}{40}$	$\frac{3}{5}$	$\frac{3}{4}$

38. Estimate the total weight of the two heaviest bells. **about $1\frac{1}{2}$ t**

39. Estimate the weight difference of the F bell and the Low F bell. **See left.**

40. Which bells weigh less than $\frac{1}{2}$ ton? **F, E, D, C, B-flat, and A**

41. Estimate the total weight of all eight bells. **about $4\frac{1}{2}$ t**

42. Estimate the average weight of the four heaviest bells. **about $\frac{1}{2}$ t**

43. **Writing in Math** You need $9\frac{9}{16}$ lb of chicken. The store sells
 chicken in half-pound quantities. How much chicken should you order? Explain. **10 lb; $9\frac{9}{16} > 9\frac{1}{2}$, so the next amount is 10 lb.**

C 44. **Challenge** Estimate the median of $9\frac{3}{5}$, $5\frac{1}{4}$, $7\frac{5}{10}$, $1\frac{7}{8}$, $6\frac{3}{4}$, and $3\frac{2}{8}$. **6**

TEKS ★ TAKS Tune-Up and Mixed Review

TAKS Objective 1
TEKS (7.2)(B)

45. Jade needs $2\frac{2}{3}$ yards of fabric to make one tablecloth. She has $11\frac{2}{3}$ yards of fabric. What is the greatest number of tablecloths Jade can make? **B**
   Ⓐ 3   Ⓑ 4   Ⓒ 5   Ⓓ 6

TAKS Objective 1
TEKS (7.2)(A)

46. The length of a piece of fabric measures between 3 and $3\frac{1}{4}$ feet. Which length could it be? **G**
   Ⓕ $\frac{72}{25}$ ft   Ⓖ $\frac{25}{8}$ ft   Ⓗ $\frac{18}{5}$ ft   Ⓙ $\frac{26}{7}$ ft

TAKS Objective 5
TEKS (7.12)(A)

47. Brian bought 4 burritos for $15. He later bought another burrito for $2.50. What was the mean cost of all the burritos? **B**
   Ⓐ $3.15   Ⓑ $3.50   Ⓒ $3.75   Ⓓ $12.50

 Lesson 2-6

Write each decimal as a mixed number or fraction in simplest form.

48. 0.04 $\frac{1}{25}$ 49. 11.125 $11\frac{1}{8}$ 50. 0.0625 $\frac{1}{16}$ 51. 3.408 $3\frac{51}{125}$

TEKS ★ TAKS Resources
- TAKS Strategies, p. 159
- TAKS Tune-Up, pp. 163–165

TAKS Tune-Up Kit
- TAKS Daily Review Transparencies
- TAKS Review and Preparation Workbook
- TAKS Strategies with Transparencies
- Texas Progress Monitoring Assessments

Lesson Quiz

Estimate.
1. $\frac{1}{8} + \frac{3}{5}$ $\frac{1}{2}$
2. $4\frac{3}{4} - 1\frac{2}{3}$ 3
3. $2\frac{5}{6} \cdot 6\frac{1}{10}$ 18
4. $43\frac{7}{8} \div 10\frac{1}{3}$ 4

Alternative Assessment

Have students work in pairs. In turn, each student chooses one exercise from each group of Exercises 11–18, 20–27, and 29–32. Each student estimates, as directed, and then explains to the partner how he or she made the estimate.

123

High-Use Academic Words

Students learn words that are not necessarily math related, but that will appear frequently in their texts. Learning these words will help them understand what to do to solve problems.

Guided Instruction

Go over the words and their meanings with students. Point out that they are all verbs, or action words, that tell you to do something.
Ask:

- *How can we use* explain *in a math problem?* **Sample: Explain why we divide the numerator by the denominator to convert a fraction to a decimal.**
- *What does* find *usually mean in a math problem?* **You may need to go through several steps to obtain the correct answer.**
- *What does the* Order of Operations *do?* **It tells in which order you should do certain operations.**

Advanced Learners **L4**
Ask students to create riddles whose answers are the vocabulary words. They can trade papers with a partner and solve each other's riddles.

TEKS ★ TAKS Resources

Dana Center TEKS Toolkit
Clarifying Activities (7.14)(A)
Visit: PHSchool.com
Web Code: arq-9045

Vocabulary Builder

High-Use Academic Words

High-use academic words are words that you will see often in textbooks and on tests. These words are not math vocabulary terms, but knowing them will help you to succeed in mathematics.

TEKS ★ TAKS
(7.14)(A) To communicate mathematical ideas using language **TAKS** **Obj. 6**

Direction Words

Some words tell what to do in a problem. I need to understand what these words are asking so that I give the correct answer.

Word	Meaning
Explain	To give details that make an idea easy to understand
Find	To obtain an answer by solving a problem
Order	To arrange or organize information in a sequence

Exercises

**Fill in the blank with *order, explain,* or *find.*

1. Question: What is the correct __?__ of a U.S. student's education? **order**

   Answer: elementary school, middle school, high school

2. In many middle schools, students must __?__ the classroom for each subject they take. **find**

3. On the first day of school, many teachers __?__ the rules of the class. **explain**

4. Explain how you know that the sum of $\frac{4}{5}$ and $\frac{14}{15}$ will be greater than 1. **See below.**

5. Find compatible numbers for $80\frac{5}{6}$ and $9\frac{2}{9}$ and estimate the quotient. $81 \div 9 = 9$

6. Order the fractions $\frac{4}{8}, \frac{2}{6}, -\frac{10}{12}, \frac{4}{4}, -\frac{1}{3}$ from least to greatest. $-\frac{10}{12}, -\frac{1}{3}, \frac{2}{6}, \frac{4}{8}, \frac{4}{4}$

7. **Word Knowledge** Think about the word *reasonable*. **7a–c. Check students' work.**
   a. Choose the letter for how well you know the word.
      A. I know its meaning.
      B. I've seen it, but I don't know its meaning.
      C. I don't know it.
   b. **Research** Look up and write the definition of *reasonable*.
   c. Use the word in a sentence involving mathematics.

4. Answers may vary. Sample: Their sum is greater than 1, because both $\frac{4}{5}$ and $\frac{14}{15}$ are approximately 1.

Hands On

TEKS ★ *TAKS*

(7.2)(B) To use addition and subtraction to solve problems involving fractions *TAKS* **Obj. 1**

(7.13)(D) To select tools such as manipulatives to solve problems

Using Fraction Models

You can use models to add and subtract fractions.

EXAMPLES **Using Fractions**

1 Find $\frac{3}{10} + \frac{1}{10}$.

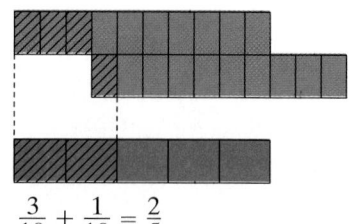

← To add, align the right side of the shaded part of the first model with the left side of the second one.

← Find a model that represents the sum of the shaded parts. If you have more than one model to choose from, use the one with the largest sections.

$\frac{3}{10} + \frac{1}{10} = \frac{2}{5}$

2 Find $\frac{3}{4} - \frac{1}{3}$.

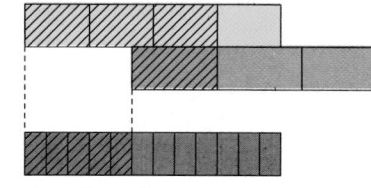

← To subtract, align the right ends of the shaded part of each model.

← Find the model that represents the difference.

$\frac{3}{4} - \frac{1}{3} = \frac{5}{12}$

Exercises

Write a number sentence for each model.

1.

? $\frac{4}{5} - \frac{2}{5} = \frac{2}{5}$

2.

? $\frac{3}{4} + \frac{1}{6} = \frac{11}{12}$

Use models to find each sum or difference. 3–6. See margin for models.

3. $\frac{3}{8} + \frac{3}{8}$ $\frac{3}{4}$

4. $\frac{5}{6} - \frac{1}{6}$ $\frac{2}{3}$

5. $\frac{2}{5} + \frac{1}{2}$ $\frac{9}{10}$

6. $\frac{7}{10} - \frac{1}{5}$ $\frac{1}{2}$

7. You need 1 lb of sugar. You have $\frac{3}{8}$ lb and $\frac{2}{5}$ lb of sugar. Do you have enough? No; $\frac{3}{8} + \frac{2}{5} = \frac{31}{40}$, which is less than 1.

3–6. See back of book.

Activity Lab

Using Fraction Models

By using models, such as fraction bars, students can gain a concrete understanding of adding and subtracting fractions.

Guided Instruction

Provide time for students to explore modeling with their fraction bars. Circulate as students work through the examples, helping them to find and align their models.

Provide additional examples, using fractions with the same denominators such as $\frac{1}{5} + \frac{3}{5}$ $\frac{4}{5}$ and $\frac{1}{6} + \frac{3}{6}$. $\frac{2}{3}$ Discuss and model that the fractions $\frac{2}{2}$, $\frac{3}{3}$, $\frac{4}{4}$, and so on, are equivalent to 1.

Exercises

Have students work independently on the Exercises. When they have finished, have them trade papers with a partner and check each other's answers.

Alternative Method

Many kinds of fraction manipulatives are useful and readily available (for use with an overhead projector, too). Your students may have success using fraction cubes, squares, tiles, attribute blocks, or Cuisenaire® rods as alternatives.

TEKS ★ *TAKS* Resources

- Activity Lab 3-2: Fraction Bar Explorations
- fraction bars
- Student Manipulatives Kit
- Classroom Aid 12–19

Dana Center TEKS Toolkit Clarifying Activities (7.2)(B), (7.13)(D)
Visit: PHSchool.com
Web Code: arq-9045

125

Adding and Subtracting Fractions

TEKS ★ 🐟AKS

(7.2)(B) To use addition and subtraction to solve problems involving fractions 🐟AKS Obj. 1
Also supports
(7.2)(F) 🐟AKS Obj. 1
(7.2)(G) 🐟AKS Obj. 1

Dana Center TEKS Toolkit Clarifying Activities (7.2)(B), (7.2)(F), (7.2)(G)
Visit: PHSchool.com
Web Code: arq-9045

TEKS ★ 🐟AKS

- (7.2)(B) To use addition and subtraction to solve problems involving fractions 🐟AKS Obj. 1
- (7.2)(F) To select and use appropriate operations to solve problems 🐟AKS Obj. 1
- (7.2)(G) To determine the reasonableness of a solution to a problem 🐟AKS Obj. 1

TEKS Math Background

To add and subtract fractions that have a common denominator, add or subtract the numerators and simplify the result. For fractions with different denominators, the fractions must be changed to a common denominator. Then add or subtract the numerators.

More Math Background: p. 118C

Lesson Planning and Resources

See p. 118E for a list of the resources that support this lesson.

✓ Check Skills You'll Need

1. Vocabulary Review
Two fractions that name the same amount are called __?__. equivalent

Find each missing number.

2. $\frac{8}{16} = \frac{\blacksquare}{8}$ 4

3. $\frac{\blacksquare}{10} = \frac{4}{5}$ 8

4. $\frac{1}{6} = \frac{4}{\blacksquare}$ 24

GO for Help
Lesson 2-3

GO 🌐nline

Video Tutor Help
Visit: PHSchool.com
Web Code: are-0775

Why Learn This?

Sometimes you want an exact answer when you add or subtract fractions.

When you are sewing, you should leave extra material to make a hem. You can add fractions to find how much extra material you need to make a hem of $\frac{5}{8}$ in. when you make clothing.

When you add or subtract fractions that have common denominators, keep the denominator the same. Add or subtract the numerators.

EXAMPLE   Common Denominators

1 Find $\frac{1}{8} + \frac{5}{8}$.

Estimate $\frac{1}{8} + \frac{5}{8} \approx 0 + \frac{1}{2}$, or $\frac{1}{2}$

$\frac{1}{8} + \frac{5}{8} = \frac{1+5}{8}$ ← Keep the denominator the same.

$= \frac{6}{8}$ ← Add the numerators.

$= \frac{3}{4}$ ✔   ← Simplify. The answer is close to the estimate.

✓ Quick Check

1. Find each sum or difference.

a. $\frac{3}{5} + \frac{1}{5}$ $\frac{4}{5}$

b. $\frac{13}{16} - \frac{9}{16}$ $\frac{1}{4}$

c. $\frac{1}{4} + \frac{3}{4}$ 1

Sometimes you add or subtract fractions with different denominators. You can use models to help you find the sum or the difference.

Bell Ringer Practice

✓ **Check Skills You'll Need**
Use student page, transparency, or PowerPoint.

🐟AKS **Daily Review 20**
Use transparency.

Differentiated Instruction   Solutions for All Learners

Special Needs L1
For Examples 2 and 3, some concrete or drawn representations will help students focus on what they are trying to find. You can use boards of different thickness for Example 3, and show that they are trying to find a fractional name for the difference.

learning style: visual

Below Level L2
Have students change the following fractions and the whole number 1 to fractions with the common denominator of
12: $\frac{1}{2}, \frac{1}{3}, \frac{1}{4}, \frac{1}{6}$, 1. $\frac{6}{12}, \frac{4}{12}, \frac{3}{12}, \frac{2}{12}, \frac{12}{12}$

learning style: visual

This model shows $\frac{1}{4} + \frac{1}{3} = \frac{7}{12}$.

This model shows $\frac{1}{2} - \frac{1}{3} = \frac{1}{6}$.

To add or subtract fractions with different denominators, first find the Least Common Denominator (LCD).

EXAMPLE **Different Denominators**

TAKS Tip

The LCD of two fractions is the least common multiple of their denominators.

2 Find $\frac{4}{5} + \frac{2}{3}$.

Estimate $\frac{4}{5} + \frac{2}{3} \approx 1 + \frac{1}{2}$, or $1\frac{1}{2}$

$\frac{4}{5} = \frac{4 \cdot 3}{5 \cdot 3} = \frac{12}{15}$ ← The LCD is 15. Write an equivalent fraction.

$+\frac{2}{3} = \frac{2 \cdot 5}{3 \cdot 5} = +\frac{10}{15}$ ← Write an equivalent fraction.

$\frac{22}{15}$ ← Add the numerators.

$1\frac{7}{15}$ ← Write as a mixed number. This is close to the estimate.

✓ Quick Check

● **2. a.** Find $\frac{3}{4} - \frac{1}{6}$. $\frac{7}{12}$ **b.** Find $\frac{3}{7} + \frac{5}{14}$. $\frac{11}{14}$

EXAMPLE **Application: Carpentry**

3 A cabinetmaker needs a board that is $\frac{9}{16}$ in. thick. By how much must he reduce the thickness of a board that is $\frac{7}{8}$ in. thick?

Estimate $\frac{7}{8} - \frac{9}{16} \approx 1 - \frac{1}{2} = \frac{1}{2}$

$\frac{7}{8} = \frac{7 \cdot 2}{8 \cdot 2} = \frac{14}{16}$ ← The LCD is 16. Write an equivalent fraction.

$-\frac{9}{16} = -\frac{9}{16} = -\frac{9}{16}$ ← Write an equivalent fraction.

$\frac{5}{16}$ ← Subtract the numerators.

The cabinetmaker should reduce the thickness of the board by $\frac{5}{16}$ in.

Check for Reasonableness The answer $\frac{5}{16}$ is close to the estimate $\frac{1}{2}$.

✓ Quick Check

● **3.** You hiked $\frac{5}{8}$ mi and $\frac{1}{4}$ mi in the afternoon. How far did you hike? $\frac{7}{8}$ mi

3-2 Adding and Subtracting Fractions **127**

2. Teach

Activity Lab

Use before the lesson.
Student Edition Activity Lab, Hands On 3-2a, Using Fraction Models, p. 125

All in One Teaching Resources

Activity Lab 3-2: Fraction Bar Exploration

Guided Instruction

Example 1
Encourage students to circle the common denominator as a reminder it stays the same when they add or subtract fractions.

Error Prevention!

Remind students if they change a denominator to make it a common denominator, the numerator of that fraction should change also.

Example 2
To help students find the LCD, suggest that they begin with the greater denominator. Have them recite its multiples until they reach a common multiple with the other denominator. Sample: $\frac{3}{4} + \frac{1}{6}$ "6, 12. 12 is also a multiple of 4."

PowerPoint
Additional Examples

1 Find $\frac{2}{7} + \frac{3}{7}$. $\frac{5}{7}$

2 Find $\frac{5}{9} + \frac{1}{6}$. $\frac{13}{18}$

3 A carpenter begins with a board that is $\frac{3}{4}$ in. thick. She removes $\frac{1}{16}$ in. from its thickness. How thick is the board now? $\frac{11}{16}$ in.

All in One Teaching Resources

• Daily Notetaking Guide 3-2 **L3**
• Adapted Notetaking 3-2 **L1**

Closure

• *What needs to be the same before you can add or subtract fractions?* their denominators
• *What part of the fractions do you actually add or subtract when you add or subtract fractions?* the numerators

Advanced Learners **L4**
Challenge students to write addition problems made up of three or more fractions, each with a different denominator. Together, the fractions should add to 1.

Sample: $\frac{1}{3} + \frac{5}{8} + \frac{1}{24}$

Pre-AP™

English Language Learners **ELL**
Students may not understand the context used for the *Why Learn This?* section of the lesson. Show a hem of a garment, the stitches, and where the seam allowance is. Then add the $\frac{5}{8}$ inches to another length to show how the hem allowance works.
learning style: visual

127

3. Practice

Assignment Guide

Check Your Understanding
Go over Exercises 1–13 in class before assigning the Homework Exercises.

Homework Exercises
A Practice by Example   14–34
B Apply Your Skills   35–45
C Challenge   46
TEKS ★ **TAKS** Tune-Up and
      Mixed Review   47–51

Homework Quick Check
To check students understanding of key skills and concepts, go over Exercises 19, 32, 38, 40, and 42.

Differentiated Instruction Resources

Check Your Understanding

1. Answers may vary. Sample: It doesn't make sense to add fractions with different denominators. For example, $\frac{1}{2} + \frac{1}{3} \neq \frac{2}{5}$.

1. Why do you need common denominators to add or subtract fractions? **See left.**

Find the least common denominator of the fractions.

2. $\frac{1}{5}, \frac{3}{4}$ 20   **3.** $\frac{5}{8}, \frac{1}{16}$ 16   **4.** $\frac{7}{10}, \frac{1}{4}$ 20   **5.** $\frac{1}{2}, \frac{2}{3}$ 6

Find each sum or difference.

6. $\frac{1}{8} + \frac{5}{8}$ $\frac{3}{4}$ **7.** $\frac{1}{2} + \frac{1}{2}$ 1   **8.** $\frac{3}{5} - \frac{2}{5}$ $\frac{1}{5}$ **9.** $\frac{5}{6} - \frac{1}{6}$ $\frac{2}{3}$

10. $\frac{1}{2} + \frac{5}{16}$ $\frac{13}{16}$ **11.** $\frac{1}{5} + \frac{3}{8}$ $\frac{23}{40}$ **12.** $\frac{9}{10} - \frac{2}{5}$ $\frac{1}{2}$ **13.** $\frac{3}{6} - \frac{4}{9}$ $\frac{1}{18}$

Homework Exercises

For more exercises, see Extra Skills and Word Problems.

 for Help

For Exercises	See Examples
14–25	1
26–34	2–3

GO Online
Homework Help
Visit: PHSchool.com
Web Code: are-0302

A **Find each sum or difference. You may find a model helpful.**

14. $\frac{1}{7} + \frac{4}{7}$ $\frac{5}{7}$ **15.** $\frac{3}{4} + \frac{3}{4}$ $1\frac{1}{2}$ **16.** $\frac{6}{8} + \frac{3}{8}$ $1\frac{1}{8}$ **17.** $\frac{1}{10} + \frac{3}{10}$ $\frac{2}{5}$

18. $\frac{4}{5} - \frac{1}{5}$ $\frac{3}{5}$ **19.** $\frac{7}{10} - \frac{1}{10}$ $\frac{3}{5}$ **20.** $\frac{5}{12} - \frac{1}{12}$ $\frac{1}{3}$ **21.** $\frac{7}{8} - \frac{5}{8}$ $\frac{1}{4}$

22. $\frac{3}{4} + \frac{1}{4}$ 1   **23.** $\frac{11}{16} - \frac{1}{16}$ $\frac{5}{8}$ **24.** $\frac{8}{9} - \frac{2}{9}$ $\frac{2}{3}$ **25.** $\frac{3}{32} + \frac{1}{32}$ $\frac{1}{8}$

Find each sum or difference by writing equivalent fractions.

26. $\frac{7}{12} + \frac{1}{6}$ $\frac{3}{4}$ **27.** $\frac{3}{3} + \frac{5}{8}$ $1\frac{5}{8}$ **28.** $\frac{4}{5} + \frac{7}{8}$ $1\frac{27}{40}$ **29.** $\frac{1}{2} + \frac{4}{5}$ $1\frac{3}{10}$

30. $\frac{5}{6} - \frac{1}{3}$ $\frac{1}{2}$ **31.** $\frac{3}{5} - \frac{1}{4}$ $\frac{7}{20}$ **32.** $\frac{5}{6} - \frac{1}{2}$ $\frac{1}{3}$ **33.** $\frac{2}{3} - \frac{1}{4}$ $\frac{5}{12}$

34. The gas tank in your family's car was $\frac{7}{8}$ full when you left your house. When you arrived at your destination, the tank was $\frac{1}{4}$ full. What fraction of a tank of gas did you use during the trip? $\frac{5}{8}$

B **GPS** **35.** **Guided Problem Solving** One third of the students in your class got an A on a test. One fourth of them got a B. What fraction of the students got an A or a B on the test? $\frac{7}{12}$
- **Make a Plan** Determine the correct operation to use. Find the LCD and write equivalent fractions.
- **Carry Out the Plan** The correct operation is __?__. The LCD of the two fractions is ▪.

36. Suppose you are using nails $\frac{5}{6}$ in. long to nail plywood $\frac{1}{4}$ in. thick to a post. How much of the nail extends into the post? $\frac{7}{12}$ in.

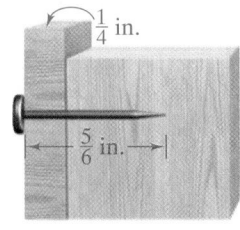

Mental Math Will each sum be *positive*, *negative*, or *zero*?

37. $-\frac{2}{3} + \frac{5}{6}$ positive

38. $-\frac{4}{5} + \frac{8}{10}$ zero

39. $-\frac{7}{8} + \frac{3}{4}$ negative

40. You rowed $\frac{2}{3}$ mi. Your friend rowed $\frac{8}{10}$ mi. Who rowed farther? How much farther? your friend; $\frac{2}{15}$ mi farther

41. What fraction, when added to $\frac{1}{6}$, results in a sum of $\frac{2}{3}$? $\frac{1}{2}$

42. **Error Analysis** A student added $\frac{2}{8} + \frac{3}{8}$ and got $\frac{5}{16}$. What was the student's mistake? What is the correct answer? The student added the denominators. The correct answer is $\frac{5}{8}$.

Use the circle graph for Exercises 43–45.

43. **Data Analysis** What fraction of takeout food is eaten at home or in a car? $\frac{7}{10}$

44. How much greater is the fraction of takeout food eaten at home than the fraction eaten at work? $\frac{7}{20}$

45. What fraction of the food is eaten at home, in a car, or at work? $\frac{17}{20}$

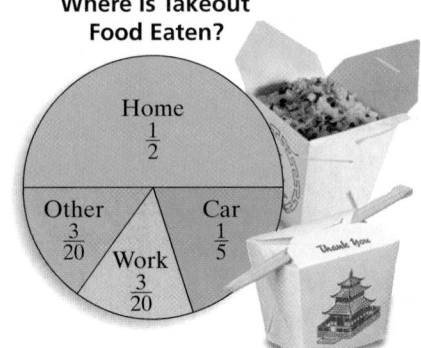

Where Is Takeout Food Eaten?

Home $\frac{1}{2}$
Other $\frac{3}{20}$
Work $\frac{3}{20}$
Car $\frac{1}{5}$

C **46.** **Challenge** Find the perimeter of the figure at the left. $1\frac{7}{8}$ in.

$\frac{3}{8}$ in.
$\frac{3}{8}$ in.
$\frac{1}{2}$ in.
$\frac{5}{8}$ in.

TEKS ★ **TAKS** **Tune-Up and Mixed Review**

TAKS Objective 1
TEKS (7.2)(B)

47. Rolf has a math test. He plans to study $\frac{5}{6}$ hour tonight and $\frac{3}{4}$ hour tomorrow. How many hours does Rolf plan to study in all? **B**

Ⓐ $1\frac{3}{4}$ h Ⓑ $1\frac{7}{12}$ h Ⓒ $\frac{4}{5}$ h Ⓓ $\frac{9}{10}$ h

TAKS Objective 1
TEKS (7.1)(A)

48. To make a noodle casserole, Jack uses $\frac{1}{3}$ cup of cream cheese, Myra uses $\frac{2}{5}$ cup, Donna uses $\frac{3}{4}$ cup, and Ernesto uses $\frac{1}{2}$ cup. Who uses the most cream cheese? **H**

Ⓕ Jack Ⓖ Myra Ⓗ Donna Ⓙ Ernesto

TAKS Objective 1
TEKS (7.2)(A)

49. Which expression can be used to find the maximum number of 0.5-inch lengths of wire that can be cut from a wire 10.2 inches long?

Ⓐ $0.5 \div 10.2$ Ⓒ $10.2 \div 0.5$ **C**
Ⓑ 0.5×10.2 Ⓓ 10.2×0.5

 for Help **Lesson 2-6**

Order from least to greatest. $-2.4, 1.34, \frac{7}{3}, \frac{25}{6}$

50. $\frac{4}{3}, 0.52, -\frac{3}{4}, 1.0$ $-\frac{3}{4}, 0.52, 1.0, \frac{4}{3}$

51. $1.34, \frac{25}{6}, -2.4, \frac{7}{3}$

Alternative Assessment

Provide students with fraction models. Have them model and record the additions and subtractions for Exercises 14–33 as demonstrated in the lesson. You may help them get started by modeling one or two exercises at the overhead as students follow along at their desks.

TEKS ★ **TAKS** **Resources**

• TAKS Strategies, p. 159
• TAKS Tune-Up, pp. 163–165

TAKS Tune-Up Kit

• TAKS Daily Review Transparencies
• TAKS Review and Preparation Workbook
• TAKS Strategies with Transparencies
• Texas Progress Monitoring Assessments

4. Assess & Reteach

PowerPoint
Lesson Quiz

Find each sum or difference.

1. $\frac{4}{5} + \frac{3}{5}$ $1\frac{2}{5}$

2. $\frac{11}{12} - \frac{10}{12}$ $\frac{1}{12}$

3. $\frac{3}{4} + \frac{5}{6}$ $1\frac{7}{12}$

4. $\frac{7}{8} - \frac{2}{3}$ $\frac{5}{24}$

Reteaching 3-2 Adding and Subtracting **L2**

Follow these steps to add or subtract fractions with different denominators.

Add: $\frac{1}{3} + \frac{1}{6}$ Subtract: $\frac{11}{12} - \frac{1}{4}$

① Write the fractions with the same denominator.
$\frac{2}{6} + \frac{1}{6}$ $\frac{11}{12} - \frac{3}{12}$

② Add or subtract the numerators.
$\frac{2}{6} + \frac{1}{6} = \frac{3}{6}$ $\frac{11}{12} - \frac{3}{12} = \frac{9}{12}$

③ Simplify the fraction.
$\frac{3}{6} = \frac{1}{2}$ $\frac{9}{12} = \frac{3}{4}$

Complete to find each sum or difference.

1. $\frac{1}{10} + \frac{3}{5}$
$\frac{1}{10} + \frac{4}{10} = \frac{7}{10}$

2. $\frac{1}{4} + \frac{1}{6}$
$\frac{3}{12} + \frac{6}{12} = \frac{9}{12} = \frac{3}{4}$

3. $\frac{5}{8} + \frac{1}{4}$
$\frac{5}{8} + \frac{2}{8} = \frac{7}{8}$

4. $\frac{3}{4} - \frac{1}{2}$
$\frac{3}{4} - \frac{1}{4} = \frac{1}{4}$

5. $\frac{5}{9} - \frac{1}{3}$
$\frac{5}{9} - \frac{3}{9} = \frac{2}{9}$

6. $\frac{3}{5} - \frac{1}{15}$
$\frac{9}{15} - \frac{1}{15} = \frac{4}{15}$

Find each sum or difference. Write in simplest form.

7. $\frac{4}{5} + \frac{2}{3}$
$1\frac{7}{15}$

8. $\frac{3}{8} - \frac{1}{4}$
$\frac{1}{8}$

9. $\frac{5}{6} - \frac{2}{3}$
$\frac{1}{6}$

10. $\frac{5}{12} - \frac{1}{4}$
$\frac{1}{6}$

11. $\frac{7}{8} + \frac{1}{4}$
$1\frac{1}{8}$

12. $\frac{3}{4} - \frac{1}{8}$
$\frac{5}{8}$

13. $\frac{2}{5} + \frac{1}{10}$
$\frac{1}{2}$

14. $\frac{7}{12} - \frac{1}{3}$
$\frac{1}{4}$

15. $\frac{1}{2} + \frac{9}{10}$
$1\frac{2}{5}$

16. $\frac{5}{6} - \frac{1}{4}$
$\frac{7}{12}$

17. $\frac{3}{8} + \frac{1}{2}$
$1\frac{1}{8}$

18. $\frac{2}{5} - \frac{3}{10}$
$\frac{1}{10}$

Enrichment 3-2 Adding and Subtracting **L4**

Critical Thinking

Using each number only once, use the numbers 2, 4, 6, and 8 to write an expression with two proper fractions that have:

a. The largest possible sum
b. The largest possible difference
c. The smallest possible sum
d. The smallest possible difference

1. What is a proper fraction?
a fraction with the numerator less than the denominator

2. How many proper fractions will you write in each expression?
2 fractions

3. How many different digits are in each pair of fractions?
4 digits

4. List all the proper fractions you can make using the numbers 2, 4, 6, and 8.
$\frac{2}{4}, \frac{2}{6}, \frac{2}{8}, \frac{4}{6}, \frac{4}{8}, \frac{6}{8}$

5. What are the pairs of fractions you can use when writing the expressions?
$\frac{2}{6}, \frac{2}{4}, \frac{2}{8}, \frac{4}{8}, \frac{6}{8}, \frac{4}{6}$

6. For each pair of fractions, find the sum and the difference.

7. Write an expression for each part of the problem.

Part a. $\frac{4}{8} + \frac{6}{2}$ Part b. $\frac{4}{2} - \frac{6}{8}$
Part c. $\frac{2}{6} + \frac{4}{8}$ Part d. $\frac{4}{2} - \frac{6}{8}$

Fraction Pairs	Sum	Difference
$\frac{4}{8}, \frac{6}{2}$	$1\frac{1}{4}$	$\frac{1}{4}$
$\frac{2}{4}, \frac{6}{8}$	$\frac{5}{6}$	$\frac{1}{6}$
$\frac{2}{6}, \frac{4}{8}$	$\frac{11}{12}$	$\frac{5}{12}$

8. How can you tell that your answers are reasonable without calculating?
Estimate the sums and differences. Use compensation to adjust for the values of the fractions.

9. Use the numbers 2, 3, 6, and 8 to write an expression with two proper fractions that have:

a. The largest possible sum
$\frac{2}{6} + \frac{3}{8}$
b. The largest possible difference
$\frac{3}{2} - \frac{6}{8}$
c. The smallest possible sum
$\frac{2}{6} + \frac{3}{8}$
d. The smallest possible difference
$\frac{3}{6} - \frac{2}{8}$

129

(7.2)(B) To use addition and subtraction to solve problems involving fractions **TAKS** Obj. 1
Also supports
(7.2)(F) **TAKS** Obj. 1
(7.2)(G) **TAKS** Obj. 1

Dana Center TEKS Toolkit Clarifying Activities (7.2)(B), (7.2)(F), (7.2)(G)
Visit: PHSchool.com
Web Code: arq-9045

Professional Development

TEKS Math Background

Adding or subtracting mixed numbers involves first adding or subtracting the fractions, and then adding or subtracting the whole numbers. When subtracting fractions, you may need to rename the mixed number. The steps for adding or subtracting mixed numbers are: Find a common denominator; rename the fraction, if needed, in subtraction problems; add or subtract; and simplify the resulting fraction.

More Math Background: p. 118C

Lesson Planning and Resources

See p. 118E for a list of the resources that support this lesson.

PowerPoint

Bell Ringer Practice

✓ **Check Skills You'll Need**
Use student page, transparency, or PowerPoint.

TAKS *Daily Review 21*
Use transparency.

3-3 Adding and Subtracting Mixed Numbers

✓ Check Skills You'll Need

1. Vocabulary Review
How does the *LCD* of two fractions help you compare the fractions?
See below.
Compare each pair of fractions. Use $<$, $=$, or $>$.

2. $\frac{3}{12} \blacksquare \frac{5}{12}$ $<$

3. $\frac{1}{6} \blacksquare \frac{1}{4}$ $<$

 GO for Help
Lesson 2-4

Check Skills You'll Need

1. When two fractions have the same denominator, you can compare them by looking at the numerators.

- (7.2)(B) To use addition and subtraction to solve problems involving fractions **TAKS** Obj. 1
- (7.2)(F) To select and use appropriate operations to solve problems **TAKS** Obj. 1
- (7.2)(G) To determine the reasonableness of a solution to a problem **TAKS** Obj. 1

Why Learn This?

Adding mixed numbers can help you find the total distance you travel, such as the number of miles you run while training for a race.

To find the sum of two mixed numbers with fraction parts that have the same denominator, you can first add the fractions and then add the whole numbers.

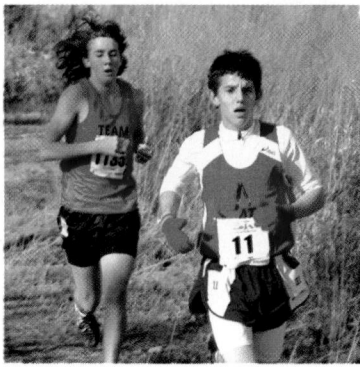

EXAMPLE **Same Denominators**

1 **Cross Country** You are training for a race. On Monday you run $2\frac{3}{4}$ mi, and on Tuesday you run $4\frac{3}{4}$ mi. What is your total mileage?

Estimate $2\frac{3}{4} + 4\frac{3}{4} \approx 3 + 5$, or 8

$2\frac{3}{4} + 4\frac{3}{4} = 6\frac{6}{4}$ ← Add the fractions. Add the whole numbers.

$= 6 + 1\frac{2}{4}$ ← Write as a sum. Write $\frac{6}{4}$ as $1\frac{2}{4}$.

$= 6 + 1\frac{1}{2}$ ← Simplify.

$= 7\frac{1}{2}$ ← Add the whole numbers.

Your total mileage is $7\frac{1}{2}$ mi.

Check for Reasonableness The answer $7\frac{1}{2}$ is close to the estimate 8.

✓ Quick Check

1. Find each sum or difference.
a. $1\frac{2}{3} + 2\frac{2}{3}$ $4\frac{1}{3}$ b. $1\frac{2}{5} + 3\frac{2}{5}$ $4\frac{4}{5}$ c. $5\frac{1}{2} - 4\frac{1}{2}$ 1

Differentiated Instruction **Solutions for All Learners**

Special Needs **L1**
Review how to change an improper fraction to a mixed number and vice versa. Use two clear glass jars marked off in fourths. Fill one to $\frac{4}{4}$ and ask: *How many more fourths do I need for $\frac{6}{4}$?* two Then fill the second jar to $\frac{2}{4}$.

learning style: visual

Below Level **L2**
Give students models such as shown. Have them write the related expression. $2\frac{1}{4} + 1\frac{1}{2}$

learning style: visual

Fractions in mixed numbers may have different denominators. You can use the LCD to rewrite them as fractions with common denominators.

EXAMPLE Different Denominators

2. Find $4\frac{1}{4} + 3\frac{2}{3}$.

Estimate $4\frac{1}{4} + 3\frac{2}{3} \approx 4 + 4$, or 8

$$4\frac{1}{4} = \quad 4\frac{3}{12} \quad \leftarrow \text{The LCD is 12. Write an equivalent fraction.}$$

$$+3\frac{2}{3} = +3\frac{8}{12} \quad \leftarrow \text{Write an equivalent fraction.}$$

$$= \quad 7\frac{11}{12} \quad \leftarrow \text{Add the fractions. Add the whole numbers.}$$

Check for Reasonableness The answer $7\frac{11}{12}$ is close to the estimate 8. The answer is reasonable.

★ TAKS Tip

When you add or subtract fractions, use the least common multiple of the denominators.

✓ **Quick Check**

2. Find each sum or difference.

   a. $2\frac{3}{4} - 1\frac{3}{4}$ 1

   b. $3\frac{1}{6} + 8\frac{7}{8}$ $12\frac{1}{24}$

   c. $6\frac{1}{2} - 2\frac{1}{5}$ $4\frac{3}{10}$

When you subtract mixed numbers, you may need to rename one of the numbers before subtracting.

EXAMPLE Subtracting With Renaming

3. **TAKS** **Multiple Choice** You bought $6\frac{1}{9}$ yd of ribbon and used $2\frac{2}{3}$ yd to make a pillow. How many yards of ribbon did you have left?

   Ⓐ $8\frac{7}{9}$ 　　　Ⓑ $4\frac{5}{9}$ 　　　Ⓒ $3\frac{2}{9}$ 　　　Ⓓ $3\frac{4}{9}$

Find $6\frac{1}{9} - 2\frac{2}{3}$.

Estimate $6\frac{1}{9} - 2\frac{2}{3} \approx 6 - 3$, or 3

$$6\frac{1}{9} = \quad 5\frac{10}{9} \quad \leftarrow \text{Rename: } 6\frac{1}{9} = 5 + 1\frac{1}{9} = 5 + \frac{10}{9}.$$

$$-2\frac{2}{3} = -2\frac{6}{9} \quad \leftarrow \text{The LCD is 9. Write an equivalent fraction.}$$

$$= \quad 3\frac{4}{9} \quad \leftarrow \text{Subtract.}$$

You have $3\frac{4}{9}$ yards of ribbon left. The correct answer is D.

Check for Reasonableness The answer $3\frac{4}{9}$ is close to the estimate 3.

✓ **Quick Check**

3. Your friend bought $4\frac{1}{3}$ ft of gift-wrap and used $2\frac{5}{6}$ ft to wrap a gift. How many feet of gift-wrap did your friend have left? $1\frac{1}{2}$ ft

---

2. Teach

Activity Lab
Use before the lesson.

All in One **Teaching Resources**
Activity Lab 3-3: Adding and Subtracting Mixed Numbers

Guided Instruction

Example 1
Collect several empty egg cartons and use them to model addition of mixed numbers. For Quick Check 1a, cut two cartons into thirds, four egg slots to each third. Place them with whole cartons to represent $1\frac{2}{3} + 2\frac{2}{3}$. As you work through the solution on the board, invite a student to act out each step with the egg cartons.

Example 2
Have students circle the denominators to reinforce that those numbers need to be the same. Point out that when they change the fractions to the LCD, the whole numbers do not change.

PowerPoint
Additional Examples

1. Find $2\frac{3}{5} + 1\frac{4}{5}$. $4\frac{2}{5}$
2. Find $5\frac{1}{2} + 3\frac{2}{3}$. $9\frac{1}{6}$
3. Find $6\frac{1}{4} - 4\frac{3}{8}$. $1\frac{7}{8}$

All in One **Teaching Resources**
• Daily Notetaking Guide 3-3 **L3**
• Adapted Notetaking 3-3 **L1**

Closure

• *How do you add or subtract mixed numbers?* Add or subtract the fractions, and then add or subtract the whole numbers.
• *When would you need to rename a fraction in a subtraction problem?* if the fraction being subtracted is greater than the first fraction

---

Advanced Learners **L4**
Challenge students to write three different mixed-number subtraction problems whose answer is $3\frac{5}{6}$.

Sample: $6\frac{1}{5} - 2\frac{11}{30} = 3\frac{5}{6}$

Pre-AP™

English Language Learners **ELL**
For Examples 1 and 2, separating the fractions from the whole numbers, and adding them separately set off by the phrases *add the whole numbers* and *add the fractions,* will help students keep track of the steps in the process. You can then recombine the sums and write as a mixed number.

learning style: verbal

131

3. Practice

Assignment Guide

Check Your Understanding
Go over Exercises 1–8 in class before assigning the Homework Exercises.

Homework Exercises
A Practice by Example   9–22
B Apply Your Skills   23–32
C Challenge   33
TEKS ★ TAKS Tune-Up and
   Mixed Review   34–39

Homework Quick Check
To check students understanding of key skills and concepts, go over Exercises 11, 20, 28, 29, and 30.

Differentiated Instruction **Resources**

Check Your Understanding

Rewrite each mixed number so that the fraction part is a proper fraction.

1. $2\frac{7}{4}$ $3\frac{3}{4}$ **2.** $3\frac{6}{5}$ $4\frac{1}{5}$ **3.** $1\frac{14}{10}$ $2\frac{2}{5}$

4. Add; when you add fractions, the sum may be greater than 1.

4. Reasoning Do you use the skill you practiced in Exercises 1–3 when you *add* or when you *subtract* mixed numbers? Explain.

Rewrite each mixed number so that the whole-number part is less by 1.

5. $4\frac{1}{2}$ $3\frac{3}{2}$ **6.** $2\frac{3}{8}$ $1\frac{11}{8}$ **7.** $1\frac{9}{10}$ $\frac{19}{10}$

8. Number Sense Suppose you want to find the difference $6 - 3\frac{2}{5}$. How would you rewrite 6 as a mixed number? $5\frac{5}{5}$

Homework Exercises

For more exercises, see Extra Skills and Word Problems.

GO for Help

For Exercises	See Examples
9–13	1
14–17	2
18–22	3

A Find each sum. $6\frac{4}{5}$

9. $6\frac{2}{5} + 1\frac{4}{5}$ $8\frac{1}{5}$ **10.** $9\frac{3}{7} + 1\frac{2}{7}$ $10\frac{5}{7}$ **11.** $3\frac{3}{8} + 4\frac{5}{8}$ **12.** $1\frac{7}{10} + 5\frac{1}{10}$
                                                                 8

13. To make lemonade, you use $3\frac{1}{3}$ cups of lemon concentrate and $1\frac{1}{3}$ cups of water. How many cups of lemonade do you make? $4\frac{2}{3}$ c

Find each sum by writing equivalent fractions.

14. $6\frac{2}{5} + 1\frac{4}{10}$ $7\frac{4}{5}$ **15.** $9\frac{1}{2} + 9\frac{1}{3}$ $18\frac{5}{6}$ **16.** $7\frac{1}{6} + 8\frac{1}{8}$ $15\frac{7}{24}$ **17.** $6\frac{1}{2} + 4\frac{5}{6}$ $11\frac{1}{3}$

Find each difference.

18. $7\frac{2}{3} - 1\frac{1}{6}$ $6\frac{1}{2}$ **19.** $15 - 3\frac{3}{4}$ $11\frac{1}{4}$ **20.** $12\frac{1}{8} - 8\frac{3}{8}$ $3\frac{3}{4}$ **21.** $14 - 5\frac{1}{5}$ $8\frac{4}{5}$

22. Cooking You have 4 cups of flour, and you need to use $1\frac{3}{4}$ cups for a cookie recipe. How much flour will you have left? $2\frac{1}{4}$ c

B **GPS** **23. Guided Problem Solving** Is a 6-quart punch bowl large enough to hold all the ingredients called for in the recipe? Explain.
• Using mental math, what is $1\frac{1}{2} + \frac{1}{2}$?
• What is the LCM of 3 and 4?
• Is the sum of all the ingredients greater than or less than 6 qt?
Yes; the total of ingredients is $5\frac{11}{12}$ qt.

Lemon Raspberry Fizz

$2\frac{1}{4}$ qt ginger ale • $1\frac{2}{3}$ qt lemon sherbet
$1\frac{1}{2}$ qt lemonade • $\frac{1}{2}$ qt raspberry juice

24. $21\frac{1}{8}$

25. $29\frac{3}{20}$

26. $5\frac{5}{6}$

27. $3\frac{5}{8}$

132   **Chapter 3**   Operations With Fractions

Adapted Practice 3-3 panel

Adapted Practice 3-3   **L1**

Practice 3-3   Adding and Subtracting Mixed Numbers   **L3**

Find each sum.
1. $5\frac{1}{3} + 3\frac{2}{3}$ 2. $7\frac{1}{4} + 4\frac{3}{8}$ 3. $2\frac{1}{8} + 6\frac{5}{8}$
   9          $11\frac{5}{8}$ $8\frac{3}{4}$

4. $8\frac{1}{2} + 4\frac{7}{10}$ 5. $9\frac{1}{6} + 6\frac{1}{4}$ 6. $3\frac{3}{4} + 10\frac{5}{8}$
   $12\frac{1}{2}$ $15\frac{5}{12}$ $14\frac{1}{2}$

Find each difference.
7. $6\frac{11}{12} - 4\frac{5}{12}$ 8. $12 - 5\frac{3}{10}$ 9. $14\frac{1}{2} - 7\frac{1}{5}$
   $2\frac{1}{2}$ $6\frac{7}{10}$ $7\frac{3}{10}$

10. $9 - 5\frac{5}{6}$ 11. $13\frac{3}{4} - 10\frac{1}{2}$ 12. $15\frac{1}{2} - 6\frac{5}{12}$
   $3\frac{1}{6}$ $3\frac{1}{4}$ $8\frac{3}{4}$

Find each sum or difference.
13. $1\frac{1}{6} - \frac{3}{4}$ 14. $4\frac{1}{2} - 2\frac{7}{8}$ 15. $9\frac{3}{4} + 7\frac{7}{8}$
   $\frac{5}{12}$ $1\frac{5}{8}$ $17\frac{5}{8}$

16. $5\frac{1}{6} - 4\frac{7}{12}$ 17. $9\frac{5}{12} + 11\frac{5}{6}$ 18. $1\frac{4}{5} - \frac{1}{6}$
   $\frac{7}{12}$ $20\frac{19}{20}$ $\frac{13}{30}$

Write a mixed number for each time period. Be sure each fraction is in lowest terms.
19. 8:00 A.M. to 9:20 A.M.   20. 9:00 A.M. to 2:45 P.M.
   $1\frac{1}{3}$ h $5\frac{3}{4}$ h

21. 11:00 A.M. to 3:55 P.M.   22. 8:30 A.M. to 10:40 P.M.
   $4\frac{11}{12}$ h $14\frac{1}{6}$ h

Guided Problem Solving panel

3-3 • Guided Problem Solving   **GPS**   **L3**

GPS Student Page 133, Exercise 29:

On Saturday you hiked $4\frac{1}{2}$ mi. On Sunday, you hiked $3\frac{3}{8}$ mi. How far did you hike during the weekend?

Understand
1. Circle the information you will need to solve.
2. What are you being asked to do?
   Find the total distance you hiked.
3. Estimate the sum of the distances.
   $4\frac{3}{8}$ is about 4, $3\frac{1}{2}$ is about 4, so $4 + 4 = 8$.

Plan and Carry Out
4. Add the whole numbers.   7
5. In order to add $\frac{3}{8} + \frac{1}{2}$, what do you need to find first?
   a common denominator
6. What is the common denominator for $\frac{3}{8} + \frac{1}{2}$?   8
7. Add. $\frac{3}{8} + \frac{1}{2}$ $\frac{7}{8}$
8. Add. $7 + \frac{7}{8}$ $7\frac{7}{8}$
9. How far did you hike during the weekend? $7\frac{7}{8}$ miles

Check
10. Is your answer reasonable according to the estimate you made in step 3?
   yes; $7\frac{7}{8}$ miles is close to the estimated total of 8 miles.

Solve Another Problem
11. On a white-water rafting trip you paddled $1\frac{3}{4}$ mi the first day and $2\frac{3}{8}$ mi the second day. How many miles did you raft on both days?
   $4\frac{1}{8}$ mi

132

Find each sum or difference. 24–27. See margin.

24. $17\frac{3}{4} + 3\frac{3}{8}$ **25.** $17\frac{2}{5} + 11\frac{3}{4}$ **26.** $15\frac{1}{3} - 9\frac{1}{2}$ **27.** $6\frac{3}{8} - 2\frac{3}{4}$

28. Error Analysis A student subtracted $10\frac{1}{7} - 3\frac{5}{7}$ and got $6\frac{6}{7}$. Find the correct answer. What mistake do you think the student made? $6\frac{3}{7}$; the student borrowed $\frac{1}{7}$ instead of $\frac{7}{7}$.

29. On Saturday you hiked $4\frac{3}{8}$ mi. On Sunday, you hiked $3\frac{1}{2}$ mi. **GPS** How far did you hike during the weekend? $7\frac{7}{8}$ mi

30. A bolt must go through a sign and a support that together are $2\frac{1}{8}$ in. thick. You need an additional $\frac{1}{16}$ in. for a washer and $\frac{1}{4}$ in. for a nut. How long should the bolt be? $2\frac{7}{16}$ in.

31. Geometry Figures A and B have a total area of $5\frac{3}{4}$ in.². The area of Figure A is $1\frac{1}{4}$ in.². Find the area of Figure B. $4\frac{1}{2}$ in.²

32. Calculator Use a calculator to find $5\frac{1}{2} + 4\frac{3}{4}$. $10\frac{1}{4}$

C **33. Challenge** A newspaper has the following advertising spaces available: $2\frac{7}{8}$ c.i. (column inches), $3\frac{1}{2}$ c.i., and $4\frac{1}{4}$ c.i. What is the total number of column inches available? $10\frac{5}{8}$ c.i.

 TEKS ★ **TAKS** **Tune-Up and Mixed Review**

TAKS Objective 1
TEKS (7.2)(B)

34. How much heavier is $28\frac{1}{2}$ pounds than $15\frac{11}{16}$ pounds? **B**

   Ⓐ $12\frac{3}{4}$ lb   Ⓑ $12\frac{13}{16}$ lb   Ⓒ $12\frac{7}{8}$ lb   Ⓓ $13\frac{13}{16}$ lb

TAKS Objective 5
TEKS (7.12)(A)

35. The table shows the number of runs Jason's baseball team, the Tigers, scored each game. What is the median number of runs the Tigers scored per game? **J**

Tigers Runs Scored

5	8	4	1	7	10	5
6	3	4	0	6	3	5

   Ⓕ 4   Ⓖ 4.5   Ⓗ 4.8   Ⓙ 5

TAKS Objective 6
TEKS (7.13)(A)

36. A submarine is located at 250 ft below sea level. At the end of the day, the submarine rises to 140 ft below sea level. Which expression represents the movement of the submarine? **B**

   Ⓐ $250 + 140$ Ⓒ $-250 + (-140)$
   Ⓑ $-250 + 140$ Ⓓ $250 - (-140)$

 for Help **Lesson 1-9**

Mental Math **Find each product using the Distributive Property.**

37. $5(23)$ 115   **38.** $7(18)$ 126   **39.** $4(62)$ 248

TEKS ★ **TAKS** **Resources**

- TAKS Strategies, p. 159
- TAKS Tune-Up, pp. 163–165

TAKS Tune-Up Kit
- TAKS Daily Review Transparencies
- TAKS Review and Preparation Workbook
- TAKS Strategies with Transparencies
- TAKS Progress Monitoring Assessments

---

4. Assess & Reteach

PowerPoint
Lesson Quiz

Find each sum or difference.

1. $8\frac{2}{3} - 4\frac{5}{6}$ $3\frac{5}{6}$

2. $7\frac{3}{5} + 3\frac{3}{4}$ $11\frac{7}{20}$

Alternative Assessment

Have students work in pairs. Each student writes one exercise for adding mixed numbers and one exercise for subtracting mixed numbers. Partners exchange papers and find the sum and difference. Then partners discuss how they found the answers.

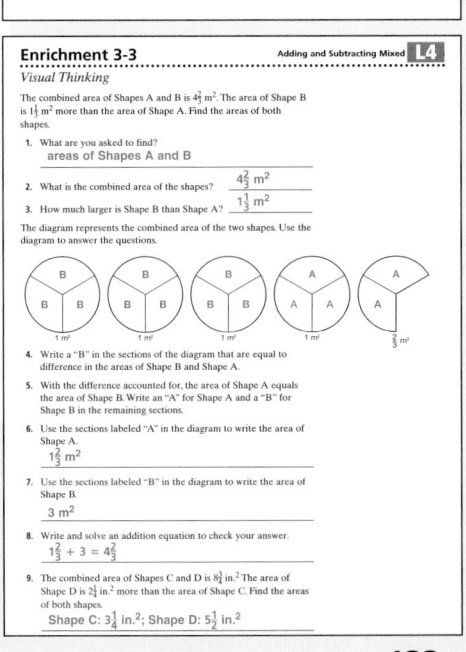

133

MATH AT WORK

Songwriter

Students may not be aware how math skills are important to certain attractive career possibilities. This feature explains an exciting career choice that makes math necessary every day.

Guided Instruction

Have different volunteers read each paragraph. Show a piece of sheet music. Point out quarter, half, and whole notes and how arranging notes differently makes the music sound different.
Ask questions, such as:
- *What beat patterns have you noticed in music you've heard?*
- *How do songwriters use fractions to write their music?*

Checkpoint Quiz 1

The table below shows the average rainfall from July through December for a city in Florida. Use benchmarks and the table to answer Exercises 1–3.

Month	July	August	September	October	November	December
Inches	$7\frac{7}{10}$	$6\frac{4}{5}$	$6\frac{3}{5}$	$3\frac{2}{5}$	$1\frac{9}{10}$	$2\frac{1}{10}$

1. Estimate the difference between rainfall in July and in December. $5\frac{1}{2}$ in.

2. Estimate the sum of rainfall in August and in September. $13\frac{1}{2}$ in.

3. Estimate the average rainfall for the six months. 5 in.

Simplify.

4. $\frac{12}{18} - \frac{9}{18}$ $\frac{1}{6}$

5. $\frac{4}{3} + \frac{2}{3}$ 2

6. $10\frac{7}{10} - 4\frac{4}{5}$ $5\frac{9}{10}$

7. $6\frac{3}{4} + 2\frac{1}{5}$ $8\frac{19}{20}$

8. $\frac{5}{9} - \frac{1}{3}$ $\frac{2}{9}$

9. $17 - 5\frac{3}{8}$ $11\frac{5}{8}$

10. **Measurement** Five years ago, Tyler's height was $43\frac{7}{8}$ in. Now his height is $65\frac{1}{2}$ in. How many inches has he grown in 5 years? $21\frac{5}{8}$ in.

MATH AT WORK

Songwriter

Songwriters need to know what types of music are "in" to compose a song that will sell. Then a songwriter must find an artist to record the song. Producers and record companies decide whether they will promote a song as a potential hit.

Songwriters use mathematics to make complex rhythms. Many hip-hop or rap beats use rhythms that follow a pattern. Songwriters write musical notes that have fractional names to create the pattern. Some common musical notes are half notes and quarter notes.

Go Online
PHSchool.com **For:** Information on songwriters **Web Code:** arb-2031

Modeling Fraction Multiplication

You can fold paper to model multiplication of fractions. Use paper folding to find $\frac{1}{3}$ of $\frac{1}{4}$, or $\frac{1}{3} \cdot \frac{1}{4}$.

TEKS ★ TAKS

(7.2)(A) To represent multiplication situations involving fractions with models TAKS Obj. 1

(7.14)(A) To communicate ideas using graphical and physical models TAKS Obj. 6

ACTIVITY

Step 1 Fold a sheet of paper into fourths as shown in the drawing at the right. Shade $\frac{1}{4}$ of it.

Step 2 Fold the same paper lengthwise into thirds as shown in the lower drawing. Shade $\frac{1}{3}$ of it.

Step 3 Count the total number of rectangles made by the folds. How many rectangles did you shade twice? What fraction of all the rectangles did you shade twice?

Step 4 Use the model to complete the equation: $\frac{1}{3} \cdot \frac{1}{4} = \blacksquare$. Explain how you found the product.

Step 5 Choose two fractions from $\frac{1}{3}$, $\frac{2}{3}$, and $\frac{3}{4}$. Use modeling to find the product of the two fractions.

Step 6 Suggest a rule for multiplying fractions.

Exercises

Complete each equation using the model shown below.

1. $\frac{1}{2} \cdot \blacksquare = \frac{1}{6}$ $\frac{1}{3}$

2. $\frac{2}{3} \cdot \frac{2}{3} = \blacksquare$ $\frac{4}{9}$

3. $\blacksquare \cdot \frac{3}{4} = \frac{3}{20}$ $\frac{1}{5}$

Make a model to represent each expression. Then find the product. 4–8. See margin for models.

4. $\frac{1}{3} \cdot \frac{2}{5}$ $\frac{2}{15}$

5. $\frac{5}{6} \cdot \frac{1}{2}$ $\frac{5}{12}$

6. $\frac{1}{2} \cdot \frac{1}{4}$ $\frac{1}{8}$

7. $\frac{3}{4} \cdot \frac{2}{3}$ $\frac{6}{12}$

8. $\frac{3}{8} \cdot \frac{1}{3}$ $\frac{3}{24}$

9. Reasoning In the exercises above, compare the product to each of its factors. Make a conjecture about the product of two numbers between 0 and 1. The product of two numbers between 0 and 1 is less than either of the two numbers.

4–8. See back of book.

Activity Lab

Modeling Fraction Multiplication

Students model multiplication of fractions. This will prepare them to calculate with fractions in Lesson 3-4.

Guided Instruction

Explain that you can multiply two fractions to find a certain part of a number that is less than one. Demonstrate how to fold the paper one way for one fraction and the other way for the other fraction. Make sure students are folding all vertical folds for one fraction and all horizontal folds for the other fraction. Ask:

- *How many sections did you make in total?* 12 *What does that number represent?* greatest common denominator
- *What does the number of vertical sections represent?* denominator of the first fraction
- *What does the number of shaded horizontal sections represent?* numerator of the second fraction

Exercises

Have students work on the Exercises. Go over the answers as a class and have them make suggestions about the formula for multiplying fractions.

Alternative Method

Have students use fraction tiles to model fraction multiplication.

TEKS ★ TAKS Resources

- Activity Lab 3-4: Multiplying Fractions
- paper
- 2 different colored pencils

Dana Center TEKS Tookit Clarifying Activities (7.2)(A), (7.14)(A)
Visit: PHSchool.com
Web Code: arq-9045

135

(7.2)(A) To represent multiplication situations involving fractions with models **TAKS** Obj. 1
Also supports
(7.2)(B) **TAKS** Obj. 1
(7.2)(F) **TAKS** Obj. 1

Dana Center TEKS Toolkit Clarifying Activities (7.2)(A), (7.2)(B), (7.2)(F)
Visit: PHSchool.com
Web Code: arq-9045

 Professional Development

TEKS Math Background

Unlike addition and subtraction of fractions, a common denominator is *not* needed when you multiply fractions. Multiply the numerators and then the denominators. The product may need to be simplified before or after you multiply. When you multiply a fraction with a whole number or mixed number, first rewrite each number as an improper fraction. After you multiply, change an improper fraction to a mixed number.

More Math Background: p. 118C

Lesson Planning and Resources

See p. 118E for a list of the resources that support this lesson.

 PowerPoint

Bell Ringer Practice

Check Skills You'll Need
Use student page, transparency, or PowerPoint.

TAKS **Daily Review 22**
Use transparency.

3-4 Multiplying Fractions and Mixed Numbers

Check Skills You'll Need

1. Vocabulary Review
In an *improper fraction,* how does the numerator compare to the denominator? **See below.**
Write each mixed number as an improper fraction.

2. $2\frac{3}{5}$ $\frac{13}{5}$ **3.** $6\frac{1}{2}$ $\frac{13}{2}$

4. $1\frac{2}{3}$ $\frac{5}{3}$ **5.** $4\frac{3}{4}$ $\frac{19}{4}$

 GO for Help
Lesson 2-4

Check Skills You'll Need

1. The numerator is greater than the denominator.

TEKS ⭐ **TAKS**
- (7.2)(A) To represent multiplication situations involving fractions with models **TAKS** Obj. 1
- (7.2)(B) To use multiplication to solve problems involving fractions **TAKS** Obj. 1
- (7.2)(F) To select and use appropriate operations to solve problems **TAKS** Obj. 1

Why Learn This?

You multiply fractions to find part of a quantity, which is useful when you cook.

A baker makes a batch of bread dough and splits it into three parts. Then she takes half of one part for one loaf. You can multiply $\frac{1}{3} \cdot \frac{1}{2}$ to find the fraction of the batch she uses for one loaf of bread.

When multiplying fractions, you do *not* need a common denominator. You multiply the numerators and multiply the denominators.

KEY CONCEPTS **Multiplying Fractions**

Arithmetic	Algebra
$\frac{1}{3} \cdot \frac{1}{2} = \frac{1 \cdot 1}{3 \cdot 2} = \frac{1}{6}$	$\frac{a}{b} \cdot \frac{c}{d} = \frac{ac}{bd}, b \neq 0$ and $d \neq 0$

EXAMPLE **Multiplying Fractions**

⭐ **TAKS** **Tip**

The model represents the product in Example 1.

1 Find $\frac{5}{8} \cdot \frac{2}{3}$.

$\frac{5}{8} \cdot \frac{2}{3} = \frac{5 \cdot 2}{8 \cdot 3}$ ← Multiply the numerators. Multiply the denominators.

$= \frac{10}{24}$ ← Find the two products.

$= \frac{5}{12}$ ← Simplify.

Quick Check

1. Find each product.

a. $\frac{3}{5} \cdot \frac{1}{4}$ $\frac{3}{20}$ **b.** $\frac{5}{6} \cdot \frac{4}{5}$ $\frac{2}{3}$ **c.** $\frac{2}{3} \cdot \frac{4}{5}$ $\frac{8}{15}$

Differentiated Instruction **Solutions for All Learners**

Special Needs L1
Help students visualize $\frac{3}{7}$ of 28 students. Ask them to look at the denominator (7), and draw rows of 7 X's until they get to 28 (4 rows of 7). Then ask them to circle columns (since 3 is the numerator). Ask: *How many X's did you circle?* **12**

learning style: visual

Below Level L2
Give students several multiplication exercises involving $\frac{1}{2}$ to simplify, such as $\frac{1}{2}$ of 3 and $\frac{1}{2}$ of 7.

$\frac{1}{2}$ of $3 = \frac{1}{2} \cdot \frac{3}{1} = \frac{3}{2} = 1\frac{1}{2}$

$\frac{1}{2}$ of $7 = \frac{1}{2} \cdot \frac{7}{1} = \frac{7}{2} = 3\frac{1}{2}$

learning style: visual

To multiply a fraction by a whole number, you can write the whole number as a fraction with a denominator of 1. When a numerator and a denominator have a common factor, you can simplify before multiplying.

EXAMPLE Multiplying by a Whole Number

2 **TAKS** Griddable Item On Friday, $\frac{3}{7}$ of the 28 students in a class went to a music competition. How many students were still in class?

Find $\frac{3}{7}$ of the 28 students, or $\frac{3}{7} \cdot 28$.

$$\frac{3}{7} \cdot 28 = \frac{3}{7} \cdot \frac{28}{1} \quad \leftarrow \text{Write 28 as } \frac{28}{1}.$$

$$= \frac{3}{\underset{1}{7}} \cdot \frac{\overset{4}{28}}{1} \quad \leftarrow \text{Simplify before multiplying.}$$

$$= \frac{12}{1} \quad \leftarrow \text{Multiply the numerators.}$$
$$\quad \leftarrow \text{Multiply the denominators.}$$

$$= 12 \quad \leftarrow \text{Simplify. There were 12 students absent.}$$

$$28 - 12 = 16 \quad \leftarrow \text{Subtract.}$$

There were 16 students still in class on Friday.

✓ Quick Check

2. There are 168 members in an orchestra, and $\frac{3}{8}$ of them play the violin. How many members play the violin? **63 members**

To multiply mixed numbers, first write them as improper fractions, and then multiply as you do with fractions.

EXAMPLE Multiplying Mixed Numbers

3 Find $2\frac{3}{5} \cdot 4\frac{1}{2}$.

Estimate $2\frac{3}{5} \cdot 4\frac{1}{2} \approx 3 \cdot 5$, or 15

$$2\frac{3}{5} \cdot 4\frac{1}{2} = \frac{13}{5} \cdot \frac{9}{2} \quad \leftarrow \text{Write the mixed numbers as improper fractions.}$$

$$= \frac{13 \cdot 9}{5 \cdot 2} \quad \leftarrow \text{Multiply numerators. Multiply denominators.}$$

$$= \frac{117}{10} \quad \leftarrow \text{Simplify.}$$

$$= 11\frac{7}{10} \quad \leftarrow \text{Write as a mixed number.}$$

Check for Reasonableness $11\frac{7}{10}$ is close to the estimate 15.

✓ Quick Check

3. Find each product.

a. $2\frac{1}{3} \cdot 4\frac{5}{8}$ $10\frac{19}{24}$ **b.** $3\frac{3}{5} \cdot 1\frac{3}{10}$ $4\frac{17}{25}$ **c.** $5\frac{3}{4} \cdot 2\frac{5}{8}$ $15\frac{3}{32}$

3-4 Multiplying Fractions and Mixed Numbers **137**

Online active math

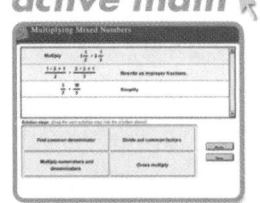

For: Multiplying Fractions Activity
Use: Interactive Textbook, 3-4

Assignment Guide

Check Your Understanding
Go over Exercises 1–6 in class before assigning the Homework Exercises.

Homework Exercises
A Practice by Example   7–31
B Apply Your Skills   32–42
C Challenge   43
TEKS ★ **TAKS** Tune-Up and
    Mixed Review   44–49

Homework Quick Check
To check students' understanding of key skills and concepts, go over Exercises 17, 28, 37, 39, and 41.

Differentiated Instruction Resources

Check Your Understanding

Complete the first step in finding each product.

1. $\frac{2}{5} \cdot \frac{3}{4} = \frac{2 \cdot \blacksquare}{5 \cdot \blacksquare}$ $\frac{3}{4}$ 2. $\frac{5}{6} \cdot 18 = \frac{5}{6} \cdot \frac{18}{\blacksquare}$ 1   3. $2\frac{1}{4} \cdot 1\frac{2}{3} = \frac{\overset{9}{\blacksquare}}{4} \cdot \frac{\overset{5}{\blacksquare}}{3}$

4. What product does the model at the left represent? $\frac{1}{4} \times \frac{5}{6}$

5. **Reasoning** When you multiply two fractions, do you need to find a common denominator first? Explain why or why not. **See margin.**

6. **Number Sense** Is $\frac{5}{7}$ of 28 *more* or *less* than 28? Explain how you know without actually multiplying.
    Less; you are finding a fraction of 28.

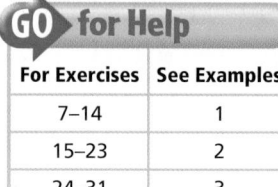

Homework Exercises

For more exercises, see Extra Skills and Word Problems.

GO for Help

For Exercises	See Examples
7–14	1
15–23	2
24–31	3

A **Find each product. Write your result in simplest form. You may find a model helpful.**

7. $\frac{1}{2} \cdot \frac{2}{3}$ $\frac{1}{3}$ 8. $\frac{1}{4} \cdot \frac{3}{5}$ $\frac{3}{20}$ 9. $\frac{1}{3} \cdot \frac{5}{6}$ $\frac{5}{18}$ 10. $\frac{9}{10} \cdot \frac{2}{3}$ $\frac{3}{5}$

11. $\frac{1}{6} \cdot \frac{3}{5}$ $\frac{1}{10}$ 12. $\frac{1}{8} \cdot \frac{4}{5}$ $\frac{1}{10}$ 13. $\frac{2}{3} \cdot \frac{2}{5}$ $\frac{4}{15}$ 14. $\frac{2}{3} \cdot \frac{4}{9}$ $\frac{8}{27}$

Find each product.

15. $\frac{3}{4} \cdot 16$ 12   16. $9 \cdot \frac{1}{3}$ 3   17. $52 \cdot \frac{1}{2}$ 26   18. $\frac{2}{5} \cdot 10$ 4

19. $\frac{1}{4}$ of 12 3   20. $\frac{3}{5}$ of 15 9   21. $\frac{2}{3}$ of 18 12   22. $\frac{5}{8}$ of 64 40

23. To make a fruit punch drink, you use $\frac{1}{3}$ cup of water. You want to make 6 drinks. How many cups of water do you need? 2 c

Find each product. Write your answer as a mixed number. $3\frac{2}{3}$

24. $2\frac{2}{5} \cdot 3\frac{3}{8}$ $8\frac{1}{10}$ 25. $5\frac{1}{4} \cdot 2\frac{2}{7}$ 12   26. $1\frac{3}{10} \cdot 6\frac{2}{3}$ $8\frac{2}{3}$ 27. $1\frac{3}{8} \cdot 2\frac{2}{3}$

28. $3\frac{1}{3} \cdot 1\frac{1}{4}$ $4\frac{1}{6}$ 29. $2\frac{1}{2} \cdot 1\frac{3}{5}$ 4   30. $4\frac{2}{3} \cdot \frac{3}{4}$ $3\frac{1}{2}$ 31. $\frac{1}{4} \cdot 3\frac{1}{5}$ $\frac{4}{5}$

B 32. **Guided Problem Solving** The largest hummingbird is the Giant Hummingbird of South America. It weighs $\frac{2}{3}$ oz. The smallest is the Bee Hummingbird of Cuba. Its weight is one tenth of the weight of a giant hummingbird. What is the total weight of both hummingbirds?
    • **Make a Plan** Find the weight of the smallest hummingbird. Then add its weight to the weight of the largest hummingbird. $\frac{11}{15}$ oz
    • **Carry Out the Plan** The weight of both hummingbirds is $\blacksquare$ oz.

33. **Baking** A recipe calls for $2\frac{3}{4}$ cups of flour. You want to triple the recipe and add another $\frac{1}{4}$ cup. How much flour will you need? $8\frac{1}{2}$ c

American

5. No; you do not need to find a common denominator, since you reduce the product anyway.

37. When multiplying, you do not need to find a common denominator.
    Example: $\frac{1}{2} \cdot \frac{1}{3} = \frac{1 \cdot 1}{2 \cdot 3} = \frac{1}{6}$

(Algebra) **Find the value of *x* using mental math.**

34. $\frac{1}{4}x = \frac{1}{4}$ **1**

35. $\frac{2}{3}x = 0$ **0**

36. $2 + \frac{3}{5}x = 2$ **0**

37. **Writing in Math** How does multiplying two fractions differ from adding two fractions? Give an example. **See margin.**

38. **Science** As a roller coaster car reaches the bottom of a slope and begins to go up the next slope, its acceleration, combined with the downward pull of gravity, can make you feel $3\frac{1}{2}$ times as heavy as you really are. This sensation is called "supergravity." How heavy would a 120-lb person experiencing supergravity feel? **420 lb**

39. The length of a track around a field is $\frac{1}{4}$ mi. You jog $3\frac{1}{2}$ times around
GPS the track. How far do you jog? $\frac{7}{8}$ **mi**

40. **Error Analysis** A student multiplies two mixed numbers, $2\frac{3}{5}$ and $1\frac{1}{3}$, and finds the product to be $2\frac{3}{15}$. Explain the student's mistake. What is the correct answer? **See left.**

40. The student did not write mixed numbers as improper fractions before multiplying; $3\frac{7}{15}$.

41. Mark has 224 board games. He bought $\frac{3}{4}$ of his games on the Internet. Of the games he bought on the Internet, $\frac{1}{6}$ are card games. How many card games did he buy on the Internet? **28 games**

42. **Calculator** Use a calculator to find $10\frac{2}{5} \cdot 4\frac{1}{2}$. $46\frac{4}{5}$

43. **Challenge** A farmer built a fence around a rectangular lot. The lot's length is $2\frac{1}{2}$ mi, and its width is $\frac{4}{5}$ its length. What is the area of the lot? How long is the fence?   **2 mi²; $6\frac{3}{5}$ mi**

 TEKS ★ **TAKS** **Tune-Up and Mixed Review**
GRIDDABLE ITEMS

TAKS Objective 1
TEKS (7.2)(B)

44. The Dancemania dancing studio sent $\frac{2}{3}$ of its dancers to a competition. If there are 36 dancers, how many dancers did the studio send to the competition? **24**

TAKS Objective 3
TEKS (7.8)(C)

45. Damien designed a thin border for his rectangular painting. The perimeter of the painting is 22 ft. The width of the painting is 4.75 ft. What is the length of the painting, in feet? **6.25**

TAKS Objective 6
TEKS (7.13)(C)

46. Helen received a gift certificate for her birthday. She spent $\frac{1}{3}$ of the gift certificate on lunch, and $\frac{1}{4}$ of the remaining amount on dessert. After she spent $3.50 for the tip, she had $4.00 left. What was the amount of Helen's gift certificate, in dollars? **15**

 for Help   **Lesson 1-1**

Estimate. Round to the nearest whole number before you calculate.

47. $19.5 + 56.13$ **76**

48. $34.3 - 18.9$ **15**

49. $26.7 \cdot 9.9$ **270**

TEKS ★ **TAKS** **Resources**

• TAKS Strategies, p. 159
• TAKS Tune-Up, pp. 163–165

TAKS Tune-Up Kit

• TAKS Daily Review Transparencies
• TAKS Review and Preparation Workbook
• TAKS Strategies with Transparencies
• Texas Progress Monitoring Assessments

---

4. Assess & Reteach

PowerPoint
Lesson Quiz

Find each product.

1. $\frac{3}{5} \cdot \frac{10}{12}$ $\frac{1}{2}$

2. $\frac{5}{8}$ of 48   30

3. $4\frac{1}{2} \cdot 2\frac{2}{10}$ $9\frac{9}{10}$

4. $3\frac{1}{4} \cdot 5\frac{1}{3}$ $17\frac{1}{3}$

Alternative Assessment

Have students work in pairs. Each student writes several fractions and mixed numbers one on each small slip of paper. Partners then pair up the fractions and work together to multiply them. Have partners record their work.

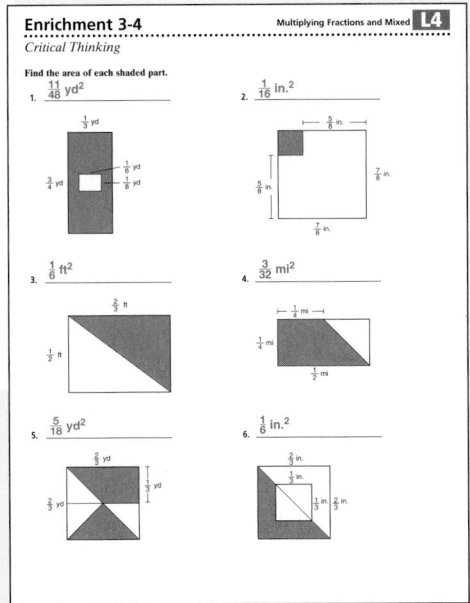

139

Modeling Fraction Division

Students use models to practice division of fractions. This will help them calculate with fractions in Lesson 3-5.

Guided Instruction

Explain that dividing fractions helps you figure how many pieces can be made from a mixed number amount. Have students give examples of times when this skill would be useful.

Ask:
- *Why must we divide each circle in half?* Alfinio wants to eat $\frac{1}{2}$ pizza each meal.

- *What is another way to say $2\frac{1}{4}$ pizzas?* $\frac{9}{4}$ pizzas

Exercises

Have students work independently on the Exercises. When they have finished, allow partners to share their work, discuss their answers, and how they arrived at the answers.

Alternative Method

Some students may prefer to continue to model the division problems by cutting out shapes and cutting them into pieces. Provide extra paper for these students.

TEKS ★ (TAKS) Resources

- Activity Lab 3-5: Dividing Fractions
- paper
- scisssors

Dana Center TEKS Toolkit Clarifying Activities (7.2)(A), (7.13)(D)
Visit: PHSchool.com
Web Code: arq-9045

140

Modeling Fraction Division

How many times does 2 go into 14? You know the answer is 7. When you divide with fractions, the answer may not be so obvious. You can use a model to help you find the answer.

TEKS ★ (TAKS)
(7.2)(A) To represent division situations involving fractions with models including pictures, words, and numbers **(TAKS) Obj. 1**
(7.13)(D) To select tools such as manipulatives to solve problems

EXAMPLE

Alfinio finds $2\frac{1}{4}$ pizzas left after his birthday party. If he decides to eat $\frac{1}{2}$ pizza per meal, how many meals does he have left?

Step 1 Cut out 3 congruent circles. Then cut $\frac{1}{4}$ of one circle. You now have $2\frac{1}{4}$ circles that represent the leftover pizza.

Step 2 Cut your circles into meals for Alfinio. Remember that Alfinio wants to eat $\frac{1}{2}$ pizza per meal.

Step 3 How many $\frac{1}{2}$-pizza meals can Alfinio make from $2\frac{1}{4}$ pizzas?

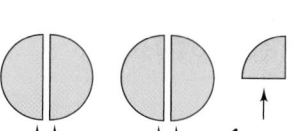

Your model shows that he had $2\frac{1}{4}$ pizzas.

So there are 4 full meals plus $\frac{1}{2}$ meal left.

● This shows that $2\frac{1}{4} \div \frac{1}{2} = 4\frac{1}{2}$.

Exercises

1. Identify the division problem shown in the model. Find the quotient. $2\frac{1}{2} \div \frac{3}{4} = 3\frac{1}{4}$

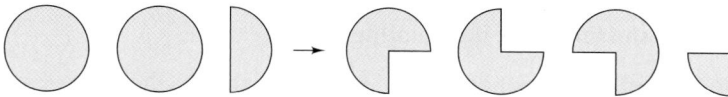

Make a model to represent each expression. Then find the quotient. 2–4. See margin for models.

2. $1\frac{2}{3} \div \frac{1}{3}$ 5

3. $1\frac{1}{2} \div \frac{1}{4}$ 6

4. $3\frac{1}{2} \div \frac{3}{4}$ $4\frac{2}{3}$

5. a. In the example above, how does the number of meals relate to the number of pizzas? Each pizza is two meals.

   b. **Number Sense** Dividing by $\frac{1}{2}$ is the same as multiplying by what number? 2

2.
, 5

3.
, 6

4.
, $4\frac{2}{3}$

3-5 Dividing Fractions and Mixed Numbers

TEKS ⭐ (TAKS)

(7.2)(A) To represent division situations involving fractions with models, including pictures, words, and numbers (TAKS) Obj. 1
Also supports
(7.2)(B) (TAKS) Obj. 1
(7.2)(G) (TAKS) Obj. 1

Dana Center TEKS Clarifying Activities (7.2)(A), (7.2)(B), (7.2)(G)
Visit: PHSchool.com
Web Code: arq-9045

Check Skills You'll Need

1. Vocabulary Review
Which operation do you use to find a *product*?
multiplication

Find each product.

2. $\frac{3}{7} \cdot \frac{2}{3}$ $\frac{2}{7}$

3. $\frac{5}{9} \cdot \frac{1}{2}$ $\frac{5}{18}$

4. $50 \cdot \frac{9}{10}$ 45

5. $2\frac{2}{9} \cdot 1\frac{4}{5}$ 4

for Help
Lesson 3-4

TEKS ⭐ (TAKS)

- **(7.2)(A)** To represent division situations involving fractions with models, including pictures, words, and numbers (TAKS) **Obj. 1**
- **(7.2)(B)** To use division to solve problems involving fractions (TAKS) **Obj. 1**
- **(7.2)(G)** To determine the reasonableness of a solution (TAKS) **Obj. 1**

🔊 **New Vocabulary** reciprocals

Why Learn This?

When you work with measurements, you will often need to divide fractions and mixed numbers. The ruler below shows there are four $\frac{3}{4}$'s in 3 wholes. So $3 \div \frac{3}{4} = 4$. Notice that $3 \cdot \frac{4}{3}$ also equals 4. The numbers $\frac{3}{4}$ and $\frac{4}{3}$ are reciprocals. Two numbers are **reciprocals** if their product is 1. To divide by a fraction, you multiply by its reciprocal.

KEY CONCEPTS   Dividing by Fractions

Arithmetic	Algebra
$3 \div \frac{3}{4} = 3 \cdot \frac{4}{3} = 4$	$\frac{a}{b} \div \frac{c}{d} = \frac{a}{b} \cdot \frac{d}{c}$ for b, c, and $d \neq 0$

Video Tutor Help
Visit: PHSchool.com
Web Code: are-0775

EXAMPLE   Dividing by a Fraction

① Find $\frac{2}{3} \div \frac{5}{6}$.

$\frac{2}{3} \div \frac{5}{6} = \frac{2}{3} \cdot \frac{6}{5}$ ← Multiply by $\frac{6}{5}$, the reciprocal of $\frac{5}{6}$.

$= \frac{2 \cdot \overset{2}{\cancel{6}}}{\underset{1}{\cancel{3}} \cdot 5}$ ← Divide 6 and 3 by their GCF, 3.

$= \frac{4}{5}$ ← Simplify.

✓ Quick Check

1. a. Find $\frac{7}{8} \div \frac{1}{4}$. $3\frac{1}{2}$ **b.** Find $\frac{5}{8} \div \frac{3}{4}$. $\frac{5}{6}$ **c.** Find $14 \div \frac{7}{10}$. 20

3-5 Dividing Fractions and Mixed Numbers **141**

Professional Development

TEKS Math Background

Two numbers are *reciprocals* if their product is 1. For example, $\frac{2}{5}$ and $\frac{5}{2}$ are reciprocals, as are 8 and $\frac{1}{8}$. To divide by a fraction, change the fraction to its reciprocal and then multiply. When dividing mixed numbers, first change the mixed numbers to improper fractions.

More Math Background: p. 118C

Lesson Planning and Resources

See p. 118E for a list of the resources that support this lesson.

Bell Ringer Practice

✓ **Check Skills You'll Need**
Use student page, transparency, or PowerPoint.

(TAKS) **Daily Review 23**
Use transparency.

Differentiated Instruction   Solutions for All Learners

Special Needs L1
Help students draw a picture for Example 2, and estimate the answer. Then ask them to work out the problem, assisting as they go through the steps. They can then compare their estimate to their calculated answer.

learning style: visual

Below Level L2
Give students fractions and have them write the reciprocal, such as these.

$\frac{2}{5}$ $\frac{5}{2}$ $\frac{3}{8}$ $\frac{8}{3}$ $\frac{1}{4}$ $\frac{4}{1}$ 6 $\frac{1}{6}$ $1\frac{1}{2}\left(=\frac{3}{2}\right)\frac{2}{3}$ $1\frac{1}{3}$ $\frac{3}{4}$

$2\frac{1}{4}$ $\frac{4}{9}$ $2\frac{3}{4}$ $\frac{4}{11}$ $3\frac{5}{8}$ $\frac{8}{29}$

learning style: visual

141

Activity Lab

Use before the lesson.
Student Edition Activity Lab,
Hands On 3-5a, Modeling
Fraction Division, p. 140

All in One Teaching Resources
Activity Lab 3-5: Dividing
Fractions

Guided Instruction

Example 1
Teach students this rhyme to help them remember how to divide fractions: *When dividing do not sigh, just invert and multiply.*

Example 2
Have students model this situation by cutting a piece of string $9\frac{1}{2}$ in. long into pieces $2\frac{3}{4}$ in. long.

Example 3
After discussing Example 3, invite students to explain alternative ways of solving the problem. For example, a student might sketch boxes for each $1\frac{1}{2}$ oz serving and keep a running total until reaching $19\frac{1}{2}$ oz.

PowerPoint

Additional Examples

1 Find $\frac{3}{10} \div \frac{2}{5}$. $\frac{3}{4}$

2 Find $4\frac{2}{3} \div 1\frac{3}{4}$. $2\frac{2}{3}$

3 You have a piece of yarn that is $12\frac{1}{2}$ ft long. You need to cut it into strips that are $1\frac{1}{4}$ ft long. How many strips will you have? **10**

Online
active math

For: Dividing Fractions Activity
Use: Interactive Textbook, 3-5

To divide mixed numbers, rewrite them as improper fractions.

EXAMPLE **Dividing Mixed Numbers**

2 **Measurement** You have a space of $9\frac{1}{2}$ in. on a poster for a row of photos. Each photo is $2\frac{3}{4}$ in. wide. How many photos can you fit?

To find how many photos you can fit, divide $9\frac{1}{2}$ by $2\frac{3}{4}$.

$$9\frac{1}{2} \div 2\frac{3}{4} = \frac{19}{2} \div \frac{11}{4} \quad \leftarrow \text{Write the mixed numbers as improper fractions.}$$

$$= \frac{19}{2} \cdot \frac{4}{11} \quad \leftarrow \text{Multiply by } \frac{4}{11}, \text{ the reciprocal of } \frac{11}{4}.$$

$$= \frac{19}{{}_1 2} \cdot \frac{4^2}{11} \quad \leftarrow \text{Divide 4 and 2 by their GCF, 2.}$$

$$= \frac{38}{11} \quad \leftarrow \text{Multiply.}$$

$$= 3\frac{5}{11} \quad \leftarrow \text{Write as a mixed number.}$$

You can fit 3 photos.

✓ Quick Check

2. a. Find $5\frac{3}{4} \div 3\frac{2}{3}$. $1\frac{25}{44}$ **b.** Find $4\frac{1}{8} \div 5\frac{1}{2}$. $\frac{3}{4}$ **c.** Find $3\frac{9}{16} \div 3$. $1\frac{3}{16}$

EXAMPLE **Application: Meal Planning**

3 How many $1\frac{1}{2}$-oz servings of cereal are in the larger cereal box at the right?

To find how many $1\frac{1}{2}$-oz servings are in $19\frac{1}{2}$ oz, divide $19\frac{1}{2}$ by $1\frac{1}{2}$.

Estimate $19\frac{1}{2} \div 1\frac{1}{2} \approx 20 \div 2$, or 10

$$19\frac{1}{2} \div 1\frac{1}{2} = \frac{39}{2} \div \frac{3}{2} \quad \leftarrow \text{Write the mixed numbers as improper fractions.}$$

$$= \frac{39}{2} \cdot \frac{2}{3} \quad \leftarrow \text{Multiply by } \frac{2}{3}, \text{ the reciprocal of } \frac{3}{2}.$$

$$= \frac{{}^{3}39 \cdot 2^{1}}{{}_1 2 \cdot 3_1} \quad \leftarrow \text{Divide 39 and 3 by their GCF. Divide 2 by itself.}$$

$$= \frac{13}{1} = 13 \quad \leftarrow \text{Simplify.}$$

There are thirteen $1\frac{1}{2}$-oz servings in the larger cereal box.

Check for Reasonableness 13 is close to 10. The answer is reasonable.

✓ Quick Check

3. One can of iced tea holds 12 fl oz. A 2-liter bottle holds $67\frac{3}{5}$ fl oz. How many cans of iced tea will you need to fill a 2-liter bottle? $5\frac{19}{30}$ cans

---

Advanced Learners **L4**
Have students use different values for *a, b, c,* and *d* in this equation $\frac{a}{b} \div \frac{c}{d} = \frac{a}{b} \cdot \frac{d}{c}$ to help show why *a* may equal 0, but *b, c,* and *d* may not. Division by 0 is not allowed; *a* is only a numerator.

Pre-AP™

English Language Learners **ELL**
To help students understand division of fractions, ask questions such as: *How many $\frac{3}{4}$-inch pieces cover 3 inches?* 4 *How many $2\frac{3}{4}$-inch sections will it take to get to cover $9\frac{1}{2}$ inches?* $3\frac{5}{11}$

learning style: visual

You want to put 4 lb of raisins in bags so that each bag contains $\frac{2}{3}$ lb. How many bags do you need?

All in One Teaching Resources
- Daily Notetaking Guide 3-5 **L3**
- Adapted Notetaking 3-5 **L1**

● More Than One Way

Kayla's Method

I can use number sense. $\frac{2}{3} + \frac{2}{3} + \frac{2}{3} = \frac{6}{3} = 2$, so three times $\frac{2}{3}$ lb is 2 lb. That means six times $\frac{2}{3}$ lb is 4 lb.

I need six bags.

Will's Method

I can divide 4 by $\frac{2}{3}$.

$$4 \div \frac{2}{3} = \frac{4}{1} \div \frac{2}{3} \quad \leftarrow \text{Write the whole number as a fraction.}$$
$$= \frac{4}{1} \cdot \frac{3}{2} \quad \leftarrow \text{Multiply by } \frac{3}{2}, \text{ the reciprocal of } \frac{2}{3}.$$
$$= \frac{\overset{2}{4} \cdot 3}{1 \cdot \underset{1}{2}} \quad \leftarrow \text{Divide 4 and 2 by their GCF, 2.}$$
$$= \frac{6}{1} = 6 \quad \leftarrow \text{Simplify.}$$

I need six bags.

Choose a Method

You want to bike 12 miles in $1\frac{1}{3}$ hours. What should your average speed be? Describe your method and explain why you chose it.
9; answers may vary. Sample: I used Kayla's method because it is quicker.

Closure

- *How do you find the reciprocal of a fraction?* Interchange the numerator and denominator.
- *How do you divide by a fraction?* Multiply by its reciprocal.
- *What is the first step in dividing mixed numbers?* Rewrite them as improper fractions.

✓ Check Your Understanding

inches

1. What quotient does the model at the left represent? $1\frac{1}{2} \div \frac{1}{2}$

Find the reciprocal of each number.

2. $\frac{5}{8}$ $\frac{8}{5}$ 3. $\frac{1}{4}$ 4   4. 9 $\frac{1}{9}$ 5. $3\frac{1}{2}$ $\frac{2}{7}$

Mental Math Match each expression to the correct quotient.

6. $6 \div \frac{1}{2}$ B   A. 25

                           B. 12
7. $5 \div \frac{1}{5}$ A   C. 90

8. $9 \div \frac{1}{10}$ C

3-5 Dividing Fractions and Mixed Numbers   **143**

Assignment Guide

Check Your Understanding
Go over Exercises 1–8 in class before assigning the Homework Exercises.

Homework Exercises
A Practice by Example   9–33
B Apply Your Skills   34–47
C Challenge   48
TEKS ★ TAKS Tune-Up and
Mixed Review   49–54

Homework Quick Check
To check students' understanding of key skills and concepts, go over Exercises 12, 29, 38, 44, and 45.

Differentiated Instruction Resources

For more exercises, see Extra Skills and Word Problems.

GO for Help

For Exercises	See Examples
9–20	1
21–33	2–3

A Find each quotient. You may find a model helpful.

9. $\frac{4}{5} \div \frac{1}{10}$ 8

10. $\frac{4}{5} \div \frac{1}{5}$ 4

11. $\frac{5}{16} \div \frac{1}{2}$ $\frac{5}{8}$

12. $\frac{7}{10} \div \frac{1}{5}$ $3\frac{1}{2}$

13. $\frac{2}{7} \div \frac{1}{9}$ $2\frac{4}{7}$

14. $\frac{1}{9} \div \frac{5}{6}$ $\frac{2}{15}$

15. $\frac{3}{4} \div \frac{2}{3}$ $1\frac{1}{8}$

16. $\frac{1}{4} \div \frac{3}{8}$ $\frac{2}{3}$

17. $\frac{3}{8} \div \frac{1}{4}$ $1\frac{1}{2}$

18. $\frac{1}{2} \div \frac{2}{7}$ $1\frac{3}{4}$

19. $\frac{3}{5} \div \frac{2}{3}$ $\frac{9}{10}$

20. $\frac{9}{10} \div \frac{1}{5}$ $4\frac{1}{2}$

Find each quotient. Write your answer as a mixed number.

21. $1\frac{1}{2} \div 3\frac{1}{4}$ $\frac{6}{13}$

22. $2\frac{1}{6} \div 3\frac{5}{6}$ $\frac{13}{23}$

23. $5\frac{1}{4} \div 3\frac{1}{2}$ $1\frac{1}{2}$

24. $5\frac{1}{3} \div 4\frac{2}{3}$ $1\frac{1}{7}$

25. $2\frac{2}{3} \div 5\frac{1}{9}$ $\frac{12}{23}$

26. $6\frac{2}{3} \div 1\frac{1}{4}$ $5\frac{1}{3}$

27. $3\frac{3}{4} \div 4\frac{1}{2}$ $\frac{5}{6}$

28. $11\frac{1}{2} \div 3\frac{1}{2}$ $3\frac{2}{7}$

29. $12\frac{3}{4} \div 4\frac{1}{2}$ $2\frac{5}{6}$

30. $11\frac{1}{3} \div 4\frac{1}{2}$ $2\frac{14}{27}$

31. $8\frac{1}{3} \div 2\frac{1}{2}$ $3\frac{1}{3}$

32. $1\frac{5}{9} \div 2\frac{1}{3}$ $\frac{2}{3}$

33. You can jog $\frac{1}{4}$ mi in 2 min. How long will it take you to jog 2 mi?
   16 min

B GPS 34. **Guided Problem Solving** Telephone cable is being installed along a $6\frac{3}{4}$-mi-long street. Workers install $\frac{9}{16}$ mi in the morning and $\frac{9}{16}$ mi in the afternoon. How long will they take to install all of the cable?
   • How many miles of cable can they install in one day?   **6 days**
   • How many miles of cable do they have to install?
   • What should you divide by to find how long the project will take?

35. Your friend found the reciprocal of $\frac{3}{8}$ without changing $5\frac{3}{8}$ to an improper fraction; $\frac{8}{43}$.

35. **Error Analysis** Your friend wrote the reciprocal of $5\frac{3}{8}$ as $5\frac{8}{3}$. Explain why your friend is incorrect. What is the correct reciprocal?

36. Estimate $8\frac{2}{5} \div 3\frac{1}{2}$. Compare your estimate to the exact quotient.
   $2; 2\frac{2}{5}$

37. A nail weighs about $\frac{1}{10}$ oz. How many nails are in a 5-lb box?
   800 nails

GO Online
Homework Help
Visit: PHSchool.com
Web Code: are-0305

38. 14 hats; answers may vary. Sample: I used number sense because it is quicker.

38. **Choose a Method** Ranchers in the American West often wear what is called a ten-gallon hat. However, a ten-gallon hat actually holds only $\frac{3}{4}$ gallon. How many ten-gallon hats would be needed to hold 10 gallons? Describe your method and explain why you chose it.   **See left.**

39. Joanne has $13\frac{1}{2}$ yd of material to make costumes. Each complete costume requires $1\frac{1}{2}$ yd for the top and $\frac{3}{4}$ yd for the bottom. How many complete costumes can she make? **6 costumes**

40. **Reasoning** Can you use the rule for multiplying by the reciprocal to divide whole numbers such as $10 \div 2$? Explain.
   yes; $10 \div 2 = 10 \cdot \frac{1}{2} = 5$

(**Algebra**) **Use number sense to find the value of *x*.**

41. $\frac{1}{4} \div x = \frac{1}{4}$ **1**

42. $x \div \frac{33}{100} = 0$ **0**

43. $x \div \frac{2}{5} = 1$ $\frac{2}{5}$

44. Biology A manatee can swim 5 mi in $1\frac{1}{4}$ h. If the manatee swims at
GPS the same average speed, how far can it swim in 1 h? **4 mi**

45. <u>Writing in Math</u> What positive number is its own reciprocal? What
number has no reciprocal? Explain. **1; 0;** $\frac{1}{1} \cdot \frac{1}{1} = 1; \frac{0}{0} \cdot \frac{0}{0} \neq 1$

46. A one-serving recipe calls for $\frac{1}{3}$ c of vegetable oil for a marinade
and $\frac{1}{6}$ c of oil for the sauce. You have $3\frac{1}{2}$ c of vegetable oil. How
many servings can you make? **7 servings**

47. The area of a rectangle is 117 ft². The length of the rectangle is $9\frac{3}{4}$ ft.
What is the width of the rectangle? **12 ft**

C 48. Challenge A rectangular floor measures 9 ft by 6 ft. You use
$1\frac{1}{2}$-ft-square tiles to cover the floor. How many tiles will you need?
24 tiles

Careers Marine biologists collect and analyze data on marine life.

TEKS ★ TAKS Tune-Up and Mixed Review

TAKS Objective 1
TEKS (7.2)(A)

49. Which model best represents the expression $4 \div \frac{2}{3}$? **B**

Ⓐ

Ⓒ

Ⓑ

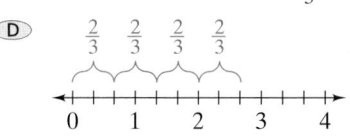
Ⓓ

TAKS Objective 5
TEKS (7.12)(B)

50. Eliza's grades on her daily math homework were 8, 10, 7, 9, 9, 4, 8, 2,
10, 8, 3, 7, 9, 8, 6, and 4. Which measure of the data is NOT
represented by a score of 8? **F**

Ⓕ Mean   Ⓖ Median   Ⓗ Mode   Ⓙ Range

TAKS Objective 6
TEKS (7.13)(B)

51. At an animal adoption center, $\frac{3}{8}$ of the animals are dogs, and $\frac{5}{16}$ are
cats. How would you find the fraction of animals that are neither
dogs nor cats? **D**

Ⓐ Add the fraction of dogs and the fraction of cats.

Ⓑ Subtract the fraction of cats from the fraction of dogs.

Ⓒ Subtract the fraction of dogs from 1 and add the fraction of cats.

Ⓓ Add both fractions and then subtract the result from 1.

GO for Help   **Lesson 2-2**   **Write in standard form.**

52. 5.5×10^4
55,000

53. 2.564×10^3
2,564

54. 5.6302×10^1
56.302

TEKS ★ TAKS Resources

• TAKS Strategies, p. 159
• TAKS Tune-Up, pp. 163–165

TAKS Tune-Up Kit

• TAKS Daily Review Transparencies
• TAKS Review and Preparation Workbook
• TAKS Strategies with Transparencies
• Texas Progress Monitoring Assessments

---

4. Assess & Reteach

PowerPoint
Lesson Quiz

Find each quotient.

1. $\frac{1}{8} \div \frac{3}{4}$ $\frac{1}{6}$

2. $\frac{2}{3} \div \frac{3}{8}$ $1\frac{7}{9}$

3. $1\frac{5}{6} \div 2\frac{2}{5}$ $\frac{55}{72}$

4. $4\frac{2}{7} \div \frac{1}{5}$ $21\frac{3}{7}$

Alternative Assessment

Make sure students have customary system rulers. Ask questions such as:

How many $\frac{1}{2}$-in. units are in $2\frac{1}{2}$ in.? **5**

How many $\frac{3}{4}$-in. units are in 3 in.? **4**

How many $1\frac{1}{2}$-in. units are in 9 in.? **6**

Have them draw line segments of the given lengths, marking off each corresponding fractional unit. Then have students write the steps involved in performing the fractional divisions represented by each model.

145

Practice Solving Problems

In this feature, students practice solving problems involving multiplication with fractions and mixed numbers. This will help them see how the skills they learned in this chapter apply to everyday situations.

Guided Instruction

Explain to students that sales in stores often offer discounts of a fraction of the price of an item. Tell them they can use multiplication with fractions to determine the sale price of the item.

Ask:
- *Why is the joke sign misleading?* $\frac{3}{2}$ of the original price is more than the original price so there is no sale.
- *Why do we add the $21 after calculating the price Freddy paid for the suit.* Tax is based on the sales price of the suit.
- *What would be a good deal on the suit?* Sample: $\frac{1}{4}$ or $\frac{1}{2}$ off the original price

TEKS ★ **TAKS Resources**

Dana Center TEKS Toolkit
   Clarifying Activities (7.2)(A),
   (7.2)(B)
Visit: PHSchool.com
Web Code: arq-9045

Practice Solving Problems

TEKS ★ **TAKS**

(7.2)(A) To represent multiplication situations involving fractions with models **TAKS** Obj. 1

(7.2)(B) To use multiplication and division to solve problems involving fractions and decimals **TAKS** Obj. 1

An employee plays a joke and posts the wrong sale sign to see if anyone notices. Freddy enters the store and buys a suit on sale. The regular price of the suit is $200. What does he pay for the suit after $21 for sales tax is added?

What You Might Think

> What do I know?
> What am I trying to find out?

> How do I show the main idea?

> How do I estimate the answer?

> How do I solve the problem?

> What is the answer?

> Is the answer reasonable?

What You Might Write

Freddy must pay $\frac{3}{2}$ of $200 and $21 for sales tax. I want to find the total after tax is added.

Draw a diagram.

$\frac{3}{2}$ is $1\frac{1}{2}$. So the suit costs $1\frac{1}{2}$ times the original price.

$1\frac{1}{2} \times \$200 = \$300$

With sales tax, the price will be over $300.

$\$300 + \$21 = \$321$

$321 is the exact answer.

Yes, it is reasonable. The answer is close to the estimate of $300.

Think It Through

1a. The $\frac{2}{2}$ mark represents all of the $200 before markup and tax.

1. **a.** In the diagram, what does it mean for $200 to be equivalent to $\frac{2}{2}$?
   b. What does the $\frac{3}{2}$ mark represent? Explain. The $\frac{3}{2}$ mark represents the cost including the markup.

2. How do you know that $1\frac{1}{2} \times \$200 = \$300$?
   See margin.

2. $1\frac{1}{2} = \frac{3}{2}$, $\frac{3}{2} \times \$200 = \$300$

Exercises

For Exercises 3 and 4, answer the questions first and then solve the problem.

3. Your friend bought a shirt at the $\frac{3}{2}$-price sale. The regular price for the shirt was \$60, and \$4.20 for sales tax was added. If your friend paid with a \$100 bill, how much change did he get? **\$5.80**
   a. What do you know?
   b. What do you want to find out?
   c. Finish drawing the diagram below to help you find the answer.

   d. Estimate the answer.

4. Harriet bought her father a tie at the $\frac{3}{2}$-price sale. The sale price was \$24, not including tax. What was the regular price? **\$16**
   a. What do you know?
   b. What do you want to find out?
   c. Make a drawing to show the main idea.
   d. Estimate the answer.

For Exercises 5–7, use the sale sign shown below.

> **SALE!**
> Belts : $\frac{1}{3}$ off   Hats : $\frac{1}{4}$ off
> Jewelry : $\frac{1}{2}$ off   Dresses : $\frac{1}{5}$ off

5. Mary buys a hat at the sale. The hat's regular price is \$24. She will pay \$1.26 for sales tax. How much change should she get from a \$20 bill? **\$.74**

6. Juanita buys a dress at the sale. The regular price of the dress is \$45. She will pay \$2.52 for sales tax. What will be the total cost? **\$38.52**

7. Xavier buys a belt at the sale. The cost was \$16 before tax was added. What was the regular price of the belt? **\$24**

3-6

TEKS ★ TAKS

(7.3)(B) To find solutions to application problems involving proportional relationships such as related measurement units **TAKS** Obj. 2

Also supports
(7.14)(A) **TAKS** Obj. 6
(7.2)(B) **TAKS** Obj. 1

Dana Center TEKS Toolkit Clarifying Activities (7.3)(B), (7.14)(A), (7.2)(B)
Visit: PHSchool.com
Web Code: arq-9045

TEKS Math Background

The units of measure commonly used in the United States are known as the Customary System. Students should know how to convert between units of measure. To change from a larger unit to a smaller unit, such as pounds to ounces, multiply. To change from a smaller unit to a larger unit, such as feet to miles, divide.

More Math Background: p. 118D

Lesson Planning and Resources

See p. 118E for a list of the resources that support this lesson.

Bell Ringer Practice

☑ **Check Skills You'll Need**
Use student page, transparency, or PowerPoint.

TAKS Daily Review 24
Use transparency.

148

3-6   Changing Units in the Customary System

☑ Check Skills You'll Need

1. **Vocabulary Review**
Why is $1\frac{3}{8}$ called a *mixed number*? See below.

Find each sum or difference.

2. $\frac{2}{3} + \frac{5}{12}$ $1\frac{1}{12}$

3. $\frac{15}{16} - \frac{5}{16}$ $\frac{5}{8}$

4. $5\frac{1}{2} + 6\frac{3}{4}$ $12\frac{1}{4}$

5. $8 - 3\frac{3}{4}$ $4\frac{1}{4}$

 for Help
Lesson 3-3

Check Skills You'll Need

1. It consists of a whole number and a fraction.

TEKS ★ TAKS

- (7.3)(B) To find solutions to application problems involving proportional relationships such as related measurement units **TAKS** Obj. 2
- (7.14)(A) To communicate ideas using appropriate units **TAKS** Obj. 6
- (7.2)(B) To use addition, subtraction, multiplication, and division to solve problems involving fractions **TAKS** Obj. 1

Why Learn This?

Most people in the United States use the customary system of measurement for length, capacity, and weight. Changing units allows you to compare measures and compute with them, as carpenters do.

Customary Units of Measure

Type	Length	Capacity	Weight
Unit	inch (in.) foot (ft) yard (yd) mile (mi)	fluid ounce (fl oz) cup (c) pint (pt) quart (qt) gallon (gal)	ounce (oz) pound (lb) ton (t)
Equivalents	1 ft = 12 in. 1 yd = 3 ft 1 mi = 5,280 ft	1 c = 8 fl oz 1 pt = 2 c 1 qt = 2 pt 1 gal = 4 qt	1 lb = 16 oz 1 t = 2,000 lb

---

Vocabulary Tip

The customary system is sometimes called the "English system," even though it is no longer used in England.

EXAMPLE   Changing Units of Length

1 **Carpentry** A carpenter has a board 10 ft long. He cuts a piece 5 ft 3 in. long from the board. What is the length in feet of the remaining piece?

You need to subtract 5 ft 3 in. from 10 ft.

$$5 \text{ ft } 3 \text{ in. } = 5\frac{3}{12} \text{ ft } = 5\frac{1}{4} \text{ ft} \quad \leftarrow \text{Write 3 in. as a fraction of a foot.}$$

$$10 - 5\frac{1}{4} = 9\frac{4}{4} - 5\frac{1}{4} \quad \leftarrow \text{Rename 10 as } 9\frac{4}{4}.$$

$$= 4\frac{3}{4} \quad \leftarrow \text{Subtract.}$$

The remaining piece is $4\frac{3}{4}$ ft long.

☑ Quick Check

$1\frac{7}{12}$ ft

1. How much shorter than a board 10 ft long is a board 8 ft 5 in. long?

148   Chapter 3   Operations With Fractions

Differentiated Instruction   Solutions for All Learners

Special Needs L1
Help students see the difference between one inch and one foot by tracing those lengths with their fingers. Help them understand weight differences by holding a 1-pound weight and a 1-ounce weight. This will help them better understand why the units are unequal.
    learning style: tactile

Below Level L2
Have students identify measurement abbreviations and write the conversion relationship.

    in. and ft **12 inches = 1 foot**
    c and fl oz **1 cup = 8 fluid ounces**
    lb and oz **1 pound = 16 ounces**
    learning style: verbal

To change from a smaller unit to a larger unit, you *divide*. To change from a larger unit to a smaller unit, you *multiply*.

EXAMPLE Changing Units of Capacity

② **Multiple Choice** Jonah has 30 fluid ounces of juice. How many $1\frac{1}{2}$-cup servings does he have altogether?

Ⓐ $2\frac{1}{2}$ Ⓑ 18   Ⓒ 20   Ⓓ $28\frac{1}{2}$

First you need to find the number of fluid ounces in $1\frac{1}{2}$ cups. Since there are 8 fluid ounces in 1 cup, you know that there are 12 fluid ounces in $1\frac{1}{2}$ cups.

Next you need to find the number of groups of 12 fluid ounces that are in 30 fluid ounces. You need to divide 30 by 12.

$$30 \div 12 = 2.5 = 2\frac{1}{2} \quad \leftarrow \text{Write as a mixed number.}$$

There are $2\frac{1}{2}$ servings in 30 fl oz of juice. The correct answer is choice A.

✓ **Quick Check**

2. How many 1-cup servings are in 50 fluid ounces of juice? $6\frac{1}{4}$ c

EXAMPLE Changing Units of Weight

③ **Cycling** The lighter the frame of a mountain bike, the easier it is to ride. In the ad shown at the left, Mountain Master weighs 76 oz and Super Cycle weighs $4\frac{1}{4}$ lb. Which bike will be easier to ride?

Think of the relationship between pounds and ounces. A pound is a larger unit of measure than an ounce. There are 16 ounces in one pound.

$1 \text{ lb} = 16 \text{ oz}$
$\searrow \times 16 \nearrow$

To change $4\frac{1}{4}$ lb to ounces, multiply $4\frac{1}{4}$ by 16.

$$4\frac{1}{4} \cdot 16 = \frac{17}{4} \cdot \frac{16}{1} \quad \leftarrow \text{Write } 4\frac{1}{4} \text{ as an improper fraction.}$$
$$= 68 \quad \leftarrow \text{Multiply.}$$

The Super Cycle will be easier to ride because it is lighter.

✓ **Quick Check**

3. Find the number of ounces in $4\frac{5}{8}$ lb. 74 oz

MOUNTAIN MASTER
76 oz frame weight
$195.95

$179.99
$4\frac{1}{4}$ lb frame weight
SUPER CYCLE

TAKS Tip

Some questions require two steps to find the answer. Read carefully, and tackle one step at a time.

3-6   Changing Units in the Customary System   **149**

Advanced Learners L4
Challenge students to find five different ways to express their height.
Sample: 5 ft 1 in.; $5\frac{1}{12}$ ft; 61 in.; $1\frac{25}{36}$ yd; about 0.0009627 mi

English Language Learners ELL
For Example 1, ask step-by-step questions. *Why is it a good idea to write 5 feet 3 inches as a mixed number?* easier to subtract *How do you know 3 inches is $\frac{3}{12}$ of a foot?* There are 12 inches in one foot. *Why did you rename 10 as $9\frac{4}{4}$?* to subtract fourths

Pre-AP™   learning style: verbal

---

2. Teach

Activity Lab

Use before the lesson.

All in One Teaching Resources

Activity Lab 3-6: Patterns in Measurement

Guided Instruction

Example 2
Display different-sized empty bottles and cartons to help students get a better sense of the units used to measure capacity.

Example 3
Some students prefer multiplying by a fraction of equivalent measures. For instance, to convert 40 ounces to pounds, you could set up this multiplication:

$$\frac{40 \text{ oz}}{1} \cdot \frac{1 \text{ lb}}{16 \text{ oz}} = \frac{40}{16} \text{ lb} =$$
$$\frac{5}{2} \text{ lb} = 2\frac{1}{2} \text{ lb}$$

Multiplying by the fraction $\frac{1 \text{ lb}}{16 \text{ oz}}$ is the same as multiplying by 1 since the values in the numerator and the denominator are equal.

PowerPoint
📥 Additional Examples

❶ A carpenter cuts a 4 ft 10 in. piece from an 8 ft board. What is the length in feet of the remaining piece? $3\frac{1}{6}$ ft

❷ How many one-cup servings are in a 30-fluid-ounce sports drink bottle? $3\frac{3}{4}$ one-cup servings

❸ Which weighs more—a $1\frac{3}{4}$-lb book or a 24 oz catalog? The book that weighs 28 oz

All in One Teaching Resources
- Daily Notetaking Guide 3-6 L3
- Adapted Notetaking 3-6 L1

Closure

- *How do you change from a smaller unit to a larger unit?* divide
- *How do you change from a larger unit to a smaller unit?* multiply

149

3. Practice

Assignment Guide

Check Your Understanding
Go over Exercises 1–8 in class before assigning the Homework Exercises.

Homework Exercises
A Practice by Example   9–29
B Apply Your Skills   30–43
C Challenge   44
TEKS ★ TAKS Tune-Up and Mixed Review   45–49

Homework Quick Check
To check students' understanding of key skills and concepts, go over Exercises 13, 21, 38, 42, and 43.

✓ Check Your Understanding

Tell whether you would *multiply* or *divide* to change from one unit of measure to the other.

1. gallons to quarts — multiply
2. ounces to pounds — divide
3. yards to feet — multiply
4. pints to cups — multiply
5. feet to miles — divide
6. tons to pounds — multiply

7. **Number Sense** Why do you *multiply* to change from a larger unit to a smaller unit?
It takes more smaller units to equal the larger units.

8. Why do you *divide* to change from a smaller unit to a larger unit?
It takes fewer larger units to equal the smaller units.

Homework Exercises

For more exercises, see Extra Skills and Word Problems.

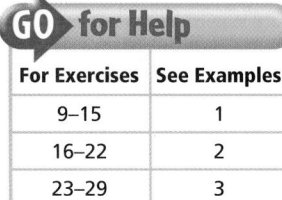

GO for Help

For Exercises	See Examples
9–15	1
16–22	2
23–29	3

Ⓐ Change each unit of length.

9. 4 ft 6 in. = ■ ft $4\frac{1}{2}$
10. 1 ft 9 in. = ■ ft $1\frac{3}{4}$
11. 6 ft 2 in. = ■ ft $6\frac{1}{6}$

12. 4 yd 2 ft = ■ yd $4\frac{2}{3}$
13. 1 yd 1 ft = ■ yd $1\frac{1}{3}$
14. 10 yd 3 ft = ■ yd   11

15. A carpenter cuts 2 ft 9 in. off a board that was 4 ft long. How long is the piece that is left, in feet and inches? $1\frac{1}{4}$ ft

Change each unit of capacity.

16. 48 fl oz = ■ c   6
17. 6 c = ■ p   3
18. 40 qt = ■ gal   10

19. 1 c = ■ p $\frac{1}{2}$
20. 9 pt = ■ qt $4\frac{1}{2}$
21. 12 c = ■ qt   3

22. How many cups are in a 12-fl oz can of lemonade? $1\frac{1}{2}$ c

Change each unit of weight.

23. $\frac{3}{4}$ lb = ■ oz   12
24. $2\frac{1}{4}$ lb = ■ oz   36
25. $2\frac{1}{2}$ t = ■ lb   5,000

26. 32 oz = ■ lb   2
27. 80 oz = ■ lb   5
28. 1000 lb = ■ t $\frac{1}{2}$

29. Which is lighter, 12 oz of cheese or 1 lb of cheese? 12 oz

Ⓑ GPS 30. **Guided Problem Solving** People in the United States discard an average of 75,000 t of food per day. If a garbage truck can hold 12,000 lb, how many trucks are needed to haul all of the food?
  • How many tons is 12,000 lb?
  • What operation should you use to find the number of garbage trucks needed?   12,500 trucks

31. You are hiking a 2-mi trail. A sign shows that you have hiked 1,000 ft. How many feet do you have left to hike? 9,560 ft

Complete.

32. 500 lb = ■ t 0.25   **33.** $1\frac{1}{5}$ t = ■ lb 2,400   **34.** $5\frac{1}{4}$ gal = ■ qt 21

35. 7 pt = ■ qt $3\frac{1}{2}$ **36.** 69 in. = ■ ft $5\frac{3}{4}$ **37.** 16 ft = ■ yd $5\frac{1}{3}$

38. Sam bought three packages of low-salt pretzels weighing 12 oz, 32 oz, and $1\frac{1}{2}$ lb. How many pounds of pretzels did Sam buy all together? $4\frac{1}{4}$ lb

39. **Biology** Baby crocodiles are about 8 in. long when they hatch, and they grow about 10 in. each year. How many feet long is a crocodile that is 4 years old? **4 ft**

40. How are the rates "6 pounds per day" and "6 days per pound" different? When would each be useful? **Check students' work.**

41. **Error Analysis** Your friend says that a quarter-pound burger is heavier than a six-ounce burger. Is your friend correct? Explain.
no; quarter pound = 4 oz

42. The length of the Amazon River in South America is about
GPS 4,000 mi. How many feet is this? **21,120,000 ft**

43. A fluid ounce measures capacity. An ounce measures weight.

43. **Writing in Math** Explain how fluid ounces and ounces differ.

C **44.** **Challenge** Three students recorded their heights as 64 in., $5\frac{1}{6}$ ft, and $1\frac{2}{3}$ yd. Find the average height in feet of the three students.
$5\frac{1}{6}$ ft

 TEKS ★ **TAKS** **Tune-Up and Mixed Review**

TAKS Objective 6
TEKS (7.13)(C)

45. An assortment of cheeses is weighed on a scale. What is the best estimate of the total weight of the 8 cheeses listed at the right? **B**
   Ⓐ Less than 5 pounds
   Ⓑ Between 5 and 10 pounds
   Ⓒ Between 10 and 15 pounds
   Ⓓ More than 15 pounds

Cheese Assortment

Quantity	Weight
1	1.1 lb
2	2 lb 4 oz
5	$\frac{1}{2}$ lb

TAKS Objective 6
TEKS (7.15)(A)

46. Mr. Paik started an 18-week training program to prepare for a marathon. The first week he jogged $1\frac{1}{2}$ mi each day, the second week he jogged 3 mi each day, and the third week he jogged $4\frac{1}{2}$ mi each day. If the pattern continues, how far will he jog each day of the sixth week? **H**
   Ⓕ 6 mi   Ⓗ 9 mi
   Ⓖ $7\frac{1}{2}$ mi   Ⓙ $10\frac{1}{2}$ mi

 for Help
Lesson 3-5

Find each quotient.

47. $\frac{3}{7} \div \frac{1}{7}$ 3   **48.** $\frac{4}{5} \div \frac{4}{10}$ 2   **49.** $\frac{3}{11} \div \frac{9}{22}$ $\frac{2}{3}$

Alternative Assessment

Provide pairs of students with tape measures or yardsticks. Have them measure various classroom objects, such as the length and width of a desk, and report the measurement in inches. Then have them write each measurement in feet and, when practical, in yards.

TEKS ★ **TAKS** **Resources**

• TAKS Strategies, p. 159
• TAKS Tune-Up, pp. 163–165

TAKS **Tune-Up Kit**
• TAKS Daily Review Transparencies
• TAKS Review and Preparation Workbook
• TAKS Strategies with Transparencies
• Texas Progress Monitoring Assessments

 PowerPoint
Lesson Quiz

Complete.

1. 56 in. = ■ ft $4\frac{2}{3}$

2. $6\frac{1}{2}$ qt = ■ pt 13

3. 26 fl oz = ■ c $3\frac{1}{4}$

4. $5\frac{1}{2}$ lb = ■ oz 88

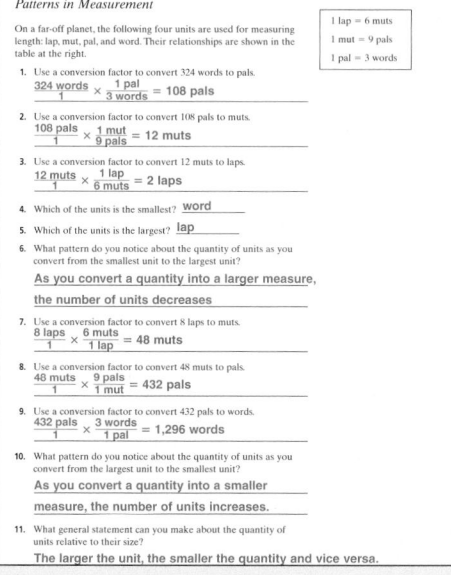

151

Solving Puzzles

Students translate word problems into numerical sentences and solve them.

Guided Instruction

Explain to students that phrases like *twice as many* and *half as much* can be translated into numerical phrases. Ask volunteers to use such phrases in sentences. Then ask questions such as:

- *Why do we multiply $\frac{2}{3}$ by 12?* Two thirds of the people are cousins and there are 12 people total.
- *How do we express 12 as a fraction?* $\frac{12}{1}$
- *If $\frac{1}{4}$ of Sandra's cousins are boys, how many boys are there?* 2

Differentiated Instruction

Below Level L2
Provide students with algebra tiles and help them model the Example. Divide the tiles into three groups and then count the number of tiles in two groups.

TEKS ★ TAKS

(7.2)(F) To select and use appropriate operations to solve problems TAKS Obj. 1

(7.2)(B) To use multiplication to solve problems involving fractions TAKS Obj. 1

Solving Puzzles

People often describe real-world situations using language that can be translated into numerical expressions. A class made some puzzles about the number of relatives who are coming to their family outings. Solve the puzzles below.

EXAMPLE

Sandra has a total of 12 aunts and cousins coming to her family outing. Two thirds are cousins, and half as many aunts as cousins are coming. How many aunts and how many cousins are coming to Sandra's outing?

Step 1 List what you know:

- $\frac{2}{3}$ cousins
- $\frac{1}{2}$ as many aunts as cousins
- 12 aunts and cousins all together

Step 2 Find the number of cousins:

$\frac{2}{3} \cdot 12 = \frac{24}{3}$ ← Multiply $\frac{2}{3}$ by 12.

$\frac{24}{3} = 8$ ← Simplify. There are 8 cousins.

Step 3 Find the number of aunts:

$\frac{1}{2} \cdot 8 = 4$ ← Multiply $\frac{1}{2}$ by 8. There are 4 aunts.

Sandra has 8 cousins and 4 aunts coming to her outing.

Exercises

1. Mark has 16 people coming to his outing. $\frac{3}{8}$ are his nieces, $\frac{1}{4}$ are his nephews, and the rest are his cousins. How many nieces, nephews, and cousins are coming to Mark's outing? **6 nieces, 4 nephews, 6 cousins**

2. Phil has 24 guests in all. Two thirds are cousins. The rest are aunts and uncles, and there are the same number of aunts as uncles. How many cousins, aunts, and uncles are coming to the outing? **16 cousins, 4 aunts, 4 uncles**

3. Create your own puzzle like the ones above. Your first clue should be the number of relatives who will come to a reunion. Then write clues using fractions, like the ones above, to describe the situation. **Check students' work.**

TEKS ★ TAKS Resources

- algebra tiles
- Student Manipulatives Kit

Dana Center TEKS Toolkit Clarifying Activities (7.2)(F), (7.2)(B)
Visit: PHSchool.com
Web Code: arq-9045

Find each product.

1. $\frac{1}{3} \cdot \frac{6}{7}$ $\frac{2}{7}$

2. $\frac{3}{4} \cdot 4\frac{1}{3}$ $3\frac{1}{4}$

3. $\frac{2}{5} \cdot \frac{1}{2}$ $\frac{1}{5}$

4. $3\frac{1}{4} \cdot 2\frac{7}{8}$ $9\frac{11}{32}$

5. $1\frac{1}{10} \cdot \frac{2}{3}$ $\frac{11}{15}$

6. What is the area of a courtyard that is $2\frac{2}{3}$ yd by $4\frac{1}{6}$ yd? $11\frac{1}{9}$ yd²

Find each quotient.

7. $\frac{5}{9} \div \frac{5}{6}$ $\frac{2}{3}$

8. $12\frac{1}{2} \div 1\frac{7}{8}$ $6\frac{2}{3}$

9. $3\frac{1}{7} \div \frac{11}{7}$ 2

10. $\frac{8}{25} \div \frac{2}{5}$ $\frac{4}{5}$

11. $5\frac{1}{5} \div \frac{4}{10}$ 13

12. You have a leaking bucket with $15\frac{1}{4}$ liters of water. Water drains out of the bucket at a rate of $\frac{1}{3}$ liter per minute. In how many minutes will the bucket be empty? $45\frac{3}{4}$ min

Change each unit of length.

13. 3 ft 4 in. = ■ ft $3\frac{1}{3}$

14. 2 ft 3 in. = ■ ft $2\frac{1}{4}$

15. 8 ft 6 in. = ■ ft $8\frac{1}{2}$

3-7a Activity Lab

Choosing Appropriate Units

When you measure an object, you should measure in an appropriate unit. For example, you would measure the length of a stapler in inches, not in miles.

TEKS ★ TAKS

(7.14)(A) To communicate mathematical ideas using appropriate units TAKS Obj. 6

Number Sense **Choose the more appropriate unit of measure.**

1. the mass of a horse	kilograms	grams	kilograms
2. the length of a marathon road race	miles	feet	miles
3. the capacity of a car's gas tank	ounces	gallons	gallons
4. the length of an eyelash	meters	millimeters	millimeters
5. the weight of a baseball	ounces	pounds	ounces

6. **Writing in Math** Choose one of your answers from Questions 1–5. Explain why you chose that unit of measure.

Answers may vary. Sample: For Question 1, I chose kilograms because horses are heavy.

153

 Checkpoint Quiz

Use this Checkpoint Quiz to check students' understanding of the skills and concepts of Lessons 3-4 through 3-6.

Resources

- All-in-One Teaching Resources Checkpoint Quiz 2
- Texas ExamView CD-ROM
- Success Tracker™ Online Intervention

Activity Lab

Choosing Appropriate Units

Students learn to choose the appropriate units to measure different objects.

Guided Instruction

Explain that objects should be measured with the unit that is appropriate to its size or length. For example, measuring a road in feet would give you a very large number, but measuring it in miles would give you a more reasonable number.

Activity

Have student work together in pairs to decide the appropriate units to measure each item. After they are finished, ask volunteers to give their answers for Exercise 6.

Differentiated Instruction

Below Level L2

Have students point to an object in the room and name an appropriate unit of measure.

TEKS ★ TAKS **Resources**

- Activity Lab 3-7: Measuring with a Ruler

Dana Center TEKS Tookit Clarifying Activities (7.14)(A)
Visit: PHSchool.com
Web Code: arq-9045

(7.2)(B) To use addition, subtraction, multiplication, and division to solve problems involving fraction and decimals (TAKS) **Obj. 1**

Dana Center TEKS Toolkit Clarifying Activities (7.2)(B)
Visit: PHSchool.com
Web Code: arq-9045

TEKS Math Background

Precision refers to the exactness of a measurement. For example, 98.6°F is more precise than 100°F. When comparing measurements, the more precise measurement has the smaller units.

More Math Background: p. 118D

Lesson Planning and Resources

See p. 118E for a list of the resources that support this lesson.

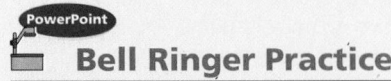

Bell Ringer Practice

✓ **Check Skills You'll Need**
Use student page, transparency, or PowerPoint.

(TAKS) **Daily Review 25**
Use transparency.

154

3-7 Precision

✓ **Check Skills You'll Need**

1. Vocabulary Review
What are the basic metric units for *length, capacity,* and *mass*?
meter; liter; gram

Complete.

2. 1 m = ■ cm 100

3. 1 m = ■ km 0.001

4. 1 cm = ■ mm 10

5. 1 kg = ■ g 1,000

6. 1 mL = ■ L 0.001

GO for Help
Lesson 1-5

Vocabulary Tip

Precise is the adjectival form of *precision*.

TEKS ★ (TAKS)

• **(7.2)(B)** To use addition, subtraction, multiplication, and division to solve problems involving fractions and decimals (TAKS) **Obj. 1**

🔊 **New Vocabulary** precision

Why Learn This?

Every measurement has a unit. Some units are more appropriate to use than others, and some units give a more precise measurement than others.

centimeters

If you measure the butterfly above to the nearest centimeter, the length is 5 cm. If you measure the butterfly to the nearest millimeter, the length is 48 mm. The measurement 48 mm is more precise than 5 cm.

The **precision** of a measurement refers to its exactness. When you compare measurements, the more precise measurement is the one that uses the smaller unit of measure.

EXAMPLES Precision in Measurement

1 Choose the more precise measurement: 12 fl oz or 2 c.

A fluid ounce is a smaller unit than a cup. So the measurement 12 fl oz is more precise than 2 c.

2 Choose the more precise measurement: 3 L or 2.5 L

One tenth of a liter is a smaller unit than a liter. So the measurement 2.5 L is more precise than 3 L.

3 Choose the more precise measurement: 8 in. or 21 in.

Both measurements use the inch as a unit. So neither measurement is more precise than the other.

✓ Quick Check

Choose the more precise measurement.

1. 2 ft, 13 in. 13 in.   **2.** 12.5 g, 11 g 12.5 g   **3.** $3\frac{1}{2}$ mi, $10\frac{1}{5}$ mi $10\frac{1}{5}$ mi

Differentiated Instruction Solutions for All Learners

Special Needs L1
Have students circle less precise numbers from sets of numbers such as 245 g or 24.7 g; 43 oz or 1 qt; 1 hr 3 min or 3 min 1 s.
24.7 g; 43 oz; 3 min 1 s

learning style: visual

Below Level L2
Guide students in measuring the length of their hand to the nearest inch, half-inch, quarter-inch, centimeter, and tenth-of-a-centimeter to help them better understand the concept of precision.

learning style: tactile

There are many different measuring tools, such as rulers, scales, and thermometers. The marks on a measuring tool tell you the precision that is possible with that tool.

EXAMPLE Finding Precision

④ **Cooking** Oven thermometers measure cooking temperatures. What is the greatest precision possible with the thermometer shown at the right?

The interval from any red dot to the next black dot is 25°F. Measurements made with this thermometer are precise to the nearest 25°F.

✓ Quick Check

4. What is the greatest precision possible with each ruler below?

a.

$\frac{1}{8}$ in.

b.

$\frac{1}{16}$ in.

A calculation is only as precise as the least precise measurement used in the calculation. When you add or subtract measurements with the same unit, round your answer to match the least precise measurement.

EXAMPLES Precision and Rounding

⑤ Find $8\frac{2}{5}$ mi + 5 mi. Round your answer appropriately.

$$8\frac{2}{5} + 5 = 13\frac{2}{5}$$

Since 5 is less precise than $8\frac{2}{5}$, round to the nearest whole number. The sum is 13 mi.

⑥ Find 9.97 cm − 5.9 cm. Round your answer appropriately.

$$9.97 - 5.9 = 4.07$$

Since 5.9 is less precise than 9.97, round to the nearest tenth. The difference is 4.1 cm.

✓ Quick Check

Find each sum or difference. Round your answer appropriately.

5. 11.4 g + 2.65 g   14.1 g

6. 45 m − 0.9 m   44 m

3-7 Precision   **155**

155

---

2. Teach

Activity Lab

Use before the lesson.
Student Edition Activity Lab 3-7a, Choosing Appropriate Units, p. 153

 Teaching Resources
Activity Lab 3-7: Measuring with a Ruler

Guided Instruction

Example 1
Name a measurement and have students give a corresponding measurement that is more precise. For example, if you say "2 inches," a student might respond "$1\frac{7}{8}$ inches."

Error Prevention!

Suggest that students identify the less precise measurement and its units before finding the sum or difference.

PowerPoint

Additional Examples

❶ Choose the more precise measurement. 3.6 cm, 9.15 cm **9.15 cm**

❷ What is the greatest precision possible with a digital clock that shows the hour and minute? **the nearest minute**

❸ Find the difference: 7 mi − $2\frac{3}{4}$ mi. Round your answer to match the less precise measurement. **4 mi**

Teaching Resources
• Daily Notetaking Guide 3-7 **L3**
• Adapted Notetaking 3-7 **L1**

Closure

• *What does it mean to round your answer to the less precise measurement?* Sample: When combining two units, such as tenths and whole numbers, round the answer to the larger unit—in this case, whole numbers.

Advanced Learners **L4**
Have students explain the difference between a rounded measurement of 1 m and 1.00 m. Sample: 1 m is between 50 and 149 cm. 1.00 m is between 99.5 and 100.49 cm.

Pre-AP™

English Language Learners **ELL**
Show students a watch with no tick marks for seconds showing. Then show them one that has the second tick marks. Point out that with one watch, you can say something took about 6 minutes. With the other, you can say it took 5 minutes and 55 seconds. That is more precise.

learning style: visual

155

Assignment Guide

Check Your Understanding
Go over Exercises 1–6 in class before assigning the Homework Exercises.

Homework Exercises
A Practice by Example 7–23
B Apply Your Skills 24–35
C Challenge 36
TEKS ★ TAKS Tune-Up and Mixed Review 37–43

Homework Quick Check
To check students' understanding of key skills and concepts, go over Exercises 11, 17, 27, 28, and 35.

Differentiated Instruction Resources

Check Your Understanding

1. Measure the pencil below to the nearest inch, to the nearest $\frac{1}{2}$ inch, and to the nearest $\frac{1}{8}$ inch.   4 in., $3\frac{1}{2}$ in., $3\frac{6}{8}$ in.

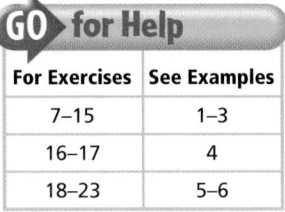

2. $\frac{1}{8}$ in.

2. **Vocabulary** Which measurement in Exercise 1 is the most precise?

3. **Number Sense** Can you use the ruler in Exercise 1 to measure the pencil to the nearest $\frac{1}{16}$ inch? Explain. $3\frac{12}{16}$ in.

Choose the more precise measurement.

4. 13 cm, 13 mm
    13 mm

5. 9 ft, $4\frac{1}{2}$ ft
    $4\frac{1}{2}$ ft

6. 8.5 kg, 2.25 kg
    2.25 kg

Homework Exercises

For more exercises, see **Extra Skills and Word Problems**.

GO for Help

For Exercises	See Examples
7–15	1–3
16–17	4
18–23	5–6

7. $11\frac{15}{16}$ in.

A **Choose the more precise measurement.**

7. 16 in., $11\frac{15}{16}$ in.
    See left.

8. 30 g, 2.5 kg 30 g

9. 37 t, 56 lb 56 lb

10. 25 qt, 38 pt 38 pt

11. 21 L, 35 mL 35 mL

12. $6\frac{1}{10}$ lb, 6.37 lb
     6.37 lb

13. 12 mo, 1 yr 12 mo

14. 0.25 g, 101 mg
     101 mg

15. 12 days, 2 wk
     12 days

Find the greatest precision possible for each scale shown.

16.

1 mm

17.

2 lb

Find each sum or difference. Round your answer appropriately.

18. 19 m $+ 4\frac{9}{10}$ m
     24 m

19. 6 ft $- 2\frac{1}{4}$ ft 4 ft

20. 7.4 L $+ 1.16$ L
     8.6 L

21. 6.53 oz $+ 2\frac{2}{5}$ oz
     8.9 oz

22. 18 g $- 3.8$ g
     14 g

23. 6.52 in. $- 5.8$ in.
     0.7 in.

B **GPS** 24. **Guided Problem Solving** You have 81 ft² of fabric. You cut a square of fabric with side length $4\frac{1}{2}$ ft. How much fabric is left?
- How many square feet of fabric did you cut out? $60\frac{3}{4}$ ft²
- What operation tells you how much fabric is left?
- What should you round to?

Find the length of each segment to the greatest precision possible.

25.
centimeters
2 cm

26.
centimeters
1.9 cm

27. **Biology** The length of a chicken egg can be $2\frac{3}{16}$ in. The length of an ostrich egg can be $6\frac{3}{8}$ in. What is the difference between the lengths of the eggs? Round your answer appropriately. about $4\frac{3}{16}$ in.

28. **Writing in Math** Your friend says that 5.25 kg is a more precise measurement than 6.2 g because a hundredths unit is smaller than a tenths unit. Do you agree? Explain. No; a gram is a smaller unit of measure.

Choose the more precise unit of measure.

29. foot, meter ft

30. gallon, liter L

31. centimeter, inch cm

32. deciliter, gallon dL

33. kilometer, mile km

34. kilogram, pound lb

35. **GPS** A climber ascends 2,458.75 ft up a 3,000-ft mountainside. How much farther does the climber have to go to reach the top? Round your answer appropriately. 541 ft

C 36. **Challenge** Three students measured the width of a bulletin board. The three measurements were 1 yd, 3 ft, and 36 in. Compare the measurements and the precision of the measurements.
They are all equal, but 36 in. is the most precise.

TEKS ⭐ TAKS Tune-Up and Mixed Review

TAKS Objective 1
TEKS (7.1)(A)

37. The fraction $\frac{3}{8}$ is found between which pair of fractions on a number line? A

Ⓐ $\frac{4}{16}$ and $\frac{13}{32}$ Ⓑ $\frac{5}{16}$ and $\frac{10}{32}$ Ⓒ $\frac{6}{16}$ and $\frac{20}{32}$ Ⓓ $\frac{7}{16}$ and $\frac{24}{32}$

TAKS Objective 6
TEKS (7.13)(A)

38. Hector bought two bags of apples. The larger bag weighed $3\frac{3}{4}$ lb. The smaller bag weighed $\frac{5}{8}$ lb less than the larger bag. Which expression can be used to find the weight, in pounds, of the smaller bag? H

Ⓕ $3\frac{3}{4} + \frac{5}{8}$ Ⓖ $3\frac{3}{4} \cdot \frac{5}{8}$ Ⓗ $3\frac{3}{4} - \frac{5}{8}$ Ⓙ $3\frac{3}{4} \div \frac{5}{8}$

TAKS Objective 1
TEKS (7.2)(E)

39. What is the value of the expression $4 + (12 \div 4)^2 - 3 \cdot 5$? B

Ⓐ -10 Ⓑ -2 Ⓒ 20 Ⓓ 50

GO for Help

Lesson 3-1   **Estimate each answer.**

40. $12\frac{1}{10} - 5\frac{7}{8}$ 41. $2\frac{2}{9} + 4\frac{1}{8}$ 42. $3\frac{1}{3} \cdot 10\frac{4}{5}$ 43. $16\frac{1}{9} \div 3\frac{6}{7}$
about 6   about 6   about 33   about 4

Alternative Assessment

Have students work in pairs. One partner names something to be measured in either the customary or the metric system, for example, "in the metric system, the length of an automobile." The other student gives a precise measurement that is appropriate, such as "2.3 meters." Students then trade roles.

TEKS ⭐ TAKS Resources

- TAKS Strategies, p. 159
- TAKS Tune-Up, pp. 163–165

TAKS Tune-Up Kit

- TAKS Daily Review Transparencies
- TAKS Review and Preparation Workbook
- TAKS Strategies with Transparencies
- Texas Progress Monitoring Assessments

---

4. Assess & Reteach

PowerPoint
Lesson Quiz

Choose the more precise measurement.

1. 12 in., $10\frac{3}{4}$ in. $10\frac{3}{4}$ in.

2. 7.78 kg, 7.8 kg 7.78 kg

Find each sum or difference. Round the answer to match the less precise measurement.

3. 3.09 L + 4.7 L 7.8 L

4. 81.2 cm − 46.08 cm 35.1 cm

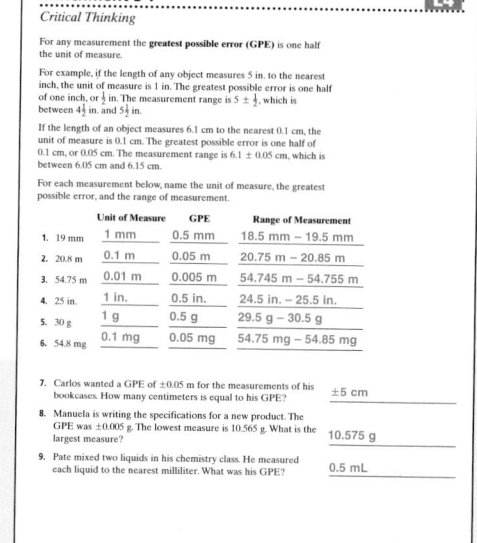

157

Estimating in Different Systems

Students practice estimating equivalent measures in the metric system and the customary system.

Guided Instruction

Have students think of examples of where and when it might be useful to approximate a measure in one measurement system when that measure is expressed in the other system. **Sample: an American traveling in Africa or a European traveling in the United States**

You may find it useful to work through how to express each of the estimates given in *reverse* order. For example, guide students to figure out how many kilometers are in a mile, or how to estimate kilograms given a weight in pounds.

Error Prevention!

As needed, review mental math procedures for multiplying and dividing by powers of 10.

Differentiated Instruction

Advanced Learners **L4**
Using the formula $F = \frac{9}{5}(C + 32)$, have students convert a few Celsius temperatures to Fahrenheit.

TEKS ★ TAKS Resources

Dana Center TEKS Toolkit Clarifying Activities (7.3)(B), (7.14)(A)
Visit: PHSchool.com
Web Code: arq-9045

3-7b Activity Lab

TEKS ★ TAKS

(7.3)(B) To find solutions to application problems involving proportional relationships such as related measurement units **TAKS Obj. 2**

(7.14)(A) To communicate mathematical ideas using appropriate units **TAKS Obj. 6**

Estimating in Different Systems

Every day you see measurements in both the customary system and the metric system. You can use estimates to help you compare measurements in the two systems.

A liter is a little more than a quart.
An inch is about 2.5 cm.
A kilometer is about 0.6 mi.
A kilogram is about 2.2 lb.

You may be more familiar with temperatures measured in Fahrenheit than in Celsius. You can use the table at the right to help you relate to Celsius temperatures.

Celsius Temperature	How It Feels
30°	hot
20°	nice
10°	cold
0°	freezing

EXAMPLE

Which measurement is longer, 15 cm or 10 in.?

One inch is about 2.5 cm.

$10 \cdot 2.5 = 25$ ← **Multiply by 10 to find the number of centimeters in 10 in.**

There are about 25 cm in 10 in. So 10 in. is longer than 15 cm.

Exercises

Which of the two measurements is greater?

1. 600 km or 200 mi   **600 km**
2. 0°C or 0°F   **0°C**
3. 80 L or 40 gal   **40 gal**
4. 50 cm or 25 in.   **25 in.**
5. 30 lb or 20 kg   **20 kg**
6. 10°F or 20°C   **20°C**

7. **Travel** A sign reads "Austin, 200 km." About how many miles would you have to drive to get to Austin?   **about 120 mi**

8. **Clothing** A sign shows that the temperature is 27°C. Would you be more comfortable in a short-sleeved shirt or in a ski parka?   **short-sleeved shirt**

9. A student tells you that he is 175 cm tall and weighs 72 kg.
   a. About how many feet tall is the student?   **about 6 ft**
   b. About how many pounds does the student weigh?   **about 158 lb**

10. You need to bring about a gallon of water for a hike. Bottled water is sold in liter bottles. How many liter bottles should you buy?   **4 L**

Strategies

Reading for Understanding

Reading-comprehension questions are based on a passage that gives you facts and information. First read the question carefully. Make sure you understand what is being asked. Then read the passage. Look for the information you need to answer the question.

EXAMPLE

Recycling Math The United States produces more than 4 pounds of trash per person each day, and recycles about one fourth of it. Canada produces about $3\frac{1}{2}$ pounds of trash per person each day, and recycles about one tenth of it. Japan produces about $2\frac{1}{2}$ of trash per person each day, and recycles about one fifth of it.

In one week, a family living in the United States produced 112 pounds of trash. About how many pounds of the trash were recycled?

What is being asked? How many pounds of trash were recycled?

Identify the information you need. The United States recycles about one fourth of the trash it produces.

Solve the problem. Pounds of recycled trash $= \frac{1}{4} \cdot 112 = 28$. About 28 pounds of the American family's trash were recycled.

Exercises

Use the passage in the example to complete Exercises 1–4.

 Objective 1
TEKS (7.2)(B)

1. a. About how many pounds of trash will a Canadian family of four produce in one week? **about 98 lb**
   b. About how many pounds of the trash will be recycled? **about 10 lb**

 Objective 1
TEKS (7.2)(B)

2. In one week, a family living in Japan produces 85 pounds of trash. About how many pounds of the trash will be recycled? **about 17 lb**

 Objective 1
TEKS (7.2)(F)

3. Suppose your family recycles one third of its trash. How much more trash does your family recycle than an average U.S. family? $\frac{1}{12}$ **lb more**

 Objective 1
TEKS (7.2)(F)

4. In one month, a school recycled two fifths of its paper and produced 25 pounds of paper. How many pounds were *not* recycled? **15 lb**

 Strategies

Reading for Understanding

This strategy provides students with pointers and practice in how to successfully approach a reading-comprehension question.

Guided Instruction

Emphasize the importance of reading the full passage carefully to identify what the question asks, what information is needed to answer the question, and what information is *not* needed. For example, students need to check whether an exact answer or an estimate is called for.

Error Prevention!

Encourage students to read the passage more than once. Encourage them to double-check that they have answered the question reasonably and not just solved the equation.

TEKS Resources

TAKS Strategies with Transparencies
• Transparency 5
• Practice sheet, p. 15

Strategies with Transparencies

Test-Taking Strategies: Reading for Understanding

Reading comprehension questions are based on a passage that gives information and facts.

To solve a problem use these steps:
• Read the directions and the passage.
• Read the questions carefully.
• Look for information that helps answer the questions.

EXAMPLE
Read the passage and answer the questions below.

Each year, more than 775,000 children and teenagers are treated in the emergency room for sports injuries. In a recent study, doctors found that 10 years ago, up to 70 percent of sports injuries in kids were acute injuries, such as a sprained ankle or a fracture. Over the past five years, however, overuse accounted for about half of all sports injuries among youngsters. Doctors are seeing a lot more elbow injuries from too much pitching and a lot more heel pain from tendinitis due to too much soccer.

This year about 25 athletes in your school will be injured. About how many of them will have injuries due to overuse?

What are you being asked?
How many of the 25 athletes will have injuries due to overuse?

What information helps you to solve the problem?
Over the past five years overuse accounted for about half of all sports injuries among youngsters.

Solve the problem: 50% of 25 students is about 13 students.

159

Chapter 3 Review

Chapter 3 Review

Vocabulary Review

 benchmark (p. 120)   precision (p. 154)   reciprocals (p. 141)

Go Online
PHSchool.com
For: Online vocabulary quiz
Web Code: arj-0351

Choose the correct vocabulary term to complete each sentence.

1. The number $\frac{7}{8}$ is the __?__ of the number $\frac{8}{7}$. **reciprocal**

2. A __?__ is a number used to replace fractions that are less than 1. **benchmark**

3. The __?__ of a measurement refers to its degree of exactness. **precision**

4. When you use a __?__ to estimate a sum, your answer has less __?__ than the exact answer. **benchmark; precision**

Skills and Concepts   TEKS ★ TAKS

Lesson 3-1
• To estimate sums, differences, products, and quotients involving fractions
• Prepares for **TEKS** (7.2)(B) To use addition, subtraction, multiplication, and division to solve problems involving fractions

You can use the **benchmarks** $0, \frac{1}{2}$, and 1 to estimate sums and difference of fractions. To estimate sums, differences, products, and quotients of mixed numbers, round to the nearest whole number or use compatible numbers.

Estimate each answer.   about $\frac{1}{2}$ about 1   about $\frac{1}{2}$

5. $\frac{3}{4} + \frac{1}{8}$ 6. $\frac{5}{6} - \frac{1}{3}$ 7. $\frac{2}{5} + \frac{3}{8}$ 8. $\frac{4}{9} - \frac{2}{18}$

about 1

Use rounding to estimate.   9–12. See left.

9. $4\frac{11}{12} - 2\frac{1}{10}$ 10. $5\frac{2}{5} \cdot 4\frac{7}{9}$ 11. $8\frac{4}{5} + 4\frac{7}{8}$ 12. $24\frac{1}{6} - 13\frac{2}{3}$

13. **Maps** A map shows three hiking trails of lengths $2\frac{1}{2}$ mi, $1\frac{4}{5}$ mi, and $3\frac{3}{10}$ mi. You want to hike the entire length of each trail. Estimate the total distance. **about 8 mi**

9. about 3
10. about 25
11. about 14
12. about 10

Lessons 3-2, 3-3
(7.2)(B) To use addition and subtraction to solve problems involving fractions **TAKS Obj. 1**

(7.2)(F) To select and use appropriate operations to solve problems **TAKS Obj. 1**

(7.2)(G) To determine the reasonableness of a solution to a problem **TAKS Obj. 1**

To add or subtract fractions, you first find a common denominator and then add or subtract the numerators. To add or subtract mixed numbers, you add or subtract the fractions first, and then the whole numbers. You may need to rename a mixed number before subtracting.

Find each sum or difference. $6\frac{13}{15}$ $15\frac{5}{12}$ $5\frac{13}{24}$

14. $2\frac{1}{3} - \frac{3}{4}$ $1\frac{7}{12}$ 15. $16\frac{2}{3} - 9\frac{4}{5}$ 16. $8\frac{1}{6} + 7\frac{3}{12}$ 17. $2\frac{1}{6} + 3\frac{3}{8}$

18. Rich walks to school in $10\frac{1}{5}$ minutes. John walks in $21\frac{1}{4}$ minutes. How many more minutes does it take John to get to school? $11\frac{1}{20}$ min

Lessons 3-4, 3-5

(7.2)(A) To represent multiplication and division situations involving fractions with models **TAKS Obj. 1**

(7.2)(B) To use multiplication and division to solve problems involving fractions **TAKS Obj. 1**

(7.2)(F) To select and use appropriate operations to solve problems **TAKS Obj. 1**

(7.2)(G) To determine the reasonableness of a solution to a problem **TAKS Obj. 1**

To multiply fractions, you multiply their numerators and multiply their denominators. To divide by a fraction, you multiply by its reciprocal.

Find each product.

$94\frac{23}{24}$

19. $\frac{2}{3} \cdot \frac{3}{8}$ $\frac{1}{4}$ **20.** $\frac{3}{5} \cdot 1\frac{1}{2}$ $\frac{9}{10}$ **21.** $2\frac{2}{3} \cdot 3\frac{3}{8}$ 9   **22.** $8\frac{5}{6} \cdot 10\frac{3}{4}$

23. What is the area of a room that is $12\frac{2}{3}$ m long and $3\frac{1}{8}$ m wide? $39\frac{7}{12}$ m²

Find each quotient.

$\frac{5}{18}$

24. $\frac{2}{3} \div \frac{4}{3}$ $\frac{1}{2}$ **25.** $5\frac{1}{4} \div \frac{7}{8}$ 6   **26.** $4\frac{4}{5} \div 1\frac{1}{3}$ $3\frac{3}{5}$ **27.** $1\frac{1}{3} \div 4\frac{4}{5}$

28. The area of Sally's garden is $17\frac{1}{2}$ square feet. If Sally's garden is $5\frac{1}{2}$ ft long, how wide is her garden? $3\frac{2}{11}$ ft

Lesson 3-6

(7.3)(B) To find solutions to application problems involving proportional relationships such as related measurement units **TAKS Obj. 2**

(7.14)(A) To communicate mathematical ideas using appropriate units **TAKS Obj. 6**

(7.2)(B) To use addition, subtraction, multiplication, and division to solve problems involving fractions **TAKS Obj. 1**

To change from a smaller unit to a larger unit, you *divide*. To change from a larger unit to a smaller unit, you *multiply*.

Complete.

29. 42 in. = ■ ft $3\frac{1}{2}$ **30.** 12 fl oz = ■ c $1\frac{1}{2}$ **31.** 80 oz = ■ lb 5

32. 10,560 ft = ■ mi 2   **33.** 2 t = ■ lb 4,000   **34.** $3\frac{1}{2}$ qt = ■ pt 7

35. The highest annual rainfall on record for the state of Texas was about 109 in., in 1873. How many feet of rain did Texas receive that year? about 9 ft

Lesson 3-7

(7.2)(B) To use addition, subtraction, multiplication, and division to solve problems involving fractions and decimals **TAKS Obj. 1**

The **precision** of a measurement refers to its degree of exactness. The smaller the units on a measuring instrument, the more precise a measurement is. When you add or subtract measurements with the same unit, round your answer to match the precision of the least precise measurement.

Choose the more precise measurement.

8.75 m

36. 12 c, 8 pt 12 c   **37.** 5.5 L, 2 L 5.5 L   **38.** 8.5 m, 8.75 m

39. 1 day, 23 h 23 h   **40.** 25 g, 3.5 kg 25 g   **41.** $11\frac{3}{16}$ in., 5 in.

$11\frac{3}{16}$ in.

45. 21.00 lb

46. 5 L

47. 5.13 m

Find each sum or difference. Round your answer appropriately.

42. 17.3 g − 10 g 7 g   **43.** $5\frac{1}{3}$ yd + 8 yd 13 yd   **44.** 7.75 cm + 3.8 cm 11.6 cm

45. 5.25 lb + 15.75 lb   **46.** 8 L − 3.005 L   **47.** 12.175 m − 7.05 m

---

TEKS ★ TAKS Resources

- **Texas ExamView CD-ROM**
  - Chapter 3 Ready-Made Test
  - Make your own Chapter 3 test
- **MindPoint Quiz Show CD-ROM**
  - Chapter 3 Review

Differentiated Instruction

All in One Teaching Resources
- Chapter 3 Test   **L2**
- Chapter 3 Test   **L3**
- Chapter 3 Alternative Assessment   **L4**

Spanish Assessment Resources ELL
- Chapter 3 Test   **L2**
- Chapter 3 Test   **L3**
- Chapter 3 Alternative Assessment   **L4**

Texas ExamView CD-ROM
- Special Needs Test   **L1**
- Special Needs Practice Bank   **L1**

Online Chapter 3 Test at
www.PHSchool.com   **L3**

Chapter Test   **L2**

Chapter Test   **L3**

Chapter Test

Chapter 3

Estimate each answer to the nearest whole number.

1. $\frac{5}{9} + 2\frac{1}{4}$ 2. $4\frac{2}{3} + 5\frac{4}{9}$ 3. $\frac{2}{7} \cdot 119$
   3   **10**   **80**

4. $2\frac{2}{3} \cdot 4\frac{1}{3}$ 5. $8\frac{1}{3} - 5\frac{5}{9}$ 6. $23\frac{9}{10} \div 12\frac{1}{4}$
   12   **2**   **2**

Write each sum or difference as a fraction or mixed number in simplest form.

7. $\frac{2}{3} - \frac{5}{12}$ 8. $\frac{3}{4} - \frac{1}{2}$ 9. $2\frac{1}{3} + 4\frac{3}{4}$
   $\frac{1}{4}$ **$\frac{1}{4}$**   **$6\frac{4}{8}$**

10. $7\frac{1}{4} + 5\frac{1}{2}$ 11. $\frac{1}{17} + \frac{5}{17}$ 12. $\frac{7}{8} - \frac{3}{5}$
    $12\frac{3}{4}$ **$\frac{6}{17}$**   **$\frac{11}{40}$**

13. The price of a company's stock was $21\frac{3}{8}$ dollars a share. Then the price went up $4\frac{1}{2}$ dollars a share. What is the new price of the stock?
    $25\frac{7}{8}$ dollars

Find each product or quotient.

14. $\frac{3}{4} \cdot \frac{2}{9}$ 15. $\frac{3}{7} \div \frac{7}{12}$ 16. $2\frac{3}{8} \cdot 4\frac{4}{5}$
    $\frac{1}{6}$ **$1\frac{2}{9}$**   **$11\frac{2}{5}$**

17. $2\frac{2}{7} \div 4$ 18. $10\frac{5}{9} \div \frac{5}{9}$ 19. $11\frac{9}{10} \cdot \frac{4}{17}$
    $\frac{4}{7}$ **$19\frac{1}{9}$**   **$1\frac{3}{5}$**

20. Tiles $\frac{1}{2}$ ft long are being placed alongside a vanity top that is $4\frac{1}{2}$ ft long. How many tiles are needed?
    6 tiles

21. A pattern for curtains requires $1\frac{3}{4}$ yd of fabric. How much fabric is needed to make 5 sets of these curtains?
    $8\frac{3}{4}$ yd

162

Estimate each answer.

1. $\frac{7}{8} + \frac{15}{16}$ about 2
2. $\frac{3}{5} - \frac{1}{2}$ about 0
3. $7\frac{1}{8} + 2\frac{3}{4}$ about 10
4. $8\frac{3}{8} - 5\frac{1}{3}$ about 3
5. $4\frac{5}{8} \cdot 2\frac{1}{10}$ about 10
6. $43\frac{1}{2} \div 5\frac{1}{5}$ about 9

7. **Tutoring** You tutored for $2\frac{1}{2}$ h on Monday, $2\frac{1}{6}$ h on Wednesday, and $1\frac{3}{4}$ h on Friday. Estimate the total number of hours you tutored during the week. **7 h**

Find each sum or difference.

8. $\frac{15}{16} - \frac{3}{16}$ $\frac{3}{4}$
9. $\frac{1}{4} + \frac{2}{3}$ $\frac{11}{12}$
10. $\frac{1}{2} - \frac{3}{8}$ $\frac{1}{8}$
11. $\frac{2}{3} + \frac{5}{6}$ $1\frac{1}{2}$
12. $8\frac{2}{5} + 5\frac{3}{5}$ 14
13. $1\frac{2}{3} - \frac{3}{4}$ $\frac{11}{12}$
14. $4\frac{3}{4} + 5\frac{1}{5}$ $9\frac{19}{20}$
15. $9\frac{3}{8} - 5\frac{1}{4}$ $4\frac{1}{8}$

16. At birth, a baby weighed $7\frac{3}{8}$ lb. The baby now weighs $8\frac{13}{16}$ lb. How much weight has the baby gained? $1\frac{7}{16}$ lb

17. You ride your bike $1\frac{3}{10}$ mi to school. At the end of the day, you stop at a park on the way home. The park is $\frac{2}{5}$ mi from school. How far is the park from your house? $\frac{9}{10}$ mi

Find each product or quotient.

18. $\frac{4}{5} \cdot \frac{1}{4}$ $\frac{1}{5}$
19. $\frac{4}{5} \div \frac{1}{4}$ $3\frac{1}{5}$
20. $\frac{3}{4} \cdot \frac{2}{3}$ $\frac{1}{2}$
21. $\frac{1}{4} \div \frac{4}{5}$ $\frac{5}{16}$
22. $1\frac{2}{3} \cdot 1\frac{1}{4}$ $2\frac{1}{12}$
23. $1\frac{2}{3} \div 1\frac{1}{4}$ $1\frac{1}{3}$
24. $150 \div 2\frac{2}{3}$ $56\frac{1}{4}$
25. $5\frac{3}{8} \cdot 3\frac{3}{4}$ $20\frac{5}{32}$

26. **Masonry** A brick is $1\frac{7}{8}$ in. high. Mortar that is $\frac{3}{8}$ in. thick is spread on each row of bricks. How many rows of bricks are needed to reach the top of a $7\frac{1}{2}$-ft doorway? **40 rows**

43. **Answers may vary.**
    Sample: A ton is 2,000 lb,
    so an object should
    weigh at least that much.

Find each answer.

27. $10\frac{3}{4} + \frac{5}{8}$ $11\frac{3}{8}$
28. $6\frac{1}{2} - 4\frac{3}{5}$ $1\frac{9}{10}$
29. $10 \div \frac{1}{4}$ 40
30. $2\frac{1}{2} \cdot 12$ 30
31. $16 \div \frac{1}{3}$ 48
32. $8\frac{3}{5} + \frac{1}{7}$ $8\frac{26}{35}$
33. $2\frac{3}{10} - 1\frac{1}{2}$ $1\frac{1}{5}$
34. $7\frac{3}{4} + \frac{3}{8}$ $8\frac{1}{8}$

35. **Earnings** You have a part-time job at a deli and work $12\frac{1}{2}$ hours in one week. You earn $6.50 per hour. How much money do you earn that week? **$81.25**

36. **Discounts** A store is having a $\frac{1}{3}$-off sale. You want to buy a jacket that originally cost $60. What is the sale price of the jacket? **$40**

Complete.

37. 38 in. = ■ ft $3\frac{1}{6}$
38. 60 oz = ■ lb $3\frac{3}{4}$
39. $3\frac{3}{4}$ qt = ■ c 15
40. $1\frac{2}{3}$ mi = ■ ft 8,800
41. $5\frac{1}{2}$ yd = ■ in. 198
42. 50 fl oz = ■ c $6\frac{1}{4}$

43. **Writing in Math** About how heavy should an object be before you start to measure the object in tons instead of pounds? Explain. **See margin.**

44. You have $1\frac{1}{2}$ lb of fish. How many 6-oz servings can you make? **4 servings**

45. You jog $8\frac{1}{2}$ times around a block. The distance around the block is 770 yd. About how many miles have you jogged? (Hint: 1 mi = 1,760 yd) $3\frac{23}{32}$ mi

Choose the more precise measurement.

46. 36 min, $1\frac{1}{4}$ h **36 min**
47. 1 t, 500 lb **500 lb**
48. 100.5 mg, 10.67 g **100.5 mg**
49. 18 months, 1 year **18 mo**

⭐ **TAKS Tips**

Some questions on TAKS tests ask you to find an expression that you could use to solve a problem.

Juan, Tina, and Ayla made friendship chains. Juan's chain is $3\frac{3}{4}$ feet long. Tina's is $2\frac{2}{3}$ feet long. Ayla's is $6\frac{1}{2}$ feet long. Which expression can be used to find how much longer Ayla's chain is than Juan's and Tina's chains combined?

Ⓐ $6\frac{1}{2} - 3\frac{3}{4} + 2\frac{2}{3}$

Ⓑ $\left(3\frac{3}{4} + 2\frac{2}{3}\right) - 6\frac{1}{2}$

Ⓒ $6\frac{1}{2} - 2\frac{2}{3} + 3\frac{3}{4}$

Ⓓ $6\frac{1}{2} - \left(3\frac{3}{4} + 2\frac{2}{3}\right)$

Tip 1
Find the expression that tells you the length of Juan's and Tina's chains combined.

Tip 2
Ayla's chain is longer. Find the expression that subtracts the combined length of Juan's and Tina's chains from Ayla's.

Think It Through
Juan's and Tina's chains are $\left(3\frac{3}{4} + 2\frac{2}{3}\right)$. You can subtract this from the length of Ayla's chain: $6\frac{1}{2} - \left(3\frac{3}{4} + 2\frac{2}{3}\right)$. The correct answer is D.

Vocabulary Builder

As you solve test items, you must understand the meanings of mathematical terms. Match each term with its mathematical meaning.

A. expression III
B. mean V
C. median IV
D. mode I
E. range II

I. the item that occurs most often in a data set

II. the difference between the greatest and least value of a data set

III. a mathematical phrase containing numbers and operation symbols

IV. the middle value when data items are arranged in numerical order

V. the sum of a data set divided by the number of data items

Multiple Choice

Read each question. Then write the letter of the correct answer on your paper.

1. Joan makes 3 kinds of fruit salad. One recipe requires $2\frac{1}{4}$ cups of grapes. Another requires $1\frac{1}{4}$ cups. The third requires $\frac{2}{3}$ cup. How many cups of grapes does she need? C

Ⓐ $3\frac{1}{2}$ cups   Ⓒ $4\frac{1}{6}$ cups

Ⓑ $3\frac{5}{6}$ cups   Ⓓ $4\frac{2}{3}$ cups

2. The map shows Lindy's daily walk. How many miles does Lindy walk to school? F

Lindy's house

$\frac{1}{5}$ mi

$1\frac{7}{10}$ mi $\frac{2}{5}$ mi

School

Ⓕ $2\frac{3}{10}$ mi   Ⓗ $1\frac{9}{10}$ mi

Ⓖ 2 mi   Ⓙ $1\frac{2}{3}$ mi

TEKS ⭐ **TAKS Resources**

TAKS Review and Preparation Workbook

Texas ExamView CD-ROM
• Instant TAKS Practice Test
• TAKS Practice Items

Differentiated Instruction

Texas Progress Monitoring Assessments
• Quarter 1 Test
  • Forms A & B   **L3**
  • Forms D & E   **L2**

Spanish Assessment Resources
• Spanish Cumulative Review **ELL**
• Spanish Quarter 1 Test
  • Forms A & B   **L3**

Texas ExamView CD-ROM
• Special Needs Practice Bank   **L1**

TAKS Daily Review Transparencies

TAKS Daily Review 1   Objective 1: (7.1)(B)
Multiple Choice

The seventh-grade class at Anarene Middle School sold $\frac{65}{10}$ of the Corsicana fruitcakes they bought. Which decimal is equivalent to the fraction sold?

A 65
B 0.65
C 6.5
D 650

Answer: B

TAKS Daily Review 2   Objective 5: (7.12)(A)
Multiple Choice

Shey has been practicing running the 200-meter foot race. Her last 6 times are shown.

23.60   24.15   24.68   28.62   24.25   23.92

What is her mean time?

F 5.02
G 23.92
H 24.21
J 24.87

3. Tammy wanted to shorten a bookshelf she made. After she cut off a piece $\frac{1}{5}$ meter long, the bookshelf was $\frac{9}{10}$ meter long. How long was the original bookshelf? **C**

   (A) $\frac{3}{5}$ m

   (B) $\frac{7}{10}$ m

   (C) $1\frac{1}{10}$ m

   (D) $1\frac{3}{5}$ m

4. Which model represents $\frac{1}{3} \cdot \frac{3}{4}$? **F**

5. It takes Mary $2\frac{1}{2}$ minutes to make one origami turtle. Which expression can be used to find how long it will take Mary to make 60 origami turtles? **A**

   (A) $60 \cdot 2\frac{1}{2}$

   (B) $60 - 2\frac{1}{2}$

   (C) $60 + 2\frac{1}{2}$

   (D) $60 \div 2\frac{1}{2}$

6. Which expression can be used to find the number of 2.5-inch pieces of tape that you can cut from a roll that is 1,295 inches long?

   (F) $1,295 \div 2.5$

   (G) $1,295 - 2.5$

   (H) $2.5 \cdot 1,295$

   (J) $2.5 \div 1,295$

   F

7. The coach of the Tigers baseball team recorded in the table below the number of runs each player scored during the season. He used the players' jersey numbers. What should the coach do to find the mean number of runs scored by each player? **C**

Jersey Number	Number of Runs Scored
3	24
5	20
12	29
17	16
25	32
26	12
31	24
33	36
37	25

   (A) He should subtract the lowest number of runs from the highest number of runs.

   (B) He should divide each number of runs scored by 9.

   (C) He should find the total number of runs scored and divide the sum by 9.

   (D) He should add all the jersey numbers together and divide the result by 9.

8. The mean of the distances Maria walked last week was 2.1 miles per day. She walked the least on Monday and the most on Saturday. On Monday, she walked 1.5 miles. On Sunday, Tuesday, and Thursday, she walked 2.2 miles. What other information is necessary to find the range of the data? **G**

   (F) The number of days she walked 1.5 miles

   (G) The number of miles Maria walked on Saturday

   (H) The number of feet in a mile

   (J) The number of miles Maria walked on Wednesday and Friday

9. What number can you add to the data set below so that the mean, median, and mode are all the same? **C**

12, 11, 22, 15, 12, 11, 15, 22

  (A) 11   (B) 12   (C) 15   (D) 22

10. The table below shows income levels of men with varying levels of education in 2001. Based on the information in the table, which of the following statements is reasonable?

H

Level of Education	Median Annual Income (dollars)
Less than 9th grade	21,361
High school diploma	34,723
Bachelor's degree	55,929
Master's degree	70,899

  (F) Men with a bachelor's degree have the highest annual income.

  (G) The income of high school graduates is about twice the income of men with less than a ninth-grade education.

  (H) The income of men with a master's degree is about twice that of men with only a high school diploma.

  (J) The income of men with a master's degree is about three times that of men with only a high school diploma.

11. A storage tank contains $30\frac{1}{2}$ gallons of water. After draining for one hour, it contains $15\frac{1}{4}$ gallons. After two hours, it contains $7\frac{5}{8}$ gallons. After three hours, it contains $3\frac{13}{16}$ gallons. If the pattern continues, how many gallons will be in the tank after 4 hours? **B**

  (A) $1\frac{27}{32}$ gal   (C) $1\frac{31}{32}$ gal

  (B) $1\frac{29}{32}$ gal   (D) $2\frac{3}{32}$ gal

12. In the United States, 390 species of animals were listed as endangered in 2000. Of those, 69 species were mammals, and 18 species were crustaceans. What fraction of the endangered species were crustaceans? **G**

  (F) $\frac{6}{195}$ (G) $\frac{3}{65}$ (H) $\frac{9}{65}$ (J) $\frac{23}{130}$

Griddable Items

Record your answer in a grid.

13. In 2002, Texas produced about 375 billion kilowatt-hours of electricity. About 138 billion of these were produced from coal. So about $\frac{138}{375}$ of the electricity came from coal. What is $\frac{138}{375}$ as a decimal? Round your answer to the nearest hundredth. **0.37**

14. Each week, the Margueles family spends about $75 on groceries. The fraction spent on fruits and vegetables is about $\frac{12}{75}$. What is $\frac{12}{75}$ as a decimal? **0.16**

TAKS GO for Help Guide

TAKS Objective	Item Number	GO To	TAKS Objective	Item Number	GO To
Obj. 1: (7.2)(B)	1–2	Lesson 3-3	Obj. 6: (7.15)(A)	10	Lesson 1-1
	3	Lesson 3-2		11	Lesson 3-5
Obj. 1: (7.2)(A)	4–5	Lesson 3-4	Obj. 1: (7.1)(B)	12	Lesson 2-3
	6	Lesson 3-5		13–14	Lesson 2-6
Obj. 6: (7.13)(B)	7–9	Lesson 1-10			

For additional TAKS practice, see the *TAKS Review and Preparation Workbook*.

TAKS Review and Preparation Workbook

Lesson 5   TAKS Grade 7 Objective 1
                            (7.2)(B)

Solving Problems with Fractions and Decimals

Most problems involving fractions and decimals require you to identify whether you need to *add, subtract, multiply,* or *divide.*

★ **TIP**

Addition and Subtraction of Decimals

To add and subtract decimals, line up the numbers on their decimal points. If there are place values that are filled in one number but not in the others, fill the empty spaces with zeros. Add or subtract just as you would with whole numbers, keeping the decimal point in the same position in the sum or difference.

- When a situation involves finding a total of several distinct pieces, use addition.
- When a situation involves finding a difference between two quantities, use subtraction.
- When a situation involves finding the total number of objects in equal-sized groups, use multiplication.
- When a situation involves separating a whole into equal parts, use division.

Examples: 72.65   89.8̶5̶
         + 3.80   − 6.75
         76.45   83.15

EXAMPLE 1

Susana took her month's allowance to the amusement park. She had $1.50 left at the end of the day. She made a list of her expenses, shown below. How much was her allowance?

Rides $3.50   Admission $1.50
Food $2.50   Toss-a-ring $2.00

Step 1 Determine what operation the problem requires. Susana's allowance is equal to the total amount of money she spent at the amusement park, *plus* the amount she had left at the end of the day. The problem can be solved with addition.

Step 2 Add the decimals, including the amount she had left at the end of the day:

Susana's monthly allowance is $11.00.

       3.50
       2.50
    + 1.50
       2.00
    _1.50_
    11.00

✓ **Quick Check 1**

1a. Ada and Jay have pet turtles. They hold a race. Below are the times the turtles took to cross the yard.

Turtle Times

Turtle	Time (seconds)
Matilda	65.7
Eugenia	75.45
Adelaide	80.12
Bertha	72.01

How many seconds longer did the slowest turtle take to cross the yard than did the fastest one?

1b. Evan has won 3 awards in the statewide Science Fair during the past few years. With each award has come a cash prize. If the 3 prizes were $24.30, $15.00, and $35.75, how much money has Evan won in the Science Fair?

4 Equations and Inequalities

Chapter at a Glance

Lesson Titles, Objectives, and Features	Assessment	NCTM Standards	TEKS ★ TAKS
4-1a Activity Lab: Describing Patterns **4-1 Evaluating and Writing Algebraic Expressions** • To write and evaluate algebraic expressions **4-1b Activity Lab, Technology:** Using Spreadsheets	Lesson Quiz	1, 2, 6, 7, 8, 9, 10	**TEKS** (7.2)(F), (7.15)(A) **TAKS** Obj. 1, 6 **TEKS** (7.13)(D); Prepares for **TEKS** (7.5)(B)
4-2 Using Number Sense to Solve Equations • To solve one-step equations using substitution, mental math, and estimation **4-2b Activity Lab, Algebra Thinking:** Keeping the Balance	Lesson Quiz	1, 2, 4, 6, 7, 8, 9, 10	**TEKS** (7.5)(B), (7.14)(A) **TAKS** Obj. 2, 6 **TEKS** (7.13)(D); Prepares for **TEKS** (7.5)(A)
4-3a Activity Lab, Hands On: Modeling Equations **4-3 Solving Equations by Adding or Subtracting** • To solve equations by adding or subtracting **Vocabulary Builder:** High-Use Academic Vocabulary	Lesson Quiz	1, 2, 6, 7, 8, 9, 10	**TEKS** (7.5)(A), (7.5)(B), (7.14)(A) **TAKS** Obj. 2, 6 **TEKS** (7.13)(D)
4-4 Solving Equations by Multiplying or Dividing • To solve equations by multiplying or dividing **Guided Problem Solving:** Practice Solving Problems	Lesson Quiz Checkpoint Quiz 1	1, 2, 4, 6, 7, 8, 9, 10	**TEKS** (7.5)(A), (7.5)(B), (7.13)(C) **TAKS** Obj. 2, 6
4-5 Exploring Two-Step Problems • To write and evaluate expressions with two operations and to solve two-step equations using number sense	Lesson Quiz	1, 2, 4, 6, 7, 8, 9, 10	**TEKS** (7.5)(A), (7.5)(B) **TAKS** Obj. 2 **TEKS** (7.13)(D)
4-6a Activity Lab, Hands On: Modeling Two-Step Equations **4-6 Solving Two-Step Equations** • To solve two-step equations using inverse operations	Lesson Quiz	1, 2, 6, 7, 8, 9, 10	**TEKS** (7.5)(A), (7.5)(B) **TAKS** Obj. 2 **TEKS** (7.13)(D)
4-7 Graphing and Writing Inequalities • To graph and write algebraic inequalities	Lesson Quiz Checkpoint Quiz 2	1, 2, 4, 6, 7, 8, 9, 10	
4-8a Activity Lab, Data Analysis: Inequalities in Bar Graphs **4-8 Solving Inequalities by Adding or Subtracting** • To solve inequalities by adding or subtracting	Lesson Quiz	1, 2, 5, 6, 7, 8, 9, 10	
4-9 Solving Inequalities by Multiplying or Dividing • To solve inequalities by multiplying or dividing	Lesson Quiz	1, 2, 4, 6, 7, 8, 9, 10	
TAKS Tune-Up: Cumulative Practice			

NCTM Standards 2000
1 Number and Operations   2 Algebra   3 Geometry   4 Measurement   5 Data Analysis and Probability
6 Problem Solving   7 Reasoning and Proof   8 Communication   9 Connections   10 Representation

Correlations to Standardized Tests

All content for these tests is contained in *Prentice Hall Math,* Course 2. This chart reflects coverage in this chapter only.

	4-1	4-2	4-3	4-4	4-5	4-6	4-7	4-8	4-9
Terra Nova CAT 6 (Level 17)									
Number and Number Relations	✔	✔	✔	✔	✔	✔	✔	✔	✔
Computation and Numerical Estimation	✔	✔	✔	✔	✔	✔	✔	✔	✔
Operation Concepts	✔	✔	✔	✔	✔	✔	✔	✔	✔
Measurement									
Geometry and Spatial Sense									
Data Analysis, Statistics, and Probability							✔		
Patterns, Functions, Algebra	✔	✔	✔	✔	✔	✔	✔	✔	✔
Problem Solving and Reasoning	✔	✔	✔	✔	✔	✔	✔	✔	✔
Communication	✔	✔	✔	✔	✔	✔	✔	✔	✔
Decimals, Fractions, Integers, and Percents	✔	✔	✔	✔	✔	✔	✔	✔	✔
Order of Operations									
Terra Nova CTBS (Level 17)									
Decimals, Fractions, Integers, Percents	✔	✔	✔	✔	✔	✔	✔	✔	✔
Order of Operations, Numeration, Number Theory	✔	✔	✔	✔	✔	✔	✔	✔	✔
Data Interpretation							✔		
Pre-algebra	✔	✔	✔	✔	✔	✔	✔	✔	✔
Measurement									
Geometry									
ITBS (Level 13)									
Number Properties and Operations	✔	✔	✔	✔	✔	✔	✔	✔	✔
Algebra	✔	✔	✔	✔	✔	✔	✔	✔	✔
Geometry									
Measurement									
Probability and Statistics									
Estimation									
SAT 10 (Int 3 Level)									
Number Sense and Operations	✔	✔	✔	✔	✔	✔	✔	✔	✔
Patterns, Relationships, and Algebra	✔	✔	✔	✔	✔	✔	✔	✔	✔
Data, Statistics, and Probability							✔		
Geometry and Measurement									
NAEP									
Number Sense, Properties, and Operations								✔	
Measurement									
Geometry and Spatial Sense									
Data Analysis, Statistics, and Probability									
Algebra and Functions	✔	✔	✔	✔	✔	✔	✔	✔	✔

CAT6 California Achievement Test, 6th Ed. **CTBS** Comprehensive Test of Basic Skills **ITBS** Iowa Test of Basic Skills, Form M
SAT10 Stanford Achievement Test, 10th Ed. **NAEP** National Assessment of Educational Progress 2005 Mathematics Objectives

TEKS Math Background

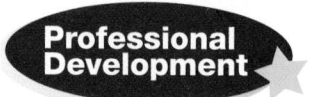

Focus on the TEKS

- At Grade 7, students extend Grade 6 skills to model and solve equations and use symbols to record actions (7.5)(A). Analysis of TAKS results shows that students should review this student expectation.

  In Lessons 4-3 and 4-4, students solve equations with variables using all four operations. Place special emphasis on these lessons because they focus on (7.5)(A).

- New at Grade 7 is to select and use appropriate operations to solve equations and justify the selections (7.2)(F).

  Students write and evaluate algebraic expressions in Lesson 4-1 (7.2)(F) and apply this skill to solve two-step equations in Lessons 4-5 and 4-6.

4-1 Evaluating and Writing Algebraic Expressions

TEKS ★ TAKS (7.2)(F), (7.15)(A) Obj. 1, 6; (7.13)(D);
Prepares for TEKS (7.5)(B)

Math Understandings

- The value of an algebraic expression varies depending on the value of the variable.
- Within a single problem, the value of the variable usually remains the same.

A **variable** is a symbol, usually a letter, that represents one or more numbers. An **algebraic expression** is a mathematical phrase with at least one variable.

Variables	Algebraic Expressions
x, y, a, c, p, m	$3x, y - 2, a \div 5, 3p + 2, 7 - m$

4-2 Using Number Sense to Solve Equations

TEKS ★ TAKS (7.5)(B), (7.14)(A) Obj. 2, 6; (7.13)(D);
Prepares for TEKS (7.5)(A)

Math Understandings

- An equation with one or more variables is an open sentence.
- An open sentence is neither true nor false until the variable is replaced with a number value.
- Some equations are easy to solve using mental math.

An **equation** is a mathematical sentence with an equal sign. A **solution of an equation** is a value for the variable that makes the equation true. An equation with one or more variables is an **open sentence**.

Equations	Open Sentences	Solutions
$6 \cdot 8 = 48$	$6y = 42$	$y = 7$
$2x + 7 = 9$	$q - 9 = 5$	$q = 14$

4-3, 4-4 Solving Equations by Adding, Subtracting, Multiplying, or Dividing

TEKS ★ TAKS (7.5)(A), (7.5)(B), (7.13)(C), (7.14)(A) Obj. 2, 6; (7.13)(D);

Math Understandings

- To solve an equation, you want to get the variable alone on one side of the equation by using the following properties.

Properties of Equality	
Arithmetic	**Algebra**
Addition Property of Equality	
$\frac{20}{2} = 10,$ so $\frac{20}{2} + 3 = 10 + 3$	If $a = b$ then $a + c = b + c$.
Subtraction Property of Equality	
$\frac{12}{2} = 6,$ so $\frac{12}{2} - 4 = 6 - 4$	If $a = b$ then $a - c = b - c$.
Division Property of Equality	
$3(2) = 6$ so, $\frac{3(2)}{2} = \frac{6}{2}$	If $a = b$ and $c \neq 0$ then $\frac{a}{c} = \frac{b}{c}$
Multiplication Property of Equality	
$\frac{12}{2} = 6,$ so $\frac{12}{2} \cdot 2 = 6 \cdot 2.$	If $a = b$ then $a \cdot c = b \cdot c.$

Inverse operations are operations that undo each other. Addition and subtraction are inverse operations. Multiplication and division are inverse operations.

<table>
<tr><td>4-5
4-6</td><td>

Exploring Two-Step Problems and Solving Two-Step Equations

</td></tr>
</table>

TEKS ★ (TAKS) (7.5)(A), (7.5)(B) Obj. 2; (7.13)(D)

Math Understandings
- To solve a two-step equation, you want to get the variable alone on one side of the equal sign using properties of equality and inverse operations.

The order for solving a two-step equation is the reverse of the order of operations: first undo addition or subtraction, then undo multiplication or division.

<table>
<tr><td>4-7</td><td>

Graphing and Writing Inequalities

</td></tr>
</table>

Math Understandings
- We can use special symbols to describe how two numbers or expressions are related to each other.

A mathematical sentence that contains one of the following symbols is an **inequality.**

$<$ is less than	$>$ is greater than
$\leq$ is less than or equal to	$\geq$ is greater than or equal to
$\neq$ is not equal to	

The **solution of an inequality** is any value that makes the inequality true. The graph of an inequality shows that an inequality can have many solutions. A closed circle indicates that a value *is* included. An open circle indicates that a value is *not* included.

Example: Graph $c \leq 3$.

<table>
<tr><td>4-8
4-9</td><td>

Solving Inequalities by Adding, Subtracting, Multiplying, or Dividing

</td></tr>
</table>

Math Understandings
- The steps for solving one-step and two-step inequalities are much the same as those for solving equations.
- Adding or subtracting from both sides of an inequality by any number does not change the direction of the inequality sign.
- Multiplying or dividing both sides of an inequality by a positive number does not change the direction of the inequality sign, but multiplying or dividing by a negative number changes the direction of the inequality sign.

Properties of Inequality	
Arithmetic	**Algebra**
Addition Property of Inequality	
Since $7 > 3$, $7 + 4 > 3 + 4$	If $a > b$, then $a + c > b + c$.
Since $1 < 3$, $1 + 4 < 3 + 4$	If $a < b$, then $a + c < b + c$.
Subtraction Property of Inequality	
Since $9 > 6$, $9 - 3 > 6 - 3$	If $a > b$, then $a - c > b - c$.
Since $7 < 20$, $7 - 4 < 20 - 4$	If $a < b$, then $a - c < b - c$.
Division Property of Inequality	
$9 > 6$, so $\frac{9}{3} > \frac{6}{3}$	If $a > b$ and $c > 0$, then $\frac{a}{c} > \frac{b}{c}$.
$15 < 20$, so $\frac{15}{5} < \frac{20}{5}$.	If $a < b$ and $c > 0$, then $\frac{a}{c} < \frac{b}{c}$.
$16 > 12$, so $\frac{16}{-4} < \frac{12}{-4}$.	If $a > b$ and $c < 0$, then $\frac{a}{c} < \frac{b}{c}$.
$10 < 18$, so $\frac{10}{-2} > \frac{18}{-2}$.	If $a < b$ and $c < 0$, then $\frac{a}{c} > \frac{b}{c}$.
Multiplication Property of Inequality	
$9 > 5$, so $9 \cdot 2 > 5 \cdot 2$	If $a > b$ and $c > 0$, then $a \cdot c > b \cdot c$.
$3 < 6$, so $3 \cdot 4 < 6 \cdot 4$	If $a < b$ and $c > 0$, then $a \cdot c < b \cdot c$.
$7 > 4$, so $7 \cdot (-2) < 4 \cdot (-2)$	If $a > b$ and $c < 0$, then $a \cdot c < b \cdot c$.
$2 < 8$, so $2 \cdot (-3) > 8 \cdot (-3)$	If $a < b$ and $c < 0$, then $a \cdot c > b \cdot c$.

Additional Professional Development Opportunities

Math Background Notes for Chapter 4: Every lesson has a Math Background in the PLAN section.

Research Overview, Mathematics Strands
Additional support for these topics and more is in the front of the Teacher's Edition.

LessonLab
LessonLab, a Pearson Education company, offers comprehensive, facilitated professional development designed to help teachers to improve student achievement. To learn more, please visit lessonlab.com.

Texas Chapter 4 Resources

	4-1	4-2	4-3	4-4	4-5	4-6	4-7	4-8	4-9	For the Chapter
Print Resources										
L3 Practice	•	•	•	•	•	•	•	•	•	
L1 Adapted Practice	•	•	•	•	•	•	•	•	•	
L3 Guided Problem Solving	•	•	•	•	•	•	•	•	•	
L2 Reteaching	•	•	•	•	•	•	•	•	•	
L4 Enrichment	•	•	•	•	•	•	•	•	•	
L3 Daily Notetaking Guide	•	•	•	•	•	•	•	•	•	
L1 Adapted Daily Notetaking Guide	•	•	•	•	•	•	•	•	•	
L3 Vocabulary and Study Skills Worksheets	•		•		•			•		•
L3 Daily Puzzles	•	•	•	•	•	•	•	•	•	
L3 Activity Labs	•	•	•	•	•	•	•	•	•	
L3 Checkpoint Quiz				•			•			
L3 Chapter Project										•
L2 Chapter Test										•
L3 Chapter Test										•
L4 Alternative Assessment										•
L3 Cumulative Review										•
Spanish Resources ELL										
L3 Practice	•	•	•	•	•	•	•	•	•	
L3 Vocabulary and Study Skills Worksheets	•		•		•		•			•
L3 Checkpoint Quiz				•			•			
L2 Chapter Test										•
L3 Chapter Test										•
L4 Alternative Assessment										•
L3 Cumulative Review										•
Transparencies										
Check Skills You'll Need	•	•	•	•	•	•	•	•	•	
Additional Examples	•	•	•	•	•	•	•	•	•	
Problem of the Day	•	•	•	•	•	•	•	•	•	
TAKS Daily Review	•	•	•	•	•	•	•	•	•	
Classroom Aid		•	•			•				
Student Edition Answers	•	•	•	•	•	•	•	•	•	•
Lesson Quiz	•	•	•	•	•	•	•	•	•	
TAKS Strategies										•
Technology										
Texas Interactive Textbook Online	•	•	•	•	•	•	•	•	•	•
Texas StudentExpress CD-ROM	•	•	•	•	•	•	•	•	•	•
Success Tracker™ Online Intervention	•	•	•	•	•	•	•	•	•	•
TeacherExpress CD-ROM	•	•	•	•	•	•	•	•	•	•
PresentationExpress CD-ROM	•	•	•	•	•	•	•	•	•	•
Texas ExamView CD-ROM with QuickTake	•	•	•	•	•	•	•	•	•	•
MindPoint Quiz Show CD-ROM	•	•	•	•	•	•	•	•	•	•
Prentice Hall Web Site: PHSchool.com	•	•	•	•	•	•	•	•	•	•

Also available: TAKS Tune-Up Kit
- TAKS Daily Review Transparencies
- TAKS Review and Preparation Workbook
- TAKS Strategies with Transparencies
- Texas Progress Monitoring Assessments
- Texas ExamView CD-ROM
- MindPoint Quiz Show CD-ROM

Other Resources
Algebra Readiness Tests
All-in-One Student Workbook
All-in-One Student Workbook, Adapted Version
Multilingual Handbook

Solution Key
Math Notes Study Folder
Spanish Cumulative Assessment

Where You Can Use the Lesson Resources

Here is a suggestion, following the four-step teaching plan, for how you can incorporate Differentiated Instruction Resources into your teaching.

	Instructional Resources **L3**	Differentiated Instruction Resources
1. Plan		
Preparation Read the Math Background in the Teacher's Edition to connect this lesson with students' previous experience. **Starting Class** **Check Skills You'll Need** Assign these exercises to review prerequisite skills. **TEKS ★ TAKS** Review the full text of the TEKS student expectations and TAKS objectives covered in this lesson. **New Vocabulary** Help students pre-read the lesson by pointing out the new terms introduced in the lesson.	**TEKS Math Background** **Math Understandings** **Transparencies & PresentationExpress CD-ROM** Check Skills You'll Need Problem of the Day TAKS Daily Review **Resources** Vocabulary and Study Skills	**Spanish Support** **ELL** Vocabulary and Study Skills
2. Teach		
L3 Guided Instruction Use the Activity Labs to build conceptual understanding. Teach each Example. Use the Teacher's Edition side column notes for specific teaching tips, including Error Prevention notes. Use the Additional Examples found in the side column (and on transparency and PowerPoint) as an alternative presentation for the content. After each Example, assign the Quick Check exercise for that Example to get an immediate assessment of student understanding. Use the Closure activity in the Teacher's Edition to help students attain mastery of lesson content.	**Student Edition** Activity Lab **Resources** Daily Notetaking Guide Activity Lab **Transparencies & PresentationExpress CD-ROM** Additional Examples Classroom Aids **Texas ExamView CD-ROM with QuickTake**	**Teacher's Edition** Every lesson includes suggestions for working with students who need special attention. **L1** Special Needs **L2** Below Level **L4** Advanced Learners **ELL** English Language Learners **Resources** **L1** Adapted Daily Notetaking Guide **Multilingual Handbook**
3. Practice		

Assignment Guide
Check Your Understanding
Use these questions to check students' understanding before you assign homework.
 	
Homework Exercises
Assign homework from these leveled exercises in the Assignment Guide.
  A Practice by Example
  B Apply Your Skills
  C Challenge
  TAKS Tune-Up and Mixed Review
Homework Quick Check
Use these key exercises to quickly check students' homework.
	Transparencies & PresentationExpress CD-ROM
	Student Answers
	Resources
	Practice
	Guided Problem Solving
	Vocabulary and Study Skills
	Activity Lab
	Daily Puzzles
	Texas ExamView CD-ROM with QuickTake
		Spanish Support
		ELL Practice
		ELL Vocabulary and Study Skills
		Resources
		L1 Adapted Practice
		L4 Enrichment

4. Assess & Reteach		
Lesson Quiz Assign the Lesson Quiz to assess students' mastery of the lesson content. **Checkpoint Quiz** Use the Checkpoint Quiz to assess student progress over several lessons.	**Transparencies & PresentationExpress CD-ROM** Lesson Quiz **Resources** Checkpoint Quiz	**Resources** **L2** Reteaching **ELL** Checkpoint Quiz Success Tracker™ Online Intervention **Texas ExamView CD-ROM with QuickTake**

KEY **L1** Special Needs   **L2** Below Level   **L3** For All Students   **L4** Advanced, Gifted   **ELL** English Language Learners

CHAPTER 4 Equations and Inequalities

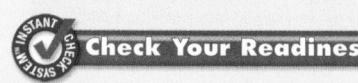
Check Your Readiness

Answers are in the back of the textbook.

For intervention, direct students to:

Adding and Subtracting Decimals
Lesson 1-2
Extra Skills and Word
Problems Practice, Ch. 1

Multiplying and Dividing Integers
Lesson 1-8
Extra Skills and Word
Problems Practice, Ch. 1

Order of Operations
Lesson 1-9
Extra Skills and Word
Problems Practice, Ch. 1

Comparing Fractions
Lesson 2-4
Extra Skills and Word
Problems Practice, Ch. 2

What You've Learned
TEKS ★ TAKS

- **(7.2)(C)** In Chapter 1, you used models to add, subtract, multiply, and divide integers. **TAKS** Obj. 1
- **(7.2)(E)** In Chapter 2, you simplified numerical expressions involving order of operations. **TAKS** Obj. 1
- **(7.2)(B)** In Chapter 3, you used addition, subtraction, multiplication, and division to solve problems involving fractions. **TAKS** Obj. 1

Check Your Readiness

For Exercises	See Lesson
1–4	1-2
5–8	1-8
9–14	1-9
15–18	2-4

GO for Help

Adding and Subtracting Decimals
Find each sum or difference.

1. $5.304 - 0.89$ **4.414**   **2.** $2.35 + 1.8 + 4.45$ **8.6**

3. $2.15 - 1.36$ **0.79**   **4.** $3.14 + 2.67 + 9.4$ **15.21**

Multiplying and Dividing Integers
Find each product or quotient.

5. $-12 \cdot 3$ **−36**   **6.** $-3 \div (-3)$ **1**   **7.** $-6 \cdot (-7)$ **42**   **8.** $-54 \div 9$ **−6**

Order of Operations
Find the value of each expression.

9. $14 + 2(15 \div 5)$ **20**   **10.** $20 \div 2 - 3 \cdot 3$ **1**   **11.** $(5 + 4) \cdot 4 \div 36$ **1**

12. $(9 - 4) \div 5 \cdot 6$ **6**   **13.** $9 \div (18 - 15) + 4$ **7**   **14.** $6 + 8 \cdot 7 - 24$ **38**

Comparing Fractions
Compare each pair of fractions. Use <, =, or >.

15. $\frac{20}{24} \; \boxed{>} \; \frac{28}{36}$ **16.** $\frac{15}{27} \; \boxed{=} \; \frac{5}{9}$ **17.** $\frac{6}{7} \; \boxed{>} \; \frac{18}{22}$ **18.** $\frac{8}{9} \; \boxed{<} \; \frac{9}{10}$

Number, Operation, and Quantitative Reasoning
TEKS (7.2)(F)
TAKS Obj. 1

Patterns, Relationships, and Algebraic Thinking
TEKS (7.5)(A), (7.5)(B)
TAKS Obj. 2

Underlying Processes and Mathematical Tools
TEKS (7.13)(C), (7.14)(A), (7.15)(A)
TAKS Obj. 6;
TEKS (7.13)(D)

Chapter 4 Overview

In this chapter, students evaluate and write algebraic expressions and write and solve both one-step and two-step equations. Then they draw upon their understanding of expressions and equations to graph, write, and solve inequalities.

Activating Prior Knowledge

In this chapter, students will build on their knowledge of the order of operations and of the distributive property to write and solve equations and inequalities. They also draw upon their understanding of mental math strategies. Ask question such as:

• *How can you find the sum of 97 and 46 using mental math?*
Sample: Use compensation; add 3 to 97, subtract 3 from 46; $100 + 43 = 143$

• *How can you use mental math to solve the following: 5×29?*
Sample: Use the distributive property;
$5 \times 29 = (5 \times 20) + (5 \times 9) = 100 + 45 = 145.$

What You'll Learn Next

TEKS ★ TAKS

• **(7.5)(A)** In this chapter, you will use models and symbols to solve equations. **TAKS** Obj. 2

• **(7.5)(B)** You will formulate problem situations when given a simple equation and formulate equations when given problem situations. **TAKS** Obj. 2

• **(7.13)(D)** You will use techniques such as mental math, estimation, and number sense to solve problems.

 TAKS Tune-Up On pages 223–225, you will review and practice the vocabulary and *TAKS* objectives you have learned.

🔊 Key Vocabulary

• Addition Property of Equality (p. 180)
• algebraic expression (p. 169)
• Division Property of Equality (p. 186)
• equation (p. 174)
• inequality (p. 205)
• inverse operations (p. 181)
• Multiplication Property of Equality (p. 188)
• open sentence (p. 174)
• solution of an equation (p. 174)
• solution of an inequality (p. 205)
• Subtraction Property of Equality (p. 180)
• variable (p. 169)

Chapter 4   **167**

167

Describing Patterns

Students identify and describe patterns in tables. Then they continue these patterns to make predictions. They use variables in their descriptions to extend patterns beyond the numbers in the tables.

Guided Instruction

Before beginning the Activity, discuss how a plane gains altitude as it takes off before maintaining a level altitude for most of a flight.
Ask:
- *Does a plane continue its rise in altitude throughout a flight?* **No, it levels off and then decreases its altitude to land.**

- *How do the Kelvin and Celsius scales differ?* **The Kelvin temperature is always 273° higher than the Celsius temperature.**

Differentiated Instruction

Advanced Learners   L4
Have students check in science books to find out about the origins of the Kelvin and Celsius scales.

TEKS ★ (TAKS) **Resources**

Dana Center TEKS Toolkit
  Clarifying Activities (7.15)(A)
Visit: PHSchool.com
Web Code: arq-9045

4-1a **Activity Lab**

TEKS ★ (TAKS)
(7.15)(A) To make conjectures from patterns
(TAKS) Obj. 6

Describing Patterns

You can identify and describe patterns to make predictions.

ACTIVITY

During part of its flight, an airplane rises 12 feet in altitude each second. Use this information to find a pattern.

1. Look at the table at the right. Explain how to find the distance the plane rises for each amount of time.
Multiply the time by 12.
2. Copy and complete the table at the right.
See right.
3. At *t* seconds, how many feet has the plane risen?
12 times t

You can use different scales to measure temperature. The Celsius and Kelvin scales have a special relationship.

Time (s)	Distance (ft)	
1	12	
5	60	
10	120	
20	■	240
25	■	300
50	■	600
100	■	1,200
200	■	2,400

4. Look at the table of temperatures at the right. Explain how to find the temperature in degrees Kelvin for each temperature in degrees Celsius.
Add 273.
5. Copy and complete the table. **See right.**

6. At *c* degrees Celsius, what is the temperature in degrees Kelvin?   **273 more than c**

Celsius (C)	Kelvin (K)	
0	273	
1	274	
5	278	
10	■	283
20	■	293
30	■	303
75	■	348
100	■	373

Exercises

Copy and complete each table. Describe the pattern you find.
1–3. See margin.

1.

A	B
1	8
2	9
5	12
10	■
30	■
50	■
n	■

2.

C	D
1	−4
2	−3
5	0
10	■
25	■
45	■
n	■

3.

E	F
1	40
2	80
5	200
10	■
100	■
500	■
n	■

4. **Reasoning** What does the letter *n* represent in each table above? How is it used to describe the pattern in the table? **See margin.**

1–4. See back of book.

Evaluating and Writing Algebraic Expressions

TEKS ★ **TAKS**

(7.2)(F) To select and use appropriate operations to solve problems **TAKS** Obj. 1
Prepares for **TEKS (7.5)(B)** To formulate problem situations when given an equation and formulate an equation when given a problem situation

 Check Skills You'll Need

1. Vocabulary Review
The set of rules for simplifying an expression is called the __?__ .
order of operations
Find the value of each expression.

2. $3 + 4 \cdot 2$ **11**

3. $12 - 6 \div 3$ **10**

4. $6 \cdot (5 - 7) + 2$ **−10**

5. $(4 + 3) \cdot 2 - 11$ **3**

GO for Help
Lesson 1-9

Why Learn This?

You can use algebraic expressions to help you make predictions based on patterns. If you know how far you can swim in 1 minute, you can estimate how far you can swim in 5 minutes.

A **variable** is a symbol that represents one or more numbers. Variables are usually letters. An **algebraic expression** is a mathematical phrase with at least one variable.

Diagrams and algebraic expressions can represent word phrases.

Word Phrase	Diagram	Algebraic Expression
a temperature of t degrees increased by 5 degrees	t | 5	$t + 5$
five cats fewer than c cats	c / ? | 5	$c - 5$
the product of 5 and n nickels	n n n n n	$5n$
a dinner bill of d dollars divided among five friends	d / $\frac{d}{5}$ $\frac{d}{5}$ $\frac{d}{5}$ $\frac{d}{5}$ $\frac{d}{5}$	$\frac{d}{5}$

EXAMPLE Writing Algebraic Expressions

 TAKS Tip

You can use diagrams to represent algebraic expressions.

❶ Write an algebraic expression for each word phrase.

a. swimming m meters per minute for 3 minutes   → $3m$

b. 12 heartbeats more than x heartbeats   → $x + 12$

✓ Quick Check

1. Write an algebraic expression for a price p decreased by 16. $p - 16$

Differentiated Instruction Solutions for All Learners

Special Needs L1
In Example 4, make sure students do not think $2p$ means $2 + 2$, since they would still get the right answer. *Ask: What if p were equal to 4, or to 5?* This lets you know they are interpreting the expression $2p$ correctly.

learning style: verbal

Below Level L2
Use several simple numerical expressions like the following to review various operation symbols.

$8 + 4$ $8 - 4$ 8×4 $8 \cdot 4$ **8(4)**

$8 \div 4$ $\frac{8}{4}$

learning style: visual

TEKS ★ **TAKS**

(7.2)(F) To select and use appropriate operations to solve problems **TAKS** Obj. 1
Prepares for **TEKS (7.5)(B)** To formulate problem situations when given an equation and formulate an equation when given a problem situation

Dana Center TEKS Toolkit Clarifying Activities (7.2)(F)
Visit: PHSchool.com
Web Code: arq-9045

TEKS Math Background

A *variable* is a placeholder for a number. A mathematical expression that contains one or more variables is called an *algebraic expression*.

When each variable in an algebraic expression is replaced by a number, the result is a numerical expression. This process is called *evaluating the algebraic expression*.

More Math Background: p. 166C

Lesson Planning and Resources

See p. 166E for a list of the resources that support this lesson.

PowerPoint
Bell Ringer Practice

✓ **Check Skills You'll Need**
Use student page, transparency, or PowerPoint.

TAKS Daily Review 26
Use transparency.

Activity Lab

Use before the lesson.
Student Edition Activity Lab 4-1a, Describing Patterns, p. 168

All in One Teaching Resources

Activity Lab 4-1: Solutions in Need of Equations

Guided Instruction

Example 4
Display $2(p + 7)$. Ask: *How would the answer be different if these parentheses were inserted?*
$2(2 + 7) \rightarrow 2(9) \rightarrow 18$

PowerPoint

Additional Examples

❶ Write an algebraic expression for each word phrase.

  a. 6 less than *d* dollars $d - 6$

  b. the sum of *s* students and 9 students $s + 9$

  c. 12 times *b* boxes $12b$

  d. 20 books divided among *s* students $\frac{20}{s}$

❷ The cost of a package of markers is *d* dollars. Write an algebraic expression for the total cost in dollars of 7 packages of markers. $7d$

❸ Write three word phrases for $2y$. Sample: the product of 2 and a number *y*; 2 times a number *y*; 2 multiplied by a number *y*

❹ Evaluate each expression. Use $r = 8$, $s = 1$, and $t = 3$.
  a. $6(t - 1)$ 12 **b.** $\frac{r}{s + t}$ 2

All in One Teaching Resources

- Daily Notetaking Guide 4-1 **L3**
- Adapted Notetaking 4-1 **L1**

Closure

- *What is an algebraic expression?* a mathematical phrase that uses variables, numbers, and operation symbols
- *How do you evaluate an algebraic expression?* Substitute a given value for each variable and simplify.

You can use algebraic expressions to represent real-world situations.

EXAMPLE **Application: Public Service**

❷ The Environmental Club is making posters. The materials for each poster cost $4. Write an algebraic expression for the cost of *p* posters.

Words	$4 per poster	times	the number of posters

| Expression | 4 | · | *p* |

An algebraic expression for the cost of the posters is $4p$.

✓ Quick Check

  2. Nine students will hang *t* posters each. Write an algebraic expression for the total number of posters the students will hang. **9t**

You can translate algebraic expressions into word phrases.

Online active math

For: Expressions Activity
Use: Interactive Textbook, 4-1

EXAMPLE **Writing Word Phrases**

❸ Write three different word phrases for $x + 2$.

> A number plus two

> A number increased by two

> Two more than a number

✓ Quick Check

  3. Write three different word phrases for $c - 50$.
Answers may vary. Sample: a number decreased by 50, 50 less than a number, 50 subtracted from a number

You can substitute for a variable to evaluate an algebraic expression.

EXAMPLE **Evaluating Algebraic Expressions**

❹ Evaluate each expression. Use the values $p = 2$, $n = 3$, and $s = 5$.

  a. $2p + 7$ **b.** $p + (n \cdot s)$

$$2p + 7 = 2(2) + 7 \quad \leftarrow \text{Substitute.} \rightarrow \quad p + (n \cdot s) = 2 + (3 \cdot 5)$$
$$= 4 + 7 \quad \leftarrow \text{Multiply.} \rightarrow \quad = 2 + (15)$$
$$= 11 \quad \leftarrow \text{Add.} \rightarrow \quad = 17$$

✓ Quick Check

  4. Use the values $n = 3$, $t = 5$, and $y = 7$ to evaluate $(n + t) \cdot y$. **56**

Advanced Learners **L4**
Write four algebraic expressions whose value is 6 when the variable *m* is replaced by 2. Samples:

$m + 4$; $8 - m$; $3m$; $\frac{12}{m}$

English Language Learners **ELL**
Alert students to translation errors. For example, *five fewer than c cats* can be misunderstood to mean $5 - c$. Often, substituting a number for the variable and working it out clarifies the confusion.

Pre-AP™

learning style: verbal

✓ Check Your Understanding

1. An algebraic expression differs from a numerical expression because it contains at least one variable, and the value changes.

1. **Vocabulary** A numerical expression is a mathematical phrase that uses numbers. What is the difference between an *algebraic* expression and a *numerical* expression?

Tell which operation you would use for each word phrase.

2. six goals fewer than g goals
subtraction

3. p people increased by two
addition

Exercises 4–7. Answers may vary. Samples are given:

4. three less than w

5. the product of five and w

6. twelve more than w

7. the quotient of w and four

Write a word phrase for each algebraic expression. 4–7. See left.

4. $w - 3$ 5. $5 \cdot w$ 6. $12 + w$ 7. $\frac{w}{4}$

Evaluate each expression. Use the value $p = 2$.

8. $p + 8$ 10   9. $3 \cdot p$ 6   10. $16 - p$ 14   11. $\frac{12}{p}$ 6

Homework Exercises

For more exercises, see Extra Skills and Word Problems.

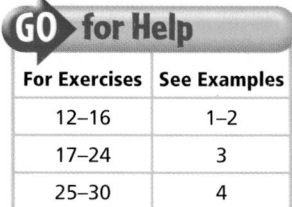

GO for Help

For Exercises	See Examples
12–16	1–2
17–24	3
25–30	4

Ⓐ Write an algebraic expression for each word phrase. You may find a diagram helpful.

12. four more than s shirts
$s + 4$

13. the quotient of p and 5 $\frac{p}{5}$

14. the sum of t TVs and 11 TVs
$t + 11$

15. five times your quiz score q
$5q$

16. Your job pays $7 per hour. Write an algebraic expression for your pay in dollars for working h hours. $7h$

Write a word phrase for each algebraic expression. 17–24. See margin.

17. $d + 2$ 18. $\frac{4}{n}$ 19. $c - 9.1$ 20. $6.5 - h$

21. $1.3 \cdot p$ 22. $10 + q$ 23. $\frac{w}{10}$ 24. $3.5v$

Evaluate each expression. Use the values $p = 4$, $n = 6$, and $s = 2$.

25. $7n$ 42   26. $-6.1p$ -24.4 27. $5 - s$ 3

28. $\frac{n}{2}$ 3   29. $8s - 6$ 10   30. $1.5(p + n)$ 15

Ⓑ **GPS** 31. **Guided Problem Solving** A student mows one lawn each week day after school and two lawns on Saturday. She earns $15.75 per lawn. Write an algebraic expression for the amount of money she makes in w weeks. **$110.25w**

- How many lawns does she mow in one week?
- *Draw a picture* to represent the amount of money she makes in one week.

Online lesson quiz, PHSchool.com, Web Code: ara-0401   4-1 Evaluating and Writing Algebraic Expressions   **171**

Exercises 17–24. Answers may vary. Samples are given:

17. 2 more than a number

18. 4 divided by a number

19. $9\frac{1}{10}$ less than a number

20. a number subtracted from $6\frac{5}{10}$

21. $1\frac{3}{10}$ and three tenths times a number

22. 10 more than a number

23. a number divided by 10

24. $3\frac{5}{10}$ times a number

3. Practice

Assignment Guide

Check Your Understanding
Go over Exercises 1–11 in class before assigning the Homework Exercises.

Homework Exercises
A Practice by Example   12–30
B Apply Your Skills   31–38
C Challenge   39
TEKS ★ **TAKS** Tune-Up and Mixed Review   40–44

Homework Quick Check
To check students' understanding of key skills and concepts, go over Exercises 13, 18, 35, 37, and 38.

Differentiated Instruction Resources

171

PowerPoint

Lesson Quiz

Evaluate when $n = 12$ and $p = 8$.

1. $2n - 9$ 15

2. $3(n + p)$ 60

3. $\frac{n}{4} + 7$ 10

Write an algebraic expression for each word phrase.

4. the number of days in w weeks
7w

5. two less than m mice $m - 2$

GO Online
Homework Help
Visit: PHSchool.com
Web Code: are-0401

35. Answers may vary. Sample: Multiply 24(60) to find the number of minutes in 24 h. Then multiply the answer by 1,260, the number of beats per minute. The heart beats 1,814,400 times in 24 h.

36. Answers may vary. Sample: Candles cost $10 each. How much do you pay for n candles?

37. Subtraction is not commutative.

Write an algebraic expression for the nth term of each table.

32.

A	0	1	2	3	5	10	n
B	5	6	7	8	10	15	?

$n + 5$

33.

C	0	1	2	3	5	10	n
D	0	10	20	30	50	100	?

$10n$

34. Write an algebraic expression to find the number of seconds in n minutes. Evaluate the expression for $n = 20$. 60n; 1,200

35. **Birds** The blue-throated hummingbird has a heart rate of about 1,260 beats per minute. Explain how you would calculate the number of times the hummingbird's heart beats in a 24-hour day. Then find the number of beats in a 24-hour day. See left.

36. Describe a situation that the expression $10n$ can model. See left.

37. <u>Writing in Math</u> You can write "twelve less than a number" as $n - 12$, but not as $12 - n$. Explain why. See left.

38. **Estimation** This section of a page from a telephone directory shows a column with 11 names in 1 inch. Each page has four 10-inch columns. Write an algebraic expression for the approximate number of names in p pages of the directory. 440p

```
6-4462  Daalling V 8 Everett All.........
2-3302  Daavis K 444 Greeley R.........
4-1775  Dabady V 94 Burnside All.....
2-0014  Dabagh L 13 Lancaster R......
6-3356  Dabagh W Dr 521 Weston All..
4-7322  Dabar G 98 River All.............
6-1530  Dabarera F 34 Roseland All....
2-2279  Dabas M 17 Riverside R........
4-9978  D'Abate D 86 Moss Hill Rd All.
2-6745  D'Abate G 111 South Central R
4-5456  Dabbous H 670 Warren Dr All.
6-3064  Dabbraccio F 151 Century All.
6-2257  Dabby D 542 Walnut All.........
2-9987  Dabcovich M G 219 Green R...
6-5643  Dabcovich M 72 Main All.......
```

39. **Challenge** A student baby-sitting for $5 per hour writes the expression $5n$ to represent the money he makes for n hours. Another student writes $3n + 15$ to represent the amount in dollars she makes. What is the second student's hourly rate? What does the number 15 represent? Answers may vary. Sample: The second student charges $15 to start and $3/h.

TEKS ★ TAKS Tune-Up and Mixed Review

TAKS Objective 6
TEKS (7.14)(A)

40. In ancient Greece, a measurement called a cubit equaled 18.3 inches. Which expression represents the number of inches in c cubits? **D**

(A) $c - 18.3$ (B) $c \div 18.3$ (C) $18.3 + c$ (D) $18.3c$

TAKS Objective 1
TEKS (7.2)(A)

41. Which expression does the model represent?

(F) $\frac{2}{3} \times \frac{3}{4}$ (H) $\frac{1}{2} \times \frac{2}{3}$

(G) $\frac{1}{3} \times \frac{3}{4}$ (J) $\frac{1}{2} \times \frac{3}{4}$

GO for Help **Lesson 1-9**   Find the value of each expression.

42. $7(1.2) + 7(0.5)$ **43.** $3(4 + 5) + 2(4 + 5)$ **44.** $5(0.25 \cdot 40)$
11.9   45   50

Reteaching 4-1   Evaluating and Writing Algebraic Ex **L2**

To evaluate an *expression*, substitute a value for the *variable* and compute.

Evaluate $5y - 8$ for $y = 7$.
$5y - 8$
$5 \times 7 - 8$ ← Substitute *y* with 7.
$35 - 8 = 27$ ← Compute.

You can use key words to write a word phrase for an algebraic expression.

$a + 5$ → *a* plus 5
or *a* increased by 5
$2n$ → the product of 2 and *n*
or 2 times *n*

Evaluate each expression using the values $m = 3$ and $x = 8$.

1. $4m + 9$
Substitute *m*: $4 \times \underline{3} + 9$
Compute: $\underline{12} + 9 = \underline{21}$

2. $4x - 7$
Substitute *x*: $4 \times \underline{8} - 7$
Compute: $\underline{32} - 7 = \underline{25}$

3. $5x + x$
Substitute *x*: $5 \times \underline{8} + 8$
Compute: $\underline{40} + 8 = \underline{48}$

4. $x + 2m$
Substitute *x* and *m*: $\underline{8} + 2 \times \underline{3}$
Compute: $\underline{8} + \underline{6} = \underline{14}$

Evaluate each expression using the values $y = 4$, $z = 8$, and $p = 10$.

5. $3y + 6 = \underline{18}$

6. $4z - 2 = \underline{30}$

7. $p + 2p = \underline{30}$

8. $3z \times z = \underline{192}$

Write a word phrase for each algebraic expression.

9. $9 + x$
9 plus a number

10. $6x$
6 times a number

11. $x - 8$
8 less than a number

12. $\frac{x}{5}$
a number divided by 5

Write an algebraic expression for each word phrase.

13. x newspapers plus 10
$x + 10$

14. 4 less than x teabags
$x - 14$

15. 3 more than x envelopes
$x + 3$

16. 6 times x school buses
$6x$

Enrichment 4-1   Evaluating and Writing Algebraic Ex **L4**
Critical Thinking

This spring the 7th graders will be going on a class trip to Space Camp. In order to raise money for their trip, the 7th grade students are selling calendars for $5 each. The students will make a profit of $2 per calendar.

Rob sells twice as many calendars as Kayla. Michael sells 6 fewer than Rob. Sherrill sells half as many as Kayla. Troy sells eight more than Rob.

1. Let c represent the number of calendars that Kayla sells. Write an expression that shows how many calendars each student sells.

a. Rob $2c$ b. Michael $2c - 6$

c. Sherrill $\frac{1}{2}c$ d. Troy $2c + 8$

2. Write the expression for the total number of calendars sold.
$c + 2c + 2c - 6 + \frac{1}{2}c + 2c + 8$

Suppose Kayla sold 100 calendars.

3. How many calendars did each of these students sell?

a. Rob 200 calendars   b. Michael 194 calendars

c. Sherrill 50 calendars   d. Troy 208 calendars

4. How many calendars were sold in all? 752 calendars

5. How much money did the students earn? $1,504

Suppose Rob sold 40 calendars.

6. How many calendars did each of these students sell?

a. Kayla 20 calendars   b. Michael 34 calendars

c. Sherrill 10 calendars   d. Troy 48 calendars

7. How many calendars were sold in all? 152 calendars

8. How much money did the students earn? $304

TEKS ★ TAKS Resources

• TAKS Tune-Up, pp. 223–225
• TAKS Strategies, p. 219

TAKS Tune-Up Kit

• TAKS Daily Review Transparencies
• TAKS Review and Preparation Workbook
• TAKS Strategies with Transparencies
• Texas Progress Monitoring Assessments

Alternative Assessment

Ask each student to write a word phrase such as "3 more than s students." Have them assign a value to the variable and exchange papers with a partner. Partners then write the corresponding algebraic expression and evaluate for the given value. Partners can repeat the process as time permits.

TEKS ★ TAKS

(7.13)(D) To select tools such as technology to solve problems

Using Spreadsheets

You can use a computer spreadsheet to keep track of the balance in a checking account. You add deposits and subtract checks. Using the formulas you supply, the spreadsheet computes values in cells.

EXAMPLE Using Spreadsheets

Use the spreadsheet. Find the balance after each entry.

	A	B	C	D
1	Date	Deposits	Checks	Balance
2				$350
3	4/29	$100		■
4	4/30		$400	■

Use the formula "= D2 + B3".
← The computer finds 350 + 100 = 450.

← Use the formula "= D3 − C4".
The computer finds 450 − 400 = 50.

● The first balance is $450. The second balance is $50.

Exercises

Use the spreadsheet at the right.

1. Find the account balance after each entry. Write the formulas you used. See margin.

2. Which formula can you use to find the balance in cell D9, whether or not a check has been written or a deposit has been made? **D**
   - Ⓐ = D8 − B9 + C9
   - Ⓑ = D8 − B9 − C9
   - Ⓒ = D8 + B9 + C9
   - Ⓓ = D8 + B9 − C9

3. **Reasoning** Suppose the balance in cell D9 is $130.34. Was the amount of a deposit entered into cell B9, or was the amount of a check entered into cell C9? Support your answer. See margin.

4. **Writing in Math** Consider your answer to Exercise 2. Explain why the formula you chose works. Give examples. See margin.

5. **Reasoning** Suppose the balance in cell D8 is $250 and you do not know the original balance. Explain how would you calculate the original balance in cell D2. Then find the original balance.

	A	B	C	D
1	Date	Deposits	Checks	Balance
2				$250
3	11/3		$25.98	■
4	11/9		$239.40	■
5	11/10	$122.00		■
6	11/13		$54.65	■
7	11/20	$350.00		■
8	11/29		$163.80	■

5. Add the values in column C and subtract the values in column B; $261.83

1. $224.02(= D2 − C3)
   −$15.38(= D3 − C4)
   $106.62(= D4 + B5)
   $51.97(= D5 − C6)
   $401.97(= D6 + B7)
   $238.17(= D7 − C8)

3. The amount of a check; the amount of money decreased from cell D8 to cell D9.

4. Answers may vary. Sample: The formula "D9 = D8 + B9 − C9" adds any deposit from cell B9 or subtracts any check from cell C9. For example, if $100 is in B9, then D9 = $401.97 + $100 − $0, or if $50 is in C9, then D9 = $401.97 + $0 − $50.

Activity Lab

Using Spreadsheets

Students can use spreadsheet software when repeated calculations (using the same math operations) are done over and over with different numbers. One common application of spreadsheets is to keep track of banking transactions accurately.

Guided Instruction

Error Prevention!

Be sure students understand what a cell is and how to identify a cell. Ask questions like: *What amount is in cell B3 of the spreadsheet in the Example?* $100 *In cell C4?* $400

Differentiated Instruction

Visual Learners
Introduce and discuss the terminology associated with the workings of a checking account: a *deposit* is money put into a bank account; a *check* is a request for money to be withdrawn from the account; the *balance* is the amount of money remaining in an account after a deposit has been made or a check has been written. If possible, show examples of a deposit slip, a check, and a balance statement.

TEKS ★ TAKS Resources

- any spreadsheet software program
- Classroom Aid 4

Dana Center TEKS Toolkit
Clarifying Activities (7.13)(D)
Visit: PHSchool.com
Web Code: arq-9045

1. Plan

TEKS ★ TAKS

(7.13)(D) To select techniques such as mental math, estimation, and number sense to solve problems

(7.5)(B) To formulate an equation when given a problem situation TAKS Obj. 2

Dana Center TEKS Toolkit Clarifying Activities (7.5)(B), (7.13)(D)
Visit: PHSchool.com
Web Code: arq-9045

TEKS Math Background

An *equation* is a mathematical sentence that contains an equal sign. This means that a statement as simple as $1 + 2 = 3$ is an equation. However, this lesson and the ones that follow focus on equations in which one side is an algebraic expression. You determine whether a number is a *solution* of such an equation by evaluating the algebraic expression when that number is substituted for the variable. If the resulting statement is true, then the number is a solution of the equation.

More Math Background: p. 166C

Lesson Planning and Resources

See p. 166E for a list of the resources that support this lesson.

Bell Ringer Practice

✓ **Check Skills You'll Need**
Use student page, transparency, or PowerPoint.

TAKS **Daily Review 27**
Use transparency.

✓ Check Skills You'll Need

1. Vocabulary Review
A _?_ is a symbol that represents one or more numbers.
variable
Write an algebraic expression for each word phrase.

2. four more than y
  $y + 4$
3. six less than v
  $v - 6$
4. k divided by 9 $\frac{k}{9}$

GO for Help
Lesson 4-1

TEKS ★ TAKS

• (7.13)(D) To select techniques such as mental math, estimation, and number sense to solve problems

• (7.5)(B) To formulate an equation when given a problem situation TAKS Obj. 2

🔊 **New Vocabulary** equation, open sentence, solution of an equation

Why Learn This?

Solving equations can help you find amounts that are not easy to measure on their own. For example, if you know the weight of the bucket, you can use an equation to find the weight of the panda.

An **equation** is a mathematical sentence with an equal sign. An equation with one or more variables is an **open sentence**. The open sentence $p + 2 = 16$ is neither true nor false until p is replaced.

You can substitute a number for the variable in an equation to see if the value makes the equation true. A **solution of an equation** is a value for a variable that makes an equation true.

$$p + 2 = 16 \qquad 20 + 2 = 16 \qquad 14 + 2 = 16$$
$$\text{false} \qquad\qquad \text{true}$$

Since 14 makes the equation true, 14 is a solution of the equation.

EXAMPLE Solving Equations Using Substitution

1. Find the solution of $12m = 108$ from the numbers 4, 7, and 9. You can test each number by substituting for m in the equation.

$$12(4) \stackrel{?}{=} 108 \qquad 12(7) \stackrel{?}{=} 108 \qquad 12(9) \stackrel{?}{=} 108$$
$$48 = 108 \text{ ✗ False} \quad 84 = 108 \text{ ✗ False} \quad 108 = 108 \text{ ✔ True}$$

Since the equation is true when you substitute 9 for m, the solution is 9.

✓ Quick Check

1. Find the solution of each equation from the given numbers.
  a. $24n = 120$; 3, 5, or 11 5
  b. $124p = 992$; 4, 6, or 8 8

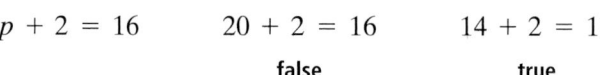
Differentiated Instruction Solutions for All Learners

Special Needs L1
Ask students to draw a picture for Example 3 to help them keep track of what they know the veterinarian weighs, and what the scale shows. They can label the line drawing of a puppy w.

learning style: visual

Below Level L2
Give students several addition and multiplication facts. Have them write the related subtractions for the addition facts and the related divisions for the multiplication facts.

learning style: visual

Sometimes you can solve an equation by using mental math.

 EXAMPLE Solving Equations Using Mental Math

2 Use mental math to solve each equation.

a. $4y \stackrel{?}{=} 20$

What you think

What number times 4 equals 20?

Since $4 \cdot 5 = 20$, $y = 5$.

b. $m + 7 = 15.5$

What you think

What number plus 7 equals 15.5?

Since $7 + 8.5 = 15.5$, $m = 8.5$.

✓ **Quick Check**

2. Use mental math to solve each equation.
   a. $t - 3 = 7$ **10**
   c. $\frac{h}{4} = 2.2$ **8.8**
   b. $n + 6 = -10.1$ **−16.1**
   d. $7x = -63$ **−9**

You can solve problems by using equations and estimation.

EXAMPLE Estimating Solutions

3 **TAKS** Multiple Choice A veterinarian holds a puppy and steps on a scale. The scale reads 134.5 lb. The veterinarian weighs 125.3 lb alone. Which is the best estimate of the weight of the puppy?

  Ⓐ Between 3 and 5 lb   Ⓒ Between 9 and 11 lb

  Ⓑ Between 6 and 8 lb   Ⓓ Between 12 and 15 lb

Words　　 weight 　plus 　 puppy's weight 　equals 　 total weight

　　　　　Let 　 w 　= the weight of the puppy.

Equation　　 125.3 　+　 w 　=　 134.5

$125.3 + w = 134.5$

$125.3 \approx 125$　$134.5 \approx 135$ ← **Choose compatible numbers.**

$125 + w = 135$ 　　　　 ← **What number added to 125 is 135?**

$w = 10$ 　　　　 ← **Use mental math.**

The puppy weighs about 10 lb. The correct answer is choice C.

✓ **Quick Check**

3. A box of machine parts weighs 14.7 lb. A forklift has a maximum weight limit of 390 lb. About how many boxes of parts can the forklift carry at one time? **about 26 boxes**

Careers A veterinarian is a health-care provider for animals.

 TAKS Tip

When writing an algebraic expression, choose a letter for the variable that will remind you of what the variable represents.

Advanced Learners L4
Use mental math to solve $3r - 5 = 7$. $12 - 5 = 7$, so $3r = 12$; $3 \cdot 4 = 12$, so $r = 4$

English Language Learners ELL
Ask students to read equations completely. For example, for $4y = 20$, ask them to say: *4 times a number y is equal to 20.* This will help them develop mathematical language and mathematical concepts.

Pre-AP™

learning style: verbal

Activity Lab
Use before the lesson.

All in One Teaching Resources
Activity Lab 4-2: Using Number Sense to Solve Equations

Guided Instruction

Example 1
Point out that the equal sign with a question mark above ($\stackrel{?}{=}$) is used immediately after a variable has been replaced by a number. It indicates that you do not yet know whether the equation is true or false.

Example 2
For part a, have students read $4y = 20$ as "4 times y equals 20." They will hear a parallel sentence structure when they read $4 \cdot 5 = 20$ as "4 times 5 equals 20."

PowerPoint
Additional Examples

1 Find the solution of $h - 18 = 54$: 3, 62, or 72? **72**

2 Use mental math to solve each equation.
   a. $s - 9 = 5$ $s = 14$
   b. $4z = 28$ $z = 7$
   c. $g + 7 = 11$ $g = 4$
   d. $\frac{c}{6} = 5$ $c = 30$

3 The weight of a packing crate is 14.65 lb. The crate and its contents together weigh 85.21 lb. Estimate the weight of the contents. **about 70 lb**

All in One Teaching Resources
• Daily Notetaking Guide 4-2 L3
• Adapted Notetaking 4-2 L1

Closure

• Explain the difference between an open sentence and a false sentence. *An open sentence is a mathematical sentence (with one or more variables) that is neither true nor false. A false sentence is false, or not true.*
• *How do you make an equation true?* Substitute the solution for the variable in the equation.

175

3. Practice

Assignment Guide

Check Your Understanding
Go over Exercises 1–9 in class before assigning the Homework Exercises.

Homework Exercises
A Practice by Example   10–23
B Apply Your Skills   24–36
C Challenge   37
TEKS ★ TAKS Tune-Up and
   Mixed Review   38–42

Homework Quick Check
To check students' understanding of key skills and concepts, go over Exercises 11, 23, 25, 34, and 35.

Differentiated Instruction Resources

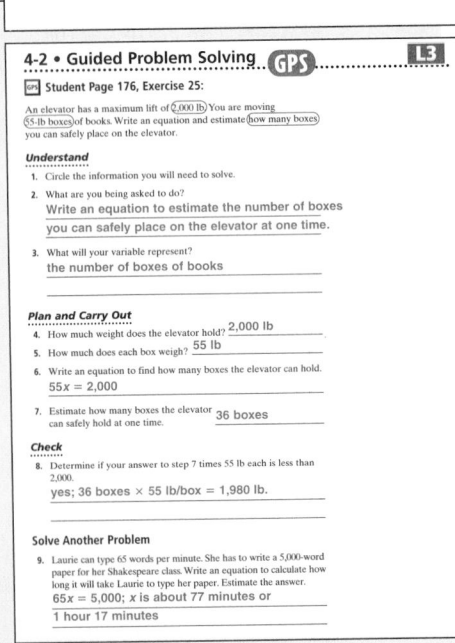

176

✓ Check Your Understanding

1. **Vocabulary** The value of a variable that makes an equation true is called the ? of the equation. **solution**

2. **Number Sense** The open sentence $14k = 0$ has ? solution(s).
   (A) no   (B) one   (C) infinitely many   **B**

Tell whether each value of the variable is a solution of the equation.

3. $5x = -35$; $x = -7$ 4. $8 - y = 2$; $y = 6$ 5. $-7 + b = 4$; $b = 3$
   yes   **yes**   **no**

Use mental math to solve each equation.

6. $10m = -90$ 7. $6 + w = 3$ 8. $\frac{40}{z} = 8$ 9. $-5p = 20$
   −9   **−3**   **5**   **−4**

Homework Exercises

For more exercises, see Extra Skills and Word Problems.

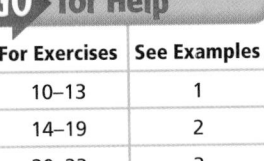

For Exercises	See Examples
10–13	1
14–19	2
20–23	3

(A) **Find the solution of each equation from the given numbers.**

10. $p + 17 = 56$; 29, 39, or 49 **39**   11. $\frac{y}{9} = 32$; 261, 279, or 288 **288**

12. $6d = -36.6$; −6.1, 0, or 6.1 **−6.1**   13. $n - 27 = 38$; 11, 51, or 65 **65**

Use mental math to solve each equation.

14. $n + 4 = 7.9$ **3.9**   15. $4d = -32$ **−8**   16. $\frac{p}{5} = 3.1$ **15.5**

17. $24 = -6w$ **−4**   18. $\frac{c}{-3} = 8$ **−24**   19. $z - 8.4 = 0$ **8.4**

Estimate the solution of each equation to the nearest whole number.

20. $3.1g = 20.9$ 21. $h - 4.9 = 13.8$ 22. $7.8 + n = 38.2$
    about 7   **about 19**   **about 30**

23. A bowling ball has a mass of 5.54 kg. A bowling pin has a mass of 1.58 kg. About how many pins are equal in mass to one ball?
    about 3 bowling pins

(B) **GPS** 24. **Guided Problem Solving** Your class has collected 84.5 lb of canned food. The school record is 103.25 lb. Write an equation and use it to estimate the amount of canned food the class still needs to collect to match the record. **84 + n = 103; about 20 lb**
   - Estimate 84.5 and 103.25 by rounding.
   - Choose a variable for the amount of food the class still needs.
   - Write an equation using your variable and your estimates.

25. An elevator has a maximum lift of 2,000 lb. You are moving 55-lb
GPS boxes of books. Write an equation and estimate how many boxes you can safely place on the elevator. **55b = 2,000; 36 boxes**

26. Check students' work.   26. Describe a situation that can be represented by $4.5 + t = 30$.

176   Chapter 4   Equations and Inequalities

Solve using mental math or estimation. If you estimate, round to the nearest whole number before you add or subtract.

27. $p - 7.35 = 46.71$
54

28. $a - 20 = 17$
37

29. $28.71 + t = 49.43$
20

30. $n - 11 = 33$
44

31. $k - 99.9 = 463.04$
563

32. $17 + p = -3$
-20

33. Baseball The total distance around a baseball diamond is 360 ft. Write an equation to represent the distance from first base to second base. $4d = 360$

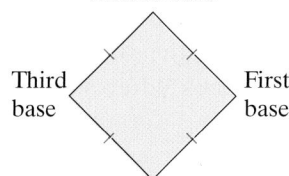
Second base

Third base   First base

Home plate

34. No; an expression has no equal sign in order to compare values.

34. Writing in Math Equations can be true or false. Can an expression like $2a + 7$ be true or false? Explain. **See left.**

Data Analysis Use the table below for Exercises 35 and 36.

35. The average precipitation for Houston is 1.5 times the average for Detroit. Find the average precipitation for Detroit. **31.89 in.**

36. The average precipitation for Raleigh is 4.3 times the average for San Diego. Find the average precipitation for San Diego. **10.01 in.**

Average Annual Precipitation

City	Precipitation (in.)
Detroit, Mich.	▬
Houston, Tex.	47.84
Raleigh, N.C.	43.05
San Diego, Calif.	▬

SOURCE: National Climatic Data Center.
Go to **PHSchool.com** for a data update.
Web Code: arg-9041

37. $4c = 67.80$; about $17; no; the total should be about 4($12.95), or $51.80.

C 37. Challenge You want to buy 4 candles that cost $12.95 each. A clerk tells you that the total, including sales tax, is $67.80. Is the clerk's total reasonable? Explain. **See left.**

TEKS ★ TAKS Tune-Up and Mixed Review

TAKS Objective 2
TEKS (7.5)(B)

38. Jane had $22.25 before baby-sitting on Saturday. After baby-sitting, she had $48.75. Which equation can be used to find b, the amount of money Jane earned from baby-sitting? **C**
Ⓐ $22.25 - b = $48.75
Ⓒ $48.75 - b = $22.25
Ⓑ $22.25 + $48.75 = b
Ⓓ $48.75 + b = $22.25

TAKS Objective 5
TEKS (7.12)(B)

39. The table shows the points the Cougars scored during their last 4 games. Which measure of data is represented by 64.5? **H**
Ⓕ mean   Ⓗ median
Ⓖ mode   Ⓙ range

Cougars Points Scored

Game	Points
1	72
2	60
3	47
4	69

GO for Help   **Lesson 1-7**

Use a number line to find each sum.

40. $-5 + 9$ 4   **41.** $-9 + 10$ 1   **42.** $-2 + -8$ -10

Alternative Assessment

Have each student write an equation and a set of possible solutions similar to Exercises 10–13. Ask students to make sure that the solution to each equation is provided in a list of possible solutions. Students then exchange papers with a partner who tries to identify the correct solution.

TEKS ★ TAKS Resources

• TAKS Strategies, p. 219
• TAKS Tune-Up, pp. 223–225

TAKS Tune-Up Kit
• TAKS Daily Review Transparencies
• TAKS Review and Preparation Workbook
• TAKS Strategies with Transparencies
• Texas Progress Monitoring Assessments

---

4. Assess & Reteach

PowerPoint
Lesson Quiz

Solve each equation. Use mental math or estimation.

1. $q - 15 = 25$ $q = 40$

2. $6r = 42$ $r = 7$

3. $17.25 + s = 21.4$ $s \approx 4$

4. $\frac{80}{t} = 8$ $t = 10$

5. $m - 39.8 = -101.03$ $m \approx -61$

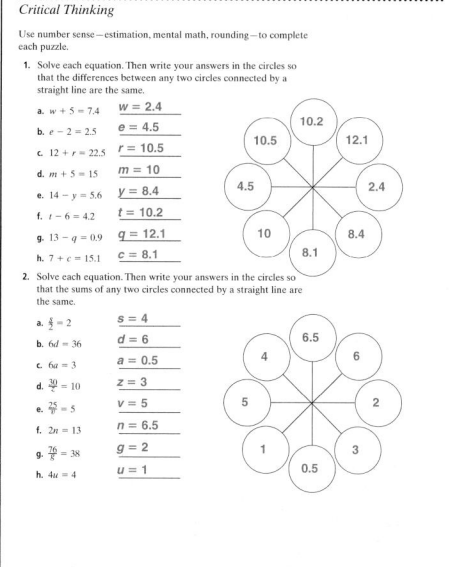

177

Keeping the Balance

Students use pictures of a scale and weights to solve equations. First they decide which scales are balanced and explain their reasoning. Then they explore rules for balancing equations.

Guided Instruction

Before beginning the Activity Lab, show a balanced scale with different weights on each side. Ask:

- *What can be removed from each pan of the first scale so that the pans remain balanced?* the ball
- *How many cubes equal 1 rectangular prism for the second scale?* 3

Differentiated Instruction

Tactile Learners
Some students may prefer using actual balances and weights to explore balancing equations.

TEKS ★ TAKS Resources

- balance scale
- weights

Dana Center TEKS Toolkit Clarifying Activities (7.14)(A)
Visit: PHSchool.com
Web Code: arq-9045

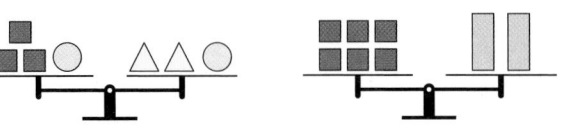

4-2b Activity Lab — Algebra Thinking x = ?

Keeping the Balance

You can use a balance-scale model to solve equations. The scales below are balanced. Use them for the activity. Objects that look identical have the same weight. Objects that look different have different weights.

TEKS ★ TAKS

(7.14)(A) To communicate mathematical ideas using graphical models TAKS Obj. 6

Prepares for **TEKS** (7.5)(A) To use pictorial models to solve equations

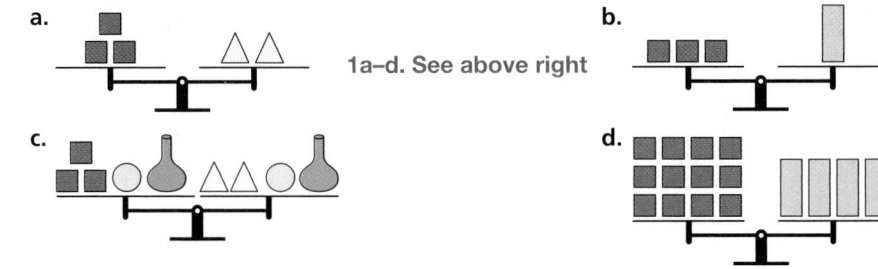

1a. Balanced; a circle was taken away from both sides.

b. Balanced; half of each side remains.

c. Balanced; a bottle was added to both sides.

d. Balanced; each side was doubled.

ACTIVITY

1. Decide whether each scale is balanced. Explain your reasoning.

   a.

   1a–d. See above right

   b.

   c.

   d.

Exercises

Tell whether each statement is true or false. Explain.
1–4. See right

1. A balanced scale will stay balanced if I add the same amount to each side.

2. A balanced scale will stay balanced if I remove the same amount from each side.

3. A balanced scale will stay balanced if I multiply each side by the same amount.

4. A balanced scale will stay balanced if I divide each side by the same amount.

Exercises 1–4. True. If you do the same thing to both sides of a balanced scale, it will stay balanced.

5. Not balanced; check students' work.

6. Balanced; check students' work.

7. Balanced; check students' work.

Decide whether each scale is balanced. Explain your reasoning.
5–7. See above right.

5.

6.

7.

178 Activity Lab Keeping the Balance

Modeling Equations

You can model and solve equations using algebra tiles.

TEKS ★ **TAKS**

(7.5)(A) To use concrete models to solve equations and use symbols to record the actions **TAKS** Obj. 2

(7.13)(D) To select tools such as manipulatives to solve problems

EXAMPLE Solving Addition Equations

1 Use algebra tiles to solve $x + 4 = 12$.

$x + 4 = 12$ ← Model the equation. Use yellow tiles for positive integers.

$x + 4 - 4 = 12 - 4$ ← Remove 4 tiles from each side.

$x = 8$ ← Simplify.

EXAMPLE Solving Multiplication Equations

2 Use algebra tiles to solve $3x = -21$.

$3x = -21$ ← Model the equation. Use red tiles for negative integers.

$\dfrac{3x}{3} = \dfrac{-21}{3}$ ← Divide each side into three equal groups.

$x = -7$ ← Simplify.

Exercises

Use algebra tiles to solve each equation.

1. $x + 12 = 18$ 6
2. $x + 3 = 16$ 13
3. $x + 8 = 17$ 9
4. $x + (-7) = 13$ 20
5. $x + (-2) = -7$ −5
6. $x + (-7) = -11$ −4
7. $3x = 18$ 6
8. $5x = -25$ −5
9. $7x = 21$ 3
10. $2x = -18$ −9
11. $4x = 28$ 7
12. $2x = 24$ 12

Modeling Equations

Students use algebra tiles to learn what an equation is and how to find its solution.

Guided Instruction

Example 2
Model the solution to the multiplication equation. Have students again follow along at their desks. Guide them to see that the equation $3x = -21$ involves multiplication. By dividing tiles into groups of equal size, they are performing the inverse operation, division.

Exercises
Have students work independently or in pairs on the Exercises. Suggest they use algebra tiles to help them with equations for which they are having difficulty.

Differentiated Instruction

Visual Learners
In Example 1, discuss with students that finding the solution to an equation means finding a value for the variable that makes the equation true. Then model the solution to the addition equation on the board or on an overhead projector. Have students follow along at their desks. Elicit from students that the equation $x + 4 = 12$ involves addition. By removing tiles they are performing the inverse operation, subtraction.

TEKS ★ **TAKS** **Resources**

- Activity Lab 4-3: Figure It Out
- algebra tiles
- Classroom Aid 37
- Student Manipulatives Kit

Dana Center TEKS Toolkit Clarifying Activities (7.5)(A), (7.13)(D)
Visit: PHSchool.com
Web Code: arq-9045

179

1. Plan

TEKS

(7.5)(A) To use models and symbols to solve equations **TAKS Obj. 2**
Also supports
(7.5)(B) **TAKS Obj. 2**

Dana Center TEKS Toolkit Clarifying Activities (7.5)(A), (7.5)(B)
Visit: PHSchool.com
Web Code: arq-9045

TEKS Math Background

Equations that have exactly the same solution or solutions are called *equivalent equations*. Solving a given equation is essentially a process of writing a series of equivalent equations until the variable is isolated by itself on one side of the equal sign. The equivalent equations that will achieve this goal are determined by a thoughtful application of the properties of equality.

More Math Background: p. 166C

Lesson Planning and Resources

See p. 166E for a list of the resources that support this lesson.

Bell Ringer Practice

✔ **Check Skills You'll Need**
Use student page, transparency, or PowerPoint.

TAKS Daily Review 28
Use transparency.

4-3

Solving Equations by Adding or Subtracting

✔ **Check Skills You'll Need**

1. **Vocabulary Review**
   A(n) __?__ is a mathematical sentence with an equal sign.
   equation

   Estimate the solution of each equation.

   2. $y + 3.14 = 11.89$
      about 9
   3. $t - 4.83 = 13.12$
      about 18
   4. $14.2 + q = 38.849$
      about 25

   GO for Help
   Lesson 4-2

TEKS ⭐ **TAKS**

• (7.5)(A) To use models and symbols to solve equations **TAKS Obj. 2**
• (7.5)(B) To formulate a problem situation when given an equation and formulate an equation when given a problem situation **TAKS Obj. 2**

🔊 **New Vocabulary** Addition Property of Equality, Subtraction Property of Equality, inverse operations

Why Learn This?

If you can solve equations, you can use known information to find unknown information.

You can think of an equation as a balance scale. When you do something to one side of an equation, you must do the same thing to the other side of the equation to keep it balanced.

You can find the value of the unknown weight above by removing four weights from each side of the scale. The result is the scale on the right.

This illustrates the Subtraction Property of Equality. You can use this property and the Addition Property of Equality to solve equations.

Video Tutor Help
Visit: PHSchool.com
Web Code: are-0775

KEY CONCEPTS **Properties of Equality**

Addition Property of Equality
If you add the same value to each side of an equation, the two sides remain equal.

Arithmetic	**Algebra**
$\frac{20}{2} = 10$, so $\frac{20}{2} + 3 = 10 + 3$.	If $a = b$, then $a + c = b + c$.

Subtraction Property of Equality
If you subtract the same value from each side of an equation, the two sides remain equal.

Arithmetic	**Algebra**
$\frac{12}{2} = 6$, so $\frac{12}{2} - 4 = 6 - 4$.	If $a = b$, then $a - c = b - c$.

Differentiated Instruction **Solutions for All Learners**

Special Needs L1
Make a double number line sketch to help students make the connection between the variables in Example 2, and the difference between the numbers. Both number lines would go from 0 – 290, but the second would stop at 244, with the difference labeled *x*.

learning style: visual

Below Level L2
Have students use a "fill-in box" to represent the solution until they become accustomed to variables.

learning style: visual

To solve an equation, you want to get the variable alone on one side of the equation. You can use **inverse operations,** operations that undo each other, to get the variable alone.

Addition and subtraction are inverse operations. You can use addition to undo subtraction.

EXAMPLE Solving Equations by Adding

1 Solve $x - 34 = -46$.

$$x - 34 = -46$$
$$x - 34 + 34 = -46 + 34 \quad \leftarrow \text{Addition Property of Equality: Add 34 to each side.}$$
$$x + 0 = -12 \quad \leftarrow \text{The numbers −34 and 34 are additive inverses.}$$
$$x = -12 \quad \leftarrow \text{Additive Identity Property}$$

Check $\quad x - 34 = -46 \quad \leftarrow$ Check the solution in the original equation.
$$-12 - 34 = -46 \quad \leftarrow \text{Substitute −12 for } x.$$
$$-46 = -46 \ \checkmark \quad \leftarrow \text{Subtract.}$$

✓ Quick Check

1. Solve the equation $x - 104 = 64$. **168**

Just as addition undoes subtraction, subtraction undoes addition.

EXAMPLE Solving Equations by Subtracting

2 Your friend's mountain bike cost $245 more than his skateboard. His mountain bike cost $290. How much did your friend's skateboard cost?

Words | cost of bike | is | $245 | more than | cost of skateboard

Let s = the cost of the skateboard.

Equation | 290 | = | 245 | + | s

$$290 = 245 + s$$
$$290 - 245 = 245 - 245 + s \quad \leftarrow \text{Subtract 245 from each side.}$$
$$45 = s \quad \leftarrow \text{Simplify.}$$

The skateboard cost $45.

✓ Quick Check

2. A hardcover book costs $19 more than its paperback edition. The hardcover book costs $26.95. How much does the paperback cost? **$7.95**

4-3 Solving Equations by Adding or Subtracting **181**

2. Teach

Activity Lab

Use before the lesson.
Student Edition Activity Lab Hands On 4-3a, Modeling Equations, p. 179

 Teaching Resources
Activity Lab 4-3: Figure It Out

Guided Instruction

Example 1
Some students are better able to visualize the process of adding the same number to each side when the addition is performed vertically.

$$\begin{array}{r} x - 34 = \quad -46 \\ + 34 = + \quad 34 \\ \hline x \quad = \quad -12 \end{array}$$

Error Prevention!

Stress the importance of checking a proposed solution by substituting it for the variable *in the original equation.*

PowerPoint
Additional Examples

1 Solve $t - 58 = 71$. Check your solution. $t = 129$

2 Solve $d + 126 = 98$. Check your solution. $d = -28$

3 Describe a problem situation that matches the equation $p - 35 = 15$. Sample: You spent $35 on a sweater and had $15 left. How much money did you have to start?

Advanced Learners L4
Solve each equation.

$x + x = 64 \quad x = 32$
$x - x = 64 \quad \text{no solution}$

Pre-AP™

English Language Learners ELL
Make the connection explicit between using inverse operations, "undoing" a subtraction or addition operation, and isolating the variable. These are often used synonymously in equations involving addition and subtraction. For example, $+3 - 3 = 0$. $x + 0$ is the same as just x by itself. **learning style: verbal**

181

Closure

- *What are inverse operations?*
  Inverse operations undo each other.
- *How can you use inverse operations to solve equations?*
  Use inverse operations to get the variable alone on one side of an equation. Add the same value to each side of an equation (to undo subtraction) or subtract the same value from each side of an equation (to undo addition).

EXAMPLE **Writing Problem Situations**

3 Describe a problem situation that matches the equation $s - 286 = 74$.

Step 1 Translate the symbols into words. The equation represents 286 subtracted from some original amount. The result of the subtraction is 74.

Step 2 Choose a context to describe the numbers and symbols.

original amount s	minus	286	is	74
↓		↓		↓
s songs	minus	286 songs	is	74 songs

Rita deleted 286 songs from her audio player. She had 74 songs left. How many songs did Rita have on her audio player before she deleted 286 songs?

You can find a solution to your equation by solving for s.

$$s - 286 = 74$$
$$s - 286 + 286 = 74 + 286 \quad \leftarrow \text{Add 286 to each side.}$$
$$s = 360 \quad \leftarrow \text{Simplify.}$$

Rita had 360 songs on her audio player.

✓ Quick Check

3. a. Describe a problem situation that matches the equation $n + 41 = 157$.   **Check students' work.**

   b. Solve the equation $n + 41 = 157$.   **116**

✓ Check Your Understanding

1. Vocabulary __?__ operations are operations that undo each other.
   Inverse

2. Jean. Dylan's error was adding 4 to both sides instead of subtracting.

2. Error Analysis Dylan and Jean tried to solve the equation $x + 4 = -9$. Who solved the equation correctly? Explain.   **See left.**

Dylan	Jean
$x + 4 = -9$	$x + 4 = -9$
$x + 4 + 4 = -9 + 4$	$x + 4 - 4 = -9 - 4$
$x = -5$	$x = -13$

Vocabulary Tip

When you get the variable alone on one side of the equation, you are "isolating the variable."

Fill in the missing numbers to solve each equation.

3. $b + 12 = 39$
   $b + 12 - \blacksquare = 39 - \blacksquare$
        12   12

4. $y - 8 = 35$
   $y - 8 + \blacksquare = 35 + \blacksquare$
        8   8

Homework Exercises

For more exercises, see Extra Skills and Word Problems.

GO for Help

For Exercises	See Examples
5–10	1
11–17	2
18–21	3

Ⓐ Solve each equation. Check your answer. You may find a model helpful.

5. $x - 6 = -55$
−49

6. $n - 255 = -455$
−200

7. $-83.4 + m = 122$
205.4

8. $t - 32.8 = -27$
5.8

9. $h - 37 = -42$
−5

10. $q - 16 = 40$
56

11. $k + 17 = 29$
12

12. $d + 261.9 = -48$
−309.9

13. $x + 34 = 212$
178

14. $253 + c = 725$
472

15. $89 + y = 100$
11

16. $62.5 + t = -77$
−139.5

17. Invisible braces cost $500 more than metal braces. Metal braces cost $4,800. How much do invisible braces cost? **$5,300**

Describe a problem situation that matches each equation. Then solve.
18–21. Answers may vary. Check student's work.

18. $t - 3.5 = 8$ **11.5**

19. $34 = g + 25$ **9**

20. $q + 12 = 100$ **88**

21. $63.8 = p - 17$ **80.8**

Ⓑ GPS **22. Guided Problem Solving** A runner's heart rate is 133 beats per minute. This is 62 beats per minute more than his resting heart rate. Write and solve an equation to find the runner's resting heart rate.
- Choose a variable to represent the resting heart rate.
- Write an equation that represents the information provided.
- Check your answer. Does it fit the details of the problem?
133 = r + 62; 71 beats/min

23. A basketball player scores 15 points in one game and p points in a second game. Her two-game total is 33 points. Write and solve an equation to find the number of points scored in the second game.
15 + p = 33; 18 points

24. Biology A student collects 12 ladybugs for a science project. This **GPS** is 9 fewer than the number of ladybugs the student collected yesterday. Write and solve an equation to find the number of ladybugs the student collected yesterday. **12 = b − 9; 21 ladybugs**

Match each equation with the graph of its solution.

25. $t + 14 = 18$ **B**   A. [number line: point at 1, marks −2, 0, 2]

26. $x - 5 = -3$ **D**   B. [number line: point at 4, marks 0, 2, 4]

27. $w + 4 = 2$ **A**   C. [number line: point at −3, marks −4, −2, 0, 2]

28. $y - 7 = -10$ **C**   D. [number line: point at 2, marks −2, 0, 2]

29. Physics At 20°C, the speed of sound in air is 343 m/s. This is 1,166 m/s slower than the speed of sound in water. Write and solve an equation to find the speed of sound in water.
343 = a − 1,166; 1,509 m/s

30. Subtract 2 from each side; Subtraction Property of Equality.

30. Reasoning How can you transform the equation $5 + x = 4$ into $3 + x = 2$? Support your answer with a property of equality.

3. Practice

Assignment Guide

Check Your Understanding
Go over Exercises 1–4 in class before assigning the Homework Exercises.

Homework Exercises
A Practice by Example   5–21
B Apply Your Skills   22–38
C Challenge   39
TEKS ★ TAKS Tune-Up and Mixed Review   40–44

Homework Quick Check
To check students' understanding of key skills and concepts, go over Exercises 7, 18, 24, 30, and 38.

Differentiated Instruction Resources

4. Assess & Reteach

PowerPoint

Lesson Quiz

Solve each equation. Check your answer.

1. $7 + a = 46$ $a = 39$

2. $b - 10 = -4$ $b = 6$

3. $9 + c = -10$ $c = -19$

4. $104 - d = 75$ $d = 29$

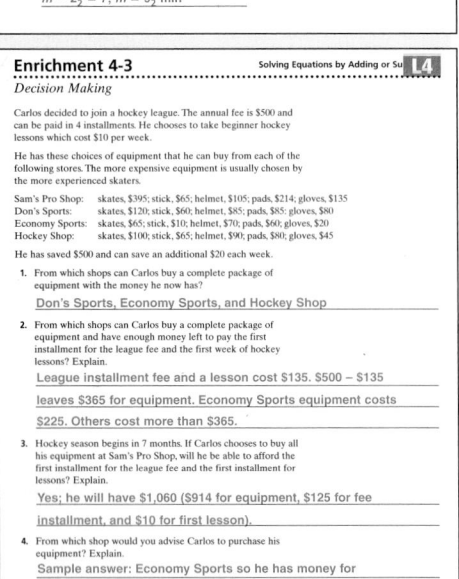

Reteaching 4-3 Solving Equations by Adding or S... **L2**

Follow these steps to solve equations.

Solve: $n + (-2) = 11$ Solve: $n - 6 = -36$

① Use the inverse operation on both sides of the equation. $n + (-2) - (-2) = 11 - (-2)$ $n - 6 + 6 = -36 + 6$

② Simplify. $n = 13$ $n = -30$

③ Check. $n + (-2) = 11$ $n - 6 = -36$
$13 + (-2) \stackrel{?}{=} 11$ $-30 - 6 \stackrel{?}{=} -36$
$11 = 11 ✔$ $-36 = -36 ✔$

Solve each equation. Check each answer.

1. $n + 6 = 8$ **2.** $n - 3 = 20$
$n + 6 - 6 = 8 - \underline{6}$ $n - 3 + \underline{3} = 20 + 3$
$n = \underline{2}$ $n = \underline{23}$

3. $n - (-3) = -1$ **4.** $-2 = n + 5$
$n - (-3) + \underline{(-3)} = -1 + \underline{(-3)}$ $-2 - \underline{5} = n + 5 - \underline{5}$
$n = \underline{-4}$ $\underline{-7} = n$

5. $n - (-4) = -2$ **6.** $n - 16 = -23$
$n - (-4) + \underline{(-4)} = -2 + \underline{(-4)}$ $n - 16 + \underline{16} = -23 + \underline{16}$
$n = \underline{-6}$ $n = \underline{-7}$

Use a calculator, pencil and paper, or mental math. Solve each equation.

7. $n + 1 = 17$ **8.** $n - (-6) = 7$ **9.** $n - 8 = -12$
$\underline{16}$ $\underline{1}$ $\underline{-4}$

10. $61 = n + 29$ **11.** $n + 84 = 131$ **12.** $-13 = n + 9$
$\underline{32}$ $\underline{47}$ $\underline{-22}$

13. In track practice, Jesse ran a mile in 7 minutes. His mile time was $2\frac{1}{2}$ minutes faster than Michael's time. Write and solve an equation to calculate Michael's mile time.
$m - 2\frac{1}{2} = 7; m = 9\frac{1}{2}$ min

Enrichment 4-3 Solving Equations by Adding or Su **L4**
Decision Making

Carlos decided to join a hockey league. The annual fee is $500 and can be paid in 4 installments. He chooses to take beginner hockey lessons which cost $10 per week.

He has these choices of equipment that he can buy from each of the following stores. The more expensive equipment is usually chosen by the more experienced skaters.

Sam's Pro Shop: skates, $395; stick, $65; helmet, $105; pads, $214; gloves, $135
Don's Sports: skates, $120; stick, $60; helmet, $85; pads, $85; gloves, $80
Economy Sports: skates, $65; stick, $10; helmet, $70; pads, $60; gloves, $20
Hockey Shop: skates, $100; stick, $65; helmet, $90; pads, $80; gloves, $45

He has saved $500 and can save an additional $20 each week.

1. From which shops can Carlos buy a complete package of equipment with the money he now has?
Don's Sports, Economy Sports, and Hockey Shop

2. From which shops can Carlos buy a complete package of equipment and have enough money left to pay the first installment for the league fee and the first week of hockey lessons? Explain.
League installment fee and a lesson cost $135. $500 − $135
leaves $365 for equipment. Economy Sports equipment costs
$225. Others cost more than $365.

3. Hockey season begins in 7 months. If Carlos chooses to buy all his equipment from Sam's Pro Shop, will he be able to afford the first installment for the league fee and the first installment for lessons? Explain.
Yes; he will have $1,060 ($914 for equipment, $125 for fee
installment, and $10 for first lesson).

4. From which shop would you advise Carlos to purchase his equipment? Explain.
Sample answer: Economy Sports so he has money for
the league fee and can begin playing immediately.
He can buy better equipment when he is sure he enjoys the sport.

184

GO Online

Homework Help
Visit: PHSchool.com
Web Code: are-0403

37. $p - 8.45 = 21.50$; $29.95

38. She has saved $135. The camp costs $250. She needs d dollars.

39. Let r = the number of runs needed; $3 + 4 + 2 + 6 + 8 + r = 30$; 7 runs.

Use a calculator, paper and pencil, or mental math. Solve each equation.

31. $n - 35 = 84$ **119**   **32.** $\frac{5}{6} = m + \frac{2}{9}$ $\frac{11}{18}$ **33.** $x + 2.5 = 1.6$ -0.9

34. $-\frac{1}{7} = x + 1\frac{2}{3}$ $-1\frac{17}{21}$ **35.** $\frac{3}{16} = c - \frac{7}{8}$ $1\frac{1}{16}$ **36.** $3\frac{1}{4} = 2\frac{1}{3} + r$ $\frac{11}{12}$

37. **Money** Use the advertisement at the right. Write and solve an equation to find the original price of the sweater.

SALE $21.50
SAVE $8.45

38. **Writing in Math** A student is saving money for field hockey camp. Her savings are modeled by the equation $135 + d = 250$. Explain what each part of the equation represents.

C **39.** **Challenge** During five baseball games, your team scores 3, 4, 2, 6, and 8 runs. How many more runs must your team score to have a total of 30 runs? Write and solve an equation.

TEKS ★ TAKS Tune-Up and Mixed Review

TAKS Objective 2
TEKS (7.5)(A)

40. The model represents the equation $x - 4 = 2$. What is the value of x? **D**

Key
$\oplus$ = +1
$\ominus$ = -1

Ⓐ 2   Ⓒ 3
Ⓑ 4   Ⓓ 6

TAKS Objective 2
TEKS (7.5)(B)

41. Which problem situation matches the equation $7.50 + x = 100$?
Ⓕ Roberto bought a box of 100 baseball cards for $7.50. What is x, the price for each baseball card?   **H**
Ⓖ Will works 7.5 hours a day. He will get a pay raise when he works 100 hours. What is x, the number of days he works to get a raise?
Ⓗ Mr. Midas bought a case of fruit for $7.50. He paid the cashier with a $100 bill. What is x, the amount of change he received?
Ⓙ Jennifer walks for 7.5 minutes. What is x, the number of miles she can walk in 100 minutes?

TAKS Objective 6
TEKS (7.13)(A)

42. The U.S. Mint made 1,303,384,000 nickels at the Denver and Philadelphia mints one year. The algebraic expression for the value in dollars of n nickels is $0.05n$. What is the value of this expression, in dollars, for the number of nickels made that year? **C**
Ⓐ 651,792,000 Ⓑ 65,179,200 Ⓒ 65,169,200 Ⓓ 6,516,920

GO for Help **Lesson 2-1** **Simplify each expression.**

43. $3 - 4 + 5 \cdot 6 - (-4)$ **33**   **44.** $4 \cdot 5 - 6 + (5 - 2)^2$ **23**

184 Chapter 4 Equations and Inequalities

TEKS ★ TAKS Resources

- TAKS Strategies, p. 219
- TAKS Tune-Up, pp. 223–225

TAKS Tune-Up Kit
- TAKS Daily Review Transparencies
- TAKS Review and Preparation Workbook
- TAKS Strategies with Transparencies
- Texas Progress Monitoring Assessments

Alternative Assessment

Provide partners with algebra tiles. Have them write several simple addition and subtraction equations similar to those in Exercises 25–28. Working together, partners should use the tiles to solve each equation and record each step of their solution process.

High-Use Academic Words

High-use academic words are words that you will see often in textbooks and on tests. These words are not math vocabulary terms, but knowing them will help you succeed in mathematics.

TEKS ★ TAKS

(7.14)(A) To communicate mathematical ideas using language *TAKS* Obj. 6

Direction Words

Some words tell what to do in a problem. I need to understand what these words are asking so that I give the correct answer.

Word	Meaning
Choose	To make a selection after analyzing given information
Describe	To tell or write about something in detail
Determine	To make a decision based on investigation

Exercises

1. Choose the colors that represent the United States of America. **C**
   - Ⓐ red, blue, green
   - Ⓒ white, blue, red
   - Ⓑ red, orange, yellow
   - Ⓓ green, purple, orange

2. Describe the design of the American flag. Determine whether there are more red stripes or white stripes on the American flag.

   2. 13 red and white stripes, 50 white stars on blue background. There are more red stripes.

3. Determine whether 2 is a solution of $8 + x = 12$. **no**

4. Describe a situation that $x - 2 = 5$ can represent. **Check students' work.**

5. Choose the model that represents "3 more than a number p." **C**

   Ⓐ   Ⓑ | p | p | p | Ⓒ

6. **Word Knowledge** Think about the word *substitute*. **6a–c. Check students' work.**
   a. Choose the letter for how well you know the word.
      - **A.** I know its meaning.
      - **B.** I've seen it, but I don't know its meaning.
      - **C.** I don't know it.
   b. **Research** Look up and write the definition of *substitute*.
   c. Use the word in a sentence involving mathematics.

Vocabulary Builder

High-Use Academic Words

Students learn a strategy for learning words that, while not math vocabulary terms, are important for success in mathematics and on tests.

Guided Instruction

Have students look through their texts for use of the terms: *choose, describe, and determine.* Ask the following questions:
- *Where do you find the term describe?* Sample: page 197, Exercise 31
- *What is another way to say "Find the solution for the equation from the given numbers"?* Sample: Determine the values for the variables that make the equation true.
- *What direction could you write for Exercise 40 on page 184 using the term,* choose? Sample: Choose the correct value for *x.*

Teaching Tip
Restate directions given in the text using *choose, describe,* and *determine* as appropriate to familiarize students with these terms.

Differentiated Instruction

English Language Learners ELL
Encourage students to write high-use academic words in their native language as needed.

TEKS ★ TAKS Resources

- Vocabulary and Study Skills Worksheets

Dana Center TEKS Toolkit Clarifying Activities (7.14)(A)
Visit: PHSchool.com
Web Code: arq-9045

TEKS ★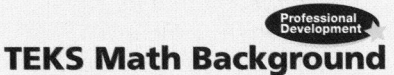

(7.5)(A) To use pictorial models and symbols to solve equations **TAKS** Obj. 2

(7.5)(B) To formulate an equation when given a problem situation **TAKS** Obj. 2

Dana Center TEKS Toolkit Clarifying Activities (7.5)(A), (7.5)(B)
Visit: PHSchool.com
Web Code: arq-9045

TEKS Math Background

The properties of equality are sometimes summarized informally as follows: *Whatever you do to one side of an equation, you must do to the other.* While this statement is essentially correct, care must be taken to note that there is an important restriction. That is, the Division Property of Equality prohibits dividing both sides of an equation by zero. This restriction is necessary because, in the system of real numbers, division by zero is undefined.

More Math Background: p. 166C

Lesson Planning and Resources

See p. 166E for a list of the resources that support this lesson.

PowerPoint
Bell Ringer Practice

✓ **Check Skills You'll Need**
Use student page, transparency, or PowerPoint.

TAKS **Daily Review 29**
Use transparency.

186

✓ Check Skills You'll Need

1. Vocabulary Review
When the GCF of a numerator and denominator is one, the fraction is in ___?___ . simplest form

Write each expression in simplest form.

2. $\frac{6}{24}$ $\frac{1}{4}$ **3.** $\frac{8(4)}{8}$ 4

4. $\frac{7(3)}{21}$ 1   **5.** $\frac{3a}{3}$ a

 for Help
Lesson 2-5

TEKS ★

- **(7.5)(A)** To use pictorial models and symbols to solve equations **TAKS** Obj. 2
- **(7.5)(B)** To formulate an equation when given a problem situation **TAKS** Obj. 2

🔊 **New Vocabulary** Division Property of Equality, Multiplication Property of Equality

Why Learn This?

If you know how to solve equations by multiplying or dividing, you can solve everyday problems such as sharing the cost of a meal with friends.

You and three friends go out for pizza. An extra-large pizza and four bottles of water cost $22.68 (including tax and a $2 coupon). How much does each person owe if you split the bill equally?

You can represent the problem with the model below. Let *p* represent the amount of money each person owes.

```
CHECK # 325   TABLE # 12
====================
ITEMS ORDERED      AMOUNT
X-LG PIZZA         18.60
$2 COUPON          -2.00
BOT WTR             1.25
BOT WTR             1.25
BOT WTR             1.25
BOT WTR             1.25
$$$$$$$$$$$$$$$$$$$$$$$$$
TAX                 1.08
                  -----
TOTAL              22.68
```

total bill	→	22.68
p | p | p | p	→	4p

The model shows that you can use the equation $4p = 22.68$. To solve this equation, you can use the Division Property of Equality.

KEY CONCEPTS **Division Property of Equality**

If you divide each side of an equation by the same nonzero number, the two sides remain equal.

Arithmetic	**Algebra**
Since $3(2) = 6$, $\frac{3(2)}{2} = \frac{6}{2}$.	If $a = b$ and $c \neq 0$, then $\frac{a}{c} = \frac{b}{c}$.

Division is the inverse operation of multiplication. When a variable is multiplied by a number, you can use division to undo the multiplication.

Division Undoes Multiplication

$$(4 \cdot 9) \div 4 = 9 \qquad\qquad 5x \div 5 = x$$

Differentiated Instruction **Solutions for All Learners**

Special Needs **L1**
Have students use number sense to check the calculation for Example 2. Ask: *What would 10 minutes cost if one minute cost 39 cents? $3.90 What would 20 minutes cost? $7.80* Since this is close to $8.58, 22 minutes makes sense.

learning style: verbal

Below Level **L2**
Make a worksheet with several multiplication and division equations in one column and solutions in a second column. Have students match equations and solutions.

learning style: visual

Video Tutor Help
Visit: PHSchool.com
Web Code: are-0775

EXAMPLE Solving Equations by Dividing

1 Solve $4p = 22.68$.

$$4p = 22.68 \quad \leftarrow \text{Notice } p \text{ is being } multiplied \text{ by 4.}$$

$$\frac{4p}{4} = \frac{22.68}{4} \quad \leftarrow \text{Divide each side by 4 to get } p \text{ alone.}$$

$$p = 5.67 \quad \leftarrow \text{Simplify.}$$

Check $\quad 4p = 22.68 \quad \leftarrow$ Check your solution in the original equation.

$$4(5.67) \stackrel{?}{=} 22.68 \quad \leftarrow \text{Replace } p \text{ with 5.67.}$$

$$22.68 = 22.68 \checkmark \quad \leftarrow \text{The solution checks.}$$

✓ Quick Check

1. Solve each equation. Check your answer.
   a. $3x = -21.6$ –7.2   **b.** $-12y = -108$ 9   **c.** $104x = 312$ 3

You can use the Division Property of Equality and inverse operations to solve real-world applications.

EXAMPLE Application: Telephone Charges

2 **TAKS** **Griddable Item** Your cellular telephone bill shows that you were charged an extra \$8.58 this month for going over your allotted minutes. The company charges \$.39 for each extra minute. How many extra minutes did you use?

Words	\$0.39 times number of minutes equals extra charge

Let n = the number of extra minutes.

Equation	0.39	·	n	=	8.58

$$0.39n = 8.58$$

$$\frac{0.39n}{0.39} = \frac{8.58}{0.39} \quad \leftarrow \text{Divide each side by 0.39.}$$

$$n = 22 \quad \leftarrow \text{Simplify.}$$

You used 22 extra minutes.

Check The charge for each extra minute is \$.39. If you use 22 extra minutes, then the total charge is $22 \cdot \$.39$, or \$8.58. The answer checks.

★ TAKS Tip

The words *each* and *per* are frequently used in problems that involve solving an equation by multiplying or dividing.

✓ Quick Check

2. Suppose you and four friends go to a baseball game. The total cost for five tickets is \$110. Write and solve an equation to find the cost of one ticket. $5c = 110$; \$22

4-4 Solving Equations by Multiplying or Dividing **187**

Advanced Learners L4
Write two equations with solution $c = -46$, one that is solved by multiplying and one by dividing.
Samples: $\frac{c}{-2} = 23$; $2c = -92$

Pre-AP™

English Language Learners ELL
Make sure students understand what the variable represents each time you have a word problem by having them tell you. In the lesson exposition, review that the *p* stands for the amount of money each person owes and not *people*.

learning style: verbal

---

2. Teach

Activity Lab
Use before the lesson.

All in One Teaching Resources
Activity Lab 4-4: Car Mileage

Guided Instruction

Example 1
Have students estimate the answer. An appropriate strategy is using compatible numbers, as follows:
Round 22.68 up to 24.
You know $4 \cdot 6 = 24$
So p is a little less than 6.

Error Prevention!

When solving equations by multiplying or dividing, students might focus on balancing the equation and neglect the sign of the solution. Have them begin their work by determining whether the solution is positive or negative and recording the sign as follows:
$r = +\blacksquare$
$n = -\blacksquare$

PowerPoint
Additional Examples

1 Solve $-3j = 44.7$. Check your answer. $j = -14.9$

2 The Art Club must buy 84 pieces of poster board. There are 6 pieces in a package. How many packages must the Art Club buy?
14 packages

3 Solve $\frac{m}{-3} = 27$, $m = -81$

187

Closure

- *Why do you use the Division Property of Equality to solve an equation with multiplication, such as 12x = 96?* To get the variable alone on one side of the equation, divide each side of the equation by 12 to undo the multiplication of 12*x*.

- *When do you use the Multiplication Property of Equality to solve an equation?* when a variable in an equation is divided by a number (value), as in $\frac{x}{3} = 5$

Another property you can use to solve equations is the Multiplication Property of Equality.

KEY CONCEPTS   **Multiplication Property of Equality**

If you multiply each side of an equation by the same number, the two sides remain equal.

Arithmetic	Algebra
$\frac{12}{2} = 6$, so $\frac{12}{2} \cdot 2 = 6 \cdot 2$.	If $a = b$, then $a \cdot c = b \cdot c$.

Multiplication is the inverse operation of division. When a variable is divided by a number, you can use multiplication to undo the division.

Multiplication Undoes Division

$$\frac{3}{5} \cdot 5 = 3 \qquad\qquad \frac{n}{3} \cdot 3 = n$$

EXAMPLE   Solving Equations by Multiplying

Vocabulary Tip

Read $\frac{t}{-45} = -5$ as "*t* divided by negative 45 equals negative 5."

3 Solve $\frac{t}{-45} = -5$.

$$\frac{t}{-45} = -5 \qquad \leftarrow \text{Notice that } t \text{ is divided by } -45.$$

$$(-45) \cdot \left(\frac{t}{-45}\right) = (-45) \cdot (-5) \qquad \leftarrow \text{Multiply side by } -45.$$

$$t = 225 \qquad \leftarrow \text{Simplify.}$$

✓ Quick Check

● **3.** Solve the equation $\frac{w}{26} = -15$. Check your answer. **−390**

✓ Check Your Understanding

1. Vocabulary The __?__ states that if you multiply each side of an equation by the same number, the two sides remain equal.
  Multiplication Property of Equality

2. Write and solve the equation modeled at the left. **10 = 3x; $\frac{10}{3}$**

3. Division Property of Equality

4. Multiplication Property of Equality

5. Division Property of Equality

Tell which property you would use to solve each equation.
3–5. See left.
3. $8g = -25.4$ **4.** $\frac{w}{26} = -15$ **5.** $5 \cdot d = 60$

Match each equation with the correct first step of the solution.

6. $-6y = 12$ **B**   **A.** Multiply both sides by −6.

7. $12y = -6$ **C**   **B.** Divide both sides by −6.

8. $\frac{y}{-6} = 12$ **A**   **C.** Divide both sides by 12.

Homework Exercises

For more exercises, see Extra Skills and Word Problems.

 for Help

For Exercises	See Examples
9–22	1–2
23–34	3

37. *m* represents the money the quintet needs to earn, 5 represents each member, and 50 represents the money each member receives.

38. $12x = -36$; -36 is the multiple of 12 that is closest to -38; $x \approx -3$.

A Solve each equation. Check your answer. You may find a model helpful.

9. $12t = 144$ 12
10. $13e = -52$ −4
11. $35q = -175$ −5
12. $-7n = -294$ 42
13. $0.2x = 4$ 20
14. $-0.5r = -8$ 16
15. $2,700 = -900w$ −3
16. $-3k = -18$ 6
17. $8n = 112$ 14
18. $0.4k = -40$ −100
19. $58 = \frac{2}{3}w$ 87
20. $-48 = \frac{1}{2}y$ −96

21. **Entertainment** A local park rents paddle boats for $5.50 per hour. You have $22 to spend. For how many hours can you rent a boat?
4 h

22. A video store charges $2.75 per day for overdue video games. You owe a late fee of $13.75. How many days overdue is the game?
5 days

Solve each equation. Check your answer.

23. $\frac{z}{8} = -3$ −24
24. $\frac{n}{3} = 9$ 27
25. $\frac{t}{8} = 12.6$ 100.8
26. $\frac{q}{2} = -1.4$ −2.8
27. $\frac{k}{-6} = -5$ 30
28. $\frac{d}{0.5} = 11$ 5.5
29. $\frac{c}{-6} = -1$ 6
30. $\frac{y}{-12} = -12$ 144
31. $\frac{n}{-5} = 1.1$ −5.5
32. $\frac{f}{7.9} = 5$ 39.5
33. $\frac{d}{6} = -4.25$ −25.5
34. $\frac{m}{-0.5} = -41$ 20.5

B **GPS** 35. **Guided Problem Solving** Julie's car travels 27 miles per gallon of gasoline used. She recently traveled 324 miles. How many gallons of gasoline did her car use? 12 gal
- **Make a Plan** Choose a variable to represent the number of gallons used. Decide what operation should be used, and write an equation.
- **Carry Out the Plan** Let ■ represent the number of gallons. The operation to use is __?__. The equation ■ can be used to solve the problem.

36. George Adrian of Indianapolis, Indiana, picked 15,830 lb of apples in 8 h. How many pounds of apples per hour is that? about 1,979 lb of apples

37. **Writing in Math** Explain why you can use the equation $\frac{m}{5} = 50$ to describe how much money a quintet has to earn for each member to receive $50. What does each part of the equation represent?
See above left.

38. **Estimation** What equation would you use to estimate the solution of $12x = -38$? Explain. Estimate the solution. See above left.

A band with five members is a quintet.

3. Practice

Assignment Guide

Check Your Understanding
Go over Exercises 1–8 in class before assigning the Homework Exercises.

Homework Exercises
A Practice by Example 9–34
B Apply Your Skills 35–51
C Challenge 52
TEKS ★ TAKS Tune-Up and Mixed Review 53–57

Homework Quick Check
To check students' understanding of key skills and concepts, go over Exercises 15, 25, 37, 45, and 47.

Differentiated Instruction Resources

4. Assess & Reteach

PowerPoint
Lesson Quiz

Solve each equation.

1. $15x = 60$ $x = 4$

2. $\dfrac{y}{12} = 8$ $y = 96$

3. $-35 = -7b$ $b = 5$

4. $\dfrac{n}{-5} = -13$ $n = 65$

Reteaching 4-4 Solving Equations by Multiplying or [L2]

Follow these steps to solve equations.

Solve: $\frac{t}{5} = -7$ Solve: $-2x = 8$

① Use the inverse operation on both sides of the equation. $(5)\frac{t}{5} = (5)(-7)$ $\frac{-2x}{-2} = \frac{8}{-2}$

② Simplify. $t = -35$ $x = -4$

③ Check. $\frac{t}{5} = -7$ $-2x = 8$
  $\frac{-35}{5} \stackrel{?}{=} -7$ $-2(-4) \stackrel{?}{=} 8$
  $-7 = -7$ ✔ $8 = 8$ ✔

Solve and check each equation.

1. $-5n = 30$ 2. $\frac{a}{2} = -16$ 3. $-2w = -4$
$\frac{-5n}{-5} = \frac{30}{-5}$ $(2)\frac{a}{2} = (2)(-16)$ $\frac{-2w}{-2} = \frac{-4}{-2}$
$n = -6$ $a = -32$ $w = 2$

4. $8t = 32$ 5. $5 = \frac{g}{6}$ 6. $\frac{n}{3} = -5$
$\frac{8t}{8} = \frac{32}{8}$ $(6)(5) = (6)\frac{g}{6}$ $(-3)\frac{n}{3} = (-3)(-5)$
$t = 4$ $30 = g$ $n = 15$

Use a calculator, pencil and paper, or mental math. Solve each equation.

7. $\frac{q}{4} = -1$ 8. $-5w = 125$ 9. $\frac{m}{8} = 10$
-4 -25 -80

10. $-2 = \frac{t}{-4}$ 11. $\frac{a}{-4} = 12$ 12. $-6b = 42$
8 -48 -7

13. $-3 = \frac{c}{-8}$ 14. $5 = \frac{q}{7}$ 15. $2t = 38$
24 35 19

16. $-9 = 9q$ 17. $n \div 6 = -3$ 18. $-8k = -40$
-1 -18 5

Enrichment 4-4 Solving Equations by Multiplying or [L4]
Critical Thinking

The equation $d = r \times t$ relates rate (r), time (t) and distance (d).

1. If you are traveling at 55 miles per hour, what formula would you use to find the distance you will travel over various time intervals? $d = 55 \times t$

2. Sometimes you are given distances and need to know how long it would take to travel at various rates. Complete the table to find the time it would take to travel 500 miles at speeds of 40, 55, 60, 65, and 70 miles per hour. Round your times to the nearest quarter hour, if necessary.

Rate (in mi/h)	40	55	60	65	70
Time (in hours)	$12\frac{1}{2}$	9	$8\frac{1}{4}$	$7\frac{3}{4}$	$7\frac{1}{4}$
Distance (in miles)	500	500	500	500	500

3. What operation did you use to find the time? Rewrite the equation so that t stands alone on one side of the equal sign.
Division; $t = \frac{d}{r}$

4. Rewrite the equation so that r stands alone on one side of the equal sign. Explain your reasoning.
$r = \frac{d}{t}$; Possible answer: To find the rate, divide the distance by the time.

5. How is rewriting an equation like solving an equation?
You use inverse operations to isolate the variable.

6. Why would you want to rewrite an equation?
Sample answer: If you needed to find many solutions using the same equation, it would be faster to have the variable isolated before doing each calculation.

7. The equation for the perimeter of a regular polygon can be written as $P = n \times s$ where P is the perimeter, n is the number of sides and s is the length of each side. How could you rewrite the equation to find the length of a side? $s = \frac{P}{n}$

190

Online
Homework Help
Visit: PHSchool.com
Web Code: are-0404

Solve each equation.

39. $\frac{1}{2}m = 25$ 50

40. $\frac{w}{-4.2} = 10.3$ −43.26

41. $\frac{1}{5}t = 17$ 85

42. $\frac{k}{21.45} = 6$ 128.7

43. $\frac{3}{4}x = 16$ $21\frac{1}{3}$

44. $\frac{y}{-5.22} = -3.11$
16.2342

45. Trees A growing tree absorbs about 26 lb of carbon dioxide
[GPS] each year. How many years will the tree take to absorb 390 lb of carbon dioxide? **15 yr**

46. The world record for playgoing is held by Dr. H. Howard Hughes of Fort Worth, Texas. He saw 6,136 plays in 31 years. How many plays did Dr. Hughes see in an average year?
about 198 plays

47. Reasoning In the equation $ab = 1$, a is an integer. Explain what you know about b. **b is the reciprocal of a and $b \neq 0$.**

48. Answers may vary. Sample: The student may have divided 12 by −6. The student should have multiplied both sides by −6 to get $n = -72$.

48. Error Analysis One student's solution for the equation $\frac{n}{-6} = 12$ is $n = -2$. Explain how the student may have found this solution. Then correct the student's mistake.

Open-Ended Write a problem that can be solved using each equation.
49–51. Check students' work.

49. $3x = 30$ **50.** $\frac{n}{5} = 2$ **51.** $2.5p = 10$

C 52. Challenge You are starting a savings account. You make an initial deposit of $100. Every week after that, you deposit $20. Your goal is to save $1,000. Write an algebraic equation and find how many weeks you will need to reach your goal. **$100 + 20w = 1,000$; 45 weeks**

TEKS ★ TAKS Tune-Up and Mixed Review

GRIDDABLE ITEMS

TAKS Objective 5
TEKS (7.12)(A)

53. The table at the right shows the number of cans each student collected for a school food drive. Which number could be added to the set of data in order for the median and the mode of the set to be equal? **72**

TAKS Objective 1
TEKS (7.2)(B)

54. A recipe calls for 3 lb of potatoes. You have one bag of potatoes that weighs 1.25 lb, and another bag that weighs 0.65 lb. How many more pounds of potatoes do you need for the recipe?
1.1

Food Drive Results

Student	Number of Cans
Abel	46
Annie	89
Cris	72
Pedro	63
Sungmee	108
Tasha	■

GO for Help **Lesson 4-3** **Solve each equation.**

55. $p - \frac{4}{7} = \frac{1}{4}$ $\frac{23}{28}$

56. $\frac{1}{2} = x - \frac{3}{4}$ $1\frac{1}{4}$

57. $\frac{1}{2} = w + \frac{5}{12}$ $\frac{1}{12}$

190 Chapter 4 Equations and Inequalities

TEKS ★ TAKS Resources

• TAKS Strategies, p. 219
• TAKS Tune-Up, pp. 223–225

TAKS Tune-Up Kit

• TAKS Daily Review Transparencies
• TAKS Review and Preparation Workbook
• TAKS Strategies with Transparencies
• Texas Progress Monitoring Assessments

Alternative Assessment

Ask students to write their own word problems similar to those in Exercises 21 and 22. Then have students exchange problems with a partner. Partners should write equations for the problems, solve the equations, and check their answers.

Write an algebraic expression for each word phrase.

1. four less than a number $x - 4$

2. three times a number $3x$

3. the quotient of 4 and a number $\frac{4}{x}$

4. nine more than a number $x + 9$

Solve each equation.

5. $g - 5 = -9.4$ -4.4

6. $y + 10.2 = 12$ 1.8

7. $-5x = 45.5$ -9.1

8. $\frac{h}{6} = 8$ 48

9. **Science** The chemical element aluminum was discovered in 1825 by Hans Christian Oersted. This was 18 years after Sir Humphry Davy discovered the element sodium. Write and solve an equation to find the year that sodium was discovered. $y + 18 = 1825; y = 1807$

10. Fingernails grow about 1.5 inches per year. How long would it take to grow nails 37 inches long? **24 years 8 months**

MATH GAMES

Evaluating Expressions

What You'll Need

- 24 index cards. Cut them in half so you have 48 smaller cards. On each card, write a different algebraic expression.
- Two number cubes

How to Play

- Deal all the cards. Each player chooses one card from his or her hand and places it face down on the table.
- A player rolls the number cubes. The sum of the numbers is the value of the variable for the first round.
- Each player turns over his or her card, evaluates the expression, and announces its value. Record the value for each player.
- Play continues until all players have rolled the number cubes.
- Find each player's total. The player with the lowest total wins.

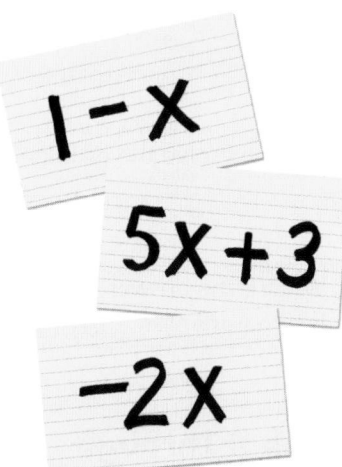

191

✓ Checkpoint Quiz

Use this Checkpoint Quiz to check students' understanding of the skills and concepts of Lessons 4-1 through 4-4.

Resources

- All-in-One Teaching Resources Checkpoint Quiz 1
- Texas ExamView CD-ROM
- Success Tracker™ Online Intervention

MATH GAMES

Evaluating Expressions

In this game, students practice evaluating expressions. Players receive algebraic expressions written on cards. They choose an expression, roll two number cubes, find the sum, and use the sum to evaluate the expression. The player with the lowest total wins.

Guided Instruction

Before they play the game, remind students that the values found can be positive or negative. Ask: *Does a negative value decrease the total?* **yes**

Resources

- 24 index cards cut in half with 48 algebraic expressions
- 2 number cubes

191

Practice Solving Problems

In this feature, students practice solving problems using diagrams. Then they use symbols to write equations that record their actions. They solve the equation and check the reasonableness of their answer.

Guided Instruction

Discuss with students the use of diagrams or models to show the information in a word problem. Then help them to use symbols to write an equation that describes what the situation is.

Have a volunteer read the word problem.
Ask:
- *How else could you have found the number of $\frac{1}{4}$ pounds in 4,000 lbs?* Multiply 4,000 by 4.
- *Why does multiplication work? Dividing by $\frac{1}{4}$ is the same as multiplying by 4.*

TEKS ★ TAKS Resources

- Classroom Aid 11

Dana Center TEKS Clarifying Activities (7.5)(A), (7.13)(C)
Visit: PHSchool.com
Web Code: arq-9045

GPS **Guided Problem Solving**

Practice Solving Problems

Big Burgers The world's largest hamburger weighed 8,266 lb. If half of the weight was meat, how many regular quarter-pound hamburgers could have been made from that burger?

TEKS ★ TAKS
(7.5)(A) To use pictorial models to solve equations and use symbols to record the actions **TAKS** Obj. 2
(7.13)(C) To select an appropriate problem-solving strategy, including drawing a picture **TAKS** Obj. 6

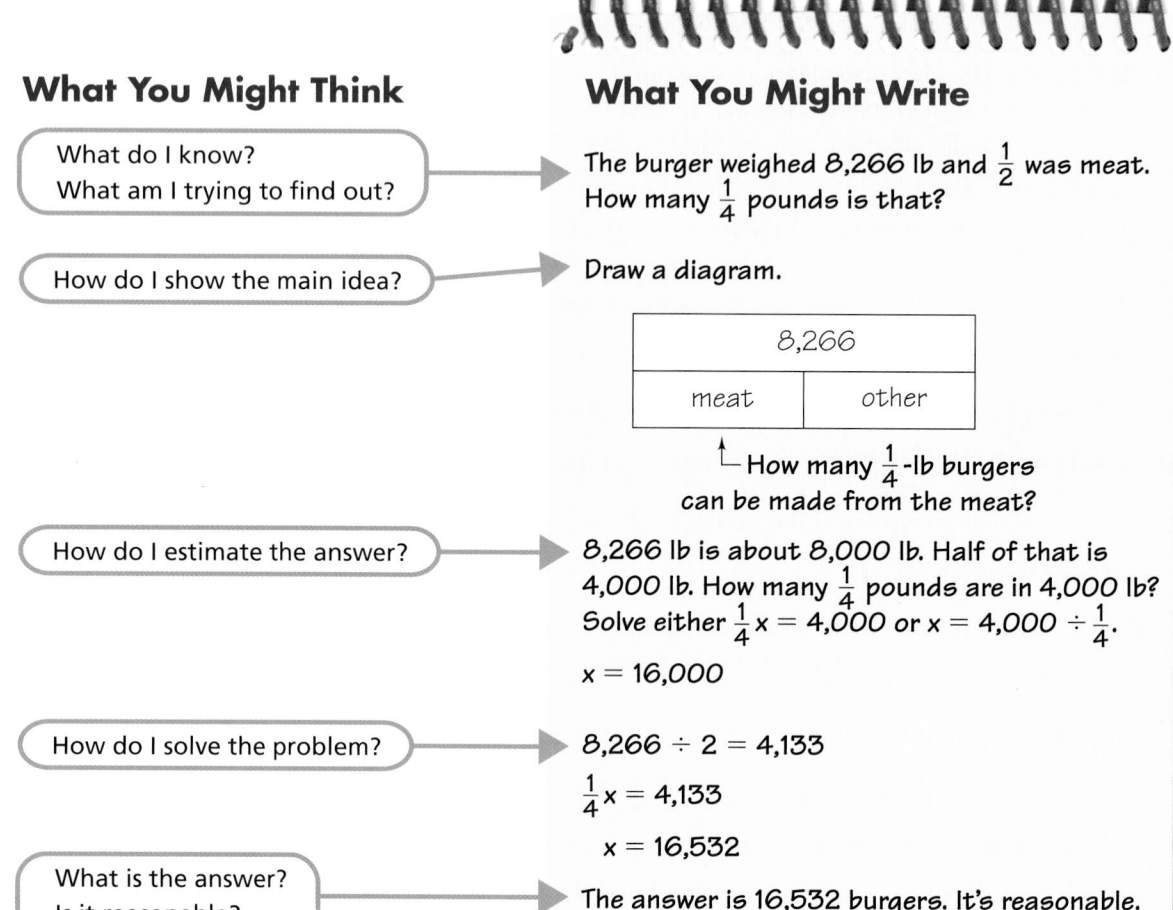

What You Might Think

- What do I know?
  What am I trying to find out?

- How do I show the main idea?

- How do I estimate the answer?

- How do I solve the problem?

- What is the answer?
  Is it reasonable?

What You Might Write

The burger weighed 8,266 lb and $\frac{1}{2}$ was meat. How many $\frac{1}{4}$ pounds is that?

Draw a diagram.

8,266	
meat	other

└ How many $\frac{1}{4}$-lb burgers can be made from the meat?

8,266 lb is about 8,000 lb. Half of that is 4,000 lb. How many $\frac{1}{4}$ pounds are in 4,000 lb? Solve either $\frac{1}{4}x = 4,000$ or $x = 4,000 \div \frac{1}{4}$.

$x = 16,000$

$8,266 \div 2 = 4,133$

$\frac{1}{4}x = 4,133$

$\quad x = 16,532$

The answer is 16,532 burgers. It's reasonable. The answer is close to the estimate of 16,000.

Think It Through

1. In the diagram, why do *meat* and *other* equally share the space under 8,266?

2. Explain why $\frac{1}{4}x = 4,000$ and $x = 4,000 \div \frac{1}{4}$ are equivalent.

1. Together, they are equal to 8,266 lb, and $\frac{1}{2}$ the weight is meat.

2. In both situations, you need to multiply 4,000 by 4.

Exercises

Solve. For Exercises 3 and 4, answer the questions first.

3. To celebrate National Hot Dog Month, a beef company made a hot dog that measured 16 feet 1 inch. A regular hot dog is $5\frac{1}{2}$ inches long. How many regular hot dogs would you need to make this hot dog?
   a. What do you know? What do you want to find out?
   b. Explain how the diagram below shows the situation. Write an equation.

   3. about 35 hot dogs

   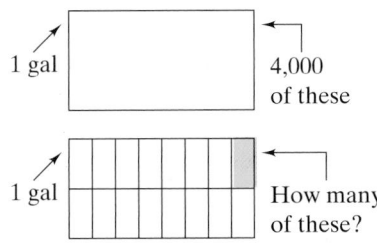

4. The world's largest glass of milk held 4,000 gallons. A gallon holds 16 cups. How many cups were in the world's largest glass of milk?
   a. Explain how the diagram below shows the situation. Write an equation.

   4. 64,000 cups

   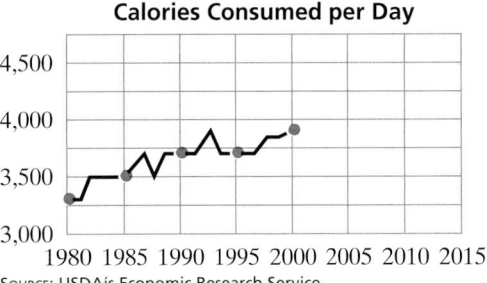

5. a. Look at the graph at the right. Estimate how many more Calories per day an American consumed in 2000 than in 1980. **600 more Calories**
   b. Suppose the increase in Calories per day was entirely from hamburgers. A quarter-pound hamburger has about 450 Calories. About how many more burgers per week did an American eat in 2000 than in 1980? **about 9 burgers**

   Calories Consumed per Day

   4,500
   4,000
   3,500
   3,000

   1980 1985 1990 1995 2000 2005 2010 2015

   Source: USDA's Economic Research Service

6. Assume the graph at the right keeps climbing at the same rate. Estimate the number of Calories an average American consumes each day this year. **Check students' work.**

7. A 125-pound soccer player burns about 65 Calories in 10 minutes. How long would the player need to play to burn up a snack that contains 260 Calories? **40 min**

TEKS ★ **TAKS**

(7.5)(A) To use pictorial models to solve equations and use symbols to record the actions **TAKS** Obj. 2
Also supports
(7.5)(B) **TAKS** Obj. 2
(7.13)(D)

Dana Center TEKS Toolkit Clarifying Activities (7.5)(A), (7.5)(B), (7.13)(D)
Visit: PHSchool.com
Web Code: arq-9045

TEKS Math Background

When each variable in an algebraic expression is replaced by a number, the result is a *numerical expression*. If the numerical expression involves more than one operation, its value is found by following the order of operations outlined in Lesson 1-9.

More Math Background: p. 166D

Lesson Planning and Resources

See p. 166E for a list of the resources that support this lesson.

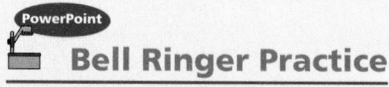

PowerPoint

Bell Ringer Practice

✓ **Check Skills You'll Need**
Use student page, transparency, or PowerPoint.

TAKS Daily Review 30
Use transparency.

194

✓ **Check Skills You'll Need**

1. **Vocabulary Review**
A(n) __?__ is a mathematical phrase with at least one variable.
algebraic expression
Evaluate each expression. Use the value $a = -4$.

2. $a + 5$ 1   3. $9 - a$ 13

4. $-6a$ 24   5. $\frac{a}{2}$ −2

GO for Help
Lesson 4-1

TEKS ★ **TAKS**
- (7.5)(A) To use pictorial models to solve equations and use symbols to record the actions **TAKS** Obj. 2
- (7.5)(B) To formulate an equation when given a problem situation **TAKS** Obj. 2
- (7.13)(D) To select techniques such as mental math and number sense to solve problems

Why Learn This?

Suppose you are ordering roses online. Roses cost $5 each, and shipping costs $10. Your total cost depends on how many roses you buy. Two-step equations can help you solve everyday problems.

You can write expressions with variables using one operation. Now you will write algebraic expressions with two operations.

EXAMPLES **Writing and Evaluating Expressions**

① Define a variable and write an algebraic expression for the phrase "$10 plus $5 times the number of roses ordered."

Let n = the number of roses ordered   ← **Define the variable.**

$10 + 5 \cdot n$ ← **Write an algebraic expression.**

$10 + 5n$ ← **Rewrite 5 · n as 5n.**

② Evaluate the expression for 12 roses.

$10 + 5n$

$10 + 5 \cdot 12$ ← **Evaluate the expression for 12 roses.**

$10 + 60$ ← **Multiply.**

70 ← **Simplify.**

If you order 12 roses, you will have to pay $70.

✓ **Quick Check**

1. Define a variable and write an algebraic expression for "a man is two years younger than three times his son's age." Let s = son's age; $3s - 2$

2. Evaluate the expression to find the man's age if his son is 13. 37

Differentiated **Instruction** **Solutions for All Learners**

Special Needs **L1**
Students may need models for all the Examples in this lesson. If the models are confusing, let them come up with a different picture to represent the problems.

learning style: visual

Below Level **L2**
Review the order of operations by having students find the value of some simple expressions such as $3 \cdot 5 + 9$ and $8 \div 4 - 2$. 24; 0

learning style: visual

Suppose your grandmother sends you 5 games for your birthday. Each game has the same weight. The box she mails them in weighs 8 ounces. The total weight is 48 ounces. What is the weight of one game?

You can represent this situation with the diagram below.

Let g represent the weight of a game.

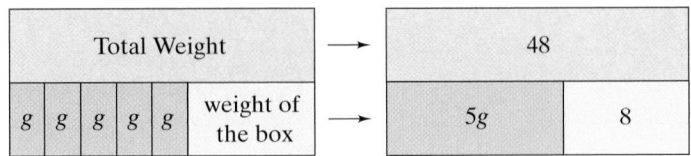

You can solve this problem using the equation $5g + 8 = 48$. Since there is more than one operation in the equation, there will be more than one step in the solution.

EXAMPLE Using Number Sense

③ Solve $5g + 8 = 48$ by using number sense.

$$5g + 8 = 48$$

$\blacksquare + 8 = 48$ ← **Cover 5g.** *Think:* **What number added to 8 is 48? Answer: 40**

$5g = 40$ ← **So** $\blacksquare$**, or 5g, must equal 40.**

$5 \cdot \blacksquare = 40$ ← **Now cover g.** *Think:* **What number times 5 is 40? Answer: 8**

$g = 8$ ← **So** $\blacksquare$**, or g, must equal 8.**

Check

$5g + 8 = 48$ ← **Check your solution in the original equation.**

$5(8) + 8 \stackrel{?}{=} 48$ ← **Substitute 8 for g.**

$40 + 8 \stackrel{?}{=} 48$ ← **Simplify.**

$48 = 48$ ✔ ← **The solution checks.**

✅ Quick Check

3. Solve each equation using number sense.

    a. $3m + 9 = 21$ **4**   **b.** $8d + 5 = 45$ **5**   **c.** $4y - 11 = 33$ **11**

TAKS Tip

When solving problems, look for opportunities to use number sense and mental math.

---

2. Teach

Activity Lab

Use before the lesson.

All in One Teaching Resources
Activity Lab 4-5: Patterns in Data

Guided Instruction

Example 2
When evaluating two-step expressions, it is important to follow the order of operations. Ask: *When you find the value of $10 + 5 \cdot 12$, why do you first multiply $5 \cdot 12$?* According to the order of operations, multiply and divide in order from left to right. Add and subtract in order from left to right.

Example 3
Display the equation $x + 8 = 48$. Ask: *What number added to 8 is 48?* **40** Write $5g + 8 = 48$ directly beneath the first equation. Have students explain how the second equation is different from the first. Then proceed with the solution in the text.

PowerPoint

Additional Examples

① ② To rent a bicycle, you pay a $12 basic fee plus $2 per hour. Write an expression for the total cost in dollars of a bicycle rental. Then evaluate the expression for an 8-hour bicycle rental. **$12 + 2h$, where h represents the number of hours; $28**

③ Solve $9k - 4 = 14$ using number sense. **$k = 2$**

Advanced Learners **L4**
Have students create original problems like the one in Example 4 using costs from a restaurant or the school cafeteria.

Pre-AP™

English Language Learners **ELL**
Ask students to work in pairs to write variables and expressions for the *Check Your Understanding* and *Homework Exercises.* Ask them to check each others to make sure they are not making errors going from words to symbols.

learning style: visual

195

Example 4

Check that students understand the problem. Ask: *What is the problem about?* friends who are having lunch together *How many people are going to share the cost of the chicken wings?* three *What does $1.50 represent?* the cost of your lemonade *Are the friends going to share the cost of the lemonade?* no

Additional Examples

④ The Healy family wants to buy a DVD player that costs $200. They have $80 saved. How much will they have to save per month for six months in order to have the whole cost saved? **$20 per month**

All in One Teaching Resources

• Daily Notetaking Guide 4-5 **L3**
• Adapted Notetaking 4-5 **L1**

Closure

• *How does solving a two-step equation differ from solving a one-step equation?* Two-step equations combine two mathematical operations. When solving two-step equations you must first undo addition or subtraction, then undo multiplication or division.

You can represent the relationships in the problem with this model.

share of total	
lemonade cost	share of chicken cost

$5.50	
$1.50	$\frac{z}{3}$

EXAMPLE Application: Food

④ Suppose you buy a jumbo lemonade for $1.50 and divide the cost of an order of chicken wings with two friends. Your share of the total bill is $5.50. Write and solve an equation to find the cost of the chicken wings.

Words   cost of lemonade   plus   (cost of wings ÷ 3)   is $5.50

Let z = the cost of the chicken wings.

Expression   1.50   + $(z \div 3)$ = $5.50

$1.50 + \frac{z}{3} = 5.50$

$1.50 + \blacksquare = 5.50$ ← Cover $\frac{z}{3}$. *Think:* What number added to 1.50 is 5.50? Answer: 4

$\frac{z}{3} = 4$ ← So $\blacksquare$, or $\frac{z}{3}$, must equal 4.

$\frac{\blacksquare}{3} = 4$ ← Now cover z. *Think:* What number divided by 3 is 4? Answer: 12

$z = 12$ ← So $\blacksquare$, or z, must equal 12.

The cost of the chicken wings is $12.

✓ Quick Check

4. **Basketball** During the first half of a game you scored 8 points. In the second half you made only 3-point baskets. You finished the game with 23 points. Write and solve an equation to find how many 3-point baskets you made. **Let b = number of 3-point baskets; 8 + 3b = 23; 5 baskets.**

✓ Check Your Understanding

1. **Vocabulary** What is the difference between a one-step expression and a two-step expression? See below left.

2. Write and solve the equation modeled at the left.
   16 = 4x − 12; 7

16				
x	x	x	x	−12

1. A one-step expression uses only one operation, while a two-step expression uses two.

Match each phrase with the correct algebraic expression.

3. 10 centimeters less than twice x, your hand length **B**   **A.** $\frac{1}{2}x - 10$

4. 10 people fewer than half x, the town's population **A**   **B.** $2x - 10$

5. 10 more than two times a number x **C**   **C.** $2x + 10$

Using number sense, fill in the missing number.

6. $4b + 5 = 17$
   $4b = \blacksquare$ 12

7. $7c - 20 = 50$
   $7c = \blacksquare$ 70

Homework Exercises

For more exercises, see Extra Skills and Word Problems.

GO for Help

For Exercises	See Examples
8–12	1
13–20	2
21–27	3–4

Ⓐ **Define a variable and write an algebraic expression for each phrase.**

8. two points fewer than 3 times the number of points scored before
Let p = number of points scored before; $3p - 2$.

9. one meter more than 6 times your height in meters
Let h = your height; $6h + 1$.

10. seven pages fewer than half the number of pages read last week
Let p = number of pages; $\frac{p}{2} - 7$.

11. eight pounds less than five times the weight of a chicken
Let w = weight; $5w - 8$.

12. twice the distance in miles flown last year, plus 100 miles
Let d = distance; $2d + 100$.

Evaluate each expression for the given value of the variable.

13. $4m - 6.5; m = 2$ **1.5**

14. $5 + 2f; f = 6.1$ **17.2**

15. $12 - 3b; b = 4.3$ **−0.9**

16. $6x + 2; x = 3$ **20**

17. $5y - 5; y = 5$ **20**

18. $7 + 8c; c = 7$ **63**

19. $2p + 4.5; p = 5.1$ **14.7**

20. $12 - 2.2s; s = 4$ **3.2**

Solve each equation using number sense. You may find a model helpful.

21. $2t + 9.4 = 39.8$ **15.2**

22. $4m + 12 = 52$ **10**

23. $10h + 14 = 84$ **7**

24. $7w + 16 = 37$ **3**

25. $3y + 13.6 = 40.6$ **9**

26. $5v + 19 = 24$ **1**

29. $40 is the hourly rate, h is the number of hours the electrician works, $35 is the fee for a house call, and $115 is the total bill. The electrician works 2 h.

27. **Money** A fitness club advertises a special for new members. Each month of membership is $19, with an initial enrollment fee of $75. Write an expression for the total cost. Then evaluate your expression for 8 months of membership.
Let m = number of months; $19m + 75$; $227.

Ⓑ **GPS** 28. **Guided Problem Solving** You want to buy an iguana that costs $49. You already have $13. If you save $9 per week, when will you have enough money to buy the iguana? **4 wk**
- How much money do you already have?
- How much more money do you need?

29. **Writing in Math** In addition to her hourly rate, an electrician charges a fee to come to your house. This can be modeled by $40h + 35 = 115$. Explain what each part of the equation represents. Then solve the equation to find the number of hours she works.
See above left.

30. You order 3 posters advertised on the Internet. Each poster costs the same amount. The shipping charge is $5. The total cost of the posters plus the shipping charge is $41. Find the cost of one poster.
$12

31. **Open-Ended** Describe a situation that can be modeled by the equation $\frac{b}{2} + 5 = 51$. **Check students' work.**

---

3. Practice

Assignment Guide

Check Your Understanding
Go over Exercises 1–7 in class before assigning the Homework Exercises.

Homework Exercises
A	Practice by Example	8–27
B	Apply Your Skills	28–41
C	Challenge	42
TEKS ★ TAKS	Tune-Up and Mixed Review	43–48

Homework Quick Check
To check students' understanding of key skills and concepts, go over Exercises 8, 14, 29, 39, and 41.

Differentiated Instruction Resources

Adapted Practice 4-5 **L1**

Practice 4-5 Exploring Two-Step Pr... **L3**

Define a variable and write an algebraic expression for each phrase.
1. six times the price of gas minus 20
Let g = the price of gas; $6g - 20$
2. one-half the distance from Boston to New York minus 25
Let d = the distance from Boston to New York; $\frac{1}{2}d - 25$
3. two fewer than five times the number of eggs needed in the recipe
Let e = the number of eggs needed in the recipe; $5e - 2$
4. 10 megabytes less than the number of megabytes in a computer, divided by 6
Let m = the number of megabytes in a computer; $\frac{m - 10}{6}$

Solve each equation using number sense.
5. $10 + 5h = 25$ — $h = 3$
6. $8s - 8 = 64$ — $s = 9$
7. $3y + 78 = 81$ — $y = 1$
8. $2g + 4 = 12$ — $g = 4$
9. $5j + 5 = 15$ — $j = 2$
10. $3w + 8 = 20$ — $w = 4$
11. $\frac{h}{3} + 1 = 4$ — $h = 6$
12. $\frac{g}{8} + 12 = 16$ — $g = 32$
13. $2 + \frac{b}{7} = 3$ — $b = 7$

14. For a walk-a-thon a sponsor committed to give you a flat fee of $5 plus $2 for every mile you walk. Write an expression for the total amount you will collect from your sponsor at the end of the walk-a-thon. Then evaluate your expression for 20 miles walked.
$5 + $2m$; $45

4-5 • Guided Problem Solving **GPS** **L3**

GPS Student Page 198, Exercise 39:

Food You are helping to prepare food for a large family gathering. You can slice 2 zucchinis per minute. You need 30 sliced zucchinis. How long will it take you to finish if you have already sliced 12 zucchinis?

Understand
1. Circle the information you will need to solve.
2. What are you being asked to do?
Find how long it will take to finish slicing the zucchinis.
3. What will your variable represent?
the number of minutes it will take to finish slicing the zucchinis

Plan and Carry Out
4. How many sliced zucchinis do you need? 30
5. How many sliced zucchinis do you already have? 12
6. Write and simplify an expression for the number of zucchinis you still need to slice. $30 - 12 = 18$
7. To calculate the number of minutes it will take to slice the remaining zucchinis, what number will you divide your answer to step 7 by? 2 minutes
8. Write an equation to solve the problem. $2t = 18$
9. How long will it take you to finish slicing the remaining zucchinis? 9 minutes

Check
10. Multiply your answer to step 9 by your answer to step 8. Does your answer match your result from step 7?
$9 \times 2 = 18$; yes

Solve Another Problem
11. Jordan skates 6 mi/h. Today she has already skated 8 miles. Her goal is to skate a total of 20 miles. How much longer does she have to skate to reach her goal?
$6t = 20 - 8$; $t = 2$; 2 hours

PowerPoint

Lesson Quiz

Solve each equation using number sense.

1. $5d + 3 = 53$ $d = 10$

2. $\frac{g}{6} - 4 = 2$ $g = 36$

3. $7h - 10 = 25$ $h = 5$

4. $\frac{k}{3} + 20 = 31$ $k = 33$

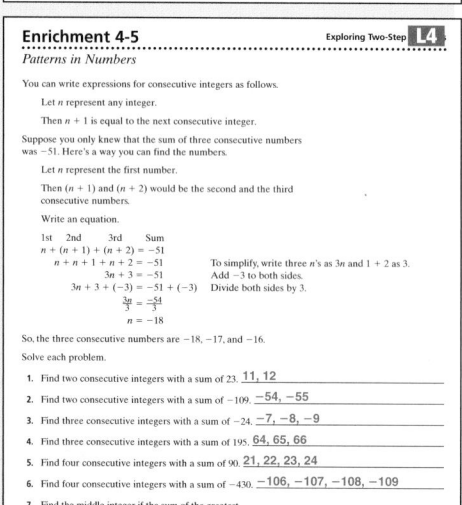

Reteaching 4-5   Exploring Two-Step **L2**

You can change a word expression into an algebraic expression by converting the words to variables, numbers, and operation symbols.

To write a two-step algebraic expression for *seven more than three times a number*, follow these steps.

① Define the variable.   Let *n* represent the number.

② Ask yourself are there any key words?   "More than" means add and
                                           "times" means multiply.

③ Write an algebraic expression. $7 + 3 \cdot n$

④ Simplify. $7 + 3n$

Define a variable and write an algebraic expression for each phrase.

1. 3 inches more than 4 times your height $4h + 3$
2. 4 less than 6 times the weight of a turkey $6t - 4$
3. 8 more than one-half the number of miles run last week $\frac{1}{2}m + 8$

Solve.

4. Three friends pay $4 per hour to rent a paddleboat plus $5 for snacks. Write an expression for the total cost of rental and snacks. Then evaluate the expression for 2 hours.
   $4h + 5$; $13

5. A lawn care service charges $10 plus $15 per hour to mow and fertilize lawns. Write an expression for the total cost of having your lawn mowed and fertilized. Then evaluate it for 4 hours.
   $10 + 15h$; $70

Solve each equation using number sense.

6. $4x - 10 = 30$ 7. $2n - 7 = 13$ 8. $\frac{s}{3} + 2 = 4$
   $x = 10$ $n = 10$ $s = 6$

Enrichment 4-5   Exploring Two-Step **L4**

Patterns in Numbers

You can write expressions for consecutive integers as follows.

   Let *n* represent any integer.

   Then *n* + 1 is equal to the next consecutive integer.

Suppose you only knew that the sum of three consecutive numbers was −51. Here's a way you can find the numbers.

   Let *n* represent the first number.

   Then (*n* + 1) and (*n* + 2) would be the second and the third consecutive numbers.

   Write an equation.

1st	2nd	3rd	Sum

$n + (n + 1) + (n + 2) = -51$
$n + n + 1 + n + 2 = -51$ To simplify, write three *n*'s as 3*n* and 1 + 2 as 3.
$3n + 3 = -51$ Add −3 to both sides.
$3n + 3 + (-3) = -51 + (-3)$ Divide both sides by 3.
$\frac{3n}{3} = \frac{-54}{3}$
$n = -18$

So, the three consecutive numbers are −18, −17, and −16.

Solve each problem.

1. Find two consecutive integers with a sum of 23. 11, 12
2. Find two consecutive integers with a sum of −109. −54, −55
3. Find three consecutive integers with a sum of −24. −7, −8, −9
4. Find three consecutive integers with a sum of 195. 64, 65, 66
5. Find four consecutive integers with a sum of 90. 21, 22, 23, 24
6. Find four consecutive integers with a sum of −430. −106, −107, −108, −109
7. Find the middle integer if the sum of the greatest and the least of three consecutive integers is 82. 40 + 42 = 82; 41

198

Online

Homework Help

Visit: PHSchool.com
Web Code: are-0405

Solve each equation using number sense.

11.5

32. $5h + 3 = 18.5$ **3.1**   **33.** $3m - 7.6 = 26.9$ **34.** $8y + 17 = 65$ **6**

35. $\frac{x}{3} - 3 = 12$ **45**   **36.** $2p - 5 = 15$ **10**   **37.** $\frac{t}{4} + 1 = 6$ **20**

38. Telephone A cellular telephone company charges $40 per month plus a $35 activation fee. Write an expression for the total cost. Then evaluate your expression for 10 months of service. **See margin.**

39. Food You are helping to prepare food for a large family gathering. You can slice 2 zucchinis per minute. You need 30 sliced zucchinis. How long will it take you to finish, if you have already sliced 12 zucchinis? **9 min**

40. Your family rented a car for a trip. The car rental cost $35 per day plus $.30/mile. After a one-day rental, the bill was $74. How many miles did your family drive? **130 mi**

41. Reasoning When you solve an equation, you must do the same operation to both sides. Explain why this is true. **See margin.**

C 42. Challenge You spend 5 minutes jogging as a warmup. Then you run 4 miles and cool down for 5 minutes. The total time you exercise is 54 minutes. What is your average time for running a mile?
11 min/mi

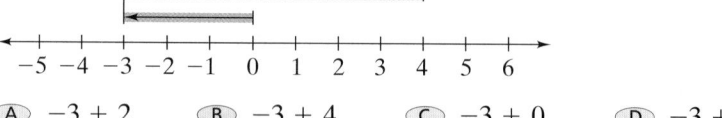

TEKS ★ TAKS Tune-Up and Mixed Review

TAKS Objective 1
TEKS (7.2)(F)

43. Daniel bought one dozen tennis balls priced at 3 balls for $1.99 and a tennis racquet for $49.99. What is the total amount he spent, not including tax, on tennis balls and a tennis racquet? **C**
  Ⓐ $51.98   Ⓒ $57.95
  Ⓑ $55.96   Ⓓ $73.87

TAKS Objective 2
TEKS (7.5)(B)

44. Medium beverages cost $1.39 and small beverages cost $0.89. Which equation can be used to find *d*, the total cost in dollars of 6 medium drinks? **J**
  Ⓕ $6 = 0.89d$ Ⓗ $6 = 1.39d$
  Ⓖ $d = 0.89(6)$ Ⓙ $d = 1.39(6)$

TAKS Objective 1
TEKS (7.2)(C)

45. Which expression is represented by the model below? **D**

  Ⓐ $-3 + 2$ Ⓑ $-3 + 4$ Ⓒ $-3 + 0$ Ⓓ $-3 + 7$

 for Help   **Lesson 2-4**   **Compare each pair of fractions. Use <, =, or >.**

46. $\frac{7}{9}$ < $\frac{4}{5}$ **47.** $\frac{9}{27}$ = $\frac{1}{3}$ **48.** $\frac{5}{12}$ > $\frac{2}{6}$

TEKS ★ TAKS Resources

- TAKS Strategies, p. 219
- TAKS Tune-Up, pp. 223–225

TAKS Tune-Up Kit
- TAKS Daily Review Transparencies
- TAKS Review and Preparation Workbook
- TAKS Strategies with Transparencies
- Texas Progress Monitoring Assessments

Alternative Assessment

Have students create word phrases similar to those in Exercises 8–12. Have partners work together to write an algebraic expression for each phrase. Partners should then incorporate each expression into an equation. Finally, have partners solve their equations.

Modeling Two-Step Equations

You can use algebra tiles to solve two-step equations.

TEKS ★ **TAKS**

(7.5)(A) To use concrete models to solve equations and use symbols to record the actions **TAKS** Obj. 2

(7.13)(D) To select tools such as manipulatives to solve problems

EXAMPLE Solving Two-Step Equations

Use algebra tiles to solve $2x + 1 = 7$.

$2x + 1 = 7$ ← Model the equation. Use yellow tiles for positive integers.

$2x + 1 - 1 = 7 - 1$
$2x = 6$ ← Remove 1 yellow tile from each side.

$\dfrac{2x}{2} = \dfrac{6}{2}$ ← Divide each side into 2 equal groups.

$x = 3$ ← Simplify.

Exercises

Write and solve the equation represented by each model.

1.

$3x - 2 = -5;\ -1$

2.

$2x - 3 = 5;\ 4$

3.

$2x + 2 = 4;\ 1$

Use algebra tiles to solve each equation.

4. $3x - 4 = 2$ 2

5. $2x - 1 = 9$ 5

6. $2x + 4 = 10$ 3

7. $3x + 4 = 7$ 1

8. $2x + 6 = -8$ −7

9. $2x - 6 = -18$ −6

10. At a county fair, an admission ticket costs $5, and each ride costs $2. You have $13. Write an algebraic equation for the number of rides you can go on. Use algebra tiles to solve the equation. **Let** x **= number of rides;** $5 + 2x = 13$**, 4 rides**

11. **Reasoning** Suppose you have 20 green, 20 red, and 20 yellow algebra tiles. Explain how you could use the tiles to model the equation $500x - 200 = 1{,}300$.   **Model an equivalent equation,** $5x - 2 = 13$**.**

38. Let m = number of months; $40m + 35$; $435

41. Answers may vary. Sample: You need to keep the equation "balanced."

Activity Lab

Modeling Two-Step Equations

Students use algebra tiles to model two-step equations and find their solutions.

Guided Instruction

Model the solution to the example. Have students follow along at their desks.
Ask:
Why did you subtract 1 yellow tile from each side? so that $2x$ is alone on the left side

- *What tells you that $-1 + 1 = 0$?* the additive inverse property
- *What two operations were used in the example?* subtraction and division

Alternative Method

Have students act out the two-step equation using chairs for the variables, boys for red tiles, and girls for yellow tiles.

TEKS ★ **TAKS** **Resources**

- Activity Lab 4-6: Critical Thinking
- algebra tiles

Dana Center TEKS Toolkit Clarifying Activities (7.5)(A), (7.13)(D)
Visit: PHSchool.com
Web Code: arq-9045

1. Plan

TEKS ★ TAKS

(7.5)(A) To use pictorial models to solve equations and use symbols to record the actions **TAKS** Obj. 2

(7.5)(B) To formulate an equation when given a problem situation **TAKS** Obj. 2

Dana Center TEKS Toolkit Clarifying Activities (7.5)(A), (7.5)(B)
Visit: PHSchool.com
Web Code: arq-9045

TEKS Math Background

The most direct approach to solving two-step equations is generally the procedure described on this page. This might be described as an "inverse order of operations." However, there are sometimes alternative procedures that are equally acceptable. For instance, in Example 2, $\frac{x}{3} + 11 = 16$, could also be solved by first multiplying both sides by 3, obtaining $x + 33 = 48$. Subtracting 33 from each side of this equation then results in the solution $x = 15$.

More Math Background: p. 166D

Lesson Planning and Resources

See p. 166E for a list of the resources that support this lesson.

Bell Ringer Practice

✓ **Check Skills You'll Need**
Use student page, transparency, or PowerPoint.

TAKS Daily Review 31
Use transparency.

✓ Check Skills You'll Need

1. Vocabulary Review
What property states that if $a = b$, then $a \cdot c = b \cdot c$?
See below.
Solve each equation.

2. $4b = 24$ 6

3. $-4d = 20$ −5

4. $\frac{k}{4} = -16$ −64

5. $\frac{h}{6} = -3$ −18

 for Help
Lesson 4-4

Check Skills You'll Need

1. Multiplication Property of Equality

TEKS ★ TAKS

- (7.5)(A) To use pictorial models to solve equations and use symbols to record the actions **TAKS** Obj. 2
- (7.5)(B) To formulate an equation when given a problem situation **TAKS** Obj. 2

Why Learn This?

Detectives often retrace steps to find missing information. You can use the strategy *Work Backward* to solve a two-step equation and find an unknown quantity.

You can solve a two-step equation by using inverse operations and the properties of equality to get the variable on one side of the equation.

For many equations, you can undo addition or subtraction first. Then you can multiply or divide to get the variable alone.

EXAMPLE Undoing Subtraction First

1 Solve $5n - 18 = -33$.

$$5n - 18 = -33$$
$$5n - 18 + 18 = -33 + 18 \quad \leftarrow \text{To undo subtraction, add 18 to each side.}$$
$$5n = -15 \quad \leftarrow \text{Simplify.}$$
$$\frac{5n}{5} = \frac{-15}{5} \quad \leftarrow \text{To undo multiplication, divide each side by 5.}$$
$$n = -3 \quad \leftarrow \text{Simplify.}$$

Check $5n - 18 = -33 \quad \leftarrow \text{Check your solution with the original equation.}$
$$5(-3) - 18 \overset{?}{=} -33 \quad \leftarrow \text{Substitute } -3 \text{ for } n.$$
$$-15 - 18 \overset{?}{=} -33 \quad \leftarrow \text{Simplify.}$$
$$-33 = -33 ✔ \quad \leftarrow \text{The solution checks.}$$

✓ Quick Check

● **1.** Solve the equation $-8y - 28 = -36$. Check your answer. 1

Differentiated Instruction Solutions for All Learners

Special Needs L1
Have students look at each Example and identify the operation they must undo first. The rules here are different from the order of operations where you multiply or divide before adding and subtracting. For many equations you undo addition or subtraction and then undo multiplication or division.
learning style: visual

Below Level L2
Have students find the missing number in several statements like the following.
$$-26 + \square = 0 \quad 26 \qquad \frac{-7}{\square} = 1 \quad -7$$
learning style: visual

EXAMPLE   Undoing Addition First

② Solve $\frac{x}{3} + 11 = 16$.

$$\frac{x}{3} + 11 = 16$$

$$\frac{x}{3} + 11 - 11 = 16 - 11 \qquad \leftarrow \text{To undo addition, subtract 11 from each side.}$$

$$\frac{x}{3} = 5 \qquad \leftarrow \text{Simplify.}$$

$$3\left(\frac{x}{3}\right) = 3(5) \qquad \leftarrow \text{To undo division, multiply each side by 3.}$$

$$x = 15 \qquad \leftarrow \text{Simplify.}$$

✓ Quick Check

● **2.** Solve the equation $\frac{x}{5} + 35 = 75$. Check your answer. *200*

You can use two-step equations to solve real-world problems.

EXAMPLE   Solving Two-Step Equations

③ **TAKS** **Multiple Choice** On weekday afternoons, a local bowling alley offers a special. Each bowling game costs $2.50, and shoe rental is $2.00. You spend $14.50 total. What is the number of games that you bowl?

⒜ 3　　　　　⒝ 5　　　　　⒞ 7　　　　　⒟ 9

Words times number of games plus is 14.50

↓ Let n = the number of games you bowl.

Equation 2.50 · n + 2.00 = 14.50

$$2.5n + 2 = 14.50$$

$$2.5n + 2 - 2 = 14.50 - 2 \qquad \leftarrow \text{Subtract 2 from each side.}$$

$$2.5n = 12.50 \qquad \leftarrow \text{Simplify.}$$

$$\frac{2.5n}{2.5} = \frac{12.50}{2.5} \qquad \leftarrow \text{Divide each side by 2.5.}$$

$$n = 5 \qquad \leftarrow \text{Simplify.}$$

You bowled 5 games. The answer is B.

★ TAKS Tip

You can eliminate answer choices using number sense. Choice D can be eliminated because it is too high. If you played 9 games, your total cost would be greater than $18.

✓ Quick Check

3. Solomon decided to make posters for the student council election. He bought markers that cost $.79 each and a poster board that cost $1.25. The total cost was $7.57. Write and solve an equation to find the number of markers that Solomon bought.
Let m = number of markers;
$0.79m + 1.25 = 7.57$; 8 markers

4-6 Solving Two-Step Equations   **201**

---

2. Teach

Activity Lab

Use before the lesson.
Student Edition Activity Lab HandsOn 4-6a, Modeling Two-Step Equations, p. 199

All in One Teaching Resources
Activity Lab 4–6: Critical Thinking

Guided Instruction

Example 1
Remind students that they have learned to solve equations involving one operation by using the inverse operation. When an equation involves two operations, they should also use an inverse order of operations: Add or subtract first, then multiply or divide.

Example 2
Students can use an inverse order on a calculator to find the solution: start with 16, subtract 11, and multiply by 3.

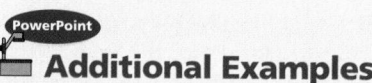

Additional Examples

① Solve $6r + 19 = 43$. $r = 4$

② Solve $\frac{a}{5} - 4 = 10$. $a = 70$

③ At the library sale, there was a $2.50 admission charge. Old paperbacks were on sale for $.25 each. If you only bought paperbacks and you spent $4.50 in all, how many paperbacks did you buy?
8 books

201

● More Than One Way

A family expects 88 people to attend its family reunion. There will be 16 children. Picnic tables seat 8 adults per table. The children will eat on blankets. How many picnic tables does the family need?

Sarah's Method

I can use number sense. First, I know that tables are needed only for adults. There are $88 - 16$, or 72, adults. Each table holds 8 adults. Since $72 \div 8 = 9$, the family needs 9 tables.

Ryan's Method

I can write and solve an equation. Let t represent the number of tables. Then $8t$ is the number of adults.

$$\text{adults} + \text{children} = 88 \text{ people}$$

$$8t + 16 = 88 \quad \leftarrow \text{Write the equation.}$$

Each term is divisible by 8. So I will divide first.

$$\frac{8t}{8} + \frac{16}{8} = \frac{88}{8} \quad \leftarrow \text{Divide each term by 8.}$$

$$t + 2 = 11 \quad \leftarrow \text{Simplify.}$$

I can use mental math to solve the equation. I know that 9 plus 2 is equal to 11. So, the family needs 9 tables.

Choose a Method

You had $25 in your savings account six weeks ago. You deposited the same amount of money each week for five weeks. Your balance is now $145. How much money did you deposit each week? Describe your method and explain why you chose it.

✓ Check Your Understanding

1. Fill in the missing numbers to make the diagram at the left represent the following situation: A taxi charges a flat fee of $2.00 plus $.50 for each mile. Your fare is $5.00. How many miles did you ride?
   Let $m=$ number of miles; $2.00 + 0.50m = 5.00$; 6 mi

Solve each equation. Check your answer.

2. $5p - 2 = 18$ 4

3. $7n - (-16) = 100$ 12

4. $\dfrac{y}{4.25} + 15 = -17$ −136

For more exercises, see Extra Skills and Word Problems.

GO for Help

For Exercises	See Examples
5–16	1
17–29	2–3

A Solve each equation. Check your answer. You may find a model helpful.

5. $8r - 8 = -32$ –3 **6.** $3w - 6 = -1.5$ 1.5 **7.** $4g - 4 = 28$ 8

8. $7t - 6 = -104$ –14 **9.** $12x - 14 = -2$ 1 **10.** $10m - \frac{2}{5} = 9\frac{3}{5}$ 1

11. $0.5y - 1.1 = 4.9$ 12 **12.** $-2d - 1.7 = -3.9$ 1.1 **13.** $-8a - 1 = -23$ $2\frac{3}{4}$

14. $2h - \frac{1}{10} = \frac{5}{8}$ $\frac{29}{80}$ **15.** $6t - \frac{1}{6} = 9$ $1\frac{19}{36}$ **16.** $5q - 3.75 = 26.25$ 6

17. $\frac{w}{5} + 3 = 6$ 15 **18.** $\frac{n}{4} + 2 = 4$ 8 **19.** $\frac{x}{8} + 4 = 13$ 72

20. $\frac{a}{7} + 10 = 17$ 49 **21.** $\frac{m}{-11} + 1 = -10$ 121 **22.** $\frac{p}{9} + 14 = 16$ 18

23. $\frac{c}{-7} + 3.2 = -2.2$ 37.8 **24.** $\frac{v}{-3} + \frac{3}{4} = -\frac{1}{8}$ $2\frac{5}{8}$ **25.** $\frac{b}{-8} + \frac{5}{7} = \frac{11}{14}$ $\frac{-4}{7}$

26. $\frac{c}{2} + 7.3 = 29.3$ 44 **27.** $\frac{m}{-10} + 12 = 67$ –550 **28.** $\frac{y}{-6.5} + 2 = -4$ 39

29. Kristine bought a vase that cost $5.99 and roses that cost $1.25 each. The total cost was $20.99. Write and solve an equation to find how many roses Kristine bought.
Let *r* = number of roses; 5.99 + 1.25*r* = 20.99; 12 roses.

B GPS 30. Guided Problem Solving Renting boats on a lake costs $22 per hour plus a flat fee of $10 for insurance. You have $98. Write and solve an equation to find the number of hours you can rent a boat.
Let *h* = number of hours; 10 + 22*h* = 98; 4 h.

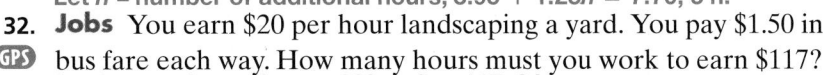

- insurance plus 22 times number of hours = total paid

Write and solve an equation for each situation.

31. A skating rink rents skates at $3.95 for the first hour plus $1.25 for each additional hour. When you returned your skates, you paid $7.70. How many additional hours did you keep the skates?
Let *h* = number of additional hours; 3.95 + 1.25*h* = 7.70; 3 h.

32. Jobs You earn $20 per hour landscaping a yard. You pay $1.50 in
GPS bus fare each way. How many hours must you work to earn $117?
Let *h* = number of hours; 20*h* − 3 = 117; 6 h.

33. Geometry The sum of the measures of the angles in a triangle is 180 degrees. One angle measures 45 degrees. The measures of the other two angles are equal. What is the measure of each of the other two angles? Let *x* = measure of each angle; 45 + 2*x* = 180; 67.5°.

34. Olympics The first modern Olympic games were held in Greece in 1896. The 2004 Olympic games in Athens had 202 participating countries. The number of countries in the 2004 Olympic games was 6 more than 14 times the number of countries in the 1896 games. How many countries participated in the 1896 Olympic games?
Let *n* = number of countries; 14*n* + 6 = 202; 14 countries.

---

3. Practice

Assignment Guide

Check Your Understanding
Go over Exercises 1–4 in class before assigning the Homework Exercises.

Homework Exercises
A Practice by Example 5–29
B Apply Your Skills 30–41
C Challenge 42
TEKS ★ TAKS Tune-Up and
   Mixed Review 43–48

Homework Quick Check
To check students' understanding of key skills and concepts, go over Exercises 12, 22, 32, 34, and 38.

Differentiated Instruction Resources

Adapted Practice 4-6 L1

Practice 4-6 Solving Two-Step Equations L3

Solve each equation. Then check your answer.
1. $7m + 8 = 71$ 9
2. $\frac{y}{7} + 6 = 11$ 35
3. $12y + 2 = 146$ 12
4. $\frac{w}{9} - 17 = 21$ 342
5. $\frac{y}{-12} + 1 = 6$ –60
6. $2a - 1 = 19$ 10
7. $\frac{b}{9} - 8 = 17$ 225
8. $-4t + 16 = 24$ –2
9. $\frac{b}{2} - 8 = -6$ –4
10. $3d + 14 = 11$ –1
11. $\frac{n}{19} - 1 = 8$ 153
12. $\frac{c}{6} - 14 = 21$ 175
13. $\frac{t}{9} + 4 = 2$ 18
14. $-2y + 16 = 10$ 3
15. $4w - 26 = 82$ 27
16. $\frac{t}{19} - 2 = -5$ –57

Solve each equation.
17. $3n - 8 = 4$ (4 + 8) ÷ 3 = 4
18. $\frac{g}{5} - 4 = 11$ (11 + 4) × 5 = 75
19. $2n - 3 = 9$ (9 + 3) ÷ 2 = 6
20. $1 + \frac{a}{4} = 9$ (9 − 1) × 4 = 32

Match each sentence with a two-step equation.
21. Half of the height of a tree minus five equals fifteen. C
22. Two less than three times the number of feet of fencing required equals twelve feet. A
23. Eight less than the quotient of Dave's golf score and four equals negative five. D
24. Three times Gail's age increased by two years equals twelve years. B
A. $3n - 2 = 12$
B. $3n + 2 = 12$
C. $\frac{a}{2} - 5 = 15$
D. $\frac{a}{4} - 8 = -5$

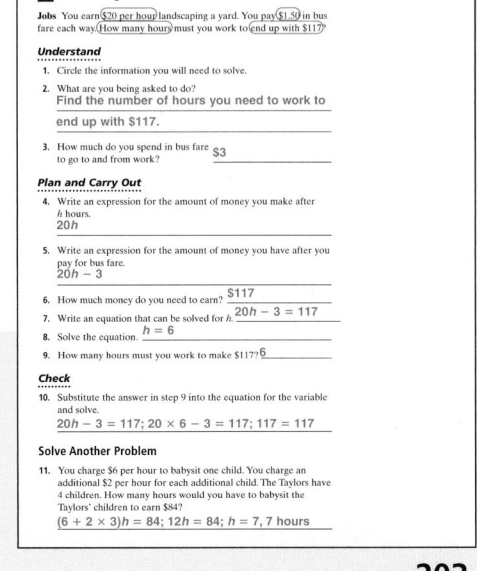

4-6 • Guided Problem Solving **GPS** L3

GPS Student Page 203, Exercise 32:

Jobs You earn $20 per hour landscaping a yard. You pay $1.50 in bus fare each way. How many hours must you work to end up with $117?

Understand
1. Circle the information you will need to solve.
2. What are you being asked to do? Find the number of hours you need to work to end up with $117.
3. How much do you spend in bus fare to go to and from work? $3

Plan and Carry Out
4. Write an expression for the amount of money you make after *h* hours. 20*h*
5. Write an expression for the amount of money you have after you pay for bus fare. 20*h* − 3
6. How much money do you need to earn? $117
7. Write an equation that can be solved for *h*. 20*h* − 3 = 117
8. Solve the equation. *h* = 6
9. How many hours must you work to make $117? 6

Check
10. Substitute the answer in step 9 into the equation for the variable and solve. 20*h* − 3 = 117; 20 × 6 − 3 = 117; 117 = 117

Solve Another Problem
11. You charge $6 per hour to babysit one child. You charge an additional $2 per hour for each additional child. The Taylors have 4 children. How many hours would you have to babysit the Taylors' children to earn $84? (6 + 2 × 3)*h* = 84; 12*h* = 84; *h* = 7, 7 hours

203

PowerPoint

Lesson Quiz

Solve each equation.

1. $9r + 7 = 79$ $r = 8$

2. $\frac{s}{4} - 6 = 14$ $s = 80$

3. $3t - 4 = 44$ $t = 16$

4. $\frac{v}{5} + 6 = -1$ $v = -35$

38. 30 = the DJ's hourly wage; x = hours the DJ works; 65 = cost of decorations; 170 = amount of money budgeted

Reteaching 4-6 Solving Two-Step **L2**

Enrichment 4-6 Solving Two-Step **L4**

204

GO Online

Homework Help
Visit: PHSchool.com
Web Code: are-0406

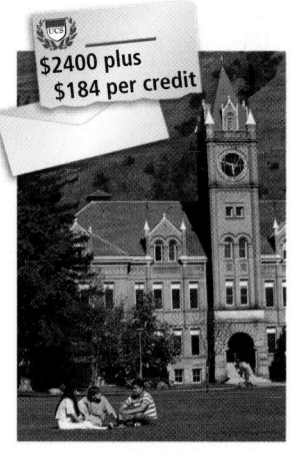

$2400 plus
$184 per credit

Solve each equation.

35. $\frac{x + 4}{5} = 3$ 11

36. $\frac{t - 7}{-2} = 11$ −15

37. $\frac{y + \frac{1}{3}}{4} = 2\frac{1}{4}$ $8\frac{2}{3}$

38. <u>**Writing in Math**</u> Your class budgets a certain amount of money from the class treasury for a dance. Expenses will include a fixed amount for decorations, plus an hourly wage for the disc jockey. This can be represented by the equation $30x + 65 = 170$. Explain how each number in the equation relates to the problem. **See margin.**

39. **College** In college, you earn credits for courses taken. For one semester, tuition at a local college is $2,400. You have financial aid that will cover $5,160 for the semester. Refer to the information at the left. How many credits can you take? **15 credits**

40. The student council sponsored a bake sale to raise money. Kim bought a slice of cake for $1.50 and also bought six cupcakes. She spent $4.20 in all. How much did each cupcake cost? **45 cents**

41. **Open-Ended** Write two different two-step equations that both have a solution of 3. **Check students' work.**

C 42. **Challenge** You buy 1.25 lb of apples and 2.45 lb of bananas. The total cost, after using a 75¢-off coupon, is $2.58. Apples and bananas sell for the same price per pound. Find their price per pound. **$.90/lb**

TEKS ★ TAKS Tune-Up and Mixed Review

TAKS Objective 2
TEKS (7.5)(A)

43. The model below represents the equation $5x + 4 = 14$.

What is the value of x? **B**

(A) $x = \frac{18}{5}$ (B) $x = 2$ (C) $x = -2$ (D) $x = 5$

TAKS Objective 6
TEKS (7.13)(B)

44. The Dead Sea is 1,345 feet below sea level. What method can be used to find the altitude of the Dead Sea in yards? **J**
(F) Multiply −1,345 by 46.   (H) Divide −1,345 by 12.
(G) Multiply −1,345 by 3.   (J) Divide −1,345 by 3.

TAKS Objective 1
TEKS (7.2)(E)

45. What is the value of the expression $2(15 - 12)^2 \div 6 + 3$?
(A) 12   (B) 9   (C) 6   (D) 2   **C**

GO for Help Lesson 4-3

Describe a problem situation that matches each equation. Then solve.

46. $r + 11 = 2$ **47.** $h - 9 = 5.5$ **48.** $\frac{1}{6}q = 9$

46–48. Check students' work.

204 **Chapter 4** Equations and Inequalities

TEKS ★ TAKS Resources

• TAKS Strategies, p. 219
• TAKS Tune-Up, pp. 223–225

TAKS Tune-Up Kit
• TAKS Daily Review Transparencies
• TAKS Review and Preparation Workbook
• TAKS Strategies with Transparencies
• Texas Progress Monitoring Assessments

Alternative Assessment

Have students work in pairs. Each partner chooses the two steps (adding or subtracting and multiplying or dividing) needed to solve an equation. Each partner writes a two-step equation that requires the chosen solution steps. Partners trade papers and each student solves the "made-to-order" equation. Students discuss their answers.

Graphing and Writing Inequalities

 Check Skills You'll Need

1. Vocabulary Review
Integers are the set of whole numbers and their __?__ .
opposites
Compare using <, =, or >.

2. 0 $\overset{>}{\blacksquare}$ −2

3. 14 $\overset{>}{\blacksquare}$ −14

4. −4 $\overset{<}{\blacksquare}$ 5

5. −17 $\overset{>}{\blacksquare}$ −18

 for Help
Lesson 1-6

What You'll Learn

To graph and write algebraic inequalities

🔊 **New Vocabulary** inequality, solution of an inequality

Why Learn This?

When you use an expression such as *at least* or *at most*, you are talking about an inequality. You can use inequalities to represent situations that involve minimum or maximum amounts.

A mathematical sentence that contains <, >, ≤, ≥, or ≠ is an **inequality.** Sometimes an inequality contains a variable, as in $x \geq 2$.

A **solution of an inequality** is any value that makes the inequality true. For example, 6, 8, and 15 are solutions of $x \geq 6$ because $6 \geq 6$, $8 \geq 6$, and $15 \geq 6$.

EXAMPLE **Identifying Solutions of an Inequality**

Vocabulary Tip

Read > as "is greater than."

Read < as "is less than."

Read ≥ as "is greater than or equal to."

Read ≤ as "is less than or equal to."

1 Find whether each number is a solution of $x \leq 2$; −3, 0, 2, 4.5.

Test each value by replacing the variable and evaluating the sentence.

$-3 \leq 2$ ← **−3 is less than or equal to 2: true.** ✔

$0 \leq 2$ ← **0 is less than or equal to 2: true.** ✔

$2 \leq 2$ ← **2 is less than or equal to 2: true.** ✔

$4.5 \leq 2$ ← **4.5 is less than or equal to 2: false.** ✗

The numbers −3, 0, and 2 are solutions of $x \leq 2$. The number 4.5 is not a solution of $x \leq 2$.

✅ **Quick Check**

● **1.** Which numbers are solutions of the inequality $m \geq -3$; −8, −2, 1.4?
−2, 1.4

A graph can show all the numbers in a solution. You use closed circles and open circles to show whether numbers are included in the solution.

Objectives

To graph and write algebraic inequalities

Examples

1 Identifying Solutions of an Inequality
2 Graphing Inequalities
3 Writing Inequalities
4 Application: Nutrition

Professional Development

Math Background

The equations that were discussed in previous lessons had a common characteristic: Each equation had exactly one solution. In contrast, each of the inequalities presented in this lesson has infinitely many solutions. Since it is impossible to list an infinite number of solutions, a number-line graph is used as a means of picturing them.

More Math Background: p. 166D

Lesson Planning and Resources

See p. 166E for a list of the resources that support this lesson.

PowerPoint

 Bell Ringer Practice

✅ **Check Skills You'll Need**
Use student page, transparency, or PowerPoint.

TAKS **Daily Review 32**
Use transparency.

Differentiated Instruction **Solutions for All Learners**

Special Needs L1
If students have difficulty graphing the solution to the inequalities, for example drawing the point or circle, ask them to work in pairs. They can provide direction while their partner graphs.

learning style: visual

Below Level L2
Read several sets of true/false exercises like these.

2 > 8 false   −2 > 8 false
2 > −8 true   −2 > −8 true

learning style: auditory

Activity Lab

Use before the lesson.

 Teaching Resources

Activity Lab 4-7: Graphing and Writing Inequalities

Guided Instruction

Example 1
Students might not understand why the statement $2 \leq 2$ is true. Tell them that $2 \leq 2$ is a short way of writing, "$2 < 2$ or $2 = 2$." A compound statement with the word *or* is true when one of the parts is true. Since $2 = 2$ is true, the entire statement is true.

Additional Examples

1 Tell whether each number is a solution of
$k > -6$: $-8, -6, 0, 3, 7$
The numbers 0, 3, and 7 are solutions of $k > -6$. The numbers -8 and -6 are not.

2 Graph the solution of each inequality on a number line.

a. $r \leq 2$

b. $m > -5$

3 Write an inequality.

Sample: $z < -4$

4 You must be at least 18 years of age to vote. Write an inequality for this. Let *a* stand for age in years; $a \geq 18$

 Teaching Resources
- Daily Notetaking Guide 4-7 **L3**
- Adapted Notetaking 4-7 **L1**

Closure

- *What is an inequality?* A mathematical sentence that contains $<$, $>$, $\leq$, or $\geq$.
- Explain what a solution of an inequality is. Any number that makes the inequality true.

EXAMPLE **Graphing Inequalities**

2 Graph the solution of each inequality.

a. $n \geq -3$

 ← Use a closed circle at -3 to show that *n* can equal -3.

b. $h < 7$

 ← Use an open circle at 7 to show that *h* cannot equal 7.

✓ Quick Check

2. Graph the solution of the inequality $w < -3$.

You can write an inequality by analyzing its graph.

EXAMPLE **Writing Inequalities**

3 Write an inequality for the graph.

 ← Since the circle at 2 is open, 2 is not a solution.

$x > 2$ ← Since the graph shows values greater than 2, use $>$.

✓ Quick Check

3. Write an inequality for the graph. $x < 4$

You can write inequalities to describe real-world situations.

EXAMPLE **Application: Nutrition**

4 To be labeled sugar free, a food product must contain less than 0.5 g of sugar per serving. Write an inequality to describe this requirement.

Words	amount of sugar	is less than	0.5 g of sugar

Let *s* = the number of grams of sugar in a serving of food.

Equation	s	<	0.5

The inequality is $s < 0.5$.

✓ Quick Check

4. Write an inequality for "To qualify for the race, your time can be at most 62 seconds." $t \leq 62$

Advanced Learners **L4**
Have students write sentences about everyday experiences that can be described by inequalities.
Sample: I ride my bike at least 5 mi each week.

English Language Learners ELL
Have students write the symbols for *is less than* or *equal to,* and *is greater than* or *equal to* on index cards. Have them write the words for the symbols, along with some examples for each one. They can refer to these cards as needed.

learning style: visual

Check Your Understanding

1. **Vocabulary** What is the name of a mathematical sentence that contains the symbols $<$, $>$, $\leq$, $\geq$, or $\neq$? **inequality**

2. **Reasoning** Is $-4 \geq 4$? Explain. **no; $-4 < 4$**

3. Which inequality does NOT have 8 as a solution? **C**
   (A) $-3 < y$ (B) $13 \geq y$ (C) $y < 8$ (D) $y \geq 8$

Which numbers are solutions of each inequality?

4. $x \geq -5$; $-6, -1, 0$ 5. $x \leq -1$; $-1, 1, 3$ 6. $x > 0$; $-1, 0, 1$
   $-1, 0$ **-1**   **1**

Homework Exercises

For more exercises, see Extra Skills and Word Problems.

GO for Help

For Exercises	See Examples
7–10	1
11–18	2
19–23	3–4

(A) **Which numbers are solutions of each inequality?**

7. $x < 1$; $-2, 1, 2$ **-2**   8. $x > -5$; $-7, -5, -1$ **-1**

9. $x \leq -9$; $-12, -4, 2$ **-12**   10. $x < -8$; $-10, -5, 0$ **-10**

Graph the solution of each inequality.
11–14. See left.

11. $x \geq 4$ 12. $x \leq -2$ 13. $x < 2$ 14. $x > -4$
   15–18. See margin.

15. $x \leq 0$ 16. $h > -5$ 17. $t \geq -5$ 18. $p < -6$

Write an inequality for each graph. $x < 2$

11.
   ```
   2 3 4 5 6 7
   ```
12.
   ```
   -6 -5 -4 -3 -2 -1
   ```
13.
   ```
   -2 -1 0 1 2 3
   ```
14.
   ```
   -5 -4 -3 -2 -1 0
   ```

19.
   ```
   0    3    6
   ```
   $x \leq 6$

20.
   ```
   -2  0  2  4  6
   ```

21.
   ```
   -2  0  2  4
   ```
   $x \geq -1$

22.
   ```
   -4  -2  0  2
   ```
   $x \leq -1$

23. Write an inequality for "Every item costs one dollar or less!" $c \leq 1.00$

(B) **GPS** 24. **Guided Problem Solving** Write an inequality for "The car ride to the park will take at least 30 minutes." $x \geq 30$
   - Choose a variable: Let x represent how long the car ride will be.
   - Read for key words: Decide whether to use $<$, $>$, $\leq$, or $\geq$.
   - Write the inequality: x ▉ 30.

Write an inequality for each statement. Graph the solution.
25–28. See margin.

25. To see the movie, you must be at least 17 years old.

26. The temperature is greater than 100°F.

27. A number p is not positive.

28. The speed limit on the highway is at most 65 mi/h.

15.
   ```
   -2 -1 0 1 2 3
   ```
16.
   ```
   -7 -6 -5 -4 -3 -2
   ```
17.
   ```
   -7 -6 -5 -4 -3 -2
   ```

18.
   ```
   -9 -8 -7 -6 -5 -4
   ```
25–28. See back of book.

3. Practice

Assignment Guide

Check Your Understanding
Go over Exercises 1–6 in class before assigning the Homework Exercises.

Homework Exercises
A   Practice by Example   7–23
B   Apply Your Skills   24–35
C   Challenge   36
TEKS ★ TAKS Tune-Up and Mixed Review   37–41

Homework Quick Check
To check students' understanding of key skills and concepts, go over Exercises 10, 19, 29, 30, and 32.

Differentiated Instruction Resources

PowerPoint

Lesson Quiz

Write an inequality for each verbal statement. Graph the solution.

1. A dog weighs less than 25 pounds. $d < 25$

$$0 \quad 10 \quad 20 \quad 30$$

2. You must be at least 18 to vote. $v \geq 18$

$$14 \quad 16 \quad 18 \quad 20 \quad 22$$

GO Online

Homework Help

Visit: PHSchool.com
Web Code: are-0407

29. Use an open circle for $<$ or $>$ and use a closed circle for $\leq$ or $\geq$.

30. Answers may vary. Sample: -17 is to the right of -22 on a number line.

Vocabulary Tip

A *compound inequality* is a number sentence with more than one inequality symbol.

29. Writing in Math Explain how you know whether to draw an open or closed circle when you graph an inequality. **See left.**

30. Reasoning Explain why $-17 > -22$. **See left.**

GPS

Use a variable to write an inequality for each situation.

31.
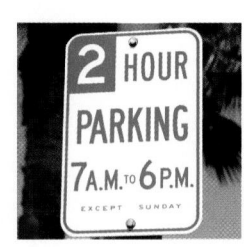
$w \leq 3$

32.
$p \leq 2$

Identify an integer that is a solution for each *compound inequality*.

33. $-3 \leq x < 0$ **34.** $-2 < y \leq 1$ **35.** $-6 \leq p \leq -4$
$-3, -2,$ or -1 $-1, 0,$ or 1 $-6, -5,$ or -4

C 36. Challenge If $a \geq 9$ and $9 \geq b$, then a ▮ b. Complete the statement using $<$, $>$, $\leq$, or $\geq$. $\geq$

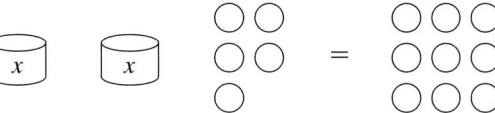

TEKS ★ TAKS Tune-Up and Mixed Review

TAKS Objective 2
TEKS (7.5)(A)

37. The model below represents the equation $2x + 5 = 9$.

What is the first step in solving the equation? **B**

Ⓐ Add 5 to each side of the equation.
Ⓑ Subtract 5 from each side of the equation.
Ⓒ Divide each side of the equation by 5.
Ⓓ Subtract 2 from each side of the equation.

TAKS Objective 6
TEKS (7.13)(B)

38. A recipe calls for 3 pounds of ground turkey. Carmen has one package of ground beef that weighs $1\frac{1}{2}$ pounds, one package of ground turkey that weighs $1\frac{1}{4}$ pound, and another package of ground turkey that weighs $1\frac{5}{8}$ pound. Which information is NOT necessary to find how much more ground turkey Carmen needs? **H**

Ⓕ Total amount of ground turkey needed for the recipe
Ⓖ Weight of Carmen's smaller package of ground turkey
Ⓗ Weight of Carmen's package of ground beef
Ⓙ Weight of Carmen's larger package of ground turkey

for Help

Lesson 1-6

Order the numbers from least to greatest.
$-4, -2, -1, 2, 4, 7$ $-9, -8, -6, 3, 12$ $-5, -2, 0, 7, 10$
39. $-2, 4, -4, 2, 7, -1$ **40.** $3, -8, -9, 12, -6$ **41.** $10, 0, -5, -2, 7$

208 Chapter 4 Equations and Inequalities

Reteaching 4-7
Graphing and Writing Ine **L2**

Two expressions separated by an inequality sign form an **inequality**. An inequality shows that the two expressions *are not* equal. Unlike the equations you have worked with, an inequality has many solutions.

The **solutions of an inequality** are the values that make the inequality true. They can be graphed on a number line. Use a closed circle (●) for $\leq$ and $\geq$ and an open circle (○) for $>$ and $<$. For example:

$x > -2$ ("greater than")
$x < -2$ ("less than")
$x \geq -2$ ("greater than or equal to")
$x \leq -2$ ("less than or equal to")

Graph the inequality $x > 4$.

The inequality is read as "x is greater than 4." Since all numbers to the right of 4 are greater than 4, you can draw an arrow from 4 to the right. Since 4 is not greater than itself, use an open circle on 4.

1. Graph the inequality $x \leq -3$.

a. Write the inequality in words.   *x is less than or equal to -3.*
b. Will the circle at -3 be open or closed?   *closed; -3 satisfies inequality*
c. Graph the solution.

2. Graph the inequality $x < 3$.

a. Write the inequality in words.   *x is less than 3.*
b. Will the circle at 3 be open or closed?   *open*
c. Graph the solution.

Enrichment 4-7
Graphing and Writing Ine **L4**

Exploring Inequalities

In order to create a sense of fairness in the sport, wrestling is divided into weight and age classes. The table below was used by the state of Florida for a 2001 junior wrestling tournament.

Division	Birthdate	Match Time Limit	Weight Classes
Bantam	Born 1994–1995 (State level program only)	Two 90-second periods 30-second rest between periods	40 lb, 45 lb, 50 lb, 55 lb, 60 lb 65 lb, 70 lb, 75 lb, 75+ lb
Midget	Born 1992–1993	Two 90-second periods 30-second rest between periods	50 lb, 55 lb, 60 lb, 65 lb, 70 lb 75 lb, 80 lb, 87 lb, 95 lb, 103 lb 112 lb, 120 lb, 120+ lb
Novice	Born 1990–1991	Two 2-minute periods 30-second rest between periods	60 lb, 65 lb, 70 lb, 75 lb, 80 lb 85 lb, 90 lb, 95 lb, 100 lb, 105 lb 112 lb, 120 lb, 130 lb, 140 lb, 140+ lb
Schoolboy/ girl	Born 1988–1989	Two 2-minute periods 30-second rest between periods	70 lb, 75 lb, 80 lb, 85 lb, 90 lb 95 lb, 100 lb, 105 lb, 110 lb 115 lb, 120 lb, 125 lb, 130 lb 140 lb, 150 lb, 160 lb, 160+ lb

For the following questions, assume the year is 2004.

1. Write an inequality to represent the age limit of a Novice wrestler. Then write another inequality to represent the weight limit for a Novice wrestler in the 90 lb weight class.
13 years $\leq x \leq$ 14 years; 90 lb $\leq x \leq$ 95 lb

2. A wrestler is 11 years old and 68 pounds. What division is the wrestler in? What is the wrestler's match time limit?
Midget; two 90-second periods

3. Write and graph an inequality to show the range of a wrestler's age in the Schoolboy/girl division.
15 years $\leq x \leq$ 16 years

4. You attend a wrestling meet to watch your friend wrestle. Use the following inequalities to determine what division your friend belongs to. 9 years $\leq x \leq$ 10 years old; 55 lb $\leq x <$ 60 lb
Bantam division

208

TEKS ★ TAKS Resources

- TAKS Strategies, p. 219
- TAKS Tune-Up, pp. 223–225

TAKS Tune-Up Kit

- TAKS Daily Review Transparencies
- TAKS Review and Preparation Workbook
- TAKS Strategies with Transparencies
- Texas Progress Monitoring Assessments

Alternative Assessment

Ask students to write four inequalities: one with $>$; one with $<$; one with $\geq$, one with $\leq$. On another sheet of paper, have them graph each inequality. Students then exchange their graphs with a partner who writes the inequality for each graph. Students should discuss their results.

Checkpoint Quiz 2

Lessons 4-5 through 4-7

Solve each equation.

1. $3x + 4 = 19$ **5**

2. $\frac{t}{5} - 2 = 6$ **40**

3. $-2y - 5 = -9$ **2**

4. $\frac{d}{-3} + 7 = 10$ **-9**

5. $6g + 6 = -6$ **-2**

6. $\frac{f}{-1} - 8 = -3$ **-5**

7. A sweater costs $12 more than twice the cost of a skirt. The sweater costs $38. Find the cost of the skirt. **Let c = the cost of a skirt; 12 + 2c = 38; $13.**

Graph the solution of each inequality. **8–10. See margin.**

8. $x > -3$

9. $y \leq -2$

10. $d \geq -1$

4-8a Activity Lab

Data Analysis

Inequalities in Bar Graphs

A class conducted a survey on free time. The standard bar graph shows the average number of hours per week students spend on various activities. The floating bar graph shows the minimum and maximum number of hours students spend on each activity.

Standard Bar Graph

Hours per week

Floating Bar Graph

Hours per week

- hanging out with friends
- watching television
- playing sports
- playing video games
- reading

1. What are the minimum and maximum hours per week that students in the survey spend hanging out with friends? **minimum 6, maximum 10**

2. Which activity is not done by all students? Which activity shows the least variety in how students responded to the survey? Explain.
2–3. See margin.

3. Let x represent the number of hours per week spent on an activity. Which activity in the floating bar graph is represented by the inequality $2 \leq x \leq 8$? Write inequalities to represent each activity on the floating bar graph.

209

Checkpoint Quiz 2

8.
$-5\ -4\ -3\ -2\ -1\quad 0$

9.
$-5\ -4\ -3\ -2\ -1\quad 0$

10.
$-4\ -3\ -2\ -1\quad 0\quad 1$

Activity Lab

2. playing video games; hanging out with friends, because the bar is the shortest

3. reading; hanging out with friends: $6 \leq x \leq 10$; watching television: $4 \leq x \leq 12$; playing sports: $2 \leq x \leq 14$; playing video games: $0 \leq x \leq 10$

209

4-8

Solving Inequalities by Adding or Subtracting

Objectives

To solve inequalities by adding or subtracting

Examples

1. Solve Inequalities by Adding
2. Solving Inequalities by Subtracting
3. Application: Transportation

TEKS Math Background

Solving an inequality involves the same basic strategy used for solving an equation: Isolate the variable. The method is the same as that used with equations. That is, you use inverse operations to "undo" the addition or subtraction.

More Math Background: p. 166D

Lesson Planning and Resources

See p. 166E for a list of the resources that support this lesson.

Bell Ringer Practice

☑ **Check Skills You'll Need**
Use student page, transparency, or PowerPoint.

(TAKS) Daily Review 33
Use transparency.

☑ Check Skills You'll Need

1. Vocabulary Review
Why are addition and subtraction called *inverse operations*?
See below.
Solve each equation.

2. $c + 4 = -2$ -6

3. $x + 9 = 10$ 1

4. $b + (-2) = 7$ 9

5. $m - (-3) = 10$ 7

 for Help
Lesson 4-3

Check Skills You'll Need

1. because they "undo" each other

 for Help

For help with graphing inequalities, see Lesson 4-7, Example 2.

What You'll Learn

To solve inequalities by adding or subtracting

🔊 **New Vocabulary** Addition Property of Inequality, Subtraction Property of Inequality

Why Learn This?

Buildings and buses have limits on the number of people they can hold. You can use inequalities to find how many people can fit safely.

You can solve inequalities using properties similar to those you used solving equations.

If you add 3 to each side of the inequality $-3 < 2$, the resulting inequality, $0 < 5$, is also true.

KEY CONCEPTS **Addition Property of Inequality**

You can add the same value to each side of an inequality.

Arithmetic	**Algebra**
Since $7 > 3$, $7 + 4 > 3 + 4$.	If $a > b$, then $a + c > b + c$.
Since $1 < 3$, $1 + 4 < 3 + 4$.	If $a < b$, then $a + c < b + c$.

EXAMPLE **Solving Inequalities by Adding**

1 Solve $n - 10 > 14$. Graph the solution.

$$n - 10 > 14$$
$$n - 10 + 10 > 14 + 10 \quad \leftarrow \text{Add 10 to each side.}$$
$$n > 24 \quad \leftarrow \text{Simplify.}$$

☑ Quick Check

$y < 7$;

1. Solve $y - 3 < 4$. Graph the solution.

Differentiated Instruction Solutions for All Learners

Special Needs **L1**
Have students draw a rectangle to represent the bus, in Example 3. Have them write 19 in the rectangle. Have them use s to represent the number of students who can board the bus keeping the total to at most 76. So they should write $19 + s$ inside the bus is less than or equal to ($\geq$) 76.
learning style: visual

Below Level **L2**
Give students several "fill in the blanks" solutions like this.
$$h - 5 < 7$$
$$h - 5 + \square < \square + 5 \quad \textbf{5; 7}$$
$$\square < \square \quad \textbf{h; 12}$$
learning style: visual

To solve an inequality involving addition, use subtraction.

Subtraction Property of Inequality

You can subtract the same value from each side of an inequality.

Arithmetic	**Algebra**
Since $9 > 6$, $9 - 3 > 6 - 3$.	If $a > b$, then $a - c > b - c$.
Since $15 < 20$, $15 - 4 < 20 - 4$.	If $a < b$, then $a - c < b - c$.

Note: The Properties of Inequality also apply to $\leq$ and $\geq$.

EXAMPLE **Solving Inequalities by Subtracting**

2. Solve $y + 7 \geq 12$. Graph the solution.

$$y + 7 \geq 12$$
$$y + 7 - 7 \geq 12 - 7 \quad \leftarrow \text{Subtract 7 from each side.}$$
$$y \geq 5 \quad \leftarrow \text{Simplify.}$$

2 a. $x > -4$;

$$-6\ -5\ -4\ -3\ -2\ -1$$

b. $y < 1$;

$$-2\ -1\ \ 0\ \ 1\ \ 2\ \ 3$$

c. $w \leq -9$;

$$-11 \qquad -9 \qquad -7$$

✓ **Quick Check**

2. Solve each inequality. Graph the solution. See left.
   a. $x + 9 > 5$ **b.** $y + 3 < 4$ **c.** $w + 4 \leq -5$

EXAMPLE **Application: Transportation**

3. A school bus can safely carry as many as 76 students. If 19 students are already on the bus, how many more can board the bus?

Words	students already on bus	plus	students remaining	is at most	76

Let s = the number of students remaining.

Expression	19	+	s	$\leq$	76

$$19 + s \leq 76$$
$$19 - 19 + s \leq 76 - 19 \quad \leftarrow \text{Subtract 19 from each side.}$$
$$s \leq 57 \quad \leftarrow \text{Simplify.}$$

At most 57 more students can board the bus.

3. Let p = number of points;
   $p + 104 > 200$; $p > 91$;
   you need more than 91 points.

✓ **Quick Check**

3. To get an A, you need more than 200 points on a two-part test. You score 109 on the first part. How many more points do you need?

Advanced Learners L4
Solve each inequality.

$x + 3 > x + 2$ all numbers
$x + 3 < x + 2$ no solution

English Language Learners ELL
Have students add the terms *open circle* and *closed circle* to their index cards. Have them describe, in words and symbols, what each means.

Pre-AP™

learning style: visual

Activity Lab

Use before the lesson.

All in One Teaching Resources

Activity Lab 4-8: Solving Inequalities by Adding and Subtracting

Guided Instruction

Example 1
Some students better visualize the process of adding the same number to each side when the addition is performed vertically.

$$n - 10 > 14$$
$$+ 10 = + 10$$
$$\overline{n > 24}$$

Error Prevention!

To check for errors in addition or subtraction, have students use the *associated equation*. In Example 1, $n > 24$ is a reasonable solution of $n - 10 > 14$ because 24 is the solution of $n - 10 = 14$.

PowerPoint
Additional Examples

1 Solve $q - 2 \geq -6$. Graph the solution. $q \geq -4$

$$-6 \quad -4 \quad -2 \quad 0 \quad 2$$

2 Solve $d + 9 < 8$. Graph the solution. $d < -1$

$$-4 \quad -2 \quad 0 \quad 2 \quad 4$$

3 The Drama Club can spend no more than $120 for costumes. They spent $79. How much more can they spend? at most $41

All in One Teaching Resources
• Daily Notetaking Guide 4-8 L3
• Adapted Notetaking 4-8 L1

Closure

• Explain how to solve inequalities by adding or subtracting. Sample: Isolate the variable; If a number has been added to the variable, subtract that number from each side. If a number has been subtracted from the variable, add that number to each side.

211

3. Practice

Assignment Guide

Check Your Understanding
Go over Exercises 1–6 in class before assigning the Homework Exercises.

Homework Exercises
A Practice by Example 7–25
B Apply Your Skills 26–38
C Challenge 39
TEKS ★ *TAKS* Tune-Up and Mixed Review 40–46

Homework Quick Check
To check students' understanding of key skills and concepts, go over Exercises 8, 17, 25, 37, and 38.

Differentiated Instruction Resources

Check Your Understanding

1. **Vocabulary** The __?__ states that you can add the same value to each side of an inequality. **Addition Property of Inequality**

2. **Reasoning** What value is a solution of $y + 7 \geq 12$ but is not a solution of $y + 7 > 12$? **5**

Match each inequality with the graph of its solution.

3. $h - 4 < 5$ **C**

4. $h + 4 \geq 5$ **D**

5. $h - 4 \leq -5$ **B**

6. $h + 4 < -5$ **A**

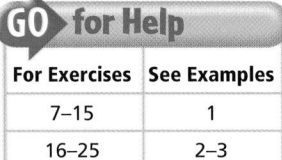

A. (number line from −12 to 9)
B. (number line from −3 to 4)
C. (number line from −9 to 12)
D. (number line from −3 to 4)

Homework Exercises

For more exercises, see **Extra Skills and Word Problems.**

GO for Help

For Exercises	See Examples
7–15	1
16–25	2–3

7. $g \leq -6$; (number line −9 to −4)

8. $m > -21$; (number line −23 to −19)

9. $y \geq 16$; (number line 14, 16, 18)

A Solve each inequality by adding. Graph the solution.
7–9. See left.
7. $g - 2 \leq -8$ 8. $m - 3 > -24$ 9. $y - 5 \geq 11$
10–15. See margin.
10. $x - 7 > -11$ 11. $n - 10 \leq 17$ 12. $p - 9 < -9$
13. $y - 5 \geq 12$ 14. $q - 2 < 4$ 15. $b - 4 > -6$

Solve each inequality by subtracting. Graph the solution.
16–24. See margin.
16. $h + 8 < -13$ 17. $n + 3 \geq 4$ 18. $r + 9 > 4$
19. $p + 10 \leq 6$ 20. $b + 22 > -1$ 21. $f + 5 \geq 0$
22. $m + 3 > 4$ 23. $x + 10 < 11$ 24. $k + 4 \leq -7$

25. **Consumer Issues** Your parents give you $35 for a scooter that **GPS** costs at least $100. How much money do you have to save to buy the scooter? Let s = amount of money to save; $s + 35 \geq 100$; $s \geq 65$; you save at least $65.

B GPS 26. **Guided Problem Solving** The weight of a loaded dump truck is less than 75,000 lb. When empty, the truck weighs 32,000 lb. Write and solve an inequality to find how much the load can weigh.

words: empty truck plus __?__ is less than 75,000 lb
inequality: 32,000 + ■ < 75,000
$\ell + 32{,}000 < 75{,}000$; $\ell < 43{,}000$

27. **Science** Water boils when the temperature is at least 212°F. A pot of water has a temperature of 109°F. How many degrees must the temperature rise for the water to boil? $109 + x \geq 212$; $x \geq 103$

10–24. See back of book.

35. No; the solution of $x + 5 \leq -2$ is $x \leq -7$, and the solution of $-2 \leq x + 5$ is $x \geq -7$.

37. $p \geq 338$; they must score at least $420 - 82$, or 338, points.

Solve each inequality by adding or subtracting.
28–30. See left.

28. $h - 9 < 1.3$ **29.** $w - \frac{1}{4} > -\frac{3}{4}$ **30.** $x + 5 \geq 98$

31. $j + 6.2 \geq 1.2$ **32.** $k + 42 \geq 36$ **33.** $a - 1\frac{4}{5} < 3\frac{7}{10}$
$j \geq -5$ $k \geq -6$ $a < 5\frac{1}{2}$

28. $h < 10.3$

29. $w > -\frac{1}{2}$

30. $x \geq 93$

34. Write an inequality for the sentence "Fifteen plus a number is greater than 10." Solve the inequality. $15 + n > 10; n > -5$

35. Reasoning Are the solutions of the inequalities $x + 5 \leq -2$ and $-2 \leq x + 5$ the same? Explain. **See margin.**

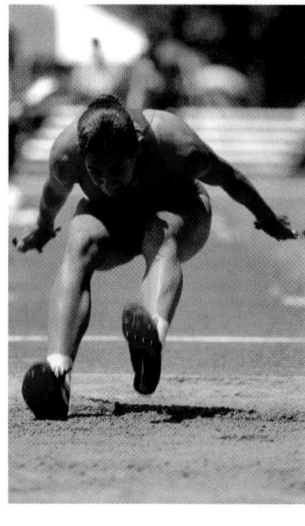

36. Sports To win the long jump, you need to jump a distance greater than 2.25 m. Your personal best jump is 2.1 m. Write and solve an inequality to find how much farther you need to jump to win.
$d + 2.1 > 2.25; d > 0.15$

37. Writing in Math The basketball team needs to score at least 420 points this season in order to set a new school record. It has already scored 82 points. Four players argue about which inequality represents the number of points yet to be scored: $p \geq 338$, $338 \geq p$, $p > 338$, or $338 > p$. Which is correct? Explain.
See margin.

38. A *compound inequality* is a number sentence with more than one inequality symbol. Solve the compound inequality $-3 \leq x + 4 < 9$.
$-7 \leq x < 5$

C 39. Challenge You want to eat no more than 3,000 Calories in a day. You consume 710 Calories for breakfast and have two bowls of soup for lunch. Each bowl contains 535 Calories. How many Calories can you consume at dinner? **no more than 1,220 Cal**

TEKS ★ TAKS Tune-Up and Mixed Review

GRIDDABLE ITEMS

TAKS Objective 1
TEKS (7.2)(F)

40. A baby who weighed 7.2 pounds at birth gained about 1.4 pounds each month. How many pounds did the baby weigh when it was 6 months old? **15.6**

TAKS Objective 1
TEKS (7.2)(B)

41. Two of the driest cities in the United States are Yuma, Arizona, and Las Vegas, Nevada. Yuma averages 3.01 inches of rain each year and Las Vegas averages 4.49 inches each year. How many more inches of rain does Las Vegas receive each year than Yuma? **1.48**

TAKS Objective 1
TEKS (7.1)(B)

42. The table shows record weights of 3 types of sunfish. In decimal form, how many pounds did the redbreast sunfish weigh? Round to the nearest hundredth. **2.06**

Fish	Weight (lb)
Green sunfish	$\frac{17}{8}$
Redbreast sunfish	$\frac{33}{16}$
Redear sunfish	$\frac{87}{16}$

Write each number as an improper fraction.

GO for Help   **Lesson 2-5**

43. $3\frac{1}{5}$ $\frac{16}{5}$ **44.** $6\frac{3}{4}$ $\frac{27}{4}$ **45.** $8\frac{1}{4}$ $\frac{33}{4}$ **46.** $7\frac{5}{8}$ $\frac{61}{8}$

Alternative Assessment

Ask students to write four different inequalities that all have the same solution, such as $h + 6 \leq 14$. $h \leq 8$ Two inequalities should be solved by adding and two by subtracting. Students then exchange papers with a partner who solves each inequality and graphs each solution. Have partners discuss their results.

TEKS ★ TAKS Resources

• TAKS Strategies, p. 219
• TAKS Tune-Up, pp. 223–225

TAKS Tune-Up Kit

• TAKS Daily Review Transparencies
• TAKS Review and Preparation Workbook
• TAKS Strategies with Transparencies
• Texas Progress Monitoring Assessments

---

4. Assess & Reteach

PowerPoint
Lesson Quiz

Solve each inequality. Graph the solution.

1. $x + 6 < 10$ $x < 4$

2. $a - 9 > 14$ $a > 23$

3. $n + 8 \leq 25$ $n \leq 17$

4. $p - 4 \geq 5$ $p \geq 9$

213

4-9

Objectives

To solve inequalities by multiplying or dividing

Examples

1. Solving Inequalities by Dividing
2. Application: Planning
3. Solving Inequalities by Multiplying

Math Background

The *rules* for solving equations and inequalities refer to the properties of equality and inequality. In Lesson 4-8, the addition and subtraction rules for inequalities were essentially the same as those for equations. In this lesson, the exposition demonstrates that multiplication and division rules for inequalities differ from the rules for equations in an important way: When multiplying or dividing each side of an inequality by a negative number, the direction of the inequality must be reversed.

More Math Background: p. 166D

Lesson Planning and Resources

See p. 166E for a list of the resources that support this lesson.

PowerPoint

Bell Ringer Practice

☑ **Check Skills You'll Need**
Use student page, transparency, or PowerPoint.

TAKS Daily Review 34
Use transparency.

214

4-9

Solving Inequalities by Multiplying or Dividing

☑ Check Skills You'll Need

1. **Vocabulary Review**
   How is the *Addition Property of Equality* similar to the *Addition Property of Inequality*?
   See below.
   Solve each inequality.

2. $x + 3 \le 5$ $x \le 2$

3. $p - 9 > -2$ $p > 7$

4. $8 \ge d + 5$ $3 \ge d$

5. $r - 2 < -8$ $r < -6$

for Help
Lesson 4-8

Check Skills You'll Need

1. You can add to each side of an equation or inequality without changing the relationship.

What You'll Learn

To solve inequalities by multiplying or dividing

 New Vocabulary Division Property of Inequality, Multiplication Property of Inequality

Why Learn This?

Inequalities can help you plan. You can solve inequalities to make sure you have enough ingredients when you are cooking.

Look at the pattern when you divide each side of an inequality by an integer.

$$18 > 12$$
$$\frac{18}{6} > \frac{12}{6}$$
$$\frac{18}{3} > \frac{12}{3}$$

← When the integer is positive, the direction of the inequality symbol stays the same.

$$\frac{18}{-2} < \frac{12}{-2}$$
$$\frac{18}{-6} < \frac{12}{-6}$$

← When the integer is negative, the direction of the inequality symbol is reversed.

KEY CONCEPTS   Division Property of Inequality

If you divide each side of an inequality by the same positive number, the direction of the inequality symbol remains unchanged.

Arithmetic	**Algebra**
$9 > 6$, so $\frac{9}{3} > \frac{6}{3}$	If $a > b$, and c is positive, then $\frac{a}{c} > \frac{b}{c}$.
$15 < 20$, so $\frac{15}{5} < \frac{20}{5}$	If $a < b$, and c is positive, then $\frac{a}{c} < \frac{b}{c}$.

If you divide each side of an inequality by the same negative number, the direction of the inequality symbol is reversed.

Arithmetic	**Algebra**
$16 > 12$, so $\frac{16}{-4} < \frac{12}{-4}$	If $a > b$, and c is negative, then $\frac{a}{c} < \frac{b}{c}$.
$10 < 18$, so $\frac{10}{-2} > \frac{18}{-2}$	If $a < b$, and c is negative, then $\frac{a}{c} > \frac{b}{c}$.

Differentiated Instruction   Solutions for All Learners

Special Needs L1
For Example 2, ask students to use a number line, and show jumps in increments of 55 until they get close to 190. Each jump represents 1 hour. It takes 3 jumps to get to 165, and you need another partial jump to get to 190, so 3 1/2 hours makes sense.

learning style: visual

Below Level L2
Have students fill in the blank for several exercises like these.

$-3t > -24$ $5w \le -15$
$t \square 8 <$ $w \square -3 \le$

learning style: visual

EXAMPLE Solving Inequalities by Dividing

1 Solve $-3y \leq -27$. Graph the solution.

$$-3y \leq -27$$
$$\frac{-3y}{-3} \geq \frac{-27}{-3} \quad \leftarrow \text{Divide each side by } -3. \text{ Reverse the direction of the symbol.}$$
$$y \geq 9 \quad \leftarrow \text{Simplify.}$$

1a. $p > -9$;

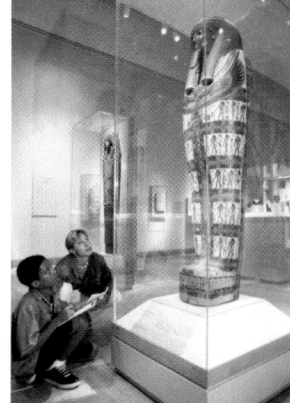

b. $m \leq 3$;

c. $n > -3$;

✓ Quick Check

1. Solve each inequality. Graph the solution. **See left.**

   a. $-4p < 36$ **b.** $-8m \geq -24$ **c.** $7n > -21$

You can solve an inequality that involves multiplication by dividing each side of the inequality by the same number.

EXAMPLE Application: Planning

2 Your class is taking a trip to a museum that is 190 miles away. The bus can travel at 55 miles per hour. At least how many hours should your class plan for the trip to the museum?

Words   55   times   number of hours   is at least   total miles

Let h = the number of hours.

Expression 55   · h $\geq$ 190

$$55h \geq 190$$
$$\frac{55h}{55} \geq \frac{190}{55} \quad \leftarrow \text{Divide each side by 55.}$$
$$h \geq 3.4545 \ldots \quad \leftarrow \text{Simplify.}$$
$$h \geq 3.5 \quad \leftarrow \text{Round up to the nearest half hour.}$$

Your class should plan for at least 3 hours and 30 minutes.

✓ Quick Check

2. A long-distance telephone company is offering a special rate of $.06 per minute. Your budget for long-distance telephone calls is $25 for the month. At most how many minutes of long distance can you use for the month with this rate? **416 min**

The properties of inequality apply to multiplication as well.

Advanced Learners   **L4**
Solve each inequality.

  $2y > y$ **all positive numbers**
  $2y < y$ **all negative numbers**

Pre-AP™

English Language Learners   **ELL**
Have students test out and explain why the inequality sign changes direction when you divide by a negative integer. Use $3 < 5$ as an example. If you divide each by -1, then the inequality becomes $-3 > -5$. Have them use and explain other examples to you.

                              learning style: verbal

---

2. Teach

Activity Lab
Use before the lesson.

All in One Teaching Resources
Activity Lab 4-9 Working with Inequalities

Guided Instruction

Example 1
Most students probably are aware that the rules for solving inequalities are very similar to the rules for solving equations. Focus their attention on the difference. Ask:
- *Why do you divide each side by -3?* to undo the multiplication by -3
- *Why do you reverse the direction of the inequality symbol?* You have divided each side by a negative number.

Error Prevention!

Watch for students who reverse the direction of the inequality whenever they see a negative number, even if the number by which they multiply or divide each side is positive.

Teaching Tip
When solving an inequality, students might find it helpful to recite the rule softly, using an abbreviated form. For example, when multiplying by a positive number, they might say, "Multiply by a positive, keep the same symbol." When dividing by a negative number, they might say, "Divide by a negative, reverse the symbol."

PowerPoint

Additional Examples

1 Solve $6a \leq -18$. Graph the solution $a \leq -3$

2 A woodworker makes a profit of $30 on each picture frame sold. How many frames must he sell to make a profit of at least $500? **17 frames**

Additional Examples

3 Solve $\frac{b}{-3} < -12$. $b > 36$

All in One Teaching Resources
- Daily Notetaking Guide 4-9 **L3**
- Adapted Notetaking 4-9 **L1**

Closure

- How do the Multiplication and Division Properties of Inequalities differ from the Multiplication and Division Properties of Equalities? **When you multiply or divide each side of an inequality by a negative number, the direction of the inequality symbol is reversed.**

KEY CONCEPTS **Multiplication Property of Inequality**

If you multiply each side of an inequality by the same positive number, the direction of the inequality symbol remains unchanged.

Arithmetic	**Algebra**
$12 > 8$, so $12 \cdot 2 > 8 \cdot 2$	If $a > b$, and c is positive, then $a \cdot c > b \cdot c$.
$3 < 6$, so $3 \cdot 4 < 6 \cdot 4$	If $a < b$, and c is positive, then $a \cdot c < b \cdot c$.

If you multiply each side of an inequality by the same negative number, the direction of the inequality symbol is reversed.

Arithmetic	**Algebra**
$6 > 2$, so $6(-3) < 2(-3)$	If $a > b$, and c is negative, then $a \cdot c < b \cdot c$.
$3 < 5$, so $3(-2) > 5(-2)$	If $a < b$, and c is negative, then $a \cdot c > b \cdot c$.

Online active math

For: Inequalities Activity
Use: Interactive
 Textbook, 4–9

EXAMPLE **Solving Inequalities by Multiplying**

3 Solve $\frac{y}{-8} \geq 2$.

$$\frac{y}{-8} \geq 2$$

$$-8 \cdot \frac{y}{-8} \leq -8 \cdot 2 \quad \leftarrow \begin{array}{l}\textbf{Multiply each side by } -8.\\ \textbf{Reverse the direction of the symbol.}\end{array}$$

$$y \leq -16 \quad \leftarrow \textbf{Simplify.}$$

Quick Check

● **3.** Solve $\frac{k}{-5} < -4$. Graph the solution.

$k > 20$

Check Your Understanding

1. The inequality symbol is reversed.

1. Vocabulary What happens when you multiply each side of an inequality by a negative number?

2. If $x > y$, which statement is NOT always true? **D**
- **A** $y < x$
- **B** $x + z > y + z$
- **C** $x - z > y - z$
- **D** $xz > yz$

Fill in the missing inequality symbol.

3. $3m > 99$
$\frac{3m}{3}$ ■ $\frac{99}{3}$ >

4. $-8z \leq 80$
$\frac{-8z}{-8}$ ■ $\frac{80}{-8}$ ≥

5. $\frac{d}{-3} < 12$
$\frac{d}{-3} \cdot (-3)$ ■ $12 \cdot (-3)$ >

216 Chapter 4 Equations and Inequalities

For more exercises, see Extra Skills and Word Problems.

GO for Help

For Exercises	See Examples
6–18	1–2
19–30	3

6. $h < 4$;

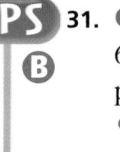

1 2 3 4 5 6

7. $p > 12$;

10 11 12 13 14 15

8. $n \leq -3$;

−6 −5 −4 −3 −2 −1

31. $c \cdot 70 \leq 6{,}000$; at most 85 cases

A **Solve each inequality by dividing. Graph the solution.**
6–8. See left.

6. $4h < 16$ **7.** $3p > 36$ **8.** $9n \leq -27$

9–17. See margin.

9. $6x < -48$ **10.** $-8b \geq -24$ **11.** $-5w \leq 30$

12. $-10d \geq -70$ **13.** $-2t > 10$ **14.** $5g < -35$

15. $-4.5p \leq 22.5$ **16.** $7y < -42.7$ **17.** $8.3w \geq 53.95$

18. A photo album page can hold six photographs. You have 296 photographs. How many pages do you need? at least 50 pages

19–30. See margin.

Solve each inequality by multiplying. Graph the solution.

19. $\frac{p}{5} < -3$ **20.** $\frac{k}{4} \geq 6$ **21.** $\frac{w}{7} \leq -3$

22. $\frac{y}{7} > -8$ **23.** $\frac{n}{-2} > -5$ **24.** $\frac{m}{-6} \geq 5$

25. $\frac{x}{10} < -4$ **26.** $\frac{c}{-5} \geq -2$ **27.** $\frac{x}{4} > -20$

28. $\frac{g}{1.2} \geq -7$ **29.** $\frac{p}{-8} < 2.1$ **30.** $\frac{f}{5} \geq -5.5$

GPS **B** **31. Guided Problem Solving** A forklift can safely carry as much as 6,000 lb. A case of paint weighs 70 lb. At most how many cases of paint can the forklift safely carry at one time? See left.
- Use number sense: How much do 100 cases weigh?
- Try the strategy *Systematic Guess and Check*: How much do 90 cases weigh? 80 cases?

32. Rides A roller coaster can carry 36 people per run. At least
GPS how many times does the roller coaster have to run to allow 10,000 people to ride? at least 278 times

33. Baking A recipe for an apple pie calls for 6 apples per pie. You have 27 apples. At most how many apple pies can you make? at most 4 pies

Write an inequality for each sentence. Solve the inequality.

34. The product of −3 and a number is greater than 12.
$-3x > 12$; $x < -4$

35. A number multiplied by 4 is at most −44. $4x \leq -44$; $x \leq -11$

36. A number divided by −9 is less than 10. $\frac{x}{-9} < 10$; $x > -90$

37. The quotient of a number and 5 is at least −8. $\frac{x}{5} \geq -8$; $x \geq -40$

38. The product of 2 and a number is less than −10. $2n < -10$; $n < -5$

39. To solve $-5x < 25$, divide each side by −5 and reverse the inequality symbol. To solve $5x < 25$, divide each side by 5 but do not reverse the symbol.

39. Writing in Math Explain how solving $-5x < 25$ is different from solving $5x < 25$. See left.

GO Online
Homework Help
Visit: PHSchool.com
Web Code: are-0409

9–17. See back of book.
19–30. See back of book.
48–49. See back of book.

---

3. Practice

Assignment Guide

Check Your Understanding
Go over Exercises 1–5 in class before assigning the Homework Exercises.

Homework Exercises
A Practice by Example   6–30
B Apply Your Skills   31–48
C Challenge   49
TEKS ★ TAKS Tune-Up and Mixed Review   50–53

Homework Quick Check
To check students' understanding of key skills and concepts, go over Exercises 13, 25, 32, 39, and 48.

Differentiated Instruction Resources

PowerPoint

Lesson Quiz

Solve each inequality. Graph the solution.

1. $8t < 32$ $t < 4$

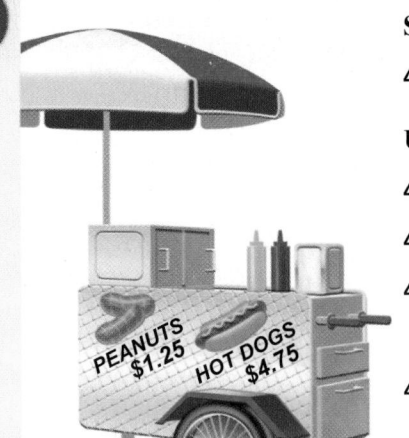

2. $\frac{s}{6} > 30$ $s > 180$

3. $-7v \geq 35$ $v \leq -5$

4. $\frac{x}{-3} < 7$ $x > -21$

Reteaching 4-9   Solving Inequalities by Multiplying and   **L2**

To solve an inequality you can multiply or divide each side by the same number. However, if the number is negative, you must also reverse the direction of the inequality sign.

Solve $-4y \geq 16$. Graph the solution.   Solve $\frac{w}{3} > 2$. Graph the solution.

$-4y \geq 16$

$\frac{-4y}{-4} \leq \frac{16}{-4}$ Divide each side by -4. $\frac{w}{3} > 2$
     of the inequality symbol.   Reverse the direction

$y \leq -4$ Simplify. $(3)\frac{w}{3} > 2(3)$ Multiply each side by 3.
     $w > 6$ Simplify.

Graph: Graph:

Solve each inequality. Graph the solution.

1. $2a > 10$ $a > 5$

2. $-4w < 16$ $w > -4$

3. $\frac{r}{2} \geq -2$ $r \geq -4$

4. $\frac{a}{4} < 1$ $a < 3$

5. $6g < 6$ $g < 1$

6. $-3x \geq -6$ $x \leq 2$

7. $\frac{m}{-2} > 0$ $m < 0$

Enrichment 4-9   Solving Inequalities by Multiplying and   **L4**

Critical Thinking

Many companies throughout the United States and Europe have been rating their customer management performance through a benchmark program. This program measures the average performance of customer satisfaction in various different categories.

The table to the right shows the average scores a computer company has received so far this year in their Information and Technology department. How does the company need to score in *managing customer information* to achieve an overall average score greater than 40?

Information and Technology	Average Score
Acquiring customer information	49
Managing customer information	?
Current system functions	32
Developing new systems	52

Source: http://www.qci.co.uk/Home_page.asp

1. Write an inequality to represent the overall score that the company wants to achieve.   average score > 40

2. What operations do you use to find an average?   addition and division

3. Let x represent the score of *managing customer information*. Write an inequality that represents the desired average of the Information and Technology department. $\frac{x + 49 + 32 + 52}{4} > 40$

4. Solve the inequality in step 3.   x > 27

5. Based on the other scores in the table, do you think the company can achieve their goal? Explain why or why not.

    Sample answer: Yes; all of the other averages listed in the table are well above 27. So it does not appear that the company should have trouble achieving their goal.

6. To be awarded a national certificate of achievement, the computer company must have an overall average in their Information and Technology Department of no less than 51.

a. Write and solve an inequality to find what the company must score in *managing customer information* to achieve the certificate. $\frac{x + 49 + 32 + 52}{4} \geq 51$; x ≥ 71

b. Based on the other scores in the table, do you think the company can achieve the certificate? Explain why or why not.

    Sample answer: No; the averages listed in the table are well below 71. It does not appear that the company will achieve the certificate.

218

Solve each inequality.

40. $9.9 < -9x$ **41.** $-25.1 > \frac{t}{-2}$ **42.** $-5.6 \leq -8p$

$-1.1 > x$ $50.2 < t$ $0.7 \geq p$

Use the drawing at the left for Exercises 43–45. You have $15.

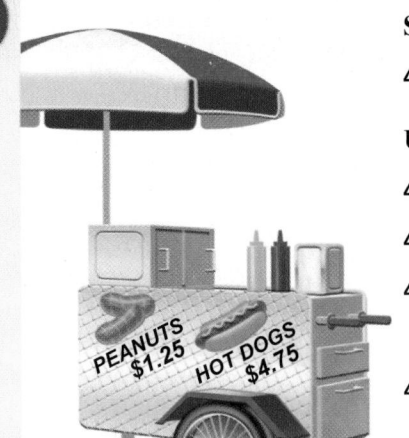

PEANUTS $1.25   HOT DOGS $4.75

43. At most how many hot dogs can you buy?   at most 3 hot dogs

44. At most how many bags of peanuts can you buy?   at most 12 bags of peanuts

45. You buy two hot dogs. How many bags of peanuts can you buy? How much money do you have left?   4 bags of peanuts; $.50

46. A 1-ton truck can haul 2,000 lb. A refrigerator weighs 302 lb. How many refrigerators can the truck carry?   at most 6 refrigerators

47. Error Analysis A student solves the inequality $5n > -25$. He says the solution is $n < -5$. Explain the student's error.   See left.

48. Reasoning Solve and graph $-18 \geq -2y$ and $-2y < -18$. Are the solutions the same? Explain.   See margin.

47. The student should not have reversed the inequality symbol.

C 49. Challenge Ten more than -3 times a number is greater than 19. Write and solve an inequality. Graph the solution.   See margin.

TEKS ★ TAKS Tune-Up and Mixed Review

TAKS Objective 2
TEKS (7.5)(B)

50. Which problem situation matches the equation below?   **A**

$$2x + 3 = 21$$

Ⓐ Janice is 3 years more than twice as old as Rashon. Janice is 21 years old. How old is Rashon?

Ⓑ Felicity has scored 2 points more than 3 times as many points as Kendra. Kendra has scored 21 points. How many points has Felicity scored?

Ⓒ Drew paid $2 more than Adam for tickets to a play. Richard's tickets cost him 3 times as much as Drew's tickets. Richard paid $21. How much did Adam pay for his tickets?

Ⓓ Nate worked 2 hours more than 3 times as many hours as Chad. Nate worked 21 hours. How many hours did Chad work?

TAKS Objective 2
TEKS (7.5)(B)

51. Arnold had a collection of baseball cards that he divided evenly among 5 friends. Each friend received 17 baseball cards. Which equation can be used to find y, the number of baseball cards Arnold had?   **G**

Ⓕ $5y = 17$ **Ⓗ** $17y = 5$

Ⓖ $\frac{y}{5} = 17$ **Ⓙ** $\frac{y}{5} - 5 = 17$

for Help   **Lesson 1-10**

Find the mean, median, and mode for each set of data.

4.875; 4; 4   3.83; 3.6; 2.2

52. 4   6   3   7   4   7   4   4   **53.** 2.2   6.4   5   2.2   2.2   5

TEKS ★ TAKS Resources

- TAKS Strategies, p. 219
- TAKS Tune-Up, pp. 223–225

TAKS Tune-Up Kit

- TAKS Daily Review Transparencies
- TAKS Review and Preparation Workbook
- TAKS Strategies with Transparencies
- Texas Progress Monitoring Assessments

Alternative Assessment

Ask students to write four different inequalities that all have the same solution. Two inequalities should be solved by multiplying. The two other inequalities should be solved by dividing. Students then trade papers with a partner who solves each inequality and graphs the solution. Have students discuss their results.

Strategies

Choosing the Process

Some test questions will ask you to choose a process or strategy for solving a problem.

EXAMPLE

Mrs. Hernandez gave students 10 points each on a test for writing the date in Spanish. She gave 4 points each for every question the students answered correctly. Hubert wrote the date correctly and received a total score of 86. How can he determine how many questions he answered correctly?

- Ⓐ Add 10 and 4 and 86.
- Ⓑ Subtract 10 from 86 and divide the difference by 4.
- Ⓒ Multiply 4 and 10 and subtract the product from 86.
- Ⓓ Divide 86 by 4.

Hubert can subtract 10 from 86 to find the number of points he received for his correct answers. Since each correct answer is worth 4 points, he can divide the difference by 4 to determine the number of questions he answered correctly. The answer is B.

 Exercises

TAKS Objective 2
TEKS (7.5)(A)

1. The model below represents the equation $2x + 3 = 10$.

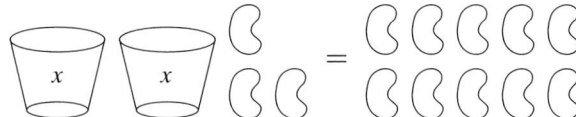

What is the first step in finding the value of x? **D**
- Ⓐ Divide the beans equally between the 2 cups.
- Ⓑ Add 10 beans to each side of the model.
- Ⓒ Add 3 beans to each side of the model.
- Ⓓ Subtract 3 beans from each side of the model.

TAKS Objective 6
TEKS (7.13)(B)

2. General admission to an amusement park costs $35.00. Each ride costs $2.50. If Jinnie has $55.00 to spend at the amusement park, what method can be used to find how many rides she can go on? **G**
- Ⓕ Add $35.00 and $2.50.
- Ⓖ Subtract $35.00 from $55.00 and divide the difference by $2.50.
- Ⓗ Multiply $2.50 and $35.00 and add the product to $55.00.
- Ⓙ Divide $55.00 by $2.50.

TAKS Strategies   Choosing the Process   **219**

 Strategies

Choosing the Process

Students learn to choose a process or strategy for solving a problem. They learn to determine what the first and second steps in solving a two-step equation are.

Guided Instruction

Example
After students read the problem and solution, ask: *Why did Hubert divide the difference by 4?* because each question was worth 4 points

Exercise
Have students find the value of x in Exercise 1. $x = 3\frac{1}{2}$

TEKS ⭐ TAKS Resources

TAKS Strategies with Transparencies
- Transparency 3
- Practice sheet, p. 16

TAKS **Strategies with Transparencies**

Test-Taking Strategies: Choosing the Process

Some test questions will ask you to choose a process or strategy for solving a problem.

Example The model represents the equation $5x + 4 = 11$.

What is the first step in finding the value of x?

A. Divide the number of circles by the number of squares.
B. Add 4 circles to each side of the model.
C. Subtract 4 circles from each side of the model.
D. Subtract 5 squares from each side of the model.

- Dividing the number of circles by the number of squares does not isolate x. Eliminate choice A.
- Adding 4 circles to each side does not simplify the model. Eliminate choice B.
- Subtracting 5 squares from each side of the model does not simplify the model, so eliminate choice D.
- Subtracting 4 circles from each side of the model moves all of the circles to one side, so the correct answer is C.

Tickets to a museum cost $7 for adults and $5 for children. Mrs. Martin is buying tickets for herself and her daughter's friends. If Mrs. Martin has $50 to spend at the museum, what method can be used to determine the number of children she can take to the museum?

A. Add 7 and 5 and subtract the result from 50.
B. Subtract 7 from 50 and divide the result by 5.
C. Multiply 7 by 5 and subtract the result from 50.
D. Subtract 5 from 50 and divide the result by 7.

TEKS ★ (TAKS) Resources

Student Edition

Extra Skills and Word Problems
   Practice, Ch. 4, p. 630
English/Spanish Glossary, p. 675
Formulas and Properties, p. 673
Tables, p. 670

All in One Teaching Resources
- Vocabulary and Study
  Skills 4F   **L3**

(TAKS) Tune-Up Kit

- TAKS Daily Review
  Transparencies
- TAKS Review and Preparation
  Workbook
- TAKS Strategies with
  Transparencies
- Texas Progress Monitoring
  Assessments
- Texas ExamView CD-ROM
- MindPoint Quiz Show CD-ROM

Differentiated Instruction

Spanish Vocabulary Workbook
   with Study Skills   **ELL**
Texas Interactive Textbook
- Audio Glossary
Online Vocabulary Quiz

Success 🔆 Tracker™
   Online at PHSchool.com

Spanish Vocabulary/Study Skills **ELL**

Vocabulary/Study Skills **L3**

4F: Vocabulary   For use with the Chapter Review

Study Skill: Review notes that you have taken in class as soon as possible to clarify any points you missed and to refresh your memory.

Circle the word that best completes the sentence.

1. A (variable, expression) is a letter that stands for a number.
2. An (expression, equation) is a mathematical statement with an equal sign.
3. A (solution, sentence) is a value for a variable that makes an equation true.
4. To solve an equation, use (inverse, variable) operations.
5. A mathematical statement that contains < or > is called an (equation, inequality).
6. The statement 4 + (9 + 3) = (4 + 9) + 3 is an example of the (Commutative Property of Addition, Associative Property of Addition).
7. The (opposite, absolute value) of 15 is −15.
8. The (mean, median) is the middle number in a data set when the data is arranged from least to greatest.
9. You can use the (commutative, identity) property to change the order in an expression.
10. The statement a + 0 = a is an example of the (Identity Property of Zero, Identity Property of Multiplication).
11. The (absolute value, opposite) of a number is its distance from 0 on a number line.
12. (Whole, integers) are the set of whole numbers, their opposites, and zero.
13. Two numbers whose sum is 0 are (additive, opposite) inverses.
14. A(n) (outlier, range) is a data value that is much greater or less than the other values in the data set.
15. Using the (distributive property, order of operations) you can calculate that 12 + 5 · 2 equals 22.

220

Vocabulary Review

 Addition Property of Equality
(p. 180)
Addition Property of
   Inequality (p. 210)
algebraic expression (p. 169)
equation (p. 174)
Division Property of Equality
(p. 186)

Division Property of
   Inequality (p. 214)
inequality (p. 205)
inverse operations (p. 181)
Multiplication Property of
   Equality (p. 188)
Multiplication Property of
   Inequality (p. 216)
open sentence (p. 174)

solution of an equation
(p. 174)
solution of an inequality
(p. 205)
Subtraction Property of
   Equality (p. 180)
Subtraction Property of
   Inequality (p. 211)
variable (p. 169)

Go Online
PHSchool.com
For: Online vocabulary quiz
Web Code: arj-0451

Choose the correct term to complete each sentence.

1. A letter that represents a number is called a(n) (equation, variable).
   variable

2. If you multiply both sides of an (equation, inequality) by the same negative number, the direction of the inequality symbol is reversed.
   inequality

3. A mathematical sentence with an equal sign is called a(n) (equation, inverse operation). *equation*

4. A mathematical phrase with at least one variable in it is a(n) (algebraic expression, solution of an equation). *algebraic expression*

5. A(n) (open sentence, solution of an inequality) is a value that makes an inequality true. *solution of an inequality*

Skills and Concepts   TEKS ★ (TAKS)

Lesson 4-1

(7.2)(F) To select and use appropriate operations to solve problems **(TAKS) Obj. 1**
Prepares for TEKS (7.5)(B) To formulate problem situations when given an equation and formulate an equation when given a problem situation

A **variable** is a letter that stands for a number. An **algebraic expression** is a mathematical phrase that uses variables, numbers, and operation symbols. To evaluate an expression, substitute a given value for each variable and then simplify.

Evaluate each expression for $n = 3$, $p = 5$, and $w = 2$.

6. $3n - 2w$ 5
7. $\dfrac{4n}{w}$ 6
8. $p + 4w$ 13
9. $7w - 2p$ 4

Lesson 4-2

(7.13)(D) To select mental math, estimation, and number sense to solve problems
(7.5)(B) To formulate an equation when given a situation **(TAKS) Obj. 2**

An **equation** is a mathematical sentence with an equal sign. An equation with one or more variables is an **open sentence**. A **solution of an equation** is a value for a variable that makes an equation true.

Use number sense to solve each equation.

10. $p + 5 = -2$ −7
11. $m - 12 = 8$ 20
12. $7t = 28$ 4
13. $\dfrac{w}{8} = 9$ 72

220   Chapter 4   Chapter Review

27–33. See back of book.

Lessons 4-3, 4-4

(7.5)(A) To use pictorial models to solve equations and use symbols to record the actions **TAKS** Obj. 2

(7.5)(B) To formulate a problem situation when given an equation and formulate an equation when given a problem situation **TAKS** Obj. 2

Whatever you do to one side of the equation, you must do the same thing to the other side of the equation. To solve a one-step equation, use **inverse operations.**

Use inverse operations to solve each equation.

14. $y + 14 = 38$ 24
15. $p - 12 = 72$ 84
16. $\frac{m}{11} = 9$ 99
17. $-7b = 84$ -12
18. $x - 8 = 44$ 52
19. $12h = 60$ 5
20. $k - 14 = 29$ 43
21. $\frac{n}{6} = -9$ -54

22. A local band had a concert and made $1,824 from tickets sales. If each ticket cost $16, how many tickets did the band sell?   **114 tickets**

Lessons 4-5, 4-6

(7.5)(A) To use pictorial models to solve equations and use symbols to record the actions **TAKS** Obj. 2

(7.5)(B) To formulate an equation when given a problem situation **TAKS** Obj. 2

(7.13)(D) To select techniques such as mental math and number sense to solve problems

You can also use inverse operations to solve two-step equations.

Solve each equation.

23. $4d + 7 = 11$ 1
24. $2m - 21 = 3$ 12
25. $-5y + 8 = 23$ -3

26. Savings You save $35 each week. You now have $140. You plan to save enough money for a cruise that costs $1,050. Write and solve an equation to find the number of weeks it will take to save for the cruise. $140 + 35w = 1,050$;   **26 wk**

Lesson 4-7

• To graph and write inequalities

A mathematical sentence that contains $<$, $>$, $\leq$, $\geq$, or $\neq$ is called an **inequality.** A **solution of an inequality** is any number that makes an inequality true. When graphing, use an open circle for $>$ and $<$ and use a closed circle for $\geq$ and $\leq$.

27–28. See margin.

Write an inequality for each statement. Then graph the inequality.

27. The ticket is at most $10.

28. The race is less than 5 miles.

Lessons 4-8, 4-9

• To solve inequalities by adding or subtracting
• To solve inequalities by multiplying or dividing

You solve inequalities just as you solve equations, but with one exception. When you multiply or divide by a negative number, you must reverse the direction of the inequality symbol.

Solve each inequality. Then graph the inequality.   29–33. See margin.

29. $h + 7 < -15$
30. $\frac{p}{5} \geq -3$
31. $g - 14 > 3$
32. $-4m \leq 28$

33. A farmer needs no less than 20 lb of seeds to plant a crop. Write an inequality for this situation. Then graph the inequality.

27–33. See back of book.

Chapter 4 Test

Go Online   For: Online chapter test
PHSchool.com   Web Code: ara-0452

Evaluate each expression for $n = 3$, $t = -2$, and $y = 4$.

1. $3n + 2t$ 5
2. $5y - 4n$ 8
3. $2(n + 3y)$ 30
4. $ny - 6$ 6
5. $\dfrac{2ny}{t}$ -12
6. $-2t + 6n$ 22

Solve each equation.

7. $x + 7 = 12$ 5
8. $m - \dfrac{1}{3} = \dfrac{1}{6}$ $\dfrac{1}{2}$
9. $13 + d = 44$ 31
10. $p - 1.8 = 6.2$ 8
11. $5n = 45.5$ 9.1
12. $\dfrac{h}{7} = 8$ 56
13. $-\dfrac{1}{3}t = 24$ -72
14. $\dfrac{k}{-4} = -12$ 48
15. $14 + 3n = 8$ -2
16. $9h - 21 = 24$ 5
17. $\dfrac{w}{5} - 10 = -4$ 30
18. $14 + \dfrac{y}{8} = 10$ -32

Define a variable. Then write and solve an equation for each problem.   19–24. See margin.

19. **Masonry** A mason is laying a brick foundation 72 in. wide. Each brick is 6 in. wide. How many bricks will the mason need across the width of the foundation?

20. **Groceries** You buy 12 apples. You also buy a box of cereal that costs $3.35. The bill is $8.75. How much does each apple cost?

21. The music boosters sell 322 music buttons and raise $483 for the music department. How much does each button cost?

22. Your family drives from Austin, Texas, to Tampa, Florida. The trip is about 1,145 mi and lasts four days. How many miles must your family drive each day?

23. **Sports** A youth soccer league recently held registration. The number of players was divided into 13 teams of 12 players. How many players registered?

24. Six friends split the cost of a party. Each person also spends $65 for a hotel room. Each person spends $160 on the party and a room. What is the cost of the party?

25. **Open-Ended** Write a problem you can represent with $2k - 10 = 6$. Solve the equation. Show your work.
8; check students' work.

Define a variable and write an inequality for each statement.

26. The game's duration is at most 3 hours.
Let d = game's duration; $d \le 3$.
27. To rent a car, you must be at least 25 years old. Let a = age; $a \ge 25$.
28. The truck can haul more than 20,000 lb.
Let h = weight hauled; $h > 20{,}000$.
29. There are fewer than 10 tickets available for the concert tonight.
Let t = number of available tickets; $t < 10$.

Solve each inequality. Graph your solution.
30–39. See margin.

30. $n + 12 \ge 15$
31. $y - 14 > 10$
32. $m - 8 \le -17$
33. $w + 22 < 14$
34. $12x < -48$
35. $10h \ge 90$
36. $\dfrac{v}{-8} > 6$
37. $\dfrac{p}{11} \le -6$
38. $-7k \le -84$
39. $\dfrac{x}{-15} < -4$

Define a variable. Then write and solve an inequality for each problem.   40–43. See margin.

40. **Transportation** A ferry can safely transport at most 220 people. There are already 143 people aboard. How many more people can the ferry take aboard?

41. **Money** A sports drink costs $1.49 per bottle. At most how many bottles can you buy if you have $12?

42. **Shopping** Alex and his mother spent at least $130 while shopping for new clothes. Alex spent $52. How much money did his mother spend?

43. **Writing in Math** Describe the similarities and differences between solving inequalities and equations. Include examples.

19–24. See back of book.
30–43. See back of book.

Cumulative Practice

 Tips

Some questions ask you to identify an equation that relates to a real-life situation.

Tip 1
The indicator words "more than" are usually used to represent addition. Look for an equation that uses addition.

Tip 2
The indicator word *twice* means "two times." Look for an equation that multiplies *n* by 2.

Maria is 27 years old. This is 3 more than twice Jesse's age. Which equation can be used to find *n*, the age of Jesse?

- Ⓐ $3n + 2 = 27$
- Ⓑ $2n + 3 = 27$
- Ⓒ $2n - 3 = 27$
- Ⓓ $3n - 2 = 27$

Think It Through

Choices C and D do not use addition. Eliminate choices C and D. Choice A uses addition but does not show *twice* Jesse's age. Eliminate choice A. The answer is B.

TEKS ★ TAKS Resources

TAKS Review and Preparation Workbook

Texas ExamView CD-ROM
- Instant TAKS Practice Test
- TAKS Practice Items

Differentiated Instruction

Texas Progress Monitoring Assessments
- Benchmark Test 2   L3

Spanish Assessment Resources
- Spanish Cumulative Review ELL

Texas ExamView CD-ROM
- Special Needs Practice Bank   L1

Vocabulary Builder

As you solve test items, you must understand the meanings of mathematical terms. Choose the correct term that correctly completes each sentence.

A. A(n) (algebraic, numerical) expression uses variables, numbers, and operation symbols. **algebraic**

B. An (equation, expression) is a mathematical sentence with an equal sign. **equation**

C. A letter that stands for a number is a(n) (expression, variable). **variable**

D. A(n) (inverse operation, solution) is a value for a variable that makes an equation true. **solution**

E. Addition and subtraction are operations that undo each other, so they are (inverse operations, equations). **inverse operations**

Multiple Choice

Read each question. Then write the letter of the correct answer on your paper.

1. In golf, scores are recorded relative to par, which is the expected number of strokes to get the ball in the holes. The table below shows the scores on the final day of a golf tournament. A negative score means that the player shot below par.

Final Golf Scores

Player	Score
Jon	−5
Alex	2
Tyler	−3
Steve	−1
Robert	−2

Which list shows the golf scores from greatest to least? **D**
- Ⓐ $-5, -3, -2, 2, -1$
- Ⓑ $2, -5, -3, -2, -1$
- Ⓒ $-5, -3, 2, -2, -1$
- Ⓓ $2, -1, -2, -3, -5$

 Daily Review Transparencies

Daily Review 1   Objective 1: (7.1)(B)
Multiple Choice

The seventh-grade class at Anarene Middle School sold $\frac{13}{20}$ of the Corsicana fruitcakes they bought. Which decimal is equivalent to the fraction sold?

A 65
B 0.65
C 6.5
D 650

Answer: B

Daily Review 2   Objective 5: (7.12)(A)
Multiple Choice

Shey has been practicing running the 200-meter foot race. Her last 6 times are shown.

23.60 24.15 24.68 28.62 24.25 23.92

What is her mean time?

F 5.02
G 23.92
H 24.21
J 24.87

Cumulative Practice (continued)

2. A scientist found the following weights for four beluga whales: $1\frac{1}{2}$ tons, $1\frac{3}{5}$ tons, $\frac{9}{10}$ tons, and $\frac{7}{5}$ tons. Which shows the weights in order from least to greatest? **J**

F $\dfrac{7}{5}, \dfrac{9}{10}, 1\dfrac{1}{2}, 1\dfrac{3}{5}$ H $1\dfrac{1}{2}, \dfrac{7}{5}, \dfrac{9}{10}, 1\dfrac{3}{5}$

G $\dfrac{9}{10}, 1\dfrac{1}{2}, \dfrac{7}{5}, 1\dfrac{3}{5}$ J $\dfrac{9}{10}, \dfrac{7}{5}, 1\dfrac{1}{2}, 1\dfrac{3}{5}$

3. Mr. Haley bought 5 dozen hot dog buns priced at 6 buns for $1.29 and 6 packages of hot dogs priced at 2 packages for $5.50. What is the total amount he spent, not including tax, on the buns and hot dogs? **C**

A $18.74   C $29.40

B $24.24   D $78.90

4. Mrs. Son bought 7 stamps for $0.80 each and 12 stamps for $0.20 each. What is the total amount she spent on her stamps? **H**

F $5.60   H $8.00

G $7.80   J $8.60

5. Which problem situation matches the equation $n = -300 - 120$? **D**

A Tom was $300 in debt when he paid off $120. How much did Tom owe then?

B Rosie drove 300 miles west of home and then drove back 120 miles east. How far was she from home then?

C What is the difference in altitude between 300 feet below sea level and 120 feet below sea level?

D A submarine was 300 feet below sea level and dove down 120 feet more. What was the submarine's final depth?

6. Parts to fix Ben's car cost $55.35. The mechanic charges $35 per hour for labor. The final bill is $177.85. Which equation can be used to find how long the mechanic takes to fix Ben's car? **H**

F $55.35x + 35 = 177.85$

G $55.35(35x) = 177.85$

H $55.35 + 35x = 177.85$

J $35x = 177.85$

7. Which situation matches the equation $\dfrac{p}{3} + 5 = 18$? **D**

A Three times the total price in dollars, added to $5, is $18.

B The total price in dollars divided by 5, plus $3, is $18.

C Five dollars more than 3 times the total price in dollars is $18.

D Five dollars more than the total price in dollars, divided by 3, is $18.

8. The model below represents the equation $x + 5 = -3$. What is the value of x? **F**

Key
$+$ = +1 $-$ = −1

F $x = -8$ H $x = 2$

G $x = -2$ J $x = 8$

9. The model below represents the equation $4x + 3 = 11$. What is the first step in finding the value of x? **A**

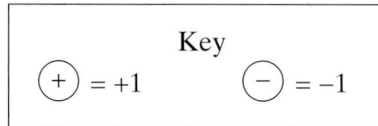

A Subtract 3 pieces of macaroni from each side of the model.

B Add 3 pieces of macaroni to each side of the model.

C Add 11 pieces of macaroni to each side of the model.

D Divide the pieces of macaroni equally among the 4 cups.

224   *TAKS* **Tune-Up**   Cumulative Practice

224

10. Each week, Mr. Farley earns between $398 and $411. Which is the best estimate of the amount he earns in 6 weeks? **G**
- (F) From $1,800 to $2,200
- (G) From $2,200 to $2,500
- (H) From $2,500 to $2,800
- (J) From $2,800 to $3,000

11. A librarian has 280 new books. Fifty of the books are reserved and kept at her desk. The remaining books are to be placed on shelves. Each shelf can hold 14 books. The equation $14s + 50 = 280$ can be used to find the number of shelves the librarian needs. About how many shelves does the librarian need? **C**
- (A) Fewer than 10
- (B) More than 30
- (C) Between 10 and 20
- (D) Between 20 and 30

12. Madison works a total of 23 hours per week at a bakery and a shoe store. She works at the bakery from 10:15 A.M. until 1:15 P.M., Monday through Friday. Which equation can be used to find s, the number of hours she works at the shoe store each week? **F**
- (F) $s = 23 - (5 \times 3)$
- (G) $s = 23 - (5 \times 4)$
- (H) $s = 23 - 3 + 3 + 3 + 3 + 3$
- (J) $s = 5 \times 3 - 23$

13. A standard bowling lane is 18.2 meters long. Which equation can be used to find c, the length of a bowling lane in centimeters? **B**
- (A) $c = \dfrac{18.2}{1,000}$
- (C) $18.2 = \dfrac{c}{1,000}$
- (B) $18.2 = \dfrac{c}{100}$
- (D) $c = \dfrac{18.2}{100}$

14. A carpenter who earns $29.50 per hour spends a total of 345 minutes on a project. How many hours does the carpenter work? **H**
- (F) $4\frac{3}{4}$ hour
- (H) $5\frac{3}{4}$ hour
- (G) $5\frac{1}{4}$ hour
- (J) $6\frac{1}{4}$ hour

Griddable Items

Record your answer in a grid.

15. It takes Brandon $2\frac{1}{2}$ minutes to cook an omelet. How many omelets can he cook in 30 minutes? **12**

16. For an art project, Juliana needs to cut out squares of paper that measure $1\frac{7}{8}$ inches on each side. She must cut the squares from a strip of paper like the one shown below.

$$\boxed{}\quad 1\frac{7}{8}\text{ in.}$$
$$10\frac{5}{8}\text{ in.}$$

How many whole squares can she cut from the paper? **5**

TAKS GO for Help Guide

TAKS Objective	Item Number	GO To	TAKS Objective	Item Number	GO To
Obj. 1: (7.1)(A)	1	Lesson 1-6	Obj. 1: (7.2)(G)	10–11	Lesson 1-1
	2	Lesson 2-7	Obj. 6: (7.14)(A)	12	Lesson 1-9
Obj. 1: (7.2)(F)	3–4	Lesson 1-3		13	Lesson 4-4
Obj. 2: (7.5)(B)	5	Lesson 1-7	Obj. 1: (7.2)(B)	14	Lesson 2-5
	6–7	Lesson 4-6		15–16	Lesson 3-5
Obj. 2: (7.5)(A)	8	Lesson 4-3			
	9	Lesson 4-6			

For additional TAKS practice, see the *TAKS Review and Preparation Workbook*.

5 Ratios, Rates, and Proportions

Chapter at a Glance

Lesson Titles, Objectives, and Features	Assessment	NCTM Standards	TEKS ★ TAKS
5-1 Ratios • To write ratios and use them to compare quantities	Lesson Quiz	1, 2, 6, 7, 8, 9, 10	**TEKS** (7.2)(D), (7.3)(B) _TAKS_ **Obj. 1, 2**
5-2 Unit Rates and Proportional Reasoning • To find unit rates and unit costs using proportional reasoning **Extension:** Using Conversion Factors	Lesson Quiz Checkpoint Quiz 1	1, 2, 6, 7, 8, 9, 10	**TEKS** (7.2)(D), (7.2)(G), (7.3)(B) _TAKS_ **Obj. 1, 2**
5-3 Proportions • To test whether ratios form a proportion by using equivalent ratios and cross products **5-3b Activity Lab, Algebra Thinking:** Interpreting Rates Visually	Lesson Quiz	1, 2, 6, 7, 8, 9, 10	**TEKS** (7.2)(D), (7.3)(B), (7.11)(B) _TAKS_ **Obj. 1, 2, 5**
5-4a Activity Lab, Data Collection: Using Proportions with Data **5-4 Solving Proportions** • To solve proportions using unit rates, mental math, and cross products **Guided Problem Solving:** Proportions and Equations	Lesson Quiz	1, 2, 6, 7, 8, 9, 10	**TEKS** (7.2)(D), (7.3)(B), _TAKS_ **Obj. 1, 2** **TEKS** (7.13)(D)
5-5a Activity Lab, Hands On: Exploring Similar Figures **5-5 Using Similar Figures** • To use proportions to find missing lengths in similar figures **5-5b Activity Lab, Technology:** Drawing Similar Figures **Vocabulary Builder:** Learning Vocabulary	Lesson Quiz Checkpoint Quiz 2	1, 2, 3, 4, 6, 7, 8, 9, 10	**TEKS** (7.3)(B), (7.6)(D), (7.14)(A), (7.15)(A) _TAKS_ **Obj. 2, 3, 6** **TEKS** (7.13)(D)
5-6a Activity Lab, Hands On: Scale Drawings and Models **5-6 Maps and Scale Drawings** • To use proportions to solve problems involving scale **5-6b Activity Lab:** Plan a Trip	Lesson Quiz	1, 2, 3, 4, 6, 7, 8, 9, 10	**TEKS** (7.3)(B), (7.4)(A), (7.8)(C), (7.14)(A) _TAKS_ **Obj. 2, 3, 6** **TEKS** (7.13)(A)
TAKS **Tune-Up: Cumulative Practice**			

NCTM Standards 2000

1 Number and Operations	**2** Algebra	**3** Geometry	**4** Measurement	**5** Data Analysis and Probability
6 Problem Solving	**7** Reasoning and Proof	**8** Communication	**9** Connections	**10** Representation

Correlations to Standardized Tests

All content for these tests is contained in *Prentice Hall Math,* Course 2. This chart reflects coverage in this chapter only.

	5-1	5-2	5-3	5-4	5-5	5-6
Terra Nova CAT6 (Level 17)						
Number and Number Relations	✔	✔	✔	✔	✔	✔
Computation and Numerical Estimation	✔	✔	✔	✔	✔	✔
Operation Concepts	✔	✔	✔	✔	✔	✔
Measurement					✔	✔
Geometry and Spatial Sense					✔	✔
Data Analysis, Statistics, and Probability						
Patterns, Functions, Algebra	✔	✔	✔	✔	✔	✔
Problem Solving and Reasoning	✔	✔	✔	✔	✔	✔
Communication	✔	✔	✔	✔	✔	✔
Decimals, Fractions, Integers, and Percent	✔	✔	✔	✔	✔	✔
Order of Operations						
Terra Nova CTBS (Level 17)						
Decimals, Fractions, Integers, Percents	✔	✔	✔	✔	✔	✔
Order of Operations, Numeration, Number Theory	✔	✔	✔	✔	✔	✔
Data Interpretation						
Pre-algebra	✔	✔	✔	✔	✔	✔
Measurement					✔	✔
Geometry					✔	✔
ITBS (Level 13)						
Number Properties and Operations	✔	✔	✔	✔	✔	✔
Algebra	✔	✔	✔	✔	✔	✔
Geometry					✔	✔
Measurement					✔	✔
Probability and Statistics						
Estimation						
SAT10 (Int 3 Level)						
Number Sense and Operations	✔	✔	✔	✔	✔	✔
Patterns, Relationships, and Algebra	✔	✔	✔	✔	✔	✔
Data, Statistics, and Probability						
Geometry and Measurement					✔	✔
NAEP						
Number Sense, Properties, and Operations		✔			✔	✔
Measurement					✔	✔
Geometry and Spatial Sense						
Data Analysis, Statistics, and Probability						
Algebra and Functions						

CAT6 California Achievement Test, 6th Ed.   **CTBS** Comprehensive Test of Basic Skills   **ITBS** Iowa Test of Basic Skills, Form M
SAT10 Stanford Achievement Test, 10th Ed.   **NAEP** National Assessment of Educational Progress 2005 Mathematics Objectives

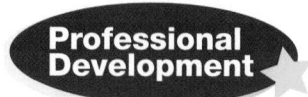
Focus on the TEKS

- At Grade 7, students use critical attributes to define similarity (7.6)(D). Analysis of TAKS results shows that students should review this student expectation.

  In Lesson 5-5, students use ratios and proportions to solve problems involving similar figures. Place special emphasis on this lesson because it focuses on (7.6)(D).

- New at Grade 7, students find ratios in proportional relationships including unit rates and unit pricing (7.2)(D).

  Students review ratios in Lesson 5-1 and extend this concept to develop proportional reasoning in Lesson 5-2. Students then set up and solve proportions in Lessons 5-3 and 5-4.

5-1 / 5-2 Ratios, Unit Rates and Proportional Reasoning

TEKS ★ TAKS (7.2)(D), (7.3)(B), (7.2)(G) Obj. 1, 2

Math Understandings

- A ratio is a multiplicative relationship between quantities.
- All ratios can be written in fraction form $\left(\frac{a}{b}\right)$.
- All fractions are ratios but not all ratios are fractions.
- Equivalent ratios can be generated using multiplication or division, just as with equivalent fractions.
- Rates are a special type of ratio.
- Unit rates and unit prices are special kinds of ratios.

A **ratio** is a pair of numbers used to show a comparison between like or unlike quantities, written x to y, $\frac{x}{y}$, $x \div y$, or $x : y (y \neq 0)$. The numbers x and y are called the **terms** of the ratio.

Two ratios are **equivalent ratios** if their corresponding fractions are equivalent or if the quotients of the respective terms are the same.

Different Types of Ratios

There are 36 seats inside a restaurant and 24 seats on the terrace.

Part to part: The ratio of indoor seats to outdoor seats is $36 : 24$ or $\frac{36}{24}$.

Part to whole: The ratio of indoor seats to the total number of seats is $36 : 60$ or $\frac{36}{60}$.

Whole to part: The ratio of the total number of seats to the number of seats indoors is $60 : 36$ or $\frac{60}{36}$.

A **rate** is a ratio comparing quantities involving different units. Twenty miles per (one) hour is an example of **unit rate** you are familiar with. It is a unit rate because the first quantity, 20 miles, is compared to one (1) of the second quantity. A **unit price** is also a unit rate, for example, $1.75 for 1 pound.

Fractions and Ratios

Students first interpret a fraction as a comparison of a part of a whole. Yet all of the ratios above were written as $\frac{x}{y}$. Remember that while all ratios can be written in $\frac{x}{y}$ form (fraction form), all ratios do not behave like fractions. This is why we use "terms" rather than numerator and denominator when working with ratios.

Example: Suppose a student played softball on two days. On each day, she got 1 hit for 2 times at bat $\left(\frac{1}{2}\right)$, so for the two days, she got 2 hits for 4 times at bat or $\frac{2}{4}$. So, for the two days, it is tempting to write $\frac{1}{2} + \frac{1}{2} = \frac{2}{4}$ but this is not correct; if we were adding fractions, we know that $\frac{1}{2} + \frac{1}{2} = \frac{2}{2} = 1$.

So, an important point in developing an understanding of ratios is that all part to whole comparisons (what we typically think of as a fraction) represent only one kind of ratio, but there are other kinds of ratios.

Models and Ratios

Models are very helpful for understanding unit rate and unit price. If 8 oz cost $2.48, the model below shows how we can think about the unit price.

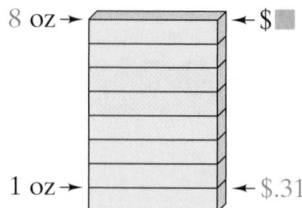

8 oz → | ← $■
1 oz → | ← $.31

The model shows why a ratio is a multiplicative relationship. One ounce costs $.31 and 8 oz cost 8 times as much.

5-3 / 5-4 Proportions and Solving Proportions

TEKS ★ TAKS (7.2)(D), (7.3)(B), Obj. 1, 2; (7.13)(D)

Math Understandings
- Equal ratios behave like equivalent fractions.
- There are different related methods for solving proportions.
- If $\frac{a}{b} = \frac{c}{d}$ (where b and d are not 0), then we can use the Multiplication Property of Equality to show cross products, ad and bc, and that $ad = bc$.
- Unit rates and unit prices are helpful for making comparisons.

A **proportion** is an equation stating that two ratios are equal. Quantities **vary proportionally** because as their corresponding values increase or decrease, the ratio of the two quantities is always equivalent.

Example: One ticket for a play costs $12. The ratio $\frac{1}{12}$ shows this comparison. The table below shows three other ratios that are equivalent to $\frac{1}{12}$.

Number of tickets	1	2	3	4
Total cost	$12	$24	$36	$48

Any pair of these equal ratios can be pulled out and written as an equation, called a proportion.

$$\frac{2}{24} = \frac{4}{48}$$

Also notice that the quotient of the total cost to the number of tickets is 12 for all of the equivalent ratios.

Methods for Solving Proportions
There are three methods commonly used for solving proportions:
- finding the unit amount
- finding the common multiplier
- using cross products

The development on p. 239 shows why the cross product method works. Be sure to connect the other two methods to the cross product method. In Example 1 on p. 244, notice that $\frac{\$2.34}{6}$ gives the unit amount and $\frac{8}{6}$ gives the common multiplier.

$$\frac{\$2.34}{6} \text{ oranges} = \frac{n}{8} \text{ oranges}$$

$\$2.34 \times 8 = 6 \times n$	using cross products
$\$2.34 \times \frac{8}{6} = n$	dividing both sides by 6

5-5 / 5-6 Using Similar Figures, Maps and Scale Drawings

TEKS ★ TAKS (7.3)(B), (7.4)(A), (7.6)(D), (7.8)(C) Obj. 2, 3

Math Understandings
- Similar figures, maps, and scale drawings have corresponding quantities that vary proportionally.

Maps and scale drawings are special types of similar figures. For all similar figures, corresponding lengths are proportional.

Proportions used for similar figures can be written in different ways as long as corresponding parts of the figures are corresponding terms in the proportion.

Example: Proportions for this situation (found on p. 253) can be set up in either of these equivalent ways.

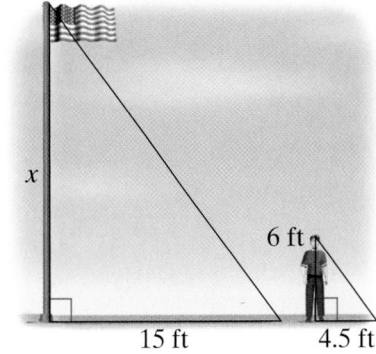

$$\frac{\text{height of pole}}{\text{shadow length of pole}} = \frac{\text{height of boy}}{\text{shadow length of boy}}$$

$$\frac{\text{height of pole}}{\text{height of boy}} = \frac{\text{shadow length of pole}}{\text{shadow length of boy}}$$

Additional Professional Development Opportunities

Math Background Notes for Chapter 5: Every lesson has a Math Backgound in the PLAN section.

Research Overview, Mathematics Strands
Additional support for these topics and more is in the front of the Teacher's Edition.

LessonLab
LessonLab, a Pearson Education company, offers comprehensive, facilitated professional development designed to help teachers to improve student achievement. To learn more, please visit lessonlab.com.

Print Resources	5-1	5-2	5-3	5-4	5-5	5-6	For the Chapter
L3 Practice	●	●	●	●	●	●	
L1 Adapted Practice	●	●	●	●	●	●	
L3 Guided Problem Solving	●	●	●	●	●	●	
L2 Reteaching	●	●	●	●	●	●	
L4 Enrichment	●	●	●	●	●	●	
L3 Daily Notetaking Guide	●	●	●	●	●	●	
L1 Adapted Daily Notetaking Guide	●	●	●	●	●	●	
L3 Vocabulary and Study Skills Worksheets	●		●	●	●	●	●
L3 Daily Puzzles	●	●	●	●	●	●	
L3 Activity Labs			●	●	●	●	
L3 Checkpoint Quiz		●			●		
L3 Chapter Project							●
L2 Chapter Test							●
L3 Chapter Test							●
L4 Alternative Assessment							●
L3 Cumulative Review							●

Spanish Resources **ELL**	5-1	5-2	5-3	5-4	5-5	5-6	For the Chapter
L3 Practice	●	●	●	●	●	●	
L3 Vocabulary and Study Skills Worksheets	●		●	●	●	●	
L3 Checkpoint Quiz		●			●		
L2 Chapter Test							●
L3 Chapter Test							●
L4 Alternative Assessment							●
L3 Cumulative Review							●

Transparencies	5-1	5-2	5-3	5-4	5-5	5-6	For the Chapter
Check Skills You'll Need	●	●	●	●	●	●	
Additional Examples	●	●	●	●	●	●	
Problem of the Day	●	●	●	●	●	●	
(TAKS) Daily Review	●	●	●	●	●	●	
Classroom Aid							
Student Edition Answers	●	●	●	●	●	●	●
Lesson Quiz	●	●	●	●	●	●	
(TAKS) Strategies							●

Technology	5-1	5-2	5-3	5-4	5-5	5-6	For the Chapter
Texas Interactive Textbook Online	●	●	●	●	●	●	●
Texas StudentExpress CD-ROM	●	●	●	●	●	●	
Success Tracker™ Online Intervention	●	●	●	●	●	●	
Texas ExamView CD-ROM with QuickTake	●	●	●	●	●	●	
TeacherExpress CD-ROM	●	●	●	●	●	●	
PresentationExpress CD-ROM	●	●	●	●	●	●	
MindPoint Quiz Show CD-ROM	●	●	●	●	●	●	
Prentice Hall Web Site: PHSchool.com	●	●	●	●	●	●	●

Also available: (TAKS) **Tune-Up Kit**
- TAKS Daily Review Transparencies
- TAKS Review and Preparation Workbook
- TAKS Strategies with Transparencies
- Texas Progress Monitoring Assessments
- Texas ExamView CD-ROM
- MindPoint Quiz Show CD-ROM

Other Resources
Algebra Readiness Tests
All-in-One Student Workbook
All-in-One Student Workbook, Adapted Version
Multilingual Handbook

Solution Key
Math Notes Study Folder
Spanish Cumulative Assessment

Where You Can Use the Lesson Resources

Here is a suggestion, following the four-step teaching plan, for how you can incorporate Differentiated Instruction resources into your teaching.

	Instructional Resources **L3**	**Differentiated Instruction Resources**
1. Plan		
Preparation Read the Math Background in the Teacher's Edition to connect this lesson with students' previous experience. **Starting Class** **Check Skills You'll Need** Assign these exercises to review prerequisite skills. **TEKS** ★ **TAKS** Review the full text of the TEKS student expectations and TAKS objectives covered in this lesson. **New Vocabulary** Help students pre-read the lesson by pointing out the new terms introduced in the lesson.	**TEKS Math Background** **Math Understandings** **Transparencies & PresentationExpress CD-ROM** Check Skills You'll Need Problem of the Day TAKS Daily Review **Resources** Vocabulary and Study Skills	**Spanish Support** ELL Vocabulary and Study Skills
2. Teach		
L3 Guided Instruction Use the Activity Labs to build conceptual understanding. Teach each Example. Use the Teacher's Edition side column notes for specific teaching tips, including Error Prevention notes. Use the Additional Examples found in the side column (and on transparency and PowerPoint) as an alternative presentation for the content. After each Example, assign the Quick Check exercise for that Example to get an immediate assessment of student understanding. Use the Closure activity in the Teacher's Edition to help students attain mastery of lesson content.	**Student Edition** Activity Lab **Resources** Daily Notetaking Guide Activity Lab **Transparencies & PresentationExpress CD-ROM** Additional Examples Classroom Aids **Texas ExamView CD-ROM with QuickTake**	**Teacher's Edition** Every lesson includes suggestions for working with students who need special attention. L1 Special Needs L2 Below Level L4 Advanced Learners ELL English Language Learners **Resources** L1 Adapted Daily Notetaking Guide **Multilingual Handbook**
3. Practice		
Assignment Guide **Check Your Understanding** Use these questions to check students' understanding before you assign homework. **Homework Exercises** Assign homework from these leveled exercises in the Assignment Guide. **A** Practice by Example **B** Apply Your Skills **C** Challenge **TAKS** Tune-Up and Mixed Review **Homework Quick Check** Use these key exercises to quickly check students' homework.	**Transparencies & PresentationExpress CD-ROM** Student Answers **Resources** Practice Guided Problem Solving Vocabulary and Study Skills Activity Lab Daily Puzzles **Texas ExamView CD-ROM with QuickTake**	**Spanish Support** ELL Practice ELL Vocabulary and Study Skills **Resources** L1 Adapted Practice L4 Enrichment
4. Assess & Reteach		
Lesson Quiz Assign the Lesson Quiz to assess students' mastery of the lesson content. **Checkpoint Quiz** Use the Checkpoint Quiz to assess student progress over several lessons.	**Transparencies & PresentationExpress CD-ROM** Lesson Quiz **Resources** Checkpoint Quiz	**Resources** L2 Reteaching ELL Checkpoint Quiz Success Tracker™ Online Intervention **Texas ExamView CD-ROM with QuickTake**

KEY **L1** Special Needs **L2** Below Level **L3** For All Students **L4** Advanced, Gifted **ELL** English Language Learners

CHAPTER
5
Ratios, Rates, and Proportions

Ratios, Rates, and Proportions

 Check Your Readiness

Answers are in the back of the textbook.

For intervention, direct students to:

Multiplying and Dividing Decimals
Lesson 1-4
Extra Skills and Word
  Problems Practice, Ch. 1

Solving Equations by Multiplying or Dividing
Lesson 4-4
Extra Skills and Word
  Problems Practice, Ch. 4

Comparing and Ordering Fractions
Lesson 2-4
Extra Skills and Word
  Problems Practice, Ch. 2

Simplifying Fractions
Lesson 2-3
Extra Skills and Word
  Problems Practice, Ch. 2

What You've Learned
TEKS ★ TAKS

- **(7.1)(A)** In Chapter 2, you compared rational numbers. **TAKS** Obj. 1
- **(7.1)(B)** You converted between fractions and decimals. **TAKS** Obj. 1
- **(7.2)(B)** In Chapter 3, you used addition, subtraction, multiplication, and division to solve problems involving fractions.
  TAKS Obj. 1

 Check Your Readiness

GO for Help

For Exercises	See Lesson
1–6	1-4
7–10	4-4
11–14	2-4
15–19	2-3

Multiplying and Dividing Decimals

Find each product or quotient.

1. $(3.6)(4)$ **14.4**
2. $(12.74)(9)$ **114.66**
3. $(15.9)(3)$ **47.7**
4. $8.96 \div 8$ **1.12**
5. $10.4 \div 4$ **2.6**
6. $52.6 \div 5$ **10.52**

Solving Equations by Multiplying or Dividing

(**Algebra**) **Solve.**

7. $4n = -32$ **–8**
8. $\frac{a}{6} = 10$ **60**
9. $18 = -9z$ **–2**
10. $-15 = \frac{p}{-5}$ **75**

Comparing and Ordering Fractions

Compare. Use <, =, or >.

11. $\frac{8}{9} \blacksquare \frac{3}{4}$ **>**
12. $\frac{7}{12} \blacksquare \frac{4}{5}$ **<**
13. $\frac{6}{3} \blacksquare \frac{24}{12}$ **=**
14. $\frac{1}{6} \blacksquare \frac{1}{7}$ **>**

Simplifying Fractions

Write each fraction in simplest form.

15. $\frac{12}{16}$ **$\frac{3}{4}$**
16. $\frac{15}{30}$ **$\frac{1}{2}$**
17. $\frac{27}{72}$ **$\frac{3}{8}$**
18. $\frac{19}{57}$ **$\frac{1}{3}$**
19. $\frac{16}{56}$ **$\frac{2}{7}$**

226   Chapter 5

Number, Operation, and Quantitative Reasoning
TEKS (7.2)(D), (7.2)(G),
 Obj. 1

Patterns, Relationships, and Algebraic Thinking
TEKS (7.3)(B), (7.4)(A)
 Obj. 2

Geometry and Spatial Reasoning
TEKS (7.6)(D), (7.8)(C)
 Obj. 3

Probability and Statistics
TEKS (7.11)(B)
 Obj. 5

Underlying Processes and Mathematical Tools
TEKS (7.14)(A), (7.15)(A)
 Obj. 6;
TEKS (7.13)(A), (7.13)(D)

Chapter 5 Overview

In this chapter, students learn to find equivalent ratios and to see if ratios can form a proportion. They use unit rates to solve proportions involving variables, and they use proportions to solve problems involving scale. They solve proportions to find missing lengths in similar figures. They solve problems using proportions and equations.

Activating Prior Knowledge

In this chapter, students will build on their knowledge of fractions by writing ratios and unit rates, solving proportions, and finding values in similar figures, maps, and scale models. Ask questions such as:

• *What are equivalent fractions?*
fractions that are equal
• *How do you find equivalent fractions?* Multiply or divide the numerator and the denominator by the same nonzero number.
• *How do you simplify fractions?* Divide the numerator and the denominator by their GCF (greatest common factor).

What You'll Learn Next
TEKS ☆

• **(7.2)(D)** In this chapter, you will find unit rates and ratios in proportional relationships.  **Obj. 1**

• **(7.3)(B)** You will find solutions to problems involving proportional relationships such as similarity, scaling, and unit costs.  **Obj. 2**

• **(7.6)(D)** You will use critical attributes to define similarity.  **Obj. 3**

(TAKS) **Tune-Up** On pages 269–271, you will review and practice the vocabulary and *TAKS* objectives you have learned.

🔊) **Key Vocabulary**

• cross products (p. 239)
• equivalent ratios (p. 229)
• indirect measurement (p. 253)
• polygon (p. 252)
• proportion (p. 238)
• rate (p. 232)
• ratio (p. 228)
• scale (p. 259)
• scale drawing (p. 259)
• similar polygons (p. 252)
• unit cost (p. 233)
• unit rate (p. 232)

Chapter 5 **227**

TEKS ★ TAKS

(7.2)(D) To use division to find ratios in proportional relationships TAKS Obj. 1

(7.3)(B) To find solutions to application problems involving proportional relationships such as related measurement units TAKS Obj. 2

Dana Center TEKS Toolkit Clarifying Activities (7.2)(D), (7.3)(B)
Visit: PHSchool.com
Web Code: arq-9045

TEKS Math Background

A ratio is a comparison of two quantities by *division*. Using a ratio to compare 2 lb and 6 lb, you can express the result in one of these forms.

2 lb to 6 lb   2 lb : 6 lb $\frac{2\ lb}{6\ lb}$

All three forms are acceptable, but in this textbook ratios are most often written in the familiar form of a fraction. Students can then connect their knowledge of fraction concepts to the task of writing equivalent ratios and writing ratios in simplest form.

More Math Background: p. 226C

Lesson Planning and Resources

See p. 226E for a list of the resources that support this lesson.

Bell Ringer Practice

✓ **Check Skills You'll Need**
Use student page, transparency, or PowerPoint.

TAKS **Daily Review 35**
Use transparency.

228

5-1 Ratios

✓ **Check Skills You'll Need**

1. **Vocabulary Review**
What are *equivalent fractions*? See below.
Write each fraction in simplest form.

2. $\frac{2}{4}$ $\frac{1}{2}$ 3. $\frac{21}{27}$ $\frac{7}{9}$

4. $\frac{36}{63}$ $\frac{4}{7}$ 5. $\frac{8}{24}$ $\frac{1}{3}$

for Help
Lesson 2-3

Check Skills You'll Need

1. Equivalent fractions are fractions that name the same amount.

TEKS ★ TAKS

- (7.2)(D) To use division to find ratios in proportional relationships TAKS Obj. 1
- (7.3)(B) To find solutions to application problems involving proportional relationships such as related measurement units TAKS Obj. 2

🔊 **New Vocabulary** ratio, equivalent ratios

Why Learn This?

The keys on a music keyboard have a repeating pattern of five black keys and seven white keys. You can use ratios to describe patterns.

The ratio of black keys to white keys in the pattern is 5 to 7. What is the ratio of black keys to all keys in the pattern?

5	7
12	

KEY CONCEPTS **Ratio**

A **ratio** is a comparison of two quantities by division. You can write a ratio in three ways.

Arithmetic	**Algebra**
5 to 7 5 : 7 $\frac{5}{7}$	a to b $a : b$ $\frac{a}{b}$
	where $b \neq 0$

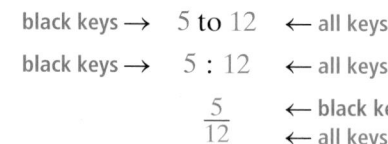

GO **Online**

Video Tutor Help
Visit: PHSchool.com
Web Code: are-0775

EXAMPLE **Writing Ratios**

① **Music** Using the pattern shown above, write the ratio of black keys to all keys in three ways.

black keys → 5 to 12 ← all keys
black keys → 5 : 12   ← all keys
                $\frac{5}{12}$ ← black keys
                     ← all keys

✓ **Quick Check**

1. Write each ratio in three ways. Use the pattern of keys shown above.
   a. white keys to all keys 7 to 12, 7 : 12, $\frac{7}{12}$
   b. white keys to black keys 7 to 5; 7 : 5; $\frac{7}{5}$

228   **Chapter 5**   Ratios, Rates, and Proportions

Differentiated **Instruction** **Solutions for All Learners**

Special Needs L1
Provide students with index cards that show different ways to write ratios. Make sure they understand that while ratios can be written like fractions, fractions are not written like ratios.

learning style: visual

Below Level L2
Review equivalent fractions. Remind students that you may multiply or divide both numerator and denominator by the same nonzero number.

learning style: auditory

Two ratios that name the same number are **equivalent ratios.** In Chapter 2, you learned to write equivalent fractions. You can find equivalent ratios by writing a ratio as a fraction and finding an equivalent fraction.

EXAMPLES Writing Equivalent Ratios

② Find a ratio equivalent to $\frac{4}{5}$.

$$\frac{4 \times 2}{5 \times 2} = \frac{8}{10} \quad \leftarrow \text{ Multiply the numerator and denominator by 2.}$$

③ Write the ratio 2 yd to 20 ft as a fraction in simplest form.

$$\frac{2\text{ yd}}{20\text{ ft}} = \frac{2 \times 3\text{ ft}}{20\text{ ft}} \quad \leftarrow \text{ There are 3 ft in each yard.}$$

$$= \frac{6\text{ ft}}{20\text{ ft}} \quad \leftarrow \text{ Multiply.}$$

$$= \frac{6\text{ ft} \div 2}{20\text{ ft} \div 2} \quad \leftarrow \text{ Divide by the GCF, 2.}$$

$$= \frac{3}{10} \quad \leftarrow \text{ Simplify.}$$

For help converting customary units, go to Lesson 3-6.

✓ **Quick Check**

2. Find a ratio equivalent to $\frac{7}{9}$. **Answers may vary. Samples:** $\frac{14}{18}$, $\frac{35}{45}$

3. Write the ratio 3 gal to 10 qt as a fraction in simplest form.
$\frac{6}{5}$

You can use decimals to express and compare ratios.

EXAMPLE Comparing Ratios

④ **Social Studies** An official U.S. flag has a length-to-width ratio of 19 : 10. The largest U.S. flag measures 505 ft by 255 ft. Is this an official U.S. flag?

official flag		largest flag
↓		↓
$\frac{19}{10}$	$\leftarrow$ length $\rightarrow$ $\leftarrow$ width $\rightarrow$	$\frac{505}{255}$

$$\frac{19}{10} = 1.9 \quad \leftarrow \begin{array}{l}\text{Write as a decimal.} \\ \text{Round if necessary.}\end{array} \rightarrow \quad \frac{505}{255} \approx 1.98$$

Since 1.98 is not equal to 1.9, the largest flag is *not* an official U.S. flag.

For: Ratios Activity
Use: Interactive Textbook, 5-1

✓ **Quick Check**

4. Tell whether the ratios are *equivalent* or *not equivalent*.

a. 7 : 3, 128 : 54
not equivalent

b. $\frac{180}{240}$, $\frac{25}{34}$
not equivalent

c. 6.1 to 7, 30.5 to 35
equivalent

5-1 Ratios **229**

2. Teach

Activity Lab

Use before the lesson.

All in One Teaching Resources
Activity Lab 5-1: Golden Ratios

Guided Instruction

Example 1
Stress the importance of the order of the numbers when writing a ratio. Ask:*Why would it not be correct to express this ratio as 12 to 5?* The ratio 12 to 5 is the ratio of all keys to black keys.

Example 2
Suggest that students use a colored pencil to write the number by which they are multiplying or dividing the numerator and denominator. This will help check that both multipliers or both divisors are the same.

PowerPoint
Additional Examples

❶ There are 7 red stripes and 6 white stripes on the flag of the United States. Write the ratio of red stripes to white stripes in three ways.
7 to 6; 7 : 6; $\frac{7}{6}$

❷ Find two ratios equivalent to $\frac{14}{4}$. Answers may vary. Samples: $\frac{7}{2}$ and $\frac{28}{8}$

❸ The ratio of girls to boys enrolled at King Middle School is 15 : 16. There are 195 girls and 208 boys in Grade 8. Is the ratio of girls to boys in Grade 8 the same as the ratio of girls to boys in the entire school? yes

All in One Teaching Resources
• Daily Notetaking Guide 5-1 **L3**
• Adapted Notetaking 5-1 **L1**

Closure
• *What is a ratio?* a comparison of two quantities by division
• *What are three different ways to write the ratio "a to b"?* a to b; a : b; $\frac{a}{b}$

Advanced Learners **L4**
Challenge students to write a ratio in simplest form when a decimal is involved.
Example:
$$\frac{2.4}{16} = \frac{2.4 \times 10}{16 \times 10} = \frac{24}{160} = \frac{24 \div 8}{160 \div 8} = \frac{3}{20}$$
Pre-AP™

English Language Learners **ELL**
For Example 1, show students a picture of a piano, with the number of keys. Say: *The number of black keys compared to all keys is a part to whole comparison. The number of black keys to white keys is a part to part comparison. Both are ratios.*

learning style: visual

229

Assignment Guide

Check Your Understanding
Go over Exercises 1–11 in class before assigning the Homework Exercises.

Homework Exercises
A Practice by Example   12–25
B Apply Your Skills   26–31
C Challenge   32
TEKS ★ TAKS Tune-Up and
Mixed Review   33–38

Homework Quick Check
To check students' understanding of key skills and concepts, go over Exercises 15, 23, 28, 29, and 31.

Differentiated Instruction Resources

Adapted Practice 5-1   **L1**

Practice 5-1   **L3**

Write a ratio for each situation in three ways.

1. Ten years ago in Louisiana, schools averaged 182 pupils for every 10 teachers.
182 to 10; 182 : 10; $\frac{182}{10}$

2. Between 1899 and 1900, 284 out of 1,000 people in the United States were 5–17 years old.
284 to 1,000; 284 : 1,000; $\frac{284}{1,000}$

Use the chart below for Exercises 3–4.

Three seventh-grade classes were asked whether they wanted chicken or pasta served at their awards banquet.

Room Number	Chicken	Pasta
201	10	12
202	8	17
203	16	10

3. In room 201, what is the ratio of students who prefer chicken to students who prefer pasta?
10 : 12; or 5 : 6

4. Combine the totals for all three rooms. What is the ratio of the number of students who prefer pasta to the number of students who prefer chicken?
39 : 34

Write each ratio as a fraction in simplest form.

5. 12 to 18 $\frac{2}{3}$ 6. 81 : 27 $\frac{3}{1}$ 7. $\frac{6}{28}$ $\frac{3}{14}$

Tell whether the ratios are equivalent or not equivalent.

8. 12 : 24, 50 : 100 Yes, they are equivalent.
9. $\frac{22}{7}$, $\frac{1}{25}$ No, they are not equivalent.
10. 2 to 3, 24 to 36 Yes, they are equivalent.

11. A bag contains green, yellow, and orange marbles. The ratio of green marbles to yellow marbles is 2 : 5. The ratio of yellow marbles to orange marbles is 3 : 4. What is the ratio of green marbles to orange marbles?
3 : 1

5-1 • Guided Problem Solving **GPS**   **L3**

GPS Student Page 231, Exercise 27:

Cooking To make pancakes, you need 2 cups of water for every 3 cups of flour. Write an equivalent ratio to find how much water you will need with 9 cups of flour.

Understand
1. Circle the information you will need to solve.
2. What are you being asked to do?
Write a ratio for the number of cups of water to the number of cups of flour.
3. Why will a ratio help you to solve the problem?
A ratio will help determine how much water you need to use with the 9 cups of flour.

Plan and Carry Out
4. What is the ratio of the cups of water to the cups of flour? $\frac{2}{3}$ or 2 : 3
5. How many cups of flour are you using? 9 cups
6. Write an equivalent ratio to use 9 cups of flour. $\frac{2}{3} = \frac{6}{9}$
7. How many cups of water are needed for 9 cups of flour? 6 cups

Check
8. Why is the number of cups of water triple the number of cups needed for 3 cups of flour?
Since 9 cups is three times 3 cups, the number of cups of water needed is also tripled.

Solve Another Problem
9. Rebecca is laying tile in her bathroom. She needs 4 black tiles for every 16 white tiles. How many black tiles are needed if she uses 128 white tiles?
$\frac{4}{16} = \frac{x}{128}$; 32 black tiles

230

---

1. Equivalent ratios name the same amount, as do equivalent fractions.

2. No; ratios can compare any two quantities. For example, a ratio may compare two parts.

1. **Vocabulary** How are equivalent ratios like equivalent fractions?

2. **Number Sense** Do all ratios compare a part to a whole? Explain.
   See left.

Find an equivalent ratio for each ratio. Answers may vary. Samples are given.

3. $\frac{1}{8}$ 2 to 16   4. 2 to 7 $\frac{4}{14}$ 5. 10 : 9 20 to 18

Write each ratio as a fraction in simplest form.

6. 2 gal to 14 qt $\frac{4}{7}$ 7. 34 in. to 4 ft $\frac{17}{24}$ 8. $\frac{4 \text{ min}}{90 \text{ s}}$ $\frac{8}{3}$

Tell whether the ratios are equivalent or not equivalent.

9. $\frac{12}{24}$, $\frac{50}{100}$ equivalent   10. 1 to 3, 2 to 9 not equivalent   11. 2 : 3, 24 : 36 equivalent

For more exercises, see Extra Skills and Word Problems.

GO for Help

For Exercises	See Examples
12–13	1
14–16	2
17–22	3
23–25	4

12. 5 to 2, 5 : 2, $\frac{5}{2}$

13. 21 to 25, 21 : 25, $\frac{21}{25}$

A Write a ratio in three ways, comparing the first quantity to the second.

12. A week has five school days and two weekend days. See left.

13. About 21 out of 25 Texans live in an urban area. See left.

Find an equivalent ratio for each ratio. 14–16. Answers may vary. Samples are given.

14. $\frac{14}{28}$ $\frac{1}{2}$ 15. 6 to 7 12 to 14   16. 4 : 5 8 : 10

Write each ratio as a fraction in simplest form.

17. $\frac{4 \text{ ft}}{8 \text{ ft}}$ $\frac{1}{2}$ 18. 10 s : 1 min $\frac{1}{6}$ 19. $\frac{30 \text{ mL}}{2 \text{ L}}$ $\frac{3}{200}$

20. 12 oz : 3 lb $\frac{1}{4}$ 21. 2 ft to 30 in. $\frac{4}{5}$ 22. $\frac{1 \text{ m}}{300 \text{ cm}}$ $\frac{1}{3}$

Tell whether the ratios are equivalent or not equivalent.

23. $\frac{18}{24}$, $\frac{3}{4}$ equivalent   24. 6 : 7, 30 : 36 not equivalent   25. 16 to 3, 27 to 5 not equivalent

B 26. **Guided Problem Solving** The students in Room 101 and Room 104 have one class together. Write the ratio of girls to boys for the combined class. $\frac{21}{36}$ or $\frac{7}{12}$

	Room 101	Room 104
Girls	12	9
Boys	16	20

• **Make a Plan** First find the total numbers of girls and boys. Then find the ratio of girls to boys for the combined class.

27. $\frac{2}{3} = \frac{6}{9}$; you need 6 c of water.

27. **Cooking** To make pancakes, you need 2 cups of water for every 3 cups of flour. Write an equivalent ratio to find how much water you will need with 9 cups of flour.

28. With the new students, the ratio of girls to boys is 16 : 11 ≈ 1.45. Without the new students, the ratio of girls to boys was 15 : 10 = 1.5.

31a. 8 : 4, 7.5 : 3, 3.5 : 1

b. 10 qt antifreeze, 5 qt water

29. Answers may vary. Sample: if the GCF of the numerator and denominator is 1

GO Online
Homework Help
Visit: PHSchool.com
Web Code: are-0501

28. Error Analysis Your math class includes 15 girls and 10 boys. Two new students, a girl and a boy, join the class. Your friend says the ratio of girls to boys is the same as before. Explain your friend's error. See margin.

29. Writing in Math How can you tell when a ratio is in simplest form? See margin.

30. Chemistry A chemical formula shows the ratio of atoms in a substance. The formula for carbon dioxide, CO_2, tells you that there is 1 atom of carbon (C) for every 2 atoms of oxygen (O). Write the ratio of hydrogen (H) atoms to oxygen atoms in water, H_2O. $\frac{2}{1}$

31. Antifreeze protects a car's radiator from freezing. In extremely cold weather, you must mix at least 2 parts antifreeze with every 1 part water.

a. List all of the ratios in the table that provide the necessary protection.

b. Reasoning How much antifreeze and how much water should you use to protect a 15-qt radiator?

31a–b. See margin.

Mixing Antifreeze

Antifreeze (qt)	Water (qt)
8	4
7.5	3
12	8
3.5	1
9	18

C 32. Challenge A bag contains colored marbles. The ratio of red marbles to blue marbles is 1 : 4. The ratio of blue marbles to yellow marbles is 2 : 5. What is the ratio of red marbles to yellow marbles? 1 : 10

TEKS ★ TAKS Tune-Up and Mixed Review

TAKS Objective 6
TEKS (7.13)(B)

33. Maria tossed a coin 20 times and got 12 heads. What is the first step to find the ratio of the number of tails to the total number of tosses? B
Ⓐ Divide 12 by 20. Ⓒ Multiply 12 by 20.
Ⓑ Subtract 12 from 20. Ⓓ Add 12 to 20.

TAKS Objective 2
TEKS (7.5)(A)

34. The model represents the equation $3x - 2 = -8$. What is the value of x? J

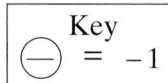

Key: $\ominus = -1$

Ⓕ $x = -6$
Ⓖ $x = -3$
Ⓗ $x = -\frac{10}{3}$
Ⓙ $x = -2$

TAKS Objective 1
TEKS (7.2)(B)

35. Emily ran $4\frac{1}{8}$ miles at track practice one day and $3\frac{3}{4}$ miles the next day. How many miles did she run in those two days? C
Ⓐ $7\frac{1}{2}$ miles Ⓑ $7\frac{3}{4}$ miles Ⓒ $7\frac{7}{8}$ miles Ⓓ $8\frac{1}{8}$ miles

 Lesson 4-4 **Algebra** Solve each equation.

36. $72 = 8k$ 9 **37.** $\frac{y}{3} = 15$ 45 **38.** $-5 = \frac{q}{7}$ −35

PowerPoint
Lesson Quiz

1. Write the ratio $\frac{9}{7}$ in two other ways. 9 to 7; 9 : 7

2. Write two other ratios equivalent to $\frac{8}{14}$. Samples: $\frac{4}{7}$, $\frac{16}{28}$

3. Compare the ratios $\frac{18}{9}$ and $\frac{16}{4}$. Are they equivalent? no

Alternative Assessment

Have students write ratios to compare various quantities within the classroom. For instance, they might write the ratio comparing the number of doors to the number of windows, or the ratio comparing the width of the door to the height of the door. Remind students that all their ratios should be written in simplest form.

TEKS ★ TAKS Resources

• TAKS Strategies, p. 265
• TAKS Tune-Up, pp. 269–271

TAKS Tune-Up Kit
• TAKS Daily Review Transparencies
• TAKS Review and Preparation Workbook
• TAKS Strategies with Transparencies
• Texas Progress Monitoring Assessments

231

(7.2)(D) To find unit rates in proportional relationships **TAKS** Obj. 1
Also supports
(7.3)(B) **TAKS** Obj. 2
(7.2)(G) **TAKS** Obj. 1

Dana Center TEKS Toolkit Clarifying Activities (7.2)(D), (7.2)(G), (7.3)(B)
Visit: PHSchool.com
Web Code: arq-9045

TEKS Math Background

The ratios in Lesson 5-1 involved quantities of the same type. That is, a number of students was compared to a number of students.

In this lesson, ratios compare different types of quantities. For instance, grams of fat are compared to servings. These ratios are called *rates*. A rate calculated for one unit of a given quantity is called a *unit rate*.

More Math Background: p. 226C

Lesson Planning and Resources

See p. 226E for a list of the resources that support this lesson.

Bell Ringer Practice

✓ Check Skills You'll Need
Use student page, transparency, or PowerPoint.

TAKS Daily Review 36
Use transparency.

✓ Check Skills You'll Need

1. Vocabulary Review
A *ratio* is a comparison of two quantities by __?__.
See below.
Write each ratio in simplest form.

2. $\frac{15}{25}$ $\frac{3}{5}$ 3. $\frac{21}{7}$ $\frac{3}{1}$

4. $\frac{22}{16}$ $\frac{11}{8}$ 5. $\frac{4}{36}$ $\frac{1}{9}$

 for Help
Lesson 5-1

Check Skills You'll Need

1. division

TEKS ★ TAKS

- (7.2)(D) To find unit rates in proportional relationships **TAKS** Obj. 1
- (7.3)(B) To estimate and find solutions to application problems involving proportional relationships such as unit cost **TAKS** Obj. 2
- (7.2)(G) To determine the reasonableness of a solution to a problem **TAKS** Obj. 1

◀» New Vocabulary rate, unit rate, unit cost

Why Learn This?

You make decisions about the foods you eat every day. Looking at rates such as grams of fat per serving can help you stay healthy.

A **rate** is a ratio that compares two quantities measured in different units. There are 15 grams of fat in 5 servings of canned soup. The rate of grams of fat per serving is $\frac{15 \text{ grams of fat}}{5 \text{ servings}}$.

The rate for one unit of a given quantity is the **unit rate.** To find a unit rate, divide the first quantity by the second quantity. For a rate of $\frac{15 \text{ grams of fat}}{5 \text{ servings}}$, the unit rate is 3 grams of fat per serving.

5 servings →   ← 15 grams of fat
1 serving →   ← 3 grams of fat

The model shows that

$$\text{total fat} \div \frac{\text{number of}}{\text{servings}} = \frac{\text{fat per}}{\text{serving}}$$

EXAMPLE   Finding a Unit Rate

1 A package of cheddar cheese contains 15 servings and has a total of 147 grams of fat. Find the unit rate of grams of fat per serving.

grams → $\frac{147}{15}$ = 9.8   ← **Divide the first quantity by the second quantity.**
servings →

The unit rate is $\frac{9.8 \text{ grams}}{1 \text{ serving}}$, or 9.8 grams of fat per serving.

✓ Quick Check

1. Find the unit rate for 210 heartbeats in 3 minutes.
70 heartbeats per min

Differentiated Instruction   **Solutions for All Learners**

Special Needs ⬛ **L1**	**Below Level** ⬛ **L2**
Help students understand that unit rates are understood to have a denominator of 1. Have them write a (1) in parentheses in colored ink. When they see a rate like miles/hour, have them rewrite it to read miles/(1) hours.	Check that students recall relationships between units of time, such as 1 h = 60 min. Also review the rules for rounding decimals.
learning style: visual	learning style: verbal

A unit rate that gives the cost per unit is a **unit cost.** Suppose a box of cereal weighs 8 oz and has a unit cost of \$.31 per ounce.

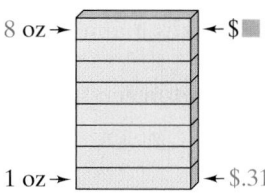

8 oz →

1 oz → ← \$.31

The model shows that

unit cost · number of ounces = total cost

EXAMPLE Using Unit Cost to Find Total Cost

2 Food Use the information at the right to find the cost of the box of cereal.

Cereal \$.31/oz

8 oz

Estimate \$.31 · 8 ≈ \$.30 · 8, or \$2.40

\$.31 · 8 = \$2.48 ← unit cost · number of units = total cost

Check for Reasonableness The total cost of \$2.48 is close to the estimate of \$2.40. So \$2.48 is reasonable.

✓ Quick Check

2. Dog food costs \$.35/lb. How much does a 20-lb bag cost? **\$7.00**

To find the unit cost, divide the total cost of the item by the number of units in the item.

EXAMPLE Using Unit Cost to Compare

★ TAKS Tip

The "better buy" is the item that has the lower unit cost.

3 Smart Shopping Two sizes of shampoo bottles are shown. Which size is the better buy? Round to the nearest cent.

Divide to find the unit cost of each size.

shampoo² shine & volume

shampoo² shine & volume

16 oz 13.5 oz

\$6.19 \$3.99

cost → $\dfrac{\$3.99}{13.5 \text{ fl oz}}$ ≈ \$.30/fl oz
size →

cost → $\dfrac{\$6.19}{16 \text{ fl oz}}$ ≈ \$.39/fl oz
size →

Since \$.30 < \$.39, the 13.5-fl-oz bottle is the better buy.

✓ Quick Check

3. Which bottle of apple juice is the better buy: 48 fl oz for \$3.05 or 64 fl oz for \$3.59? **\$.064/fl oz, \$.056/fl oz; the 64-fl-oz bottle is the better buy.**

Advanced Learners L4
Suppose you could bicycle from Earth to the moon. The distance is about 239,000 mi, and your speed is 12 mi/h. How long would it take to get to the moon? ≈ **830 days**

Pre-AP™

English Language Learners ELL
As students are learning English, they might equate better with bigger, both because of examples they have seen and the similarity between the words. Make sure they understand the *better* buy has the *smallest* price per unit.

learning style: verbal

---

2. Teach

Activity Lab
Use before the lesson.

 Teaching Resources
Activity Lab 5-2: Unit Rates

Guided Instruction

Example 3
Have students use calculators to find unit prices. Focus attention on the concept of unit prices. Stress the importance of writing the $\frac{price}{size}$ ratio, to identify which order they should enter the numbers into the calculator.

Error Prevention!

Remind students to assess their work for reasonableness using general guidelines.

speed = $\dfrac{distance}{time}$

unit price = $\dfrac{total\ price}{size}$

PowerPoint

Additional Examples

1 Find the unit rate: earn \$33 for 4 hours of work **\$8.25/h**

2 Use the unit cost to find the total cost: 7 yd of ribbon at \$.39 per yard **\$2.73**

3 Find each unit cost. Then determine the better buy. 3 lb of potatoes for \$.89 5 lb of potatoes for \$1.59 ≈ **\$.30/lb;** ≈ **\$.32/lb; The better buy is 3 lb for \$.89.**

 Teaching Resources

• Daily Notetaking Guide 5-2 L3
• Adapted Notetaking 5-2 L1

Closure

• *What is the relationship between a rate and a ratio?* A rate is a ratio that compares two different types of quantities.
• *What is a unit rate?* a rate that compares a quantity to one unit of a second quantity
• *What is a unit price?* a unit rate that identifies the cost of one unit of a given item

233

Assignment Guide

Check Your Understanding
Go over Exercises 1–5 in class before assigning the Homework Exercises.

Homework Exercises

A Practice by Example   6–18
B Apply Your Skills   19–28
C Challenge   29
TEKS ★ TAKS Tune-Up and
   Mixed Review   30–35

Homework Quick Check
To check students' understanding of key skills and concepts, go over Exercises 12, 17, 25, 27, and 28.

Differentiated Instruction Resources

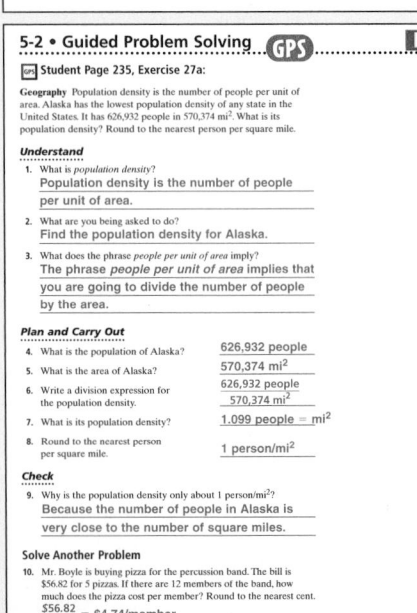

Check Your Understanding

1. **Vocabulary** What makes a unit rate a unit cost?
Answers may vary. Sample: It gives the cost of one item.

Find the unit rate for each situation by filling in the blanks.

2. skating 1,000 m in 200 s: $\frac{\text{meters}}{\text{seconds}} \rightarrow \frac{1,000}{\blacksquare} = 5$ meters per second   200

3. earning \$147 in 21 h: $\frac{\text{dollars}}{\text{hours}} \rightarrow \frac{\blacksquare}{21} = \blacksquare$ dollars per hour   147; 7

4. spending \$89 in 5 h: $\frac{\text{dollars}}{\text{hours}} \rightarrow \frac{89}{\blacksquare} = \blacksquare$ dollars per hour   5; 17.80

5. Use the model at the right to find the total amount of fat in 4 servings. **8 g**

4 servings → ▢ ← ■ grams
1 serving → ▢ ← 2 grams

Homework Exercises

For more exercises, see Extra Skills and Word Problems.

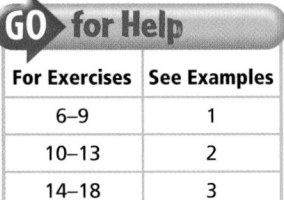

GO for Help

For Exercises	See Examples
6–9	1
10–13	2
14–18	3

A **Find the unit rate for each situation. Round to the nearest hundredth, if necessary.**

6. traveling 1,200 mi in 4 h   **300 mi/h**

7. scoring 96 points in 6 games   **16 points/game**

8. reading 53 pages in 2 h   **26.5 pages/h**

9. 592 students in 17 classrooms   **34.8 students/classroom**

Find the total cost using each unit cost.

10. 5 ft at \$3 per foot   **\$15**

11. 15 yd^2 at \$2 per square yard   **\$30**

12. 10 gal at \$2.40 per gallon   **\$24**

13. 26 oz at \$.15 per ounce   **\$3.90**

★ TAKS Tip

Drawing a model can help you find unit rates.

Find each unit cost.

14. \$12 for 4 yd^2 **\$3/yd^2**

15. \$3.45 for 3.7 oz   **\$.93/oz**

16. \$9 for 5 L   **\$1.80/L**

Which size is the better buy? 17–18. See margin.

17. detergent: 32 fl oz for \$1.99
     50 fl oz for \$2.49

18. crackers: 12 oz for \$2.69
     16 oz for \$3.19

B GPS

19. **Guided Problem Solving** A school has 945 students and 35 teachers. If the numbers of teachers and students both increase by 5, does the unit rate remain the same? Explain. **See margin.**

• Find unit rates. $\frac{\text{students}}{\text{teachers}} \rightarrow \frac{\blacksquare}{\blacksquare} = \blacksquare$ students per teacher

20. 0.1738 km/min; 173.8 m/min

20. **Biking** You bike 18.25 km in 1 h 45 min. What is the unit rate in kilometers per minute? In meters per minute? **See left.**

21. \$2.94 for 6 yd

21. **Crafts** The costs for three different types of ribbon are \$.79 for 1 yd, \$1.95 for 3 yd, and \$2.94 for 6 yd. Which is the best buy?

234   Chapter 5   Ratios, Rates, and Proportions

17. \$.06/fl oz, \$.05/fl oz; the 50-fl-oz detergent is the better buy.

18. \$.22/oz, \$.20/oz; the 12-oz crackers is the better buy.

19. No; the new student-to-teacher ratio would be 950 students : 40 teachers, or 23.75 students : 1 teacher.

GO Online
Homework Help
Visit: PHSchool.com
Web Code: are-0502

28. A rate is a ratio that compares two quantities measured in different units. A unit rate is the rate for one unit of something.

Find each unit cost.

22. 2 qt $3.69 — **$1.85/qt**

23. 2 pt $1.49 — **$.75/pt**

24. 11 oz $.99 — **$.09/oz**

25. 5 lb $2.99 — **$.60/lb**

26. The world record for the women's 3,000-m steeplechase is 9 min 1.59 s. Find the runner's speed in meters per second. Round your answer to the nearest hundredth. **5.54 m/s**

27. **Geography** Population density is the number of people per unit of area. **1 person/mi²**
   a. Alaska has the lowest population density of any state in the United States. It has 626,932 people in 570,374 mi². What is its population density? Round to the nearest person per square mile.
   b. **Reasoning** New Jersey has 1,134.5 people/mi². Can you conclude that 1,134.5 people live in every square mile in New Jersey? Explain. **No; answers may vary. Sample: Some regions of the state are more densely populated than others.**

28. **Writing in Math** Explain the difference between a rate and a unit rate. **See above left.**

C 29. **Challenge** A human heart beats an average of 2,956,575,000 times in 75 years. About how many times does a heart beat in one year? In one day? In one minute?
   about 39,421,000 times; about 108,000 times; about 75 times

TEKS ★ TAKS Tune-Up and Mixed Review

TAKS Objective 1
TEKS (7.2)(D)

30. A grocery store sells apple juice in these sizes: 64 ounces for $2.48, 128 ounces for $4.48, and 48 ounces for $1.92. Which size has the lowest unit cost? **C**
   Ⓐ 48-oz only   Ⓒ 128-oz only
   Ⓑ 64-oz only   Ⓓ 128-oz and 64-oz

TAKS Objective 6
TEKS (7.13)(C)

31. There are 12 teams in a soccer league. Each team must play every other team once. How many games will be played in all? **G**
   Ⓕ 60 games   Ⓖ 66 games   Ⓗ 72 games   Ⓙ 132 games

TAKS Objective 5
TEKS (7.12)(B)

32. Aaron received the following scores on different tests: 98, 79, 85, 92, 88. Which measure of the data is represented by 19 points? **B**
   Ⓐ median   Ⓑ range   Ⓒ mean   Ⓓ mode

 GO for Help **Lesson 2-1**

Use paper and pencil, mental math, or a calculator to simplify.

33. $3^2 + 4 \cdot 5$ **29**   34. $(6 - 3)^3 - 1$ **26**   35. $2 \cdot 4 - 5^2$ **−17**

PowerPoint
Lesson Quiz

1. It took Anthony 5 h 45 min to complete a 25-mi walkathon. What was his average speed in miles per hour? Round your answer to the nearest hundredth. ≈ **4.35 mi/h**

2. A 20-lb bag of dog food costs $21.50. A 30-lb bag of the same dog food costs $32.90. Find each unit cost. Then determine the better buy.
   ≈ $1.08/lb;
   ≈ $1.10/lb; 20 lb for $21.50

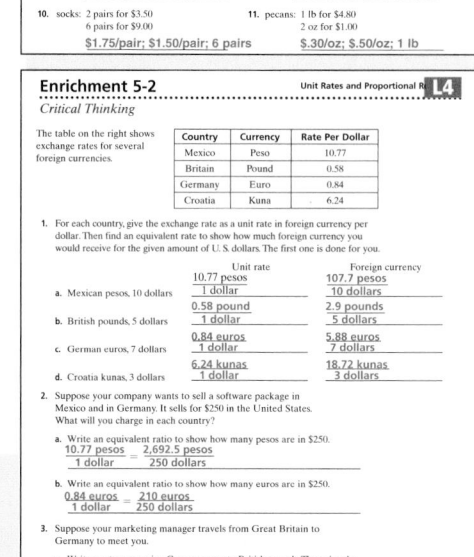

Alternative Assessment

Ask each student to write the steps needed to find the better buy, given two costs. Have students trade steps with a partner and use the partner's steps to do Exercises 17 and 18. Afterwards, partners should discuss their steps and revise them accordingly.

TEKS ★ TAKS Resources

- TAKS Strategies, p. 265
- TAKS Tune-Up, pp. 269–271

TAKS Tune-Up Kit
- TAKS Daily Review Transparencies
- TAKS Review and Preparation Workbook
- TAKS Strategies with Transparencies
- Texas Progress Monitoring Assessments

235

Using Conversion Factors

This extension of Lesson 5-2 teaches students how to generate formulas involving unit conversions. Students learn to use ratios as a means of converting a measurement from one system of measurement to another.

Guided Instruction

Ask students what measures they often see in metric units and why they might want to convert to customary units. Then ask what measures they see in customary units that they might want to convert to metric.

Example 1

Ask: *Is an inch or a centimeter longer?* inch *How do you know?* There are 2.54 cm in an inch. *Should there be more or fewer centimeters in 15 inches?* more

Science Connection

The metric system measures mass, not weight, in grams and kilograms. In order to make conversions, the language "weighs as much as" is used.

Using Conversion Factors

A conversion factor is a rate that equals 1. For example, since 60 min = 1 h, both $\frac{60 \text{ min}}{1 \text{ h}}$ and $\frac{1 \text{ h}}{60 \text{ min}}$ equal 1. You can use $\frac{60 \text{ min}}{1 \text{ h}}$ as a conversion factor to change hours into minutes.

$$7 \text{ h} = \frac{7 \cancel{\text{h}}}{1} \cdot \frac{60 \text{ min}}{1 \cancel{\text{h}}} = 420 \text{ min} \quad \leftarrow \begin{array}{l} \textbf{Divide the common unit, hours (h).} \\ \textbf{The result is in minutes.} \end{array}$$

The table shows some common conversion factors for converting between the metric system and the customary system.

EXAMPLE **Converting to the Metric System**

1 Convert 15 inches to centimeters.

$$15 \text{ in.} = \frac{15 \cancel{\text{in.}}}{1} \cdot \frac{2.54 \text{ cm}}{1 \cancel{\text{in.}}} \quad \leftarrow \begin{array}{l} \textbf{Use } \frac{2.54 \text{ cm}}{1 \text{ in.}} \textbf{ since conversion is to} \\ \textbf{centimeters. Divide the common units.} \end{array}$$
$$= (15)(2.54) \text{ cm} \quad \leftarrow \textbf{Simplify.}$$
$$= 38.1 \text{ cm} \quad \leftarrow \textbf{Multiply.}$$

Conversion Factors
Length
1 in. = 2.54 cm
1 km ≈ 0.62 mi
Capacity
1 L ≈ 1.06 qt
Weight and Mass
1 oz ≈ 28 g
1 kg ≈ 2.2 lb

EXAMPLE **Converting to the Customary System**

2 The mass of a western diamondback rattlesnake is about 6.7 kg. How many pounds does the snake weigh? Round to the nearest tenth.

$$6.7 \text{ kg} = \frac{6.7 \cancel{\text{kg}}}{1} \cdot \frac{2.2 \text{ lb}}{1 \cancel{\text{kg}}} \quad \leftarrow \textbf{Use } \frac{2.2 \text{ lb}}{1 \text{ kg}} \textbf{ since conversion is to pounds.}$$
$$= (6.7)(2.2) \text{ lb} \quad \leftarrow \textbf{Simplify.}$$
$$= 14.74 \text{ lb} \quad \leftarrow \textbf{Multiply.}$$
$$\approx 14.7 \text{ lb} \quad \leftarrow \textbf{Round to the nearest tenth.}$$

Exercises

Write a conversion factor you can use to convert each measure.

1. kilometers to miles $\frac{0.62 \text{ mi}}{1 \text{ km}}$

2. liters to quarts $\frac{1.06 \text{ qt}}{1 \text{ L}}$

3. ounces to grams $\frac{28 \text{ g}}{1 \text{ oz}}$

Use a conversion factor to convert each measure. Round to the nearest tenth.

4. 22 in. ≈ ■ cm 55.9

5. 26.4 lb ≈ ■ kg 12

6. 20.5 oz ≈ ■ g 574

7. 500 g ≈ ■ oz 17.9

8. 5 km ≈ ■ mi 3.1

9. 20 L ≈ ■ qt 21.2

1. Write the ratio 7 : 52 in two other ways. **7 to 52, $\frac{7}{52}$**

Write each ratio in simplest form.

2. $\frac{4}{6}$ **$\frac{2}{3}$**

3. $\frac{16}{48}$ **$\frac{1}{3}$**

4. 24 to 14 **12 to 7**

5. 18 : 27 **2 : 3**

Write a unit rate for each situation.

6. typing 126 words in 3 min **42 words/min**

7. scoring 45 points in 5 games **9 points/game**

Find each unit cost. Which is the better buy?

8. 3 for $.79, 4 for $.99 **$.2633, $.2475; the second item is the better buy.**

9. 5 for $39, 7 for $46 **$7.80, $6.57; the second item is the better buy.**

10. The last time you bought pizza, 3 pizzas were just enough for 7 people. At that rate, how many pizzas should you buy for a party for 35 people? **15 pizzas**

MATH AT WORK

Automotive Engineer

Automotive engineers design, develop, and test all kinds of vehicles. They also test and evaluate a design's cost, reliability, and safety.

Engineers have many opportunities to use math skills. They use problem-solving skills to find out why cars break down.

Computer-aided design systems help automotive engineers plan the cars of the future. Computer simulations allow them to test for quality and to predict how their designs will work in the real world.

Go Online
PHSchool.com

For: Information on automotive engineers
Web Code: arb-2031

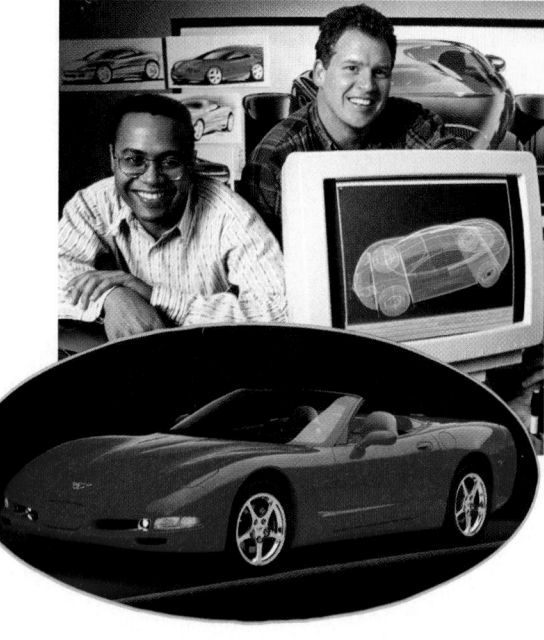

5-3

1. Plan

TEKS ★ 〔TAKS〕

(7.2)(D) To use division to find ratios in proportional relationships 〔TAKS〕 **Obj. 1**
(7.3)(B) To find solutions to application problems involving proportional relationships 〔TAKS〕 **Obj. 2**

Dana Center TEKS Toolkit Clarifying Activities (7.2)(D), (7.3)(B)
Visit: PHSchool.com
Web Code: arq-9045

TEKS Math Background

A ratio is an expression that shows a comparison of two numbers by division. That is, a ratio is a "mathematical phrase." In contrast, a proportion is a "mathematical sentence." It is an equation that declares the equality of two ratios. You can determine if two ratios form a proportion by looking for equivalent fractions or by using *cross products*.

More Math Background: p. 226D

Lesson Planning and Resources

See p. 226E for a list of the resources that support this lesson.

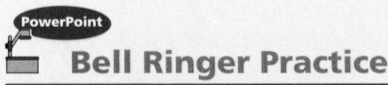
Bell Ringer Practice

✓ **Check Skills You'll Need**
Use student page, transparency, or PowerPoint.

〔TAKS〕 **Daily Review 37**
Use transparency.

238

✓ **Check Skills You'll Need**

1. Vocabulary Review
The *LCD* of two fractions is the ___?___ of the fractions' denominators.
1–5. See below.
Compare. Use <, =, or >.

2. $\frac{3}{4} \blacksquare \frac{5}{8}$ **3.** $\frac{3}{7} \blacksquare \frac{12}{28}$

4. $\frac{2}{3} \blacksquare \frac{11}{15}$ **5.** $\frac{1}{6} \blacksquare \frac{1}{12}$

 for Help
Lesson 2-4

Check Skills You'll Need

1. LCM
2. >
3. =
4. <
5. >

 GO **Online**

Video Tutor Help
Visit: PHSchool.com
Web Code: are-0775

TEKS ★ 〔TAKS〕

- **(7.2)(D)** To use division to find ratios in proportional relationships 〔TAKS〕 **Obj. 1**
- **(7.3)(B)** To find solutions to application problems involving proportional relationships 〔TAKS〕 **Obj. 2**

◀)) **New Vocabulary** proportion, cross products

Why Learn This?

Pollsters conduct surveys. They ask different groups of people the same questions. You can use proportions to compare the answers from the different groups.

Did You See a Movie This Weekend?

Class	Yes	Total Number
A	10	24
B	25	60

A **proportion** is an equation stating that two ratios are equal. One method of testing whether ratios form a proportion is to write both ratios in simplest form. Then see if they are equal.

EXAMPLE **Writing Ratios in Simplest Form**

❶ **Surveys** Refer to the table above. For each class, write the ratio of the number of students who saw a movie to the total number of students. Do the ratios form a proportion?

Class A: $\frac{10}{24} = \frac{10 \div 2}{24 \div 2} = \frac{5}{12}$ ← **Divide 10 and 24 by their GCF, which is 2.**

Class B: $\frac{25}{60} = \frac{25 \div 5}{60 \div 5} = \frac{5}{12}$ ← **Divide 25 and 60 by their GCF, which is 5.**

Since both ratios are equal to $\frac{5}{12}$, the ratios are proportional.

✓ Quick Check

1. Do $\frac{10}{12}$ and $\frac{40}{56}$ form a proportion? no; $\frac{5}{6} \neq \frac{5}{7}$

KEY CONCEPTS **Proportion**

Ratios that are equal form a proportion.

Arithmetic	**Algebra**
$\frac{6}{8} = \frac{9}{12}$	$\frac{a}{b} = \frac{c}{d}, b \neq 0, d \neq 0$

Differentiated Instruction Solutions for All Learners

Special Needs **L1**
To visualize proportions, show students a one inch length and a one foot length. Ask: *If we wanted to measure the distance across your desk, we would need more of one of these units than the other. Which one? Why?* The shorter one. It takes up less distance so you need more.

learning style: visual

Below Level **L2**
Give students a ratio such as $\frac{12}{18}$ and have them write as many ratios equal to it as they can in two minutes. Discuss their results.

$\frac{12}{18} = \frac{6}{9} = \frac{4}{6} = \frac{2}{3} = \frac{8}{12} = \frac{16}{24} = \frac{24}{36} \cdots$

learning style: visual

You can use the properties of equality to discover another way to determine whether ratios form a proportion.

$$\frac{6}{8} = \frac{9}{12}$$ ← Use the ratios from the beginning of the lesson.

$$\frac{6}{8}\left(\frac{8}{1} \cdot \frac{12}{1}\right) = \frac{9}{12}\left(\frac{8}{1} \cdot \frac{12}{1}\right)$$ ← Use the Multiplication Property of Equality. Multiply each side by both denominators.

$$\frac{6}{{}_1\cancel{8}}\left(\frac{\cancel{8}^{1}}{1} \cdot \frac{12}{1}\right) = \frac{9}{{}_1\cancel{12}}\left(\frac{8}{1} \cdot \frac{\cancel{12}^{1}}{1}\right)$$ ← Divide numerators and denominators by their GCF.

$$6 \cdot 12 = 9 \cdot 8$$

The products $6 \cdot 12$ and $9 \cdot 8$ are called cross products. For two ratios, the **cross products** are the two products found by multiplying the denominator of each ratio by the numerator of the other ratio.

$6 \cdot 12$ 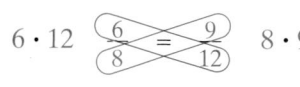 $8 \cdot 9$

KEY CONCEPTS   **Cross-Products Property**

If two ratios form a proportion, the cross products are equal. If two ratios have equal cross products, they form a proportion.

Arithmetic	**Algebra**
$\frac{6}{8} = \frac{9}{12}$	$\frac{a}{b} = \frac{c}{d}$
$6 \cdot 12 = 8 \cdot 9$	$ad = bc$, where $b \neq 0$ and $d \neq 0$

The lengths of the bones in your hands form a proportion.

SOURCE: *Fascinating Fibonaccis*

You can use the Cross-Products Property to determine whether ratios form a proportion.

EXAMPLE   **Using Cross Products**

2 Do the ratios in each pair form a proportion?

a. $\frac{5}{9}, \frac{30}{34}$

$\frac{5}{9} \stackrel{?}{=} \frac{30}{54}$ ← Test each pair of ratios. →

$5 \cdot 54 \stackrel{?}{=} 9 \cdot 30$ ← Write cross products. →

$270 = 270$ ← Simplify. →

Yes, $\frac{5}{9}$ and $\frac{30}{54}$ form a proportion.

b. $\frac{7}{8}, \frac{55}{65}$

$\frac{7}{8} \stackrel{?}{=} \frac{55}{65}$

$7 \cdot 65 \stackrel{?}{=} 8 \cdot 55$

$455 \neq 440$

No, $\frac{7}{8}$ and $\frac{55}{65}$ do *not* form a proportion.

Quick Check

2. Determine whether the ratios form a proportion.

  a. $\frac{3}{8}, \frac{6}{16}$ yes; 48 = 48   **b.** $\frac{6}{9}, \frac{4}{6}$ yes; 36 = 36   **c.** $\frac{4}{8}, \frac{5}{9}$ no; 36 ≠ 40

Advanced Learners **L4**
Have students write four proportions for which $4 \cdot 20$ and $5 \cdot 16$ can be the cross products.

$\frac{4}{5} = \frac{16}{20}, \frac{5}{4} = \frac{20}{16}, \frac{4}{16} = \frac{5}{20}, \frac{16}{4} = \frac{20}{5}$

Pre-AP™

English Language Learners **ELL**
Remind students that when they convert units, this rule usually applies: To convert from larger to smaller units, multiply. To convert from smaller to larger, divide. Have them talk about why this is true, and use several examples to verify it.

learning style: verbal

Activity Lab

Use before the lesson.

All in One Teaching Resources
Activity Lab 5-3: Math Reasoning

Guided Instruction

Example 1
Students might recall that another method for determining whether two ratios are equivalent is to write each as a decimal. If students use calculators to do this, suggest that they store the decimal for the first ratio in the calculator's memory in order to have it available for comparison.

Example 2
Reinforce the concept of cross products by pointing out that the ovals connecting the pairs of numbers form a large "X," which is a symbol for multiplication.

PowerPoint
Additional Examples

Determine if the ratios can form a proportion.

1 $\frac{42}{56}, \frac{56}{64}$ no

2 **a.** $\frac{2}{3}, \frac{18}{24}$ no   **b.** $\frac{5}{4}, \frac{30}{24}$ yes

3 **a.** $\frac{4}{10}, \frac{6}{15}$ yes   **b.** $\frac{8}{6}, \frac{9}{7}$ no

All in One Teaching Resources
• Daily Notetaking Guide 5-3 **L3**
• Adapted Notetaking 5-3 **L1**

Closure

• Define proportion. An equation stating that two ratios are equal.
• Summarize the three methods for determining whether a pair of ratios can form a proportion. Write ratios in simplest form and check for equality, find a common multiplier between numerators and denominators, and find cross products and check for equality.

Assignment Guide

Check Your Understanding
Go over Exercises 1–9 in class before assigning the Homework Exercises.

Homework Exercises
A Practice by Example   10–27
B Apply Your Skills   28–38
C Challenge   39
TEKS ★ TAKS Tune-Up and
    Mixed Review   40–45

Homework Quick Check
To check students' understanding of key skills and concepts, go over Exercises 14, 22, 29, 34, and 38.

Differentiated Instruction Resources

✓ Check Your Understanding

2. If you multiply both the numerator and denominator of the first fraction by 3, you get the second fraction. $\frac{3}{5} \times \frac{3}{3} = \frac{9}{15}$

9. No; you need to multiply the numerator of one by the denominator of the other.
$$\frac{3}{4} \stackrel{?}{=} \frac{12}{16}$$
$$3 \cdot 16 \stackrel{?}{=} 4 \cdot 12$$
$$48 = 48$$
They do form a proportion.

1. **Vocabulary** A proportion states that two __?__ are equal. ratios

2. **Number Sense** Without writing $\frac{3}{5}$ and $\frac{9}{15}$ in simplest form or using the Cross-Products Property, how can you tell whether the ratios form a proportion? See left.

Fill in the blank so that each pair of ratios forms a proportion.

3. $\frac{1}{2}, \frac{4}{\blacksquare}$ 8

4. $\frac{3}{3}, \frac{9}{\blacksquare}$ 9

5. $\frac{3}{4}, \frac{\blacksquare}{12}$ 9

6. $\frac{4}{7}, \frac{8}{\blacksquare}$ 14

7. $\frac{2}{3}, \frac{\blacksquare}{18}$ 12

8. $\frac{\blacksquare}{5}, \frac{6}{10}$ 3

9. **Error Analysis** A student used the Cross-Products Property to determine that $\frac{3}{4}$ and $\frac{12}{16}$ do not form a proportion. His work is shown at the right. Is he correct? Explain. See left.

$$\frac{3}{4} \stackrel{?}{=} \frac{12}{16}$$
$$3 \cdot 12 \stackrel{?}{=} 4 \cdot 16$$
$$36 \neq 64$$

Homework Exercises

For more exercises, see Extra Skills and Word Problems.

GO for Help

For Exercises	See Examples
10–18	1
19–27	2

A Determine whether the ratios can form a proportion.

10. $\frac{1}{2}, \frac{14}{28}$ yes

11. $\frac{6}{8}, \frac{4}{3}$ no

12. $\frac{8}{18}, \frac{20}{45}$ yes

13. $\frac{21}{24}, \frac{56}{64}$ yes

14. $\frac{15}{45}, \frac{3}{15}$ no

15. $\frac{45}{9}, \frac{10}{2}$ yes

16. $\frac{19}{76}, \frac{5}{20}$ yes

17. $\frac{17}{34}, \frac{2}{3}$ no

18. $\frac{40}{12}, \frac{160}{3}$ no

19. $\frac{6}{10}, \frac{9}{15}$ yes

20. $\frac{4}{5}, \frac{10}{13}$ no

21. $\frac{7}{8}, \frac{15}{18}$ no

22. $\frac{6}{14}, \frac{3}{7}$ yes

23. $\frac{7}{22}, \frac{28}{77}$ no

24. $\frac{12}{15}, \frac{20}{25}$ yes

25. $\frac{6}{10}, \frac{24}{42}$ no

26. $\frac{5}{9}, \frac{15}{27}$ yes

27. $\frac{3}{10}, \frac{15}{25}$ no

28. No; $\frac{5}{2}$ and $\frac{34}{12}$ are not proportional because $5 \times 12 \neq 2 \times 34$.

B **GPS** 28. **Guided Problem Solving** Your boat engine needs 5 fl oz of oil mixed with every 2 gal of gas. A gas container has 12 gal of gas mixed with 34 fl oz of oil. Is this the correct mixture? Explain.
  • **Make a Plan** Write the ratio of oil to gas for the boat and for the gas container. Determine whether the ratios form a proportion.
  • **Carry Out the Plan** The ratios of oil to gas are $\frac{\blacksquare \text{ fl oz}}{2 \text{ gal}}$ and $\frac{\blacksquare \text{ fl oz}}{12 \text{ gal}}$.
  See above left.

29. No; $\frac{4}{5}$ and $\frac{1}{2}$ are not proportional because $4 \times 25 \neq 5 \times 16$.

29. **Decorating** A certain shade of green paint requires 4 parts blue to 5 parts yellow. If you mix 16 quarts of blue paint with 25 quarts of yellow paint, will you get the desired shade of green? Explain.
See left.

240   Chapter 5   Ratios, Rates, and Proportions

34. Answers may vary. Sample: Use cross products to find that $ab = ab + b^2$, which is only true if $b = 0$, which makes the ratios undefined.

35. Yes; the weight ratios $\frac{174}{29}$ and $\frac{102}{17}$ are proportional because $174 \cdot 17 = 102 \cdot 29$.

36. Yes; $\frac{b}{h} = \frac{20}{15} = \frac{12}{9}$ is a proportion.

37. yes; $\frac{26}{1} = \frac{104}{4}$

38. No, the ratios $\frac{18}{6}$ and $\frac{12}{3}$ are not proportional because $18 \times 3 \neq 6 \times 12$.

39. $\frac{4n}{3}$ and $\frac{12n}{9}$ will always form a proportion because $36n = 36n$ for all values of n.

Do the ratios in each pair form a proportion?

30. $\frac{56}{2}, \frac{110}{3}$ no   **31.** $\frac{18}{12}, \frac{4.8}{3.6}$ no   **32.** $\frac{20}{1.5}, \frac{60}{4.5}$ yes   **33.** $\frac{3.5}{35}, \frac{2.04}{204}$ no

34. Writing in Math Explain why $\frac{a}{b}$ and $\frac{a+b}{b}$ can *never* form a proportion. **See margin.**

35. Space An astronaut who weighs 174 lb on Earth weighs 29 lb on the moon. If you weigh 102 lb on Earth, would you weigh 17 lb on the moon? Explain. **See margin.**

36. Geometry Is the ratio of b to h the same in both triangles? Explain your reasoning. **See margin.**

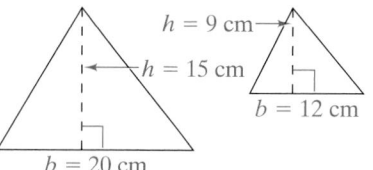
$h = 9$ cm
$h = 15$ cm
$b = 12$ cm
$b = 20$ cm

37. An elephant's heart rate was measured at 26 beats in 1 minute and 104 beats in 4 minutes. Are the rates proportional? **See margin.**

38. Physical Science Eighteen-karat gold contains 18 parts gold and 6 parts other metals. A ring contains 12 parts gold and 3 parts other metals. Is the ring eighteen-karat gold? Explain. **See margin.**

Careers Astronauts pilot spacecraft or work on science projects in space.

Ⓒ **39. Challenge** Determine whether $\frac{4n}{3}$ and $\frac{12n}{9}$ *always, sometimes,* or *never* form a proportion. Explain. **See margin.**

TEKS ★ TAKS Tune-Up and Mixed Review

TAKS Objective 1
TEKS (7.2)(D)

40. Which ratio does NOT form a proportion with $\frac{5}{8}$? **C**

Ⓐ $\frac{20}{32}$ Ⓑ $\frac{100}{160}$ Ⓒ $\frac{45}{56}$ Ⓓ $\frac{10}{16}$

TAKS Objective 1
TEKS (7.2)(A)

41. Which expression does the model below represent? **H**

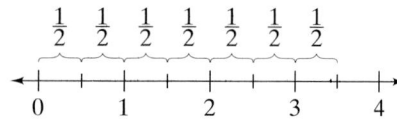
$\frac{1}{2}$ $\frac{1}{2}$ $\frac{1}{2}$ $\frac{1}{2}$ $\frac{1}{2}$ $\frac{1}{2}$ $\frac{1}{2}$
0   1   2   3   4

Ⓕ $3\frac{1}{2} - \frac{1}{2}$ Ⓖ $\frac{1}{2} \div 3\frac{1}{2}$ Ⓗ $3\frac{1}{2} \div \frac{1}{2}$ Ⓙ $\frac{1}{2} \times 3\frac{1}{2}$

TAKS Objective 6
TEKS (7.13)(B)

42. Carrie buys T-shirts for $6.25 each. After paying to have her school mascot printed on the shirts, she sells each one for $9.50. Carrie plans to sell 12 T-shirts at a basketball game. What missing information is needed to find how much profit per shirt she will make? **A**

Ⓐ Cost to print the mascot   Ⓒ Sizes of the T-shirts
Ⓑ Number of fans at the game   Ⓓ Price of each T-shirt

GO for Help   **Lesson 4-3**   **Algebra** Solve each equation.

43. $y - 37 = 68$ 105   **44.** $m + 59 = -348$ −407   **45.** $b + 175 = 102$ −73

TEKS ★ TAKS Resources

• TAKS Strategies, p. 265
• TAKS Tune-Up, pp. 269–271

TAKS Tune-Up Kit
• TAKS Daily Review Transparencies
• TAKS Review and Preparation Workbook
• TAKS Strategies with Transparencies
• Texas Progress Monitoring Assessments

---

4. Assess & Reteach

PowerPoint
Lesson Quiz

Determine if the ratios can form a proportion.

1. $\frac{35}{56}, \frac{45}{63}$ no   **2.** $\frac{9}{13}, \frac{18}{26}$ yes

3. $\frac{12}{9}, \frac{16}{12}$ yes   **4.** $\frac{30}{16}, \frac{45}{12}$ no

Alternative Assessment

Give students the following ratios.

$\frac{2}{3}$ $\frac{10}{16}$ $\frac{48}{56}$ $\frac{24}{36}$ $\frac{6}{4}$ $\frac{15}{24}$ $\frac{36}{42}$ $\frac{26}{36}$

Have them use the ratios to form as many proportions as possible.

$\frac{2}{3} = \frac{24}{36}; \frac{10}{16} = \frac{15}{24}; \frac{48}{56} = \frac{36}{42}$

241

Interpreting Rates Visually

5-3b Activity Lab   Algebra Thinking   x = ?

TEKS ★ TAKS
(7.11)(B) To make inferences and convincing arguments based on an analysis of given data TAKS Obj. 5

Interpreting Rates Visually

You can describe real-world situations using rates.

ACTIVITY

Manny mowed lawns to earn spending money. He charged $10 per hour. Ilene earned money by baby-sitting at $8 per hour, plus a $5 travel fee. Who earned the most for a 3-hour job?

1. Copy and complete the table below to show how much each person earns. **See margin.**

Earnings

	1 hour	2 hours	3 hours	4 hours	5 hours
Manny	■	■	■	■	■
Ilene	■	■	■	■	■

2. Graph the data above on a coordinate system like the one below. Make Manny's line solid and make Ilene's line dashed. **See margin.**

3. Why does the line for Manny's earnings start at $0 for zero hours worked? Why does the line for Ilene's earnings start at $5 for zero hours worked? **Manny does not charge a travel fee. Ilene charges a $5 travel fee.**

4. An expression for Manny's earnings is $10x$, where x is the number of hours worked. Write an expression for Ilene's earnings. **$5 + 8x$**

5. Estimate the time at which the lines cross. What does this point represent? **2.5 hrs. It means they are earning the same amount for the same number of hours worked.**

6. According to the graph, who earned more for a 3-hour job?   **Manny earned more.**

7. Estimate each person's earnings for a $1\frac{1}{2}$-hour job. Estimate each person's earnings for a $2\frac{1}{2}$-hour job. **Manny: $15, Ilene $17; Manny: $25, Ilene $25**

1–2. See back of book.

5-4a Activity Lab

Data Collection

Using Proportions With Data

You can use proportions to estimate the number of times your heart beats in one minute, which is called your heart rate.

TEKS ★ TAKS

(7.2)(D) To use division to find unit rates and ratios in proportional relationships **TAKS Obj. 1**

(7.3)(B) To estimate and find solutions to application problems involving proportional relationships **TAKS Obj. 2**

ACTIVITY

Copy and complete the table below. Use your data from Steps 1–4.

My Heart Rate Data

Ratio: $\dfrac{\text{counted beats}}{10 \text{ seconds}}$	■
Resting Heart Rate	■
Minimum Target Value	■
Maximum Target Value	■
Exercising Heart Rate	■

Step 1 Count the number of times your heart beats in 10 seconds. Write this value as a ratio.

Step 2 Let x = your heart rate. Use your data to write a proportion.

$$\frac{\text{counted beats}}{10 \text{ seconds}} = \frac{x \text{ beats}}{60 \text{ seconds}}$$

Use mental math to find x. This is your resting heart rate.

Step 3 When you exercise, your heart rate should fall within a target zone. Calculate the values for your target zone.

Minimum value = $0.6(220 - \text{your age})$
Maximum value = $0.8(220 - \text{your age})$

Step 4 Jog in place for one minute. Repeat Steps 1 and 2 to estimate your exercising heart rate.

Exercises

1. Compare your exercising rate with your target zone. **Answers may vary. Sample: My exercising heart rate is less than my minimum target rate.**

2. Explain why counting your heartbeats for 10 seconds, rather than for a full minute, gives you a more accurate estimate of your exercising heart rate. **Your heart rate will decrease rapidly when you stop exercising.**

3. Express your resting heart rate as a unit rate and estimate the number of times your heart beats in 24 hours. **Check students' work.**

Activity Lab

Using Proportions with Data

Students use a sample of data to arrive at a proportional unit rate. This will prepare them to solve proportions in Lesson 5-4.

Guided Instruction

Before beginning the Activity, ask students to name different kinds of exercise and their unit rates (*e.g.* jogging in miles per hour). Ask:

- *Why would you monitor your heart rate when you exercise?* **to make sure your heart is beating at a healthy rate**
- *What other body activities could you measure with a unit rate?* **breaths per minute, eye blinks per minute**

Exercises

Have students work independently on the Exercises. Then have them trade papers with a partner and compare answers. Students with errors should correct their papers.

Alternative Method

Some students may prefer to represent data visually to arrive at an answer. Have them create a table for number of heartbeats at ten second intervals and help them find a unit rate.

TEKS ★ TAKS Resources

- Activity Lab 5-4: Decision Making
- Student Manipulatives Kit

Dana Center TEKS Toolkit Clarifying Activities (7.2)(D), (7.3)(B)
Visit: PHSchool.com
Web Code: arq-9045

5-4

1. Plan

TEKS

(7.2)(D) To use division to find unit rates and ratios in proportional relationships
TAKS Obj. 1
Also supports
(7.3)(B) **TAKS** Obj. 2
(7.13)(D)

Dana Center TEKS Toolkit Clarifying Activities (7.2)(D), (7.3)(D), (7.13)(D)
Visit: PHSchool.com
Web Code: arq-9045

TEKS Math Background

In a proportion, such as $\frac{3}{4} = \frac{18}{24}$, each of the four *terms* is a number, and the proportion is a true statement. In many situations one of the terms of a proportion is unknown. The unknown term is represented by a variable, as in $\frac{r}{3} = \frac{36}{27}$. This statement is neither true nor false. Solve the proportion by finding the value of the variable that makes the statement true. Since $\frac{4}{3} = \frac{36}{27}$, the solution of $\frac{r}{3} = \frac{36}{27}$ is 4.

More Math Background: p. 226D

Lesson Planning and Resources

See p. 226E for a list of the resources that support this lesson.

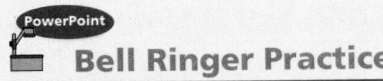
Bell Ringer Practice

✓ **Check Skills You'll Need**
Use student page, transparency, or PowerPoint.

TAKS Daily Review 38
Use transparency.

244

✓ Check Skills You'll Need

1. Vocabulary Review
When is a ratio a *unit rate*?
1–5. See below.
Write the unit rate for each situation.

2. 192 km in 24 d

3. 248 mi in 4 h

4. 50 push-ups in 2 min

5. 180 words in 3 min

 for Help
Lesson 5-2

Check Skills You'll Need

1. A ratio is a unit rate when you are finding the rate for one unit of something.

2. 8 km/d

3. 62 mi/h

4. 25 push-ups/min

5. 60 words/min

TEKS

- (7.2)(D) To use division to find unit rates and ratios in proportional relationships **TAKS** Obj. 1
- (7.3)(B) To find solutions to application problems involving proportional relationships such as unit costs **TAKS** Obj. 2
- (7.13)(D) To select techniques such as mental math to solve problems

Why Learn This?

You know the price of six oranges, but you want to buy eight. You can solve a proportion to find the total cost of the quantity that you want to buy.

You can use unit rates to solve a proportion. First find the unit rate. Then multiply to solve the problem.

6 for $2.34

EXAMPLE **Using Unit Rates**

① **Shopping** Use the information above to find the cost in dollars of 8 oranges.

Solve the proportion $\frac{2.34 \text{ dollars}}{6 \text{ oranges}} = \frac{x \text{ dollars}}{8 \text{ oranges}}$.

Step 1 Find the unit price.

$$\frac{2.34 \text{ dollars}}{6 \text{ oranges}}$$

$\$2.34 \div 6 \text{ oranges}$ ← **Divide to find the unit price.**

$\$.39/\text{orange}$

Step 2 You know the cost of one orange. Multiply to find the cost of 8 oranges.

$\$.39 \cdot 8 = \$3.12$ ← **Multiply the unit rate by the number of oranges.**

The cost of 8 oranges is $3.12.

✓ Quick Check

$6.37

1. a. Postcards cost $2.45 for 5 cards. How much will 13 cards cost?

b. Swimming goggles cost $84.36 for 12. At this rate, how much will new goggles for 17 members of a swim team cost? $119.51

Differentiated Instruction Solutions for All Learners

Special Needs L1	**Below Level** L2
To help students with their proportional reasoning, have them use fraction kits or strips to show how $\frac{6}{8}$ and $\frac{9}{12}$ are equal and therefore proportional. Repeat with $\frac{4}{6}$ and $\frac{10}{15}$.	Review the process of solving simple multiplication equations such as $3x = 12$ and $54 = -9y$. $x = 4$, $y = -6$
learning style: tactile	learning style: visual

You can use mental math to solve some proportions. When a proportion involves a variable, you solve the proportion by finding the value of the variable.

EXAMPLE   Solving Using Mental Math

② **Algebra** Solve each proportion using mental math.

a. $\dfrac{z}{12} = \dfrac{21}{36}$

$$\overset{\times 3}{\underbrace{\dfrac{z}{12} = \dfrac{21}{36}}_{\times 3}} \quad \leftarrow \text{Since } 12 \times 3 = 36, \text{ the common multiplier is 3.}$$

$z = 7 \quad \leftarrow$ Use mental math to find what number times 3 equals 21.

b. $\dfrac{8}{10} = \dfrac{n}{40}$

$$\overset{\times 4}{\underbrace{\dfrac{8}{10} = \dfrac{n}{40}}_{\times 4}} \quad \leftarrow \text{Since } 10 \times 4 = 40,\ 8 \times 4 = n.$$

$n = 32 \quad \leftarrow$ Use mental math.

✓ Quick Check

2. Solve each proportion using mental math.

a. $\dfrac{3}{8} = \dfrac{b}{24}$ **9**

b. $\dfrac{m}{5} = \dfrac{16}{40}$ **2**

c. $\dfrac{15}{30} = \dfrac{5}{p}$ **10**

Many proportions cannot easily be solved with mental math. In these situations, you can use cross products to solve a proportion.

EXAMPLE   Solving Using Cross Products

Before you use cross products to solve a proportion, check whether you can use mental math.

③ **TAKS** Griddable Item Solve $\dfrac{25}{38} = \dfrac{15}{x}$ using cross products.

$\dfrac{25}{38} = \dfrac{15}{x}$

$25x = 38(15) \quad \leftarrow$ Write the cross products.

$25x = 570 \quad \leftarrow$ Simplify.

$\dfrac{25x}{25} = \dfrac{570}{25} \quad \leftarrow$ Divide each side by 25.

$x = 22.8 \quad \leftarrow$ Simplify.

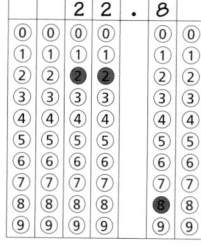

✓ Quick Check

3. Solve each proportion using cross products.

a. $\dfrac{12}{15} = \dfrac{x}{21}$ **16.8**

b. $\dfrac{16}{30} = \dfrac{d}{51}$ **27.2**

c. $\dfrac{20}{35} = \dfrac{110}{m}$ **192.5**

Advanced Learners **L4**
Challenge students to solve this proportion.

$\dfrac{32}{m} = \dfrac{m}{2}$ $m = 8$ or $m = -8$

Pre-AP™

English Language Learners **ELL**
Make sure to clearly distinguish between a common *multiple* and a common *multiplier*. The similarity in the terms can cause confusion.

learning style: verbal

245

---

2. Teach

Activity Lab

Use before the lesson.
Student Edition Activity Lab, Data Collection 5-4a, Using Proportions With Data, p. 243

All in One Teaching Resources
Activity Lab 5-4: Decision Making

Guided Instruction

Example 2
Have students describe each part orally, using a parallel structure to state the relationship between the denominators and the relationship between the numerators. Have them say for part a: 12 times 3 equals 36. z times 3 equals 21. z must be what number? **7**

The method of solving proportions using a common multiplier is sometimes called the "factor of change" method. You can scale a ratio up or down to an equivalent ratio by multiplying its terms by a common multiplier, just as you can generate equivalent fractions by multiplying the numerator and denominator of a fraction by a common multiplier.

Error Prevention!

When solving a proportion, students might multiply all the numbers. Stress that the process of solving a proportion involves a series of equations. It is important to write an *equation* involving the cross products. After writing the correct cross-product equation, highlight the number next to the variable. Focus attention on this number and use it as a divisor, not a multiplier.

Additional Examples

1 The cost of 4 light bulbs is $3. At this rate, what is the cost of 10 light bulbs? **$7.50**

2 Solve each proportion using mental math.

a. $\frac{5}{c} = \frac{30}{42}$ **c = 7**

b. $\frac{9}{4} = \frac{72}{t}$ **t = 32**

3 Solve $\frac{6}{8} = \frac{9}{a}$ using cross products. **a = 12**

All in One Teaching Resources

- Daily Notetaking Guide 5-4 **L3**
- Adapted Notetaking 5-4 **L1**

Closure

Give students the following equations.

$\frac{4}{5} = \frac{20}{25}$ $\frac{3}{8} = \frac{18}{w}$

- Ask: *Why is each equation a proportion?* **Each is a statement that shows two ratios are equivalent.** *How is the second proportion different from the first?* **One number in the proportion is unknown and is represented by a variable.**

- Discuss the three methods for solving proportions that were presented in Examples 1 through 3. Tell students to choose the method they think most appropriate and use it to solve $\frac{3}{8} = \frac{18}{w}$. **w = 48**

● More Than One Way

Nature An oyster bed covers 36 m². Your class studies 4 m² of the oyster bed. In those 4 m² you count 96 oysters. Predict the number of oysters in the entire bed.

Carlos's Method

I will let x represent the number of oysters in the 36-m² bed.

$$\text{oysters} \rightarrow \frac{96}{4} = \frac{x}{36} \leftarrow \text{oysters} \quad \leftarrow \text{Write a proportion.}$$
$$\text{area} \rightarrow \quad \quad \leftarrow \text{area}$$

$96(36) = 4x$ ← Write the cross products.

$3,456 = 4x$ ← Simplify.

$\frac{3,456}{4} = \frac{4x}{4}$ ← Divide each side by 4.

$864 = x$ ← Simplify.

There are about 864 oysters in the oyster bed.

Brianna's Method

Since $9 \cdot 4 \text{ m}^2 = 36 \text{ m}^2$, the entire bed is 9 times as large as the portion studied. So I know there should be about $9 \cdot 96$, or 864, oysters in the oyster bed.

Choose a Method

You buy a bag of 400 marbles. In a handful of 20 marbles, you find 8 red marbles. About how many red marbles are in the bag? Explain why you chose the method you used.
Check students' methods: about 160 red marbles.

✓ Check Your Understanding

1. Answers may vary. Sample: Finding a unit rate gives you a denominator of 1, so you only need to multiply to solve the proportion. $\frac{5}{1} = \frac{x}{8}$, x = 40

1. **Writing in Math** How does a unit rate help you solve a proportion?

2. **Number Sense** Does the proportion $\frac{3}{7} = \frac{x}{21}$ have the same solution as $\frac{7}{3} = \frac{21}{x}$? Explain. **Yes; both give the cross products of 7x = 3 · 21.**

Solve each proportion using mental math.

3. $\frac{2}{5} = \frac{m}{10}$

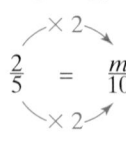

$m = \blacksquare 4$

4. $\frac{1}{6} = \frac{4}{y}$

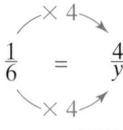

$y = \blacksquare 24$

5. $\frac{7}{3} = \frac{28}{b}$

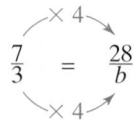

$b = \blacksquare 12$

For more exercises, see Extra Skills and Word Problems.

GO for Help

For Exercises	See Examples
6–10	1
11–16	2
17–25	3

A Solve each problem by finding a unit rate and multiplying.

6. If 5 goldfish cost $6.45, what is the cost of 8 goldfish? $10.32

7. If 12 roses cost $18.96, what is the cost of 5 roses? $7.90

8. If 3 onions weigh 0.75 lb, how much do 10 onions weigh? 2.5 lb

9. If 13 key chains cost $38.35, what is the cost of 20 key chains? $59.00

10. At a telethon, a volunteer can take 48 calls over a 4-hour shift. At this rate, how many calls can 12 volunteers take in a 4-hour shift? 576 calls

Solve each proportion using mental math.

11. $\frac{2}{7} = \frac{x}{21}$ 6

12. $\frac{18}{32} = \frac{m}{16}$ 9

13. $\frac{c}{10} = \frac{36}{60}$ 6

14. $\frac{c}{35} = \frac{4}{7}$ 20

15. $\frac{16}{38} = \frac{b}{19}$ 8

16. $\frac{9}{w} = \frac{36}{20}$ 5

Solve each proportion using cross products.

17. $\frac{8}{12} = \frac{y}{30}$ 20

18. $\frac{15}{33} = \frac{m}{22}$ 10

19. $\frac{c}{28} = \frac{49}{16}$ 85.75

20. $\frac{y}{18} = \frac{21}{63}$ 6

21. $\frac{14}{34} = \frac{x}{51}$ 21

22. $\frac{9}{30} = \frac{p}{16}$ 4.8

23. $\frac{20}{w} = \frac{12}{3}$ 5

24. $\frac{27}{20} = \frac{36}{v}$ $26\frac{2}{3}$

25. $\frac{19}{r} = \frac{152}{4}$ 0.5

29. Yes; when you simplify a ratio, it is still equivalent to the original ratio.

B **GPS** **26. Guided Problem Solving** You received $57.04 for working 8 h. At that rate, how much would you receive for working 11 h? $78.43

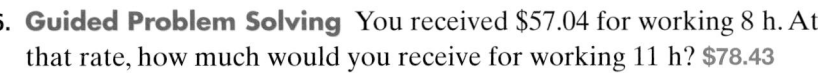

hours → $\frac{8}{\blacksquare} = \frac{\blacksquare}{x}$ ← You would receive x dollars for ■ hours.
pay →

27. History Franklin D. Roosevelt was elected president in 1932 with about 22,800,000 votes. The ratio of the number of votes he received to the number of votes the other candidates received was about 4 : 3. About how many votes did the other candidates receive? 17,100,000 votes

28. There are 450 students and 15 teachers in a school. The school hires **GPS** 2 new teachers. To keep the student-to-teacher ratio the same, how many students in all should attend the school? 510 students

29. Reasoning Brian solved the proportion $\frac{18}{45} = \frac{a}{20}$ at the right. His first step was to simplify the ratio $\frac{18}{45}$. Is his answer correct? Explain. See above left.

$2\frac{18}{\underset{5}{45}} = \frac{a}{20}$
×4
$\frac{2}{5} = \frac{a}{20}$
×4
$a = 8$

30. A jet takes $5\frac{3}{4}$ h to fly 2,475 mi from New York City to Los Angeles. About how many hours will a jet flying at the same average rate take to fly 5,452 mi from Los Angeles to Tokyo? about $12\frac{1}{2}$ h

President Franklin D. Roosevelt

3. Practice

Assignment Guide

Check Your Understanding
Go over Exercises 1–5 in class before assigning the Homework Exercises.

Homework Exercises
A Practice by Example   6–25
B Apply Your Skills   26–37
C Challenge   38
TEKS ★ **TAKS** Tune-Up and
Mixed Review   39–44

Homework Quick Check
To check students' understanding of key skills and concepts, go over Exercises 8, 21, 28, 36, and 37.

Differentiated Instruction Resources

PowerPoint
Lesson Quiz

1. The cost of 5 CDs is $42. At this rate, what is the cost of 7 CDs?
$58.80

Solve each proportion.

2. $\frac{72}{45} = \frac{8}{n}$ n = 5

3. $\frac{b}{18} = \frac{9}{5}$ b = 32.4

Alternative Assessment

Have each student in a pair write two equivalent ratios and use them to form a proportion. Each student should then erase one of the four numbers and replace it with a variable. Now have students exchange papers and solve each other's proportions. Partners should discuss their results.

GO Online
Homework Help
Visit: PHSchool.com
Web Code: are-0504

Solve each proportion using cross products. Round to the nearest tenth, if necessary.

31. $\frac{1.7}{2.5} = \frac{3.4}{d}$ 5

32. $\frac{y}{9.3} = \frac{12.6}{5.4}$ 21.7

33. $\frac{33.1}{x} = \frac{6.2}{1.3}$ 6.9

34. $\frac{16.9}{13.5} = \frac{t}{7.4}$ 9.3

35. **Error Analysis** A videocassette recorder uses 2 m of tape in 3 min when set on extended play. To determine how many minutes a tape that is 240 m long can record on extended play, one student wrote the proportion $\frac{2}{3} = \frac{n}{240}$. Explain why this proportion is incorrect. Then write a correct proportion. 240 should be the numerator. $\frac{2}{3} = \frac{240}{n}$

36. **Health** Your heart rate is the number of heartbeats per minute.
   a. What is your heart rate if you count 18 beats in 15 seconds?
   b. **Choose a Method** How many beats do you count in 15 seconds if your heart rate is 96 beats/min? Explain the method you chose.
   36a–b. See left.

37. **Writing in Math** You estimate you will take 75 min to bike 15 mi to a state park. After 30 min, you have traveled 5 mi. Are you on schedule? Explain. See margin.

36a. 72 beats/min

b. 24; answers may vary.

C 38. **Challenge** A recipe for fruit salad serves 4 people. It calls for $2\frac{1}{2}$ oranges and 16 grapes. You want to serve 11 people. How many oranges and how many grapes will you need?
7 oranges, 44 grapes

TEKS ★ TAKS Tune-Up and Mixed Review
GRIDDABLE ITEMS

TAKS Objective 2
TEKS (7.3)(B)

39. An antelope ran 237 ft in 3 seconds. If the antelope continued to run at the same rate, how many seconds would it take him to run 790 ft?
10

TAKS Objective 1
TEKS (7.2)(D)

40. The table below shows the leaders in punt returns for the National Football Conference during one season.

Punt Return Leaders

Name	Number of Returns	Yards
Brian Westbrook	20	306
Allen Rossum	39	545
Reggie Swinton	23	318
R. W. McQuarters	37	452

What was the unit rate of yards per return for Reggie Swinton? Round to the nearest hundredth. 13.83

TAKS Objective 1
TEKS (7.2)(B)

41. A restaurant bill for four people is $37.80. How much money, in dollars, should each person contribute to share the cost evenly?
9.45

GO for Help   Lesson 1-6

Order the numbers from least to greatest.

42. 16, −12, 10, −3
−12, −3, 10, 16

43. −6, −3, 8, −2, 1
−6, −3, −2, 1, 8

44. 5, 0, −1, 2, −5
−5, −1, 0, 2, 5

TEKS ★ TAKS Resources

• TAKS Strategies, pp. 269–271
• TAKS Tune-Up, p. 265

TAKS Tune-Up Kit

• TAKS Daily Review Transparencies
• TAKS Review and Preparation Workbook
• TAKS Strategies with Transparencies
• Texas Progress Monitoring Assessments

37. No; answers may vary. Sample: 15 mi in 75 min gives a unit rate of 0.2 mi/min. 5 mi in 30 min is behind schedule with a unit rate of 0.17 mi/min.

Enrichment 5-4   L4

Reteaching 5-4   Solving Pro L2

Solving a proportion means finding a missing part of the proportion. You can use unit rates to solve a proportion. First find the unit rate. Then multiply to solve the proportion.

Shawn filled 8 bags of leaves in 2 hours. At this rate, how many bags would he fill in 6 hours?

① Find a unit rate for the number of bags per hour. Divide by the denominator.
$\frac{8 \text{ bags}}{2 \text{ hours}} = \frac{8 \text{ bags} \div 2}{2 \text{ hours} \div 2} = \frac{4 \text{ bags}}{1 \text{ hour}}$ The unit rate is 4 bags per hour.

② Multiply the unit rate by 6 to find the number of bags he will fill in 6 hours.

Unit rate		Number of hours		Total
↓		↓		↓
4	×	6	=	24

At this rate, Shawn can fill 24 bags in 6 hours.

If two ratios form a proportion, the **cross products** are equal.

Solve. $\frac{n}{15} = \frac{9}{5}$

① Write the cross products.   5 · 3 = 15 · n
② Simplify.   15 = 15n
③ Solve the equation.   n = 1

Solve.

1. The bookstore advertises 5 notebooks for $7.75. At this rate, how much will 7 notebooks cost? $10.85

2. Leroy can lay 144 bricks in 3 hours. At this rate, how many bricks can he lay in 7 hours? 336

Solve each proportion using cross products.

3. $\frac{5}{24} = \frac{n}{6}$ 4 · 6 = 24 · n   n = 1

4. $\frac{30}{4} = \frac{n}{4}$ 30 = 30n   n = 1

5. $\frac{6}{9} = \frac{27}{n}$ 162 = 9n   n = 18

Solve each proportion.

6. $\frac{4}{10} = \frac{n}{15}$ n = 6

7. $\frac{4}{200} = \frac{n}{100}$ n = 2

8. $\frac{6}{n} = \frac{5}{10}$ n = 12

9. $\frac{33}{22} = \frac{96}{n}$ n = 66

10. $\frac{6}{3} = \frac{n}{5}$ n = 10

11. $\frac{2}{n} = \frac{4}{10}$ n = 5

248

Proportions and Equations

Often you can translate a proportion problem into an equation. You can then use the equation to solve similar problems.

Muscles   For each 5 pounds of body weight, about 2 pounds is muscle. How much of a 125-pound student is muscle?

TEKS ★

(7.2)(D) To use division to find unit rates in proportional relationships **TAKS** Obj. 1

(7.3)(B) To find solutions to application problems involving proportional relationships **TAKS** Obj. 2

What You Might Think

What do I know?

What am I trying to find out?

How do I solve the problem?

What is the answer?

What You Might Write

Each 5 lb of weight includes 2 lb of muscle.

How many pounds of muscle are in 125 lb of body weight?

I can write an equation to find the muscle weight for any student weight. A proportion that represents the situation is

$$\frac{x}{125} = \frac{2}{5}.$$

To solve for x, I can multiply each side by 125.

$$x = \frac{2}{5}(125)$$

125 represents the student's weight. So if a student's weight is w, then the equation

$x = \frac{2}{5}w$ gives the amount of muscle for any weight w.

$$x = \frac{2}{5}(125)$$
$$= 250 \div 5$$
$$= 50$$

The 125-lb student has about 50 lb of muscle.

Think It Through   When you find the cross products, you get $2w = 5x$. To solve for x, you divide by 5, which results in $x = \frac{2}{5}w$.

1. Show how solving the equation $\frac{2}{5} = \frac{x}{w}$ for x gives the equation $x = \frac{2}{5}w$.

2. Explain why you can use the equation $x = \frac{2}{5}w$ as a shortcut for finding the amount of muscle for any student.
   If you substitute the weight of the student, you only need to multiply.

Proportions and Equations

In this feature, students write a proportion for a situation and translate the proportion into an equation. Then they use the equation to solve the problem. Students apply the problem solving steps to this process.

Guided Instruction

Discuss with students situations in which they can make proportions, then use equations to solve real-world problems.

Have a volunteer read the problem. Ask:
- *What do you know from the problem that will let you set up a proportion?* for each 5 pounds of body weight about 2 pounds is muscle
- *What ratio can you set up?* 2 to 5 or $\frac{2}{5}$
- *What are you trying to find out?* how many pounds of muscle a 125-pound student has
- *What proportion can you set up?* $\frac{2}{5} = \frac{x}{125}$

Science Connection

Have students check in science books to find out about the origins of the Kelvin and Celsius scales.

TEKS ★ **TAKS Resources**

Dana Center TEKS Toolkit
   Clarifying Activities (7.2)(D), (7.3)(B)
Visit: PHSchool.com
Web Code: arq-9045

Error Prevention!

Some students may have difficulty understanding the equation $x = \frac{2}{5}w$ where w is a student's weight. You may want to make a table with several weights and have students find the amount of muscle for each weight.

Exercises

Have students work through Exercises 3 and 4 in pairs. For Exercises 5–7, you may wish to ask questions similar to the **a** and **b** questions in Exercises 3 and 4.

Differentiated Instruction

English Language Learners ELL

You may need to explain some of the terms in Exercises 6 and 7, for example *concession, equator,* and *rotation.* You may want to draw a picture for *equator* and show *rotation* with arrows.

Exercises

Solve each problem. For Exercises 3 and 4, answer the questions first.

3. During one season, a basketball player made 353 of 765 free throws. At that rate, how many free throws would the player make in another 600 attempts? **about 277 free throws**
   a. What do you know? What do you want to find out?
   b. Can you write an equation to predict the number of free throws x the player will make for any number of shots s?

4. Jess wants to sell fruit punch on a hot day. The punch is 2 parts grape juice to 3 parts apple juice. Jess has 5 quarts of apple juice. How many quarts of grape juice does she need? **$3\frac{1}{3}$ qt**
   a. What do you know? What do you want to find out?
   b. Can you write an equation to find the number of quarts of grape juice g needed for a quarts of apple juice?

5. Jess makes the graph below so that she does not have to keep calculating amounts of juice. Use the graph to find how much grape juice is needed for 15 quarts of apple juice. Then find how much apple juice is needed for 12 quarts of grape juice. **10 qt; 18 qt**

Fruit Punch Mix

6. A concession stand needs 3 hot dogs for every 7 people who attend a football game. If 1,400 fans are expected to attend the game, how many hot dogs are needed? **600 hot dogs**

7. Earth is about 25,000 mi around at the equator. If you are sitting on the equator, about how fast are you traveling? (*Hint:* Earth makes one rotation in 24 hours.) **about 1,042 mi/h**

Exploring Similar Figures

In everyday language, two items are *similar* if they are the same in some, but not necessarily all, ways. In math, similarity has a related meaning. Complete the activity to find out what makes two figures mathematically similar.

TEKS ★ TAKS

(7.6)(D) To use critical attributes to define similarity TAKS Obj. 3

(7.14)(A) To communicate mathematical ideas using efficient tools TAKS Obj. 6

(7.15)(A) To make conjectures from patterns or sets of examples TAKS Obj. 6

ACTIVITY

Figures 1 and 2 below are similar. Figures 3 and 4 are similar, too. You can test whether two figures are similar by measuring their angles and side lengths.

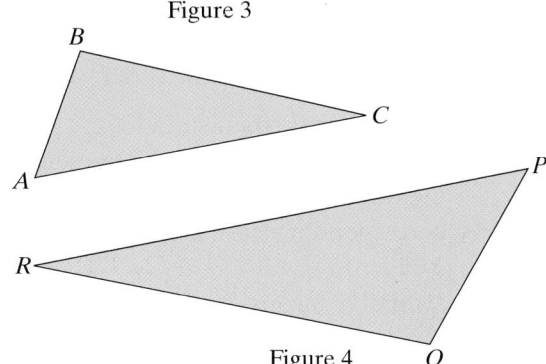

1. Copy the table at the right. Use a protractor to measure each angle of Figure 1 and Figure 2 above. Fill in the missing information in the table. What do you notice about the angle measures in each row of your table? **See margin.**

2. Copy the table at the right. Use a centimeter ruler to measure each side of Figure 1 and Figure 2 to the nearest tenth of a centimeter. Fill in the missing information in the table. What pattern do you notice in the length of the sides in each row of the table? **See margin.**

3. Repeat Steps 1 and 2 for Figures 3 and 4. **See margin.**

4. Make a conjecture about the angle measures and side lengths of similar figures. **See margin.**

Fig. 1	Angle Measure	Fig. 2	Angle Measure
∠A	■	∠P	■
∠B	■	∠Q	■
∠C	■	∠R	■

Fig. 1	Side Length (cm)	Fig. 2	Side Length (cm)
AB	■	PQ	■
BC	■	QR	■
CA	■	RP	■

1–4. See back of book.

Activity Lab

Exploring Similar Figures

Students learn a mathematical definition for similar figures and learn what makes figures similar. This will help them work with similar figures in Lesson 5-5.

Guided Instruction

Before beginning the Activity, ask students what the word *similar* means. Ask them to name pairs of things that are similar and tell why they are similar. Then ask questions, such as:

- *What makes two shapes similar?* same number of sides, same number of angles, same shape
- *Are all triangles similar?* No, corresponding angles must have the same measure and lengths of corresponding sides must form equal ratios.

Activity

Have students work in pairs on the Activity. Circulate and provide assistance where needed with measuring angles and lengths. Make sure students have the numbers in their proportions in the proper positions.

Alternative Method
Students may prefer to work with paper models of the triangles. Provide paper triangle cutouts that are to scale with the triangles on the page.

TEKS ★ TAKS Resources

- Activity Lab 5-5: Indirect Measurement
- protractor
- centimeter ruler
- Student Manipulatives Kit

Dana Center TEKS Toolkit Clarifying Activities (7.6)(D), (7.14)(A), (7.15)(A)
Visit: PHSchool.com
Web Code: arq-9045

TEKS ★ TAKS

(7.3)(B) To estimate and find solutions to application problems involving proportional relationships such as similarity **TAKS** Obj. 2

(7.6)(D) To use critical attributes in defining similarity **TAKS** Obj. 3

Dana Center TEKS Toolkit Clarifying Activities (7.3)(B), (7.6)(D)
Visit: PHSchool.com
Web Code: arq-9045

TEKS Math Background

Similar figures have the same shape but not necessarily the same size. For two *polygons* to be similar, corresponding angles must have the same measure, and the lengths of corresponding sides must be proportional. When it is known that two polygons are similar, it may be possible to find an unknown length by writing and solving a proportion.

More Math Background: p. 226D

Lesson Planning and Resources

See p. 226E for a list of the resources that support this lesson.

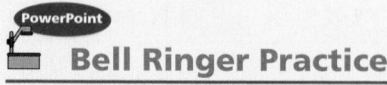
Bell Ringer Practice

✓ **Check Skills You'll Need**
Use student page, transparency, or PowerPoint.

TAKS Daily Review 39
Use transparency.

✓ **Check Skills You'll Need**

1. Vocabulary Review
An equation stating that two ratios are equal is a __?__.
1–5. See below.
Solve each proportion.

2. $\frac{x}{4} = \frac{12}{8}$ **3.** $\frac{4}{b} = \frac{16}{48}$

4. $\frac{84}{12} = \frac{g}{6}$ **5.** $\frac{6}{3} = \frac{19}{m}$

GO for Help
Lesson 5-4

TAKS Tip

When solving problems involving similar figures, make sure you are working with corresponding angles and sides.

Check Skills You'll Need

1. proportion
2. 6
3. 12
4. 42
5. 9.5

TEKS ★ TAKS

• **(7.3)(B)** To estimate and find solutions to application problems involving proportional relationships such as similarity **TAKS** Obj. 2
• **(7.6)(D)** To use critical attributes to define similarity **TAKS** Obj. 3

🔊 **New Vocabulary** polygon, similar polygons, indirect measurement

Why Learn This?

The heights of objects such as totem poles may be difficult to measure directly. You can measure indirectly by using figures that have the same shape. When two figures have the same shape, but not necessarily the same size, they are similar.

In the similar triangles below, corresponding angles have the same measure. Since $\frac{40}{60} = \frac{50}{75} = \frac{34}{51}$, the corresponding sides are proportional. You write $\triangle ABC \sim \triangle FGH$. The symbol $\sim$ means "is similar to."

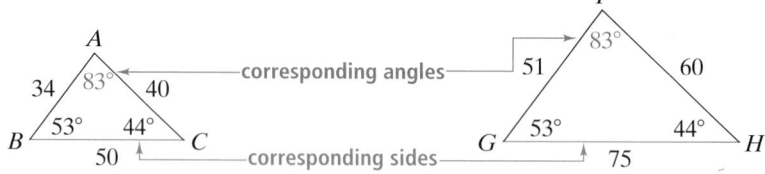

A **polygon** is a closed plane figure formed by three or more line segments that do not cross.

KEY CONCEPTS **Similar Polygons**

Two polygons are **similar polygons** if
• corresponding angles have the same measure, and
• the lengths of the corresponding sides form equivalent ratios.

You can use proportions to find missing side lengths in similar polygons.

Differentiated Instruction **Solutions for All Learners**

Special Needs **L1**
If available, take students out to see a flagpole and its shadow, or a tree and its shadow. Let them stand next to the taller structure, and show them how you might actually determine the height of the flagpole by using corresponding sides.

learning style: visual

Below Level **L2**
In Example 1, students may better visualize the proportion by aligning the triangle names vertically.

$\triangle CAT$
$\triangle DOG$ → $\frac{CA}{DO} = \frac{AT}{OG}$

learning style: visual

EXAMPLE Finding a Missing Measure

① **Algebra** $\triangle ACT$ and $\triangle ODG$ are similar.
Find the value of x.

$\dfrac{AC}{OD} = \dfrac{AT}{OG}$ ← Write a proportion.

$\dfrac{x}{50} = \dfrac{24}{30}$ ← Substitute.

$\dfrac{x}{50} = \dfrac{4}{5}$ ← Write $\dfrac{24}{30}$ in simplest form.

$\dfrac{x}{50} = \dfrac{4}{5}$ ← Find the common multiplier. ×10

$x = 40$ ← Use mental math.

✓ Quick Check

1. The trapezoids are similar. Find x.
20

You can use **indirect measurement** to measure distances that are difficult to measure directly. You do this by using proportions and similar figures.

EXAMPLE Application: Indirect Measurement

② **TAKS** **Multiple Choice** A 6-ft-tall person standing near a flagpole casts a shadow 4.5 ft long. The flagpole casts a shadow 15 ft long. What is the height of the flagpole?

Ⓐ 11.25 ft   Ⓑ 18 ft   Ⓒ 20 ft   Ⓓ 360 ft

Draw a picture and let x represent the height of the flagpole.

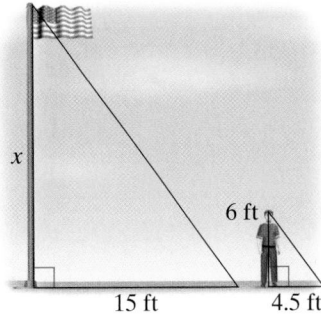

$\dfrac{x}{6} = \dfrac{15}{4.5}$ ← Write a proportion.

$4.5x = 6 \cdot 15$ ← Write the cross products.

$\dfrac{4.5x}{4.5} = \dfrac{6 \cdot 15}{4.5}$ ← Divide each side by 4.5.

$x = 20$ ← Simplify.

The height of the flagpole is 20 ft. The answer is C.

✓ Quick Check

2. A 6-ft person has a shadow 5 ft long. A nearby tree has a shadow 30 ft long. What is the height of the tree? **36 ft**

TAKS Tip

Drawing a picture can help you see what quantities you know and what quantities you are looking for.

---

2. Teach

Activity Lab

Use before the lesson.
Student Edition Activity Lab,
Hands On 5-5a, Exploring Similar
Figures, p. 251

All in One **Teaching Resources**
Activity Lab 5-5: Indirect
Measurement

Guided Instruction

Example 2
Some students might perceive the heights and lengths as a maze, and have difficulty writing a proportion. Suggest that they first write the proportion using words.

$\dfrac{\text{height of flagpole}}{\text{height of person}} = \dfrac{\text{shadow of flagpole}}{\text{shadow of person}}$

Substitute the numbers and variable for the words they represent.

PowerPoint
Additional Examples

① $\triangle ABC$ is similar to $\triangle DEF$. Find the value of c. **12**

② A 5-ft person near a tree has a shadow 12 ft long. The tree has a shadow 42 ft long. What is the height of the tree? $17\frac{1}{2}$ ft

All in One **Teaching Resources**
• Daily Notetaking Guide 5-5 **L3**
• Adapted Notetaking 5-5 **L1**

Closure

• *The angle measures of a triangle are 40°, 60°, and 80°. What are the angle measures of a similar triangle?* **40°, 60°, and 80°**
• *The side lengths of a triangle are 40 cm, 60 cm, and 80 cm. The smallest side length of a similar triangle is 120 cm. What are the lengths of the other two sides?* **180 cm, 240 cm**

Advanced Learners **L4**
Have students decide whether each statement is *true* or *false*.

All squares are similar. **true**
All rectangles are similar. **false**

English Language Learners **ELL**
Make sure students can identify which sides and angles are corresponding. They can label or name each side, and make an organized list of which sides correspond.

Pre-AP™

learning style: visual

253

Assignment Guide

Check Your Understanding
Go over Exercises 1–5 in class before assigning the Homework Exercises.

Homework Exercises

A Practice by Example   6–10
B Apply Your Skills   11–18
C Challenge   19
TEKS ★ TAKS Tune-Up and Mixed Review   20–25

Homework Quick Check
To check students' understanding of key skills and concepts, go over Exercises 7, 10, 13, 17, and 18.

Differentiated Instruction **Resources**

Check Your Understanding

1. Two polygons are similar if corresponding angles have the same measure and the lengths of the corresponding sides form equivalent ratios.

4. No; the lengths of corresponding sides do not form equivalent ratios.

1. **Vocabulary** What must be true about the corresponding angles and the corresponding sides for two polygons to be similar?

△*ABC* is similar to △*RST*. Complete each statement.

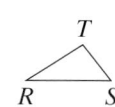

2. ∠*B* corresponds to __?__. ∠*S*

3. $\overline{RS}$ corresponds to __?__. $\overline{AB}$

4. **Geometry** Are the rectangles similar? Explain. See left.

5. **Open-Ended** Think of a distance that is difficult to measure directly. How would you find it indirectly? Check students' work.

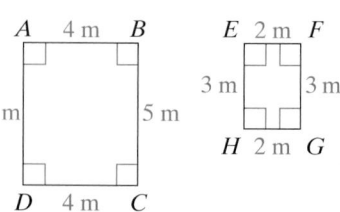

Homework Exercises

For more exercises, see **Extra Skills and Word Problems.**

GO for Help

For Exercises	See Examples
6–9	1
10	2

A **Algebra** △*ABC* is similar to △*PQR*. Find each measure.

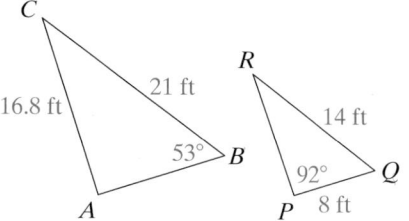

6. length of $\overline{AB}$ **12 ft**

7. length of $\overline{RP}$ **11.2 ft**

8. measure of ∠*A* **92°**

9. measure of ∠*Q* **53°**

10. A woman is 5 ft tall and her shadow is 4 ft long. A nearby tree has a shadow 30 ft long. How tall is the tree? **37.5 ft**

B **GPS** 11. **Guided Problem Solving** An image is 16 in. by 20 in. You want to make a copy that is similar. Its longer side will be 38 in. The copy costs $.60 per square inch. Estimate the copy's total cost. **about $600**
  • What is the approximate length of the shorter side of the copy?
  • What is the approximate area of the copy?

12. **Social Studies** You want to enlarge a copy of the flag of the Philippines that is 4 in. by 8 in. The two flags will be similar. How long should you make the shorter side if the long side is 6 ft? **3 ft**

GO Online
Homework Help
Visit: PHSchool.com
Web Code: are-0505

13. **Geometry** A rectangle with an area of 32 in.² has one side
  GPS measuring 4 in. A similar rectangle has an area of 288 in.². How long is the longer side in the larger rectangle? **24 in.**

Each pair of figures below is similar. Find the value of each variable.

14.

15.

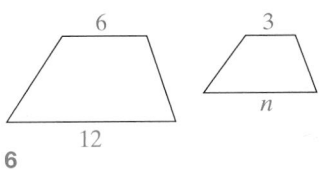

16. A burro is standing near a cactus. The burro is 59 in. tall. His shadow is 4 ft long. The shadow of the cactus is 7 ft long. Estimate the height of the cactus. **about 9 ft**

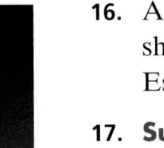

17. Surveying Surveyors know that △PQR and △STR are similar. They cannot measure the distance *d* across the lake directly. Find the distance across the lake. **2.88 km**

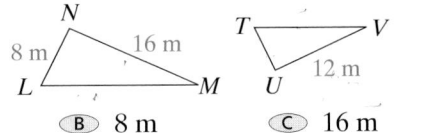

18. Writing in Math Give three examples of real-world objects that are similar. Explain why they are similar. **Check students' work.**

C 19. Challenge The ratio of the corresponding sides of two similar triangles is 4 : 9. The sides of the smaller triangle are 10 cm, 16 cm, and 18 cm. Find the perimeter of the larger triangle. **99 cm**

TEKS ★ TAKS Tune-Up and Mixed Review

TAKS Objective 2
TEKS (7.3)(B)

20. In the figure, △LMN ~ △TVU. What is the length of $\overline{UT}$? **A**

Ⓐ 6 m   Ⓑ 8 m   Ⓒ 16 m   Ⓓ 24 m

TAKS Objective 1
TEKS (7.2)(D)

21. The cost of two pounds of pears is $1.78. How much will five pounds of pears cost? **H**

Ⓕ $0.71   Ⓖ $2.67   Ⓗ $4.45   Ⓙ $8.90

TAKS Objective 6
TEKS (7.14)(A)

22. Which algebraic expression represents five inches less than twice last year's rainfall *f* in inches? **B**

Ⓐ $5 - 2f$ Ⓑ $2f - 5$ Ⓒ $2 - 5f$ Ⓓ $5f - 2$

 Lesson 4-6

Algebra Solve each equation.

23. $3x + 2 = 17$ **5**   **24.** $\frac{x}{5} + 5 = 21$ **80**   **25.** $2a - 4 = 8$ **6**

Alternative Assessment

Have students work in pairs. Each partner should draw two figures that appear to be similar and two figures that appear not to be similar. Then have the partners explain to each other why the pairs of figures they drew are similar or not similar.

TEKS ★ TAKS Resources

- TAKS Strategies, p. 265
- TAKS Tune-Up, pp. 269–271

TAKS Tune-Up Kit

- TAKS Daily Review Transparencies
- TAKS Review and Preparation Workbook
- TAKS Strategies with Transparencies
- Texas Progress Monitoring Assessments

Drawing Similar Figures

In Lesson 5-5, students studied the properties of similar figures and learned how to determine whether two figures are similar. Here they will learn how to create figures similar to a given figure by using geometry software.

Guided Instruction

Error Prevention!

Some students might have difficulty using the software. Have students do the Activity with a partner. Pair students who are less proficient on the computer with those who are comfortable using the geometry software.

Teaching Tip

Depending on the size of $\triangle ABC$ and the position of point D, the sides of the similar triangle might extend beyond the bounds of the viewing window. If this occurs, suggest that students select the entire drawing, click on any part of it, and drag it until it is entirely visible. If the drawing is too large to be displayed on the screen in its entirety, suggest that students open a new window and begin with a smaller $\triangle ABC$.

Exercises

For Exercise 3, note that many geometry software programs do not display arrowheads at the ends of lines. Watch for students who believe they have made an error because they do not see the arrowheads.

TEKS ★ TAKS Resources

- computer
- geometry software program
- Students Manipulatives Kit

Dana Center TEKS Toolkit Clarifying Activities (7.6)(D), (7.13)(D)
Visit: PHSchool.com
Web Code: arq-9045

256

Drawing Similar Figures

Using a computer is an excellent way to explore similar figures. For this activity you need geometry software.

TEKS ★ TAKS
(7.6)(D) To use critical attributes to define similarity TAKS Obj. 3
(7.13)(D) To select technology to solve problems

ACTIVITY

Follow these steps to draw two similar triangles like those at the right.

Step 1 Draw a triangle and label it ABC.

Step 2 Draw a point D not on the triangle.

Step 3 Draw a triangle similar to $\triangle ABC$ using the dilation command. To use this command, you will need to enter a scale factor and name one point as the center of the dilation. Use 2 as a scale factor and name point D as the center.

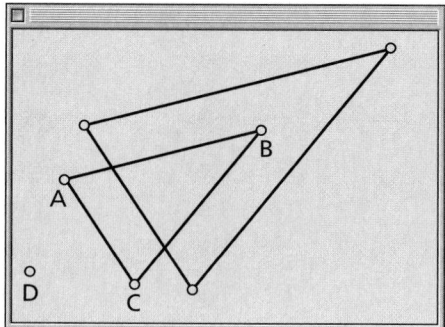

Exercises

1. Change the shape of $\triangle ABC$ by dragging point A, B, or C. What happens to the larger triangle each time? The larger triangle is always similar to $\triangle ABC$.

2. Drag point D to different locations. Describe what happens in each case below.
   a. D is inside $\triangle ABC$.   The larger triangle is outside $\triangle ABC$.
   b. D is on $\overline{AB}$.   One side of the larger triangle contains $\overline{AB}$.
   c. D is on top of point C.   The larger triangle has $\angle C$ as one of its angles.

3. Use the software to draw $\overleftrightarrow{AD}$ (line AD), $\overleftrightarrow{BD}$, and $\overleftrightarrow{CD}$.
   a. What do you notice about the lines and the larger triangle? Each line goes through a vertex of the larger triangle.
   b. Why do you think that point D is called the center of the dilation? Answers may vary. Sample: The lines that connect corresponding vertices meet at D.

4. Draw a third triangle similar to $\triangle ABC$. This time use 0.5 as the scale factor. Keep D as the center. What do you notice about the new triangle? The new triangle is smaller than $\triangle ABC$.

5. a. **Open-Ended** Draw more triangles similar to $\triangle ABC$ by choosing other scale factors. Again keep D as the center. Check students' work.
   b. **Writing in Math** Explain how your choice of scale factor affects the final figure. See margin.
   c. Use what you have learned to write a definition for scale factor. See margin.

5b. Answers may vary. Sample: A scale factor greater than 1 creates a triangle larger than $\triangle ABC$; a scale factor less than 1 creates a triangle smaller than $\triangle ABC$.

c. Answers may vary. Sample: The scale factor is the ratio of the sides of the created triangle to the corresponding sides of $\triangle ABC$.

Determine whether the ratios form a proportion.

1. $\frac{5}{8}, \frac{12}{20}$ no

2. $\frac{4}{10}, \frac{2}{5}$ yes

3. $\frac{24}{15}, \frac{4}{3}$ no

4. $\frac{8}{3}, \frac{48}{18}$ yes

5. The last time your family bought hamburgers, 5 hamburgers cost $5.25. At this rate, what is the cost of 8 hamburgers? **$8.40**

6. 7 movie tickets cost $57.75. What is the cost of 2 movie tickets? **$16.50**

△ABC is similar to △WXY. Find each measure.

7. $\angle X$ 120°

8. $\angle C$ 26°

9. length of $\overline{AB}$ 9

10. length of $\overline{WY}$ 12

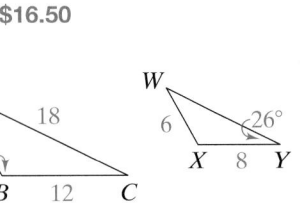

Checkpoint Quiz

Use this Checkpoint Quiz to check students' understanding of the skills and concepts of Lessons 5-3 through 5-5.

Resources

- All-in-One Teaching Resources Checkpoint Quiz 2
- Texas ExamView CD-ROM
- Success Tracker™ Online Intervention

Vocabulary Builder

Learning Vocabulary

You can make your own dictionary of new math vocabulary terms.

EXAMPLE

Write entries for your dictionary for the terms *ratio* and *rate*.

Term	Definition	Example
Ratio	Comparison of two different quantities by division	$\frac{20 \text{ people}}{5 \text{ people}}$
Rate	Ratio that compares two quantities measured in different units	$\frac{20 \text{ people}}{5 \text{ cars}}$

← Make a table with 3 columns. Label the columns "Term," "Definition," and "Example."

← Write the vocabulary term and its definition. Then give an example of the term.

Exercises

Write an entry for your dictionary for each term. 1–3. Check students' work.

1. proportion

2. similar figures

3. cross products

Vocabulary Builder

Learning Vocabulary

Students create their own dictionaries with examples to learn math vocabulary words.

Guided Instruction

Ask students how they use a dictionary to learn new words. Point out the definitions in the glossary at the back of this book. Ask:
- *How does the example help you to understand the word's meaning?* It shows how the word is used, demonstrates its meaning.
- *Why is a dictionary a useful tool?* You can use it at any time to help you understand how a word is being used.

Exercises

Have students share their dictionary entries with a partner. Invite pairs to discuss ways to improve each other's entries.

257

257

Students use drawings and measurements to make accurate scale models. This will help them understand the concept of maps and scale drawings in Lesson 5-6.

Guided Instruction

Before beginning the Activity, discuss models that students have seen or built themselves. Ask:

• *Why is it important for models to be to scale?* People use models to learn information about the actual item the model represents. To have accurate information about that item, the model must have the same proportions.

• *Who would use a model in their work? Why?* Sample: an architect to plan a building he or she is designing; a doctor to study a body part she or he is going to work with

Exercises

Have students work independently on the Exercises. Have them compare models and discuss why they are the same or why they are different.

Alternative Method

Some students may prefer to use three-dimensional objects, such as blocks, to build a model. Provide these materials to help students understand the concept of models.

TEKS ★ TAKS Resources

• Activity Lab 5-6: Exploring Scale
• grid paper
• Student Manipulatives Kit

Dana Center TEKS Toolkit Clarifying Activities (7.3)(B), (7.8)(C), (7.14)(A)
Visit: PHSchool.com
Web Code: arq-9045

258

5-6a Activity Lab

Hands On

Scale Drawings and Models

The sketches below show the measurements of Jackie's bedroom. You can use these sketches to make a model of Jackie's bedroom.

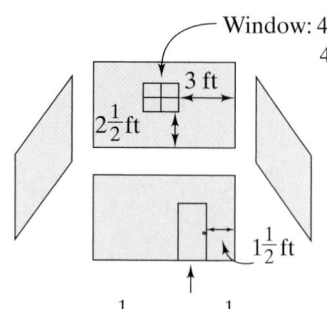

Window: $4\frac{1}{2}$ ft wide
4 ft tall

3 ft

$2\frac{1}{2}$ ft

$1\frac{1}{2}$ ft

Door: $3\frac{1}{3}$ ft wide, $6\frac{1}{2}$ ft tall

8 ft

8 ft

10 ft

TEKS ★ **TAKS**

(7.3)(B) To find solutions to application problems involving proportional relationships such as scaling **TAKS Obj. 2**

(7.8)(C) To use geometric concepts and properties to solve problems in fields such as art and architecture **TAKS Obj. 3**

(7.14)(A) To communicate ideas using physical models **TAKS Obj. 6**

ACTIVITY

Step 1 Make a drawing on graph paper of the floor and walls of Jackie's room as shown. Let one unit on the graph paper represent one foot. Include the windows and doors.

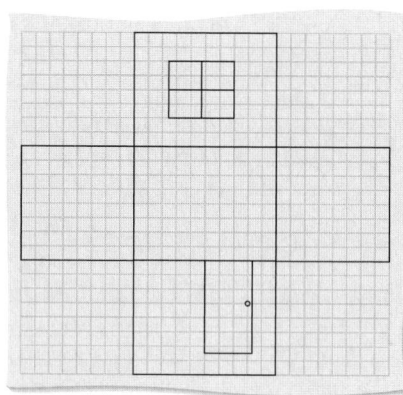

Step 2 Cut around your drawing and tape up the walls to make your model.

Model

Exercises

1–4. Check students' work.

1. Jackie's bedroom bureau is shown at the right. Use the same steps as above to make a drawing and a model of the bureau.

2. Measure the heights and lengths of the walls of your classroom. Use graph paper to make an accurate drawing of the floor and walls.

3. Cut around your drawing and make a model of your classroom.

4. Explain how you can use ratios and proportions to find the dimensions of your model.

4 ft

2 ft

$3\frac{1}{2}$ ft

5-6 — Maps and Scale Drawings

Check Skills You'll Need

1. Vocabulary Review
What are *cross products*?
See back of book.
Solve each proportion.

2. $\frac{2}{3} = \frac{x}{12}$ 8
3. $\frac{9}{5} = \frac{27}{y}$ 15
4. $\frac{5}{m} = \frac{25}{5}$ 1
5. $\frac{t}{21} = \frac{6}{18}$ 7

 for Help
Lesson 5-5

TEKS

- **(7.3)(B)** To find solutions to application problems involving proportional relationships such as scaling *TAKS* **Obj. 2**
- **(7.4)(A)** To generate formulas involving scaling *TAKS* **Obj. 2**
- **(7.8)(C)** To use geometric concepts in art and architecture *TAKS* **Obj. 3**

🔊 **New Vocabulary** scale drawing, scale

Why Learn This?

When you know how scales work, you can see them in everything from maps to giant sculptures.

A **scale drawing** is an enlarged or reduced drawing of an object that is similar to the actual object.

A **scale** is the ratio that compares a length in a drawing or model to the corresponding length in the actual object. If a 15-foot boat is 1 inch long on a drawing, you can write the scale of the drawing in these three ways.

$$1 \text{ in. } : 15 \text{ ft} \qquad \frac{1 \text{ in.}}{15 \text{ ft}} \qquad 1 \text{ in. } = 15 \text{ ft}$$

↑ ↑
drawing actual

Vocabulary Tip

On a map, the equal sign in 1 in. = 15 ft does not mean that the two quantities are equal, as it would in an equation.

1 cm = 2.5 m

EXAMPLE Using a Scale Drawing

1 **Algebra** The length of the side of a house is 3 cm on a scale drawing. What is the actual length of the side of the house?

You can write the scale of the drawing as $\frac{1 \text{ cm}}{2.5 \text{ ft}}$. Then write a proportion. Let n represent the actual length of the house.

drawing (cm) → $\frac{1}{2.5}$ = $\frac{3}{n}$ ← drawing (cm)
actual (m) →   ← actual (m)

$1n = 2.5(3)$ ← **Write the cross products.**

$n = 7.5$ ← **Simplify.**

The actual length is 7.5 m.

✓ Quick Check

1. The chimney of the house is 4 cm tall on the drawing. How tall is the chimney of the actual house? **10 m**

TEKS

(7.3)(B) To find solutions to application problems involving proportional relationships such as scaling *TAKS* **Obj. 2**
Also supports
(7.4)(A) *TAKS* **Obj. 2**
(7.8)(C) *TAKS* **Obj. 3**

Dana Center TEKS Toolkit Activities (7.3)(B), (7.4)(A), (7.8)(C)
Visit: PHSchool.com
Web Code: arq-9045

TEKS Math Background

A *scale drawing* is a two-dimensional representation of a real object. The ratio $\frac{\text{drawing length}}{\text{corresponding actual length}}$ is the same throughout the drawing. This ratio is called the *scale* of the drawing. An artist uses the scale and actual lengths to create the drawing; the reader uses the scale and drawing lengths to interpret the drawing. Both creating and interpreting the drawing require proportional reasoning.

More Math Background: p. 226D

Lesson Planning and Resources

See p. 226E for a list of the resources that support this lesson.

Bell Ringer Practice

✓ **Check Skills You'll Need**
Use student page, transparency, or PowerPoint.

TAKS **Daily Review 40**
Use transparency.

Differentiated Instruction Solutions for All Learners

Special Needs **L1**
Provide students with experiences using map scales. Let them measure the actual distance between two points on a map, then compare that distance to the scale and find the actual distance.

Below Level **L2**
Give students blank templates for organizing their work.

drawing → ■ = ■ ← drawing
actual → ■   ■ ← actual

learning style: visual
learning style: visual

Activity Lab

Use before the lesson.
Student Edition Activity Lab,
Hands On 5-6a, Scale Drawings
and Models, p. 58

All in One Teaching Resources
Activity Lab 5-6: Exploring Scale

Guided Instruction

Example 2
Students will need metric rulers.
The map distance between
Charlotte and Raleigh is about
2.8 cm. The map distance
between Raleigh and Winston-
Salem is about 1.9 cm.

Error Prevention!

In Quick Check, students might
record the map distance in
millimeters and use this number in
their proportions. For instance, if
they record the distance from
Charlotte to Raleigh as 28 mm,
they might write $\frac{1}{75} = \frac{28}{n}$. Suggest
that they include the units in their
proportions and highlight the
units. This should focus their
attention on the need to convert
the measure.

$$\frac{1 \text{ cm}}{75 \text{ km}} = \frac{28 \text{ mm}}{n \text{ km}} \rightarrow \frac{1 \text{ cm}}{75 \text{ km}} = \frac{2.8 \text{ cm}}{n \text{ km}}$$

★ TAKS Tip

When writing a proportion,
make sure each ratio
compares the same types
of quantities.

EXAMPLE Application: Geography

2 Find the actual distance from Charlotte to Winston-Salem.

1 cm : 75 km

Step 1 Use a centimeter ruler to find the map distance from Charlotte
to Winston-Salem. The map distance is about 1.6 cm.

Step 2 Use a proportion to find the actual distance. Let n represent the
actual distance.

$$\begin{array}{l} \text{map (cm)} \rightarrow \\ \text{actual (m)} \rightarrow \end{array} \frac{1}{75} = \frac{1.6}{n} \begin{array}{l} \leftarrow \text{map (cm)} \\ \leftarrow \text{actual (m)} \end{array} \quad \leftarrow \text{Write a proportion.}$$

$$1n = 75(1.6) \qquad \leftarrow \text{Write the cross products.}$$

$$n = 120 \qquad \leftarrow \text{Simplify.}$$

The actual distance from Charlotte to Winston-Salem is about 120 km.

✓ Quick Check

2. Find the actual distance from Charlotte to Raleigh.
   about 206 km

You can use the GCF to find the scale of a drawing or a model.

EXAMPLE Finding the Scale

3 **Models** Refer to the model
boxcar shown at the right. The
actual length of a boxcar is 609 in.
What is the scale of the model?

7 in.

$$\begin{array}{l} \text{scale length} \rightarrow \\ \text{actual length} \rightarrow \end{array} \frac{7}{609} = \frac{7 \div 7}{609 \div 7} = \frac{1}{87} \quad \leftarrow \text{Write the ratio in simplest form.}$$

The scale is 1 in. : 87 in.

✓ Quick Check

3. The length of a room in an architectural drawing is 10 in. Its actual
   length is 160 in. What is the scale of the drawing? **1 in. : 16 in.**

Advanced Learners L4
The scale of a map is 1 : 250,000. What is the actual
distance in miles for each inch of map distance? **about
3.9 miles**

Pre-AP™

English Language Learners ELL
Have students read scales on atlases, maps, and
globes. Ask them to talk about what they notice about
the map scales. *How are the map scales different?*
How are they similar? Why is a map scale useful?
Could a map be drawn with the real distance? no

learning style: verbal

EXAMPLE   **Application: Models**

4 **TAKS** **Multiple Choice** You want to make a scale model of a sailboat that is 51 ft long and 48 ft tall. You plan to make the model 17 in. long. Which equation can you use to find x, the height of the model?

  Ⓐ $\dfrac{48}{51} = \dfrac{17}{x}$ Ⓑ $\dfrac{17}{51} = \dfrac{x}{48}$ Ⓒ $\dfrac{48}{17} = \dfrac{x}{51}$ Ⓓ $\dfrac{x}{17} = \dfrac{51}{48}$

$$\begin{array}{l}\text{model (in.)} \rightarrow \dfrac{17}{51} = \dfrac{\blacksquare}{\blacksquare} \leftarrow \text{model (in.)} \\ \text{actual (ft)} \rightarrow \qquad\qquad \leftarrow \text{actual (ft)}\end{array} \quad \leftarrow \textbf{Write a proportion.}$$

$$\dfrac{17}{51} = \dfrac{x}{48} \quad \leftarrow \begin{array}{l}\textbf{Fill in the information you know.} \\ \textbf{Use } x \textbf{ for the information you do not know.}\end{array}$$

The correct answer is choice B.

You can solve the proportion to find the height of the model. You can simplify $\dfrac{17}{51}$ to make calculating easier.

$$\dfrac{\overset{1}{\cancel{17}}}{\underset{3}{\cancel{51}}} = \dfrac{x}{48} \quad \leftarrow \textbf{Simplify } \dfrac{17}{51} \textbf{ by dividing by the GCF, 17.}$$

$$\dfrac{1}{3} = \dfrac{x}{48}$$

$$\overset{\times 16}{\dfrac{1}{3}} = \underset{\times 16}{\dfrac{x}{48}} \quad \leftarrow \textbf{Find the common multiplier, 16.}$$

$$x = 16 \quad \leftarrow \textbf{Use mental math.}$$

The height of the model is 16 inches.

✓ Quick Check

● **4.** If the sailboat is 15 ft wide, how wide should the model be?
    5 in.

GO for Help

For help with simplifying ratios, go to Lesson 5-3, Example 1.

✓ Check Your Understanding

2. Larger; since a scale is a ratio of $\frac{\text{drawing}}{\text{actual}}$, then in $\frac{5 \text{ cm}}{1 \text{ mm}}$, the drawing is larger than the actual figure.

1. Vocabulary A scale is a __?__ that compares a length in a drawing to the corresponding __?__ in the actual object. ratio; length

2. Reasoning The scale of a drawing is 5 cm : 1 mm. Is the scale drawing larger or smaller than the actual figure? Explain. See left.

3. Error Analysis A student wants to write the scale of a statue of President Kennedy, who was 6 ft tall. The statue is 8 ft tall. The student writes the scale as 6 ft : 8 ft. Is the student correct? Explain.
No; the scale should be written as model : actual, or 8 ft : 6 ft.

The scale of a map is 1 inch : 5 miles. Find each distance.

                                                15 mi
4. A road is 3 in. long on the map. Find the actual length of the road.

5. A lake is 35 miles long. Find the length of the lake on the map.
    7 in.

5-6 Maps and Scale Drawings   **261**

PowerPoint
Additional Examples

1 The scale of a drawing is 1 in. : 6 ft. Find the actual length for a drawing length of 4.5 in. **27 ft**

2 On the map of North Carolina, the map distance from Asheville to Raleigh would be about 4.4 cm. Find the actual distance from Asheville to Raleigh. **about 330 km**

3 The actual length of the wheelbase of a mountain bike is 260 cm. The length of the wheelbase in a scale drawing is 4 cm. Find the scale of the drawing. **1 cm : 65 cm**

4 An architect's model of a house is 44 in. high. The actual house is 20 ft high and 45 ft wide. What should the width of the architect's model be? **99 in.**

All in One Teaching Resources
- Daily Notetaking Guide 5-6 **L3**
- Adapted Notetaking 5-6 **L1**

Closure

- Explain how maps and scale drawings are related to ratios and proportions. **Sample: The scale of a map or drawing is a ratio that compares each length in the map or drawing to a corresponding actual length. You use a proportion involving the scale and a known map or drawing length to find an unknown actual length.**

3. Practice

Assignment Guide

Check Your Understanding
Go over Exercises 1–5 in class before assigning the Homework Exercises.

Homework Exercises
A Practice by Example   6–17
B Apply Your Skills   18–25
C Challenge   26
TEKS ★ TAKS Tune-Up and
 Mixed Review   27–30

Homework Quick Check
To check student's understanding of key skills and concepts, go over Exercises 9, 15, 21, 24, and 25.

Differentiated Instruction Resources

262

For more exercises, see Extra Skills and Word Problems.

for Help

For Exercises	See Examples
6–11	1
12–15	2
16–17	3–4

Ⓐ **Algebra** A scale drawing has a scale of 1 in. : 11 ft. Find the actual length for each drawing length.

6. 21 in. **231 ft**   **7.** 15 in. **165 ft**   **8.** 6 in. **66 ft**

9. 45 in. **495 ft**   **10.** 13.5 in. **148.5 ft**   **11.** 1.5 in. **16.5 ft**

Geography Find the actual distance between each pair of cities. Use a ruler to measure. Round to the nearest mile.

12. Hartford and Danbury **about 47 mi**

13. Norwich and Hartford **about 38 mi**

14. New Haven and Norwich **about 47 mi**

15. New Haven and Danbury **about 28 mi**

16. In a scale drawing, the width of a sofa is 15 cm. The actual width of the sofa is 150 cm. What is the scale of the drawing? **1 cm : 10 cm**

17. A certain car is about 100 in. long and 60 in. wide. You plan to make a model of this car that is 9 in. wide. How long will your model be?
 15 in.

Ⓑ GPS **18. Guided Problem Solving** The height of a building on a blueprint is 10 in. Its actual height is 150 ft. What is the scale of the drawing?
 • What ratio can you use to find the scale? **1 in. : 15 ft**
 • How can finding the GCF help you to simplify your answer?

19. The scale of a model is 0.5 in. : 6 ft. Find the length of the model for an actual length of 204 ft. **8.5 in.**

20. Geography Dallas is $6\frac{3}{4}$ in. from Houston on a map of Texas with a scale of $\frac{3 \text{ in.}}{100 \text{ mi}}$. What is the actual distance from Dallas to Houston?
 225 mi

21. Architecture The blueprint below is a scale drawing of an apartment. The scale is $\frac{1}{4}$ in. : 4 ft. Sketch a copy of the floor plan. Write the actual dimensions in place of the scale dimensions.

GO **Online**
Homework Help
Visit: PHSchool.com
Web Code: are-0506

See margin.

21.

16 ft   20 ft
20 ft   16 ft 12 ft

24. Answers may vary. Sample: Set up the proportion $\frac{2 \text{ in.}}{17 \text{ ft}} = \frac{x}{51 \text{ ft}}$. Solve the proportion by mental math or cross products. $x = 6$, so the drawing will have a length of 6 in.

Use a centimeter ruler to measure the length of the segment shown in each figure below. Find the scale of each drawing. Answers may vary. Samples are given.

22. Peach Aphid

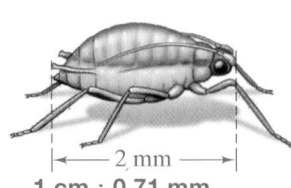

← 2 mm →
1 cm : 0.71 mm

23. Killer Whale

← 8 m →
1 cm : 1.9 m

24. <u>Writing in Math</u> **GPS** You are making a scale drawing with a scale of 2 in. = 17 ft. Explain how you find the length of the drawing of an object that has an actual length of 51 ft. **See margin.**

25. Special Effects A special-effects artist has made a scale model of a dragon for a movie. In the movie, the dragon will appear to be 16 ft tall. The model is 4 in. tall.
 a. What scale has the artist used? **1 in. : 4 ft**
 b. The same scale is used for a model of a baby dragon, which will appear to be 2 ft tall. What is the height of the model? **0.5 in.**

C 26. Challenge A building is drawn with a scale of 1 in. : 3 ft. The height of the drawing is 1 ft 2 in. After a design change, the scale is modified to be 1 in. : 4 ft. What is the height of the new drawing? $10\frac{1}{2}$ in.

TEKS ★ TAKS Tune-Up and Mixed Review

TAKS Objective 2
TEKS (7.3)(B)

27. Doug drew a map with a scale of 1 inch : 5 miles. What distance on Doug's map should represent 4.5 miles? **B**
 Ⓐ 0.45 in. Ⓑ 0.9 in. Ⓒ 0.95 in. Ⓓ 4.5 in.

TAKS Objective 3
TEKS (7.6)(D)

28. In the figure at the right, $ABCD \sim STUV$. Which of the following statements is NOT true? **J**
 Ⓕ $\overline{UV}$ corresponds to $\overline{CD}$.
 Ⓖ $\overline{AD}$ corresponds to $\overline{SV}$.
 Ⓗ $\angle A$ corresponds to $\angle S$.
 Ⓙ $\angle D$ corresponds to $\angle U$.

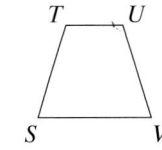

TAKS Objective 6
TEKS (7.14)(A)

29. A cycling route is 56 miles long. There is a water station every $3\frac{3}{4}$ mi. Which equation represents the total number of water stations w? **B**
 Ⓐ $56w = 3\frac{3}{4}$ Ⓒ $3\frac{3}{4} - w = 56$
 Ⓑ $3\frac{3}{4}w = 56$ Ⓓ $w + 3\frac{3}{4} = 56$

GO for Help Lesson 5-5

30. Find the values of x and y in the similar triangles at the right. $x = 40, y = 32$

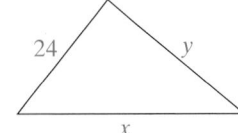

Alternative Assessment

Display a map of your state and assign students to groups of four. Ask students to find and explain the scale on the map. Then have them find the distance between two cities.

TEKS ★ TAKS Resources

- TAKS Strategies, p. 265
- TAKS Tune-Up, pp. 269–271

TAKS Tune-Up Kit
- TAKS Daily Review Transparencies
- TAKS Review and Preparation Workbook
- TAKS Strategies with Transparencies
- Texas Progress Monitoring Assessments

263

Plan a Trip

Students use the scale of a map to find the lengths of different routes between two cities, and then to calculate the amount of time to drive each route.

Guided Instruction

Before assigning the Exercises, be sure students understand the map scale: 1 in. : 85 mi.

Ask questions such as:
- *How many miles does 1 inch represent?* 85 mi
- *How many miles do 3 inches represent?* 255 mi
- *Why can't you measure the shortest straight line from Indianapolis to Cleveland to plan your trip?* **Sample: You have to drive on the roads, and there is no road shown that goes straight from Indianapolis to Cleveland.**

Activity

Have students work in pairs. For Exercise 1, one partner can make the measurements and the other can record the measurements.

Exercises 2–4 The partners should work independently and then compare results.

Exercise 5 can be used as a short-term project that can be displayed in the classroom.

Differentiated Instruction

Advanced Learners　　L4
Have students calculate the map distance and actual distance of a round trip from Indianapolis to Columbus to Cleveland and back to Indianapolis through Toledo and Fort Wayne.

TEKS ★ TAKS Resources

- inch ruler
- map of the United States
- Student Manipulatives Kit

Dana Center TEKS Toolkit Clarifying Activities (7.3)(B), (7.13)(A)
Visit: PHSchool.com
Web Code: arq-9045

5-6b Activity Lab

Plan a Trip

TEKS ★ TAKS

(7.3)(B) To estimate and find solutions to application problems involving proportional relationships such as scaling and related measurement units TAKS Obj. 2

(7.13)(A) To identify and apply mathematics to activities in and outside of school

0 ——————— 85 mi
1 in. : 85 mi

ACTIVITY

Answers may vary. Samples are given.
Use the map above to plan a trip from Indianapolis to Cleveland.

1. Measure the distances on Routes 69 and 90 from Indianapolis to Fort Wayne, Fort Wayne to Toledo, and Toledo to Cleveland. Add them to get the total map distance. **3.75 in.**

Located on the shore of Lake Erie, the 150,000-square-foot Rock and Roll Hall of Fame and Museum is a landmark for the city of Cleveland, Ohio.

2. Locate the scale on the map. Use the scale to convert the map distance into the actual distance for your trip. **320 mi**

3. Use an average speed of 50 mi/h. Find the time it will take to drive the total actual distance. If you plan to drive no more than 4 hours per day, how many days will your trip take? **6.3 h; 2 days**

4. Suppose you want to make the same trip, but you want to visit a friend in Columbus. Plan your trip from Indianapolis to Cleveland to pass through Columbus. Compare the two trips. **The trip will be a little shorter.**

5. **Research** Now suppose that you are planning a cross-country road trip from Trenton, New Jersey, to San Francisco, California. Locate a map of the United States and plan your trip. Decide which cities you would like to visit along the way. How long will your trip take you? **Check students' work.**

Using a Variable

You can solve many problems by using a variable to represent an unknown quantity.

EXAMPLE

Purple is a mixture of the primary colors red and blue. A certain shade of purple paint requires 6 parts red paint to 7 parts blue paint. If you have 16 quarts of red paint, how many quarts of blue paint do you need to make the desired shade of purple? How many quart cans of blue paint do you need to buy?

The problem is asking for the amount of blue paint needed to make a shade of purple. You can write and solve a proportion.

Let b represent the number of quarts of blue paint you need.

$$\text{red paint} \rightarrow \frac{6}{7} = \frac{16}{b} \leftarrow \text{red paint} \qquad \leftarrow \textbf{Write a proportion.}$$
$$\text{blue paint} \rightarrow \qquad \qquad \leftarrow \text{blue paint}$$

$$6b = 112 \qquad \leftarrow \textbf{Write the cross products and simplify.}$$

$$\frac{6b}{6} = \frac{112}{6} \qquad \leftarrow \textbf{Divide each side by 6.}$$

$$b = 18\frac{2}{3} \qquad \leftarrow \textbf{Simplify.}$$

You need $18\frac{2}{3}$ quarts of blue paint. You should buy 19 cans.

Exercises

Use a variable to write and solve an equation.

TAKS Objective 1
TEKS (7.2)(D)

1. To serve 16 people, 96 pieces of fruit are needed. How many pieces of fruit are needed to serve 22 people? **C**

   Ⓐ $18\frac{2}{3}$ Ⓑ 11   Ⓒ 132   Ⓓ 144

TAKS Objective 2
TEKS (7.3)(B)

2. A paper distributor is shipping mailing tubes to an art gallery. The distributor has previously shipped 560 tubes in 16 boxes. At this rate, how many boxes would the distributor need to ship 112 tubes? **F**

   Ⓕ 4   Ⓖ 5   Ⓗ 12   Ⓙ 35

TAKS Objective 6
TEKS (7.13)(C)

3. A class of 37 students is making origami boxes. Each box requires 8 pieces of origami paper. The class will split into groups of at most 3 students per group. If each group is going to make one box, what is the least number of pieces of paper needed by the class? **C**

   Ⓐ 24   Ⓑ 96   Ⓒ 104   Ⓓ 296

TAKS Strategies

Using a Variable

Students learn to use a variable as the placeholder for an unknown quantity in a problem. They then write and solve an equation involving that variable. The solution of the equation leads to the solution of the problem.

Guided Instruction

After students read the problem, write $\frac{\text{red}}{\text{blue}} = \frac{\text{red}}{\text{blue}}$ on the chalkboard or on a transparency. As students watch, erase the words one at a time, replacing each with the corresponding number until $\frac{6}{7} = \frac{16}{\text{blue}}$ is displayed. Lead students to see that the remaining word *blue* represents the unknown number of quart-cans of blue paint needed to make the shade of purple. Now replace *blue* with the variable *b*. Proceed to solve the proportion and answer the question.

TEKS ★ TAKS Resources

TAKS Strategies with Transparencies
- Transparency 11
- Practice sheet, p. 17

TAKS Strategies with Transparencies

Test-Taking Strategies: Using a Variable

You can solve many problems by using a variable to represent an unknown quantity.

Let the variable be the quantity that you are looking for.

> **Examples**
> Let x = the number of hours worked.
> Let t = the amount of time spent.
> Let A = the area of the backyard.

Then use the variable to write an equation.

> You attend a cheerleading clinic with your team every Saturday morning. The clinic costs $6.50 per person. It costs $78 for your entire team to attend the clinic. How many cheerleaders are on your team?
>
> Let c = the number of cheerleaders.
>
> Write and solve an equation to find the number of cheerleaders.
>
> $$6.50c = 78$$
> $$\frac{6.50c}{6.50} = \frac{78}{6.50} \qquad \text{There are 12 cheerleaders on your team.}$$
> $$c = 12$$

Define a variable. Then, write and solve an equation for each problem.

1. An illustrator charges $75 per picture. Find the total number of pictures in a children's book if the illustrator earned $3,000.

2. There are 12 songs on a CD. The CD lasts 42 minutes. About how long is the average song on the CD?

TEKS ⭐ TAKS Resources

Student Edition
Extra Skills and Word Problems
  Practice, Ch. 5, p. 638
English/Spanish Glossary, p. 675
Formulas and Properties, p. 673
Tables, p. 670
All in One Teaching Resources
• Vocabulary and Study
  Skills 5F   **L3**

TEKS ⭐ TAKS Resources

TAKS Tune-Up Kit
• TAKS Daily Review
  Transparencies
• TAKS Review and Preparation
  Workbook
• TAKS Strategies with
  Transparencies
• Texas Progress Monitoring
  Assessments
• Texas ExamView CD-ROM
• MindPoint Quiz Show CD-ROM

Differentiated Instruction

Spanish Vocabulary Workbook
with Study Skills   **ELL**
Texas Interactive Textbook
• Audio Glossary
Online Vocabulary Quiz

Success 🔧 Tracker™
Online at PHSchool.com

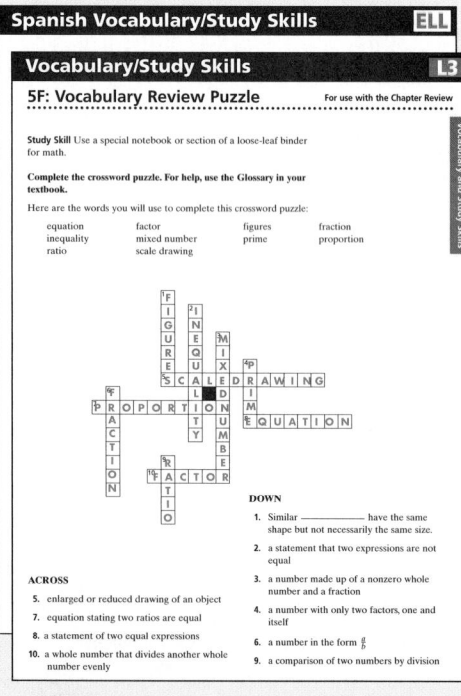

Vocabulary Review

🔊 **cross products** (p. 239)   **proportion** (p. 238)   **scale drawing** (p. 259)
   equivalent ratios (p. 229)   **rate** (p. 232)   **similar polygons** (p. 252)
   indirect measurement (p. 253)   **ratio** (p. 228)   **unit cost** (p. 233)
   polygon (p. 252)   **scale** (p. 259)   **unit rate** (p. 232)

Choose the correct term to complete each sentence.

1. A street map is an example of (a scale drawing, cross products).
   a scale drawing
2. Knowing a(n) (indirect measurement, unit cost) is helpful for
   getting the best buy when you shop. unit cost
3. A speed limit of 40 mi/h is an example of a (rate, proportion).
   rate
4. A ratio that compares a length in a drawing to the actual length of
   an object is a (scale, proportion). scale
5. When two polygons have corresponding angles with equal measures
   and corresponding sides with proportional lengths, the polygons are
   (cross products, similar). similar

Go Online
PHSchool.com
For: Online vocabulary quiz
Web Code: arj-0551

Skills and Concepts   TEKS ⭐ TAKS

Lesson 5-1
(7.2)(D) To use division to
find ratios in proportional
relationships **TAKS** Obj. 1
(7.3)(B) To find solutions to
application problems
involving proportional
relationships such as related
measurement units
TAKS Obj. 2

A **ratio** is a comparison of two quantities by division. You can write the
same ratio in three ways. To find equal ratios, multiply or divide the
numerator and denominator by the same nonzero number.

Write each ratio in simplest form.

6. $\frac{9}{30}$ $\frac{3}{10}$ 7. $\frac{64}{20}$ $\frac{16}{5}$ 8. 99 : 33 3 : 1 9. 75 : 20   10. $\frac{45}{180}$ $\frac{1}{4}$
                                                                                  15 : 4

11. **Sports** During a recent Olympics, the United States won 97 medals,
    including 39 gold medals. Write the ratio of gold medals to total
    medals in three ways. $\frac{39}{97}$, 39 to 97, 39 : 97

Lesson 5-2
(7.2)(D) To find unit rates in
proportional relationships
TAKS Obj. 1
(7.3)(B) To estimate and
find solutions to application
problems involving
proportional relationships
TAKS Obj. 2

A **rate** is a ratio that compares two quantities measured in different
units. A **unit rate** has a denominator of 1. Find a **unit cost** by dividing the
price of an item by the size of the item.

Write the unit rate for each situation.

12. 282 passengers in 47 cars
    6 passengers/car
13. 600 Calories in 8 servings
    75 Cal/serving
14. 414 students in 18 classrooms
    23 students/classroom
15. $136 for 34 kg $4/kg

(7.2)(G) To determine the reasonableness of a solution to a problem **TAKS Obj. 1**

16. $.28/oz, $.31/oz; the 10-oz size is the better buy.

16. Shopping A 10-oz box of cereal costs $2.79. A 13-oz box of the same brand of cereal costs $3.99. Find the unit cost for each item and determine which is the better buy. **See left.**

17. A carpenter renovating a house is sanding the dining room floor. She sands 300 ft² of wood floor in 1 h 40 min. What is the unit rate in square feet per minute? **3 ft² per minute**

Lessons 5-3, 5-4

(7.2)(D) To use division to find unit rates and ratios in proportional relationships **TAKS Obj. 1**

(7.3)(B) To find solutions to application problems involving proportional relationships **TAKS Obj. 2**

(7.13)(D) To select techniques such as mental math to solve problems

22. $\frac{5}{3} = \frac{x}{250,000}$; 417,000 board feet

A proportion is an equation stating that two ratios are equal. If two ratios form a proportion, the **cross products** are equal.

Solve each proportion.

18. $\frac{3}{7} = \frac{n}{28}$ 12   **19.** $\frac{3}{5} = \frac{15}{x}$ 25   **20.** $\frac{a}{18} = \frac{12}{72}$ 3   **21.** $\frac{32}{c} = \frac{4}{17}$ 136

22. Wood A local lumberyard sells a total of 250,000 board feet of hardwood each year. The ratio of softwood sold to hardwood sold is 5 : 3. Write and solve a proportion to find the amount of softwood sold each year. Round your answer to the nearest thousand. **See left.**

23. The ratio of the width of a rectangle to its length is 5 : 8. What is the width in feet if the length is 12 ft? **7.5 ft**

Lesson 5-5

(7.3)(B) To estimate and find solutions to application problems involving proportional relationships such as similarity **TAKS Obj. 2**

(7.6)(D) To use critical attributes to define similarity **TAKS Obj. 3**

Two polygons are **similar polygons** if corresponding angles have equal measures and the lengths of corresponding sides form equivalent ratios.

24. A fire hydrant is 30 in. tall and casts a shadow 8 in. long. How tall is a nearby tree that casts a shadow 4 ft long? **15 ft**

Each pair of figures is similar. Find each missing value.

25.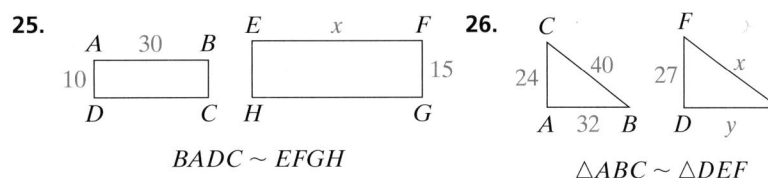

$BADC \sim EFGH$

45

26. $\triangle ABC \sim \triangle DEF$

$x = 45, y = 36$

Lesson 5-6

(7.3)(B) To find solutions to problems involving proportional relationships such as scaling **TAKS Obj. 2**

(7.4)(A) To generate formulas involving scaling **TAKS Obj. 2**

(7.8)(C) To use geometric concepts in art and architecture **TAKS Obj. 3**

A **scale drawing** is an enlarged or reduced drawing of an object that is similar to the actual object. A **scale** is a ratio that compares a length in a drawing to the corresponding length in an actual object.

27. Maps The scale on a map is 1 in. : 525 mi. The map distance from Chicago to Tokyo is 12 in. Find the actual distance between the cities. **6,300 mi**

28. Architecture A drawing's scale is 0.5 in. : 10 ft. A room is 15 ft long. How long is the room on the drawing? **0.75 in.**

Chapter 5 Chapter Review **267**

Chapter 5 Test

TEKS ★ TAKS Resources

- Texas ExamView CD-ROM
  - Ch. 5 Ready-Made Test
  - Make your own Ch. 5 test
- MindPoint Quiz Show CD-ROM
  - Ch. 5 Review

Differentiated Instruction

All in One Teaching Resources
- Chapter 5 Test **L2**
- Chapter 5 Test **L3**
- Chapter 5 Alternative
  Assessment **L4**

Spanish Assessment Resources **ELL**
- Chapter 5 Test **L2**
- Chapter 5 Test **L3**
- Chapter 5 Alternative
  Assessment **L4**

Texas ExamView CD-ROM
- Special Needs Test **L1**
- Special Needs Practice
  Bank **L1**

Online Chapter 5 Test at
www.PHSchool.com **L3**

Chapter Test L2

Chapter Test L3

Chapter Test Form A
Chapter 5

1. There are 14 boys and 16 girls in a class. Write the ratio of boys to girls in simplest form.
   7 : 8

Determine whether the ratios in each pair are proportional.

2. 1 : 10; 2 : 5 — no
3. 4 to 7; 28 to 49 — yes
4. — no

5. Which is a better buy, 6 apples for $1.74 or 5 apples for $1.20? Why?
   5 apples for $1.20; the unit rate, $.24 < $.29.

Write the unit rate for each situation.

6. bike 21 km in 50 min — 0.42 km/min
7. earn $18 for 1 hr 15 min work — $.24/min
8. sew 9 curtain panels in 15 days — 0.6 curtain panels per day
9. Wyatt spent ¼ of his money on a train set and ½ on tickets to a play. He now has $18. How much money did Wyatt start with? Explain why you chose the method you did.
   $72; sample answer: Work backwards.

Write each ratio in two other ways.

10. — 5 to 9; 5 : 9
11. 8 to 3 — 8 : 3; 8/3
12. 12 : 15 — 12 to 15; 12/15

Solve each proportion.

13. — n = 5
14. — x = 9.15
15. — t = 16

16. Alonso can jog 2 miles in 16 minutes. Is it reasonable to assume that it will take him 24 minutes to jog 3 miles? Explain.
   Yes; sample answer: The ratios form a proportion; 24 min/3 mi = 16 min/2 mi.

268

1. Write a ratio for the following information in three ways: In the United States, 98 million out of 99.6 million homes have at least one television. $98 : 99.6$, $\frac{98}{99.6}$, 98 to 99.6

Write each ratio in two other ways. 2–7. See margin.

2. $\frac{9}{7}$

3. $48 : 100$

4. 33 to 9

5. $46 : 50$

6. 19 to 91

7. $6 : 7$

8. **Gas Mileage** Engineers test four cars to find their fuel efficiency. Use the information in the table below. Which car gets the most miles per gallon? **Car C**

Car	Miles	Gallons Used
A	225	14
B	312	15
C	315	10
D	452	16

Find the unit rate for each situation.

9. running 2.3 km in 7 min **0.33 km/min**

10. earning $36.00 in 4 h **$9.00/h**

11. **Writing in Math** You need to buy 10 lb of rice. A 2-lb bag costs $1.29. A 10-lb bag costs $6.99. You want to buy a 10-lb bag. Your friend thinks buying five 2-lb bags is a better deal because the unit rate is lower. Is your friend correct? Explain. **See margin.**

Solve each proportion.

12. $\frac{6}{5} = \frac{n}{7}$ **8.4**

13. $\frac{3}{7} = \frac{8}{x}$ **$18\frac{2}{3}$**

14. $\frac{k}{4} = \frac{9}{32}$ **$1\frac{1}{8}$**

15. $\frac{3.5}{d} = \frac{14}{15}$ **3.75**

16. $\frac{80}{35} = \frac{w}{7}$ **16**

17. $\frac{y}{18} = \frac{2.4}{15}$ **2.88**

18. The ratio of teachers to students in a middle school is 2 to 25. There are 350 students in the school. Find the number of teachers.
    28 teachers

19. **Maps** A map with a scale of 1 in. : 175 mi shows two cities 5 in. apart. How many miles apart are the cities? **875 mi**

Write each ratio in simplest form.

20. $\frac{7}{49}$ $\frac{1}{7}$

21. $\frac{12}{4}$ $\frac{3}{1}$

22. $\frac{8}{2}$ $\frac{4}{1}$

23. $\frac{14}{18}$ $\frac{7}{9}$

24. $\frac{68}{100}$ $\frac{17}{25}$

25. $\frac{15}{95}$ $\frac{3}{19}$

26. In the figure below, $\triangle JKL \sim \triangle PQR$. Find x and y. **$x = 12$, $y = 14$**

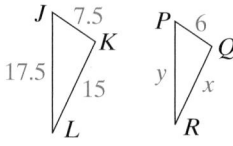

27. **Utilities** Last month, your electric bill was $25.32 for 450 kilowatt-hours of electricity. At that rate, what would be the bill for 240 kilowatt-hours? **$13.50**

28. A person who is 60 in. tall casts a shadow that is 15 in. long. How tall is a nearby tree that casts a shadow that is 40 in. long?
    160 in.

Use mental math to solve each proportion.

29. $\frac{14}{36} = \frac{7}{x}$ **18**

30. $\frac{40}{16} = \frac{x}{2}$ **5**

31. $\frac{x}{1} = \frac{24}{2}$ **12**

32. $\frac{4}{9} = \frac{12}{x}$ **27**

33. Suppose you are making a scale drawing of a giraffe that is 5.5 m tall. The drawing is 7 cm tall. Find the scale of the drawing.
    See margin.

34. **Ballooning** A hot-air balloon 2,100 ft above the ground can descend at the rate of 1.5 ft/s. The balloon is scheduled to land at 3:30 P.M. When should the balloonist start descending? **about 3:07 P.M.**

35. **Science** A 380-cubic-centimeter sample of titanium has a mass of 1,170 g. Find the mass of a titanium sample that has a volume of 532 cubic centimeters. **1,638 g**

2. $9 : 7$, 9 to 7

3. $\frac{48}{100}$, 48 to 100

4. $33 : 9$, $\frac{33}{9}$

5. $\frac{46}{50}$, 46 to 50

6. 19 : 91, $\frac{19}{91}$

7. $\frac{6}{7}$, 6 to 7

11. Yes; the 2-lb bag for $.65/lb is a better buy than the 10-lb bag for $.70/lb.

33. Answers may vary.
    Sample: 1 cm : 78.6 cm

★ TAKS Tips

Some TAKS tests ask you to use similar figures to find missing lengths. Read the question at the right and review the answer choices. Then follow the tips to answer the sample question.

> **Tip 2**
> Create a proportion using the ratios of the corresponding sides.

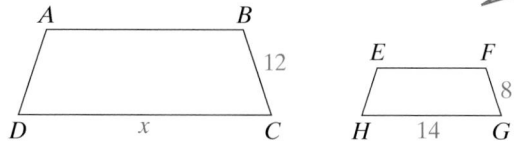

ABCD and *EFGH* are similar.

Which equation can be used to find *x*?

Ⓐ $\frac{8}{12} = \frac{x}{14}$ Ⓒ $\frac{12}{8} = \frac{14}{x}$

Ⓑ $\frac{14}{12} = \frac{8}{x}$ Ⓓ $\frac{8}{12} = \frac{14}{x}$

> **Tip 1**
> Identify the corresponding sides.

Think It Through
The ratios of corresponding sides must be equal, therefore 8 : 12 must be equal to 14 : *x*. So the correct answer is D.

TEKS ★ TAKS Resources

TAKS Review and Preparation Workbook

Texas ExamView CD-ROM
- Instant TAKS Practice Test
- TAKS Practice Items

Differentiated Instruction

Spanish Assessment Resources
- Spanish Cumulative Review ELL

Texas ExamView CD-ROM
- Special Needs Practice Bank L1

Vocabulary Builder

As you solve test items, you must understand the meanings of mathematical terms. Match each term with its mathematical meaning.

A. proportion III

B. ratio II

C. unit rate V

D. scale IV

E. rate I

I. a ratio that compares two quantities measured in different units

II. a comparison of two quantities by division

III. an equation stating that two ratios are equal

IV. a ratio that compares a length in a drawing to the corresponding length of an actual object

V. the rate for one unit of a given quantity

Multiple Choice

Read each question. Then write the letter of the correct answer on your paper.

1. The table below shows the test scores for Mrs. Heppler's social studies class.

First Period Test Scores

Grade Range	Number of Tests
0 to 49	1
50 to 59	1
60 to 69	4
70 to 79	7
80 to 89	8
90 to 100	3

Which of the following statements is supported by the data in the table? **A**

Ⓐ One fourth of the students got a grade less than 70.

Ⓑ One fourth of the students got a grade greater than 90.

Ⓒ Half of the students got a grade of 60 or greater.

Ⓓ The highest grade in the class was 85.

2. The students in Mr. Linn's class made paper airplanes and flew them. The distances, in inches, that the airplanes flew are below.

160, 162, 172, 175, 176, 178, 179, 183, 185, 190, 193, 198, 200, 201, 204, 205

Which of the following statements is NOT supported by the data? **H**

Ⓕ About one fourth of the airplanes flew less than 176 inches.

Ⓖ The range of the distances was 45 inches.

Ⓗ About half of the airplanes flew more than 193 inches.

Ⓙ About one fourth of the airplanes flew 200 inches or more.

3. The table below shows the amount of time it took for six stores to sell out of a new video game on the day of its release.

Sell-Out Times of New Video Game

Stores	Time (hr)
Store 1	$4\frac{1}{3}$
Store 2	$1\frac{2}{5}$
Store 3	$3\frac{1}{3}$
Store 4	$\frac{5}{8}$
Store 5	$2\frac{1}{4}$
Store 6	$\frac{3}{4}$

Which of the following statements is NOT supported by the data? **D**

Ⓐ It took Store 2 almost twice as long as Store 6 to sell out.

Ⓑ It took Store 5 almost three times as long as Store 6 to sell out.

Ⓒ The mean time for all 6 stores was a little over 2 hours.

Ⓓ The total number of hours of the first three stores equals the total number of hours of the last three stores.

270 *TAKS* **Tune-Up** Cumulative Practice

4. A wall 66 feet long is made of concrete blocks. Each block is $1\frac{3}{4}$ feet long. Which equation represents the total number of blocks b? **G**

Ⓕ $66b = 1\frac{3}{4}$ Ⓗ $1\frac{3}{4} - b = 66$

Ⓖ $1\frac{3}{4}b = 66$ Ⓙ $b + 1\frac{3}{4} = 66$

5. Which situation matches the equation below? **D**

$$5x = 75$$

Ⓐ The cost of each piece of beef jerky is \$.75. Daniel wants to buy 5 pieces. What is x, the total cost of the beef jerky?

Ⓑ Lindsey has \$5. She needs \$75 to buy a new bicycle. What is x, the amount she needs to save?

Ⓒ On the football team, 5 of the 75 players are also in the band. What is x, the number of players who are not in band?

Ⓓ Five people want to split the cost of rodeo tickets. The total cost of the tickets is \$75. What is x, the cost for each person?

6. Clara can walk 5 miles in 1 hr 40 minutes. How far can she walk in 1 minute? **G**

Ⓕ 0.04 mi   Ⓗ 0.4 mi

Ⓖ 0.05 mi   Ⓙ 0.5 mi

7. A recipe for 12 cups of fruit punch calls for $\frac{1}{2}$ cup of sugar. How much sugar is needed to make 18 cups of fruit punch using this recipe? **D**

Ⓐ $\frac{1}{8}$ Ⓑ $\frac{1}{2}$ Ⓒ $\frac{12}{18}$ Ⓓ $\frac{3}{4}$

8. Kyla can eat 32 grapes in 18 seconds. If she continues to eat at the same rate, how long will it take her to eat 128 grapes? **G**

Ⓕ 64 seconds   Ⓗ 128 seconds

Ⓖ 72 seconds   Ⓙ 178 seconds

9. The area of the garden in the diagram can be found by evaluating the expression below. What is the value of this expression? **C**

$$(5 + 3)^2 + 9 \times 5$$

	5 ft	3 ft	9 ft
5 ft	Tomatoes	Okra	Watermelon
3 ft	Peppers	Onions	

Ⓐ 365   Ⓑ 85   Ⓒ 109   Ⓓ 61

10. What is the value of the expression $6 \cdot (7 - 5) + (8 + 4) \div 3$? **F**

Ⓕ 16   Ⓖ 12   Ⓗ 8   Ⓙ 4

11. Last week, Luz bought several pounds of shrimp for $11.94. Now she wants to buy 4 more pounds of the same shrimp for a party. What other information is necessary to find the cost of the 4 pounds of shrimp?

Ⓐ total cost of other groceries   **D**
Ⓑ reason for the party
Ⓒ amount of change she received
Ⓓ number of pounds she bought last week

12. △ABC and △PQR are similar.

Which choice shows the process used to find the length of $\overline{PQ}$? **G**

Ⓕ Use the same length as $\overline{AB}$.
Ⓖ Set up a proportion using corresponding sides from △ABC and △PQR.
Ⓗ Write a ratio comparing $\overline{PQ}$ and $\overline{BC}$.
Ⓙ Add 10 to the length of $\overline{AB}$.

Griddable Items
Record your answer in a grid.

13. Pam earns $9.45 for working 3 hours. If she gets paid at the same rate, how many dollars does she earn for working 8 hours? **25.20**

14. A map scale says 1 cm : 5 km. The actual distance between two cities is 112 km. How many centimeters apart are the cities on the map? **22.4**

GO for Help Guide

TAKS Objective	Item Numbers	GO To	TAKS Objective	Item Numbers	GO To
Obj. 5: (7.11)(B)	1	Lesson 2-3	Obj. 6: (7.13)(B)	11	Lesson 5-4
	2–3	Lesson 3-4		12	Lesson 5-5
Obj. 1: (7.5)(B)	4–5	Lesson 4-4	Obj. 2: (7.3)(B)	13	Lesson 5-4
Obj. 1: (7.2)(D)	6	Lesson 5-2		14	Lesson 5-6
	7–8	Lesson 5-4			
Obj. 1: (7.2)(E)	9	Lesson 2-1			
	10	Lesson 1-9			

For additional TAKS Practice, see the *TAKS Review and Preparation Workbook*.

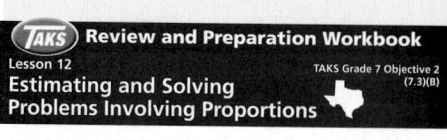

6 Percents

Chapter at a Glance

Lesson Titles, Objectives, and Features	Assessment	NCTM Standards	TEKS ★ TAKS
6-1 Understanding Percents • To model percents and to write percents using equivalent ratios	Lesson Quiz	1, 2, 6, 7, 8, 9, 10	**TEKS** (7.1)(B), (7.14)(A) TAKS **Obj. 1, 6**
6-2a Activity Lab, Hands On: Rational Number Cubes **6-2 Percents, Fractions, and Decimals** • To convert between fractions, decimals, and percents	Lesson Quiz	1, 2, 6, 7, 8, 9, 10	**TEKS** (7.1)(A), (7.1)(B) TAKS **Obj. 1**, Prepares for **TEKS** (7.1)(B)
6-3 Percents Greater Than 100% or Less Than 1% • To convert between fractions, decimals, and percents greater than 100% or less that 1%	Lesson Quiz Checkpoint Quiz 1	1, 2, 6, 7, 8, 9, 10	**TEKS** (7.1)(B), (7.3)(A) TAKS **Obj. 1, 2**
6-4a Activity Lab, Data Analysis: Using Percent Data in a Graph **6-4 Finding a Percent of a Number** • To find and estimate the percent of a number	Lesson Quiz	1, 2, 5, 6, 7, 8, 9, 10	**TEKS** (7.1)(B), (7.3)(A), (7.11)(B) TAKS **Obj. 1, 2, 5** **TEKS** (7.13)(D)
6-5 Solving Percent Problems Using Proportions • To use proportions to solve problems involving percent	Lesson Quiz	1, 2, 6, 7, 8, 9, 10	**TEKS** (7.3)(A), (7.3)(B) TAKS **Obj. 2**
6-6 Solving Percent Problems Using Equations • To use equations to solve problems involving percent **Guided Problem Solving:** Solving Percent Problems	Lesson Quiz	1, 2, 6, 7, 8, 9, 10	**TEKS** (7.1)(B), (7.3)(A) TAKS **Obj. 1, 2**
6-7 Applications of Percent • To find and estimate solutions to application problems involving percent **6-7b Activity Lab, Algebra Thinking:** Percent Equations	Lesson Quiz Checkpoint Quiz 2	1, 2, 6, 7, 8, 9, 10	**TEKS** (7.1)(B), (7.3)(A) TAKS **Obj. 1, 2** **TEKS** (7.13)(D)
6-8a Activity Lab, Data Analysis: Exploring Percent of Change **6-8 Finding Percent of Change** • To find percents of increase and percents of decrease	Lesson Quiz	1, 2, 5, 6, 7, 8, 9, 10	**TEKS** (7.1)(B), (7.3)(A), (7.11)(B) TAKS **Obj. 1, 2, 5**
TAKS **Tune-Up: Cumulative Practice**			

NCTM Standards 2000
1 Number and Operations	**2** Algebra	**3** Geometry	**4** Measurement	**5** Data Analysis and Probability
6 Problem Solving	**7** Reasoning and Proof	**8** Communication	**9** Connections	**10** Representation

Correlations to Standardized Tests

All content for these tests is contained in *Prentice Hall Math,* Course 2. This chart reflects coverage in this chapter only.

	6-1	6-2	6-3	6-4	6-5	6-6	6-7	6-8
Terra Nova CAT6 (Level 17)								
Number and Number Relations	✔	✔	✔	✔	✔	✔	✔	✔
Computation and Numerical Estimation	✔	✔	✔	✔	✔	✔	✔	✔
Operation Concepts	✔	✔	✔	✔	✔	✔	✔	✔
Measurement								
Geometry and Spatial Sense								
Data Analysis, Statistics, and Probability				✔				✔
Patterns, Functions, Algebra	✔	✔	✔	✔	✔	✔	✔	✔
Problem Solving and Reasoning	✔	✔	✔	✔	✔	✔	✔	✔
Communication	✔	✔	✔	✔	✔	✔	✔	✔
Decimals, Fractions, Integers, and Percent	✔	✔	✔	✔	✔	✔	✔	✔
Order of Operations								
Terra Nova CTBS (Level 17)								
Decimals, Fractions, Integers, Percents	✔	✔	✔	✔	✔	✔	✔	✔
Order of Operations, Numeration, Number Theory	✔	✔	✔	✔	✔	✔	✔	✔
Data Interpretation				✔				✔
Pre-algebra	✔	✔	✔	✔	✔	✔	✔	✔
Measurement								
Geometry								
ITBS (Level 13)								
Number Properties and Operations	✔	✔	✔	✔	✔	✔	✔	✔
Algebra	✔	✔	✔	✔	✔	✔	✔	✔
Geometry								
Measurement								
Probability and Statistics								
Estimation				✔		✔		✔
SAT10 (Int 3 Level)								
Number Sense and Operations	✔	✔	✔	✔	✔	✔	✔	✔
Patterns, Relationships, and Algebra	✔	✔	✔	✔	✔	✔	✔	✔
Data, Statistics, and Probability				✔				✔
Geometry and Measurement								
NAEP								
Number Sense, Properties, and Operations	✔		✔	✔	✔		✔	✔
Measurement								
Geometry and Spatial Sense								
Data Analysis, Statistics, and Probability								
Algebra and Functions						✔		

CAT6 California Achievement Test, 6th Ed.   **CTBS** Comprehensive Test of Basic Skills   **ITBS** Iowa Test of Basic Skills, Form M
SAT10 Stanford Achievement Test, 10th Ed.   **NAEP** National Assessment of Educational Progress 2005 Mathematics Objectives

TEKS Math Background

Professional Development

Focus on the TEKS

- At Grade 7, students estimate and find solutions involving percents (7.3)(A). Analysis of TAKS results shows that students struggle with this student expectation.

  In Lessons 6-3 through 6-8 students solve various percent problems including finding the percent of a number or the percent of change, and problems using proportions and equations. Place special emphasis on these lessons because they all focus on (7.3)(A).

- New at Grade 7 is generating equivalent rational numbers including fractions, decimals, and percents (7.1)(B). Students build upon Grade 6 skills to find equivalent numbers for percents in Lessons 6-1 and 6-2 (7.1)(B).

Example: You say 0.75 as "seventy-five hundredths," which you can write as the fraction $\frac{75}{100}$ or 75%.

Converting Percents, Decimals, and Fractions	
To rewrite this:	**Do this:**
a decimal as a percent	multiply by 100 OR move the decimal point two places to the right
a percent as a decimal	divide by 100 OR move the decimal point two places to the left
a fraction as a percent	rewrite with a denominator of 100 OR convert to a decimal and write as a percent
a percent as a fraction	rewrite with a denominator of 100 and simplify

6-1 Understanding Percents

TEKS ★ *TAKS* (7.1)(B), (7.14)(A) Obj. 1, 6

Math Understandings
- A percent expresses parts per 100. The percent symbol, %, means "per 100" or "/100."
- A percent is a relative, rather than an absolute amount. For example, 25% of a greater number represents a different value from 25% of a lesser number.

A **percent** is a ratio that compares a number to 100. For example, you can express 3 out of 4 as the equivalent ratio 75 out of 100, or $\frac{75}{100}$, which is 75%.

6-2 Percents, Fractions, and Decimals

TEKS ★ *TAKS* (7.1)(A), (7.1)(B) Obj. 1

Math Understandings
- You can represent a percent in different but related ways, such as a ratio, a fraction, and a decimal.
- You can rewrite a decimal that names hundredths directly as the same percent.

6-3 Percents Greater Than 100% or Less Than 1%

TEKS ★ *TAKS* (7.1)(B), (7.3)(A) Obj. 1, 2

Math Understandings
- A fraction or a decimal that is less than $\frac{1}{100}$ or 0.01 can be expressed as a percent less than 1%.
- A number that is greater than 1 can be expressed as a percent greater than 100%.

If the number compared to 100 is less than 1, the percent is less than 1%. If the number compared to 100 is greater than 100, the percent is greater than 100%. A mixed number such as $4\frac{1}{2}$ represents a percent greater than 100%. A fraction less than $\frac{1}{100}$ represents a percent less than 1%.

6-4 Finding a Percent of a Number

TEKS ★ *TAKS* (7.1)(B), (7.3)(A) Obj. 1, 2; (7.13)(D)

Math Understandings
- You can find a given percent of a number by rewriting the percent as either a decimal or a fraction and then multiplying.
- You can use compatible numbers (numbers easy to calculate with mental math) to estimate a percent.

Knowing the fraction equivalents of common percents can make it easier to find percents of a number using mental math.

Percent	10%	25%	33.33%	50%	66.67%	75%
Fraction	$\frac{1}{10}$	$\frac{1}{4}$	$\frac{1}{3}$	$\frac{1}{2}$	$\frac{2}{3}$	$\frac{3}{4}$

6-5 6-6 Solving Percent Problems Using Proportions and Equations

TEKS ★ (TAKS) (7.1)(B), (7.3)(A), (7.3)(B) Obj. 1, 2

Math Understandings
- Percent problems involve a part, a percent, and a whole.
- If you know two of the three quantities, you can find the missing one by using either a proportion or an equation.
- You can write proportions in different equivalent ways.

In a problem, you can identify the percent by the % sign, and the whole usually follows the word *of*. The model below shows the relationship among the part, whole, and percent.

You can write and solve the proportion $\frac{part}{whole} = \frac{percent}{100}$ to find the missing number, percent, or whole. To find the missing number, percent, or whole, you can also write and solve the equation (whole) × (percent) = part.

6-7 Applications of Percent

TEKS ★ (TAKS) (7.1)(B), (7.3)(A) Obj. 1, 2

Math Understandings
- You often use percent in daily transactions such as paying sales tax, estimating the amount of the tip on a bill, and figuring commission.

In many towns and states, you pay a sales tax that is a percent of the purchase price. A **tip** is a percent of a bill that you give to the person providing a service. Some sales jobs pay a **commission**, a percent of the amount you sell.

Example: A lunch costs $7.95. The sales tax is 5% and you want to leave a 20% tip. What is the total you pay for lunch?
Total = Cost + Tax + Tip = $7.95 + $.40 + $1.59 = $9.94

6-8 Finding Percent of Change

TEKS ★ (TAKS) (7.1)(B), (7.3)(A) Obj. 1, 2

Math Understandings
- A percent of change may be an increase or a decrease.
- The percent of change is a ratio, expressed as a percent. It compares the amount of change to the original amount. The amount of change is the difference between the original amount and the amount that results after the change.

The **percent of change** is the percent a quantity increases or decreases from its original amount. The difference between the selling price and the store's original cost of an item is called the **markup**. So a common percent of increase is the ratio of the amount of markup to the original cost of an item. The difference between the original price and the sale price of an item is called a **discount**.

Additional Professional Development Opportunities

Professional Development

Math Background Notes for Chapter 6: Every lesson has a Math Background in the PLAN section.

Research Overview, Mathematics Strands Additional support for these topics and more is in the front of the Teacher's Edition.

LessonLab LessonLab, a Pearson Education company, offers comprehensive, facilitated professional development designed to help teachers to improve student achievement. To learn more, please visit lessonlab.com.

Texas Chapter 6 Resources

	6-1	6-2	6-3	6-4	6-5	6-6	6-7	6-8	For the Chapter
Print Resources									
L3 Practice	●	●	●	●	●	●	●	●	
L1 Adapted Practice	●	●	●	●	●	●	●	●	
L3 Guided Problem Solving	●	●	●	●	●	●	●	●	
L2 Reteaching	●	●	●	●	●	●	●	●	
L4 Enrichment	●	●	●	●	●	●	●	●	
L3 Daily Notetaking Guide	●	●	●	●	●	●	●	●	
L1 Adapted Daily Notetaking Guide	●	●	●	●	●	●	●	●	
L3 Vocabulary and Study Skills Worksheet	●		●				●	●	●
L3 Daily Puzzles	●	●	●	●	●	●	●	●	
L3 Activity Labs	●	●	●	●	●	●	●	●	
L3 Checkpoint Quiz		●					●		
L3 Chapter Project									●
L2 Chapter Test									●
L3 Chapter Test									●
L4 Alternative Assessment									●
L3 Cumulative Review									●
Spanish Resources ELL									
L3 Practice	●	●	●	●	●	●	●	●	
L3 Vocabulary and Study Skills Worksheets	●		●		●		●	●	●
L3 Checkpoint Quiz			●				●		
L2 Chapter Test									●
L3 Chapter Test									●
L4 Alternative Assessment									●
L3 Cumulative Review									●
Transparencies									
Check Skills You'll Need	●	●	●	●	●	●	●	●	
Additional Examples	●	●	●	●	●	●	●	●	
Problem of the Day	●	●	●	●	●	●	●	●	
TAKS Daily Review	●	●	●	●	●	●	●	●	
Classroom Aid									
Student Edition Answers	●	●	●	●	●	●	●	●	●
Lesson Quiz	●	●	●	●	●	●	●	●	
TAKS Strategies									●
Technology									
Texas Interactive Textbook Online	●	●	●	●	●	●	●	●	●
Texas StudentExpress CD-ROM	●	●	●	●	●	●	●	●	●
Success Tracker™ Online Intervention	●	●	●	●	●	●	●	●	●
TeacherExpress CD-ROM	●	●	●	●	●	●	●	●	●
PresentationExpress CD-ROM	●	●	●	●	●	●	●	●	●
Texas ExamView CD-ROM with QuickTake	●	●	●	●	●	●	●	●	●
MindPoint Quiz Show CD-ROM	●	●	●	●	●	●	●	●	●
Prentice Hall Web Site: PHSchool.com	●	●	●	●	●	●	●	●	●

Also available: **TAKS Tune-Up Kit**
- TAKS Daily Review Transparencies
- TAKS Review and Preparation Workbook
- TAKS Strategies with Transparencies
- Texas Progress Monitoring Assessments
- Texas ExamView CD-ROM
- MindPoint Quiz Show CD-ROM

Other Resources
Algebra Readiness Tests
All-in-One Student Workbook
All-in-One Student Workbook, Adapted Version
Multilingual Handbook

Solution Key
Math Notes Study Folder
Spanish Cumulative Assessment

Where You Can Use the Lesson Resources

Here is a suggestion, following the four-step teaching plan, for how you can incorporate Differentiated Instruction Resources into your teaching.

	Instructional Resources　L3	Differentiated Instruction Resources
1. Plan		
Preparation Read the Math Background in the Teacher's Edition to connect this lesson with students' previous experience. **Starting Class** **Check Skills You'll Need** Assign these exercises to review prerequisite skills. **TEKS** ★ *TAKS* Review the full text of the TEKS student expectations and TAKS objectives covered in this lesson. **New Vocabulary** Help students pre-read the lesson by pointing out the new terms introduced in the lesson.	**TEKS Math Background** **Math Understandings** **Transparencies & PresentationExpress CD-ROM** Check Skills You'll Need Problem of the Day TAKS Daily Review **Resources** Vocabulary and Study Skills	**Spanish Support** ELL Vocabulary and Study Skills
2. Teach		
L3 Guided Instruction Use the Activity Labs to build conceptual understanding. Teach each Example. Use the Teacher's Edition side column notes for specific teaching tips, including Error Prevention notes. Use the Additional Examples found in the side column (and on transparency and PowerPoint) as an alternative presentation for the content. After each Example, assign the Quick Check exercise for that Example to get an immediate assessment of student understanding. Use the Closure activity in the Teacher's Edition to help students attain mastery of lesson content.	**Student Edition** Activity Lab **Resources** Daily Notetaking Guide Activity Lab **Transparencies & PresentationExpress CD-ROM** Additional Examples Classroom Aids **Texas ExamView CD-ROM with QuickTake**	**Teacher's Edition** Every lesson includes suggestions for working with students who need special attention. L1 Special Needs L2 Below Level L4 Advanced Learners ELL English Language Learners **Resources** L1 Adapted Daily Notetaking Guide **Multilingual Handbook**
3. Practice		
Assignment Guide **Check Your Understanding** Use these questions to check students' understanding before you assign homework. **Homework Exercises** Assign homework from these leveled exercises in the Assignment Guide. 　A Practice by Example 　B Apply Your Skills 　C Challenge 　*TAKS* Tune-Up and Mixed Review **Homework Quick Check** Use these key exercises to quickly check students' homework.	**Transparencies & PresentationExpress CD-ROM** Student Answers **Resources** Practice Guided Problem Solving Vocabulary and Study Skills Activity Lab Daily Puzzles **Texas ExamView CD-ROM with QuickTake**	**Spanish Support** ELL Practice ELL Vocabulary and Study Skills **Resources** L1 Adapted Practice L4 Enrichment
4. Assess & Reteach		
Lesson Quiz Assign the Lesson Quiz to assess students' mastery of the lesson content. **Checkpoint Quiz** Use the Checkpoint Quiz to assess student progress over several lessons.	**Transparencies & PresentationExpress CD-ROM** Lesson Quiz **Resources** Checkpoint Quiz	**Resources** L2 Reteaching ELL Checkpoint Quiz Success Tracker™ Online Intervention **Texas ExamView CD-ROM with QuickTake**

KEY　L1 Special Needs　L2 Below Level　L3 For All Students　L4 Advanced, Gifted　ELL English Language Learners

Percents

CHAPTER
6
Percents

 Check Your Readiness

Answers are in the back of the textbook.

For intervention, direct students to:

Using Estimation Strategies
Lesson 1-1
Extra Skills and Word
Problems Practice, Ch. 1

Fractions and Decimals
Lesson 2-6
Extra Skills and Word
Problems Practice, Ch. 2

Solving Equations by Multiplying or Dividing
Lesson 4-4
Extra Skills and Word
Problems Practice, Ch. 4

Using Proportional Reasoning
Lesson 5-4
Extra Skills and Word
Problems Practice, Ch. 5

 What You've Learned

TEKS ★ **TAKS**

- **(7.1)(B)** In Chapter 2, you converted between decimals, fractions, and whole numbers. **TAKS** Obj. 1
- **(7.3)(B)** In Chapter 5, you estimated and found solutions to application problems involving proportional relationships. **TAKS** Obj. 2

Check Your Readiness

GO for Help

For Exercises	See Lesson
1–4	1-1
5–9	2-6
10–13	4-4
14–16	5-4

Using Estimation Strategies

Use compatible numbers to estimate each quotient.

1. $74.89 \div 14.7$ 5

2. $1,409 \div 102.4$ 14

3. $495.89 \div 99.3$ 5

4. $1,913 \div 188$ 10

Fractions and Decimals

Write each decimal as a fraction in simplest form.

5. 0.85 $\frac{17}{20}$

6. 0.4 $\frac{2}{5}$

7. 0.68 $\frac{17}{25}$

8. 1.25 $\frac{5}{4}$

9. 0.01 $\frac{1}{100}$

Solving Equations by Multiplying or Dividing

(Algebra) **Solve each equation.**

10. $0.8t = 24$ 30

11. $0.35w = 280$ 800

12. $\frac{n}{0.6} = 14$ 8.4

13. $\frac{z}{0.25} = 12$ 3

Using Proportional Reasoning

Solve each proportion.

14. $\frac{4}{5} = \frac{n}{100}$ 80

15. $\frac{x}{8} = \frac{27}{100}$ 2.16

16. $\frac{6}{a} = \frac{3}{100}$ 200

272   Chapter 6

Number, Operation, and Quantitative Reasoning
TEKS (7.1)(A), (7.1)(B)
TAKS Obj. 1

Patterns, Relationships, and Algebraic Reasoning
TEKS (7.3)(A), (7.3)(B)
TAKS Obj. 2

Probability and Statistics
TEKS (7.11)(B)
TAKS Obj. 5

Underlying Processes and Mathematical Tools
TEKS (7.14)(A)
TAKS Obj. 6;
TEKS (7.13)(D)

Chapter 6 Overview

In this chapter, students work with percents, including percents less than 1 or greater than 100. They begin by comparing percents to fractions and decimals. Then, using real-world applications, they solve problems involving percents, including finding a percent of a number and finding percent of change.

Activating Prior Knowledge

In this chapter, students will build on their knowledge of proportions and proportional reasoning to solve problems involving applications of percents. They also draw upon their understanding of the relationship between decimals and fractions to express both as percents. Ask:

• *How can you write a decimal as a fraction?* Sample: Write a fraction in tenths, hundredths, thousandths, and so on, and then express that fraction in simplest form.

• *What is the missing term in the proportion:* $\frac{n}{12} = \frac{5}{6}$? $n = 10$

What You'll Learn Next

TEKS ⭐ **TAKS**

• **(7.1)(B)** You will convert between fractions, decimals, whole numbers, and percents. *TAKS* Obj. 1

• **(7.3)(A)** You will estimate and find solutions to application problems involving percent. *TAKS* Obj. 2

 Key Vocabulary

• commission (p. 305)
• discount (p. 311)
• markup (p. 311)
• percent (p. 274)
• percent of change (p. 310)

 Tune-Up On pages 319–321, you will review and practice the vocabulary and *TAKS* objectives you have learned.

TEKS ★ TAKS

(7.1)(B) To convert between fractions, whole numbers, and percents TAKS Obj. 1

(7.14)(A) To communicate mathematical ideas using numerical and graphical models TAKS Obj. 6

Dana Center TEKS Toolkit Clarifying Activities (7.1)(B), (7.14)(A)
Visit: PHSchool.com
Web Code: arq-9045

TEKS Math Background

While a ratio compares any two numbers, such as $\frac{4}{5}$, a percent is a ratio that compares a number to 100, such as $\frac{80}{100}$ or 80%. Any ratio can be expressed as a percent by writing an equal ratio with a denominator of 100.

$$\frac{4}{5} = \frac{4 \cdot 20}{5 \cdot 20} = \frac{80}{100} = 80\%$$

More Math Background: p. 272C

Lesson Planning and Resources

See p. 272E for a list of the resources that support this lesson.

Bell Ringer Practice

✓ **Check Skills You'll Need**
Use student page, transparency, or PowerPoint.

TAKS **Daily Review 41**
Use transparency.

274

✓ Check Skills You'll Need

1. Vocabulary Review
What are *equivalent ratios?* 1–5. See below.

Find two equivalent ratios for each ratio.

2. $\frac{2}{5}$ $\frac{4}{10}, \frac{6}{15}$ 3. $\frac{13}{50}$ $\frac{26}{100}, \frac{39}{150}$

4. $\frac{3}{25}$ $\frac{6}{50}, \frac{9}{75}$ 5. $\frac{1}{10}$ $\frac{2}{20}, \frac{3}{30}$

 for Help
Lesson 5-1

Check Skills You'll Need

1. Equivalent ratios have the same value.

2–5. Answers may vary. Samples are given.

Vocabulary Tip

Percent means "per hundred." The root *cent* appears in words such as century, centimeter, and centipede.

2.

Why Learn This?

Percents make ratios easier to understand and compare. You can use a percent to represent the floor space needed for each piece of furniture in a room.

A **percent** is a ratio that compares a number to 100. You can use a model to find a percent. You can model a percent using a 10 × 10 grid.

EXAMPLES Using Models With Percents

1 The floor plan above shows a bedroom with an area of 100 ft². Find the percent of floor space needed for each piece of furniture.

Count the number of grid spaces for each piece. Write each number as a ratio to the total number of grid spaces, 100. Then write it as a percent.

Bed $\frac{28}{100} = 28\%$ **Bureau** $\frac{10}{100} = 10\%$ **Desk** $\frac{8}{100} = 8\%$

2 Model 25% on a 10 × 10 grid.

Shade 25 of the 100 grid spaces. →

✓ Quick Check

1. Write a ratio and a percent to represent the unused floor space.
$\frac{54}{100}$; 54%

2. Model 80% on a 10 × 10 grid. See left.

274 Chapter 6 Percents

Differentiated Instruction Solutions for All Learners

Special Needs L1
For Quick Check 3, have students overlay a hundred grid on the grids shown. Then they can see, for example, that a ratio of $\frac{3}{4}$ is equal to $\frac{75}{100}$ or 75%.

learning style: visual

Below Level L2
The following numbers are denominators in ratios. By what number do you need to multiply each denominator to find a percent?

5 20   20 5   25 4   4 25

learning style: verbal

For help with finding equivalent fractions, go to Lesson 2-3, Example 1.

The factors of 100 are 1, 2, 4, 5, 10, 20, 25, 50, and 100. Any ratio written as a fraction with a denominator that is a factor of 100 is easy to write as a percent. You can use common multiples to write an equivalent ratio that has a denominator of 100. When you have a fraction with a denominator of 100, look at the numerator to find the percent.

EXAMPLE   Finding Percents Using Models

③ What percent does each shaded area represent?

a.

b.

c.

$$\frac{20}{100} = 20\%$$ $$\frac{2}{10} = \frac{20}{100} = 20\%$$ $$\frac{1}{5} = \frac{20}{100} = 20\%$$

✓ Quick Check

3. Write a ratio and a percent for each shaded area.

a.

b.

c.

$\frac{3}{4}$; 75% $\frac{1}{2}$; 50% $\frac{7}{10}$; 70%

EXAMPLE   Using Equivalent Ratios

TAKS Tip

When answering questions in Griddable format, enter only the numerical portion of your answer in the grid.

④ **TAKS Griddable Item** You take a quiz that has 20 questions and get only 3 incorrect answers. What is your percent grade on the quiz?

First find the number of correct answers. Then write a ratio.

$\frac{17}{20}$ ← number of correct answers
  ← total number of answers

$\frac{17 \cdot 5}{20 \cdot 5}$ ← Since 20 · 5 is 100, multiply numerator and denominator by 5.

$\frac{85}{100}$ ← Simplify.

85% ← Write as a percent.

Your percent grade is 85%. Fill in 85 on your answer grid.

✓ Quick Check

4. A tennis team played a total of 25 games and won 20 of them. What percent of the games did the team win? 80%

Advanced Learners L4
Your collection of books has five types: $\frac{1}{5}$ are mysteries, $\frac{8}{50}$ are biographies, $\frac{2}{10}$ are joke books, and $\frac{10}{100}$ are books about animals. What percent are science fiction, the last type? 34%

English Language Learners ELL
Some students have a difficult time understanding that $\frac{17}{20}$ is = 85%, even when they do the calculations correctly. Use alternate ways to explain that no matter what the denominator is, the ratio is equal to a part out of a whole with a denominator of 100.

Pre-AP™

learning style: verbal

---

2. Teach

Activity Lab
Use before the lesson.

All in One Teaching Resources
Activity Lab 6-1: Fractions, Decimals, Percents

Guided Instruction

Example 3
Have students practice repeating the factor pairs of 100. 2, 50; 4, 25; 5, 20; 10,10

Additional Examples

❶ In a floor plan of a 10 × 10 room, a chair takes up 4 spaces. Write the ratio and percent of the chair space to the total floor space. $\frac{4}{100}$; 4%

❷ Model 82% in a 10 × 10 grid.

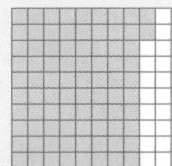

❸ What percent does the shaded area represent? 60%

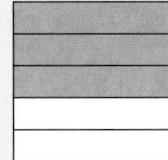

❹ Write each ratio as a percent.
a. $\frac{3}{10}$ 30% b. $\frac{4}{5}$ 80%

All in One Teaching Resources
• Daily Notetaking Guide 6-1 **L3**
• Adapted Notetaking 6-1 **L1**

Closure

• *What is a percent?* a ratio that compares a number to 100
• *How do you write a ratio with any denominator as a percent?* Write as an equal ratio with a denominator of 100. The numerator is the percent.

275

Assignment Guide

Check Your Understanding
Go over Exercises 1–6 in class before assigning the Homework Exercises.

Homework Exercises
A Practice by Example 7–18
B Apply Your Skills 19–33
C Challenge 34
TEKS ★ TAKS Tune-Up and Mixed Review 35–40

Homework Quick Check
To check students' understanding of key skills and concepts, go over Exercises 8, 13, 26, 30, and 32.

Differentiated Instruction Resources

276

✓ Check Your Understanding

1. Write a ratio and a percent for the shaded area in the diagram. $\frac{32}{100}$; 32%

2. Model 15% on a 10 × 10 grid. **See margin.**

Write each ratio as a percent.

3. $\frac{67}{100}$ 67%

4. $\frac{4}{5}$ 80%

5. $\frac{9}{10}$ 90%

6. **Reasoning** How can you use percents to compare two ratios with different denominators? **Answers may vary. Sample: Write each ratio as a percent and compare the two percents.**

Homework Exercises

For more exercises, see Extra Skills and Word Problems.

Ⓐ **Write a ratio and a percent for each shaded figure.**

GO for Help

For Exercises	See Examples
7–9	1
10–14	2
15–18	3–4

7.
$\frac{64}{100}$; 64%

8.
$\frac{48}{100}$; 48%

9.
$\frac{60}{100}$; 60%

Model each percent on a 10 × 10 grid. 10–14. See margin.

10. 35% **11.** 78% **12.** 10% **13.** 8% **14.** 90.5%

Write a ratio and a percent for each shaded area.

15.
$\frac{4}{5}$, 80%

16.
$\frac{1}{10}$, 10%

17.
$\frac{11}{20}$, 55%

18. **Geography** The area of Argentina is about three tenths the area of the United States. Write this ratio as a percent. **30%**

Ⓑ **GPS** 19. **Guided Problem Solving** In a litter of 10 puppies, exactly six puppies are black. What percent of the puppies are not black? **40%**
   • How many puppies are not black?
   • How many puppies are in the litter?

20. **Government** An amendment to the U.S. Constitution must be ratified by at least three fourths of the states to become law. Write this ratio as a percent. **75%**

2.

10–14. See back of book.

Write each ratio as a percent.

21. $\frac{3}{5}$ 60%　**22.** $\frac{1}{2}$ 50%　**23.** $\frac{21}{25}$ 84%　**24.** $\frac{9}{50}$ 18%　**25.** $\frac{11}{20}$ 55%

26. **Writing in Math** Explain how to model 25% two different ways.
　　See left.

26. Answers may vary. Sample: Shade 25 squares on a 10 × 10 grid or shade 1 section of a square divided into 4 equal areas.

Find what percent of a dollar each set of coins makes.

27. 2 quarters and 2 dimes **70%**　　**28.** 3 quarters, 1 dime, 3 pennies **88%**

29. Your class has 12 boys and 13 girls. What percent of the students in your class are girls? **52%**

30. **History** Before the Battle of Tippecanoe, nineteen twentieths of General William Harrison's troops had never before been in a battle. What percent of the troops had previously been in a battle? **5%**

Estimate the percent of each figure that is shaded.

31.
about 19%

32.
about 22%

33.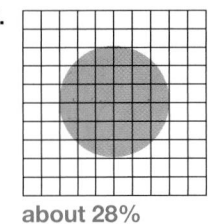
about 28%

C 34. **Challenge** You shade four squares in a grid. How many squares are there if the shaded portion represents 20% of the grid? **20 squares**

 TEKS ★ TAKS Tune-Up and Mixed Review

GRIDDABLE ITEMS

TAKS Objective 1
TEKS (7.1)(B)

35. The table shows the ratios of people who prefer four popular yogurt flavors. What is the percent of people surveyed who prefer blueberry? **12**

Most Popular Yogurt Flavors

Personal Favorite	Ratio
Strawberry	$\frac{2}{5}$
Blueberry	$\frac{3}{25}$
Vanilla	$\frac{3}{50}$
Peach	$\frac{3}{100}$

TAKS Objective 1
TEKS (7.2)(B)

36. Five students in Ms. Power's class ran for charity. The distances they ran were as follows: 5.8 mi, $4\frac{1}{2}$ mi, 2.4 mi, $3\frac{9}{10}$ mi, and 7 mi. What was the distance, in miles, the students ran altogether? **23.6**

TAKS Objective 5
TEKS (7.12)(A)

37. Arthur scored 87 on each of his first three tests. He scored 93 and 95 on his next two tests. What was the mean score of all his tests? **89.8**

 GO for Help
Lesson 4-7

Which numbers are solutions of each inequality?

38. $x > -3; -4, 0, 3$
0, 3

39. $x \le -2; 0, -2, -3$
−2, −3

40. $x < 5; 5, 3, -1$
3, −1

Online lesson quiz, PHSchool.com, Web Code: ara-0601

6-1　Understanding Percents　**277**

PowerPoint
Lesson Quiz

1. Write a ratio and a percent for the shaded figure. $\frac{30}{100}$; 30%

Write each ratio as a percent.

2. $\frac{1}{10}$ 10%　　3. $\frac{11}{50}$ 22%

Reteaching 6-1

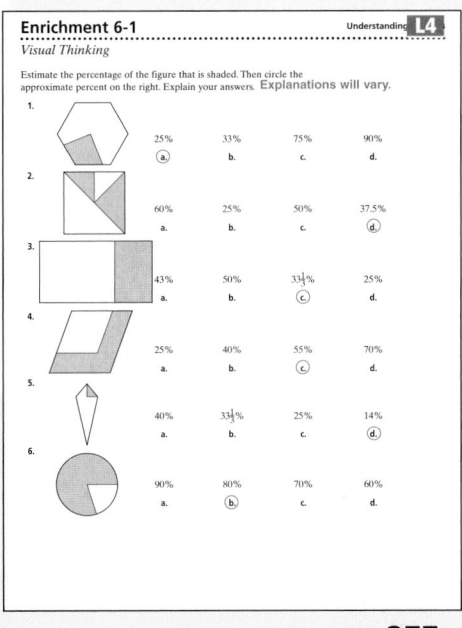

Enrichment 6-1

Alternative Assessment

Provide student pairs with hundredths-decimal grids. Each partner shades different parts of five grids. Partners exchange squares and write a ratio and a percent for the shaded part of each square.

TEKS ★ TAKS Resources

• TAKS Strategies, p. 315
• TAKS Tune-Up, pp. 319–321

TAKS Tune-Up Kit

• TAKS Daily Review Transparencies
• TAKS Review and Preparation Workbook
• TAKS Strategies with Transparencies
• Texas Progress Monitoring Assessments

Rational Number Cubes

Students order rational numbers using greater than, less than, and equal symbols. This will help them become familiar with how numbers can be equivalent fractions, decimals, and percents.

Guided Instruction

Explain the steps of the Activity. Point out that the numbers on each cube are equivalent. Ask:

• *If you rolled 3 cubes and got $\frac{1}{8}$, =, and 0.75, could you use that roll?* no *Why?* $\frac{1}{8}$ does not equal 0.75

• *How many squares of the grid should you shade to equal 12.5%?* twelve full squares and one half square

Activity

Have students work in pairs. They should toss the cubes until all the numbers and symbols fit in the chain. They can take turns tossing the cubes and recording the results and work together to decide where each number or symbol should be placed.

Alternative Method

Some students may have an easier time with simpler fractions. Provide these students with cubes reflecting decimals, fractions, and percents of 0, $\frac{1}{2}$, and 1.

Teaching Tip

Have students study the table to help them convert mentally between fractions, decimals, and percents.

TEKS ★ TAKS Resources

• Activity Lab 6-2: Critical Thinking
• number cube patterns
• scissors
• tape

Dana Center TEKS Toolkit Clarifying Activities (7.1)(A)
Visit: PHSchool.com
Web Code: arq-9045

Rational Number Cubes

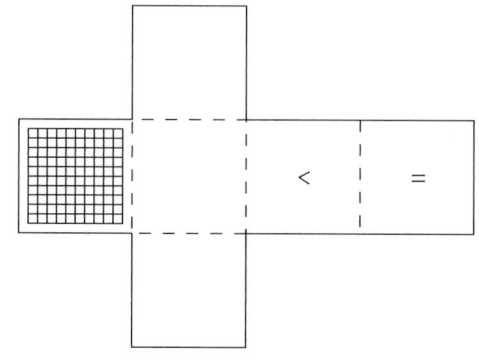

TEKS ★ TAKS
(7.1)(A) To compare and order positive rational numbers TAKS Obj. 1
Prepares for **TEKS** (7.1)(B) To convert between fractions, decimals, and percents

You can write equivalent rational numbers in several different ways. The table below shows common rational numbers in equivalent forms. The fraction, decimal, and percent in each column are equivalent.

Fraction	$\frac{1}{8}$	$\frac{1}{4}$	$\frac{1}{3}$	$\frac{1}{2}$	$\frac{2}{3}$	$\frac{3}{4}$
Decimal	0.125	0.25	$0.33\overline{3}$	0.5	$0.66\overline{6}$	0.75
Percent	12.5%	25%	$33\frac{1}{3}\%$	50%	$66\frac{2}{3}\%$	75%

ACTIVITY   Check students' work.

Step 1 A net of a cube is shown at the right. Make six copies of the net.

Step 2 Use the first column from the table above. Fill in the squares of the first net. Write $\frac{1}{8}$ in the first empty square. Write 0.125 and 12.5% in the other two empty squares. Then shade the 10×10 grid to model this rational number.

Step 3 Repeat Step 2 with the other nets and the other columns of the table.

Step 4 Cut out each net. Fold each net along its dotted lines. Tape the edges to form a cube.

Step 5 Work in pairs. Toss the 12 cubes. Use the top views of the cubes. Arrange as many as you can into a chain that reads correctly from left to right. (You can use the inequality symbol as either "less than" or "greater than.")

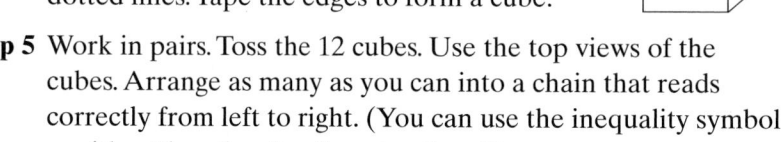

Top Views of the Cubes   Unused Cubes

Step 6 Pick up the unused cubes and toss them again. Insert these cubes into the chain wherever they fit. Repeat until you can successfully place all 12 cubes in the chain.

Percents, Fractions, and Decimals

 Check Skills You'll Need

1. **Vocabulary Review**
   What is a *repeating decimal?*
   1–2. See below.
   Write each fraction as a decimal.

2. $\frac{5}{16}$ 3. $\frac{11}{40}$ 0.275

4. $\frac{4}{9}$ 0.$\overline{4}$ 5. $\frac{2}{15}$ 0.1$\overline{3}$

GO for Help
Lesson 2-6

Check Skills You'll Need

1. A repeating decimal is a decimal that repeats without end.

2. 0.3125

TEKS ★ TAKS

• (7.1)(B) To convert between fractions, decimals, whole numbers, and percents
   TAKS Obj. 1

• (7.1)(A) To compare and order integers and positive rational numbers
   TAKS Obj. 1

Why Learn This?

The food labels below all use a different form of $\frac{1}{2}$. Any rational number can be written as a fraction, a decimal, or a percent.

50% of the minimum daily amount

Same taste $\frac{1}{2}$ the sugar

This product has 0.5g of fat.

KEY CONCEPTS **Fractions, Decimals, and Percents**

The model at the right shows 21 out of 100 squares shaded. You can write the shaded part of the model as a fraction, a decimal, or a percent.

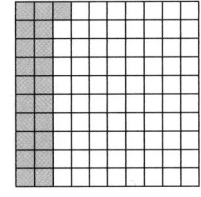

Fraction	Decimal	Percent
$\frac{21}{100}$	0.21	21%

 Tip

When you multiply a decimal by 100, the decimal point moves 2 places to the right.

To write a decimal as a percent, you can multiply the decimal by 100.

EXAMPLE **Writing Decimals as Percents**

1 Write 0.759 as a percent.

$0.759 = \frac{759}{1,000}$ ← Write as a fraction.

$= \frac{75.9}{100}$ ← Write an equivalent fraction with 100 in the denominator.

$= 75.9\%$ ← Write as a percent.

✓ **Quick Check**

1. Write 0.607 as a percent. 60.7%

TEKS ★ TAKS

(7.1)(B) To convert between fractions, decimals, whole numbers, and percents
   TAKS Obj. 1
(7.1)(A) To compare and order integers and positive rational numbers
   TAKS Obj. 1

Dana Center TEKS Toolkit Clarifying Activities (7.1)(B), (7.1)(A)
Visit: PHSchool.com
Web Code: arq-9045

Professional Development

TEKS Math Background

You can convert between decimals, fractions, and percent by using the definition of percent as a quantity over 100. For instance, 0.5 is $\frac{5}{10}$, which is the same as $\frac{50}{100}$ or 50%. A decimal can easily be changed to a percent by multiplying by 100, or by moving the decimal point two places to the right and using the % symbol.

More Math Background: p. 272C

Lesson Planning and Resources

See p. 272E for a list of the resources that support this lesson.

PowerPoint
Bell Ringer Practice

✓ **Check Skills You'll Need**
Use student page, transparency, or PowerPoint.

TAKS **Daily Review 42**
Use transparency.

Differentiated Instruction Solutions for All Learners

Special Needs L1
Make sure students understand that moving the decimal point two places to the right is the same as multiplying by 100. Underline the two 0's in 100, and underline the two decimal places so they see the connection.

learning style: visual

Below Level L2
Have students complete a table such as the one below.

Fraction	$\frac{1}{10}$	$\frac{1}{5}$	$\frac{1}{4}$	$\frac{3}{4}$
Decimal	0.1	0.2	0.25	0.75
Percent	10%	20%	25%	75%

learning style: visual

2. Teach

Activity Lab

Use before the lesson.
Student Edition Activity Lab,
Hands On 6-2a, Rational Number
Cubes, p. 278

All in One Teaching Resources
Activity Lab 6-2: Critical Thinking

Guided Instruction

Error Prevention!

In Quick Check 2, make sure
students do not keep the percent
sign when they convert percents
to decimals.

Example 4

If students have difficulty finding
the GCF (Greatest Common
Factor), have them factor the
numerator and use those factors
to rewrite 100 as shown below:

$$\frac{15}{100} = \frac{5 \cdot 3}{5 \cdot 20} = \frac{3}{20}$$

Example 5

To help students remember which
way to move the decimal point,
tell them this story. When the
percent symbol (%) is written to
the right of a number, the decimal
point moves two places to be
closer to the symbol. When the
symbol is removed, the decimal
point "goes back home" two
places to the left.

Online active math

For: Rational Number
Activity
Use: Interactive
Textbook, 6-2

To write a percent as a decimal, you can divide it by 100, or move the
decimal point two places to the left.

EXAMPLE **Writing Percents as Decimals**

2 Write 47.5% as a decimal.

$$47.5\% = \frac{47.5}{100} \quad \leftarrow \text{Write the percent as a fraction.}$$
$$= 0.475 \quad \leftarrow \text{Divide.}$$

✓ Quick Check

2. Write each percent as a decimal.
   a. 35% 0.35   **b.** 12.5% 0.125   **c.** 7.8% 0.078

When the denominator of a fraction is a factor of 100, you can easily use
equivalent ratios to convert the fraction to a percent. For fractions with
other denominators, you can use a calculator to convert the fraction into
a decimal, and then rewrite the decimal as a percent.

EXAMPLE **Writing Fractions as Percents**

3 **Nutrition** In a slice of cheese pizza, 45 Calories are from fat. The total
number of Calories in each slice is 158. About what percent of the
Calories are *not* from fat? Round to the nearest tenth of a percent.

Step 1 Find the number of Calories that are not from fat.

$$158 - 45 = 113$$

Step 2 Estimate.
$$\frac{113}{158} \approx \frac{120}{160}, \text{ which is } \frac{3}{4}, \text{ or } 75\%.$$

Step 3 Write the ratio.

$$\frac{113}{158} \quad \begin{array}{l} \leftarrow \text{Calories from fat} \\ \leftarrow \text{total Calories} \end{array}$$

$$113 \div 158 = 0.71518987 \quad \leftarrow \text{Use a calculator.}$$
$$= 71.518987\% \quad \leftarrow \text{Write as a percent.}$$
$$\approx 71.5\% \quad \leftarrow \text{Round to the nearest tenth of a percent.}$$

About 71.5% of the Calories are not from fat.

Check for Reasonableness Since 71.5% is close to the estimate 75%,
the answer is reasonable.

✓ Quick Check

3. Write $\frac{21}{40}$ as a percent. Round to the nearest tenth of a percent. 52.5%

Advanced Learners **L4**
You go to a restaurant with $8.73. You want to have
enough money to give your waitress a 15% tip for
your lunch. What is the most money you can spend on
the meal? **$7.59**

Pre-AP™

English Language Learners **ELL**
Ask: *What happens to the decimal point when you
multiply or divide a decimal by 100?* **Answers may
vary.** Have students work with a partner to explain
and test their ideas. They will be less prone to errors if
they understand the movement of the decimal point.

learning style: verbal

You can write a percent as a fraction. First write the percent as a fraction with a denominator of 100. Then simplify the fraction.

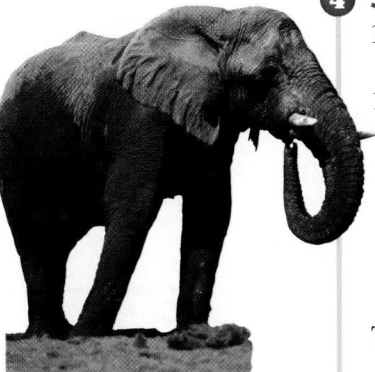

EXAMPLE **Writing Percents as Fractions**

4 **Science** Behavioral scientists observed an elephant that slept about 12.5% of each day. What fraction of each day did the elephant sleep?

$$12.5\% = \frac{12.5}{100}$$ ← **Write 12.5% as a fraction with a denominator of 100.**

$$= \frac{12.5 \times 10}{100 \times 10}$$ ← **Multiply the numerator and denominator by 10.**

$$= \frac{125 \div 125}{1,000 \div 125}$$ ← **Divide both numerator and denominator by the GCF, 125.**

$$= \frac{1}{8}$$ ← **Simplify the fraction.**

The elephant slept about $\frac{1}{8}$ of each day.

✓ **Quick Check**

4. An elephant eats about 6% of its body weight in vegetation each day. Write this as a fraction in simplest form. $\frac{3}{50}$

To compare rational numbers in different forms, you can write all the numbers in the same form. Then graph each number on a number line.

EXAMPLE **Ordering Rational Numbers**

5 Order 0.52, 37%, 0.19, and $\frac{1}{4}$ from least to greatest.

Write all the numbers as decimals. Then graph them.

0.52 ← **This number is already in decimal form.**

$37\% = 0.37$ ← **Move the decimal point two places to the left.**

0.19 ← **This number is already in decimal form.**

$\frac{1}{4} = 0.25$ ← **Divide the numerator by the denominator.**

```
           0.19  1/4      37%    0.52
    ─┼───┼───┼───┼───┼───┼───┼───┼───┼───┼─
     0  0.1 0.2 0.3 0.4 0.5 0.6 0.7 0.8 0.9  1
```

From least to greatest, the numbers are 0.19, $\frac{1}{4}$, 37%, and 0.52.

✓ **Quick Check**

5. Order from least to greatest.

a. $\frac{3}{10}$, 0.74, 29%, $\frac{11}{25}$
   29%, $\frac{3}{10}$, $\frac{11}{25}$, 0.74

b. 15%, $\frac{7}{20}$, 0.08, 50%
   0.08, 15%, $\frac{7}{20}$, 50%

GO for Help

For help converting a fraction to a decimal, go to Lesson 2-6.

Assignment Guide

Check Your Understanding
Go over Exercises 1–4 in class before assigning the Homework Exercises.

Homework Exercises

A Practice by Example   5–29
B Apply Your Skills   30–35
C Challenge   36

TEKS ★ **TAKS** Tune-Up
and Mixed Review   37–41

Homework Quick Check
To check students' understanding of key skills and concepts, go over Exercises 12, 21, 31, 34, and 35.

Differentiated Instruction **Resources**

Check Your Understanding

1. Write the shaded part of the model at the left as a percent, a fraction, and a decimal. 62%, $\frac{62}{100}$, 0.62

2. In each set, find the number that does *not* equal the other two.
   a. 9.9%, $\frac{99}{100}$, 0.99   **b.** 64%, $\frac{16}{50}$, 0.64 $\frac{16}{50}$ **c.** 12%, $\frac{3}{25}$, 1.2 **1.2**
   9.9%

3. **Mental Math** Order 0.54, 55%, and $\frac{1}{2}$ from least to greatest. **See left.**

3. $\frac{1}{2}$, 0.54, 55%

4. **Reasoning** When you write a percent as a decimal, why do you move the decimal point 2 units to the left? **You are dividing by 100.**

Homework Exercises

For more exercises, see Extra Skills and Word Problems.

GO for Help

For Exercises	See Examples
5–9	1
10–14	2
15–20	3
21–26	4
27–29	5

(A) Write each decimal as a percent.

5. 0.57   6. 0.375   7. 0.09   8. 0.155   9. 0.6
   57%   37.5%   9%   15.5%   60%

Write each percent as a decimal.

10. 32%   11. 88%   12. 19.1%   13. 3%   14. 1.25%
    0.32   0.88   0.191   0.03   0.0125

Write each fraction as a percent to the nearest tenth of a percent.

15. $\frac{45}{50}$ 90%   16. $\frac{7}{8}$ 87.5%   17. $\frac{1}{12}$ 8.3%   18. $\frac{5}{6}$ 83.3%   19. $\frac{3}{11}$
                                                                                                  27.3%

20. Out of 49 fish, 31 are goldfish. About what percent are goldfish?
    about 63%

Write each percent as a fraction in simplest form.

21. 15% $\frac{3}{20}$ 22. 6% $\frac{3}{50}$ 23. 20% $\frac{1}{5}$ 24. 37.5% $\frac{3}{8}$ 25. 17%
                                                                                               $\frac{17}{100}$

26. **Computers** A computer screen shows the print on a page at 78% of its actual size. Write 78% as a fraction in simplest form. $\frac{39}{50}$

Order from least to greatest.

27. $\frac{1}{2}$, 12%, 0.25   28. 68%, 0.37, $\frac{3}{10}$ 29. 0.81, $\frac{4}{5}$, 90%
    12%, 0.25, $\frac{1}{2}$ $\frac{3}{10}$, 0.37, 68% $\frac{4}{5}$, 0.81, 90%

B GPS 30. **Guided Problem Solving** In your class, 9 of the 26 students are in the chorus. What percent of your class is in the chorus? Round to the nearest tenth of a percent. **34.6%**
   • What ratio can help to find the percent of students in the chorus?
   • Should you multiply or divide by 100 to find the percent?

31. No, 0.4% is equal to 0.004 as a decimal.

31. **Writing in Math** Does 0.4 equal 0.4%? Explain. **See left.**

32. Compare 0.32 and 3.2%. Use <, =, or >. **0.32 > 3.2%**

33. See back of book.

33. Math in the Media Use the cartoon below to complete the table.

Topping	With Olives	Plain	With Onions and Green Peppers
Percent of the Pizza	■	■	■
Number of Slices	■	■	■

See margin.

34. Nutrition The tables at the left give data on two different foods. A gram of fat has 9 Calories. A gram of carbohydrates and a gram of protein both have 4 Calories. What percent of the Calories in each food are from carbohydrates? Round to the nearest percent.
macaroni and cheese, 30%; spaghetti and meat sauce, 46%

35. Your teacher uses different methods of grading quizzes. Your quiz
GPS grades are 85%, $\frac{9}{10}$, $\frac{16}{20}$, 92%, $\frac{21}{25}$, and 79%. 79%, $\frac{16}{20}$, $\frac{21}{25}$, 85%, $\frac{9}{10}$, 92%
a. Write your quiz grades in order from least to greatest.
b. Find the average percent grade of your quizzes. 85%

36. Challenge Write 3.75% as a fraction in simplest form. $\frac{3}{80}$
C

Macaroni & Cheese

Nutrition	
Fat	33 g
Carbohydrates	40 g
Protein	17 g

Spaghetti & Meat Sauce

Nutrition	
Fat	12 g
Carbohydrates	39 g
Protein	19 g

TEKS ★ TAKS Tune-Up and Mixed Review

TAKS **Objective 2**
TEKS (7.5)(B)

37. Nathan runs m miles each weekday and $3\frac{1}{4}$ times farther on Saturday. He runs $6\frac{1}{2}$ miles on Saturday. Which equation can be used to find the number of miles Nathan runs each weekday? **A**

Ⓐ $3\frac{1}{4}m = 6\frac{1}{2}$ Ⓒ $m + 3\frac{1}{4} = 6\frac{1}{2}$

Ⓑ $6\frac{1}{2}m = 3\frac{1}{4}$ Ⓓ $m \div 3\frac{1}{4} = 6\frac{1}{2}$

TAKS **Objective 2**
TEKS (7.3)(B)

38. The prices of 3 different bags of onions are given in the table below. Which size bag has the lowest price per pound? **H**

Bag (lb)	Price
5	$3.49
10	$6.70
15	$10.33

Ⓕ The 5-lb bag only
Ⓖ The 5-lb bag and the 15-lb bag
Ⓗ The 10-lb bag only
Ⓙ The 15-lb bag only

GO for Help **Lesson 4-9** Solve each inequality.

39. $6.3 \geq -7x$ **40.** $-12 < \frac{m}{2}$ $-24 < m$ **41.** $-10.2 \leq -0.2y$
$-0.9 \leq x$ $51 \geq y$

TEKS ★ TAKS Resources

• TAKS Strategies, p. 315
• TAKS Tune-Up, pp. 319–321

TAKS Tune-Up Kit

• TAKS Daily Review Transparencies
• TAKS Review and Preparation Workbook
• TAKS Strategies with Transparencies
• Texas Progress Monitoring Assessments

4. Assess & Reteach

PowerPoint

Lesson Quiz

Write in order from least to greatest.

1. 30%, 0.24, $\frac{2}{5}$ 0.24, 30%, $\frac{2}{5}$

2. 0.9, $\frac{7}{8}$, 9% 9%, $\frac{7}{8}$, 0.9

3. $\frac{1}{4}$, 40%, 0.35 $\frac{1}{4}$, 0.35, 40%

4. $\frac{7}{10}$, 0.77, 7% 7%, $\frac{7}{10}$, 0.77

Alternative Assessment

Each student in a pair writes one decimal, one fraction, and one percent. Partners exchange papers and write the partner's decimals and fractions as percents. Students write percents as decimals and each other's fractions in simplest form. Then partners work together to arrange the six original fractions, decimals, and percents in order from least to greatest.

283

TEKS ★ TAKS

(7.1)(B) To convert between factions, decimals, whole numbers, and percents
TAKS Obj. 1

(7.3)(A) To estimate and find solutions to application problems involving percent
TAKS Obj. 2

Dana Center TEKS Toolkit Clarifying Activities (7.1)(B), (7.3)(A)
Visit: PHSchool.com
Web Code: arq-9045

TEKS Math Background

A percent can be greater than 100% or less than 1%. Percents greater than 100% convert to mixed numbers. Percents less 1% convert to fractions less than $\frac{1}{100}$.

$150\% \rightarrow \frac{150}{100} \rightarrow 1\frac{1}{2}$

$0.15\% \rightarrow \frac{15}{10,000} \rightarrow \frac{3}{2,000}$

To convert a mixed number to a percent, first write it as a decimal.

More Math Background: p. 272C

Lesson Planning and Resources

See p. 272E for a list of the resources that support this lesson.

Bell Ringer Practice

☑️ **Check Skills You'll Need**
Use student page, transparency, or PowerPoint.

TAKS Daily Review 43
Use transparency.

6-3 Percents Greater Than 100% or Less Than 1%

☑️ **Check Skills You'll Need**

1. Vocabulary Review
A *percent* is a ratio that compares a number to __?__ .100

Write each ratio as a percent.

2. $\frac{1}{100}$ 1%   3. $\frac{49}{50}$ 98%

4. $\frac{19}{20}$ 95%   5. $\frac{2}{25}$ 8%

GO for Help
Lesson 6-1

TEKS ★ TAKS
• (7.1)(B) To convert between fractions, decimals, whole numbers, and percents
TAKS Obj. 1
• (7.3)(A) To estimate and find solutions to application problems involving percent
TAKS Obj. 2

Why Learn This?

You can get 110% of one day's Recommended Dietary Allowance of vitamin C by eating one half of a grapefruit.

In a percent, if the number compared to 100 is greater than 100, the percent is greater than 100%. If the number compared to 100 is less than 1, the percent is less than 1%.

You can rewrite these percents as decimals or fractions.

EXAMPLES   Rewriting Percents

1 Write 110% as a decimal and as a fraction.

$110\% = 1.10$ ← **Move the decimal point two places to the left.**

$110\% = \frac{110}{100} = \frac{11}{10} = 1\frac{1}{10}$ ← **Use the definition of percent. Simplify the fraction.**

110% equals 1.10 in decimal form and $1\frac{1}{10}$ in fraction form.

2 Write 0.7% as a decimal and as a fraction in simplest form.

$0.7\% = 0.007$ ← **Move the decimal point two places to the left.**

$0.7\% = \frac{0.7}{100}$ ← **Use the definition of percent.**

$= \frac{0.7 \cdot 10}{100 \cdot 10} = \frac{7}{1,000}$ ← **Multiply numerator and denominator by 10 to get a whole number numerator. Simplify.**

0.7% equals 0.007 in decimal form and $\frac{7}{1,000}$ in fraction form.

☑️ Quick Check

1. Write 125% as a decimal and as a fraction.   1.25; $\frac{5}{4}$ or $1\frac{1}{4}$

2. Write 0.35% as a decimal and as a fraction in simplest form. 0.0035; $\frac{7}{2,000}$

284   Chapter 6   Percents

Differentiated Instruction   Solutions for All Learners

Special Needs L1
Give students a 100-grid and ask them to color in 120% of the whole grid. As they run out of room, ask them whether they need another grid. Show them that 120% is one whole and 20% of another whole.

learning style: visual

Below Level L2
To change percents less than 1 into fractions, review place values with students. "Count off" the decimal places (*tenths, hundredths, thousandths*) and write the correct number as the denominator.

learning style: verbal

A mixed number represents a percent greater than 100%.

EXAMPLE **Writing Mixed Numbers as Percents**

③ **Entertainment** A movie ticket costs $1\frac{7}{8}$ times as much as renting a video. Write this mixed number as a percent.

$$1\frac{7}{8} = 1 \; \boxed{+} \; 7 \; \boxed{\div} \; 8 \; \boxed{=} \; 1.875 \quad \leftarrow \text{Use a calculator.}$$
$$= 1.87.5 = 187.5\% \quad \leftarrow \begin{array}{l}\text{Move the decimal point two}\\ \text{places to the right.}\end{array}$$

A movie ticket costs 187.5% of the cost of renting a video.

✓ Quick Check

3. You plan to run $2\frac{4}{5}$ times the distance you ran yesterday. Write this number as a percent. **280%**

A proper fraction represents a percent less than 100%.

EXAMPLE **Application: Government**

A fraction less than $\frac{1}{100}$ represents a percent less than 1%. You can use percents less than 1% to describe small numbers.

④ **⊙** **Multiple Choice** West Virginia has 3 members in the U.S. House of Representatives. There are 432 other representatives who are not from West Virginia. What percent of the representatives are from West Virginia?

  Ⓐ 70%   Ⓑ 7%   Ⓒ 0.7%   Ⓓ 0.007%

The total number of representatives is $432 + 3$, or 435.

Estimate Round 435 to 400. 4 is close to 3. Then $\frac{4}{400} = 0.01$, or 1%.

$$\frac{\text{West Virginia representatives}}{\text{total number of representatives}} = \frac{3}{435} \quad \leftarrow \textbf{Write the fraction.}$$
$$= 0.0068965517 \quad \leftarrow \textbf{Use a calculator.}$$
$$\approx 0.7\% \quad \leftarrow \textbf{Write as a percent and round.}$$

About 0.7% of the representatives are from West Virginia. The correct answer is choice C.

Check for Reasonableness Since 0.7% is close to the estimate 1%, the answer is reasonable.

✓ Quick Check

4. Idaho has 2 members in the U.S. House of Representatives. What percent of the representatives are from Idaho? Round to the nearest hundredth of a percent. **0.46%**

Advanced Learners L4
Change each to a decimal. Place in order from least to greatest. If necessary, round to the nearest hundredth.
$\frac{7}{400}$ 0.0175   0.08%   0.0008 $2\frac{3}{5}$ 2.60   6.2%   0.062
0.0008, 0.0175, 0.062, 2.60

English Language Learners ELL
To clarify the explanations for percents greater and less than one, make sure that students understand that 100% can be thought of as one whole. Percents greater or less than 100% are greater or less than one whole.

(Pre-AP™)

learning style: verbal

Activity Lab
Use before the lesson.

All in One Teaching Resources
Activity Lab 6-3: Percents Greater than 100 or Less than 1

Guided Instruction

Example 1
Provide students with two 10 × 10 grids to model percents greater than 100. One grid will become completely shaded and the part greater than 100 will be shaded in the second grid.

Example 2
Remind students that they can write zeros to the right of decimals without changing the value of the decimals. Encourage students to insert these zeros before moving the decimal point.

PowerPoint
Additional Examples

Write each percent as a decimal and a fraction in simplest form.

① 140% 1.40; $1\frac{2}{5}$

② 0.75% 0.0075; $\frac{3}{400}$

Write each fraction or decimal as a percent. Round to the nearest hundredth of a percent.

③ a. $4\frac{2}{3}$ 466.67%
    b. 2.557 255.7%

④ a. $\frac{1}{325}$ 0.31%   b. $\frac{6}{875}$ 0.69%

All in One Teaching Resources
• Daily Notetaking Guide 6-3 L3
• Adapted Notetaking 6-3 L1

Closure

• *How do you write a percent greater than 100 as a mixed number?* Sample: Rewrite the percent as a fraction with denominator of 100, simplify, and write the improper fraction as a mixed number.

• *How do you write a percent greater than 100 or less than 1 as a decimal?* Move the decimal point two places to the left.

Assignment Guide

Check Your Understanding
Go over Exercises 1–7 in class before assigning the Homework Exercises.

Homework Exercises
A Practice by Example   8–32
B Apply Your Skills   33–49
C Challenge   50
TEKS ★ *TAKS* Tune-Up
   and Mixed Review   51–56

Homework Quick Check
To check students' understanding of key skills and concepts, go over Exercises 15, 28, 40, 43, and 46.

Differentiated Instruction **Resources**

✓ Check Your Understanding

Write each percent as a decimal and as a fraction in simplest form.

1. 150%   1.5; $\frac{3}{2}$ or $1\frac{1}{2}$

2. 0.2%   0.002; $\frac{1}{500}$

Write each decimal or fraction as a percent.

3. 8.25   825%

4. $\frac{1}{160}$ 0.625%

5. **Mental Math** Write 400% as a whole number.   4

6. **Number Sense** Compare the numerator and denominator of a fraction that is greater than 100%.   The numerator is greater than the denominator.

7. How can you decide whether a decimal is less than 1%? More than 100%? Give an example for each case.   See left.

7. Answers may vary. Sample: A decimal that is less than 1% has zeros in the tenths and hundredths place, such as 0.009. A decimal that is greater than 100% has a number other than zero before the decimal point, such as 1.01.

Homework Exercises

For more exercises, see Extra Skills and Word Problems.

 GO for Help

For Exercises	See Examples
8–13	1
14–19	2
20–32	3–4

8. 1.8; $1\frac{4}{5}$

9. 1.3; $1\frac{3}{10}$

10. 1.75; $1\frac{3}{4}$

11. 3.45; $3\frac{9}{20}$

12. 2.4; $2\frac{2}{5}$

13. 4.52; $4\frac{13}{25}$

14. 0.001; $\frac{1}{1,000}$

15. 0.0075; $\frac{3}{400}$

A **Write each percent as a decimal and as a fraction in simplest form.**
8–15. See left.

8. 180%   **9.** 130%   **10.** 175%   **11.** 345%

12. 240%   **13.** 452%   **14.** 0.1%   **15.** 0.75%

16. 0.09%   **17.** 0.16%   **18.** 0.5%   **19.** 0.05%

0.0009; $\frac{9}{10,000}$ 0.0016; $\frac{1}{625}$ 0.005; $\frac{1}{200}$ 0.0005; $\frac{1}{2,000}$

Write each number as a percent to the nearest hundredth of a percent.

20. $4\frac{3}{4}$ 475%   **21.** $1\frac{3}{5}$ 160%   **22.** $1\frac{1}{100}$ 101%   **23.** $2\frac{29}{50}$ 258%

24. $3\frac{7}{20}$ 335%   **25.** $2\frac{3}{8}$ 237.5%   **26.** $\frac{5}{684}$ 0.73%   **27.** $\frac{2}{329}$ 0.61%

28. $\frac{7}{1,000}$ 0.7%   **29.** $\frac{1}{400}$ 0.25%   **30.** $\frac{3}{500}$ 0.6%   **31.** $\frac{7}{998}$ 0.70%

32. **Social Studies** About 4 of every 804 people in the world are citizens of Canada. Write this number as a percent. Round to the nearest hundredth of a percent.   0.50%

B **GPS** **33.** **Guided Problem Solving** Interlibrary loans of reference books have increased to $1\frac{9}{10}$ of what they were 15 years ago. If a library loaned 100 books 15 years ago, how many would it loan today?
   • What is $1\frac{9}{10}$, written as a decimal?   190 books
   • How do you write a decimal as a percent?

34. **Geography** The world's total land area is about 57.9 million square miles. Luxembourg has an area of 999 square miles. What percent of the world's total land area does Luxembourg occupy?
   0.00001725%

286   Chapter 6   Percents

41–44. See back of book.

Write each mixed number as a percent.   1,001%   1,015%

35. $2\frac{7}{10}$ 270%   **36.** $5\frac{6}{100}$ 506%   **37.** $10\frac{1}{100}$ **38.** $10\frac{3}{20}$

Write each percent as a decimal and as a fraction in simplest form.

39. Jewelry sales in December were 166% of sales in November. 1.66; $1\frac{33}{50}$

40. **Weather** On March 1, the snowpack in the Northern Great Basin
GPS of Nevada was 126% of the average snowpack. 1.26; $1\frac{13}{50}$

Model each percent using one or more 10 × 10 grids.   41–44. See margin.

41. 175%   **42.** 120%   **43.** 200%   **44.** 0.5%

45. **Science** The number of known living species is about 1.7 million. About 4,500 species are mammals. What percent of known living species are mammals? Round to the nearest hundredth of a percent.   0.26%

46. **Writing in Math** What does it mean to reach 120% of a savings goal? Answers may vary. Sample: Your actual savings were 1.2 times your goal.

Decide whether each percent is reasonable. Explain why or why not.

47. Buttermilk is 105% milk fat. No; it cannot be more than 100% fat.

48. Rainfall in Oregon this year is reported to be 160% of the average. Yes; the rainfall can be 1.6 times the average.

49. A scientific study concluded that 0.5% of the seeds will not grow. Yes; it is reasonable that $\frac{1}{2}$ of 1% of the seeds will not grow.

C **50.** **Challenge** Recently, a near-mint copy of the Baltimore Orioles 1966 Yearbook was auctioned for $15. The yearbook cost $.50 in 1966. Write a ratio of the auction price to the original price. Find the percent. $\frac{15}{0.5}$, or $\frac{150}{5}$, or 30; **3,000%**

The male platypus has a poisonous spur to use against attackers.

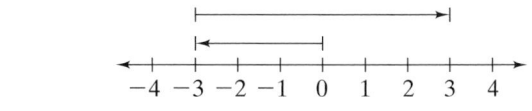
TEKS ★ TAKS Tune-Up and Mixed Review

TAKS Objective 1
TEKS (7.1)(B)

51. The arctic and antarctic icecaps and glaciers make up about 2.3% of the world's water. Which fraction equals 2.3%? **C**

Ⓐ $\frac{23}{100}$ Ⓑ $\frac{1}{5}$ Ⓒ $\frac{23}{1,000}$ Ⓓ $\frac{23}{10,000}$

TAKS Objective 1
TEKS (7.2)(C)

52. Which expression is represented by the model below? **F**

$$-4\ -3\ -2\ -1\ \ 0\ \ 1\ \ 2\ \ 3\ \ 4$$

Ⓕ $-3+6$ Ⓖ $-3+3$ Ⓗ $6-3$ Ⓙ $3+3$

GO for Help   **Lesson 6-2**

Write each percent as a fraction in simplest form.

53. 28% $\frac{7}{25}$ **54.** 37.5% $\frac{3}{8}$ **55.** 80% $\frac{4}{5}$ **56.** 74% $\frac{37}{50}$

---

4. Assess & Reteach

PowerPoint
Lesson Quiz

Write each as a decimal and a fraction or mixed number in simplest form.

1. 112% 1.12; $1\frac{3}{25}$

2. 0.8% 0.008; $\frac{1}{125}$

Write each as a percent.

3. $3\frac{1}{2}$ 350%

4. 0.0045 0.45%

Reteaching 6-3   Percents Greater Than 100% or Less **L2**

You can express a percent that is less than 1% or greater than 100% as a decimal or as a fraction. A percent that is less than 1% is a quantity that is less than $\frac{1}{100}$. A percent that is greater than 100% is a quantity that is greater than 1.

- Write 0.5% as a decimal and as a fraction.

  Move the decimal point two places to the left to write a percent as a decimal. Add zeros as needed.   00.5% = 0.005

  Since percent means per 100, you can write the percent as a fraction with a denominator of 100.   0.5% = $\frac{0.5}{100}$

  Then rewrite the numerator as a whole number. Since 10 × 0.5 = 5, multiply the numerator and denominator by 10. Then simplify. $\frac{0.5}{100} = \frac{0.5 \times 10}{100 \times 10} = \frac{5}{1,000} = \frac{1}{200}$

  So, 0.5% = 0.005 = $\frac{1}{200}$

- Write 125% as a decimal and as a fraction.

  Move the decimal point two places to the left to write a percent as a decimal. Add zeros as needed.   125% = 1.25

  Since percent means per 100, you can write the percent as a fraction with a denominator of 100.   125% = $\frac{125}{100}$

  Then simplify. $\frac{125}{100} = \frac{125 \div 25}{100 \div 25} = \frac{5}{4} = 1\frac{1}{4}$

  So, 125% = 1.25 = $1\frac{1}{4}$

Write each percent as a fraction in simplest form and as a decimal.

1. 0.01% $\frac{1}{10,000}$; 0.0001
2. 0.45% $\frac{9}{2,000}$; 0.0045
3. 0.2% $\frac{1}{500}$; 0.002
4. 0.67% $\frac{67}{10,000}$; 0.0067
5. 150% $\frac{3}{2} = 1\frac{1}{2}$; 1.5
6. 225% $\frac{9}{4} = 2\frac{1}{4}$; 2.25
7. 186% $\frac{93}{50} = 1\frac{43}{50}$; 1.86
8. 201% $\frac{201}{100} = 2\frac{1}{100}$; 2.01

Enrichment 6-3   Percents Greater Than 100% or Less **L4**
Critical Thinking

Answer the questions with the information given.

A small percent of bats carries rabies—generally, about $\frac{1}{2}$%. In how large a group of bats would you expect to find exactly one bat carrying rabies? Explain how you found your answer.

1. What percent of bats carries rabies?   about $\frac{1}{2}$%
2. Write $\frac{1}{2}$% as a fraction. $\frac{0.5}{100}$
3. Write your fraction from Exercise 2 with a whole number in the numerator. $\frac{5}{1,000}$
4. Explain what your fraction means by giving the number of bats that may have rabies and the group size.   Sample answer: About 5 bats in a group of 1,000 bats have rabies.
5. Write a fraction with a numerator of 1 equivalent to the fraction you wrote in Exercise 3. $\frac{1}{200}$
6. About how large would you expect a group of bats to be if one bat carries rabies?   200 bats
7. Explain how you found your answer.   Sample answer: Write $\frac{1}{2}$% as a fraction. Then find an equivalent fraction with a numerator of 1.
8. Does your answer mean that every group of bats this size will have exactly one bat with rabies? Explain.   Sample answer: No, it is only an average. Some groups will have more than one rabid bats and others will have none.

Alternative Assessment

Each student in a pair writes two percents greater than 100 and two percents less than 1. Partners exchange papers and write each percent as a decimal and as a fraction. Then partners work together to arrange the eight original percents in order from least to greatest.

TEKS ★ TAKS Resources

- TAKS Strategies, p. 315
- TAKS Tune-Up, pp. 319–321

TAKS Tune-Up Kit

- TAKS Daily Review Transparencies
- TAKS Review and Preparation Workbook
- TAKS Strategies with Transparencies
- Texas Progress Monitoring Assessments

287

Use this Checkpoint Quiz to check students' understanding of the skills and concepts of Lessons 6-1 through 6-3.

Resources

- All-in-One Teaching Resources Checkpoint Quiz 1
- Texas ExamView CD-ROM
- Success Tracker™ Online Intervention

MATH GAMES

Order, Please!

In this game, students practice comparing and ordering fractions, decimals, and percents. Each player receives a number and the players must order themselves from least to greatest.

Guided Instruction

Before they play the game, remind students that they may need to convert their numbers to different forms in order to figure out the order.
Ask:
- *Is a mixed number greater than or less than a percent over 100%?* greater than
- *Is a decimal that is less than 1 greater than or less than a percent over 100%?* less than

Resources

- construction paper

288

 Checkpoint Quiz 1

Write each percent as a decimal and as a fraction in simplest form.

1. 45% 0.45; $\frac{9}{20}$

2. 135% 1.35; $1\frac{7}{20}$

3. 0.98% 0.0098; $\frac{49}{5,000}$

4. Write $\frac{14}{25}$ as a percent. 56%

5. Order 0.245, $\frac{1}{6}$, 20%, and $\frac{1}{4}$ from least to greatest. $\frac{1}{6}$, 20%, 0.245, $\frac{1}{4}$

6. Write a ratio and a percent for the shaded area below. $\frac{16}{25}$; 64%

7. Model 47% on a 10 × 10 grid.

8. One hour is what percent of one week? Round to the nearest tenth of a percent. about 0.6%

9. A club has 100 members. Five of the members are officers. Each officer gets six other members to help them decorate for a club party. What percent of the club members help decorate? 35%

10. You walked to school on 135 days out of 180 days. What percent of the days did you walk? Round to the nearest tenth of a percent. 75%

MATH GAMES

Order, Please!

What You'll Need

- 30 pieces of construction paper, each with a fraction, decimal, or a percent written on it. Include mixed numbers or the equivalent decimals and percents.

How To Play

- Select two teams of five players. Each player receives one piece of construction paper.
- When play begins, team members must order their numbers from the least to the greatest number.
- The first team to order their numbers correctly is the winner.

Using Percent Data in a Graph

TEKS ★ TAKS

(7.3)(A) To estimate and find solutions to application problems involving percent TAKS **Obj. 2**

(7.11)(B) To make inferences based on an analysis of given data TAKS **Obj. 5**

You can use percent data in a graph to interpret and understand the information that is shown.

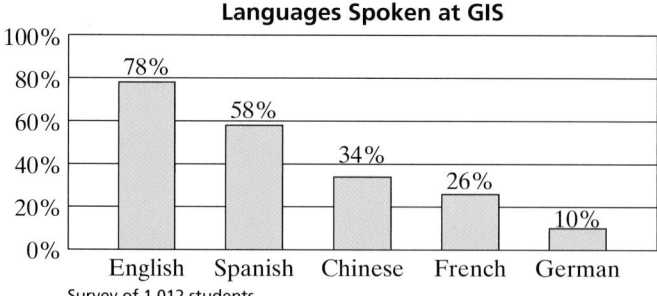

Languages Spoken at GIS

Survey of 1,012 students

The bar graph at the left shows which languages are spoken at Gould International School.

ACTIVITY

Work with a partner to analyze the graph and answer the following questions.

1. What language do most of the students speak?
   English
2. How many students were surveyed? **1,012 students**

3. Copy and complete the table at the right. Estimate the number of students who speak each language.
   See margin.
4. What language do about $\frac{1}{3}$ of the students speak?
   Chinese
5. What language do about $\frac{1}{4}$ of the students speak?
   French
6. Why do you think the sum of the percents is greater than 100%? **Answers may vary. Sample: Some students speak more than one language, so they were counted more than once.**

Language	Percent	Number of Students
English	78%	■
Spanish	■	■
Chinese	■	■
French	■	■
German	10%	~101

Exercises

Based on the graph above, tell whether each of the following statements is reasonable. Explain.

1. More than half of the students at Gould speak English or Spanish. **Yes; both 78% and 58% are greater than 50%.**

2. Everyone who speaks French also speaks German. **No; there are no data about which students speak both French and German.**

3. Exactly 20 students speak English but not Spanish. **No; there are more than 200 more students who speak English than Spanish.**

4. There could be a student at Gould International School who speaks all five languages shown in the bar graph. **Yes; the total is more than 100%, so some students speak more than one language.**

3. See back of book.

Activity Lab

Using Percent Data in a Graph

Students analyze data in a graph that is in the form of percents. This will prepare them to compare percents in Lesson 6-4.

Guided Instruction

Before beginning the Activity, review the information in the graph. You may wish to draw the graph on the board. Ask:
- *What does having the longest bar mean for that language?* **Most students speak that language.**
- *Do the percents on the bars add to more than 100%?* **yes**
- *Why is that?* **Some students speak more than one language.**
- *What important pieces of information does the graph tell us?* **number of students at the school, percent of total students that speak each language**

Activity

Have students work together to answer the questions. Circulate and check students' work. Discuss the Exercises as a class explaining why the statements are reasonable or unreasonable.

Alternative Method

Students may be more comfortable with another kind of graph. Provide them with a circle graph, pictogram, or other visual data display.

TEKS ★ TAKS Resources

- Activity Lab 6-4: Decision Making

Dana Center TEKS Toolkit Clarifying Activities (7.3)(A), (7.11)(B)
Visit: PHSchool.com
Web Code: arq-9045

TEKS ★ TAKS

(7.3)(A) To estimate and find solutions to problems involving percent TAKS Obj. 2

Also supports
(7.1)(B) TAKS Obj. 1
(7.13)(D)

Dana Center TEKS Toolkit Clarifying Activities (7.3)(A), (7.1)(B), (7.13)(D)
Visit: PHSchool.com
Web Code: arq-9045

TEKS Math Background

To find a percent of a number, simply multiply the number by the decimal or fraction equivalent of the percent. In word problems, it is helpful to know that the word *of* indicates multiplication.

More Math Background: p. 272C

Lesson Planning and Resources

See p. 272E for a list of the resources that support this lesson.

PowerPoint
 Bell Ringer Practice

☑ **Check Skills You'll Need**
Use student page, transparency, or PowerPoint.

TAKS Daily Review 44
Use transparency.

290

6-4 Finding a Percent of a Number

 Check Skills You'll Need

1. Vocabulary Review
The *Distributive Property* combines the operation of _?_ with addition or subtraction.
multiplication
Find each product using the Distributive Property and mental math.

2. 80 · 15 **1,200**

3. 75 · 18 **1,350**

4. 78 · 0.9 **70.2**

5. 27 · 1.1 **29.7**

GO for Help
Lesson 1-9

TEKS ★ TAKS

- (7.3)(A) To estimate and find solutions to problems involving percent TAKS Obj. 2
- (7.1)(B) To convert between fractions, decimals, whole numbers, and percents TAKS Obj. 1
- (7.13)(D) To select techniques such as mental math and estimation to solve problems

Why Learn This?

You can use a percent of a number to help you analyze statistics, such as how many students in each grade participate in school activities.

Suppose your choir has 44 students, and 25% of the students are in eighth grade. Then 25% of 44 is the number of eighth-graders in the choir.

To find 25% of 44, you can write 25% as a decimal or as a fraction, and then multiply by 44.

EXAMPLE Finding Percent of a Number

GO for Help
For help in writing a percent as a decimal, go to Lesson 6-2, Example 2.

1 Find 25% of 44.

Method 1 Write the percent as a decimal.

$$25\% = 0.25$$ ← Change 25% to an equivalent form. →

$$0.25 \cdot 44 = 11$$ ← Multiply. →

25% of 44 is 11.

Method 2 Write the percent as a fraction.

$$25\% = \frac{1}{4}$$

$$\frac{1}{4} \cdot 44 = 11$$

☑ **Quick Check**

1. Find 75% of 140. **105**

Differentiated Instruction Solutions for All Learners

Special Needs L1
In Example 3, check for students who might write $\frac{3}{2}$ or $\frac{2}{3}$ for 32%. To help them, provide a list of commonly used benchmark fraction, percent, and decimal equivalencies.

learning style: visual

Below Level L2
Have students practice basic percents for mental math.

10% of 65 **6.5**   50% of 22 **11**
10% of 349 **34.9**   50% of 640 **320**
10% of 784 **78.4**   50% of 584 **292**

learning style: visual

You can use mental math with some percents.

- 100% of a number is the number itself. 100% of 190 is 190.
- 50% of a number is $\frac{1}{2}$ of the number. 50% of 190 is 95.
- 10% of a number is 0.1 of the number. 10% of 190 is 19.
- 1% of a number is 0.01 of the number. 1% of 190 is 1.9.

EXAMPLE **Using Mental Math**

② Find 11% of 840.

What You Think

11% = 10% + 1%.

10% of 840 is 0.1 · 840, or 84.

1% of 840 is 0.01 · 840, or 8.4.

So 84 + 8.4 = 92.4.

Why It Works

$$11\% \text{ of } 840 = 0.11 \cdot 840 \quad \leftarrow \textbf{Write 11\% as a decimal.}$$
$$= (0.10 + 0.01) \cdot 840 \quad \leftarrow \textbf{Substitute 0.10 + 0.01 for 0.11.}$$
$$= (0.10 \cdot 840) + (0.01 \cdot 840) \quad \leftarrow \textbf{Use the Distributive Property.}$$
$$= 84 + 8.4 \quad \leftarrow \textbf{Multiply.}$$
$$= 92.4 \quad \leftarrow \textbf{Add.}$$

✓ Quick Check

2. Use mental math to find 40% of 2,400. **960**

For help with estimating using compatible numbers, go to Lesson 1-1, Example 3.

You can use compatible numbers to estimate a percent.

EXAMPLE **Estimating a Percent**

③ **Elections** The candidate you voted for received 32% of the votes in an election. If 912 votes were counted, about how many votes did your candidate receive?

$$32\% \cdot 912 \quad \leftarrow \textbf{Write an expression.}$$
$$\downarrow \qquad \downarrow$$
$$\frac{1}{3} \cdot 900 = 300 \quad \leftarrow \textbf{Use compatible numbers such as } \frac{1}{3} \textbf{ and 900.}$$

Your candidate received about 300 votes.

✓ Quick Check

3. Estimate each answer.
   a. 24% of 238 **about 60** b. 19% of 473 **about 100** c. 82% of 747 **about 600**

6-4 Finding a Percent of a Number **291**

2. Teach

Activity Lab

Use before the lesson.
Student Edition Activity Lab, Data Analysis 6-4a, Using Percent Data in a Graph, p. 289

All in One Teaching Resources
Activity Lab 6-4: Decision Making

Guided Instruction

Example 3
Remind students that compatible numbers are numbers that are easy to divide. For example, the numbers 20 and 4 are compatible but 20 and 6 are not.

PowerPoint

Additional Examples

① Find each answer.
   a. 15% of 40 **6**
   b. 80% of 460 **368**

② Find each answer using mental math.
   a. 49% of 300 **147**
   b. 11% of 720 **79.2**

③ Estimate each answer.
   a. 76% of 405 **300**
   b. 12% of 5,575 **560**
   c. 48% of 925 **450**

All in One Teaching Resources

- Daily Notetaking Guide 6-4 **L3**
- Adapted Notetaking 6-4 **L1**

Closure

- *How can you find a percent of a number?* **Sample: Change the percent into either a fraction or a decimal. Then multiply and simplify the product.**
- *How can you use mental math to find a percent of a number?* **Sample: Use the Distributive Property.**
- *How can you estimate a percent of a number?* **Sample: Use compatible numbers.**

Advanced Learners **L4**
Which expression will *not* help you find the price of a $60 item on sale for 25% off? **D**

A 60 − 0.25(60)   B 0.75(60)
C 60(1 − 0.25)   D 60 − 0.75(60)

Pre-AP™

English Language Learners **ELL**
For Example 1, ask students to solve the problem in different ways. Ask them what fraction 25% is equal to, then ask them to mentally calculate what $\frac{1}{4}$ of 44 is. Finally, have them draw it.

learning style: visual

3. Practice

Assignment Guide

Check Your Understanding
Go over Exercises 1–9 in class before assigning the Homework Exercises.

Homework Exercises
A Practice by Example   10–34
B Apply Your Skills   35–44
C Challenge   45
TEKS ★ TAKS Tune-Up
and Mixed Review   46–50

Homework Quick Check
To check students' understanding of key skills and concepts, go over Exercises 24, 31, 41, 43, and 44.

Differentiated Instruction Resources

Adapted Practice 6-4   L1

Practice 6-4   *Finding a Percent of ...*   L3

Find each answer.
1. 20% of 560 — 112
2. 42% of 200 — 84
3. 9% of 50 — 4.5
4. 40% of 70 — 28
5. 25% of 80 — 20
6. 50% of 80 — 40
7. 40% of 200 — 80
8. 5% of 80 — 4
9. 75% of 200 — 150

Find each answer using mental math.
10. 14% of 120 — 16.8
11. 30% of 180 — 54
12. 62.5% of 24 — 15
13. 34% of 50 — 17
14. 25% of 240 — 60
15. 85.5% of 23 — 19.665
16. 120% of 56 — 67.2
17. 80% of 90 — 72
18. 42% of 120 — 50.4

Solve.
19. A farmer grew a watermelon that weighed 20 lb. From his experience with growing watermelons, he estimated that 95% of the watermelon's weight is water.
  a. How much of the watermelon is water? 19 lb
  b. How much of the watermelon is not water? 1 lb
  c. The watermelon was shipped off to market, where it sat until it had dehydrated (lost water). If the watermelon is still 90% water, what percent of it is not water? 10%
  d. The solid part of the watermelon still weighs the same. What was the weight of the watermelon at this point? 18.1 lb
20. A bicycle goes on sale at 75% of its original price of $160. What is its sale price? $120

6-4 • Guided Problem Solving GPS   L3

Student Page 293, Exercise 41:
Forestry Russia had 17,000 forest fires in 2001. Aircraft put out 40% of the fires. How many of the fires were put out by aircraft?

Understand
1. What is the relevant information in the problem?
17,000 forest fires, 40%
2. What are you being asked to do?
Find 40% of 17,000.
3. How will changing 40% to an equivalent decimal help you solve the problem?
You can multiply 17,000 by the equivalent decimal to find the percentage

Plan and Carry Out
4. What is the percent of fires in Russian forests that were put out by aircraft?
40%
5. Write 40% as a decimal. 0.4
6. What is the total number of Russian forest fires? 17,000
7. Multiply your decimal answer from step 5 by 17,000.
17,000 · 0.4 = 6,800
8. How many of the fires were put out by aircraft? 6,800

Check
9. What is 50% of 17,000? Is the number of fires put out by aircraft less than this?
17,000 · 0.5 = 8,500; yes

Solve Another Problem
10. Your mother says that 80% of your shirts are dirty. If you have 30 shirts, how many are dirty?
30 · 0.8 = 24 dirty shirts

292

✓ Check Your Understanding

9. Answers may vary. Sample: You would probably use a fraction when the percent can be written as a fraction that is compatible with the other number. You would use a decimal for all other cases.

Use mental math, paper and pencil, or a calculator to find each answer.

1. 58% of 50   **29**
2. 8% of 400   **32**
3. 48% of 121   **58.08**
4. 10% of 70   **7**

Estimation Write an expression and estimate each answer.

5. 19% of 63 $\frac{1}{5} \cdot 60 = 12$
6. 73% of 80 $\frac{3}{4} \cdot 80 = 60$
7. 15% of 39 $\frac{3}{20} \cdot 40 = 6$
8. What is 12% of 100? What is $n\%$ of 100?   12; n

9. **Reasoning** When would you use a decimal to find a percent of a number? When would you use a fraction instead of a decimal?
See left.

Homework Exercises

For more exercises, see Extra Skills and Word Problems.

GO for Help

For Exercises	See Examples
10–18	1
19–27	2
28–34	3

A Find each answer.

10. 6% of 90 5.4
11. 20% of 80 16
12. 27% of 120 32.4
13. 12% of 230 27.6
14. 75% of 240 180
15. 15% of 45 6.75
16. 3% of 12 0.36
17. 150% of 17 25.5
18. 7% of 300 21

Mental Math Find each answer using mental math.

19. 11% of 520 57.2
20. 9% of 780 70.2
21. 50% of 948 474
22. 40% of 216 86.4
23. 51% of 840 428.4
24. 100% of 194 194
25. 60% of 520 312
26. 49% of 150 73.5
27. 90% of 345 310.5

Estimate each answer.

28. 27% of 162 about 40
29. 33% of 88 about 30
30. 53% of 721 about 360
31. 19% of 399 about 80
32. 98% of 65 about 64
33. 73% of 522 about 400

34. There are 75 students at tryouts for the basketball team. Of this number, about 65% are in the seventh grade. About how many seventh-grade students are trying out for the team? about 49 seventh-graders

B GPS 35. **Guided Problem Solving** Of 90 coins in a piggy bank, 20% are quarters. What is the least possible amount of money in the bank? $5.22
  • How many coins in the bank are quarters?
  • What is the value of the coins that are quarters?
  • What is the least possible value of the coins that are not quarters?

36. **Sales** The regular price of a calculator is $15.98. Today you can buy it on sale for 70% of the regular price. Estimate the sale price. about $11.00

43. Yes; $0.03 \times 96 = 2.88$ and $0.96 \times 3 = 2.88$.

44a. Ceramics: $23.\overline{3}\%$; Typing: $11.\overline{3}\%$; Cooking: $45.\overline{3}\%$; Others: 20%

  b. Ceramics: about 583 students; Typing: about 283 students; Cooking: about 1,133 students; Others: about 500 students

First estimate. Then check your estimate by finding the answer.

37. 66% of 243
160.38

38. 48% of 658
315.84

39. 13% of 326
42.38

40. A nurse earning an annual salary of $39,235 gets a 4% raise. What is the amount of the raise? **$1,569.40**

41. **Forestry** Russia had 17,000 forest fires in 2001. Aircraft put out **GPS** 40% of the fires. How many of the fires were put out by aircraft?
6,800 forest fires

42. You take a test with 25 questions on it. Your grade on the test is 84%. How many questions do you get right? **21 questions**

43. **Writing in Math** Is 3% of 96 the same value as 96% of 3? Explain.
See margin.

44. **Data Analysis** At a high school, 150 students are surveyed about their electives.
a. Find the percent of the students surveyed taking each elective. **44a–b. See margin.**
b. **Estimation** The school population is about 2,500. Estimate the number of students taking each elective.

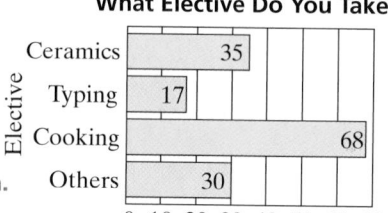
What Elective Do You Take?

45. **Challenge** The number of students in this year's class is 110% of the number in last year's class. If last year's class had 260 students, how many more students are in this year's class? **26 students**

TEKS ★ TAKS Tune-Up and Mixed Review

TAKS Objective 2
TEKS (7.3)(A)

46. At a sale, everything is 70% of the original price. Marc bought a jacket originally priced at $58.90 and a pair of jeans originally priced at $29.95. Which is the best estimate of the total cost? **B**
Ⓐ $30   Ⓑ $60   Ⓒ $90   Ⓓ $120

TAKS Objective 1
TEKS (7.2)(A)

47. Which model best represents the expression $\frac{1}{2} \times \frac{2}{5}$? **H**

Ⓕ

Ⓗ

Ⓖ

Ⓙ

for Help
Lesson 5-4

Algebra **Solve each proportion.**

48. $\frac{13}{39} = \frac{n}{60}$ **20**

49. $\frac{7}{15} = \frac{28}{m}$ **60**

50. $\frac{21}{x} = \frac{5}{8}$ **33.6**

TEKS ★ TAKS Resources

• TAKS Strategies, p. 315
• TAKS Tune-Up, pp. 319–321

TAKS Tune-Up Kit

• TAKS Daily Review Transparencies
• TAKS Review and Preparation Workbook
• TAKS Strategies with Transparencies
• Texas Progress Monitoring Assessments

---

4. Assess & Reteach

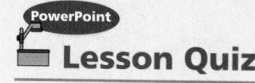
PowerPoint
Lesson Quiz

Find the percent of each number.

1. 40% of 90 **36**

2. 120% of 45 **54**

3. 3.5% of 700 **24.5**

4. 90% of 650 **585**

Alternative Assessment

Have students work in pairs on Exercises 10–18 as you randomly write the answers on the board. Have pairs check their work by matching their answers to those on the board. Direct students to show their work.

293

6-5 Solving Percent Problems Using Proportions

TEKS ★ TAKS

(7.3)(A) To find solutions to application problems involving percent TAKS Obj. 2

(7.3)(B) To find solutions to application problems involving proportional relationships TAKS Obj. 2

Dana Center TEKS Toolkit Clarifying Activities (7.3)(A), (7.3)(B)
Visit: PHSchool.com
Web Code: arq-9045

TEKS Math Background

A proportion is an equation stating that two ratios are equal. Because the ratios part to whole and percent to 100 are equal, they form the proportion $\frac{\text{part}}{\text{whole}} = \frac{\text{percent}}{100}$. Proportions can be solved using cross products, which are numerators that result if you multiply denominators to find a common denominator. For $\frac{3}{4} = \frac{9}{12}$, the cross products are $3 \cdot 12 = 4 \cdot 9$, or $36 = 36$. And 36 is the numerator for each fraction when the common denominator is $4 \cdot 12$, or 48.

More Math Background: p. 272D

Lesson Planning and Resources

See p. 272E for a list of the resources that support this lesson.

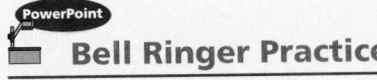
Bell Ringer Practice

☑ **Check Skills You'll Need**
Use student page, transparency, or PowerPoint.

TAKS **Daily Review 45**
Use transparency.

☑ Check Skills You'll Need

1. Vocabulary Review
A *proportion* is an equation stating that two __?__ are equal. **ratios**

Solve each proportion.

2. $\frac{n}{32} = \frac{1}{4}$ **8**

3. $\frac{6}{n} = \frac{2}{5}$ **15**

4. $\frac{7}{8} = \frac{n}{100}$ **87.5**

 for Help
Lesson 5-4

TEKS ★ TAKS

• (7.3)(A) To find solutions to application problems involving percent TAKS Obj. 2

• (7.3)(B) To find solutions to application problems involving proportional relationships TAKS Obj. 2

Why Learn This?

Survey and poll results are often reported using percents.

In a survey of 2,000 people in the United States, 204 said they are left-handed. You can use this information to find the percent of people who are left-handed.

You can use a model to help find this percent.

```
                      part          whole
                       ↓              ↓
Number    0    204                 2,000
          |————————————————————————————|
Percent  0%   n%                   100%
```

$\frac{204}{2,000} = \frac{n}{100}$ ← The part, 204, corresponds to n in the model.
← The whole, 2,000, corresponds to 100.

Online
active math

For: Percents Activity
Use: Interactive Textbook, 6-5

EXAMPLE Finding a Percent

① What percent of 2,000 is 204?

Using the model above, you can write and solve a proportion.

$\frac{204}{2,000} = \frac{n}{100}$ ← Write a proportion.

$2000n = 204(100)$ ← Write cross products.

$\frac{2,000n}{2,000} = \frac{204(100)}{2,000}$ ← Divide each side by 2,000.

$n = 10.2$ ← Simplify.

204 is 10.2% of 2,000.

☑ Quick Check

1. What percent of 92 is 23? **25%**

Differentiated Instruction Solutions for All Learners

Special Needs L1
Help students draw pictures for each of the examples in this lesson, using hundreds grids. Then help them transition to the percent model.

learning style: visual

Below Level L2
Have students use the proportion $\frac{\text{is}}{\text{of}} = \frac{\text{percent}}{100}$ to solve percent problems such as these.

50% of what number is 75? **150**
What percent of 90 is 18? **20%**

learning style: verbal

EXAMPLES Finding a Part and the Whole

② 20% of 55 is what number?

part   whole
0   n 55
0%   20%   100%

$\dfrac{n}{55} = \dfrac{20}{100}$ ← Write a proportion.

$\dfrac{n}{55} = \dfrac{1}{5}$ ← Simplify the fraction.

$\dfrac{n}{55} = \dfrac{1}{5}$ ×11 ... ×11 ← Use the common multiplier, 11.

$n = 11$ ← Simplify.

11 is 20% of 55.

③ **Budgets** Suppose your entertainment budget is 30% of your weekly wages from a job. You plan to spend $10.50 on a movie night. How much will you need to earn at your job in order to stay within your budget?

part   whole
0    $10.50 n
0%   30%   100%

$\dfrac{10.50}{n} = \dfrac{30}{100}$ ← Write a proportion.

$30n = 10.50(100)$ ← Write cross products.

$\dfrac{30n}{30} = \dfrac{10.50(100)}{30}$ ← Divide.

$n = 35$ ← Simplify.

You need to earn $35 to stay within your budget.

✓ Quick Check

2. 85% of 20 is what number? **17**

3. Your math teacher assigns 25 problems for homework. You have done 60% of them. How many problems have you done? **15 problems**

KEY CONCEPTS **Percents and Proportions**

Finding a Percent	**Finding a Part**	**Finding a Whole**
What percent of 25 is 5?	What is 20% of 25?	20% of what is 5?
0 5 25 0% n% 100%	0 n 25 0% 20% 100%	0 5 n 0% 20% 100%
$\dfrac{5}{25} = \dfrac{n}{100}$	$\dfrac{n}{25} = \dfrac{20}{100}$	$\dfrac{5}{n} = \dfrac{20}{100}$
$n = 20$	$n = 5$	$n = 25$
20% of 25 is 5.	5 is 20% of 25.	20% of 25 is 5.

6-5 Solving Percent Problems Using Proportions **295**

Advanced Learners **L4**

Rob's score on a math test was 88% of Cathy's score. Cathy's score was 97% of Bill's score. Bill's score was 92% of Lynn's score. Lynn's score was 94 out of 100. *What was Rob's score?* **74**

Pre-AP™

English Language Learners **ELL**

Take some time talking about the scales in the Key Concepts section. Ask students questions like: *Why is the 25 in the same location as the 100%? Why does* n *change location in the proportions?* Make sure they understand part and whole to prevent errors in setting up proportions.

learning style: visual

Activity Lab

Use before the lesson.

All in One Teaching Resources

Activity Lab 6-5: Using Proportions to Find Percents

Guided Instruction

Example 1

Review the concept of cross products by circling the terms of the diagonals, making two ovals. Point out that the ovals connecting the pairs of numbers form a large "X," which is a symbol for multiplication.

Example 3

If students are having trouble writing the proportion for Quick Check 3, have them draw models. Remind them that the whole line segment represents the whole amount that they are looking for.

PowerPoint

Additional Examples

❶ What percent of 150 is 45?
30%

❷ 35% of 90 is what number?
31.5

❸ 117 is 45% of what number?
260

All in One Teaching Resources

- Daily Notetaking Guide 6-5 **L3**
- Adapted Notetaking 6-5 **L1**

Closure

- *What are the three basic types of percent problems?* finding a part, finding a percent, and finding a whole
- *How do you use a proportion to solve each type of percent problem?* Sample: For each type of problem, you use the proportion $\dfrac{\text{part}}{\text{whole}} = \dfrac{\text{percent}}{100}$, substitute for two pieces, and solve for the missing piece using cross products.

295

Assignment Guide

Check Your Understanding
Go over Exercises 1–7 in class before assigning the Homework Exercises.

Homework Exercises
A Practice by Example 8–24
B Apply Your Skills 25–35
C Challenge 36
TEKS ★ (TAKS) Tune-Up
and Mixed Review 37–43

Homework Quick Check
To check students' understanding of key skills and concepts, go over Exercises 10, 18, 33, 34, and 35.

Differentiated Instruction Resources

Check Your Understanding

Tell whether the answer to the question is a *percent*, a *part*, or a *whole*. Then answer the question.

1. What percent of 200 is 50?
percent; 25%

2. 12 is 80% of what?
whole; 15

3. 50% of what number is 8?
whole; 16

4. What is 30% of 90?
part; 27

Match each question with the proportion you could use to answer it.

5. What is 40% of 15? C

6. 15 is what percent of 40? A

7. 40% of what number is 15? B

A. $\dfrac{15}{40} = \dfrac{n}{100}$

B. $\dfrac{15}{n} = \dfrac{40}{100}$

C. $\dfrac{n}{15} = \dfrac{40}{100}$

Homework Exercises

For more exercises, see Extra Skills and Word Problems.

GO for Help

For Exercises	See Examples
8–13	1
14–19	2
20–24	3

(TAKS) Tip

You can use a model to help you solve percent problems.

A Use a proportion to find the percent.

8. 24 is what percent of 32? 75%

9. What percent of 230 is 23? 10%

10. What percent of 25 is 23? 92%

11. 8 is what percent of 400? 2%

12. What percent of 600 is 84? 14%

13. 21 is what percent of 168? 12.5%

Use a proportion to find the part.

14. What is 4% of 350? 14

15. 1% of 500 is what number? 5

16. What number is 62% of 50? 31

17. 15% of 15 is what number? 2.25

18. 40% of 25 is what number? 10

19. What is 37.5% of 8? 3

Use a proportion to find the whole.

20. 36 is 72% of what number? 50

21. 80% of what number is 15? 18.75

22. 21 is 84% of what number? 25

23. 28 is 35% of what number? 80

24. A sweater is on sale for $33. This is 75% of the original price. Find the original price. $44

B **GPS** **25. Guided Problem Solving** In a market, 44 of the 80 types of vegetables are grown locally. What percent of the vegetables are grown locally? 55%
   • Identify the part. Identify the whole.
   • Complete and solve the proportion: $\dfrac{\blacksquare}{\blacksquare} = \dfrac{\blacksquare}{100}$.

26. A school holds classes from 8:00 A.M. to 2:00 P.M. For what percent of a 24-hour day does this school hold classes? 25%

Write a proportion for each model. Solve for *n*. 27–30. See margin.

27.
0   90   *n*
0%   40%   100%

28.
0   *n*   80
0%   70% 100%

29.
0   54   144
0%   *n*%   100%

30.
0   139.1   *n*
0%   65%   100%

31. **Music** In a school band of 24 students, 9 students play brass instruments. What percent of the members play brass instruments? **37.5%**

32. You purchase a telescope in a state with a 5% sales tax. You pay $14.85 in tax. Estimate the price of the telescope. **about $300**

33. **Open-Ended** Write a percent problem that compares the number of boys to the number of girls in your class. **Check students' work.**

34. At the library, you find 9 books on a certain topic. The librarian tells **(GPS)** you that 55% of the books on this topic have been signed out. How many books does the library have on the topic? **20 books**

35. **Writing in Math** A proportion that models a percent problem has four numbers. One of the numbers is always the same. Explain why. **See left.**

35. The number 100 always appears as the denominator of one of the ratios, since percent means "out of 100."

C 36. **Challenge** A car dealer advertises "All cars 19% off sticker price!" A buyer pays $15,930.95 for a car. Estimate the sticker price. **about $20,000**

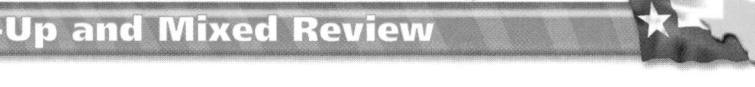 **TEKS ★ TAKS Tune-Up and Mixed Review**

TAKS Objective 2
TEKS (7.3)(A)

37. Out of 45 students, 29 go on a field trip. Which best represents the percent of the students who do NOT go on the trip? **B**
Ⓐ 16%   Ⓑ 36%   Ⓒ 64%   Ⓓ 84%

TAKS Objective 2
TEKS (7.3)(A)

38. In 2001, 56.5% of households in the United States had a computer. Which expression provides the best estimate for the number of households with computers in a survey of 621 households in 2001? **H**
Ⓕ 60% of 650   Ⓗ 60% of 600
Ⓖ 50% of 600   Ⓙ 50% of 650

TAKS Objective 2
TEKS (7.5)(A)

39. The model below represents $4n + 6 = 18$. What is the value of *n*? **C**

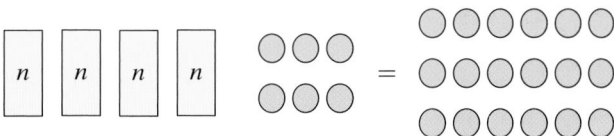

Ⓐ $n = 24$ Ⓑ $n = 6$ Ⓒ $n = 3$ Ⓓ $n = -3$

 for Help   **Lesson 2-3**   **Write each fraction in simplest form.**

40. $\frac{8}{10}$ $\frac{4}{5}$ **41.** $\frac{4}{12}$ $\frac{1}{3}$ **42.** $\frac{5}{100}$ $\frac{1}{20}$ **43.** $\frac{16}{24}$ $\frac{2}{3}$

Online lesson quiz, PHSchool.com, Web Code: ara-0605   **6-5** Solving Percent Problems Using Proportions   **297**

27. $\frac{90}{n} = \frac{40}{100}$; 225

28. $\frac{n}{80} = \frac{70}{100}$; 56

29. $\frac{54}{144} = \frac{n}{100}$; 37.5

30. $\frac{139.1}{n} = \frac{65}{100}$; 214

TEKS ★ TAKS Resources

- TAKS Strategies, p. 315
- TAKS Tune-Up, pp. 319–321

TAKS Tune-Up Kit
- TAKS Daily Review Transparencies
- TAKS Review and Preparation Workbook
- TAKS Strategies with Transparencies
- Texas Progress Monitoring Assessments

---

4. Assess & Reteach

PowerPoint
Lesson Quiz

Use a proportion to solve.

1. What percent of 240 is 60? **25%**
2. 90 is what percent of 120? **75%**
3. 75% of what number is 66? **88**
4. 24 is 96% of what number? **25**

Alternative Assessment

Have students work in pairs. Partners take turns drawing models for Exercises 8–23. Then they work together to complete the exercises.

Reteaching 6-5   Solving Percent Problems Using Pro **L2**

You can use proportions to solve percent problems. Remember, the percent is compared to 100.

Finding the part:
10% of 40 is _?_.
$\frac{10}{100} = \frac{n}{40}$
$100 \cdot n = 10 \cdot 40$
$n = 4$
10% of 40 is 4.

Finding the whole:
20% of _?_ is 8.
$\frac{20}{100} = \frac{8}{n}$
$20 \cdot n = 100 \cdot 8$
$n = 40$
20% of 40 is 8.

Finding the percent:
_?_ % of 25 is 20.
$\frac{n}{100} = \frac{20}{25}$
$25 \cdot n = 100 \cdot 20$
$n = 80$
80% of 25 is 20.

Complete to solve for *n*.

1. 75% of _?_ is 12.
$\frac{75}{100} = \frac{12}{n}$
$75 \cdot n = 100 \cdot 12$
$n = 16$

2. 20% of _?_ is 82.
$\frac{20}{100} = \frac{82}{n}$
$20 \cdot n = 100 \cdot 82$
$n = 410$

3. 5% of _?_ is 9.
$\frac{5}{100} = \frac{9}{n}$
$5n = 100 \cdot 9$
$n = 180$

4. 60 is 5% of *n*.
$\frac{5}{100} = \frac{60}{n}$
$5n = 100 \cdot 60$
$n = 1,200$

5. 6% of *n* is 4.8.
$\frac{6}{100} = \frac{4.8}{n}$
$6n = 100 \cdot 4.8$
$n = 80$

6. 51 is 170% of *n*.
$\frac{170}{100} = \frac{51}{n}$
$170n = 100 \cdot 51$
$n = 30$

Use a proportion to solve.

7. 12% of *n* is 9.
$n = 75$

8. 49% of *n* is 26.95.
$n = 55$

9. 18% of *n* is 27.
$n = 150$

10. What is 210% of 44?
92.4

11. What is 30% of 200?
60

12. 64 is what percent of 80?
80%

Enrichment 6-5   Solving Percent Problems Using Pr **L4**
Decision Making

A library conducted a survey of the community about the kind of novels they read most often. A total of 40,000 people were surveyed. The results are shown in the circle graph at the right.

Fantasy 10%   Historical 11%
Science Fiction 19%
Mystery 35%
Romance 25%

1. Use the information in the circle graph to find the number of people preferring each kind of book. Use a proportion to solve.

Kind of Novel	Percent of Community	Number of People in Community	Budget
Fantasy	10%	4,000	$25,000
Historical	11%	4,400	$27,500
Science Fiction	19%	7,600	$47,500
Romance	25%	10,000	$62,500
Mystery	35%	14,000	$87,500

Sample answers: Exercises 2, 3, and 4.

2. Why is a circle graph a good way to show percent information?
Since the circle represents 100% of the whole, it gives a visual idea of how the data relates to the whole.

3. You can spend $250,000 on new library books. Write the amount you would spend for each kind of book in the table. Explain.
Would spend the same percentage as the kind of books preferred.

4. A patron gave the library $50,000 to expand the children's fiction section. How would you decide which kinds of books to buy? Would you use the survey results above?
Would use children's books recommended by various national groups. Survey results probably are not valid for children, since adults are more likely to be surveyed.

297

TEKS ✦ (TAKS)

(7.3)(A) To estimate and find solutions to application problems involving percent (TAKS) **Obj. 2**

(7.1)(B) To convert between fractions, decimals, whole numbers, and percents (TAKS) **Obj. 1**

Dana Center TEKS Toolkit Clarifying Activities (7.3)(A), (7.1)(B)
Visit: PHSchool.com
Web Code: arq-9045

TEKS Math Background

You can solve many percent problems by directly translating the words into an equation. In these equations, two quantities are known and the third unknown quantity is represented by a variable.

More Math Background: p. 272D

Lesson Planning and Resources

See p. 272E for a list of the resources that support this lesson.

PowerPoint
Bell Ringer Practice

✓ **Check Skills You'll Need**
Use student page, transparency, or PowerPoint.

(TAKS) **Daily Review 46**
Use transparency.

298

✓ **Check Skills You'll Need**

1. **Vocabulary Review**
   State the *Division Property of Equality*.
   See below.
   Solve each equation.

2. $3n = 51$ **17**

3. $\frac{x}{4} = 12$ **48**

GO for Help
Lesson 4-4

GO Online

Video Tutor Help
Visit: PHSchool.com
Web Code: are-0775

Check Skills You'll Need

1. If both sides of an equation are divided by the same nonzero number, the results are equal.

TEKS ✦ (TAKS)

- (7.3)(A) To estimate and find solutions to application problems involving percent (TAKS) **Obj. 2**
- (7.1)(B) To convert between fractions, decimals, whole numbers, and percents (TAKS) **Obj. 1**

Why Learn This?

Suppose a ski resort reports that 60% of its trails are open. If you know how many trails are open, you can solve an equation to find the total number of trails in the park.

You can translate percent problems into equations to find parts, wholes, or percents.

EXAMPLE Finding a Whole

1 (TAKS) **Multiple Choice** A ski resort in New Hampshire begins the season with 60% of its trails open. There are 27 trails open. How many trails does the ski resort have?

Ⓐ 5   Ⓑ 16   Ⓒ 22   Ⓓ 45

Words | 60% of | the number of trails | is | 27

Let x = the number of trails at this ski resort.

Equation | 0.60 · | x | = 27

$0.60x = 27$ ← Write the equation.

$\dfrac{0.60x}{0.60} = \dfrac{27}{0.60}$ ← Divide each side by 0.60.

$x = 45$ ← Simplify.

The ski resort has 45 trails. The correct answer is choice D.

✓ **Quick Check**

1. A plane flies with 54% of its seats empty. If 81 seats are empty, what is the total number of seats on the plane?   **150 seats**

Differentiated Instruction **Solutions for All Learners**

Special Needs **L1**
For each of the examples, ask students to predict whether the product will be less than or greater than the given number in the problem. For example: *Will the product be greater than 27 in Example 1, greater than 377 in Example 2? Why?*

learning style: verbal

Below Level **L2**
Use a single set of values to underscore how to use the equations, such as these.

What is 20% of 65? **13**
20% of what number is 13? **65**
What percent of 65 is 13? **20%**

learning style: verbal

You can use an equation to find a whole, a part, or a percent.

EXAMPLE   **Finding a Part**

2 What number is 39% of 377?

| Words | A number is 39% of 377 |

Let *n* = the number.

| Equation | $n = 0.39 \cdot 377$ |

$n = 0.39 \cdot 377 = 147.03$ ← Simplify.

✓ Quick Check

● **2.** 27% of 60 is what number?   16.2

EXAMPLE   **Finding a Percent**

3 **Recreation** Of 3,072 teens surveyed, 2,212 say they read for fun. What percent of the teens surveyed say they read for fun?

Estimate About 2,000 of 3,000 teens read for fun.

$\dfrac{2,000}{3,000} = \dfrac{2}{3} \approx 0.67 = 67\%$

$3,072p = 2,212$ ← Write an equation. Let *p* = the percent of teens who read for fun.

$\dfrac{3,072p}{3,072} = \dfrac{2,212}{3,072}$ ← Divide each side by 3,072.

$p \approx 0.7200520833$ ← Use a calculator.

$p \approx 72\%$ ← Write the decimal as a percent.

About 72% of the teens surveyed say they read for fun.

Check for Reasonableness 72% is close to the estimate 67%.

✓ Quick Check

● **3.** It rained 75 days last year. About what percent of the year was rainy?
     about 20.5%

KEY CONCEPTS   **Percents and Equations**

Finding a Percent	**Finding a Part**	**Finding a Whole**
What percent of 25 is 5?	What is 20% of 25?	20% of what is 5?
$n \cdot 25 = 5$	$n = 0.2 \cdot 25$	$0.2 \cdot n = 5$
$n = 0.2$	$n = 5$	$n = 25$
5 is 20% of 25.	5 is 20% of 25.	20% of 25 is 5.

---

2. Teach

Activity Lab

Use before the lesson.

All in One Teaching Resources
Activity Lab 6-6: Patterns in Data

Guided Instruction

Example 2
Write the "general form" equation on the board in words. Box the parts shown. As a student reads Quick Check 2, have another student write the equation below the sentence as shown.

A |*number*| is a |*percent*| of a |*whole*|.

    n   =   27%   •   60

Error Prevention!

Remind students that a percent needs to be changed to a decimal before they do any calculations.

PowerPoint
Additional Examples

1 Use an equation to solve: 18% of what number is 81?
$81 = 18\% \cdot n$;   450

2 Use an equation to solve: 32% of 40 is what number?
$n = 32\% \cdot 40$;   12.8

3 Use an equation to solve: What percent of 200 is 45?
$45 = n\% \cdot 200$;   22.5%

All in One Teaching Resources
- Daily Notetaking Guide 6-6 **L3**
- Adapted Notetaking 6-6 **L1**

Closure

- *How can you solve percent problems with equations?*
  Translate the words into an equation that relates the percent, the part, and the whole. Solve for the unknown quantity.

Advanced Learners **L4**
Cheryl bought stock for $20 and sold it for $40, saying her stock went up 100%. Mark said she sold it for 200% of its value. Who is right? Explain.   both; $20 gain is 100%; 40 is 200% of 20

Pre-AP™

English Language Learners   **ELL**
Spend some time translating percent word problems to equations before asking the students to calculate. Students need practice analyzing the word problems and rewording them, as in Example 1, so that they then lead more naturally to an equation.

learning style: verbal

3. Practice

Assignment Guide

Check Your Understanding
Go over Exercises 1–6 in class before assigning the Homework Exercises.

Homework Exercises
A Practice by Example 7–20
B Apply Your Skills 21–31
C Challenge 32
TEKS ★ **TAKS** Tune-Up
and Mixed Review 33–39

Homework Quick Check
To check students' understanding of key skills and concepts, go over Exercises 9, 17, 28, 29, and 30.

Differentiated Instruction Resources

Check Your Understanding

1. No; "20% of 40" asks for a part, "20 is what percent of 40" asks for a percent, and "20 is 40% of what number" asks for a whole.

1. Do the following questions mean the same thing? Explain. *What is 20% of 40? 20 is what percent of 40? 20 is 40% of what number?*
See left.

Match each question with the equation you could use to answer it.

2. What is 16% of 200? **B**

3. 16 is what percent of 200? **C**

4. 16% of what number is 200? **A**

A. $0.16n = 200$
B. $n = 0.16(200)$
C. $16 = 200n$

Write an equation for each question. Then answer the question.

5. What percent of 625 is 500?
$625p = 500;$ 80%

6. What number is 5% of 520?
$n = 0.05 \cdot 520;$ 26

Homework Exercises

For more exercises, see Extra Skills and Word Problems.

GO for Help

For Exercises	See Examples
7–11	1
12–15	2
16–20	3

A Use an equation to find the whole.

7. 96% of what number is 24?
$0.96x = 24;$ 25

8. 40% of what number is 30?
$0.40x = 30;$ 75

9. 50.4 is 36% of what number?
$50.4 = 0.36x;$ 140

10. 12.8 is 32% of what number?
$12.8 = 0.32x;$ 40

11. You answered 22 questions correctly and scored 88% on a test. How many questions were on the test in all? **25 questions**

Use an equation to find a part.

12. 18% of 90 is what number?
$0.18 \cdot 90 = x;$ 16.2

13. What number is 41% of 800?
$x = 0.41 \cdot 800;$ 328

14. What number is 56% of 48?
$x = 0.56 \cdot 48;$ 26.88

15. 70% of 279 is what number?
$0.70 \cdot 279 = x;$ 195.3

Use an equation to find the percent.

16. What percent of 496 is 124?
$496x = 124;$ 25%

17. 18 is what percent of 48?
$18 = 48x;$ 37.5%

18. 39 is what percent of 260?
$39 = 260x;$ 15%

19. What percent of 620 is 372?
$620x = 372;$ 60%

20. A sports team has won 21 out of the 40 games it has played. About what percent of the games has the team won? **about 52.5**

B **GPS** 21. **Guided Problem Solving** Suppose 24% of a 1,500-Calorie diet is from protein. How many Calories are *not* from protein? **1,140 Calories**
   - **Make a Plan** Find the number of Calories that are from protein. Subtract that number from the daily total number of Calories.
   - **Carry Out the Plan** 24% of 1,500 is ▓. Subtract ▓ from 1,500.

22. A water tank containing 496 gallons is 62% full. How many more gallons are needed to fill the tank? **304 gallons**

30. If 25% of a number is 45, the number is more than 45, because 45 is a part of the whole number. If 150% of a number is 45, the number is less than 45, because 150% is more than the whole number.

Use the table at the right. Find the percent of days in a 365-day year that are school days in each country. Round to the nearest percent.

58%

23. China 69%   **24.** Israel 59%   **25.** Russia

26. Scotland 55%   **27.** United States 49%

Length of School Year

Country	Days
China	251
Israel	215
Russia	210
Scotland	200
United States	180

Source: *The Top 10 of Everything*

28. **Food** You make 72 cookies for a bake sale.
GPS This is 20% of the cookies at the bake sale. How many cookies are at the bake sale?

360 cookies

29. The attendance at the school play on Friday was 95% of the attendance on Saturday night. If 203 people attended on Saturday night, estimate how many attended on Friday night. about 190 people

30. **Writing in Math** If 25% of a number is 45, is the number greater than or less than 45? If 150% of a number is 45, is the number greater than or less than 45? Explain how you can tell. See margin.

31. Of the 60 members of a choir, 30% sing alto and 45% sing soprano. How many members of the choir sing alto or soprano? 45 members

C **32.** **Challenge** You plant 40 pots with seedlings. Eight of the pots contain tomato plants. What percent of your seedlings are *not* tomato plants? 80%

TEKS ★ **TAKS** **Tune-Up and Mixed Review**

TAKS Objective 2
TEKS (7.3)(A)

33. About 12% of an iceberg's mass is above water. If the mass above water is 9,000,000 kg, what is the mass of the entire iceberg? C

    A 108,000 kg   C 75,000,000 kg

    B 1,080,000 kg   D 120,000,000 kg

TAKS Objective 6
TEKS (7.14)(A)

34. On average, a group of 25 college students contains 14 females. Which equation can be used to find x, the percent of females in a typical group of college students? F

  F $\frac{x}{100} = \frac{14}{25}$ G $\frac{x}{25} = \frac{14}{100}$ H $\frac{x}{25} = \frac{14}{39}$ J $\frac{x}{14} = \frac{25}{100}$

TAKS Objective 1
TEKS (7.2)(A)

35. The model at the right represents which expression? C

  A $\frac{1}{5} \times \frac{3}{5}$ C $\frac{1}{2} \times \frac{3}{5}$

  B $\frac{1}{3} \times \frac{3}{5}$ D $\frac{2}{3} \times \frac{7}{10}$

GO for Help

Lesson 5-3

Determine whether the ratios in each pair can form a proportion.

36. $\frac{4}{12}$, $\frac{140}{360}$ no   **37.** $\frac{7}{9}$, $\frac{35}{45}$ yes   **38.** $\frac{12}{28}$, $\frac{3}{7}$ yes   **39.** $\frac{45}{60}$, $\frac{3}{4}$ yes

Alternative Assessment

Students work in pairs and take turns posing questions such as those in Exercises 7–20. The partner writes an equation to solve. Together they solve the equation.

TEKS ★ **TAKS** **Resources**

• TAKS Strategies, p. 315
• TAKS Tune-Up, pp. 319–321

TAKS Tune-Up Kit

• TAKS Daily Review Transparencies
• TAKS Review and Preparation Workbook
• TAKS Strategies with Transparencies
• Texas Progress Monitoring Assessments

4. Assess & Reteach

PowerPoint

Lesson Quiz

Write and solve an equation.

1. 6% of 38 is what number?
$n = 6\% \cdot 38$; 2.28

2. 40% of what number is 24?
$24 = 40\% \cdot n$; 60

3. What percent of 52 is 13?
$13 = n\% \cdot 52$; 25%

4. 96% of what number is 240?
$240 = 96\% \cdot n$; 250

301

Solving Percent Problems

In this feature, students practice solving application problems involving percents. They estimate using benchmark fractions and then multiply to find parts of a whole.

Guided Instruction

Explain to students that percents can be applied to real-life situations, such as survey data. Have a volunteer read the problem aloud. Ask:

- *What information do you need to solve the problem?* number of total children with braces, percent of mothers who said children "felt cool," number of children each mother has

- *How would the answer be different if the mothers had two children each and both said they "felt cool" with braces?* The 406 children would double to 812 and the answer would be 69% of 812 or double 280.

- *How do you know that your answer is reasonable?* 280 is close to the estimate we got by rounding the percent and the total number of children.

TEKS ★ TAKS Resources

Dana Center TEKS Toolkit Clarifying Activities (7.3)(A), (7.1)(B)
Visit: PHSchool.com
Web Code: arq-9045

Solving Percent Problems

TEKS ★ TAKS
(7.3)(A) To estimate and find solutions to application problems involving percent **TAKS** Obj. 2
(7.1)(B) To convert between fractions, decimals, whole numbers, and percents **TAKS** Obj. 1

Braces are cool! A recent survey of 406 mothers by the American Association of Orthodontists reported that 69% felt that wearing braces makes their children feel cool. If each mother had only one child with braces, how many children would that be?

What You Might Think

- What do I know?
- What am I trying to find out?
- How do I show the main idea?
- How can I estimate the answer?
- How do I solve the problem?
- Is the answer reasonable?

What You Might Write

69% of 406 mothers said their children felt cool. Each mother had 1 child, so that's 69% of 406 children.

The number of children who felt cool.

Make a diagram.

Number of Mothers

69% is close to 75%, which is $\frac{3}{4}$.

406 is close to 400.

$\frac{3}{4}$ and 400 are compatible; $\frac{3}{4}$ of 400 is 300.

69% is 0.69.

$0.69 \times 406 = n$

$280.14 = n$

280.14 can be rounded to 280.

280 is close to the estimate of 300. The answer is reasonable.

Think It Through

1. What percent of 406 mothers did not say their children "felt cool?" How many children is that? **31%; about 126 children**

2. How does the diagram above help show the main idea? See margin.

2. Answers may vary. Sample: It compares the number of mothers who said their children felt cool to the total number of mothers.

Exercises

For Exercises 3 and 4, answer the questions first, and then solve the problem.

3. A solo guitarist received a royalty payment of 9% based on the sales of her CD. If she received a check for $5,238, what were the total sales of her CD? $58,200
   a. What do you know?
   b. What do you want to find out?
   c. How can the diagram below help you write an equation?

   $0 $5,238 n

   0% 9%   50%   100%

4. The human body is about 67% water. A student weighs 130 pounds. How much of his weight is water? about 87.1 lb
   a. What do you know?
   b. What do you want to find out?
   c. What diagram would help you show the main idea?

5. Teenagers were asked how many hours per week they worked. The data are shown below. Assume they were paid $5.50 per hour. About how much per week would the largest category of students make? The second-largest? between $49.50 and $66.00; between $33.00 and $49.50

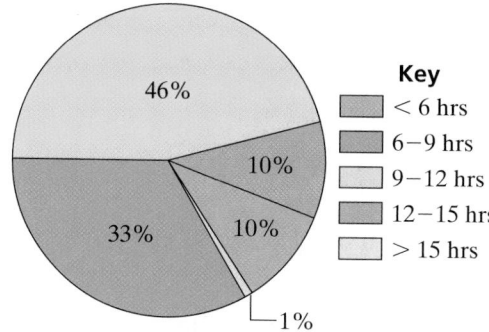

Key
- < 6 hrs
- 6–9 hrs
- 9–12 hrs
- 12–15 hrs
- > 15 hrs

6. When water freezes, its volume increases by 9%. If you freeze one gallon of water to make ice for a party, how many cubic inches of ice will you have? (*Hint*: 1 gallon = 231 in.^{3}) about 252 in.^{3}

7. Research says that humans learn through listening 11% of the time and through observing 83% of the time. In a 50-minute math class, how much of the time would you be learning by listening? By observing? 5.5 minutes; 41.5 minutes

Applications of Percent

Dana Center TEKS Toolkit Clarifying Activities (7.3)(A), (7.1)(B)
Visit: PHSchool.com
Web Code: arq-9045

TEKS Math Background

Sales tax can be calculated using the word equation
sales tax = tax% · purchase price.
Similarly, a tip is a percent of a bill. You can easily calculate tips of 15% by finding 10% of the bill (move the decimal 1 place to the left) and adding $\frac{1}{2}$ of this result. Commission is a percent of sales earned by a salesperson as part of a salary.

More Math Background: p. 272D

Lesson Planning and Resources

See p. 272E for a list of the resources that support this lesson.

PowerPoint

Bell Ringer Practice

✓ **Check Skills You'll Need**
Use student page, transparency, or PowerPoint.

TAKS **Daily Review 47**
Use transparency.

304

✓ **Check Skills You'll Need**

1. Vocabulary Review
To write a *percent* as a decimal, move the decimal point two places to the __?__ .
left
Write each percent as a decimal.

2. 6.5% **3.** 4.25%
0.065   0.0425

4. 15%   **5.** 20%
0.15   0.2

GO **for Help**
Lesson 6-2

TEKS ⭐ **TAKS**
• (7.3)(A) To estimate and find solutions to application problems involving percent
TAKS Obj. 2
• (7.1)(B) To convert between fractions, decimals, whole numbers, and percents
TAKS Obj. 1

🔊 **New Vocabulary** commission

Why Learn This?

You use percents to calculate taxes, tips, and commissions.

In many states, you must pay a sales tax on items you buy. The sales tax is a percent of the purchase price. A tax percent is also called a tax rate.

To find sales tax, you can use the formula
sales tax = tax rate · purchase price.

EXAMPLE **Finding Sales Tax**

1 **Shopping** The price of a bicycle you plan to buy is $159.99. The sales tax rate is 6%. How much will you pay for the bicycle?

$0.06 \cdot 159.99 \approx 9.60$ ← Find the sales tax. Round to the nearest cent.

$159.99 + 9.60 = 169.59$ ← Add the sales tax to the purchase price.

You will pay $169.59 for the bicycle.

✓ **Quick Check**

1. Find the total cost for a purchase of $185 if the sales tax rate is 5.5%.
$195.18

A tip is a percent of a bill that you give to someone who provides a service. You can use estimation and mental math to find a 15% tip.

Step 1 Round the bill to the nearest dollar.

Step 2 Find 10% of the bill by moving the decimal point one place to the left.

Step 3 Find 5% of the bill by taking one half of the result of Step 2.

Step 4 Add the amounts of Step 2 and Step 3 together to find 15%.

Differentiated Instruction Solutions for All Learners

Special Needs L1
For Example 1, draw a number line that sets $159.99 equal to 100%. Show students that they are finding the cost of the bike (100%) plus the tax, so their answer must be greater than the cost of the bike.

learning style: visual

Below Level L2
Have students practice manipulating decimal points by calculating 10% tips. Ask: *How would you calculate a 10% tip?* Sample: Move the decimal point one place to the left and round to hundredths.

learning style: verbal

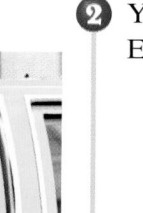

EXAMPLE Estimating a Tip

② Your family takes a taxi to the train station. The taxi fare is $17.85. Estimate a 15% tip to give the driver.

$$17.85 \approx 18 \quad \leftarrow \text{Round to the nearest dollar.}$$
$$0.1 \cdot 18 = 1.8 \quad \leftarrow \text{Find 10\% of the bill.}$$
$$\frac{1}{2} \cdot 1.8 = 0.9 \quad \leftarrow \text{Find 5\% of the bill. 5\% is } \frac{1}{2} \text{ of the 10\% amount.}$$
$$1.8 + 0.9 = 2.7 \quad \leftarrow \text{Add the 10\% and 5\% amounts to get 15\%.}$$

For a $17.85 taxi fare, a 15% tip is about $2.70.

✓ Quick Check

2. Estimate a 15% tip for each amount.
  a. $58.20 about $8.70   **b.** $61.80 about $9.30   **c.** $49.75 about $7.50

Some sales jobs pay you a **commission**, a percent of the amount of your sales. To find a commission, use *commission = commission rate · sales.*

EXAMPLES Finding a Commission

③ Find the commission on a $500 sale with a commission rate of 12.5%.

$$0.125 \cdot 500 = 62.5 \quad \leftarrow \text{Write 12.5\% as 0.125 and multiply.}$$

The commission on the sale is $62.50.

Video Tutor Help
Visit: PHSchool.com
Web Code: are-0775

④ A sales agent earns a weekly salary of $650, plus a commission of 4% on all sales. His sales this week are $1,250. How much does he earn?

Words total earnings = salary + commission

Let t = total earnings.

Equation t =   650   +   0.04 · 1,250

$$t = 650 + 0.04 \cdot 1,250 \quad \leftarrow \text{Write the equation.}$$
$$= 650 + 50 \quad \leftarrow \text{Multiply.}$$
$$= 700 \quad \leftarrow \text{Simplify.}$$

The sales agent earns $700 this week.

✓ Quick Check

3. Find the commission on a $3,200 sale with a commission rate of 6%.

4. Suppose you earn a weekly salary of $800 plus a commission of 3.5% on all sales. Find your earnings for a week with total sales of $1,400.

3. $192

4. $849

6-7 Applications of Percent **305**

Advanced Learners L4
Ben's weekly salary is $850. He also earns a 6% commission on sales. Last week, his total salary with commission was $959.80. What were Ben's sales?
$1,830

English Language Learners ELL
Act out examples of someone giving or getting a tip, paying sales tax, or getting a commission on a sale. These words and concepts can be difficult to grasp. Students need experience with the language and the concept before they can do the calculation.

Pre-AP™

learning style: visual

---

2. Teach

Activity Lab
Use before the lesson.

All in One Teaching Resources
Activity Lab 6-7: Commission

Guided Instruction

Example 2
Explain that a tip is money given to someone, such as a waitperson or taxi driver, for doing a good job. Emphasize that a tax is a required amount, while a tip is voluntary and is generally determined by the person giving the tip.

PowerPoint
Additional Examples

① A video game costs $34.98. The sales tax rate is 5.5%. Find the total cost. $36.90

② Use estimation to calculate a 15% tip for each amount.
  a. $34.50 $5.25
  b. $11.84 $1.80

③ Find the commission on a $450 sale when the commission rate is 7%. $31.50

④ Find the total earnings for a salesperson with a salary of $550 plus a 4% commission on sales of $1,485. $609.40

All in One Teaching Resources
• Daily Notetaking Guide 6-7 L3
• Adapted Notetaking 6-7 L1

Closure

• *What is the word equation you use to find sales tax?*
  sales tax =
  percent of tax · purchase price

• *What is the word equation you use to find commissions?*
  commission =
  percent of sales · sales

• *What is the word equation for the total cost of a meal and tip?*
  total = cost of food +
  (percent of tip · cost of food)

305

Assignment Guide

Check Your Understanding
Go over Exercises 1–7 in class before assigning the Homework Exercises.

Homework Exercises
A Practice by Example 8–19
B Apply Your Skills 20–27
C Challenge 28
TEKS ★ TAKS Tune-Up and Mixed Review 29–33

Homework Quick Check
To check student's understanding of key skills and concepts, go over Exercises 9, 14, 22, 24, and 26.

Differentiated Instruction Resources

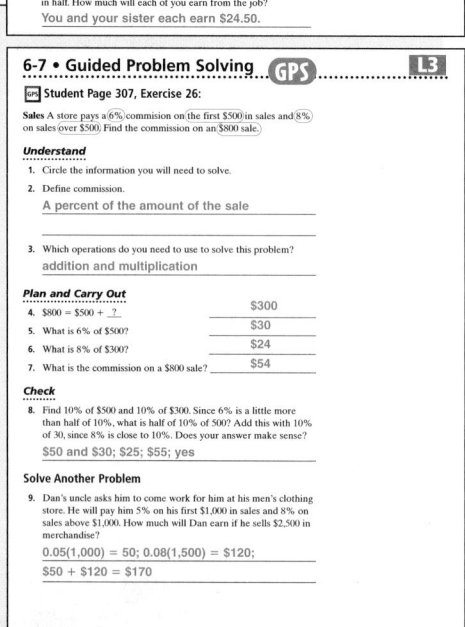

Check Your Understanding

1. **Vocabulary** What does it mean to earn an 8% commission?
You earn 8% of the amount you sell.
2. **Number Sense** Is 4% sales tax on a $250 item *greater than, less than,* or *equal to* 4% commission on a $250 sale? **equal to**
3. **Mental Math** Calculate a 15% tip on a restaurant bill of $24. **$3.60**

Find the sales tax for each item. The tax rate is 6%.

4. a CD priced at $12.99 **$.78**   5. a $450 TV **$27**

Find each commission, given the sale.

6. 5% on a $900 sale **$45**   7. 2% on a $35.50 sale **$.71**

Homework Exercises

For more exercises, see Extra Skills and Word Problems.

GO for Help

For Exercises	See Examples
8–10	1
11–14	2
15–19	3–4

A **Find the total cost.**

8. $35.99 with a 5% sales tax
$37.79
9. $72.75 with a 6% sales tax
$77.12
10. The price of a coat is $114 before sales tax. The sales tax is 7%. Find the total cost of the coat. **$121.98**

Estimate a 15% tip for each amount.

11. $68.50
about $10.35
12. $30.80
about $4.65
13. $9.89
about $1.50
14. $27.59
about $4.20

Find each commission, given the sale and the commission rate.

15. $800, 12%
$96
16. $2,500, 8%
$200
17. $2,000, 7.5%
$150
18. $600, 4.5%
$27

19. Suppose your boss owes you $800, plus a commission of 2.5% on a sale of $1,000. How much does your boss owe you? **$825**

B **GPS** 20. **Guided Problem Solving** Your lunch bill is $19.75. A 5% sales tax will be added, and you want to give a tip of about 20% of $19.75. Estimate how much you will pay for lunch. **about $25**
   • To what number should you round the bill?
   • About how much tip should you give?

21. Your neighbor pays $40 to have her lawn mowed and always adds a 15% tip. You and your friend decide to mow the lawn together and split the earnings evenly. How much will each of you make? **$23**

GO Online
Homework Help
Visit: PHSchool.com
Web Code: are-0607

22. **Writing in Math** Explain how you can use estimation and mental math to calculate a 20% tip. **See margin.**

22. Answers may vary. Sample: Find 10% of the bill by moving the decimal point one place to the left. Then double this number.

23. A purchase costs $25.79 with a tax of $1.29. Find the sales tax rate. **5%**

24. **Art** For a craft project, you select the four packages of modeling clay and the set of tools shown at the right. If there is a 6% sales tax, what is the total cost? **$13.73**

$2.79 ea. plus tax

CLAY

$1.79 plus tax

25. A real estate agent earns a weekly salary of $200. This week, the agent sold a home for $120,000 and was paid a 5.5% commission. Find the agent's earnings for the week. **$6,800**

26. **Sales** A store pays a 6% commission on the first $500 in sales and **GPS** 8% on sales over $500. Find the commission on an $800 sale. **$54**

27. **Open-Ended** If your employer gave you a choice between earning a fixed salary and earning a commission based on your sales, how would you choose? Explain your reasoning and give an example.
Check students' work.

C **28.** **Challenge** Find the commission rate if the total earnings are $970, including a salary of $350 and a commission on sales of $12,400.
5%

TEKS ★ TAKS Tune-Up and Mixed Review

TAKS Objective 2
TEKS (7.3)(A)

29. Laundry workers can expect a tip between 15% and 20%. Which is closest to the amount Diane should offer in order to give the minimum tip for a laundry service of $11.50? **D**

(A) $4.00 (B) $2.50 (C) $2.00 (D) $1.75

TAKS Objective 3
TEKS (7.8)(C)

30. A surveyor drew this diagram to find the distance across a small lake. If $\triangle RSV$ is similar to $\triangle UST$, what is the width w? **H**

(F) 44 m (H) 41.25 m
(G) 21.8 m (J) 11.7 m

U
w
30 m
T
S
16 m
V
22 m
R

TAKS Objective 6
TEKS (7.13)(B)

31. Raul bought 3 posters for $2.59 each and 2 posters for $1.98 each. He paid 59 cents tax. What other information is necessary to find Raul's correct change? **A**

(A) The amount of money Raul gave the cashier
(B) Whether the posters were on sale
(C) The total amount of money Raul spent
(D) How Raul got to the store

 for Help **Lesson 5-2**

Write each unit rate.
34 mi/gal
$2.35/lb
32. 408 mi on 12 gal of gasoline **33.** $16.45 for 7 lb of fish

Alternative Assessment

Each student in a pair writes three problems: one for finding total cost including sales tax; one for finding a tip; and one for finding a commission. Partners exchange papers and solve each other's problems. Partners check each other's work and discuss their results.

TEKS ★ TAKS Resources

- TAKS Strategies, p. 315
- TAKS Tune-Up, pp. 319–321

TAKS Tune-Up Kit
- TAKS Daily Review Transparencies
- TAKS Review and Preparation Workbook
- TAKS Strategies with Transparencies
- Texas Progress Monitoring Assessments

Lesson Quiz

1. Find the payment for a $75 purchase with a sales tax rate of 5%. **$78.75**

2. Find a 15% tip for a $27.60 bill. **$4.14**

3. Find the commission on $3,580 in sales when commission is paid at 6%. **$214.80**

Reteaching 6-7   Applications of **L2**

Finding Sales Tax
sales tax = percent of tax · purchase price
Find the amount of sales tax on a television that costs $350 with an 8% sales tax.
sales tax = 8% · $350
sales tax = 0.08 · 350
sales tax = 28
The sales tax is $28.
How much does the television cost with sales tax?
$350 + $28 = $378

Finding a Commission
commission = commission rate · sales
Find the commission earned with a 3% commission rate on $3,000 in sales.
commission = 3% · $3,000
commission = 0.03 · 3,000
commission = 90
The commission earned is $90.
How much do you earn if you have a base salary of $500 plus 3% commission on sales of $3,000?
$90 + $500 = $590

Find the total cost.
1. $10.00 with a 4% sales tax — $10.40
2. $8.75 with a 5.25% sales tax — $9.21
3. $61.00 with an 7% sales tax — $65.27
4. $320.00 with a 6.5% sales tax — $340.80
5. $6.30 with a 8% sales tax — $6.80
6. $26.75 with a 7.5% sales tax — $28.76

Find each commission.
7. 6% on $3,000 in sales — $180
8. 1.5% on $400,000 in sales — $6,000
9. 8% on $1,200 in sales — $96
10. 5.5% on $2,400 in sales — $132

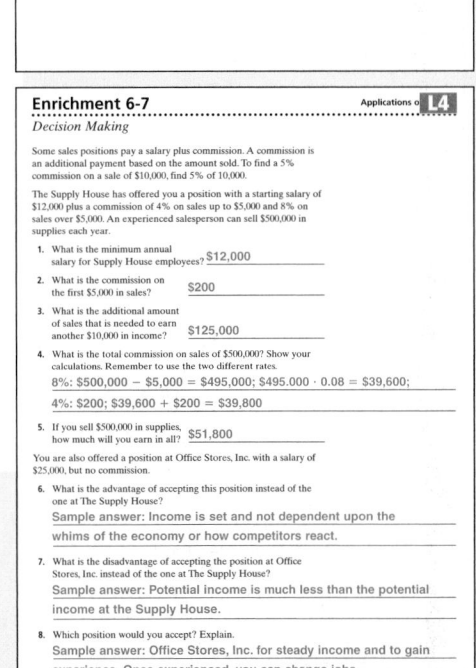

Enrichment 6-7   Applications of **L4**
Decision Making

Some sales positions pay a salary plus commission. A commission is an additional payment based on the amount sold. To find a 5% commission on a sale of $10,000, find 5% of 10,000.

The Supply House has offered you a position with a starting salary of $12,000 plus a commission of 4% on sales up to $5,000 and 8% on sales over $5,000. An experienced salesperson can sell $500,000 in supplies each year.

1. What is the minimum annual salary for Supply House employees? $12,000
2. What is the commission on the first $5,000 in sales? $200
3. What is the additional amount of sales that is needed to earn another $10,000 in income? $125,000
4. What is the total commission on sales of $500,000? Show your calculations. Remember to use the two different rates.
8%: $500,000 − $5,000 = $495,000; $495.000 · 0.08 = $39,600;
4%: $200; $39,600 + $200 = $39,800
5. If you sell $500,000 in supplies, how much will you earn in all? $51,800

You are also offered a position at Office Stores, Inc. with a salary of $25,000, but no commission.

6. What is the advantage of accepting this position instead of the one at The Supply House?
Sample answer: Income is set and not dependent upon the whims of the economy or how competitors react.
7. What is the disadvantage of accepting the position at Office Stores, Inc. instead of the one at The Supply House?
Sample answer: Potential income is much less than the potential income at the Supply House.
8. Which position would you accept? Explain.
Sample answer: Office Stores, Inc. for steady income and to gain experience. Once experienced, you can change jobs.

307

Percent Equations

Students are given percent equations and answer multiple-choice questions about them. They eliminate answer choices by telling whether they are true or false. This will extend the percent skills they learned in Lesson 6-7.

Guided Instruction

Review the Example with students. Explain that only one choice can be correct and they must find the correct answer by process of elimnation. Ask questions, such as:

- *How can you use estimation to help solve this problem?* 49% is about 50% and $\frac{1}{2}$ of x is 30. D is the only correct choice because 60 > 30. So x must be about 60.
- *How would you solve the equation to prove that D is true?* Convert 49% to 0.49. Multiply 30 by the 0.49. $30 \times 0.49 \approx 61.2$, $61.2 > 30$

TEKS ★ **TAKS** Resources

Dana Center TEKS Toolkit
 Clarifying Activities (7.13)(D)
Visit: PHSchool.com
Web Code: arq-9045

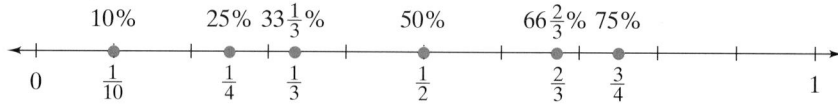

6-7b **Activity Lab**   **Algebra Thinking** ○○   x = ?

TEKS ★ **TAKS**
(7.13)(D) To select techniques such as mental math and estimation to solve problems

Percent Equations

When you have a multiple-choice question with an equation using percent, you can quickly eliminate some of the choices. Use benchmark numbers for percents to help you. Here are some benchmarks:

```
        10%        25% 33⅓%       50%        66⅔% 75%
 ←──┬────●────┬────●───●────┬────●────┬───●───●────┬───────┬──→
    0    1/10       1/4  1/3      1/2       2/3  3/4              1
```

EXAMPLE

Which statement is true for $49\% \times x = 30$? Explain.

Ⓐ $x \approx 30$ Ⓑ x is negative.   Ⓒ $x < 60$ Ⓓ $x > 30$

Choice A is not true.   ← 49% is about $\frac{1}{2}$ and $\frac{1}{2}$ of 30 is 15. So $x \approx 30$ isn't close.

Choice B is not true.   ← That would make the left side a negative number.

Choice C is not true.   ← 49% is a little less than $\frac{1}{2}$, and $\frac{1}{2}$ of 60 is 30.

Choice D is true.   ← x must be big enough that half of it is 30. x must be about twice 30.

● The correct answer is choice D.

Exercises

Reasoning Which choice is true for the equation? Use benchmark numbers to explain. Check each answer choice. Do not compute.

1. $31\% \times x = 23.1$ B; $x < 100$ is true because $\frac{1}{3}$ of 100 is more than 23.1.
   Ⓐ $x < 23.1$ Ⓑ $x < 100$ Ⓒ $x \approx 90$ Ⓓ $x \approx \frac{2}{3}$

2. $90 \times x\% = 8.9$ F; $x \approx 10$ is true because 8.9 is about $\frac{1}{10}$ of 90.
   Ⓕ $x \approx 10$ Ⓖ $x > 30$ Ⓗ $x \approx 50$ Ⓙ $x > 10$

3. $251 \div 500 = x\%$ B; $x \approx 50$ is true because 251 is about $\frac{1}{2}$ of 500.
   Ⓐ $x < 0$ Ⓑ $x \approx 50$ Ⓒ $x \approx 2$ Ⓓ $x < 45$

Write three statements about the variable for each equation. Make somes statements true and some false. Circle the ones that are true.   4–6. Check students' work.

4. $26\% \times x = 101$ 5. $500 \div 1007 = x\%$ 6. $20 \times x\% = 10.5$

Find each answer using a proportion.

1. 35 is what percent of 60?
   58.3%

2. 14.4 is 90% of what number?
   16

3. What percent of 75 is 63?
   84%

Find each answer using an equation.

4. What percent of 120 is 54?
   45%

5. What is 72% of 95?
   68.4

6. What is 120% of 185?
   222

Find the price of each item.

7. originally $299; 5% markup
   $313.95

8. originally $97; 15% discount
   $82.45

9. price $32.79; 8.25% tax
   $35.50

10. **Sales** Find the commission for a rate of 5.5% and $1,400 in sales. $77

6-8a Activity Lab

Data Analysis

Exploring Percent of Change

TEKS ★ TAKS

(7.3)(A) To find solutions to application problems involving percent **TAKS** Obj. 2

(7.11)(B) To make inferences and arguments based on an analysis of data **TAKS** Obj. 5

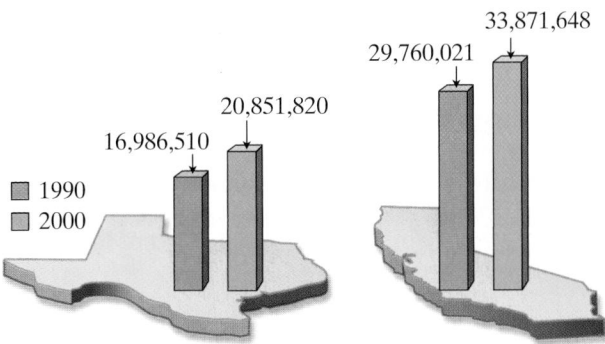

16,986,510   20,851,820

29,760,021   33,871,648

■ 1990
■ 2000

Texas Population   **California Population**

Use the graph above to complete the following exercises.

1. Find the population change from 1990 to 2000 for each state. Texas: 3,865,310; California: 4,111,627

2. Which state had the greater change in population? California

3. For each state, write the ratio $\frac{\text{change in population}}{\text{1990 population}}$. Write each as a percent.
   Texas: $\frac{3,865,310}{16,986,510}$; 22.8%
   California: $\frac{4,111,627}{29,760,021}$; 13.8%

4. Which state had the greater population change in terms of percent? Texas

5. **Reasoning** Why are your answers to 2 and 4 above different? See margin.

309

5. Answers may vary. Sample: California had a greater increase in population, but because it started with a greater population, it had a lesser percent of change.

✓ Checkpoint Quiz

Use this Checkpoint Quiz to check students' understanding of the skills and concepts of Lessons 6-4 through 6-7.

Resources

- All-in-One Teaching Resources Checkpoint Quiz 2
- Texas ExamView CD-ROM
- Success Tracker™ Online Intervention

Activity Lab

Exploring Percent of Change

Students compare data to find a percent of change over time. This will familiarize them with the concept that they will work on in Lesson 6-8.

Guided Instruction

Define percent of change for students. Explain that percent of change is found by using a proportion.

Exercises
Work on the exercises as a class. Ask volunteers to provide each answer and discuss why that answer is correct or incorrect.

Differentiated Instruction

Advance Learners **L4**
Have students create a graph for 2000 to 2010, using the same percent of change rates.

TEKS ★ TAKS Resources

- Activity Lab 6-8: Percent Change

Dana Center TEKS Toolkit Clarifying Activities (7.3)(A), (7.11)(B)
Visit: PHSchool.com
Web Code: arq-9045

TEKS ✯ **TAKS**

(7.3)(A) To estimate and find solutions to application problems involving percent **TAKS** Obj. 2

(7.1)(B) To convert between fractions, decimals, whole numbers, and percents **TAKS** Obj. 1

Dana Center TEKS Tookit Clarifying Activities (7.3)(A), (7.1)(B)
Visit: PHSchool.com
Web Code: arq-9045

TEKS Math Background

The *percent of change* is the percent a quantity increases or decreases from its original amount. To find the percent of change, you first find the amount of change and divide it by the original amount. A *markup* is the amount of increase in the price of an item. A *discount* is the amount of decrease in an item. So, a *percent of markup* is the percent increase in price and a *percent of discount* is the percent decrease in price.

More Math Background: p. 272D

Lesson Planning and Resources

See p. 272E for a list of the resources that support this lesson.

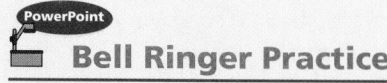

Bell Ringer Practice

☑ **Check Skills You'll Need**
Use student page, transparency, or PowerPoint.

TAKS **Daily Review 48**
Use transparency.

✓ Check Skills You'll Need

1. Vocabulary Review
What are the *cross products* in the proportion $\frac{5}{16} = \frac{n}{100}$? **500 and 16n**

Solve each proportion.

2. $\frac{2}{20} = \frac{n}{100}$ **10**

3. $\frac{1}{8} = \frac{n}{100}$ **12.5**

4. $\frac{6.5}{13} = \frac{n}{100}$ **50**

GO for Help
Lesson 5-4

TEKS ✯ **TAKS**

- **(7.3)(A)** To estimate and find solutions to application problems involving percent **TAKS** Obj. 2
- **(7.1)(B)** To convert between fractions, decimals, whole numbers, and percents **TAKS** Obj. 1

🔊 **New Vocabulary** percent of change, markup, discount

Why Learn This?

You can use percent of change to describe how much an amount increases or decreases over time. For example, every 10 years, the number of U.S. representatives for a state may change, based on the change in the state's population.

A **percent of change** is the percent a quantity increases or decreases from its original amount. Use a proportion to find a percent of change.

$$\frac{\text{amount of change}}{\text{original amount}} = \frac{\text{percent of change}}{100}$$

EXAMPLE **Finding a Percent of Increase**

1 **Government** North Carolina had 12 seats in the U.S. House of Representatives in the 1990s. After the 2000 census, North Carolina had 13 seats. Find the percent of increase in the number of representatives.

$13 - 12 = 1$ ← **Find the amount of change.**

$\frac{1}{12} = \frac{n}{100}$ ← **Write a proportion. Let n = percent of change.**

$100 \cdot \frac{1}{12} = \frac{n}{100} \cdot 100$ ← **Multiply each side by 100.**

$\frac{100}{12} = n$ ← **Simplify.**

$8.3 \approx n$ ← **Divide.**

The number of North Carolina representatives increased by about 8%.

✓ Quick Check

1. In 2000, California went from 52 to 53 representatives. Find the percent of increase in the number of representatives. **1.9%**

Differentiated Instruction **Solutions for All Learners**

Special Needs **L1**
Help students draw double number lines for Examples 1–3, with one of them showing percents 0–150%. Highlight the distance that corresponds to the percent students are trying to find.

learning style: visual

Below Level **L2**
Remind students that the amount of increase and the percent of increase are not the same. Ask: *A store buys an item for $4 and sells it for $6. Is $2 the percent of increase or the markup?* the markup

learning style: verbal

To make a profit, stores charge more for items than they pay for them. The difference between the selling price and the store's cost of an item is called the **markup**. The percent of markup is a percent of increase.

$$\frac{\text{amount of markup}}{\text{original cost}} = \frac{\text{percent of markup}}{100}$$

EXAMPLE Finding a Percent of Markup

2 An electronics store orders sets of walkie-talkies for $14.85 each. The store sells each set for $19.90. What is the percent of markup?

$$19.90 - 14.85 = 5.05 \qquad \leftarrow \textbf{Find the amount of markup.}$$

$$\frac{5.05}{14.85} = \frac{n}{100} \qquad \leftarrow \textbf{Write a proportion. Let } n \textbf{ be the percent of markup.}$$

$$14.85n = 5.05(100) \qquad \leftarrow \textbf{Write cross products.}$$

$$\frac{14.85n}{14.85} = \frac{5.05(100)}{14.85} \qquad \leftarrow \textbf{Divide each side by 14.85.}$$

$$n \approx 34 \qquad \leftarrow \textbf{Simplify.}$$

The percent of markup is about 34%.

✓ Quick Check

2. Find the percent of markup for a $17.95 headset marked up to $35.79.
99.4%

The difference between the original price and the sale price of an item is called a **discount**. The percent of discount is a percent of decrease.

$$\frac{\text{amount of discount}}{\text{original cost}} = \frac{\text{percent of discount}}{100}$$

EXAMPLE Finding a Percent of Discount

★ (TAKS) Tip

Before you find the percent of change, decide whether the change is an increase or a decrease.

3 **Music** During a clearance sale, a keyboard that normally sells for $49.99 is discounted to $34.99. What is the percent of discount?

$$49.99 - 34.99 = 15.00 \qquad \leftarrow \textbf{Find the amount of discount.}$$

$$\frac{15}{49.99} = \frac{n}{100} \qquad \leftarrow \textbf{Write a proportion. Let } n \textbf{ be the percent of discount.}$$

$$49.99n = 15(100) \qquad \leftarrow \textbf{Write cross products.}$$

$$\frac{49.99n}{49.99} = \frac{15(100)}{49.99} \qquad \leftarrow \textbf{Divide each side by 49.99.}$$

$$n \approx 30 \qquad \leftarrow \textbf{Simplify.}$$

The percent of discount for the keyboard is about 30%.

✓ Quick Check

3. Find the percent of discount of a $24.95 novel on sale for $14.97.
40%

---

2. Teach

Activity Lab

Use before the lesson.
Student Edition Activity Lab, Data Analysis 6-8a, Exploring Percent of Change, p. 309

All in One Teaching Resources
Activity Lab 6-8: Percent Change

Guided Instruction

Example 1
Be sure students understand the difference between the *amount of change* and the *percent of change*. Amount of change is found by subtraction and refers to the number of seats (or individuals). The percent of change is found by solving the proportion and refers to the percent of increase in the number of seats, which relates a part to a whole (the number of new seats to the original number of seats).

Example 3
Help students understand that the same steps are used to find percent of markup and percent of discount. You may want them to write the following proportions to help illustrate this point.

$$\frac{\text{amount of change}}{\text{original amount}} = \frac{\text{percent of change}}{100}$$

$$\frac{\text{amount of markup}}{\text{original cost}} = \frac{\text{percent of markup}}{100}$$

$$\frac{\text{amount of discount}}{\text{original cost}} = \frac{\text{percent of discount}}{100}$$

PowerPoint
Additional Examples

1 Last year, a school had 632 students. This year the school has 670 students. Find the percent of increase in the number of students. **6%**

2 Find the percent markup for a car that a dealer buys for $10,590 and sells for $13,775. **30%**

3 Find the percent of discount for a $74.99 tent that is discounted to $48.75. **35%**

Closure

- *What is the percent of change?*
  the percent a quantity
  increases or decreases from its
  original amount
- *What is the proportion you use
  to find percent increase?*
  $\dfrac{\text{amount of change}}{\text{original amount}} = \dfrac{\text{percent of change}}{100}$
- *What is the word equation you
  use to find markup?* markup =
  selling price − original price

● More Than One Way

A jacket goes on sale with a discount of 40% off the original price. The
original price of the jacket is $42.95. What is the sale price of the jacket?

Anna's Method

I can find the amount of the discount by multiplying $42.95 by 40%.
Then I will subtract the discount from the original price.

$42.95 \cdot 0.40 = 17.18$ ← **Find the amount of the discount.**

$42.95 - 17.18 = 25.77$ ← **Subtract the discount from the original price.**

The sale price of the jacket is $25.77.

Chris's Method

The jacket is discounted by 40%, so I will pay 60% of the
original price. I can multiply the original price of $42.95
by the percent I need to pay.

$42.95 \cdot 0.60 = 25.77$ ← **Find the discounted price.**

The sale price of the jacket is $25.77.

Choose a Method

You get a discount of 20% on a $27.50 ticket. How much
will your ticket cost? Describe your method and explain
why it is appropriate.

More Than One Way

Answers may vary.
Sample: Chris's method is
simpler because you can
use mental math to find
that you have to pay 80%
of the original price, and
then you need only one
step to calculate
(0.80)($27.50) = $22.

✓ Check Your Understanding

1. Answers may vary.
Sample: They both
involve the difference
between the original
price and the selling
price. Percent of
markup is a percent
of increase and
percent of discount is
a percent of decrease.

1. **Vocabulary** How are percent of markup and percent of discount
   similar? How are they different? See left.

2. **Number Sense** Is it possible for a markup to be 200%? Give an
   example and explain. Yes; for example, an item's cost could be $10,
   and it could be sold for $30, which is a markup price of $20 or 200%.

Write the proportion to find percent of change.

3. $35 to $50
   $\frac{15}{35}$, 43% increase

4. 98 to 72
   $\frac{26}{98}$, 27% decrease

5. 748 to 374
   $\frac{374}{748}$, 50% decrease

Matching Match each situation with the correct percent of change.

6. Boots first priced at $110 go on sale for $88. B

7. A radio costs a store $88 but sells for $110. A

A. 25% markup

B. 20% discount

31. Find the difference in the number of
    students for last year and this year,
    divide that by last year's number, and
    express the result as a percent. If this
    year's number is greater than last year's
    number, the change is an increase. If this
    year's number is less, the change is a
    decrease.

For more exercises, see Extra Skills and Word Problems.

GO for Help

For Exercises	See Examples
8–16	1
17–21	2
22–26	3

Ⓐ Find each percent of increase. Round to the nearest percent.

8. 60 to 75   25%

9. 88 to 99   13%

10. 135 to 200   48%

11. 12 to 18   50%

12. 2 to 7   250%

13. 12 to 63   425%

14. 120 to 240   100%

15. 15 to 35   133%

16. Business A worker earning $5.15/h receives a raise. She now earns $6/h. Find the percent of increase in her hourly rate of pay.   17%

Find each percent of markup. Round to the nearest percent.

17. $22 marked up to $33   50%

18. $15 marked up to $60   300%

19. $13.50 marked up to $25   85%

20. $40 marked up to $59.75   49%

21. Clothing Find the percent of markup for a shirt that a store buys for $3.25 and sells for $7.50.   131%

Find each percent of discount. Round to the nearest percent.

22. $70 discounted to $63   10%

23. $9 discounted to $4   56%

24. $10 discounted to $7   30%

25. $480 discounted to $300   38%

26. Crafts A package of poster board usually sells for $8.40. This week the package is on sale for $6.30. What is the percent of discount?   25%

Ⓑ GPS 27. Guided Problem Solving The annual precipitation for a city dropped from 65 cm to 47 cm over the course of 5 years. What is the average percent of change in the amount of precipitation for 1 year?
- What was the amount of change in the precipitation over 5 years?
- What was the percent of change over 5 years?   5.5% decrease

28. A scientist earning an annual salary of $49,839 gets a 4% raise. Estimate the new annual salary for this scientist.   about $52,000

29. Sports A football player gained 1,200 yd last season and 900 yd this **GPS** season. Find the percent of change. State whether the change is an increase or a decrease.   25% decrease

30. The student should have divided by 1,938 instead of 2,128.

30. Error Analysis The number of students enrolled in a school has increased from 1,938 to 2,128. A student calculates the percent of increase. His work is shown at right. Explain the student's mistake.

$$2{,}128 - 1{,}938 = 190$$
$$190 \div 2{,}128 \approx 0.089$$
$$0.089 = 8.9\%$$

See above left.

31. Writing in Math Describe how you can find the percent of change in the number of students in your school from last year to this year.   See margin.

Careers Scientists develop vaccines and treatments.

---

3. Practice

Assignment Guide

Check Your Understanding
Go over Exercises 1–7 in class before assigning the Homework Exercises.

Homework Exercises
- **A** Practice by Example   8–26
- **B** Apply Your Skills   27–35
- **C** Challenge   36
- **TEKS ★ TAKS** Tune-Up and Mixed Review   37–41

Homework Quick Check
To check students' understanding of key skills and concepts, go over Exercises 14, 22, 29, 31, and 34.

Differentiated Instruction Resources

Adapted Practice 6-8   L1

Practice 6-8   Finding Percent of   L3

Find each percent of change. State whether the change is an increase or a decrease.

1. A $50 coat is put on sale for $35.   30% decrease
2. Mayelle earns $18,000 a year. After a raise, she earns $19,500.   8.3% increase
3. Last year Anthony earned $24,000. After a brief lay-off this year, Anthony's income is $18,500.   22.9% decrease
4. In 1981, about $1.1 million was lost due to fires. In 1988, the loss was about $9.6 million.   873% increase
5. In a recent year, certain colleges and universities received about $268 million in aid. Ten years later, they received about $94 million.   65% decrease
6. A coat regularly costing $125 is put on sale for $75.   40% decrease

7. Complete the table.

Enrollment in Center City Schools From 1995 to 2000

Year	Enrollment	Change from Last Year (number of students)	Change from Last Year (%)	Increase or Decrease
1995	18,500	—	—	—
1996	19,300	800	4%	increase
1997	19,700	400	2%	increase
1998	19,500	200	1%	decrease
1999	19,870	370	2%	increase
2000	19,200	670	3%	decrease

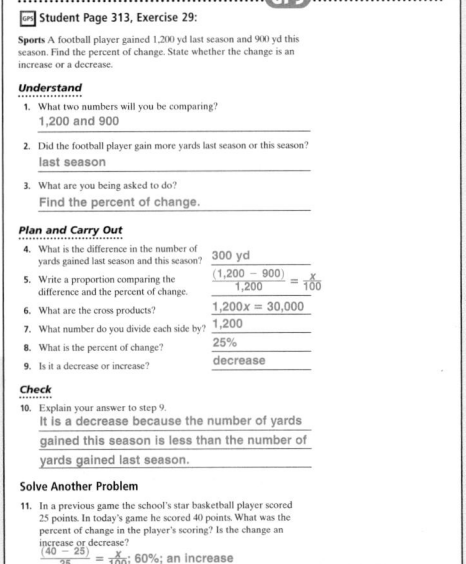

6-8 • Guided Problem Solving   **GPS**   L3

Student Page 313, Exercise 29:

Sports A football player gained 1,200 yd last season and 900 yd this season. Find the percent of change. State whether the change is an increase or a decrease.

Understand
1. What two numbers will you be comparing?   1,200 and 900
2. Did the football player gain more yards last season or this season?   last season
3. What are you being asked to do?   Find the percent of change.

Plan and Carry Out
4. What is the difference in the number of yards gained last season and this season?   300 yd
5. Write a proportion comparing the difference and the percent of change. $\frac{(1{,}200 - 900)}{1{,}200} = \frac{x}{100}$
6. What are the cross products? $1{,}200x = 30{,}000$
7. What number do you divide each side by?   1,200
8. What is the percent of change?   25%
9. Is it a decrease or increase?   decrease

Check
10. Explain your answer to step 9.   It is a decrease because the number of yards gained this season is less than the number of yards gained last season.

Solve Another Problem
11. In a previous game the school's star basketball player scored 25 points. In today's game he scored 40 points. What was the percent of change in the player's scoring? Is the change an increase or decrease? $\frac{(40 - 25)}{25} = \frac{x}{100}$; 60%; an increase

Lesson Quiz

Find each percent of change and round to the nearest tenth. State whether it is an increase or decrease.

1. 10 to 25   150% increase

2. 95 to 76   20% decrease

3. 36 to 30   16.7% decrease

4. 70 to 82   17.1% increase

35. See back of book.

Reteaching 6-8   Finding Percent o **L2**

Percent of change is the percent something increases or decreases from its original amount.

	Find the percent of increase from 12 to 18.	Find the percent of decrease from 20 to 12.
① Subtract to find the amount of change.	$18 - 12 = 6$	$20 - 12 = 8$
② Write a proportion. $\frac{change}{original} = \frac{percent}{100}$	$\frac{6}{12} = \frac{n}{100}$ $6 \cdot 100 = 12n$	$\frac{8}{20} = \frac{n}{100}$ $8 \cdot 100 = 20n$
③ Solve for n.	$n = 50$ The percent of increase is 50%.	$n = 40$ The percent of decrease is 40%.

State whether the change is an *increase* or *decrease*. Complete to find the percent of change.

1. 40 to 60
$60 - 40 = 20$
$\frac{20}{40} = \frac{n}{100}$
$20 \cdot 100 = 40n$
$n = 50$
increase of 50%

2. 15 to 9
$15 - 9 = 6$
$\frac{6}{15} = \frac{n}{100}$
$6 \cdot 100 = 15n$
$n = 40$
decrease of 40%

3. 0.4 to 0.9
$0.9 - 0.4 = 0.5$
$\frac{0.5}{0.4} = \frac{n}{100}$
$0.5 \cdot 100 = 0.4n$
$n = 125$
increase of 125%

Find the percent of *increase*.

4. 16 to 40   150%

5. 20 to 22   10%

6. 9 to 18   100%

7. 28 to 35   25%

8. 80 to 112   40%

9. 150 to 165   10%

Find the percent of *decrease*.

10. 20 to 15   25%

11. 100 to 57   43%

12. 52 to 26   50%

13. 140 to 126   10%

14. 75 to 72   4%

15. 1000 to 990   1%

Enrichment 6-8   Finding Percent o **L4**

Decision Making

Answer the questions given the information.

A softball diamond is a 60 ft by 60 ft square. The sides of a baseball diamond are 50% longer than this. What is the percent increase in the area from the softball diamond to the baseball diamond?

1. Will you find the percent increase or decrease?   percent increase

2. What are the dimensions of a softball diamond?   60 ft by 60 ft

3. How much longer is the side of a baseball diamond than the side of a softball diamond?   50% longer

4. Draw a diagram to show the areas of the two fields. Use another piece of paper if you need more space.

5. Which expression gives you the length of one side of the baseball diamond?   a
a. $60 + 0.5(60)$ b. $60 - (60 \cdot 0.5)$ c. $(60 \cdot 0.5) \div 60$

6. What is the length of the side of the baseball diamond?   90 ft

7. What is the formula for the area of a square? $A = s^2$

8. What is the area of the softball diamond?   3,600 ft²

9. What is the area of the baseball diamond?   8,100 ft²

10. How much larger is the area of the baseball diamond?   4,500 ft²

11. What is the percent increase?   125%

12. What other strategies could you use to find the answer?   Sample answer: Solve a simpler problem, make a table

Baseball / Softball (diagram)

314

GO Online
Homework Help
Visit: PHSchool.com
Web Code: are-0608

Find the price of each item.

32. originally $35.75; 65% markup $58.99

33. originally $82; 35% discount $53.30

34. Choose a Method A TV goes on sale with a discount of 28%. The original price of the TV is $942. What is the sale price of the TV? $678.24

35. Business A toy store opened five years ago. The owner uses a computer to track sales. She uses a program that prints @@@ in some cells instead of numbers. Copy and complete the spreadsheet.
See margin.

	A	B	C	D	
1	Year	Sales ($)	Change From Last Year ($)	Change From Last Year (%)	
2	1	200,000	(not open last year)	(not open last year)	
3	2	240,000	40,000	@@@	
4	3	300,000	@@@	@@@	
5	4	330,000	@@@	@@@	

36. Challenge A storeowner buys a case of 144 pens for $28.80. Tax and shipping cost an additional $8.64. He sells the pens for $.59 each. What is the markup per pen? What is the percent of markup? $.33; 126.9%

TEKS ★ TAKS Tune-Up and Mixed Review

TAKS Objective 2
TEKS (7.3)(A)

37. Which of the following represents the least percent of change?   **A**
Ⓐ A child grew from 40 inches to 46 inches in one year.
Ⓑ Internet service costs increased from $21 to $25 per month.
Ⓒ An after-school program enrollment was 72 and is now 84.
Ⓓ A child's weekly allowance is changed from $5 to $6.

TAKS Objective 2
TEKS (7.3)(A)

38. Mr. Chun earns a salary of $150 a week plus 8% commission on all sales. How much will he earn if his sales in one week are $2,990?   **G**
Ⓕ $3,002   **Ⓖ** $389.20   **Ⓗ** $251.20   **Ⓙ** $239.20

TAKS Objective 6
TEKS (7.13)(A)

39. Julie took a taxi from school to her home. The taxi rate started at $2.00 and then $0.50 was added for every $\frac{1}{4}$ mile traveled. What information is needed to find the cost of the taxi ride?   **B**
Ⓐ Number of minutes she rode in the taxi
Ⓑ Number of miles Julie's home is from the school
Ⓒ Number of gallons of gasoline used for the trip
Ⓓ Average speed of the taxi

for Help   **Lesson 6-7**   **(Algebra) Find each payment.**

40. $231.63

$471.30

40. $218 with a 6.25% sales tax

41. $451 with a 4.5% sales tax

TEKS ★ TAKS Resources

• TAKS Strategies, p. 315
• TAKS Tune-Up, pp. 319–321

TAKS Tune-Up Kit
• TAKS Daily Review Transparencies
• TAKS Review and Preparation Workbook
• TAKS Strategies with Transparencies
• Texas Progress Monitoring Assessments

Alternative Assessment

Provide pairs of students with 10 index cards. Each partner writes a different number on each of five of the cards. Partners mix the cards, make two piles, and designate one as the original number. Partners work together to find the percent of increase or decrease for each pair of numbers.

Working Backward

A useful problem solving strategy for answering multiple-choice questions is to *Work Backward*. Check to see which choice results in a correct answer by substituting the answers into the problem.

EXAMPLE

In a pile of dimes and quarters, there are twice as many dimes as quarters. The total value of the coins is $9.45. How many quarters are in the pile?

  Ⓐ 11   Ⓑ 18   Ⓒ 21   Ⓓ 24

Check each answer to see whether it works.

Choice A   11 quarters: 2.75   22 dimes: 2.20   2.75 + 2.20 = 4.95 ✗
Choice B   18 quarters: 4.50   36 dimes: 3.60   4.50 + 3.60 = 8.10 ✗
Choice C   21 quarters: 5.25   42 dimes: 4.20   5.25 + 4.20 = 9.45 ✔
Choice D   24 quarters: 6.00   48 dimes: 4.80   6.00 + 4.80 = 10.80 ✗

The correct answer is choice C.

Exercises

Solve each problem by working backward.

 Objective 1
TEKS (7.2)(B)

1. What is the greatest number of movie tickets you can buy if you have $33.48 and each movie ticket costs $6.75? **B**
  Ⓐ 3   Ⓑ 4   Ⓒ 5   Ⓓ 6

 Objective 5
TEKS (7.12)(A)

2. Your grades on four math tests are 97, 88, 79, and 92. What grade do you need on the fifth test to have a mean of 90? **H**
  Ⓕ 90   Ⓖ 92   Ⓗ 94   Ⓙ 96

Objective 6
TEKS (7.13)(C)

3. If you start with a number, add 5, and then multiply by 7, the result is 133. What is the number? **B**
  Ⓐ 12   Ⓑ 14   Ⓒ 15   Ⓓ 21

Objective 6
TEKS (7.13)(C)

4. For your birthday, you receive $48 and a $15 gift certificate to a department store. The store is having a sale that takes 40% off the price of all items. What is the total value of the merchandise you can buy and still have $7.50 left for lunch? **H**
  Ⓕ $70.50   Ⓖ $88.20   Ⓗ $92.50   Ⓙ $100

Chapter 6 Review

Vocabulary Review

 commission (p. 305)
discount (p. 311)

markup (p. 311)
percent (p. 274)

percent of change (p. 310)

Choose the vocabulary term from the column on the right that completes the sentence.

1. The difference between the selling price and a store's cost is the __?__. **C**

2. A __?__ can be an increase or a decrease. **E**

3. A __?__ is a ratio that compares a number to 100. **D**

4. The difference between the original price and the sale price is the __?__. **B**

5. A __?__ is a percent of the sales made by a salesperson. **A**

A. commission
B. discount
C. markup
D. percent
E. percent of change

Go Online
PHSchool.com
For: Online vocabulary quiz
Web Code: arj-0651

Skills and Concepts   TEKS ★ TAKS

Lessons 6-1, 6-2

(7.1)(A) To compare and order integers and positive rational numbers **TAKS Obj. 1**

(7.1)(B) To convert between fractions, decimals, whole numbers, and percents **TAKS Obj. 1**

(7.14)(A) To communicate mathematical ideas using numerical and graphical models **TAKS Obj. 6**

A **percent** is a ratio that compares a number to 100.

To write a decimal as a percent, multiply the decimal by 100, or move the decimal point two places to the right. To write a percent as a decimal, divide by 100, or move the decimal point two places to the left.

To write a fraction as a percent, first convert the fraction into a decimal. To write a percent as a fraction, write the percent with a denominator of 100 and simplify.

Write each percent as a decimal and as a fraction in simplest form.

6. 65% $0.65; \frac{13}{20}$ 7. 2% $0.02; \frac{1}{50}$ 8. 1.8% $0.018; \frac{9}{500}$ 9. $62\frac{1}{2}\%$ $0.625; \frac{5}{8}$

10. Write $\frac{3}{8}$ as a percent. 37.5%   11. Write 0.16 as a percent. 16%

Lessons 6-3, 6-4

(7.3)(A) To estimate and find solutions to problems involving percent **TAKS Obj. 2**

(7.1)(B) To convert between fractions, decimals, whole numbers, and percents **TAKS Obj. 1**

A mixed number represents a percent greater than 100%. A proper fraction represents a percent less than 100%. To find a percent of a whole, write the percent as a decimal or fraction and then multiply.

Find each answer.

12. Find 83% of 54. 44.82

13. What is 4% of 16? 0.64

14. Find 135% of 72. 97.2

Lessons 6-5, 6-6

(7.3)(A) To estimate and find solutions to application problems involving percent **TAKS Obj. 2**

(7.3)(B) To find solutions to application problems involving proportional relationships **TAKS Obj. 2**

(7.1)(B) To convert between fractions, decimals, whole numbers, and percents **TAKS Obj. 1**

Percent problems are solved by using a proportion or an equation.

Use a proportion or an equation to solve.

15. What percent of 40 is 28? **70%**

16. 38 is 80% of what number? **47.5**

17. What is 60% of 420? **252**

18. 80% of 15 is what number? **12**

19. **72**

20. **20%**

21. Technology The price of a new version of a computer game is 120% of the price of the original version. The original version cost $48. What is the cost of the new version? **$57.60**

Lesson 6-7

(7.3)(A) To estimate and find solutions to application problems involving percent **TAKS Obj. 2**

(7.1)(B) To convert between fractions, decimals, whole numbers, and percents **TAKS Obj. 1**

A tip is a percent of a bill that you give to the person providing a service. A **commission** is a percent of a sale.

22. You go to a restaurant with four other people. The total for the food is $43.85. You need to add 5% for tax and 15% for tip. If you decide to split the bill evenly, estimate how much you will pay. **about $10.52**

23. Diamonds Find the commission on a diamond that is sold for $6,700 when the commission paid is 4%. **$268**

Find each commission, given the sale and the commission rate.

24. $700, 9%
$63

25. $3,600, 6%
$216

26. $5,000, 5.5%
$275

27. Insurance An insurance company pays its agents 40% commission on the first year's premium and 5% on the second year's premium for life insurance policies. If the premiums are $500 per year, what is the total commission that will be paid during the two years? **$225**

Lesson 6-8

(7.3)(A) To estimate and find solutions to application problems involving percent **TAKS Obj. 2**

(7.1)(B) To convert between fractions, decimals, whole numbers, and percents **TAKS Obj. 1**

A **percent of change** is the percent a quantity increases or decreases from its original amount. Use the proportion $\dfrac{\text{amount of change}}{\text{original amount}} = \dfrac{\text{percent change}}{100}$.

Markup is an example of a percent of increase. **Discount** is an example of a percent of decrease.

Find each percent of change. Tell whether it is an increase or a decrease.

28. $90 to $75
16.7% decrease

29. 3.5 ft to 4.2 ft
20% increase

30. 120 lb to 138 lb
15% increase

31. 300 cm to 420 cm
40% increase

32. 80.5 g to 22.5 g
72% decrease

33. 108 kg to 90 kg
16.7% decrease

34. 31% decrease

34. Shopping The sale price of a game is $24.95. Its original price was $36.00. Find the percent of change. Round to the nearest percent.

Go Online For: Online chapter test
PHSchool.com **Web Code:** ara-0652

TEKS ★ TAKS Resources

- Texas ExamView CD-ROM
  - Chapter 6 Ready-Made Test
  - Make your own Chapter 6 test
- MindPoint Quiz Show CD-ROM
  - Chapter 6 Review

Differentiated Instruction

All-in-One Teaching Resources
- Chapter 6 Test **L2**
- Chapter 6 Test **L3**
- Chapter 6 Alternative Assessment **L4**

Spanish Assessment Resources **ELL**
- Chapter 6 Test **L2**
- Chapter 6 Test **L3**
- Chapter 6 Alternative Assessment **L4**

Texas ExamView CD-ROM
- Special Needs Test **L1**
- Special Needs Practice Bank **L1**

Online Chapter 6 Test at www.PHSchool.com **L3**

Write each decimal as a percent and write each percent as a decimal.

1. 5% 0.05
2. 0.3 30%
3. 125% 1.25
4. 0.0045 0.45%
5. 0.39% 0.0039
6. 3.4 340%

Write each fraction as a percent. Write each percent as a fraction.

7. 35% $\frac{7}{20}$
8. 125% $\frac{5}{4}$
9. 2% $\frac{1}{50}$
10. $\frac{7}{8}$ 87.5%
11. $\frac{3}{4}$ 75%
12. $\frac{6}{5}$ 120%

13. According to the U.S. Census Bureau, 0.98% of females in the United States in 1990 were named Barbara. Express this percent as a fraction. $\frac{49}{5,000}$

Model each percent on a 10 × 10 grid.
14–16. See margin.
14. 34%
15. 285%
16. $12\frac{1}{2}$%

17. You work 20 hours per week at a grocery store during the summer. Sixty percent of your job is restocking the shelves. How many hours per week do you spend restocking the shelves? 12 h

18. Draw a model and write a proportion to find the answer to "25 percent of what number is 30?" See margin.

Write an equation for each question. Then solve the equation.

19. What percent of 82 is 10.25?
    $82x = 10.25$; 12.5%
20. 108% of 47 is what number?
    $(1.08)(47) = x$; 50.76
21. 99 is 72% of what number?
    $99 = 0.72x$; 137.5
22. 12 is what percent of 1,920?
    $12 = 1,920x$; 0.625%
23. What is 62% of 128?
    $x = (0.62)(128)$; 79.36
24. 168% of what number is 714?
    $1.68x = 714$; 425
25. In a grade of 250 students, there are 6 sets of twins. What percent of the students in this grade have a twin? 4.8%

Write a proportion for each model. Solve for *n*.

26.
```
0        50      80    50   n
                       -- = --- ; 62.5
0%      n%    100%     80   100
```

27.
```
0            60   n    60   80
                       -- = -- ; 75
0%        80% 100%     n    100
```

28. **Shopping** You buy a sweater for $18.75, which is 25% off the original price. What was the original price? $25

29. To prepare for competitions, your swimming coach required you to swim 8 lengths in the pool. You swam 10 lengths. What percent of the required practice did you swim? 125%

Find each percent of change. Round to the nearest tenth of a percent. State whether the change is an increase or a decrease.

30. 4.15 to 4.55 9.6% increase
31. 379 to 302 20.3% decrease
32. 72 to 102 41.7% increase

33. **Jobs** According to the U.S. Department of Labor, total employment is expected to increase from 146 million in 2000 to 168 million in 2010. Find the percent of increase. 15.1% increase

34. **Restaurants** You order items from a menu that total $7.85. Your bill comes to $8.30, including tax. What is the percent of the tax? Round to the nearest tenth of a percent. 5.7%

35. A salesperson receives a salary of $300 per week and a 6% commission on all sales. How much does this salesperson earn in a week with $2,540 in sales? $452.40

36. A bicycle store pays $29.62 for a helmet. The store sells the helmet for $39.99. Find the percent of markup. 35% markup

37. **Writing in Math** How do you determine whether you are finding a percent of increase or a percent of decrease between two values? Explain. See margin.

14–16. See back of book.

18.
```
0    30              n


0%  25%           100%

30    25
-- = --- ; 120
n    100
```

37. If the original value is less than the new value, it is an increase. If the original value is greater than the new value, it is a decrease.

Cumulative Practice

 Tips

Some TAKS tests ask you questions about percent. This question asks you to study a graph and determine the percent of a figure that is shaded.

Tip 1
Find the number of shaded squares and the total number of squares.

The diagram below shows the number of lots sold in a housing development. The dark squares indicate lots that have been sold. What percent of the total number of lots have been sold?

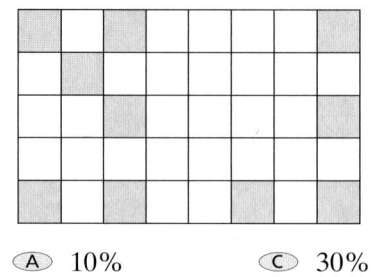

- Ⓐ 10%
- Ⓑ 25%
- Ⓒ 30%
- Ⓓ 40%

Tip 2
Make a proportion,
$$\frac{\text{number shaded}}{\text{total number}} = \frac{x}{100}.$$

Think It Through
Keep in mind that *percent* means a ratio that compares a number to 100. There are 10 shaded squares and 40 squares in all. The proportion is $\frac{10}{40} = \frac{x}{100}$. So $x = 25$. The correct answer is choice B, 25%.

Vocabulary Builder

As you solve test items, you must understand the meanings of mathematical terms. Choose the term that correctly completes each sentence.

A. A ratio that compares a number to 100 is a (proportion, percent). **percent**

B. A mathematical sentence with an equal sign is a(n) (solution, equation). **equation**

C. The (mean, mode) of a data set is the sum of the data divided by the number of data items. **mean**

D. The (range, median) of a data set is the middle value when the data are arranged in numerical order. **median**

Multiple Choice

Read each question. Then write the letter of the correct answer on your paper.

1. The table shows the ancestry claimed by a sample of 200 U.S. citizens. Which statement is best supported by the data? **D**

Ancestry of U.S. Population

Ancestry Group	Number
African American	18
English	18
German	30
Irish	22
Mexican	13
Other	117

- Ⓐ Exactly 18% consider their ancestry to be African American.
- Ⓑ Twice as many citizens claim Mexican ancestry as German ancestry.
- Ⓒ Five ancestry groups make up the U.S. population.
- Ⓓ Less than 12% claim Irish ancestry.

 Tune-Up

TEKS ★ TAKS Resources

TAKS Review and Preparation Workbook

Texas ExamView CD-ROM
- Instant TAKS Practice Test
- TAKS Practice Items

Differentiated Instruction

Texas Progress Monitoring Assessments
- Benchmark Test 3   **L3**
- Quarter 2 Test
  - Forms A & B   **L3**
  - Forms D & E   **L2**
- Mid-Course Test
  - Forms A & B   **L3**
  - Forms D & E   **L2**

Spanish Assessment Resources
- Spanish Cumulative Review **ELL**
- Spanish Quarter 2 Test
  - Forms A & B   **L3**
- Spanish Mid-Course Test
  - Forms A & B   **L3**

Texas ExamView CD-ROM
- Special Needs Practice Bank   **L1**

TAKS Daily Review Transparencies

TAKS Daily Review 1   Objective 1: (7.1)(B)
Multiple Choice
The seventh-grade class at Anarene Middle School sold $\frac{13}{20}$ of the Corsicana fruitcakes they bought. Which decimal is equivalent to the fraction sold?
A   65
B   0.65
C   6.5
D   650

Answer: B

TAKS Daily Review 2   Objective 5: (7.12)(A)
Multiple Choice
Shey has been practicing running the 200-meter foot race. Her last 6 times are shown.
23.60   24.15   24.68   28.62   24.25   23.92
What is her mean time?
F   5.02
G   23.92
H   24.21
J   24.87

Answer: J

2. The table below shows the highest level of education for 500 people.

Highest Level of Education

Education Level	Number
High school graduate	160
Some College	85
College Associate's degree	41
College Bachelor's degree	89
College Graduate degree	45
Other	80

Which statement is NOT supported by these data? **G**

Ⓕ At least thirty-two percent graduated high school.

Ⓖ Eighty-five percent attended college.

Ⓗ About twice as many have a bachelor's degree as have a graduate degree.

Ⓙ Some people in the survey may not have finished high school.

3. Nathan used black tiles for $\frac{2}{3}$ of his mosaic, as shown below.

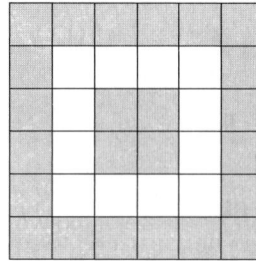

What percent of his mosaic uses black tiles?

Ⓐ 12% Ⓒ 24% **D**

Ⓑ $33\frac{1}{3}$% Ⓓ $66\frac{2}{3}$%

4. Texas is the leading cotton producer in the United States. In 2003, about 0.24 of U.S. cotton bales were produced in Texas. What percent of the cotton was this? **H**

Ⓕ 0.24% Ⓗ 24%

Ⓖ 2.4% Ⓙ 240%

5. In Canada, 23.2% of the residents speak French. Which of the following is NOT equal to 23.2%? **C**

Ⓐ 0.232 Ⓒ $\frac{232}{100}$

Ⓑ $\frac{29}{125}$ Ⓓ $23\frac{1}{5}$%

6. Kimberly has completed $\frac{1}{3}$, $\frac{2}{5}$, $\frac{3}{4}$, and $\frac{1}{4}$ of the assignments in her four subjects. Which of the following shows the percent of Kimberly's assignments completed in order from least to greatest? **F**

Ⓕ 25%, 33%, 40%, 75%

Ⓖ 3%, 4%, 25%, 75%

Ⓗ 1.5%, 2.5%, 4%, 7.5%

Ⓙ 4%, 25%, 33%, 75%

7. The fraction $\frac{3}{8}$ is found between which pair of decimals on a number line? **B**

Ⓐ 0.18 and 0.24

Ⓑ 0.31 and 0.39

Ⓒ 0.42 and 0.58

Ⓓ 0.62 and 0.78

8. In the last gymnastics meet, Diane got scores of $8\frac{1}{2}$ points on the bars, 8.25 points on the beam, $8\frac{3}{8}$ points on the vault, and 8.4 points on the floor exercise. Which of the following lists her events in order from the greatest score to the least? **J**

Ⓕ Floor exercise, vault, beam, bars

Ⓖ Beam, vault, floor exercise, bars

Ⓗ Bars, vault, floor exercise, beam

Ⓙ Bars, floor exercise, vault, beam

9. In the United States, 12% of those in the labor force carpool to work. If 12%, or 23 people, carpool in a business, which equation can be used to find the number of people the business employs? **D**

Ⓐ $x = 0.12(23)$ Ⓒ $23x = 12$

Ⓑ $23 = 12x$ Ⓓ $0.12x = 23$

320

10. A pair of in-line skates is on sale for $65. This is $5 less than the original price. Which equation CANNOT be used to find the original price *g*? **J**

 Ⓕ $g - 5 = 65$ Ⓗ $65 = g - 5$
 Ⓖ $65 + 5 = g$ Ⓙ $g + 5 = 65$

11. According to the USDA, a healthy daily diet for most children includes 7 servings of bread or grains, 5 servings of vegetables, 4 servings of fruit, 3 servings of dairy products, and 2 servings of meat. A student following this eating plan eats 28 oz of food. About how many ounces should be fruit? **B**

 Ⓐ 2 oz   Ⓒ 8 oz
 Ⓑ 5 oz   Ⓓ 12 oz

12. The retail price of an item is $14, and with sales tax the total cost is $14.84. In the same store, how much would another item that is $112 cost with sales tax? **H**

 Ⓕ $112.84   Ⓗ $118.72
 Ⓖ $115.00   Ⓙ $120.00

13. A hot-air balloon travels as fast as the wind speed of the day. If a hot-air balloon travels due east 24.5 miles in 3.5 hours, about how far would the balloon travel in 5 hours? **A**

 Ⓐ 35 mi   Ⓒ 86 mi
 Ⓑ 50 mi   Ⓓ 113 mi

14. Which expression is represented by the model below? **F**

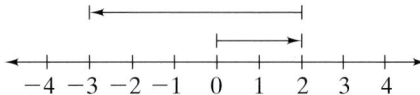

 Ⓕ $2 + -5$ Ⓗ $-5 - 2$
 Ⓖ $-2 + 5$ Ⓙ $2 - (-5)$

15. Which expression is represented by the model below? **A**

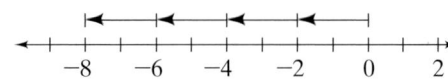

 Ⓐ 4×-2 Ⓒ -4×-2
 Ⓑ $4 - (-2)$ Ⓓ $-4 + 2$

Griddable Items

Record your answer in a grid.

16. Mr. Williams purchased 25 shares of a stock for $912.50 and later purchased 10 shares of the same stock for $181.25. What is the mean price in dollars per share for all the shares purchased? **31.25**

17. Ivana saw four different pairs of gloves that cost $9.95, $12.65, $15.00, and $11.75. What is the median cost, in dollars, of the gloves? **12.20**

TAKS GO for Help Guide

TAKS Objective	Item Numbers	GO To	TAKS Objective	Item Numbers	GO To
Obj. 5: (7.11)(B)	1–2	Lesson 6-2	Obj. 2: (7.3)(B)	11–13	Lesson 5-4
Obj. 1: (7.1)(B)	3–5	Lesson 6-2	Obj. 1: (7.2)(C)	14	Lesson 1-7
Obj. 1: (7.1)(A)	6–7	Lesson 6-2		15	Lesson 1-8
	8	Lesson 2-7	Obj. 5: (7.12)(A)	16–17	Lesson 1-10
Obj. 6: (7.14)(A)	9	Lesson 6-6			
	10	Lesson 4-3			

For additional TAKS practice, see the *TAKS Review and Preparation Workbook*.

321

7 Geometry

Chapter at a Glance

Lesson Titles, Objectives, and Features	Assessment	NCTM Standards	TEKS ★ (TAKS)
7-1 Lines and Planes • To identify segments, rays, and lines **Vocabulary Builder:** High-Use Academic Words	Lesson Quiz	3, 6, 9, 10	**TEKS** (7.14)(A) (TAKS) **Obj. 6;** Prepares for **TEKS** (7.6)(A)
7-2a Activity Lab, Hands On: Measuring Angles **7-2 Identifying and Classifying Angles** • To classify angles and to work with pairs of angles	Lesson Quiz	3, 6, 9, 10	**TEKS** (7.6)(A) (TAKS) **Obj. 3;** **TEKS** (7.13)(D); Prepares for **TEKS** (7.6)(A)
7-3a Activity Lab, Hands On: Sides and Angles of a Triangle **7-3 Triangles** • To classify triangles and to find the angle measures of triangles	Lesson Quiz	3, 6, 9, 10	**TEKS** (7.6)(B), (7.8)(C), (7.15)(A), (7.15)(B) (TAKS) **Obj. 3, 6;** Prepares for **TEKS** (7.6)(B)
7-4 Quadrilaterals and Other Polygons • To classify polygons and special quadrilaterals	Lesson Quiz Checkpoint Quiz 1	3, 6, 9, 10	**TEKS** (7.6)(B), (7.8)(C) (TAKS) **Obj. 3**
7-5 Congruent Figures • To identify congruent figures and to use them to find missing measures	Lesson Quiz	3, 6, 9, 10	**TEKS** (7.6)(D), (7.8)(C) (TAKS) **Obj. 3**
7-6 Circles • To identfy parts of a circle	Lesson Quiz	3, 6, 9, 10	Prepares for **TEKS** (7.9)(A)
7-7 Circle Graphs • To analyze and construct circle graphs 7-7b Activity Lab, Data Collection: Making a Circle Graph **Guided Problem Solving:** Percents and Circle Graphs	Lesson Quiz Checkpoint 2	3, 5, 6, 9, 10	**TEKS** (7.3)(A), (7.11)(A), (7.11)(B) (TAKS) **Obj. 2, 5**
7-8 Constructions • To construct congruent segments and perpendicular bisectors	Lesson Quiz	3, 6, 9, 10	
(TAKS) Tune-Up: Cumulative Practice			

NCTM Standards 2000
1 Number and Operations   2 Algebra   3 Geometry   4 Measurement   5 Data Analysis and Probability
6 Problem Solving   7 Reasoning and Proof   8 Communication   9 Connections   10 Representation

Correlations to Standardized Tests

All content for these tests is contained in *Prentice Hall Math,* Course 2. This chart reflects coverage in this chapter only.

	7-1	7-2	7-3	7-4	7-5	7-6	7-7	7-8
Terra Nova CAT6 (Level 17)								
Number and Number Relations								
Computation and Numerical Estimation								
Operation Concepts								
Measurement		✔						
Geometry and Spatial Sense	✔	✔	✔	✔	✔	✔	✔	✔
Data Analysis, Statistics, and Probability								
Patterns, Functions, Algebra								
Problem Solving and Reasoning	✔	✔	✔	✔	✔	✔	✔	✔
Communication								
Decimals, Fractions, Integers, and Percents							✔	
Order of Operations								
Terra Nova CTBS (Level 17)								
Decimals, Fractions, Integers, Percents								
Order of Operations, Numeration, and Number Theory								
Data Interpretation							✔	
Pre-Algebra								
Measurement		✔						
Geometry	✔	✔	✔	✔	✔	✔	✔	✔
ITBS (Level 13)								
Number Properties and Operations								
Algebra								
Geometry	✔	✔	✔	✔	✔	✔	✔	✔
Measurement		✔						
Probability and Statistics							✔	
Estimation								
SAT10 (Int 3 Level)								
Number Sense and Operations								
Patterns, Relationships, and Algebra								
Data, Statistics, and Probability							✔	
Geometry and Measurement	✔	✔	✔	✔	✔	✔	✔	✔
NAEP								
Number Sense, Properties, and Operations								
Measurement		✔						
Geometry and Spatial Sense	✔							
Data Analysis, Statistics, and Probability							✔	
Algebra and Functions								

CAT6 California Achievement Test, 6th Ed.   **CTBS** Comprehensive Test of Basic Skills   **ITBS** Iowa Test of Basic Skills, Form M
SAT10 Stanford Achievement Test, 10th Ed.   **NAEP** National Assessment of Educational Progress 2005 Mathematics Objectives

TEKS Math Background

Professional Development

Focus on the TEKS

- At Grade 7, students use properties to classify triangles and quadrilaterals (7.6)(B). Analysis of TAKS results shows that students struggle with this expectation.

  In Lessons 7-3, students classify triangles using congruent sides and angle measures. Students also classify quadralaterals and other polygons using relationships among sides and angles in Lesson 7-4. Place special emphasis on these lessons because they both focus on (7.6)(B).

- New at Grade 7 is classifying pairs of angles (7.6)(A). Students identify properties of points, lines, and planes in Lesson 7-1 (prepares for (7.6)(A)) and apply these properties to angle measures and sums of angles in Lesson 7-2 (7.6)(A).

An **angle** is formed by two rays with a common endpoint called the **vertex.** You can classify angles by their measures.

| **acute angle** | **right angle** | **obtuse angle** | **straight angle** |
| between 0° and 90° | 90° | between 90° and 180° | 180° |

If the sum of the measures of two angles is 90°, the angles are **complementary** angles. If the sum of two angles is 180°, the angles are **supplementary. Adjacent angles** share a vertex and a side but have no interior points in common. **Vertical angles** are formed by two intersecting lines and are opposite each other. Vertical angles have equal measures. Angles with equal measures are **congruent angles.**

7-1 Lines and Planes

TEKS ★ *TAKS* **Prepares for (7.6)(A)**

Math Understandings
- *Line, point,* and *plane* are the basic geometric concepts used to define all other geometric terms.
- Points, lines, and planes are ideas that do not physically exist.

A **plane** is a flat surface that extends indefinitely in all directions. **Intersecting lines** have exactly one point in common. **Parallel lines** are lines in the same plane that never intersect. **Skew lines** lie in different planes and are neither parallel nor intersecting.

7-2 Identifying and Classifying Angles

TEKS ★ *TAKS* **(7.6)(A) Obj. 3**

Math Understandings
- The measure of an angle describes the opening between the two sides, or rays, that form the angle. It does not depend on the lengths of the sides.
- You usually measure angles in terms of a circle, using the unit of a degree, or $\frac{1}{360}$, of a complete rotation about a point.

7-3 Triangles

TEKS ★ *TAKS* **(7.6)(B), (7.8)(C), (7.15)(B) Obj. 3, 6**

Math Understandings
- You can classify a triangle by the number of congruent sides it has or by its angle measures.

Congruent sides have the same length. A **scalene triangle** has no congruent sides. An **isosceles triangle** has at least two congruent sides. An **equilateral triangle** has three congruent sides. An equilateral triangle is always an isosceles triangle.

Angle Sum of a Triangle
The sum of the measures of the angles of a triangle is 180°.

A **right triangle** has one right angle. An **acute triangle** has three acute angles. An **obtuse triangle** has one obtuse angle.

7-4 Quadrilaterals and Other Polygons

TEKS ★ *TAKS* **(7.6)(B), (7.8)(C) Obj. 3**

Math Understandings
- You can classify polygons by the relationships among sides and angles.

A **polygon** is a closed plane figure with sides formed by three or more line segments. The sides meet only at endpoints.

A **parallelogram** is a quadrilateral with both pairs of opposite sides parallel.

Polygon Names	Number of Sides
triangle	3
quadrilateral	4
pentagon	5
hexagon	6
octagon	8
decagon	10

There are three special types of parallelograms: a **rectangle** has four right angles; a **rhombus** has four congruent sides; a **square** has four right angles and four congruent sides.

7-5 Congruent Figures

TEKS ★ *TAKS* (7.6)(D), (7.8)(C) Obj. 3

Math Understandings
- Corresponding parts (sides and angles) of congruent polygons are congruent.

Congruent polygons are polygons with the same size and shape. Two congruent figures have exactly the same size and shape, and you can move them so that they will coincide exactly with each other.

7-6 Circles
7-7 and Circle Graphs

TEKS ★ *TAKS* (7.11)(A), (7.11)(B) Obj. 5

Math Understandings
- In every circle, the radius is half the diameter and the diameter is twice the radius.
- A circle graph represents one whole. Percents can be used to describe parts of the whole.

A **circle** is the set of points in a plane that are all the same distance from a given point, called the *center*. A **radius** is a segment that connects the center of a circle to the circle. A **chord** is a segment that has both endpoints on the circle. A **diameter** is a segment that passes through the center of a circle and has both endpoints on the circle. A **semicircle** is an arc that is half of the circumference of a circle. A **central angle** is an angle with its vertex at the center of the circle.

7-8 Constructions

Math Understandings
- You can draw many geometric constructions using only an unmarked straightedge and a compass.
- You can use a compass and a straightedge to construct a segment congruent to a given segment.
- Any point on the perpendicular bisector of a line segment is equidistant from the endpoints of the segment.

The **midpoint** of a segment is the point that divides the segment into two segments of equal length. A **segment bisector** is a line, segment, or ray that goes through the midpoint of a segment. **Perpendicular lines** intersect to form right angles. A segment bisector that is perpendicular to a segment is the **perpendicular bisector** of the segment.

A **compass** is a geometric tool used to draw circles and arcs. An **arc** is part of a circle.

Additional Professional Development Opportunities

Math Background Notes for Chapter 7: Every lesson has a Math Backgound in the PLAN section.

Research Overview, Mathematics Strands
Additional support for these topics and more is in the front of the Teacher's Edition.

LessonLab
LessonLab, a Pearson Education company, offers comprehensive, facilitated professional development designed to help teachers to improve student achievement. To learn more, please visit lessonlab.com.

Texas Chapter 7 Resources

	7-1	7-2	7-3	7-4	7-5	7-6	7-7	7-8	For the Chapter
Print Resources									
L3 Practice	●	●	●	●	●	●	●	●	
L1 Adapted Practice	●	●	●	●	●	●	●	●	
L3 Guided Problem Solving	●	●	●	●	●	●	●	●	
L2 Reteaching	●	●	●	●	●	●	●	●	
L4 Enrichment	●	●	●	●	●	●	●	●	
L3 Daily Notetaking Guide	●	●	●	●	●	●	●	●	
L1 Adapted Daily Notetaking Guide	●	●	●	●	●	●	●	●	
L3 Vocabulary and Study Skills Worksheets	●		●	●		●		●	●
L3 Daily Puzzles	●	●	●	●	●	●	●	●	
L3 Activity Labs	●	●	●	●	●	●	●	●	
L3 Checkpoint Quiz				●			●		
L3 Chapter Project									●
L2 Chapter Test									●
L3 Chapter Test									●
L4 Alternative Assessment									●
L3 Cumulative Review									●
Spanish Resources ELL									
L3 Practice	●	●	●	●	●	●	●	●	●
L3 Vocabulary and Study Skills Worksheet	●		●	●		●		●	●
L3 Checkpoint Quiz				●			●		
L2 Chapter Test									●
L3 Chapter Test									●
L4 Alternative Assessment									●
L3 Cumulative Review									●
Transparencies									
Check Skills You'll Need	●	●	●	●	●	●	●	●	
Additional Examples	●	●	●	●	●	●	●	●	
Problem of the Day	●	●	●	●	●	●	●	●	
TAKS Daily Review	●	●	●	●	●	●	●	●	
Classroom Aid							●		
Student Edition Answers	●	●	●	●	●	●	●	●	●
Lesson Quiz	●	●	●	●	●	●	●	●	
TAKS Strategies									●
Technology									
Texas Interactive Textbook Online	●	●	●	●	●	●	●	●	●
Texas StudentExpress CD-ROM	●	●	●	●	●	●	●	●	●
Success Tracker™ Online Intervention	●	●	●	●	●	●	●	●	●
TeacherExpress CD-ROM	●	●	●	●	●	●	●	●	●
PresentationExpress CD-ROM	●	●	●	●	●	●	●	●	●
Texas ExamView CD-ROM with QuickTake	●	●	●	●	●	●	●	●	●
MindPoint Quiz Show CD-ROM	●	●	●	●	●	●	●	●	●
Prentice Hall Web Site: PHSchool.com	●	●	●	●	●	●	●	●	●

Also available: **TAKS Tune-Up Kit**
- TAKS Daily Review Transparencies
- TAKS Review and Preparation Workbook
- TAKS Strategies with Transparencies
- Texas Progress Monitoring Assessments
- Texas ExamView CD-ROM
- MindPoint Quiz Show CD-ROM

Other Resources
Algebra Readiness Tests
All-in-One Student Workbook
All-in-One Student Workbook, Adapted Version
Multilingual Handbook

Solution Key
Math Notes Study Folder
Spanish Cumulative Assessment

Where You Can Use the Lesson Resources

Here is a suggestion, following the four-step teaching plan, for how you can incorporate Differentiated Instruction resources into your teaching.

	Instructional Resources L3	Differentiated Instruction Resources
1. Plan		
Preparation Read the Math Background in the Teacher's Edition to connect this lesson with students' previous experience. **Starting Class** **Check Skills You'll Need** Assign these exercises to review prerequisite skills. **TEKS** ★ **TAKS** Review the full text of the TEKS student expectations and TAKS objectives covered in this lesson. **New Vocabulary** Help students pre-read the lesson by pointing out the new terms introduced in the lesson.	**TEKS Math Background** **Math Understandings** **Transparencies & PresentationExpress CD-ROM** Check Skills You'll Need Problem of the Day TAKS Daily Review **Resources** Vocabulary and Study Skills	**Spanish Support** ELL Vocabulary and Study Skills
2. Teach		
L3 Guided Instruction Use the Activity Labs to build conceptual understanding. Teach each Example. Use the Teacher's Edition side column notes for specific teaching tips, including Error Prevention notes. Use the Additional Examples found in the side column (and on transparency and PowerPoint) as an alternative presentation for the content. After each Example, assign the Quick Check exercise for that Example to get an immediate assessment of student understanding. Use the Closure activity in the Teacher's Edition to help students attain mastery of lesson content.	**Student Edition** Activity Lab **Resources** Daily Notetaking Guide Activity Lab **Transparencies & PresentationExpress CD-ROM** Additional Examples Classroom Aids **Texas ExamView CD-ROM with QuickTake**	**Teacher's Edition** Every lesson includes suggestions for working with students who need special attention. L1 Special Needs L2 Below Level L4 Advanced Learners ELL English Language Learners **Resources** L1 Adapted Daily Notetaking Guide **Multilingual Handbook**
3. Practice		
Assignment Guide **Check Your Understanding** Use these questions to check students' understanding before you assign homework. **Homework Exercises** Assign homework from these leveled exercises in the Assignment Guide. 　A Practice by Example 　B Apply Your Skills 　C Challenge 　**TAKS** Tune-Up and Mixed Review **Homework Quick Check** Use these key exercises to quickly check students' homework.	**Transparencies & PresentationExpress CD-ROM** Student Answers **Resources** Practice Guided Problem Solving Vocabulary and Study Skills Activity Lab Daily Puzzles **Texas ExamView CD-ROM with QuickTake**	**Spanish Support** ELL Practice ELL Vocabulary and Study Skills **Resources** L1 Adapted Practice L4 Enrichment
4. Assess & Reteach		
Lesson Quiz Assign the Lesson Quiz to assess students' mastery of the lesson content. **Checkpoint Quiz** Use the Checkpoint Quiz to assess student progress over several lessons.	**Transparencies & PresentationExpress CD-ROM** Lesson Quiz **Resources** Checkpoint Quiz	**Resources** L2 Reteaching ELL Checkpoint Quiz Success Tracker™ Online Intervention **Texas ExamView CD-ROM with QuickTake**

KEY　L1 Special Needs　L2 Below Level　L3 For All Students　L4 Advanced, Gifted　ELL English Language Learners

Check Your Readiness

Answers are in the back of the textbook.

For intervention, direct students to:

Comparing Integers
Lesson 1-6
Extra Skills and Word
  Problems Practice, Ch. 1

Solving One-Step Equations
Lesson 4-3
Extra Skills and Word
  Problems Practice, Ch. 4

Solving Proportions
Lesson 5-4
Extra Skills and Word
  Problems Practice, Ch. 5

Finding a Percent of a Number
Lesson 6-4
Extra Skills and Word
  Problems Practice, Ch. 6

What You've Learned
TEKS ★ TAKS

- **(7.6)(D)** In Chapter 5, you used critical attributes to define similarity. **TAKS** Obj. 3
- **(7.3)(B)** You found solutions to application problems involving proportional relationships, such as similarity, scaling, and related measurement units. **TAKS** Obj. 2
- **(7.3)(A)** In Chapter 6, you found solutions to application problems involving percent. **TAKS** Obj. 2

 Check Your Readiness

Comparing Integers

Compare using <, =, or >.

1. $83\ \boxed{<}\ 90$
2. $120\ \boxed{>}\ 99$
3. $0\ \boxed{>}\ -47$
4. $-21\ \boxed{<}\ -11$

Solving One-Step Equations

Solve each equation.

5. $d + 17 = 19$ 2
6. $m - 12 = 3$ 15
7. $j - 5 = 7$ 12
8. $m - 15 = 90$ 105
9. $58 + n = 63$ 5
10. $y + 86 = 180$ 94

Solving Proportions

Solve each proportion.

11. $\frac{5}{16} = \frac{25}{w}$ 80
12. $\frac{n}{12} = \frac{20}{15}$ 16
13. $\frac{18}{k} = \frac{6}{37}$ 111
14. $\frac{23}{12} = \frac{x}{24}$ 46

Finding a Percentage of a Number

Find each answer.

15. 30% of 360
    108
16. 24% of 360
    86.4
17. 4.5% of 360
    16.2
18. 18% of 360
    64.8

GO for Help

For Exercises	See Lesson
1–4	1-6
5–10	4-3
11–14	5-4
15–18	6-4

Patterns, Relationships, and Algebraic Thinking
TEKS (7.3)(A)
TAKS Obj. 2

Geometry and Spatial Reasoning
TEKS (7.6)(A), (7.6)(B), (7.6)(D), (7.8)(C)
TAKS Obj. 3

Probability and Statistics
TEKS (7.11)(A), (7.11)(B)
TAKS Obj. 5

Underlying Processes and Mathematical Tools
TEKS (7.14)(A), (7.15)(A), (7.15)(B)
TAKS Obj. 6;
TEKS (7.13)(D)

Chapter 7 Overview

In this chapter, students work with plane geometry concepts. They learn about the properties of lines and angles. Then they classify angles according to their degree measures. They work with triangles, quadrilaterals, and other polygons, including congruent figures. Next, they investigate circles and circle graphs. They conclude the chapter by focusing on constructions.

Activating Prior Knowledge

In this chapter, students will build on their knowledge of angles such as adjacent angles, supplementary angles, and complementary angles. They learn to classify angles by their degree measures and their relationship to other angles. They draw upon their knowledge of triangles to classify and name them by the measures of their angles and lengths of their sides.
Ask questions such as:
• *What are some names for different types of triangles?*
Sample: an equilateral triangle, an isosceles triangle, a scalene triangle
• *Describe an angle.* Sample: the opening formed by two lines that intersect

What You'll Learn Next
TEKS ★ TAKS

• **(7.6)(A)** In this chapter, you will use angle measurements to classify pairs of angles as complementary or supplementary. **TAKS** Obj. 3

• **(7.6)(B)** You will use properties to classify triangles and quadrilaterals. **TAKS** Obj. 3

• **(7.11)(A)** You will select and use an appropriate presentation for presenting and displaying relationships among collected data, including circle graphs. **TAKS** Obj. 5

TAKS Tune-Up On pages 369–371, you will review and practice the vocabulary and *TAKS* objectives you have learned.

🔊 Key Vocabulary

• acute triangle (p. 337)
• circle graph (p. 354)
• complementary (p. 331)
• equilateral triangle (p. 336)
• isosceles triangle (p. 336)
• obtuse triangle (p. 337)
• parallel lines (p. 325)
• parallelogram (p. 341)
• rectangle (p. 341)
• regular polygon (p. 340)
• rhombus (p. 341)
• right triangle (p. 337)
• scalene triangle (p. 336)
• square (p. 341)
• supplementary (p. 331)
• trapezoid (p. 341)

Chapter 7 **323**

323

Lines and Planes

What You'll Learn

To identify segments, rays, and lines

- Prepares for **TEKS (7.6)(A)** To use angle measurements to classify pairs of angles as complementary or supplementary

 New Vocabulary point, line, ray, segment, plane, intersecting lines, parallel lines, skew lines

TEKS Math Background

Points are the basis of all geometry. Points have no height, width, or length so they are called zero-dimensional. A *point* indicates an exact position. A *line* is a series of points that extends in opposite directions without end, making a line one-dimensional. A *ray* is part of a line with one endpoint and extends forever in one direction. A *line segment* is a part of a line with two endpoints. A *plane* is a two-dimensional figure that extends indefinitely.

More Math Background: p. 322C

Lesson Planning and Resources

See p. 322E for a list of the resources that support this lesson.

 Bell Ringer Practice

✓ Check Skills You'll Need
Use student page, transparency, or PowerPoint.

TAKS Daily Review 49
Use transparency.

✓ Check Skills You'll Need

1. Vocabulary Review
List the five *inequality* symbols.
$<, >, \le, \ge, \ne$
Graph the solution of each inequality.

2. $x \le -3$ **3.** $x < 1$

4. $x \le 2$ **5.** $x \ge 5$

6. $x > 1$ **7.** $x < 4$

2–7. See back of book.

GO for Help
Lesson 4-7

Why Learn This?

City maps show parallel and intersecting streets. A statement such as "W. 4th St. runs parallel to W. 3rd St." can help you give and understand directions.

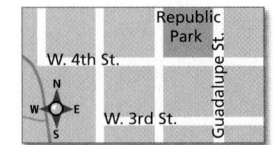

A **point** is a location. A point has no size. You name a point by a capital letter.

A **line** is a series of points that extend in opposite directions without end. You name a line by any two points on the line or by a lowercase letter.

$\overleftrightarrow{AB}, \overleftrightarrow{BA}, n$

A **ray** is part of a line with one endpoint and all the points of the line on one side of the endpoint. You name a ray using two points, starting with the endpoint.

$\overrightarrow{BA}$, ray BA

A **segment** is part of a line with two endpoints and all points in between. You name a segment by its endpoints.

$\overline{AB}, \overline{BA}$

EXAMPLE Naming Segments, Rays, and Lines

1 Use the points in each diagram to name the figure shown.

a. $\overline{XY}$ **b.** $\overleftrightarrow{GR}$ **c.** $\overrightarrow{JT}$

✓ Quick Check

1. Use the points in each diagram to name the figure shown.

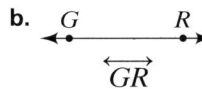

a. $\overrightarrow{PD}$ **b.** $\overline{RS}$ **c.** $\overleftrightarrow{AV}$

Differentiated Instruction Solutions for All Learners

Special Needs L1
Students often have a difficult time visualizing skew lines, since they are neither parallel nor intersecting. Take opportunities to show them skew lines around the classroom. Have them trace with their finger a pair of skew lines on their desks.

learning style: tactile

Below Level L2
Have students model parallel, intersecting, and skew lines as shown in Example 2 with toothpicks or pipe cleaners.

learning style: tactile

A **plane** is a flat surface that extends indefinitely in all directions and has no thickness. There are two planes in the diagram below.

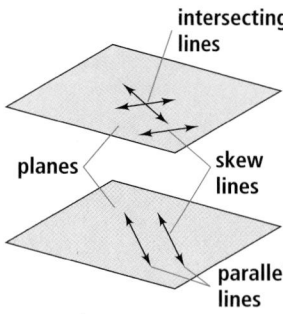

intersecting lines

planes

skew lines

parallel lines

Intersecting lines lie in the same plane. **Intersecting lines** have exactly one point in common. **Parallel lines** are lines in the same plane that never intersect. Parallel segments and rays lie in parallel lines.

Skew lines lie in different planes. They are neither parallel nor intersecting.

EXAMPLE Intersecting, Parallel, and Skew

2 **Architecture** Use the information in the photograph and diagram below to name a segment with the given description.

a. a segment parallel to $\overline{AB}$

$\overline{GH}$ lies in the same plane as $\overline{AB}$. $\overline{GH}$ does not intersect $\overline{AB}$.

$\overline{GH}$ is parallel to $\overline{AB}$.

b. a segment skew to $\overline{AB}$

$\overline{EF}$ lies in a different plane. $\overline{EF}$ is not parallel to $\overline{AB}$ and does not intersect $\overline{AB}$.

$\overline{EF}$ is skew to $\overline{AB}$.

2a. $\overline{EF}, \overline{HD}$
b. $\overline{EB}, \overline{CB}, \overline{AB}, \overline{GH}, \overline{DH}$
c. $\overline{FC}, \overline{EF}, \overline{BC}, \overline{HD}$

✓ **Quick Check**

2. Name the segments in the diagram that fit each description.
   a. parallel to $\overline{BC}$ b. intersect $\overline{BH}$ c. skew to $\overline{AG}$

---

2. Teach

Activity Lab

Use before the lesson.

All in One Teaching Resources
Activity Lab 7-1: Lines and Planes

Guided Instruction

Example 1
• *Which of the figures could be named differently?* $\overrightarrow{XY}$ can be $\overrightarrow{YX}$ and $\overleftrightarrow{GR}$ can be $\overleftrightarrow{RG}$.
• *Why can ray JT not be named differently?* The name of the ray begins with the endpoint.

PowerPoint

Additional Examples

1 Use the points in each diagram to name the figure.
   a. $R \quad\quad S$ $\overline{RS}$
   b. $J \quad K$ $\overleftrightarrow{JK}$
   c. $A \quad\quad B$ $\overrightarrow{BA}$

2 Name all the segments that have each characteristic.

   a. parallel to $\overline{UT}$ $\overline{RS}, \overline{WZ}$
   b. intersecting $\overline{RU}$ $\overline{WU}, \overline{TU}, \overline{WR}, \overline{RS}$
   c. skew to $\overline{RS}$ $\overline{WU}, \overline{ZT}$

All in One Teaching Resources
• Daily Notetaking Guide 7-1 **L3**
• Adapted Notetaking 7-1 **L1**

Closure

• Describe a line, a line segment, and a ray. A line is a series of points that extends in two directions indefinitely. A line segment is part of a line with two endpoints. A ray is part of a line with one endpoint.

---

3. Practice

Assignment Guide

Check Your Understanding
Go over Exercises 1–8 in class before assigning the Homework Exercises.

Homework Exercises
A Practice by Example 9–17
B Apply Your Skills 18–30
C Challenge 31
TEKS ★ TAKS Tune-Up and Mixed Review 32–36

Homework Quick Check
To check students' understanding of key skills and concepts, go over Exercises 11, 16, 23, 27, and 30.

Differentiated Instruction **Resources**

326

✓ Check Your Understanding

2. No. The lines could be either skew or parallel. If they were in the same plane, then they would be parallel.

1. **Vocabulary** __?__ are lines that are neither parallel nor intersecting. Skew lines
2. **Reasoning** Two lines do not intersect. Can you conclude that they are parallel? Explain. See left.

Use the points in each diagram to name the figure shown.

3. L ———————— C $\overline{LC}$

4. ←— M R —→ $\overleftrightarrow{MR}$

5. ←—— K E $\overrightarrow{KE}$

6. O D ——→ $\overrightarrow{OD}$

Use the diagram for Exercises 7 and 8.

7. Name all the segments parallel to $\overline{AD}$. $\overline{BC}$, $\overline{FE}$

8. Name all the segments intersecting $\overline{FG}$. $\overline{BC}$, $\overline{AD}$, $\overline{FE}$

Homework Exercises

For more exercises, see Extra Skills and Word Problems.

Ⓐ Use the points in each diagram to name the figure shown.
9–14. See left.

GO for Help

For Exercises	See Examples
9–14	1
15–17	2

9. L ———————— C

10. ←— W A —

11. ←— Z V

12. P F —→

13. Q ———————— S

14. ←— G H —→

9. $\overline{LC}$
10. $\overrightarrow{AW}$
11. $\overleftrightarrow{ZV}$
12. $\overrightarrow{PF}$
13. $\overline{QS}$
14. $\overleftrightarrow{GH}$

Buildings Use the diagram at the right for Exercises 15–17.

15. Name all the segments skew to $\overline{BC}$. $\overline{AE}$, $\overline{EF}$, $\overline{DH}$, $\overline{GH}$

16. Name all the segments intersecting $\overline{AD}$. $\overline{AB}$, $\overline{AE}$, $\overline{CD}$, $\overline{DH}$

17. Name all the segments parallel to $\overline{EH}$. $\overline{AD}$, $\overline{FG}$

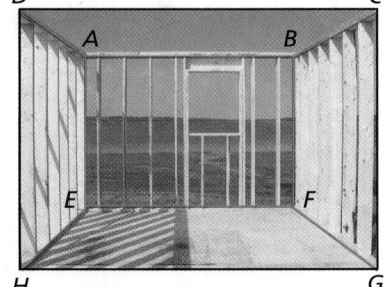

Ⓑ GPS 18. **Guided Problem Solving** Describe a route from A to B that includes Main St. and a street parallel to Main St.
   • What street is parallel to Main St.?
   • What street(s) connect Main St. and Lee Ave.? 18–19. See margin.

19. Use the map shown in Exercise 18. Describe a route from A to B that includes Oak St. and a street that intersects Oak St.

Exercises 18–19. Answers may vary. Samples are given.

18. From point A, go along Clark St to Main Street. Turn right on Main Street. Turn left on Lee Street. Then turn right on Hope Street. Continue on Hope Street to point B at the corner of Hope and Oak Streets.

19. From point A, go along Clark Street to Main Street. Turn right on Main Street. Then turn left on Oak Street. Continue on Oak Street to point B at the corner of Hope and Oak Streets.

Tell whether each figure below contains ray AB.

20.
A B
no

21.
A B
yes

22.
A B
no

23. Are the rungs on a ladder parallel, intersecting, or skew?
GPS parallel

Draw each figure. 24–28. See margin.

24. $\overleftrightarrow{AD}$

25. $\overline{QW}$

26. $\overleftrightarrow{PR}$

27. $\overrightarrow{FG}$ intersecting $\overleftrightarrow{TU}$

28. $\overrightarrow{TB}$ and $\overrightarrow{TA}$ on the same line

29. **Error Analysis** Jim says that in the box shown at the left $\overleftrightarrow{EF}$ and $\overleftrightarrow{GH}$ are parallel, since they do not intersect. Why is Jim incorrect?
See left.

30. **Writing in Math** Describe examples of parallel, intersecting, and skew lines in your classroom.
See left.

29. $\overleftrightarrow{EF}$ and $\overleftrightarrow{GH}$ do not lie in the same plane.

30. Answers may vary. Samples are given. Parallel: top and bottom edges of a doorway; Intersecting: the lines in the addition symbol; Skew: the top of a doorway and the side of a desk

C 31. **Gabge** Name each segment, ray, and line in the figure below.

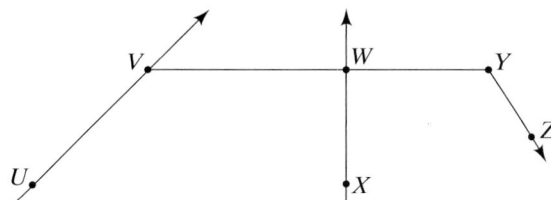

$\overleftrightarrow{UV}, \overrightarrow{UV}, \overrightarrow{UV}, \overrightarrow{VU}, \overrightarrow{VW}, \overrightarrow{VY},$
$\overrightarrow{WY}, \overleftrightarrow{WX}, \overrightarrow{WX}, \overrightarrow{XW}, \overline{WX},$
$\overrightarrow{YZ}, \overline{YZ}$

  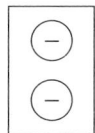 **TEKS ★ TAKS Tune-Up and Mixed Review**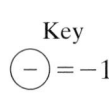

TAKS Objective 1
TEKS (7.1)(B)

32. An advertisement offers you 0.3% off your next purchase. What fraction of the original price does this represent? **C**

Ⓐ $\frac{3}{10}$ Ⓑ $\frac{3}{100}$ Ⓒ $\frac{3}{1,000}$ Ⓓ $\frac{3}{10,000}$

TAKS Objective 1
TEKS (7.2)(C)

33. Which expression does the model represent? **F**

Key
$\ominus = -1$

Ⓕ $3 \times (-2)$ Ⓖ $2 \times (-3)$ Ⓗ $2 \times (-2)$ Ⓙ 3×3

TAKS Objective 2
TEKS (7.4)(A)

34. Which formula shows z, the number of milliliters that result when you add x milliliters to y liters? **D**

Ⓐ $z = 100x + y$ Ⓒ $z = 100y + x$
Ⓑ $z = 1,000x + y$ Ⓓ $z = 1,000y + x$

GO for Help   Lesson 6-8

Find the percent of change. Is the change an increase or a decrease?

35. original: $5.75; new: $6.25
about 9% increase

36. original: 380 ft; new: 320 ft
about 16% decrease

24–28. See back of book.

TEKS ★ TAKS Resources

• TAKS Strategies, p. 365
• TAKS Tune-Up, pp. 369–371

TAKS Tune-Up Kit

• TAKS Daily Review Transparencies
• TAKS Review and Preparation Workbook
• TAKS Strategies with Transparencies
• Texas Progress Monitoring Assessments

Lesson Quiz

Use the diagram for questions 1–3.

1. parallel lines Sample: $\overleftrightarrow{AC}$ and $\overleftrightarrow{BD}$

2. all the rays that have B as an endpoint $\overrightarrow{BJ}, \overrightarrow{BG}, \overrightarrow{BD}, \overrightarrow{BA}$ or $\overrightarrow{BE}$

3. a segment on $\overleftrightarrow{AC}$ $\overline{AC}$ or $\overline{CA}, \overline{AI}$ or $\overline{IA}, \overline{CI}$ or $\overline{IC}$

Alternative Assessment

Have students work in pairs. Each student takes a turn drawing and labeling one of the figures discussed in this lesson. His or her partner names the figure verbally and with symbolic notation.

327

High-Use Academic Words

Students learn a strategy for learning words that, while not math vocabulary terms, are important for success in mathematics and on tests.

Guided Instruction

Have students look through their texts for use of the terms: *classify, sketch,* and *identify.* Ask the following questions:
- *Where do you find the term* classify? Sample: page 13, above Exercises 6–8
- *What is another way to say "Which of the triangles are congruent?"* Sample: Identify the congruent triangles.
- *If you sketched a quadrilateral, what would you sketch?* Sample: a closed plane figure with sides formed by four line segments

Teaching Tip
Restate directions given in the text using *classify, sketch,* and *identify* as appropriate to familiarize students with these terms.

Differentiated Instruction

English Language Learners   **ELL**
Encourage students to write high-use academic words in their native language as needed.

TEKS ★ (TAKS) Resources

- Vocabulary and Study Skills Worksheets

Dana Center TEKS Toolkit Clarifying Activities (7.14)(A)
Visit: PHSchool.com
Web Code: arq-9045

328

Vocabulary Builder

High-Use Academic Words

High-use academic words are words that you will see often in textbooks and on tests. These words are not math vocabulary terms, but knowing them will help you succeed in mathematics.

TEKS ★ (TAKS)
(7.14)(A) To communicate mathematical ideas using language (TAKS) Obj. 6

Direction Words

Some words tell what to do in a problem. I need to understand what these words are asking so that I give the correct answer.

Word	Meaning
Classify	To arrange or group things according to their characteristics
Sketch	To draw something without using a scale
Identify	To recognize and be able to tell what something is

Exercises

1. Identify the sport in which the ball shown at the right is used.
   football
2. Classify each sport as played by a *team* or by an *individual.*
   a. basketball team   b. golf individual   c. volleyball team   d. billiards individual

3. There are six pairs of lines in the diagram at the right. Classify each pair of lines as *intersecting* or *parallel.* See margin.

4. Sketch a floor plan of your school's cafeteria.
   Check students' work.
5. Sketch a line segment and a ray that share endpoint *T.* Check students' work.

6. Identify the ray shown at the right.

7. **Word Knowledge** Think about the word *justify.* 7a–c. Check students' work.
   a. Choose the letter for how well you know the word.
      A. I know its meaning.
      B. I've seen it, but I don't know its meaning.
      C. I don't know it.
   b. **Research** Look up and write the definition of *justify.*
   c. Use the word in a sentence involving mathematics.

328   Vocabulary Builder   High-Use Academic Words

3. $\overleftrightarrow{FG}$ and $\overleftrightarrow{RS}$, parallel
   $\overleftrightarrow{FG}$ and $\overleftrightarrow{BC}$, intersect
   $\overleftrightarrow{FG}$ and $\overleftrightarrow{KL}$, intersect
   $\overleftrightarrow{RS}$ and $\overleftrightarrow{BC}$, intersect
   $\overleftrightarrow{RS}$ and $\overleftrightarrow{KL}$, intersect
   $\overleftrightarrow{BC}$ and $\overleftrightarrow{KL}$, parallel

Hands On

TEKS ★ TAKS

(7.13)(D) To select tools such as real objects to solve problems

Prepares for **TEKS** (7.6)(A) To use angle measurements to classify pairs of angles as complementary or supplementary

Measuring Angles

An angle (∠) has two sides and a vertex. Angles are measured in degrees (°). You can estimate the measure of an angle before measuring.

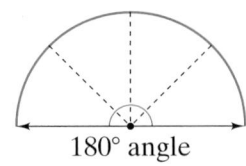

45° angle
(half of a right angle)

180° angle
(a straight angle)

90° angle
(a right angle)

135° angle
(a right angle and a 45° angle)

EXAMPLE Measuring Angles

What is the measure of ∠X at the right?

Estimate ∠X is larger than a 90° angle and smaller than a 135° angle. You can estimate that the measure of ∠X is between 90° and 135°.

Step 1 Place your protractor on the vertex of the angle, as shown.

Step 2 Make sure that one side of the angle passes through zero on one of the protractor's scales.

Step 3 Read the same scale where it intersects the second side of the angle.

The measure of ∠X is 110°. You can write this as $m\angle X = 110°$.

Check for Reasonableness The measure of ∠X is between 90° and 135°. The protractor measure of 110° is reasonable.

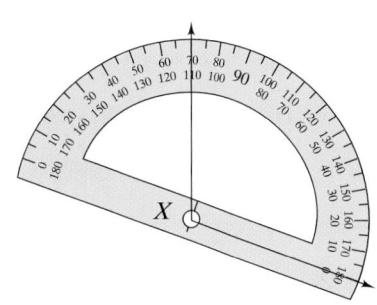

Exercises

Estimate each angle. Then use your protractor to measure each angle.

1.

A

21°

2.

B

120°

3.

C

166°

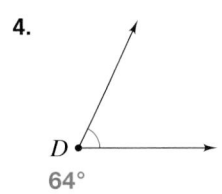

4.

D

64°

Activity Lab

Measuring Angles

Guided Instruction

Ask: *Which scale on the protractor are you using to measure the angle, the upper scale or lower scale?* lower

Activity

Have students work in pairs to do Exercises 1–4. One student estimates the angle for Exercises 1 and 2; the other measures it. Students reverse roles for Exercises 3 and 4.

TEKS ★ TAKS Resources

• Activity Lab 7-2: Angles and Parallel Lines
• protractor

Dana Center TEKS Toolkit Clarifying Activities (7.13)(D)
Visit: **Visit:** PHSchool.com
Web Code: arq-9045

329

TEKS ★ TAKS

(7.6)(A) To use angle measurements to classify pairs of angles as complementary or supplementary **TAKS** Obj. 3

Dana Center TEKS Toolkit Clarifying Activities (7.6)(A)
Visit: PHSchool.com
Web Code: arq-9045

TEKS Math Background

An *angle* is formed when two lines, line segments, or rays meet at a common point called the *vertex*. An angle formed by rays $\overrightarrow{BA}$ and $\overrightarrow{BC}$ can be named: ∠ABC, ∠CBA, or ∠B for short. The *measure* of an angle is indicated by the lowercase *m*, as in *m*∠B, in degrees.

When two lines intersect, four pairs of adjacent angles and two pairs of vertical angles are formed. *Adjacent angles* share a side and are supplementary (add to 180°). *Vertical angles* are opposite each other and are congruent (have equal measures).

More Math Background: p. 322C

Lesson Planning and Resources

See p. 2E for a list of the resources that support this lesson.

PowerPoint
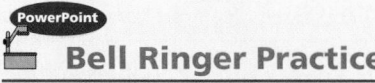
Bell Ringer Practice

☑ **Check Skills You'll Need**
Use student page, transparency, or PowerPoint.

TAKS **Daily Review 50**
Use transparency.

✓ Check Skills You'll Need

1. Vocabulary Review
What do you call a mathematical sentence with an equal sign? **equation**

Use mental math to solve each equation.

2. $\ell + 20 = 90$ **70**

3. $n + 40 = 180$ **140**

4. $p + 16 = 90$ **74**

5. $s + 22 = 180$ **158**

  for Help
Lesson 4-2

Vocabulary Tip

The ⌐ symbol indicates a right angle. Write "the measure of ∠C" as *m*∠C.

TEKS ★ TAKS

• (7.6)(A) To use angle measurements to classify pairs of angles as complementary or supplementary **TAKS** Obj. 3

🔊 **New Vocabulary** angle, vertex, acute angle, right angle, obtuse angle, straight angle, complementary, supplementary, adjacent angles, vertical angles, congruent angles

Why Learn This?

Architects think about angles in the structures they design. If you can measure angles, you can predict how different geometric figures can fit together.

The design of a geodesic dome requires triangles, because triangles have exactly three angles. They make the dome stable.

An **angle** (∠) is a figure formed by two rays with a common endpoint. You can call the angle below ∠DCE, ∠ECD, ∠C, or ∠1.

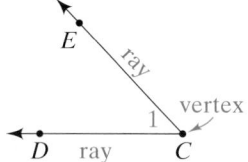

A **vertex** is the point of intersection of two sides of an angle or figure. The plural of *vertex* is *vertices*.

You can classify angles by their measures.

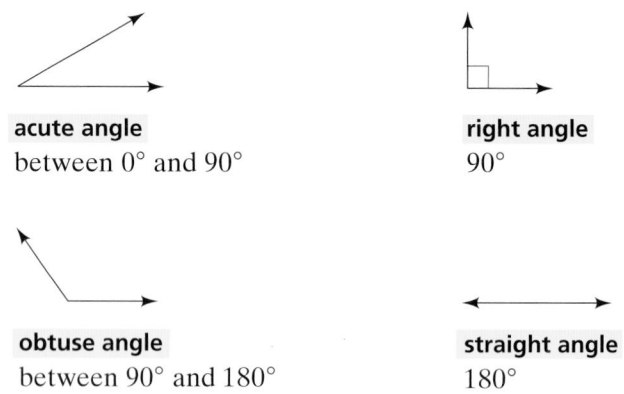

acute angle
between 0° and 90°

right angle
90°

obtuse angle
between 90° and 180°

straight angle
180°

Differentiated Instruction **Solutions for All Learners**

Special Needs L1
It may be hard for some students to see the angle in the straight line. Redraw the angles, and erase everything but the vertical line along the bottom. Explain that the angles form this line which is equal to 180°.

learning style: visual

Below Level L2
Have students fold three pieces of cardstock in half and turn them on edge. Students can adjust the fold to model acute, right, and obtuse angles.

learning style: tactile

EXAMPLE Identifying Angles

① **Architecture** Part of a geodesic dome is shown at the right. Identify all the acute angles.

∠NEF, ∠FAN, ∠NAB, ∠ABN, ∠BNA, ∠NBC, ∠CDN, ∠NDE, ∠DEN, and ∠END are acute.

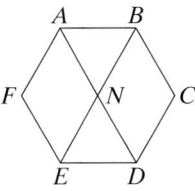

✓ **Quick Check**

● 1. Classify ∠AFE as *acute, right, obtuse,* or *straight.* obtuse

If the sum of the measures of two angles is 90°, the angles are **complementary.** If the sum is 180°, the angles are **supplementary.**

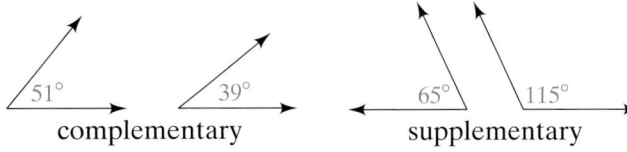

complementary   supplementary

EXAMPLE Finding Complements and Supplements

② **TAKS Multiple Choice** If ∠A and ∠B are supplementary and the measure of ∠A is 37°, what is the measure of ∠B?

Ⓐ 43°   Ⓑ 53°   Ⓒ 143°   Ⓓ 153°

Write an equation. Let x = the measure of ∠B.

$x + 37° = 180°$ ← The angles are supplementary.

$x + 37° - 37° = 180° - 37°$ ← Subtract 37° from each side.

$x = 143°$ ← Simplify.

The measure of ∠B is 143°. The answer is C.

✓ **Quick Check**

● 2. Find the measure of the complement of ∠A in Example 2. 53°

Adjacent angles share a vertex and a side but have no interior points in common. Angles 1 and 2 are adjacent angles. Adjacent angles formed by two intersecting lines are supplementary.

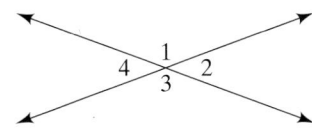

Angles 1 and 3 above are vertical angles. **Vertical angles** are formed by two intersecting lines and are opposite each other. Vertical angles have equal measures. Angles with equal measures are **congruent angles.**

7-2 Identifying and Classifying Angles   **331**

---

2. Teach

Activity Lab

Use before the lesson.
Student Edition Activity Lab, Hands On 7-2a Measuring Angles, p. 329

All in One Teaching Resources

Activity Lab 7-2: Angles and Parallel Lines

Guided Instruction

Example 1
Ask: *Put the four types of angles in order from greatest measure to least measure.* straight, obtuse, right, acute

Error Prevention!

Students may confuse the terms *supplementary* and *complementary.* Invite them to suggest mnemonic devices to remember how they differ. For example, *complementary* is before *supplementary* alphabetically, and 90 is before 180 numerically.

Science Connection

An astrolabe measures the angles formed by a star in the sky and the horizon. Early sailors used the astrolabe to navigate the seas.

PowerPoint
Additional Examples

① Identify the acute angles, obtuse angles, and straight angles in the figure.

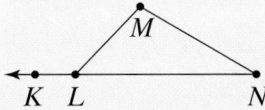

acute: ∠MLN, ∠MNL
obtuse: ∠KLM, ∠LMN
straight: ∠KLN

② The measure of ∠Q is 49°. Find the measure of its complement. 41°

Advanced Learners L4
Can an angle be larger than 180°? Explain. Sample: Yes, the exterior angle for any angle less than 180° is greater than 180°.

Pre-AP™

English Language Learners ELL
Help students use language to connect terms to one another. For example, ask them to state the relationship between vertical angles and congruent angles. Vertical angles are congruent, but not all congruent angles are vertical.

learning style: verbal

331

Additional Examples

3 Find the measures of ∠1, ∠2, and ∠4, if m∠3 = 32°.
m∠1 = 32°, m∠2 = 148°, and m∠4 = 148°

Closure

- *What are acute, obtuse, right, and straight angles?* Acute angles are greater than 0° and less than 90°; obtuse angles are greater than 90° and less than 180°; right angles are equal to 90°, and straight angles are equal to 180° or a straight line.
- *What are complementary and supplementary angles?* Complementary angles are two angles that add to 90°. Supplementary angles are two angles that add to 180°.
- *What are vertical and adjacent angles?* When two lines intersect, vertical angles are opposite each other; adjacent angles share a side and a vertex and are supplementary.

EXAMPLE Finding Angle Measures

3 (**Algebra**) Find the measures of ∠1, ∠2, and ∠3, for m∠4 = 128°.

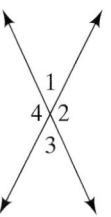

$m\angle 1 = 180° - 128°$ ← ∠1 and ∠4 are supplementary.
$= 52°$

$m\angle 2 = 128°$ ← ∠2 and ∠4 are vertical angles.

$m\angle 3 = 52°$ ← ∠1 and ∠3 are vertical angles.

✓ Quick Check

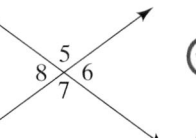

3. In the diagram at the left, $m\angle 8 = 72°$. Find the measures of ∠5, ∠6, and ∠7. **108°; 72°; 108°**

● More Than One Way

If $m\angle 1 = 140°$ and $m\angle 2 = 40°$, what is $m\angle 3$?

Carlos's Method

∠3 and ∠1 are across from each other, so they are vertical angles. Since vertical angles have the same measure, $m\angle 3 = m\angle 1$.

So $m\angle 3 = 140°$.

Brianna's Method

∠2 and ∠3 together form a straight angle, so their measures add up to 180°. This means that they are supplementary angles.

$$40° + m\angle 3 = 180°$$
$$40° - 40° + m\angle 3 = 180° - 40°$$ ← Subtract 40° from each side.
$$m\angle 3 = 140°$$ ← Simplify.

So $m\angle 3$ is 140°.

More Than One Way

155°; methods and explanations may vary.

Choose a Method

In the figure at the right, $m\angle BEC = 25°$ and $m\angle CED = 155°$. Find $m\angle AEB$. Explain why you chose the method you used.

Check Your Understanding

1. Vertical angles lie opposite each other, while adjacent angles lie next to each other.

1. **Vocabulary** How are vertical angles and adjacent angles different? **See left.**

2. **Reasoning** What is the sum of the measures of the four angles formed by intersecting lines?
   360°

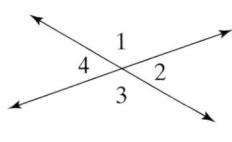

Classify each angle as *acute, right, obtuse,* or *straight*. Then find the measures of the complement and the supplement of each angle.

3. $m\angle A = 45°$
   acute, 45°, 135°

4. $m\angle B = 105°$
   obtuse, none, 75°

5. $m\angle C = 75°$
   acute, 15°, 105°

Homework Exercises

For more exercises, see Extra Skills and Word Problems.

 GO for Help

For Exercises	See Examples
6–8	1
9–17	2
18–20	3

Ⓐ **Classify each angle as *acute, right, obtuse,* or *straight*.**

6.
   acute

7.
   obtuse

8.
   straight

9. 11°; 101°

10. 23°; 113°

11. 78°; 168°

12. 66.5°; 156.5°

13. 52.4°; 142.4°

14. 42.1°; 132.1°

15. 33.6°; 123.6°

16. 14.9°; 104.9°

17. 7.8°; 97.8°

(**Algebra**) **Find the measures of the complement and the supplement of each angle.** **9–17. See left.**

9. $m\angle G = 79°$

10. $m\angle H = 67°$

11. $m\angle J = 12°$

12. $m\angle A = 23.5°$

13. $m\angle B = 37.6°$

14. $m\angle C = 47.9°$

15. $m\angle D = 56.4°$

16. $m\angle E = 75.1°$

17. $m\angle F = 82.2°$

(**Algebra**) **In the diagram at the right, $m\angle 2 = 123°$. Find the measure of each angle.**

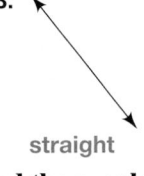

18. $m\angle 1$ **57°**

19. $m\angle 3$ **57°**

20. $m\angle 4$ **123°**

Ⓑ **GPS** 21. **Guided Problem Solving** Engineers designed a metal support that forms a 65° angle with a dam. Find the measure of the angle's supplement. **115°**

$$x + 65° = \blacksquare$$
$$x + 65° - \blacksquare = 180° - \blacksquare$$
$$x = \blacksquare$$

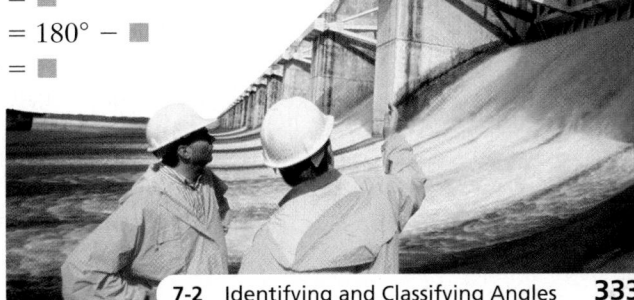

◐nline lesson quiz, PHSchool.com, **Web Code:** ara-0702

7-2 Identifying and Classifying Angles **333**

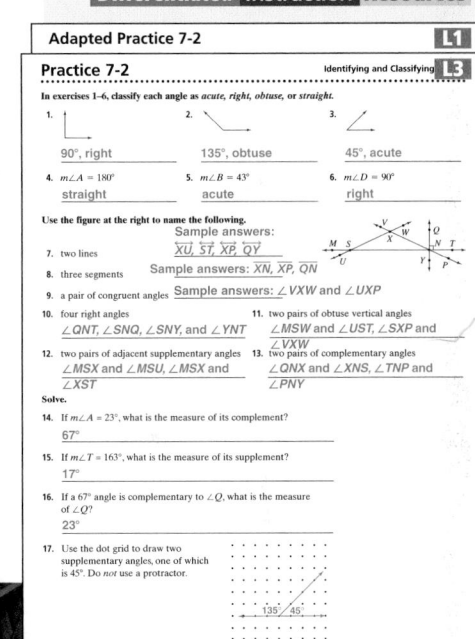

Assignment Guide

Check Your Understanding
Go over Exercises 1–5 in class before assigning the Homework Exercises.

Homework Exercises
A Practice by Example   6–20
B Apply Your Skills   21–31
C Challenge   32
TEKS ★ **TAKS** Tune-Up and Mixed Review   33–35

Homework Quick Check
To check student's understanding of key skills and concepts, go over Exercises 7, 13, 25, 26, and 28.

Differentiated Instruction Resources

Adapted Practice 7-2   **L1**

Practice 7-2   Identifying and Classifying   **L3**

In exercises 1–6, classify each angle as *acute, right, obtuse,* or *straight.*
1.
90°, right
2.
135°, obtuse
3.
45°, acute
4. $m\angle A = 180°$ straight
5. $m\angle B = 43°$ acute
6. $m\angle D = 90°$ right

Use the figure at the right to name the following.
7. two lines   Sample answers: $\overline{XU}, \overline{ST}, \overline{XP}, \overline{QY}$
8. three segments   Sample answers: $\overline{XN}, \overline{XP}, \overline{QN}$
9. a pair of congruent angles   Sample answers: $\angle XNT, \angle UXP$
10. four right angles $\angle QNT, \angle SNQ, \angle SNY,$ and $\angle YNT$
11. two pairs of obtuse vertical angles $\angle MSW$ and $\angle UST, \angle SXP$ and $\angle VXW$
12. two pairs of adjacent supplementary angles $\angle MSX$ and $\angle MSU, \angle MSX$ and $\angle XST$
13. two pairs of complementary angles $\angle QNX$ and $\angle XNS, \angle TNP$ and $\angle PNY$

Solve.
14. If $m\angle A = 23°$, what is the measure of its complement?   67°
15. If $m\angle T = 163°$, what is the measure of its supplement?   17°
16. If a 67° angle is complementary to $\angle Q$, what is the measure of $\angle Q$?   23°
17. Use the dot grid to draw two supplementary angles, one of which is 45°. Do *not* use a protractor.   135° 45°

7-2 • Guided Problem Solving   **GPS**   **L3**

Student Page 334, Exercise 26:

Writing in Math Can an angle ever have the same measure as its complement? Explain.

Understand
1. What are you being asked to do?
   Determine if an angle can ever have the same measure as its complement.
2. What do you have to do to explain your answer?
   If there is an angle that has the same measure as its complement, show that the sum of the angles is 90°. If there is not an angle that has the same measure as its complement, explain why.

Plan and Carry Out
3. What is the definition of complementary angles?
   two angles whose sum measures 90°
4. If an angle and its complement have the same measure, explain the relationship between the angle and 90°.
   The angle is half of 90°.
5. Determine the measure of the angle.   45°
6. Can an angle ever have the same measure as its complement?   yes

Check
7. Explain your answer.
   Sample answer: The complement of a 45° angle is a 45° angle and the sum of 45° and 45° is 90°.

Solve Another Problem
8. Can an angle ever have the same measure as its supplement? Explain.
   Yes; 90° + 90° = 180° which is the definition of supplementary angles.

333

PowerPoint

Lesson Quiz

Use the diagram for questions 1–3.

1. Find the measures of ∠2 and ∠3. m∠2 = 40° m∠3 = 90°

2. Name a pair of adjacent, complementary angles. ∠1 and ∠2

3. Name a pair of supplementary angles. ∠3 and ∠4 or ∠4 and ∠5

Alternative Assessment

Each student in a pair uses a protractor to draw three adjacent angles whose sum is greater than 180° and less than 360°. Students exchange papers and find the measure of each other's angles. Then they classify each angle as acute, obtuse, right, or straight.

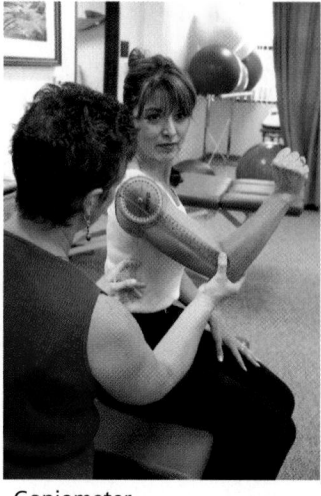

GO Online
Homework Help
Visit: PHSchool.com
Web Code: are-0702

25. The student used the wrong scale on the protractor.

Goniometer

Find the measures of the supplement and the complement of each angle.

22. m∠Q = 48°
132° and 42°

23. m∠R = 20.2°
159.8° and 69.8°

24. m∠S = 77.7°
102.3° and 12.3°

25. Error Analysis A student measured ∠XYZ and said that m∠XYZ = 120°. Explain the student's error. **See left.**

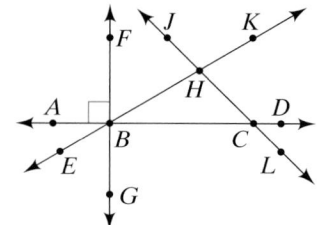

26. Writing in Math Can an angle ever have the same measure as its complement? Explain. **See margin.**

27. Physical Therapy Physical therapists use goniometers to measure the amount of motion a person has in a joint, such as an elbow or a knee. Estimate the measure of the angle shown by the goniometer in the photo at the left. **about 65°**

Use the figure to name the following.
28–29. See margin.

28. two pairs of adjacent supplementary angles

29. two pairs of obtuse vertical angles

30. two pairs of complementary angles
∠ABE and ∠EBG, ∠FBH and ∠HBC

31. an angle congruent to ∠DCL
∠HCB

C **32. Challenge** You know that ∠B is the complement of ∠A, that m∠B = 51°, and that m∠A = (3x − 12)°. Find x. **See margin.**

TEKS ★ TAKS Tune-Up and Mixed Review

TAKS Objective 3
TEKS (7.6)(A)

33. In the diagram at the right, which pair of angles form complementary angles? **C**
Ⓐ ∠AFB and ∠AFC
Ⓑ ∠BFC and ∠CFD
Ⓒ ∠AFB and ∠CFD
Ⓓ ∠AFB and ∠EFD

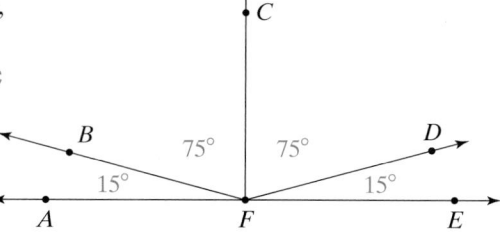

TAKS Objective 1
TEKS (7.1)(A)

34. The five countries in northern Africa that border the Mediterranean Sea are shown in the table, along with the lowest elevation in each country. Which country contains the lowest point? **H**
Ⓕ Algeria
Ⓖ Morocco
Ⓗ Egypt
Ⓙ Tunisia

Country	Elevation
Algeria	−40 m
Egypt	−133 m
Libya	−47 m
Morocco	−55 m
Tunisia	−17 m

GO for Help
Lesson 5-6

35. For a scale of 1 cm : 12 km, find the actual length represented by the length 1.7 cm in a drawing. **20.4 km**

TEKS ★ TAKS Resources

- TAKS Strategies, p. 365
- TAKS Tune-Up, pp. 369–371

TAKS Tune-Up Kit
- TAKS Daily Review Transparencies
- TAKS Review and Preparation Workbook
- TAKS Strategies with Transparencies
- Texas Progress Monitoring Assessments

26. A 45° angle has the same measure as its complement.

28. Answers may vary. Sample: ∠BHJ and ∠JHK, ∠JHK and ∠KHC

29. Answers may vary. Sample: ∠JHK and ∠BHC, ∠HCD and ∠BCL

32. See back of book.

Hands On

TEKS ★ **TAKS**

(7.15)(A) To make conjectures from patterns or sets of examples **TAKS** **Obj. 6**

Prepares for **TEKS** (7.6)(B) To use properties to classify triangles

Sides and Angles of a Triangle

You need three sides and three angles to form a triangle. Can you make a triangle with *any* three sides? The activity below will help you understand the relationship between the side lengths of a triangle and its angles.

ACTIVITY Check students' work.

Step 1 Cut five straws to the following lengths: 2 in., 4 in., 5 in., 8 in., and 10.5 in.

Step 2 Using any three pieces, try to form a triangle. When you find three lengths that can form a triangle, trace the perimeter of the triangle on a sheet of paper. Label the triangles △A, △B, △C, and so on.

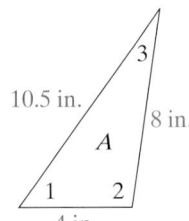

Step 3 Using all possible combinations of three pieces, repeat Step 2 and make as many triangles as you can.

Step 4 Make a list of the side lengths of all the triangles that you made. Record your results in a table like the one below.

Triangle	Shortest Side	Middle Side	Longest Side
A	4 in.	8 in.	10.5 in.
B	■	■	■
C	■	■	■

Step 5 Analyze your table. For each triangle, make a conjecture about the sum of any two side lengths compared to the length of the third side.

Step 6 Now use a protractor to measure the three angles in each triangle. Record your results in a table like the one below.

Triangle	$m \angle 1$	$m \angle 2$	$m \angle 3$	Total
A	■	■	■	■
B	■	■	■	■
C	■	■	■	■

Step 7 Analyze your table. Make a conjecture about the sum of the angles in each triangle.

Activity Lab

Sides and Angles of a Triangle

Students use pipe cleaners to discover relationships among the sides and angles of triangles.

Guided Instruction

Before beginning the Activity, have students decide if they think a triangle can be made with any three sides. Tell them they will answer this question as they do the Activity. They will also learn what the sum of the angles of any triangle is.

You may want students to write their opinions before doing the Activity and revise them afterwards.

Differentiated Instruction

Tactile Learners

If students have trouble seeing that the sum of the measures of any triangle is 180°, have them cut out a paper triangle, number the angles of the triangle and cut them off. Then they place the three angles side by side to form non-overlapping adjacent angles. The three angles will form a straight angle, which will measure 180°. So the sum of the angles of the triangle is 180°.

Visual Learners

Using pipe cleaners of different colors will help students to differentiate lengths more easily.

TEKS ★ **TAKS** **Resources**

- Activity Lab 7-3: Triangles
- pipe cleaners
- protractor

Dana Center TEKS Toolkit Clarifying Activities (7.15)(A)
Visit: PHSchool.com
Web Code: arq-9045

TEKS ★ (TAKS)

(7.6)(B) To use properties to classify triangles (TAKS) Obj. 3
Also supports
(7.8)(C) (TAKS) Obj. 3
(7.15)(B) (TAKS) Obj. 6

Dana Center TEKS Toolkit Clarifying Activities (7.6)(B), (7.8)(C), (7.15)(B)
Visit: PHSchool.com
Web Code: arq-9045

Professional Development

TEKS Math Background

Triangles can be classified by the number of their *congruent sides*. *Scalene triangles* have no congruent sides. *Isosceles triangles* have two or more congruent sides. *Equilateral triangles* have three congruent sides and are therefore also isosceles triangles.

Triangles can also be classified by their angle measures. A *right triangle* has one right angle. An *acute triangle* has three acute angles. An *obtuse triangle* has one obtuse angle.

More Math Background: p. 322C

Lesson Planning and Resources

See p. 322E for a list of the resources that support this lesson.

PowerPoint
Bell Ringer Practice

✓ **Check Skills You'll Need**
Use student page, transparency, or PowerPoint.

(TAKS) **Daily Review 51**
Use transparency.

7-3 Triangles

✓ Check Skills You'll Need

1. Vocabulary Review
How does the measure of an *acute angle* compare to 90°?
See below.
Classify each angle as *acute, right, obtuse,* or *straight*.

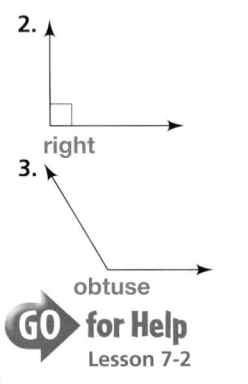

2. right

3. obtuse

GO for Help
Lesson 7-2

Check Skills You'll Need

1. an angle with a measure greater than 0° and less than 90°

TEKS ★ (TAKS)

• (7.6)(B) To use properties to classify triangles (TAKS) Obj. 3
• (7.8)(C) To use geometric concepts in art and architecture (TAKS) Obj. 3
• (7.15)(B) To validate conclusions using mathematical properties (TAKS) Obj. 6

🔊 **New Vocabulary** congruent sides, scalene triangle, isosceles triangle, equilateral triangle, right triangle, acute triangle, obtuse triangle

Why Learn This?

When you can classify triangles, you will recognize them in art and architecture.

Origami is the art of paper folding. At the right is an origami crane. The folds form a variety of triangles.

Congruent sides have the same length. You can classify a triangle by the number of congruent sides it has.

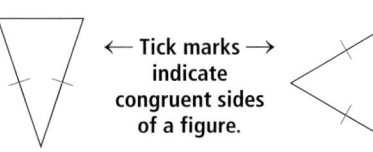

← Tick marks →
indicate
congruent sides
of a figure.

scalene triangle
no congruent sides

isosceles triangle
at least two congruent sides

equilateral triangle
three congruent sides

EXAMPLE   Classifying Triangles by Sides

❶ (TAKS) **Multiple Choice** Which of the following best describes △ABC based on its sides?

  Ⓐ Scalene   Ⓒ Isosceles
  Ⓑ Right   Ⓓ Equilateral

△ABC has no congruent sides. Therefore, it is a scalene triangle. The correct answer is A.

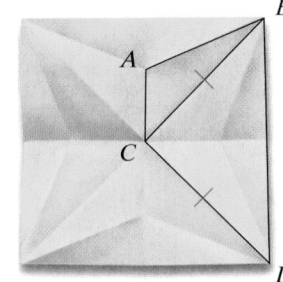

✓ Quick Check

● **1.** Classify △BCD by its sides.   isosceles

You can also classify a triangle by its angle measures.

Differentiated Instruction Solutions for All Learners

Special Needs L1
Have students highlight the angles when classifying triangles by their angle measures. Have them highlight the sides when classifying triangles by sides. This will help them keep track of their triangles.

learning style: visual

Below Level L2
Have students cut out a variety of triangles. Then have them use a ruler and protractor to classify their triangles by side and angle measures.

learning style: tactile

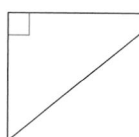

right triangle
one right angle

acute triangle
three acute angles

obtuse triangle
one obtuse angle

Online active math

For: Triangle Activity
Use: Interactive Textbook, 7-3

EXAMPLE Classifying Triangles by Angles

2 Classify the triangle shown at the right by its angle measures.

The triangle has one obtuse angle, so it is an obtuse triangle.

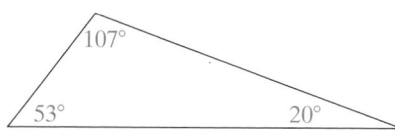

✓ **Quick Check**

2. Classify each triangle by its angle measures.

a.
right

b.
acute

There is a very important property of the angles of a triangle: the sum of the measures of the angles of every triangle is the same.

KEY CONCEPTS Angle Sum of a Triangle

The sum of the measures of the angles of any triangle is 180°.

Suppose you know the measures of two of the angles of a triangle. You can write and solve an equation to find the third angle measure.

EXAMPLE Finding an Angle Measure

GO for Help

For help solving equations, go to Lesson 4-3, Example 1.

3 (Algebra) Find the value of x in the triangle.

$$x + 53° + 61° = 180°$$
$$x + 114° = 180°$$
$$x + 114° - 114° = 180° - 114°$$
$$x = 66°$$

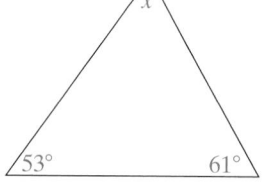

✓ **Quick Check**

3. Find the value of x in the triangle.
22°

7-3 Triangles **337**

---

2. Teach

Activity Lab

Use before the lesson.
Student Edition Activity Lab, Hands On 7-3a, Sides and Angles of a Triangle, p. 335

All in One Teaching Resources
Activity Lab 7-3: Triangles

Guided Instruction

Example 2
One right angle classifies a triangle as a right triangle; one obtuse angle classifies it as an obtuse triangle; but three acute angles are necessary for it to be classified as an acute triangle.

PowerPoint
Additional Examples

1 Classify each triangle by its sides.

a.
isosceles

b.
scalene

2 Classify each by its angle measures.

a.
obtuse

b.
acute

3 Find the value of x below. **46°**

All in One Teaching Resources
- Daily Notetaking Guide 7-3 **L3**
- Adapted Notetaking 7-3 **L1**

Closure

- *How are triangles classified as scalene, isosceles, and equilateral?* See back of book.
- *How are triangles classified as acute, obtuse, and right?* See back of book.
- *How can you find the measure of a missing angle in a triangle?* See back of book.

Advanced Learners **L4**
Is it possible for a triangle to have two right angles? Two obtuse angles? Justify your response. No. The sum of the angles in a triangle is always 180°. The sum of any two angles must be < 180°.

Pre-AP™

English Language Learners **ELL**
Have students draw six triangles on an index card. Three should be classified by their angles (right, obtuse, acute), and three by their sides (scalene, isosceles, equilateral).

learning style: visual

3. Practice

Assignment Guide

Check Your Understanding
Go over Exercises 1–5 in class before assigning the Homework Exercises.

Homework Exercises
A Practice by Example   6–14
B Apply Your Skills   15–22
C Challenge   23
TEKS ★ TAKS Tune-Up and Mixed Review   24–30

Homework Quick Check
To check students' understanding of key skills and concepts, go over Exercises 8, 13, 19, 21, and 22.

Differentiated Instruction Resources

Check Your Understanding

2. Check students' work. An example is given.

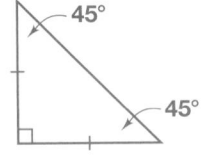

1. **Vocabulary** A scalene triangle has __?__ congruent sides. no

2. **Open-Ended** Draw an isosceles right triangle. Label the angle measures and use tick marks to indicate congruent sides.

Classify each triangle by its angle measures and by its sides.

3.

obtuse scalene

4.

right isosceles

5.

acute isosceles

Homework Exercises

For more exercises, see Extra Skills and Word Problems.

A **Classify each triangle by its sides.**

GO for Help	
For Exercises	**See Examples**
6–8	1
9–11	2
12–14	3

6. isosceles

7. scalene

8. equilateral

Classify each triangle by its angle measures.

9.
obtuse

10.
acute

11.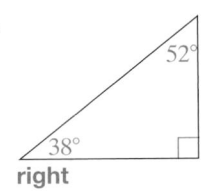
right

Algebra Find the value of *x* in each triangle.

12.
80°

13.
64°

14.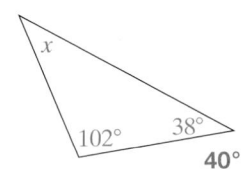
40°

B **GPS** 15. **Guided Problem Solving** The angles of a triangle measure *x*°, 2*x*°, and 3*x*°. Classify the triangle by its angles.   See left.

15. right triangle

- Use the strategy *Systematic Guess and Check*.
- Continue until the sum of the measures is 180°.
- Classify the triangle.

x°	2*x*°	3*x*°	Sum of Angle Measures	Result
10	20	30	60	Too low
■	■	■	■	■

338   Chapter 7   Geometry

22b. Complementary; the sum of the angles of a triangle is 180°, and if one of the angles is 90°, the other two must add up to 90°.

23. An equilateral triangle is always isosceles because it has 3 congruent sides. An isosceles triangle is not always equilateral because it has at least 2 congruent sides.

19. 64°; 180° − (93° + 31°) = 56°; 56° + 60° = 116°; 180° − 116° = 64°

(**Algebra**) **Suppose the sides of a triangle have each of the given measures. Classify each triangle by its sides.**

16. *j, j, j*
equilateral

17. 3*a*, 3*a*, 5*a*
isosceles

scalene
18. 3*w*, 4*w*, 8*w*

19. **Writing in Math** What is the
GPS measure of ∠*E*? Show your work and justify your steps. **See left.**

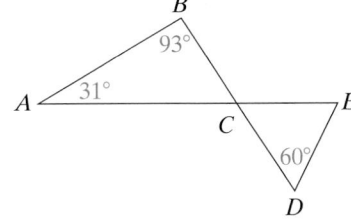

20. The traffic sign at the left is used in Norway. Classify the shape of the sign by its sides. **equilateral**

21. (**Algebra**) A triangle has two angles that both measure 68°. What is the measure of the third angle? **44°**

22. The triangles shown are right triangles.
  a. What is the sum of the measures of the two acute angles in each triangle? **90°**
  b. Reasoning What is the relationship between the two acute angles in any right triangle? Explain. **See margin.**

C 23. Challenge Are all equilateral triangles isosceles? Are all isosceles triangles equilateral? Explain. **See margin.**

 TEKS ★ TAKS Tune-Up and Mixed Review

TAKS Objective 3
TEKS (7.6)(B)

24. The side view of a ramp has the shape of a triangle. Which of the following best describes the triangle with the given measures? **B**
  Ⓐ Right isosceles triangle
  Ⓑ Right scalene triangle
  Ⓒ Acute isosceles triangle
  Ⓓ Acute scalene triangle

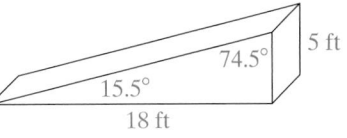

TAKS Objective 2
TEKS (7.3)(B)

25. On a scale drawing, one side of a box is 2 inches long. The actual length of the box is 6 feet. What is the scale of the drawing? **G**
  Ⓕ 6 in. : 2 ft   Ⓖ 1 in. : 3 ft   Ⓗ 3 in. : 1 ft   Ⓙ 3 ft : 2 in.

TAKS Objective 1
TEKS (7.2)(F)

26. Three seventh-grade classes go on a camping trip together. The classes have 21, 20, and 19 students. If four students sleep in each tent, how many tents are needed? **C**
  Ⓐ 10   Ⓑ 12   Ⓒ 15   Ⓓ 20

 for Help
Lesson 6-3

Write each percent as a decimal and as a fraction in simplest form.

27. 116%
1.16; $\frac{29}{25}$

28. 137%
1.37; $\frac{137}{100}$

29. 155%
1.55; $\frac{31}{20}$

30. 175%
1.75; $\frac{7}{4}$

Alternative Assessment

Ask each student to draw five different triangles and then exchange papers with a partner. Partners classify each triangle by its sides and by the measures of its angles. To extend the activity, have students measure and label each angle.

TEKS ★ TAKS Resources

• TAKS Strategies, p. 365
• TAKS Tune-Up, pp. 369–371

TAKS Tune-Up Kit
  • TAKS Daily Review Transparencies
  • TAKS Review and Preparation Workbook
  • TAKS Strategies with Transparencies
  • Texas Progress Monitoring Assessments

---

4. Assess & Reteach

PowerPoint
Lesson Quiz

Classify each triangle by its sides and by its angle measures. Then find the measure of the missing angle.

1.
isosceles; acute; 30°

2.
scalene; obtuse; 19°

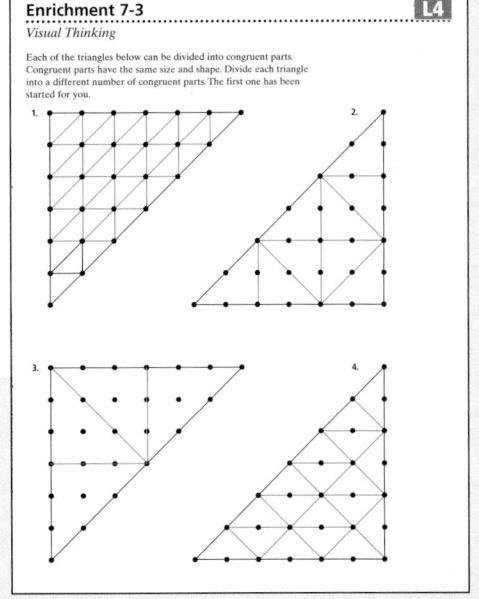

339

1. Plan

TEKS ★ TAKS

(7.6)(B) To use properties to classify quadrilaterals TAKS Obj. 3

(7.8)(C) To use geometric concepts in art and architecture TAKS Obj. 3

Dana Center TEKS Toolkit Clarifying Activities (7.6)(B), (7.8)(C)
Visit: PHSchool.com
Web Code: arq-9045

TEKS Math Background

A *polygon* is a closed, two-dimensional figure classified by its number of sides.

The only regular quadrilateral is a *square*. A *rhombus* has four congruent sides, and opposite parallel sides, so it is a *parallelogram*. A quadrilateral with parallel opposite sides can also be a *parallelogram*. A *trapezoid* is not a parallelogram because only one pair of sides is parallel. A parallelogram with four right angles is a *rectangle*. So a square is also a rectangle.

More Math Background: p. 322C

Lesson Planning and Resources

See p. 322E for a list of the resources that support this lesson.

Bell Ringer Practice

✓ **Check Skills You'll Need**
Use student page, transparency, or PowerPoint.

TAKS **Daily Review 52**
Use transparency.

340

✓ Check Skills You'll Need

1. Vocabulary Review
What kind of triangle will always have three congruent sides?
1–4. See below.
Classify each triangle by its sides.

2.

3.

4.

 for Help
Lesson 7-3

Check Skills You'll Need

1. an equilateral triangle
2. equilateral
3. isosceles
4. scalene

TEKS ★ TAKS

- (7.6)(B) To use properties to classify quadrilaterals TAKS Obj. 3
- (7.8)(C) To use geometric concepts in art and architecture TAKS Obj. 3

🔊 **New Vocabulary** quadrilateral, pentagon, hexagon, octagon, decagon, regular polygon, irregular polygon, trapezoid, parallelogram, rectangle, rhombus, square

Why Learn This?

Artists and designers use quadrilaterals and other polygons in their work because these shapes are pleasing to the eye. The artist Piet Mondrian is known for painting rectangles.

A polygon is a closed plane figure with sides formed by three or more line segments. The sides meet only at their endpoints.

You classify polygons by their number of sides.

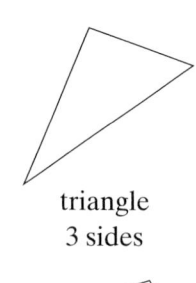
triangle
3 sides

quadrilateral
4 sides

pentagon
5 sides

hexagon
6 sides

octagon
8 sides

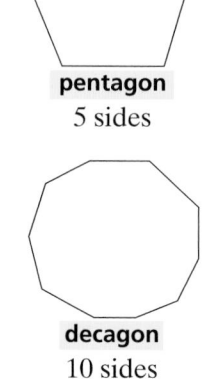
decagon
10 sides

A **regular polygon** is a polygon with all sides congruent and all angles congruent. An **irregular polygon** is a polygon with sides that are not all congruent or angles that are not all congruent.

340 Chapter 7 Geometry

Differentiated Instruction Solutions for All Learners

Special Needs L1
Some students my have difficulty drawing the quadrilaterals in Example 3. Have them trace the drawn figure with their fingers, counting each side as they trace. Then, pair them up with a student who can draw.

learning style: tactile

Below Level L2
Have students cut various polygons from index cards and label them on one side. Have students mix up the cards and use them like flashcards to practice the naming of polygons.

learning style: tactile

EXAMPLE Identifying Regular Polygons

Vocabulary Tip

Regular means "consistent" or "the same."

1 Identify each polygon and classify it as *regular* or *irregular*.

a.

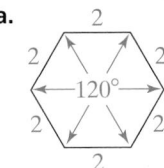

The figure has 6 sides. All sides are congruent. The hexagon is regular.

b.

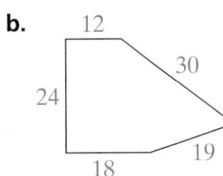

The figure has 5 sides. Not all sides are congruent. The pentagon is irregular.

Quick Check

1a. The octagon is irregular because the sides are not all congruent.

b. The triangle is regular because all sides and all angles are congruent.

1. Identify each polygon and classify it as *regular* or *irregular*.

a.

b.

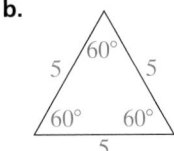

c. **Reasoning** How would you find the perimeter of a regular polygon? Explain. **Multiply the side length by the number of sides the polygon has.**

Some quadrilaterals have special names.

  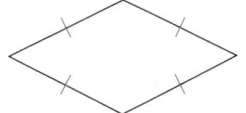

$\overline{AB}$ is parallel to $\overline{CD}$.

A **trapezoid** is a quadrilateral with exactly one pair of parallel sides. The arrows indicate parallel sides.

A **parallelogram** is a quadrilateral with both pairs of opposite sides parallel.

GO for Help

For help with parallel lines, go to Lesson 7-1, Example 2.

There are three special types of parallelograms.

rectangle
four right angles

rhombus
four congruent sides

square
four right angles and four congruent sides

2. Teach

Activity Lab

Use before the lesson.

All in One Teaching Resources

Activity Lab 7-4: Shapes and Angles

Guided Instruction

Error Prevention!
Some students may have difficulty drawing the figures. Provide them with a set of pattern blocks to trace. You may want students to measure the sides and angles of their tracings to reinforce the relationships between sides and angles of a given figure.

PowerPoint

Additional Examples

1 Identify the polygon and classify it as *regular* or *irregular*.

a.

hexagon; irregular

b.

triangle; regular

2 Identify the polygons in the design. **The outside polygon is a decagon. Inside are octagons, quadrilaterals, triangles and a hexagon.**

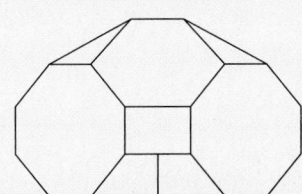

3 Draw a regular parallelogram on graph or dot paper.

  square

7-4 Quadrilaterals and Other Polygons **341**

Advanced Learners **L4**
What are the different ways you can classify a square?
A square is a rectangle, a rhombus, a quadrilateral, a parallelogram, and a regular polygon.

English Language Learners **ELL**
Have students draw a classification chart for quadrilaterals. It should show rectangles, rhombi, and squares as subsets of parallelograms.

Pre-AP™

learning style: visual

341

Closure

- *What is a regular polygon?* a closed plane figure with all sides and all angles congruent
- *How do you classify a polygon by its number of sides?* Sample: A triangle has 3 sides; a quadrilateral has 4 sides; a pentagon has 5 sides; a hexagon has 6 sides; etc.
- *What are the five special quadrilaterals?* trapezoid, parallelogram, rectangle, rhombus, square

EXAMPLE **Classifying Polygons**

2 **Architecture** Use the best names to identify the polygons in the window shown at the right.

The outside frame is an octagon. Inside the frame there are triangles, rectangles, trapezoids, and squares.

3. Check student's work. An example is given.

☑ **Quick Check**

2. Use the best names to identify the polygons in each pattern.

   a.

   hexagons, triangles

   b.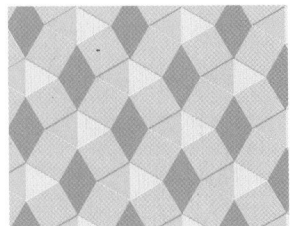

   squares, triangles, rhombuses

EXAMPLE **Using Dot Paper**

Online
active math

For: Quadrilateral Activity
Use: Interactive Textbook, 7-4

3 Draw each of the following figures on dot paper.

a. a parallelogram that is not a rectangle or a rhombus

b. a rhombus that is not a square

☑ **Quick Check**

3. Draw a trapezoid with a pair of congruent opposite sides.
   See above left.

Check Your Understanding

1. A trapezoid is a quadrilateral with only one pair of parallel sides. A parallelogram is a quadrilateral with two pairs of parallel sides.

1. **Vocabulary** How do parallelograms and trapezoids differ? Explain.

2. **Reasoning** Can you draw a square that is not a rhombus? Explain.
   2–5. See margin.

List all the names that apply to each figure.

3.

4.

5.

2. No. All squares have four congruent sides. Every square is a rhombus.

3. quadrilateral, parallelogram

4. quadrilateral

5. quadrilateral, parallelogram, rhombus, rectangle, square

For more exercises, see Extra Skills and Word Problems.

GO for Help

For Exercises	See Examples
6–8	1
9–10	2
11–12	3

Ⓐ **Identify each polygon and classify it as *regular* or *irregular*. Explain.**

6.

7.

8.

6–8. See left.

6. The pentagon is regular because all sides and angles are congruent.

7. The parallelogram is irregular because the sides are not all congruent.

8. The quadrilateral is irregular because the sides are not all congruent.

Use the best names to identify the polygons in each pattern.

9.

rectangles, trapezoids

10.

squares, trapezoids, triangles

Use dot paper or graph paper to draw each quadrilateral.

11. a trapezoid with vertical sides parallel   11–12. See margin.

12. two squares, the second of which has twice the perimeter of the first

Ⓑ **GPS** **13. Guided Problem Solving** Find the length of a side of a regular decagon that has a perimeter of 22 ft.   **2.2 ft**
  • How many sides does a decagon have?
  • Can you write a formula for the perimeter of a regular decagon?

Judging by appearance, classify each quadrilateral in the photos below. Then name the parallel sides.

14. Parallelogram; $\overline{AB}$ is parallel to $\overline{DC}$, and $\overline{AD}$ is parallel to $\overline{BC}$.

15. Trapezoid; $\overline{PQ}$ is parallel to $\overline{RS}$.

14.

15.

List all side lengths and angle measures you can find for each polygon.

17. $JN = 5$ in.; $m\angle J = m\angle K = m\angle L = m\angle N = 90°$

16. rhombus $WXYZ$, $WX = 4$ cm   **17.** rectangle $JKLN$, $KL = 5$ in.
    $XY = YZ = ZW = 4$ cm
18. parallelogram $ABCD$, $AB = 6$ cm, $m\angle A = 65°$
    $DC = 6$ cm

For Exercises 11 and 12, check students' work. Examples are given.

11.

12.

Adapted Practice 7-4   **L1**

Practice 7-4   Quadrilaterals and Other P   **L3**

Identify each polygon and classify it as *regular* or *irregular*.

1. quadrilateral; irregular   2. octagon; irregular   3. hexagon; regular

State all correct names for each quadrilateral. Then circle the best name.

4. parallelogram rectangle   5. parallelogram rhombus   6. trapezoid

Use dot paper to draw each quadrilateral.

7. a rectangle that is not a square   Sample drawings are shown.

8. a rhombus with two right angles

9. a trapezoid with no right angles

10. List all additional side lengths and angle measures you can find for the trapezoid JKLM, where $\overline{KL}$ is parallel to $\overline{JM}$, ∠K is a right angle, and the length of $\overline{LM}$ is 10 cm.
Check students' answers. Sample answer: ∠P is a right angle.

7-4 • Guided Problem Solving GPS   **L3**

GPS Student Page 344, Exercise 22:

Writing in Math Can a quadrilateral be both a rhombus and a rectangle? Explain.

Understand
1. What are you being asked to do?
   Determine if a quadrilateral can be both a rhombus and a rectangle.
2. In order to answer this question, what definitions do you need to know?
   quadrilateral, rhombus, and rectangle

Plan and Carry Out
3. What is a quadrilateral?
   A quadrilateral is a polygon that has 4 sides.
4. What is a rhombus?
   A rhombus is a parallelogram with 4 congruent sides.
5. What is a rectangle?
   A rectangle is a parallelogram with 4 right angles.
6. Can a quadrilateral be both a rhombus and a rectangle?
   yes

Check
7. Explain your answer to step 6 by giving an example of a shape that is both a rhombus and a rectangle.
   A square is a quadrilateral because it has four sides. It is a rhombus because it has four congruent sides. It is a rectangle because it has four right angles.

Solve Another Problem
8. If all squares are types of rectangles, are all rhombuses types of rectangles? Explain.
   No, rectangles are rhombuses with four right angles.

343

4. Assess & Reteach

Lesson Quiz
PowerPoint

Identify each polygon. Then classify it as *regular* or *irregular*.

1. rectangle; irregular

2. hexagon; regular

3. octagon; regular

4. trapezoid; irregular

Alternative Assessment

Provide pairs of students with graph paper or dot paper. One partner names one of the polygons in this lesson while the other draws and labels the polygon. Have partners alternate roles.

19.

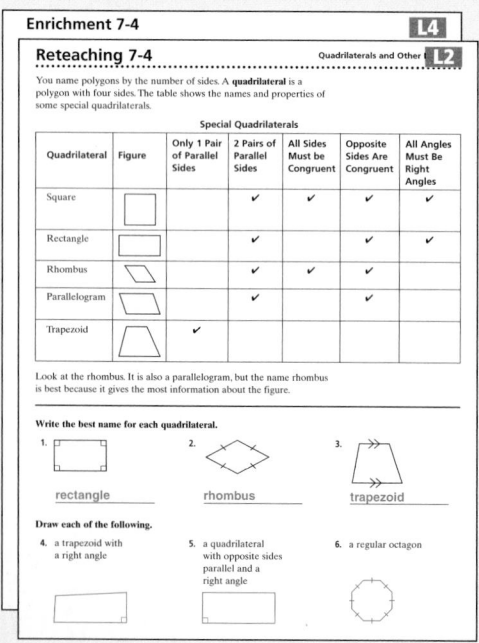

Enrichment 7-4 | **L4**

Reteaching 7-4 | Quadrilaterals and Other | **L2**

You name polygons by the number of sides. A **quadrilateral** is a polygon with four sides. The table shows the names and properties of some special quadrilaterals.

Special Quadrilaterals

Quadrilateral	Figure	Only 1 Pair of Parallel Sides	2 Pairs of Parallel Sides	All Sides Must be Congruent	Opposite Sides Are Congruent	All Angles Must Be Right Angles
Square			✔	✔	✔	✔
Rectangle			✔		✔	✔
Rhombus			✔	✔	✔	
Parallelogram			✔		✔	
Trapezoid		✔				

Look at the rhombus. It is also a parallelogram, but the name rhombus is best because it gives the most information about the figure.

Write the best name for each quadrilateral.

1. rectangle 2. rhombus 3. trapezoid

Draw each of the following.

4. a trapezoid with a right angle
5. a quadrilateral with opposite sides parallel and a right angle
6. a regular octagon

344

Sketch each polygon. 19–21. See margin.

19. pentagon **20.** octagon **21.** regular quadrilateral

Math in the Media Use the cartoon for Exercises 22 and 23.

LET'S ASK SQUARE... HE ALWAYS HAS THE RIGHT ANGLE ON THINGS.

23. No; it would be a rectangle.

24a.

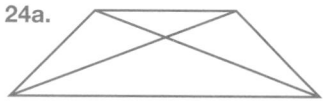

b. The diagonals have the same length.

25.

22. **Writing in Math** Can a quadrilateral be both a rhombus and a **GPS** rectangle? Explain. Yes; a square is both a rhombus and a rectangle.

23. **Reasoning** Can a trapezoid have three right angles? Draw a diagram to support your answer. See left.

24. a. Use a ruler to draw a trapezoid with opposite sides congruent.
b. A diagonal joins two vertices that are not endpoints of the same side of a polygon. Draw and measure the diagonals of the figure you drew in part (a). What do you notice? See left.

C **25.** **Challenge** Draw a quadrilateral with exactly one pair of congruent opposite angles. See left.

TEKS ★ TAKS Tune-Up and Mixed Review

TAKS Objective 3
TEKS (7.6)(B)

26. Which statement is always true about a rhombus? **B**
  A It has four congruent angles.
  B It has four congruent sides.
  C It has four right angles.
  D It has exactly one pair of parallel sides.

TAKS Objective 2
TEKS (7.3)(B)

27. A punch recipe calls for 6 cups of pineapple juice. Alicia has 1 quart of pineapple juice. How much more does she need? **F**
  F $\frac{1}{2}$ qt   G $1\frac{1}{2}$ qt   H 3 c   J 2 pt

TAKS Objective 5
TEKS (7.12)(A)

28. An art collector bought five paintings for a total of $3,600. Then he bought another painting for $1,200. What was the mean cost for all of the paintings? **B**
  A $720   B $800   C $960   D $4,800

GO for Help Lesson 2-6

Write each fraction as a decimal.

29. $\frac{5}{3}$ $1.\overline{6}$ **30.** $\frac{7}{16}$ 0.4375   **31.** $\frac{15}{18}$ $0.8\overline{3}$ **32.** $\frac{10}{6}$ $1.\overline{6}$

TEKS ★ TAKS Resources

• TAKS Strategies, p. 366
• TAKS Tune-Up, pp. 369–371

TAKS Tune-Up Kit
• TAKS Daily Review Transparencies
• TAKS Review and Preparation Workbook
• TAKS Strategies with Transparencies
• Texas Progress Monitoring Assessments

20.

21.

Use the points in each diagram to name the figure shown.

1.
X   Z $\overrightarrow{XZ}$

2.
N   M $\overleftrightarrow{NM}$

3.
K   V $\overline{KV}$

Find the measures of the complement and the supplement of each angle.

4. $m\angle T = 12°$ **78°; 168°**

5. $m\angle R = 47°$ **43°; 133°**

6. $m\angle U = 65°$ **25°; 115°**

7. A triangle has angles that measure 63° and 47°. What is the measure of the third angle? **70°**

Classify the triangles in the figure at the right.

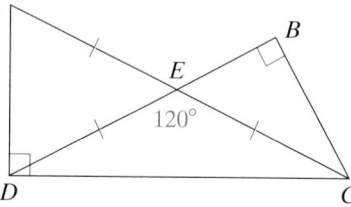

8. $\triangle ADE$
equilateral

9. $\triangle DEC$
obtuse isosceles

10. $\triangle ACD$
right scalene

11. In the figure below, all six segments are congruent. Identify the three polygons that are formed by the segments and classify them as *regular* or *irregular*.

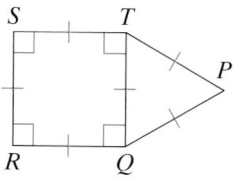

Equilateral $\triangle PQT$ is regular, square QRST is regular, and pentagon PQRST is irregular.

MATH AT WORK

Architect

Do you have an eye for design? If so, then architecture could be a career for you. Architects use creativity, math, science, and art to plan buildings that are beautiful, functional, safe, and economical.

Architects use geometry to understand spatial relationships. They use ratios and percents to plan scale drawings and to build scale models, too.

Architects also must be able to manage projects, supervise people, and communicate complex ideas.

 Go Online
PHSchool.com
For: Information about architects
Web Code: arb-2031

TEKS ★ TAKS

(7.6)(D) To use critical attributes to define similarity TAKS Obj. 3

(7.8)(C) To use geometric concepts and properties to solve problems in fields such as architecture TAKS Obj. 3

Dana Center TEKS Toolkit Clarifying Activities (7.6)(D), (7.8)(C)
Visit: PHSchool.com
Web Code: arq-9045

TEKS ★ TAKS

- (7.6)(D) To use critical attributes to define similarity TAKS Obj. 3
- (7.8)(C) To use geometric concepts and properties to solve problems in fields such as architecture TAKS Obj. 3

◀)) **New Vocabulary** congruent polygons

Professional Development
TEKS Math Background

Two congruent polygons have *corresponding parts*: each angle and each side in the first polygon is congruent to an angle and a side in the second polygon. The symbol ≅ means "is congruent to." To name congruent figures, write vertices in corresponding order: △ABC ≅ △XYZ. Tick marks can indicate corresponding parts.

More Math Background: p. 322D

Lesson Planning and Resources

See p. 322E for a list of the resources that support this lesson.

PowerPoint

Bell Ringer Practice

✓ **Check Skills You'll Need**
Use student page, transparency, or PowerPoint.

TAKS **Daily Review 53**
Use transparency.

✓ **Check Skills You'll Need**

1. Vocabulary Review
What makes two polygons *similar*?
See below.
△ABC ~ △PQR. Find each measure.

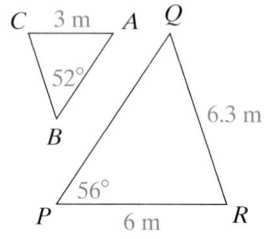

2. length of $\overline{BC}$ 5

3. $m\angle A$ **4.** $m\angle Q$
   56°   52°

GO for Help
Lesson 5-5

Why Learn This?

A manufacturer that makes large quantities of the same item must be sure that the items are all the same shape and size.

Similar polygons have the same shape. **Congruent polygons** are polygons with the same shape *and* the same size. The corresponding parts (sides and angles) of congruent polygons are congruent. The symbol ≅ means "is congruent to."

$\overline{AB} \cong \overline{ED}$ $\overline{BC} \cong \overline{DF}$ $\overline{CA} \cong \overline{FE}$

$\angle A \cong \angle E$ $\angle B \cong \angle D$ $\angle C \cong \angle F$

$\triangle ABC \cong \triangle EDF$

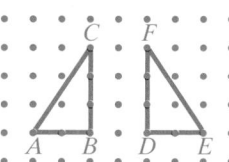

Write the vertices of congruent triangles in corresponding order.

EXAMPLE **Identifying Congruent Figures**

① Are the figures *congruent* or *not congruent*? Explain.

$\overline{KN} \cong \overline{PS}$ and $\overline{NM} \cong \overline{SR}$, but $\overline{LM}$ is not congruent to $\overline{QR}$.

The figures are not congruent.

✓ **Quick Check**

1. Are the figures *congruent* or *not congruent*? Explain.   See left.

Check Skills You'll Need

1. Two polygons are similar if corresponding angles are congruent and corresponding side lengths have the same proportion.

1. Congruent; the sides and angles all have the same measure.

346   Chapter 7   Geometry

Differentiated Instruction **Solutions for All Learners**

Special Needs L1
Have students cut out congruent figures drawn on grid or dot paper. Ask them to place one on top of another to show that they have equal angle measures and equal side lengths.

learning style: visual

Below Level L2
Have students take turns describing a polygon while the rest of the group draws it on graph paper. Have students compare their drawings to see which ones are congruent.

learning style: visual

EXAMPLE Application: Manufacturing

2 Assembly-line workers compare manufactured parts to a sample part to see if they are congruent. Is △UVW congruent to the sample triangle, △RST?

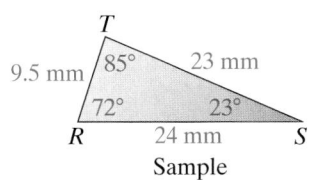
Sample

$\overline{UV} \cong \overline{RS}$, $\overline{VW} \cong \overline{ST}$, $\overline{WU} \cong \overline{TR}$, $\angle U \cong \angle R$, $\angle V \cong \angle S$, and $\angle W \cong \angle T$.

△UVW ≅ △RST

✓ Quick Check

2. Is the right figure congruent to the sample figure? Explain.

Sample

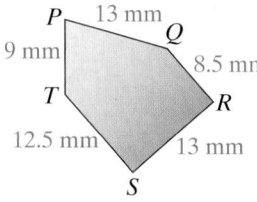

No; the sides are different lengths.

If you know that figures are congruent, you can use information about one figure to find information about the other.

EXAMPLE Working With Congruent Figures

★ TAKS Tip

If two angles in one triangle are congruent to two angles in another triangle, then both triangles' third angles must also be congruent.

3 The triangles at the right are congruent.

a. Write six congruences for the corresponding parts of the triangles.

$\angle X \cong \angle T$ $\angle Y \cong \angle S$ $\angle Z \cong \angle R$
$\overline{XY} \cong \overline{TS}$ $\overline{ZY} \cong \overline{RS}$ $\overline{ZX} \cong \overline{RT}$

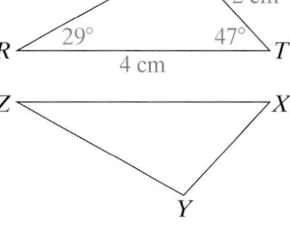

b. Find ZY and m∠X.

$ZY = 3$ cm ← $\overline{ZY} \cong \overline{RS}$, so ZY = RS

$m\angle X = 47°$ ← $\angle X \cong \angle T$, so m∠X = m∠T

✓ Quick Check

3a. $\overline{AB} \cong \overline{FG}$; $\overline{BC} \cong \overline{GH}$; $\overline{CD} \cong \overline{HI}$; $\overline{DA} \cong \overline{IF}$; $\angle A \cong \angle F$; $\angle B \cong \angle G$; $\angle C \cong \angle H$; $\angle D \cong \angle I$

b. 15.5; 139°

3. The quadrilaterals are congruent. **See left.**

a. Write the congruences for the corresponding parts.

b. Find AD and m∠G.

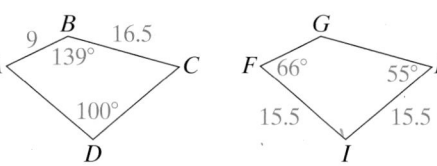

7-5 Congruent Figures **347**

Advanced Learners **L4**
Have students predict how many ways a square can be divided into two congruent figures. **There are an infinite number of ways.**

English Language Learners **ELL**
Have students label each of the following symbols: =, ?, ≥, ≤, ≈, ≅, ≠. Have them practice reading the symbols to each other.

Pre-AP™

learning style: verbal

---

2. Teach

Activity Lab

Use before the lesson.

All in One Teaching Resources
Activity Lab 7-5: Congruent Figures

Guided Instruction

Example 3
Have students repeat aloud, "triangle *XYZ* is congruent to triangle *TSR*." This helps students identify corresponding angles.

PowerPoint
Additional Examples

1 Are the figures *congruent*? Explain. **See back of book.**

2 Are the figures congruent? **yes**

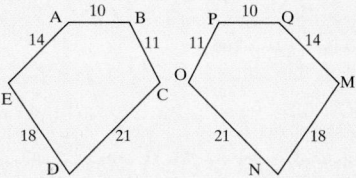

3 The triangles are congruent.

a. Write six congruences for the corresponding parts. **See back of book.**

b. Find *OP* and m∠Q **See back of book.**

All in One Teaching Resources
• Daily Notetaking Guide 7-5 **L3**
• Adapted Notetaking 7-5 **L1**

Closure

• *What are congruent polygons?* **polygons with the same size and shape**
• *How do you identify congruent polygons?* **Compare that corresponding angle and side measures are the same.**

347

Assignment Guide

Check Your Understanding
Go over Exercises 1–4 in class before assigning the Homework Exercises.

Homework Exercises
A Practice by Example   5–8
B Apply Your Skills   9–21
C Challenge   22
TEKS ★ (TAKS) Tune-Up and Mixed Review   23–26

Homework Quick Check
To check students' understanding of key skills and concepts, go over Exercises 5, 7, 13, 20, and 21.

Differentiated Instruction Resources

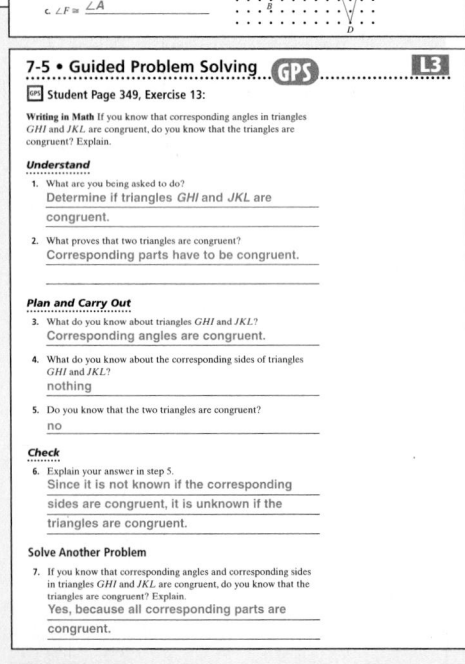

✓ Check Your Understanding

1. Yes. Similar polygons have congruent angles and sides in proportion. If the proportion is 1 to 1, then the polygons are not just similar, but congruent.

3. Congruent; all corresponding sides and angles are congruent.

4. Not congruent; not all corresponding sides and angles are congruent.

1. **Vocabulary** Is it possible for two similar polygons to be congruent polygons? Explain.

2. **Reasoning** If you know that two polygons are congruent, can you conclude that they are similar? Explain.
   Yes. The ratio is 1 : 1, and the angles are congruent.

Are the figures *congruent* or *not congruent*? Explain.

3.

4.

Homework Exercises

For more exercises, see Extra Skills and Word Problems.

GO for Help

For Exercises	See Examples
5–6	1–2
7–8	3

A **Are the figures *congruent* or *not congruent*? Explain.**

5. Not congruent; not all corresponding sides and angles are congruent.

See left.

6.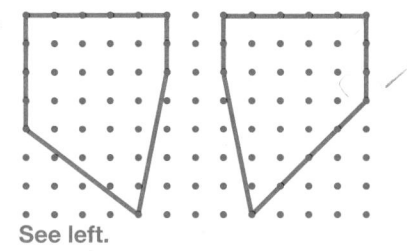
Sample
Not congruent; not all corresponding sides and angles are congruent.

Each pair of figures is congruent. Write six congruences for the corresponding parts of the figures. Then find the missing side lengths and angle measures.   7–8. See margin.

7.

8.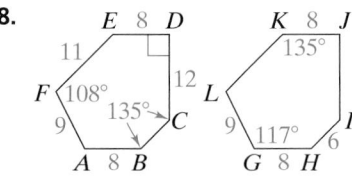

B **GPS** 9. **Guided Problem Solving** Complete the congruence statement: △RST ≅ ■.
   • **Make a Plan** List pairs of congruent corresponding angles to find corresponding vertices.
   • **Carry Out the Plan**
     ∠R ≅ ■, ∠S ≅ ■, ∠T ≅ ■; △RST ≅ ■   See left.

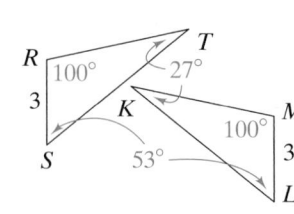

9. △MLK; ∠M; ∠L; ∠K
   △MLK

7–8. See back of book.

Adapted Practice 7-5   L1

Practice 7-5   Congruent L3

Are the figures congruent or not congruent? Explain.

1. Congruent, because all corresponding angles and corresponding sides are congruent.
2. Congruent, because all corresponding angles and corresponding sides are congruent.
3. Not congruent, because corresponding sides are not congruent.

Complete each congruence statement.

4. △ABC ≅ △NLM   5. △ABC ≅ △FED   6. △ABC ≅ △RTS

Write six congruences involving corresponding sides and angles for each pair of triangles.

7. △ABC ≅ △DEF
   AB ≅ DE, BC ≅ EF,
   AC ≅ DF, ∠A ≅ ∠D,
   ∠B ≅ ∠E, ∠C ≅ ∠F

8. △JKL ≅ △MNO
   JK ≅ MN, KL ≅ NO,
   JL ≅ MO, ∠J ≅ ∠M,
   ∠K ≅ ∠N, ∠L ≅ ∠O

Use the diagram at the right to complete each of the following.

9. a. ∠ABC ≅ ___∠FED___
   b. AB ≅ ___FE___
   c. ∠F ≅ ___∠A___

7-5 • Guided Problem Solving **GPS**   L3

GPS Student Page 349, Exercise 13:

Writing in Math If you know that corresponding angles in triangles GHI and JKL are congruent, do you know that the triangles are congruent? Explain.

Understand
1. What are you being asked to do?
   Determine if triangles GHI and JKL are congruent.
2. What proves that two triangles are congruent?
   Corresponding parts have to be congruent.

Plan and Carry Out
3. What do you know about triangles GHI and JKL?
   Corresponding angles are congruent.
4. What do you know about the corresponding sides of triangles GHI and JKL?
   nothing
5. Do you know that the two triangles are congruent?
   no

Check
6. Explain your answer in step 5.
   Since it is not known if the corresponding sides are congruent, it is unknown if the triangles are congruent.

Solve Another Problem
7. If you know that corresponding angles and corresponding sides in triangles GHI and JKL are congruent, do you know that the triangles are congruent? Explain.
   Yes, because all corresponding parts are congruent.

Complete each congruence statement.

10. △ABC ≅ ■ △FDE

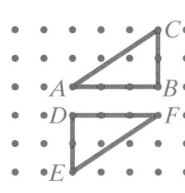

11. △ABC ≅ ■ △SRT

12. △ABC ≅ ■ △ZXY

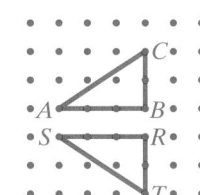

13. **Writing in Math** If you know that corresponding angles in triangles
GPS GHI and JKL are congruent, do you know that the triangles are
congruent? Explain. No; you must also know that the sides
are congruent.

B Apply **Complete each congruence statement.** △ABC ≅ △ABD

14. $\overline{AC}$ ≅ ■ $\overline{AD}$

15. $\overline{BC}$ ≅ ■ $\overline{BD}$

16. $\overline{AB}$ ≅ ■ $\overline{AB}$

17. ∠D ≅ ■ ∠C

18. ∠CAB ≅ ■ ∠DAB

19. ∠ABC ≅ ■ ∠ABD

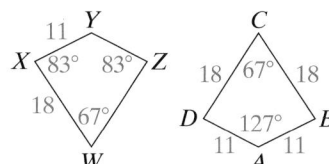

20. **Open-Ended** Draw a pair of congruent triangles. Label the
vertices. Then list the pairs of congruent sides and congruent angles.
Answers will vary. Check students' work.

21. $\overline{XY}$ ≅ $\overline{BA}$; $\overline{YZ}$ ≅ $\overline{AD}$;
$\overline{ZW}$ ≅ $\overline{DC}$; $\overline{WX}$ ≅ $\overline{CB}$;
∠Y ≅ ∠A; ∠Z ≅ ∠D;
∠W ≅ ∠C; ∠X ≅ ∠B
YZ = 11; ZW = 18;
m∠Y = 127°; m∠D = 83°;
m∠B = 83°

21. The pair of figures is congruent.
Write six congruences for the
corresponding parts of the
figures. Then find the missing side
lengths and angle measures.

22. No; the order of letters
is different, so different
angles are congruent.

C 22. **Challenge** Does the statement △JKL ≅ △MNO say the same
thing as the statement △JKL ≅ △NOM? Explain.

TAKS Objective 3
TEKS (7.6)(D)

23. △QRS is similar to △UTS. Which of the following is NOT true
about △QRS and △UTS? D
Ⓐ $\overline{QS}$ corresponds to $\overline{US}$.   Ⓒ ∠S corresponds to ∠S.
Ⓑ $\overline{RQ}$ corresponds to $\overline{TU}$.   Ⓓ ∠Q corresponds to ∠T.

TAKS Objective 3
TEKS (7.6)(A)

24. The measure of ∠DHE is 65°. Which
angle is supplementary to ∠DHE? J
Ⓕ ∠CHD   Ⓗ ∠DHB
Ⓖ ∠CHB   Ⓙ ∠DHA

 for Help   **Lesson 6-5**   **Use a proportion to find the percent.**

25. 12 is what percent of 48? 25%   26. 2 is what percent of 100? 2%

TEKS ★ TAKS Resources
• TAKS Strategies, p. 365
• TAKS Tune-Up, pp. 369–371
TAKS Tune-Up Kit
  • TAKS Daily Review Transparencies
  • TAKS Review and Preparation Workbook
  • TAKS Strategies with Transparencies
  • Texas Progress Monitoring Assessments

PowerPoint
Lesson Quiz

△ABC ≅ △QRP.

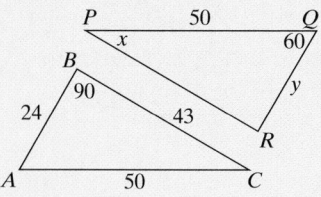

1. Write the congruences.

$\overline{AB}$ ≅ $\overline{QR}$; $\overline{BC}$ ≅ $\overline{RP}$;
$\overline{CA}$ ≅ $\overline{PQ}$; ∠A ≅ ∠Q;
∠B ≅ ∠R; ∠C ≅ ∠P

2. Find the values of x and y.
x = 30°; y = 24 units

Alternative Assessment

Have students work in pairs with
geoboards. One student makes a
figure and challenges the partner
to make one congruent and one
non-congruent figure. Partners
must agree which figure is
congruent and which is non-
congruent. Partners trade roles as
time permits.

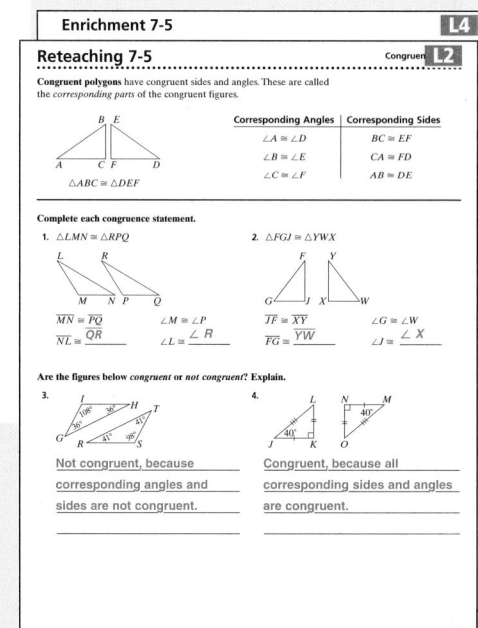

349

TEKS ★ TAKS

Prepares for **TEKS (7.9)(A)** To solve problems involving circumference and area of circles

TEKS Math Background

A *circle* is formed by a set of points that are all equidistant from the center point. If the chord passes through the center of the circle, then it is a *diameter*. Two radii drawn on a circle form a *central angle*. The central angle forms two arcs, one inside the angle, and the other outside the angle. A diameter forms two *semicircles,* one on each side of the diameter.

More Math Background: p. 322D

Lesson Planning and Resources

See p. 322E for a list of the resources that support this lesson.

Bell Ringer Practice

☑ **Check Skills You'll Need**
Use student page, transparency, or PowerPoint.

TAKS Daily Review 54
Use transparency.

✓ Check Skills You'll Need

1. Vocabulary Review
How many endpoints does a *segment* have? **2**

Use the points in each diagram to name the figure shown.

2. •———————•
   F   R

3. •————————•——
   Z   J

4. ◄—•————————•—►
      N   K

2–4. See below.

GO for Help
Lesson 7-1

Check Skills You'll Need

2. $\overline{FR}$

3. $\overrightarrow{ZJ}$

4. $\overleftrightarrow{NK}$

Any two hands of a clock form a central angle on the circular face of the clock.

7-6 Circles

What You'll Learn

To identify parts of a circle

• Prepares for **TEKS (7.9)(A)** To solve problems involving circumference and area of circles

🔊 **New Vocabulary** circle, radius, diameter, central angle, chord, arc, semicircle

Why Learn This?

In a pizza, each slice is part of a whole pie. In geometry, a central angle is part of a full circle. Just as you can use slices to measure a portion of a pizza, you can use central angles to measure a portion of a circle.

A **circle** is the set of points in a plane that are all the same distance from a given point, called the center. You name a circle by its center. Circle O is shown at the right.

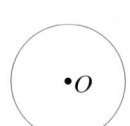

A **radius** is a segment that connects the center of a circle to the circle.

$\overline{OB}$ is a radius of circle O.

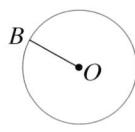

A **diameter** is a segment that passes through the center of a circle and has both endpoints on the circle.

$\overline{AC}$ is a diameter of circle O.

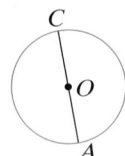

A **central angle** is an angle with its vertex at the center of a circle.

$\angle AOB$ is a central angle of circle O.

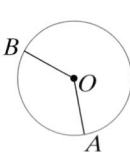

A **chord** is a segment that has both endpoints on the circle.

$\overline{AD}$ is a chord of circle O.

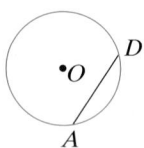

Notice that a central angle is formed by two radii. Two radii lying on the same line form a diameter of a circle. So a radius is half a diameter.

350   Chapter 7   Geometry

Differentiated Instruction Solutions for All Learners

Special Needs L1
Give students a picture of a circle with all the parts labeled. Include circumference and area by having the inside of the circle shaded. They can use this to help them work through the exercises.

learning style: visual

Below Level L2
Have students draw circles that include a radius, a diameter, and a chord with endpoints labeled. Students should then name every segment and arc.

learning style: visual

You can use points on a circle as well as the circle's center to name parts of the circle.

EXAMPLE Naming Parts Inside a Circle

① Name all the radii, diameters, and chords shown for circle O.

radii: $\overline{OA}$, $\overline{OB}$, $\overline{OC}$, and $\overline{OD}$

diameter: $\overline{AC}$

chords: $\overline{AB}$, $\overline{BC}$, $\overline{CD}$, $\overline{DA}$, and $\overline{AC}$

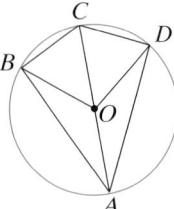

Vocabulary Tip

The plural of *radius* is *radii* (RAY dee eye).

✓ Quick Check

● 1. Name all the central angles shown in circle O.
∠AOB, ∠AOC, ∠AOD,
∠BOC, ∠BOD, ∠COD

An **arc** is part of a circle. A **semicircle** is half of a circle. In circle P, $\overset{\frown}{ST}$ and $\overset{\frown}{TW}$ are arcs less than the length of a semicircle. $\overset{\frown}{STW}$ is a semicircle. You use three letters to name an arc that is a semicircle or longer.

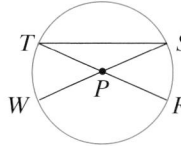

EXAMPLE Naming Arcs

② Name three of the arcs in circle O.

Three arcs are $\overset{\frown}{XZ}$, $\overset{\frown}{XY}$, and $\overset{\frown}{ZXY}$.

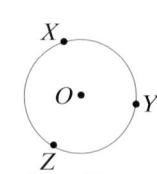

✓ Quick Check

● 2. Name three other arcs in circle O. $\overset{\frown}{ZY}$, $\overset{\frown}{ZYX}$, $\overset{\frown}{YZX}$

You can use arcs to describe real-world situations involving circles.

EXAMPLE Application: Amusement Parks

③ You are in the red car of a Ferris wheel. Your friend is in the green car. Name two different arcs between you and your friend.

The shorter arc is $\overset{\frown}{DE}$.

The longer arc is $\overset{\frown}{DCE}$.

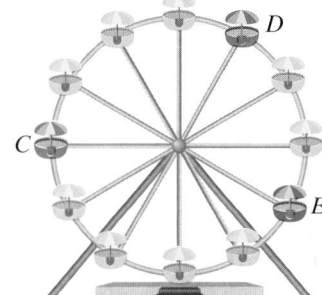

✓ Quick Check

● 3. Name two different arcs from the blue car to the green car. $\overset{\frown}{CDE}$, $\overset{\frown}{CE}$

7-6 Circles **351**

---

2. Teach

Activity Lab

Use before the lesson.

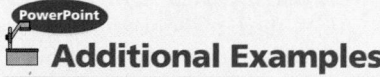 **Teaching Resources**
Activity Lab 7-6: Circles

Guided Instruction

Error Prevention!

Watch for students who confuse the terms *chord* and *diameter*.

PowerPoint
Additional Examples

Use circle F to answer 1–3.

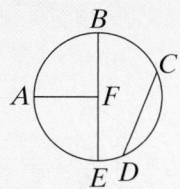

① Name all the radii, diameters, central angles, and chords shown in circle F. radii: $\overline{FB}$, $\overline{FE}$, $\overline{FA}$; diameter: $\overline{EB}$; chords: $\overline{EB}$, $\overline{CD}$; central angles: ∠BFA, ∠BFE, ∠EFA

② Name three of the arcs in circle F. Sample: $\overset{\frown}{AB}$, $\overset{\frown}{AE}$, and $\overset{\frown}{BCE}$

③ Name two different arcs between points C and D. Sample: $\overset{\frown}{CD}$, and $\overset{\frown}{CBD}$

Teaching Resources

• Daily Notetaking Guide 7-6 **L3**
• Adapted Notetaking 7-6 **L1**

Closure

• *What is a circle?* a set of points in a plane that are all the same distance from the center
• *What is the difference between a central angle and an arc?* A central angle is an angle formed by two radii. The part of the circle cut by the angle is an arc.

Advanced Learners **L4**
If two circles have congruent central angles, are the circles congruent? Explain. **No. The size of the angle is not related to the length of the radius or diameter.**

Pre-AP™

English Language Learners **ELL**
Ask students to tell you what is similar and different between a chord, a radius, and a diameter. Ask them to use the words *endpoints* and *segment* in their explanations.

learning style: verbal

351

3. Practice

Assignment Guide

Check Your Understanding
Go over Exercises 1–7 in class before assigning the Homework Exercises.

Homework Exercises
A Practice by Example   8–16
B Apply Your Skills   17–30
C Challenge   31
TEKS ★ TAKS Tune-Up and
   Mixed Review   32–37

Homework Quick Check
To check students' understanding of key skills and concepts, go over Exercises 10, 15, 25, 26, and 29.

Differentiated Instruction Resources

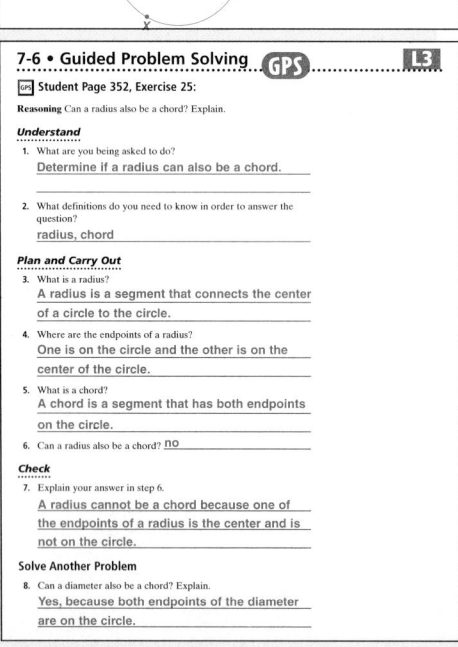

✓ Check Your Understanding

1. A radius is a line from the center of a circle to a point on the circle. A diameter is a line between two points on a circle that passes through the center of the circle.

1. **Vocabulary** Explain how a radius is different from a diameter.

2. **Reasoning** Must a diameter also be a chord? Explain. See margin.

Name each of the following for circle M.

3. center
   M

4. radii
   $\overline{ML}$, $\overline{MK}$, $\overline{MJ}$

5. chords
   $\overline{JL}$

6. diameter
   $\overline{JL}$

7. central angles
   ∠JMK, ∠KML, ∠JML

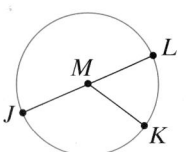

Homework Exercises

For more exercises, see Extra Skills and Word Problems.

GO for Help

For Exercises	See Examples
8–12	1
13–16	2–3

A **Name each of the following for circle O.**
8–12. See left.

8. center   9. radii   10. chords

11. diameter   12. central angles

8. O

9. $\overline{OC}$, $\overline{OK}$, $\overline{OD}$

10. $\overline{CK}$, $\overline{KD}$, $\overline{DE}$, $\overline{CE}$, $\overline{CD}$

11. $\overline{CD}$

12. ∠COK, ∠KOD, ∠COD

13. $\overline{TR}$, $\overline{RS}$, $\overline{ST}$

14. $\overarc{TRS}$, $\overarc{RST}$, $\overarc{STR}$

15. $\overarc{CD}$, $\overarc{DB}$, $\overarc{CB}$

16. $\overarc{DBC}$, $\overarc{DCB}$

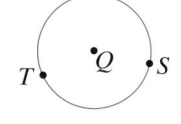

Name the following arcs for circle Q.
13–14. See left.

13. all arcs shorter than a semicircle

14. all arcs longer than a semicircle

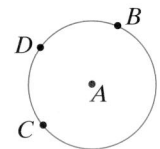

Name the following arcs for circle A.
15–16. See left.

15. all arcs shorter than a semicircle

16. all arcs longer than a semicircle

B **GPS** 17. **Guided Problem Solving** The spoke of the wheel extends from the center of the wheel to the outer edge of the wheel. If a spoke is 26 cm long, what is the diameter of the wheel?   52 cm
  • What part of a circle does a spoke represent?

Name each of the following for circle D.
18–23. See margin.

18. two chords   19. two central angles

20. a diameter   21. an isosceles triangle

22. five arcs   23. the longest chord

24. If $m\angle FDG = 90°$, find $m\angle HDG$.   90°

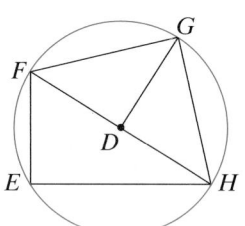

25. **Reasoning** Can a radius also be a chord? Explain.
GPS No; only one endpoint is on the circle.

26. a. **Open-Ended** Draw a design that includes a quadrilateral with vertices on a circle.   a–b. Check students' work.

b. **Writing in Math** Describe your design so someone can draw it without looking at your drawing.

GO Online
Homework Help
Visit: PHSchool.com
Web Code: are-0706

2. Yes. The diameter is the longest chord in a circle. It has both endpoints on the circle.

Exercises 18–22. Answers may vary. Samples are given.

18. $\overline{FG}$, $\overline{EF}$

19. ∠FDG, ∠GDH

20. $\overline{FH}$

21. △FDG

22. $\overarc{FG}$, $\overarc{FGH}$, $\overarc{GH}$, $\overarc{HE}$, $\overarc{GHE}$

23. $\overline{FH}$

29–30. See back of book.

Careers Fabric designers use geometric shapes, including circles, to create beautiful patterns on fabrics.

Find each length for radius *r* and diameter *d*.

27. $d = 45.2$ cm, $r = \blacksquare$ 22.6 cm   **28.** $r = 2.9$ mm, $d = \blacksquare$ 5.8 mm

Draw several diagrams that fit each description. Then make a conjecture. 29–30. See margin.

29. A quadrilateral has vertices that are the endpoints of two diameters.

30. A triangle has all its vertices on a circle. One of its sides is a diameter of the circle.

C **31. Challenge** You are running around a circular track. The distance around the track is 200 m. Points *A*, *B*, *C*, *D*, and *E* are spaced evenly around the track. If you run along $\overset{\frown}{ABD}$, $\overset{\frown}{DEB}$, and $\overset{\frown}{BCA}$, how far have you run?   400 m

TEKS ★ TAKS Tune-Up and Mixed Review

TAKS Objective 3
TEKS (7.6)(B)

32. Jorge drew the figure shown at the right, with *O* at the center of the circle. What kind of triangle is $\triangle COB$?   **D**

Ⓐ Acute isosceles triangle
Ⓑ Right isosceles triangle
Ⓒ Obtuse scalene triangle
Ⓓ Obtuse isosceles triangle

TAKS Objective 6
TEKS (7.14)(A)

33. Tickets to a sporting event that cost $25 last year cost $32 now. Which equation can be used to find *n*, the percent of increase in the ticket price?   **J**

Ⓕ $\dfrac{25}{32} = \dfrac{n}{100}$ Ⓖ $\dfrac{32}{25} = \dfrac{n}{100}$ Ⓗ $\dfrac{7}{32} = \dfrac{n}{100}$ Ⓙ $\dfrac{7}{25} = \dfrac{n}{100}$

TAKS Objective 6
TEKS (7.15)(A)

34. Kiera bought a new computer on sale for $50 less than the original selling price. What other information is necessary to find the percent of the discount?   **B**

Ⓐ The store where the computer was purchased
Ⓑ The original price of the computer
Ⓒ The amount of tax charged
Ⓓ The reason for buying a new computer

GO for Help   **Lesson 7-2**

Classify each angle as *acute*, *right*, *obtuse*, or *straight*.

35.   **36.**   **37.**

35. acute
36. obtuse
37. right

Online lesson quiz, PHSchool.com, Web Code: ara-0706

Alternative Assessment

Each student draws a circle and labels several of its parts. Partners exchange circles and identify all diameters, radii, chords, central angles, and arcs.

TEKS ★ TAKS Resources

• TAKS Strategies, p. 365
• TAKS Tune-Up, pp. 369–371

TAKS Tune-Up Kit

• TAKS Daily Review Transparencies
• TAKS Review and Preparation Workbook
• TAKS Strategies with Transparencies
• Texas Progress Monitoring Assessments

---

4. Assess & Reteach

PowerPoint
Lesson Quiz

Use circle *O* for questions 1–3.

1. Name the radii, diameter, and chords. radii: $\overline{OQ}$, $\overline{OR}$, $\overline{OS}$; diameter: $\overline{QS}$; chords: $\overline{PQ}$, $\overline{PR}$, $\overline{QR}$, $\overline{SQ}$

2. Name two central angles. Sample: $\angle SOR$, $\angle QOR$

3. Name three arcs. Sample: $\overset{\frown}{PQ}$, $\overset{\frown}{QRS}$, $\overset{\frown}{SP}$

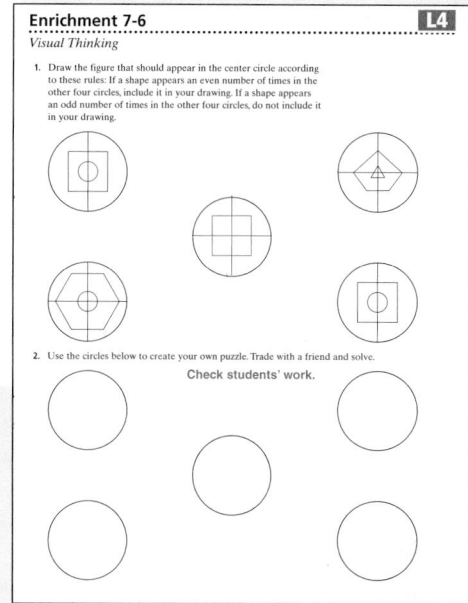

353

TEKS ★ TAKS

(7.11)(A) To select and use an appropriate representation for presenting and displaying relationships among collected data TAKS Obj. 5

Also supports
(7.11)(B) TAKS Obj. 5

Dana Center TEKS Toolkit Clarifying Activities (7.11)(A) (7.11)(B)
Visit: PHSchool.com
Web Code: arq-9045

TEKS Math Background

Circle graphs provide a quick way to visualize the size of parts of a whole. To make a circle graph you need to find the central angle for each part or section by solving the proportion $\frac{part}{whole} = \frac{angle}{360°}$.

More Math Background: p. 322D

Lesson Planning and Resources

See p. 322E for a list of the resources that support this lesson.

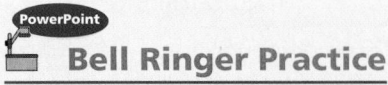

Bell Ringer Practice

✓ **Check Skills You'll Need**
Use student page, transparency, or PowerPoint.

TAKS **Daily Review 55**
Use transparency.

7-7 Circle Graphs

✓ Check Skills You'll Need

1. Vocabulary Review
How is finding the percent of a number like multiplying decimals?
See below.

Find each answer.

2. 25% of 360   90

3. 60% of 360   216

4. 72% of 360   259.2

for Help
Lesson 6-4

Check Skills You'll Need

1. Every percent can be written as a decimal by moving the decimal point two places to the left. Thus 25% becomes 0.25. So taking the percent of a number is the same as multiplying by a decimal.

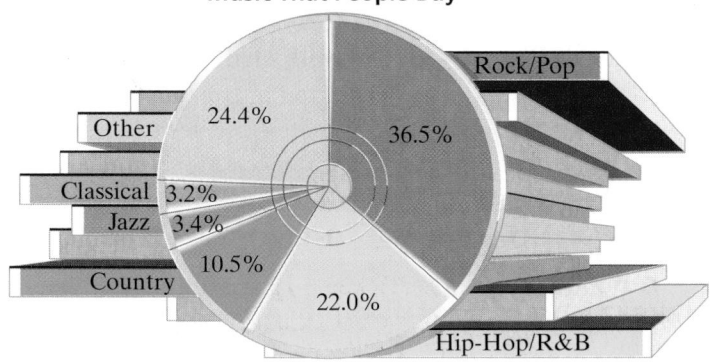

Video Tutor Help
Visit: PHSchool.com
Web Code: are-0775

TEKS ★ TAKS

- (7.11)(A) To select and use an appropriate representation for presenting and displaying relationships among collected data TAKS Obj. 5
- (7.11)(B) To make inferences and convincing arguments based on an analysis of given or collected data TAKS Obj. 5

🔊 **New Vocabulary** circle graph

Why Learn This?

You can use a circle graph like the one below to display survey or research results. You can see at a glance how the parts compare to one another and to the whole amount.

Music That People Buy

- Rock/Pop 36.5%
- Other 24.4%
- Classical 3.2%
- Jazz 3.4%
- Country 10.5%
- Hip-Hop/R&B 22.0%

SOURCE: Recording Industry Association of America

A **circle graph** is a graph of data in which a circle represents the whole. Each wedge, or sector, is part of the whole. The total must be 100%. You can use a circle graph to see how the whole breaks down into parts.

EXAMPLE Analyzing a Circle Graph

① TAKS **Griddable Item** In a recent year, consumers spent $13.7 billion on music recordings. Use the circle graph above to find how many dollars, to the nearest tenth of a billion, were spent on country music.

Find 10.5% of $13.7 billion.

0.105 · $13.7 billion ≈ $1.4 billion

✓ Quick Check

1. Approximately how much money was spent on jazz? about 470 million

---

354 Chapter 7 Geometry

Differentiated Instruction Solutions for All Learners

Special Needs L1
Some students may have difficulty drawing a circle graph. If so, pair them up with students who can do the drawing while they check the sections against the data in the table.

learning style: visual

Below Level L2
Use circle graph paper for Example 2. Shade the angle measures on the circle graph based on the scale of the graph paper rather than using compass measurements.

learning style: visual

A circle graph is divided into sectors. Each sector is determined by a central angle. The sum of the measures of the central angles is 360°.

 Constructing a Circle Graph

2 **Science** Use the information in the table below to make a circle graph.

NASA Space Shuttle Expenditures

Category	Cost (millions of dollars)
Orbiter	698.8
Propulsion	1,053.1
Operations	738.8
Upgrades	488.8

Source: *Statistical Abstract of the United States*
Go to **PHSchool.com** for a data update.
Web Code: arg-9041

Step 1 Add to find the total space shuttle expenditures.
$$698.8 + 1,053.1 + 738.8 + 488.8 = 2,979.5$$

Step 2 For each central angle, set up a proportion to find the angle measure. Use a calculator to solve. Round to the nearest tenth.

$$\frac{698.8}{2,979.5} = \frac{a}{360} \quad a \approx 84.4° \qquad \frac{1,053.1}{2,979.5} = \frac{b}{360} \quad b \approx 127.2°$$

$$\frac{738.8}{2,979.5} = \frac{c}{360} \quad c \approx 89.3° \qquad \frac{488.8}{2,979.5} = \frac{d}{360} \quad d \approx 59.1°$$

Step 3 Draw a circle. Draw the central angles using the measures found in Step 2. Label each section. Include a title and a key.

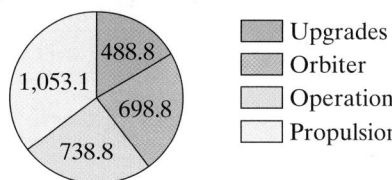

NASA Space Shuttle Expenditures (millions of dollars)

☐ Upgrades
☐ Orbiter
☐ Operations
☐ Propulsion

Quick Check

2. **a.** Find the measure of the central angle that you would draw to represent summer. **144°**

b. Use the information in the table at the right to make a circle graph. *See back of book.*

Favorite Season

Season	Percent
Summer	40%
Spring	11%
Winter	4%
Fall	45%

---

2. Teach

Activity Lab

Use before the lesson.

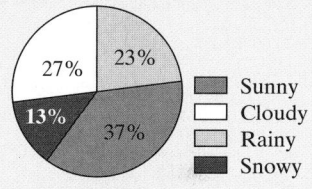 **Teaching Resources**
Activity Lab 7-7: Circle Graphs

Guided Instruction

Technology
Students can use a spreadsheet program to draw circle graphs.

PowerPoint
Additional Examples

1 Use the circle graph below.

November Weather (30 days)

27% 23%
13% 37%

☐ Sunny
☐ Cloudy
☐ Rainy
☐ Snowy

a. What percent of the days was snowy? **13%**

b. How many days were cloudy? **8 days**

2 Use the information in the table to make a circle graph.

Size of U.S. Households (2000)

No. of People in Household	Number (in thousands)
1	26,724
2	34,666
3	17,152
4	15,309
5 or more	10,854

See back of book.

Teaching Resources
• Daily Notetaking Guide 7-7 L3
• Adapted Notetaking 7-7 L1

Closure

• *How do you make a circle graph?* See back of book.

Assignment Guide

Check Your Understanding
Go over Exercises 1–6 in class before assigning the Homework Exercises.

Homework Exercises
A Practice by Example   7–11
B Apply Your Skills   12–18
C Challenge   19
TEKS ★ TAKS Tune-Up and
Mixed Review   20–26

Homework Quick Check
To check students' understanding of key skills and concepts, go over Exercises 8, 11, 14, 17, and 18.

Differentiated Instruction Resources

356

✓ Check Your Understanding

1. **Vocabulary** In a circle graph, the sum of the sectors must equal ■.
   the whole circle, 360°, 100%
2. **Number Sense** A circle graph has five sectors. Two sectors are equal to 25% each. The third sector is equal to 35%. Which CANNOT be the value of either of the remaining two sectors? **A**
   - Ⓐ 22%   Ⓑ 11%   Ⓒ 10%   Ⓓ 1%

Find the measure of the central angle that you would draw to represent each percent in a circle graph.

3. 25% **90°**   4. 50% **180°**   5. 10% **36°**   6. 12.5% **45°**

Homework Exercises

For more exercises, see Extra Skills and Word Problems.

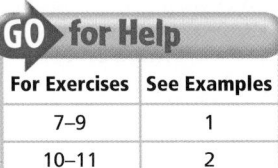

A Use the circle graph for Exercises 7–9.

For Exercises	See Examples
7–9	1
10–11	2

7. What takes up the largest portion of Royston's day? **sleeping**

8. What percent of the day does Royston typically spend doing homework? **12.5%**

9. How many hours a day does Royston spend sleeping? **about 8 hours**

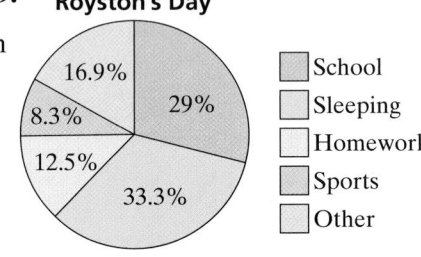
Royston's Day

16.9% 29% 8.3% 12.5% 33.3%

□ School
□ Sleeping
□ Homework
□ Sports
□ Other

Use the information in each table to make a circle graph.

10. **Frozen Yogurt Sales**

Flavor	Scoops
Vanilla	84
Chocolate	107
Strawberry	43

11. **Movie Rentals**

Type	Number
Action	7
Comedy	9
Other	5

10–11. See margin.

B GPS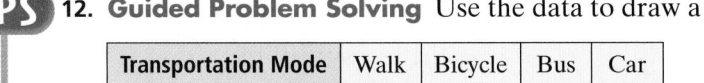

12. **Guided Problem Solving** Use the data to draw a circle graph.

See margin.

Transportation Mode	Walk	Bicycle	Bus	Car
Number of Students	252	135	432	81

- **Make a Plan** First find the total number of students. Then set up a proportion for each mode to find its central angle measure.
- **Carry Out the Plan** The total number of students is ■. Use the proportions below.

$$\frac{252}{■} = \frac{w}{360} \qquad \frac{135}{■} = \frac{b}{360} \qquad \frac{432}{■} = \frac{u}{■} \qquad \frac{■}{■} = \frac{c}{■}$$

10–12. See back of book.

14. No, "other" and Europe both indicate many different countries.

Use the circle graph for Exercises 13–16.

13. Which country or region is most visited by United States travelers? **Mexico**

14. **Reasoning** Can you tell which country or region is least visited by United States travelers? Explain.

15. Approximately how many people travel to Europe from the United States each year? **11.6 million people**

16. **Writing in Math** Why use Europe rather than list every country individually? **The angles would be too small to display.**

U.S. Foreign Travel (millions of people per year)

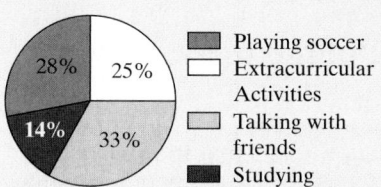

| Mexico | Europe |
| Canada | Other |

Source: Statistical Abstract of the United States

17. The table shows how many days each week students do volunteer work. Use the table to make a circle graph. **See margin.**

Days	1	2	3	4	5
Students	11	5	5	2	2

18. **Open-Ended** Describe a situation for which a circle graph is an appropriate display to represent the data. Describe a situation for which a circle graph is *not* an appropriate display to represent the data. **See margin.**

C **19.** **Challenge** A circle graph shows a survey of the favorite ice cream flavors of all the students at Park School. Vanilla is the favorite flavor of 28 students. The central angle measure for vanilla is 72° in the circle graph. How many students are at Park School? **140 students**

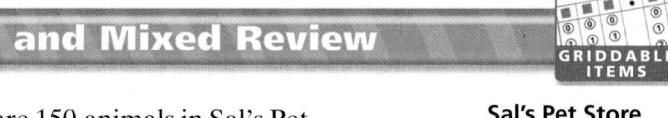
TEKS ★ TAKS Tune-Up and Mixed Review

TAKS Objective 5
TEKS (7.11)(A)

20. There are 150 animals in Sal's Pet Store. According to the circle graph, how many of the animals are dogs? **45**

Sal's Pet Store

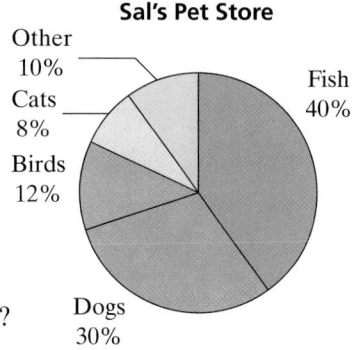

Other 10%
Cats 8%
Birds 12%
Fish 40%
Dogs 30%

TAKS Objective 1
TEKS (7.2)(D)

21. A carpenter renovating a house is sanding the dining room floor. She sands 300 ft² of wood floor in 1 hour and 40 minutes. What is the unit rate in square feet per minute?
3

TAKS Objective 3
TEKS (7.6)(A)

22. The measure of ∠ABC is 128°. What is the measure of its supplement in degrees? **52**

GO for Help
Lesson 3-3

Find each sum or difference. $10\frac{7}{18}$

23. $\frac{2}{3} + \frac{3}{8}$ $1\frac{1}{4}$ **24.** $4\frac{1}{6} + 6\frac{2}{9}$ **25.** $\frac{7}{8} - \frac{1}{4}$ $\frac{5}{8}$ **26.** $14\frac{5}{8} - 6\frac{5}{12}$ $8\frac{5}{24}$

---

4. Assess & Reteach

Lesson Quiz

The circle graph below shows how a class of 48 students spends free time after lunch.

28% | 25%
14% | 33%

■ Playing soccer
□ Extracurricular Activities
▨ Talking with friends
■ Studying

1. What percent study or do extracurricular activities? **39%**

2. How many students spend time on extracurricular activities? **12**

3. Find the measure of the central angle that you would draw to represent 15% in a circle graph. **54°**

17–18. See back of book.

Alternative Assessment

Have students work in pairs to complete Exercises 10 and 11. First they list the steps they need to take before they can make the graph, such as: find the total, find the percent each item is of the total, and find the measure of the central angle to the nearest whole number. Then each pair makes its graphs.

TEKS ★ TAKS Resources

- TAKS Strategies, p. 365
- TAKS Tune-Up, pp. 369–371

TAKS Tune-Up Kit
- TAKS Daily Review Transparencies
- TAKS Review and Preparation Workbook
- TAKS Strategies with Transparencies
- Texas Progress Monitoring Assessments

357

Making a Circle Graph

Students will use a spinner to generate data that they will then present in a circle graph.

Guided Instruction

Teaching Tip
Tell students that they will make 100 spins so that the numbers they work with will be easy to convert to decimals or percents.

TEKS ★ **TAKS Resources**

• Classroom Aid 27

Dana Center TEKS Toolkit Clarifying Activities (7.11)(A)
Visit: PHSchool.com
Web Code: arq-9045

Checkpoint Quiz

Use this Checkpoint Quiz to check students' understanding of the skills and concepts of Lessons 7-5 through 7-7.

Resources

• spinner
• paper and writing instruments

Activity Lab

1. The *tallies* column should total 100. The *fraction* column should total 1. The *angle* column should total 360°.

3. Answers may vary. Sample: The results are very close. The circle graph might be even closer if I used 1,000 spins. The fact that each spin is random means the experimental probability might be different from the theoretical probability.

358

7-7b Activity Lab

TEKS ★ **TAKS**
(7.11)(A) To select and use an appropriate representation for presenting and displaying relationships among collected data, including circle graph
TAKS Obj. 5

Making a Circle Graph

You can use a spinner to generate data. You can use circle graphs to present the data.

ACTIVITY

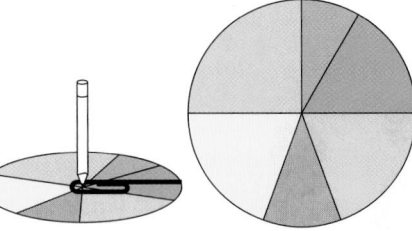

Step 1 Copy the spinner at the right. Use a protractor to measure and copy the central angles of the spinner.

Step 2 Straighten half a paper clip to use as the pointer. Use a pencil point to keep the loop of the paper clip at the center of the spinner.

Step 3 Make a table like the one at the right. Spin the paper clip. Use your frequency column to record the results of 100 spins.

Category	Tallies	Fraction	Angle
Red	■	■	■
Blue	■	■	■
Green	■	■	■
Yellow	■	■	■
Gray	■	■	■
Orange	■	■	■

1. Fill in the fraction of tallies for each color and the number of degrees in that fraction of a circle. What should be the sum of each column? **See margin.**

2. Make a circle graph for your data. Use a protractor to draw the central angles for your graph. Label each sector of your graph. **Check students' work.**

3. Compare your circle graph to the spinner that you used. Are they exactly the same? Explain. **See margin.**

✓ Checkpoint Quiz 2

Lessons 7-5 through 7-7

1. If two squares have the same area, are they congruent? Explain. **See margin.**

2. Use the information in the table to make a circle graph. **See margin.**

Name each of the following for circle P.

3. two chords $\overline{RS}$ and $\overline{ST}$

4. a diameter $\overline{TR}$

5. two central angles
∠RPS, ∠SPT, ∠TPQ, and ∠QPR

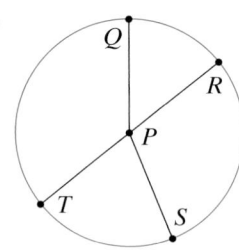

Town Middle School

Grade	6	7	8
Number of Students	75	100	125

358

Checkpoint Quiz 2

1. Yes. The square root of the area is the side length. Since both squares have the same area, they have the same side length. Being squares, they both have four right angles. Congruent sides and congruent angles means the squares are congruent.

2. See back of book.

Percents and Circle Graphs

The circle graph shows people's milk preferences. If your school cafeteria ordered pints of milk for 450 milk-drinking students, how many pints of each type should the cafeteria order?

School Milk Preferences

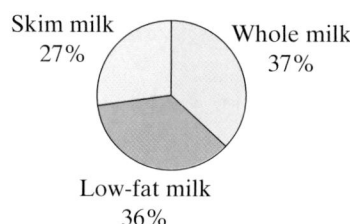

Skim milk 27%

Whole milk 37%

Low-fat milk 36%

TEKS ★ TAKS

(7.11)(B) To make inferences and convincing arguments based on analysis of given or collected data **TAKS** Obj. 5

(7.3)(A) To estimate and find solutions to application problems involving percent **TAKS** Obj. 2

What You Might Think

> What do I know?
> What do I want to find out?

> How do I solve the problem?

> What is the answer?

> Is it reasonable?

What You Might Write

The graph shows whole, low-fat, and skim milk preferences. I want to find each percent for 450 students.

Whole milk: 37% · 450 = 166.5
Low-fat milk: 36% · 450 = 162
Skim milk: 27% · 450 = 121.5

Round: 166.5 rounds to 170.
         162 rounds to 160.
         121.5 rounds to 120.

Order 170 pints of whole milk, 160 pints of low-fat milk, and 120 pints of skim milk.

The numbers add to 450, with skim milk a smaller number than the other two. The answer is reasonable.

Think It Through

1. Do you think these data will change in ten years? In what way? Explain your reasoning. See margin.

1.   Answers may vary. Sample: Yes; students are more diet conscious, and preferences for low-fat and skim milk would be increasing.
4.   See back of book.

GPS Guided Problem Solving

Percent and Circle Graphs

In this feature, students learn to solve problems using percents and circle graphs. The circle graph shows milk preferences in percents using 450 as a base.

Guided Instruction

Discuss with students the percent equation: percent × base = part. Have them identify or find each percent for the various milk types.

TEKS ★ TAKS Resources

• Classroom Aids 27, 28

Dana Center TEKS Toolkit
   Clarifying Activities (7.3)(A), (7.11)(B)
Visit: PHSchool.com
Web Code: arq-9045

Error Prevention!

Error Prevention!

Be sure students understand that the base remains the same although the percents and parts change.

Exercises

Work through Exercise 1 as a class. Then assign students to work with partners to complete Exercises 2–4.

For Exercise 4, have partners work together to choose five categories. If they disagree on the categories, help them broaden the categories, for example, from soccer and band to after school activities.

Differentiated Instruction

English Language Learners   ELL

For Exercise 3, be sure students understand what blood typing is. Ask if any students know their own blood type.

Exercises

Solve the problems. For Exercises 2 and 3, answer the questions first.

2. The circle graph shows different age groups in the population of the United States as reported in the 2000 U.S. Census. If the population of the United States is about 281 million, approximately how many people are in your age group?   about 31.2 million

Age Groups

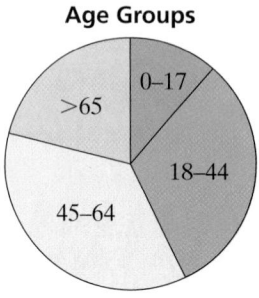

a. What do you know? What do you want to find out?
b. How can you estimate the percent of people in your age group?

3. A study collected percents of male and female teachers across the nation. The results are shown in the table below. If you have five classes each year, how many male teachers can you expect during your three middle school years? How many female teachers can you expect?   4 male teachers; 11 female teachers

Teachers

Female	Male
72%	28%

a. What do you know? What do you want to find out?
b. Can a model help you find the answers?

4. Blood typing is important in transfusions and organ transplants. Use the data in the table to make a circle graph showing the percents of blood types in the United States. Use a calculator to find the number of U. S. citizens with each blood type. Use 281 million as the population of the United States. See margin.

U.S. Blood Type Percentages

Type	Positive	Negative
O	38%	7%
A	34%	6%
B	9%	2%
AB	3%	1%

5. Make a circle graph of how you spend time during a typical day in school. Limit your graph to five categories.   Check students' work.

Constructions

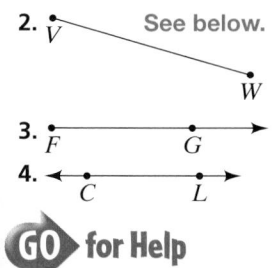
What You'll Learn

To construct congruent segments and perpendicular bisectors

🔊 **New Vocabulary** compass, midpoint, segment bisector, perpendicular lines, perpendicular bisector

Why Learn This?

Architects use congruent segments and perpendicular lines when they design buildings. Congruent segments and perpendicular lines can give a design a sense of balance.

You can use a geometric tool called a **compass** to draw a circle, or a part of a circle, called an arc.

You can use a compass and a straightedge (an unmarked ruler) to construct a congruent segment for a given segment.

EXAMPLE **Constructing a Congruent Segment**

1 Construct segment $\overline{CD}$ congruent to $\overline{AB}$.

A ———— B

Step 1 Draw a ray with endpoint C.

C ————————→

Step 2 Open the compass to the length of $\overline{AB}$.

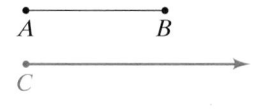
A   B

Step 3 Keep the compass open to the same width. Put the compass point on point C. Draw an arc that intersects the ray. Label the point of intersection D.

C   D

$\overline{CD}$ is congruent to $\overline{AB}$.

1.

T 25 mm R

S   V

✔ **Quick Check**

1. Draw a segment $\overline{TR}$ 25 mm long. Construct $\overline{SV}$ congruent to $\overline{TR}$.
   See left.

Objectives
To construct congruent segments and perpendicular bisectors

Examples
1 Constructing a Congruent Segment
2 Constructing a Perpendicular Bisector

Professional Development

TEKS Math Background

You can use a *compass* to draw circles and parts of circles, called *arcs*. Some basic constructions are constructing congruent segments and bisecting a segment. A *segment bisector* is a line, or segment, or ray that divides a segment at its midpoint into two congruent segments. An infinite number of segment bisectors can divide one segment into two equal segments. However, it has only one *perpendicular bisector* that intersects the segment at a right angle.

More Math Background: p. 322D

Lesson Planning and Resources

See p. 322E for a list of the resources that support this lesson.

PowerPoint

Bell Ringer Practice

✔ **Check Skills You'll Need**
Use student page, transparency, or PowerPoint.

TAKS Daily Review 56
Use transparency.

Differentiated Instruction Solutions for All Learners

Special Needs L1
Some students may have difficulty handling the compass to complete the constructions. Pair them up with a student who can draw while they read the directions out loud. They can trace the drawing after it is constructed.

learning style: tactile

Below Level L2
Use a ruler to measure the segments in Example 2 and find the midpoint arithmetically. Students should verify that the midpoint by construction matches the measured one.

learning style: tactile

361

Activity Lab

Use before the lesson.

All in One Teaching Resources

Activity Lab 7-8: Constructions

Guided Instruction

Example 1
Have students practice drawing circles with a compass. Show students that the tip must remain anchored while drawing an arc. Make sure students draw without putting too much pressure on the compass because this can change the size of the opening.

Technology Tip
Geometry software programs allow students to perform compass and straightedge constructions.

PowerPoint

Additional Examples

① Construct a segment $\overline{RS}$ that is congruent to $\overline{PQ}$.

② Construct the perpendicular bisector of $\overline{PQ}$.

All in One Teaching Resources
- Daily Notetaking Guide 7-8 **L3**
- Adapted Notetaking 7-8 **L1**

Closure

- *How are a segment bisector and midpoint of a segment related?*
  The bisector cuts the segment into two segments of equal length by intersecting the segment at the midpoint.

362

The **midpoint** of a segment is the point that divides the segment into two segments of equal length.

A **segment bisector** is a line, segment, or ray that goes through the midpoint of a segment.

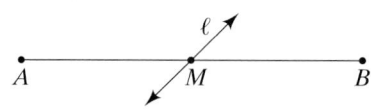

$\overline{AM}$ is congruent to $\overline{MB}$.

M is the midpoint of $\overline{AB}$.

Line ℓ is a segment bisector of $\overline{AB}$.

Perpendicular lines are lines that intersect to form right angles.

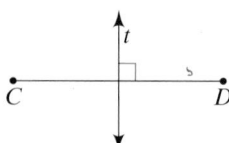

A segment bisector that is perpendicular to a segment is the **perpendicular bisector** of the segment. You can use a compass and a straightedge to construct the perpendicular bisector of a given segment.

EXAMPLE **Constructing a Perpendicular Bisector**

② Construct the perpendicular bisector of $\overline{AB}$.

Step 1 Set the compass to more than half the length of $\overline{AB}$. Put the tip of the compass at *A* and draw an arc intersecting $\overline{AB}$.

Step 2 Keeping the compass set at the same width, put the tip at *B* and draw another arc intersecting $\overline{AB}$. Points *C* and *D* are where the arcs intersect.

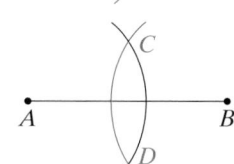

Step 3 Draw $\overleftrightarrow{CD}$. The intersection of $\overline{AB}$ and $\overleftrightarrow{CD}$ is point *M*. $\overleftrightarrow{CD}$ is the perpendicular bisector of $\overline{AB}$. Point *M* is the midpoint of $\overline{AB}$.

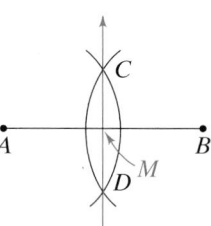

✓ Quick Check

2. Draw a segment 3 in. long. Label the segment $\overline{XY}$. Construct the perpendicular bisector of $\overline{XY}$.

This 1482 edition of Euclid's *Elements of Geometry* was the first math book produced on a printing press.

SOURCE: Wellesley College Library

2.

$\overline{XY}$ = 3 in.

Advanced Learners **L4**
How many segment bisectors of $\overline{AB}$ are there? **an infinite number**
How many perpendicular segment bisectors of $\overline{AB}$ are there? **one**

English Language Learners **ELL**
Have students pair up and take turns, with one partner reading the data and one drawing. Then switch roles. Both students practice speaking about, and listening to, the terms used in the constructions.

learning style: verbal

Check Your Understanding

1. Answers may vary. Since *Q* is the midpoint of $\overline{PR}$, $\overline{PQ}$ and $\overline{QR}$ are congruent.

Vocabulary Tip

$\overline{AB}$ means the length of $\overline{AB}$.

1. **Vocabulary** *Q* is the midpoint of $\overline{PR}$. Write a statement about two congruent segments having endpoint *Q*.

2. **Reasoning** Can you construct a different perpendicular bisector of $\overline{AB}$ in Example 2? Explain. **No. The perpendicular bisector is unique in the plane.**

Point *B* is the midpoint of $\overline{AC}$. Complete each statement.

3. $AB = 4$ in., $AC = \blacksquare$ **8 in.**

4. $AC = 9$ m, $AB = \blacksquare$ **$4\frac{1}{2}$ m**

5. $AC = 7$ m, $BC = \blacksquare$ **$3\frac{1}{2}$ m**

6. $BC = 5$ ft, $AB = \blacksquare$ **5 ft**

Homework Exercises

For more exercises, see Extra Skills and Word Problems.

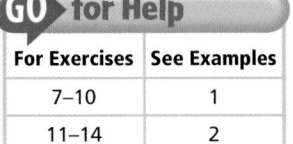

For Exercises	See Examples
7–10	1
11–14	2

7–14. Check students' work.

A Copy each segment. Then construct a congruent segment.

7. $\overset{\bullet}{A} \rule{3cm}{0.4pt} \overset{\bullet}{B}$

8. $\overset{\bullet}{S} \rule{3cm}{0.4pt} \overset{\bullet}{T}$

9. $\overset{\bullet}{C} \rule{3cm}{0.4pt} \overset{\bullet}{D}$

10. $\overset{\bullet}{K} \rule{3cm}{0.4pt} \overset{\bullet}{L}$

Draw each segment. Then construct its perpendicular bisector.

11. a segment 4 in. long

12. a segment 10 cm long

13. a segment 5 in. long

14. a segment 13.5 cm long

B   **GPS** 15. **Guided Problem Solving** Draw $\overline{CD}$ at least 3 in. long. Construct and label a segment one fourth as long as $\overline{CD}$. See margin.
- **Make a Plan** One half of one half is one fourth. So bisecting half of a line segment will give you one fourth of a line segment.
- **Carry Out the Plan** Bisect $\overline{CD}$ and label the midpoint *E*. Then bisect $\overline{CE}$. That segment will be one fourth as long as $\overline{CD}$.

16. Draw $\overline{MN}$ about 4 in. long. Then construct $\overline{JK}$ two and one half **GPS** times as long as $\overline{MN}$. See margin.

17. Draw $\overline{AB}$ about 5 in. long. Then construct $\overline{XY}$ so that the two line segments are perpendicular bisectors of each other. See margin.

18. **Patterns** Draw two large triangles, one acute and one obtuse. Construct the perpendicular bisector of each side. Make a conjecture about the perpendicular bisectors of the sides of any triangle. See margin.

19. 1, infinite, 1; a segment can only have one exact midpoint or perpendicular bisector. A segment be bisected by an infinite number of lines.

19. **Writing in Math** How many midpoints does a segment have? How many segment bisectors does it have? How many perpendicular bisectors does it have? Explain. See left.

15–18. See back of book.

---

3. Practice

Assignment Guide

Check Your Understanding
Go over Exercises 1–6 in class before assigning the Homework Exercises.

Homework Exercises
A	Practice by Example	7–14
B	Apply Your Skills	15–27
C	Challenge	28

TEKS ★ TAKS Tune-Up and Mixed Review 29–34

Homework Quick Check
To check students' understanding of key skills and concepts, go over Exercises 8, 12, 16, 19, and 26.

Differentiated Instruction Resources

Lesson Quiz

1. Construct a segment congruent to this segment.

2. Draw a segment 9.5 cm long. Then construct its perpendicular bisector.

31. $\frac{5}{7}$, 5 : 7

32. 6 to 13, $\frac{6}{13}$

33. 9 to 4, 9 : 4

34. 16 to 25, 16 : 25

364

GO Online
Homework Help
Visit: PHSchool.com
Web Code: are-0708

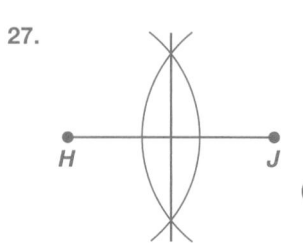

27.

Point B is the midpoint of AC. Complete each statement.

20. $AB = 2.25$ in., $AC = \blacksquare$ 4.5 in.

21. $AC = 8.4$ cm, $AB = \blacksquare$ 4.2 cm

22. $BC = 1.7$ ft, $AB = \blacksquare$ 1.7 ft

23. $AB = 17$ mm, $AC = \blacksquare$ 34 mm

24. $AC = 3$ in., $BC = \blacksquare$ 1.5 in.

25. $BC = 75$ cm, $AC = \blacksquare$ 150 cm

26. Follow the steps to construct $\triangle EFG$ with all sides congruent to $\overline{XY}$.

  Step 1 Draw a segment $\overline{XY}$. Use a compass to construct $\overline{EF} \cong \overline{XY}$.

  Step 2 Using the same compass width, place the compass tip on point F and draw an arc above $\overline{EF}$.

  Step 3 Using the same compass width, place the compass tip on point E and make another arc above $\overline{EF}$, intersecting the first arc. Label the intersection G.

  Step 4 Draw $\overline{EG}$ and $\overline{FG}$ to form $\triangle EFG$.   **Check students' work.**

27. Use the construction techniques you learned in this lesson to draw a 90° angle without using a protractor. **See left.**

C 28. **Challenge** A is the midpoint of $\overline{XY}$. Y is the midpoint of $\overline{XZ}$. Z is the midpoint of $\overline{AB}$. $\overline{XA}$ is 2 cm long. How long is $\overline{XB}$? **14 cm**

TEKS ★ TAKS Tune-Up and Mixed Review

TAKS Objective 1
TEKS (7.2)(B)

29. Don bought items that cost $2.59, $3.48, $1.75, $0.63, and $0.98. He used a coupon worth $0.80. The tax totaled $0.73. If he gave the clerk a $10 bill, how much change did he receive? **A**

  Ⓐ $0.64   Ⓑ $0.96   Ⓒ $1.37   Ⓓ $9.36

TAKS Objective 2
TEKS (7.5)(B)

30. Which problem situation matches the equation $0.80x = 400$? **J**

  Ⓕ In a recent election, 80% of the people voted for a new tax to repair streets. Four hundred people voted. What is x, the number who voted for the tax?

  Ⓖ Eighty out of 400 of the items at one manufacturing plant were found to have flaws. What is x, the percent of items that contained flaws?

  Ⓗ The Drake family has driven 80 miles. They need to travel 400 miles to reach their destination. What is x, the percent of their trip completed?

  Ⓙ In a school survey, 400 students said they would like more variety in the cafeteria. This was 80% of those surveyed. What is x, the total number of students who were surveyed?

 Lesson 5-1   **Write each ratio in two other ways.**   31–34. See margin.

31. 5 to 7   32. 6 : 13   33. $\frac{9}{4}$ 34. $\frac{16}{25}$

TEKS ★ TAKS Resources

- TAKS Strategies, p. 365
- TAKS Tune-Up, pp. 369–371

TAKS Tune-Up Kit
- TAKS Daily Review Transparencies
- TAKS Review and Preparation Workbook
- TAKS Strategies with Transparencies
- Texas Progress Monitoring Assessments

Alternative Assessment

Each student in a pair draws a line segment. Partners exchange drawings. Each student constructs a segment congruent to the partner's segment and then constructs the perpendicular bisector of the segment. Students can share their work and their methods with the class.

Drawing a Picture

Sometimes a picture is not supplied with a problem. Then you can draw a picture to help you solve the problem. Make sure your picture is large enough to allow you to label all the parts.

EXAMPLE

$\triangle CRT \cong \triangle POV$. The measure of $\angle C$ is 41°, and the measure of $\angle T$ is 104°. What is the measure of $\angle O$?

Draw and label triangles CRT and POV. Label angles C and T. Label the corresponding angles in $\triangle POV$.

 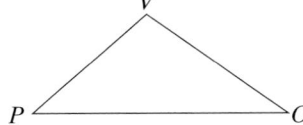

Write an equation to find the measure of $\angle O$.

Let $x = m\angle O = m\angle R$.

$$x + 41° + 104° = 180°$$
$$x + 145° = 180°$$
$$x + 145° - 145° = 180° - 145°$$
$$x = 35°$$

● The measure of $\angle O$ is 35°.

Exercises

Draw a picture to solve each problem.

TAKS Objective 3
TEKS (7.6)(A)

1. $\overleftrightarrow{QR}$ intersects $\overleftrightarrow{ST}$ at point U. The measure of $\angle QUT$ is 123°, and the measure of $\angle TUR$ is 57°. What is the measure of $\angle SUR$?   **C**
   - Ⓐ 57°
   - Ⓑ 90°
   - Ⓒ 123°
   - Ⓓ 133°

TAKS Objective 3
TEKS (7.6)(B)

2. A right triangle has one angle that measures 16°. Which of the following could be the measures of the other two angles?   **G**
   - Ⓕ 16°, 148°
   - Ⓖ 74°, 90°
   - Ⓗ 84°, 90°
   - Ⓙ 82°, 82°

TAKS Objective 4
TEKS (7.9)(A)

3. Rectangle $ABCD$ shares $\overline{BC}$ with equilateral triangle BCE. The length of $\overline{CD}$ is 4 cm, and the perimeter of $ABCD$ is 14 cm. What is the perimeter of $\triangle BCE$?   **C**
   - Ⓐ 3 cm
   - Ⓑ 6 cm
   - Ⓒ 9 cm
   - Ⓓ 14 cm

TAKS Strategies

Drawing a Picture

This feature presents the effective test-taking strategy of drawing a picture to help solve a problem.

Guided Instruction

Discuss with students that drawing a picture or sketch can help them more clearly understand the relationships presented in words.

Error Prevention!

Stress that the picture they draw accurately represents the data provided in the text. Guide students to reread the text after drawing the picture to make sure it expresses the identical information.

TEKS ★ **TAKS** Resources

TAKS Strategies with Transparencies
- Transparency 9
- Practice sheet, p. 19

TAKS **Strategies with Transparencies**

Test-Taking Strategies: Drawing a Picture

A diagram can help you see how to solve a problem.

Example A square quilt has 6 in. by 6 in. fabric squares. The outside perimeter is 144 in. How many squares are on the quilt perimeter?

A. 144   B. 36   C. 24   D. 20

Each side must be 144 ÷ 4 = 36 in.

Let one unit on graph paper represent 6 in.

There must be 36 ÷ 6 = 6 squares on each side.

Draw a diagram, and count the perimeter squares.

The answer is 20, or choice D.

Use a diagram to find the answer. Explain your reasoning.

1. Tess wants to fence in her garden, which is 5 ft long and 4 ft wide. She will put a post at each corner and at every foot. How many fence posts will she need?

   A. 14   B. 20   C. 18   D. 19

2. What is the area of the shaded square in the figure?

   F. 50 cm²
   G. 100 cm²
   H. 200 cm²
   J. 400 cm²

Chapter 7 Review

TEKS ★ TAKS Resources

Student Edition
Extra Skills and Word Problems
  Practice, Ch. 7, p. 642
English/Spanish Glossary, p. 675
Formulas and Properties, p. 673
Tables, p. 670
All in One Teaching Resources
- Vocabulary and Study
  Skills 7F   L3

TAKS Tune-Up Kit
- TAKS Daily Review
  Transparencies
- TAKS Review and Preparation
  Workbook
- TAKS Strategies with
  Transparencies
- Texas Progress Monitoring
  Assessments
- Texas ExamView CD-ROM
- MindPoint Quiz Show CD-ROM

Differentiated Instruction

Spanish Vocabulary Workbook
  with Study Skills   ELL
Texas Interactive Textbook
- Audio Glossary
Online Vocabulary Quiz

Success ✶ Tracker™
Online at PHSchool.com

Vocabulary Review

 acute angle (p. 330)
  acute triangle (p. 337)
  adjacent angles (p. 331)
  angle (p. 330)
  arc (p. 351)
  central angle (p. 350)
  chord (p. 350)
  circle (p. 350)
  circle graph (p. 354)
  compass (p. 361)
  complementary (p. 331)
  congruent angles (p. 331)
  congruent polygons (p. 346)
  congruent sides (p. 336)
  decagon (p. 340)
  diameter (p. 350)
  equilateral triangle (p. 336)
  hexagon (p. 340)

intersecting lines (p. 325)
irregular polygon (p. 340)
isosceles triangle (p. 336)
line (p. 324)
midpoint (p. 362)
obtuse angle (p. 330)
obtuse triangle (p. 337)
octagon (p. 340)
parallel lines (p. 325)
parallelogram (p. 341)
pentagon (p. 340)
perpendicular bisector (p. 362)
perpendicular lines (p. 362)
plane (p. 325)
point (p. 324)
quadrilateral (p. 340)
radius (p. 350)
ray (p. 324)

rectangle (p. 341)
regular polygon (p. 340)
rhombus (p. 341)
right angle (p. 330)
right triangle (p. 337)
scalene triangle (p. 336)
segment (p. 324)
segment bisector (p. 362)
semicircle (p. 351)
skew lines (p. 325)
straight angle (p. 330)
square (p. 341)
supplementary (p. 331)
trapezoid (p. 341)
vertex (p. 330)
vertical angles (p. 331)

Go Online
PHSchool.com
For: Online vocabulary quiz
Web Code: arj-0751

Choose the correct term to complete each sentence.

1. (Parallel, Skew) lines lie in the same plane. **parallel**

2. A (decagon, pentagon) is a polygon with five sides. **pentagon**

3. Angles whose sum is 180° are (complementary, supplementary).
    supplementary

4. A(n) (isosceles, scalene) triangle has no congruent sides. **scalene**

5. An (acute, obtuse) angle measures less than 90°. **acute**

Skills and Concepts   TEKS ★ TAKS

Lessons 7-1, 7-2
(7.6)(A) To use angle
measurements to classify
pairs of angles as
complementary or
supplementary **TAKS** Obj. 3

A **plane** is a flat surface that extends indefinitely in all directions and has
no thickness. **Parallel lines** are lines that lie in the same plane and have
no points in common. **Skew lines** do not lie in the same plane.

An **angle** is formed by two rays with a common endpoint. The sum of
two **complementary** angles is 90°. The sum of two **supplementary**
angles is 180°.

Find the complement and the supplement of each angle.

6. $m\angle A = 55°$ 7. $m\angle B = 27°$ 8. $m\angle C = 87°$ 9. $m\angle D = 12°$
    35°, 125°   63°, 153°   3°, 93°   78°, 168°

Spanish Vocabulary/Study Skills   ELL

Vocabulary/Study Skills   L3

7F: Vocabulary Review   For use with the Chapter Review

Study Skill Write assignments down; do not rely only on your memory.

Below is a list of clues grouped by the number of letters in the answer.
Identify the word each clue represents, and fit each word into the puzzle grid.

3 letters
• part of a circle
5 letters
• angle that measures between
  0° and 90°
• formed by two rays with a
  common endpoint
• segment that has both
  endpoints on the circle
• flat surface that extends
  indefinitely in all directions

6 letters
• point of intersection of two
  sides on an angle or figure
• set of all points in a plane
  that are the same distance
  from a given point
• angle that measures between
  90° and 180°

7 letters
• tool used to draw circles and
  arcs
• polygon with 10 sides
• type of triangle with no
  congruent sides
• polygon with all sides and
  angles congruent
8 letters
• point that divides a segment
  into two segments of equal
  length
• polygon with 5 sides
9 letters
• sides that have the same
  length
• type of triangle with at least
  two sides congruent
• parallelogram with four right
  angles
• quadrilateral with exactly one
  pair of parallel sides
11 letters
• triangle with three congruent
  sides
12 letters
• lines that have exactly one
  point in common
13 letters
• two angles whose sum is 180°
• two angles whose sum is 90°

Lessons 7-3, 7-4

(7.6)(B) To use properties to classify triangles and quadrilaterals **TAKS Obj. 3**

(7.8)(C) To use geometric concepts and properties to solve problems in fields such as art and architecture **TAKS Obj. 3**

(7.15)(B) To validate conclusions using mathematical properties **TAKS Obj. 6**

You can classify a triangle by the measure of its sides and angles. The sum of the measures of the angles of any triangle is 180°. A **polygon** is classified by the number of sides it has. A **regular polygon** has congruent sides and congruent angles.

Find the value of x. Then classify each triangle by its sides and angles.

10.

120°; isosceles; obtuse

11.

60°; equilateral; acute

12.

31°; scalene; right

Identify each polygon and classify it as *regular* or *irregular*.

pentagon; regular

square, regular

octagon, irregular

13.

14.

15.

16. $m\angle M = 30°$,
$m\angle C = m\angle P = 46°$,
$m\angle B = 104°$, $AC = 22$,
$BC = 12$, $MN = 17$

Lesson 7-5

(7.6)(D) To use critical attributes to define similarity **TAKS Obj. 3**

(7.8)(C) To use geometric concepts and properties to solve problems in fields such as architecture **TAKS Obj. 3**

Congruent polygons have the same size and shape. **Corresponding parts** of congruent polygons are congruent.

16. In the diagram, $\triangle ABC \cong \triangle MNP$. Find the missing side lengths and angle measures for the figures. See left.

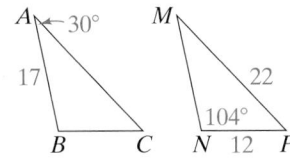

Lessons 7-6, 7-7

(7.11)(A) To select and use an appropriate representation for displaying data, including circle graph **TAKS Obj. 5**

(7.11)(B) To make inferences based on an analysis of data **TAKS Obj. 5**

Prepares for **TEKS (7.9)(A)** To solve problems involving circumference and area of circles

A **circle** is the set of points in a plane that are all the same distance from the center. A circle can have **radii, diameters, central angles, chords,** and **arcs. Circle graphs** present data as percents or fractions of a total.

Name each of the following for circle T.

17. radii
$\overline{TW}, \overline{TY}, \overline{TK}, \overline{TM}$

18. diameters
$\overline{MY}$

19. center T

20. chords
$\overline{WY}; \overline{KY}$

21. arcs longer than a semicircle
$\overarc{WYM}, \overarc{YKW}, \overarc{KMY}, \overarc{MWK}, \overarc{WYK}$

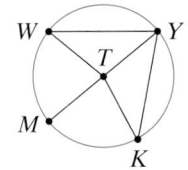

Lesson 7-8

• To construct congruent segments and perpendicular bisectors

You can use a **compass** to construct congruent segments and **perpendicular bisectors.** 22–23. See margin.

22. Draw a segment. Construct a segment congruent to it.

23. Draw a segment. Construct its perpendicular bisector.

22.

23.
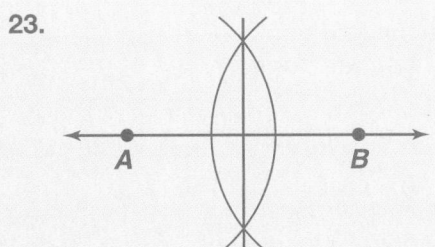

Alternative Assessment **L4**

Alternative Assessment
Chapter 7

POLYGONS TO WEAR

An art class is making T-shirt designs. The teacher has given the following guidelines:

• Create your design by repeating *one regular polygon.*
• The polygons that make up your design must completely cover the design area; there may not be any space between the polygons. In other words, the sides of each polygon must meet exactly with the sides of other polygons.
• Do not worry about the edges of the patterns because fabrics will be cut where necessary.

Show all of your work on a separate sheet of paper.

1. Tamika drew the design shown below. On dot paper, make a *different* design, using the same type of polygon that Tamika used.

2. Travis decided to pattern his design after Tamika's by adding vertical lines to her pattern, as shown below. Did Travis's design meet the teacher's requirements? Explain.

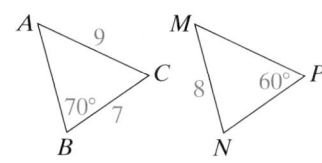
TEKS ★ TAKS Resources

- Texas ExamView CD-ROM
  - Ch. 7 Ready-Made Test
  - Make your own Ch. 7 test
- MindPoint Quiz Show CD-ROM
  - Chapter 7 Review

Differentiated Instruction

All in One Teaching Resources
- Chapter 7 Test **L2**
- Chapter 7 Test **L3**
- Chapter 7 Alternative Assessment **L4**

Spanish Assessment Resources **ELL**
- Chapter 7 Test **L2**
- Chapter 7 Test **L3**
- Chapter 7 Alternative Assessment **L4**

Texas ExamView CD-ROM
- Special Needs Test **L1**
- Special Needs Practice Bank **L1**

Online Chapter 7 Test at
www.PHSchool.com **L3**

Use the diagram for Exercises 1–3.

1. Name all the segments parallel to $\overline{AB}$.
   $\overline{MH}, \overline{GC}, \overline{FD}$

2. Name all the segments intersecting $\overline{FG}$.
   $\overline{MF}, \overline{FD}, \overline{AG}, \overline{GC}$

3. Name all the segments skew to $\overline{DH}$.
   $\overline{GC}, \overline{AB}, \overline{MA}, \overline{FG}$

Use a protractor to measure each angle.

4. 40°

5. 100°

Find the measures of the complement and the supplement of each angle.

6. $m\angle H = 45°$
   45°, 135°

7. $m\angle R = 7°$
   83°, 173°

8. $m\angle K = 89°$
   1°, 91°

9. $m\angle P = 25°$
   65°, 155°

10. What is the supplement of a 102° angle?
   a 78° angle

11. Does a 98° angle have a complement? Explain.   No, it would have to be a −8° angle.

12. Draw a segment. Construct its perpendicular bisector. See margin.

13. Draw a segment $\overline{AB}$. Construct a congruent segment $\overline{CD}$.   See margin.

Find the value of x in each triangle. Classify each triangle by its side lengths and its angle measures.

14.
92°; isosceles; obtuse

15.
150°; scalene; obtuse

Identify each polygon.

16.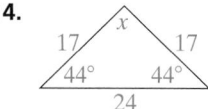
rhombus

17.
rectangle

12–13. See back of book.
32–33. See back of book.

---

18. What is the name of a polygon with one pair of parallel sides?   **trapezoid**

In the diagram below, $\triangle ABC \cong \triangle MNP$. Complete each statement.

19. $\overline{AC} \cong \blacksquare$ $\overline{MP}$

20. $\angle P \cong \blacksquare$ $\angle C$

21. $\blacksquare \cong \overline{PN}$ $\overline{CB}$

22. $\angle B \cong \blacksquare$ $\angle N$

23. $\blacksquare \cong \angle M$ $\angle A$

24. $AB = \blacksquare$ 8

25. $m\angle N = \blacksquare$ 70°

26. $MP = \blacksquare$ 9

Name each of the following for circle W.

27. three radii
   $\overline{WA}, \overline{WT}, \overline{WM}$

28. two chords
   Any two of $\overline{AC}, \overline{TM}, \overline{AM}$

29. two central angles
   $\angle AWT, \angle TWM$

30. one diameter
   $\overline{AM}$

31. three arcs shorter than half the circle
   any three of $\overarc{AC}, \overarc{CM}, \overarc{MT}, \overarc{TA}$

32. **Class Trip** Students earned the following amounts of money to pay the transportation costs of a class trip. Make a circle graph for the data.   See margin.

Fundraiser	Money
Car wash	$150
Paper drive	$75
Book sale	$225
Food stand	$378

33. **Writing in Math** Briefly explain the differences and similarities among a rectangle, a rhombus, and a square.   See margin.

Tips

Some TAKS test questions ask you to study a graph and determine information about the data.

The tuition at a school is shown below. If the trend continues, which is the best prediction of the tuition in year 5?

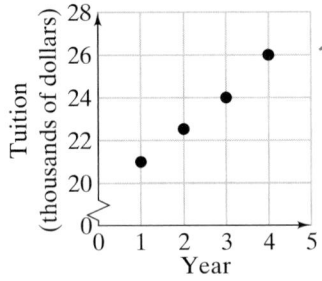

Tip 2
Estimate how much the tuition has increased each year.

Tip 1
Notice that the trend for the cost of tuition is increasing each year.

Ⓐ Less than $26,000
Ⓑ Between $26,000 and $28,000
Ⓒ Between $28,000 and $30,000
Ⓓ More than $35,000

Think It Through

The graph shows that tuition in year 4 is about $26,000. The trend is about a $1,000 increase in tuition each year. The best prediction for tuition in year 5 is between $26,000 and $28,000. The answer is B.

TEKS ★ Resources

TAKS Review and Preparation Workbook

Texas ExamView CD-ROM
• Standardized Test Practice
• TAKS Practice Items

Differentiated Instruction

Spanish Assessment Resources
• Spanish Cumulative Review **ELL**

Texas ExamView CD-ROM
• Special Needs Practice Bank **L1**

Vocabulary Builder

As you solve test items, you must understand the meanings of mathematical terms. Select the correct term from the pair in each sentence.

A. Two angles whose measures sum to 180° are (complementary, supplementary).
supplementary
B. A portion of a circle is a(n) (arc, radius).
arc
C. If part of a circle graph represents 25%, then the corresponding (central angle, vertical angle) must be 90°.
central angle
D. If two polygons are the same shape and the same size, they are (congruent, regular) polygons. **congruent**
E. Every square is both a rectangle and a (rhombus, trapezoid). **rhombus**

Multiple Choice

Read each question. Then write the letter of the correct answer on your paper.

1. The graph below shows the number of students who participated in various activities. Which statement is best supported by these data? **C**

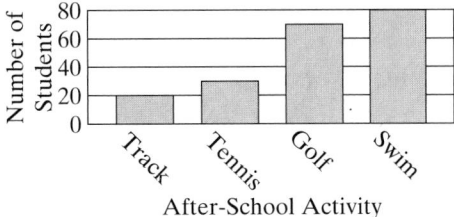

Ⓐ Golf is the most popular sport.
Ⓑ The same number of students participated in track and in tennis.
Ⓒ Track had about 20 students.
Ⓓ Half the students in the school swim.

2. The table shows the number of students who bought school lunches during the week. Which statement is NOT supported by these data? **F**

School Lunch

Day	Number of Students
Monday	62
Tuesday	45
Wednesday	58
Thursday	39
Friday	21

Ⓕ Almost twice as many students bought lunch on Tuesday as on Friday.

Ⓖ More students bought lunch on Monday than on Thursday and Friday combined.

Ⓗ Almost twice as many students bought lunch on Thursday as on Monday.

Ⓙ More than 200 students bought school lunches during the week.

3. Which could NOT describe a triangle with two congruent sides? **C**

Ⓐ Equilateral   Ⓒ Scalene

Ⓑ Obtuse   Ⓓ Isosceles

4. What is NOT a name for the figure below? **F**

Ⓕ Equilateral   Ⓗ Parallelogram

Ⓖ Quadrilateral   Ⓙ Rhombus

5. Which statement is always true about a rhombus? **B**

Ⓐ It has 4 congruent angles.

Ⓑ It has 4 congruent sides.

Ⓒ The sum of the 4 angles is 180°.

Ⓓ It has 4 right angles.

6. If $\angle G$ and $\angle H$ are supplementary and the measure of $\angle G$ is 78°, what is the measure of $\angle H$? **H**

Ⓕ 12°   Ⓗ 102°

Ⓖ 22°   Ⓙ 132°

7. If $\angle K$ and $\angle L$ are complementary, and the measure of $\angle K$ is 36°, what is the measure of $\angle L$? **A**

Ⓐ 54°   Ⓑ 64°   Ⓒ 144°   Ⓓ 154°

8. The model below represents the equation $3x + 5 = 8$. What is the first step in finding the value of x? **G**

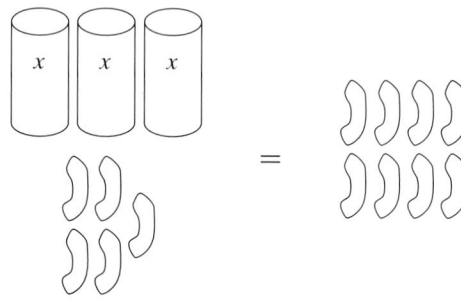

Ⓕ Subtract 5 pieces of macaroni from each side of the model.

Ⓖ Add 5 pieces of macaroni to each side of the model.

Ⓗ Subtract 8 pieces of macaroni from each side of the model.

Ⓙ Divide the pieces of macaroni equally among the 3 cups.

9. The model represents the equation $x - 4 = 4$. What is the value of x? **D**

Key
⊕ = +1   ⊖ = −1

Ⓐ $x = 0$ Ⓒ $x = 4$

Ⓑ $x = -4$ Ⓓ $x = 8$

Spanish Cumulative Review   **ELL**

Cumulative Review   **L3**

Cumulative Review

Chapter 1–7

Multiple Choice. Choose the letter of the best answer.

1. Compare. -14×10 ___?___ $-28 + (-102)$.
   Ⓐ <
   B. >
   C. ≥
   D. =

2. What is the value of $5 \times 6 - 7 \times 3$?
   F. −15
   Ⓖ 9
   H. 51
   J. 69

3. What is $\frac{19}{25}$ written as a decimal?
   A. 0.91
   B. 0.1925
   C. 0.25
   Ⓓ 0.76

4. John has $4\frac{1}{2}$ lb of halibut. He wants each person to get a 6-oz serving. How many people can he feed?
   F. 6 people
   Ⓖ 12 people
   H. 27 people
   J. 75 people

5. What is the value of 1^{20}?
   Ⓐ 1
   B. 5
   C. 10
   D. 20

6. What is the range of the data given below? 13.4, 24.2, 33.0, 11.5, 21.0, 35.9, 40.2
   F. 22.5
   G. 26.8
   H. 27.0
   Ⓙ 28.7

7. Which fraction is equivalent to $\frac{8}{12}$?
   A. $\frac{2}{6}$
   Ⓑ $\frac{10}{15}$
   C. $\frac{3}{4}$
   D. $\frac{16}{20}$

8. Solve $-3n - 1 = -25$.
   F. −24
   G. −8
   H. 3
   Ⓙ 8

9. Complete. 153 in. = _____ ft
   A. 4.25
   Ⓑ 12.75
   C. 51
   D. 459

10. What is the prime factorization for 210?
    Ⓕ $2 \times 3 \times 5 \times 7$
    G. $5 \times 6 \times 7$
    H. $2 \times 7 \times 15$
    J. $2 \times 5 \times 21$

11. $\triangle FGH$ has angle measures of 78° and 54°. What is the measure of the third angle?
    A. 12°
    B. 36°
    Ⓒ 48°
    D. 96°

12. A scale on a map is 1.5 in. : 200 mi. The map distance from Miami to Chicago is 9 in. What is the actual distance between the cities?
    F. 600 mi
    Ⓖ 1,200 mi
    H. 1,800 mi
    J. 2,700 mi

13. Which one of the following is a regular quadrilateral?
    A. trapezoid
    B. triangle
    Ⓒ square
    D. pentagon

370

10. Carmen is painting a picture that is 15 inches long. The ratio of the length to the width of the painting is the golden ratio, approximately 3 : 2. What is the approximate width of the painting? **H**

   (F) 2 inches   (H) 10 inches

   (G) 5 inches   (J) 27.5 inches

11. An architect is designing the roof of a building, as shown in the diagram below. If the peak of the roof needs to form a 120° angle, what should the measure of ∠D be? **A**

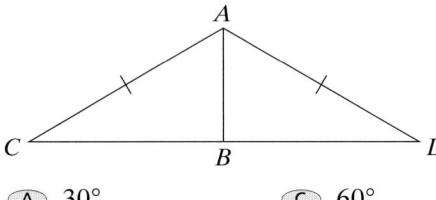

   (A) 30°   (C) 60°

   (B) 45°   (D) 75°

12. A good tip for a hair stylist is 15%. Miguel got a haircut and gave a $2.70 tip, which was the appropriate 15%. What was the price of his haircut? **H**

   (F) $4.50   (H) $18

   (G) $15   (J) $40.50

13. What is the total cost of a $6.99 item with 6.5% sales tax? **C**

   (A) $6.92   (C) $7.44

   (B) $7.41   (D) $7.83

14. Mrs. Binetti saves $\frac{6}{15}$ of her plastic bottles so that her students can use them for projects. What percent of her plastic bottles does Mrs. Binetti save? **H**

   (F) 15%   (H) 40%

   (G) 20%   (J) 65%

15. It is estimated that 87.6% of the parents will volunteer in school activities this year. Which number is NOT equivalent to 87.6%? **D**

   (A) $\frac{876}{1,000}$ (C) 0.876

   (B) $\frac{87.6}{100}$ (D) 8.76

16. Malcolm served cake at a dinner party. His guests ate about $\frac{7}{8}$ of the cake. About what percent of the cake was eaten? **J**

   (F) 50%   (H) 75%

   (G) 62.5%   (J) 87.5%

Griddable Items

Record your answer in a grid.

17. Mixing 3 ounces of vinegar with 16 ounces of water makes a cleaning solution. To make the same solution, how many ounces of vinegar should Robert mix with 128 ounces of water? **24**

18. A 2.5-m stick casts a 3.2-m shadow. How many meters tall is a nearby building that casts a shadow that is 19.2 m long? **15**

TAKS GO for Help Guide

TAKS Objective	Item Number	GO To	TAKS Objective	Item Number	GO To
Obj. 5: (7.11)(B)	1–2	Lesson 7-7	Obj. 6: (7.13)(A)	10	Lesson 5-5
				11	Lesson 7-3
Obj. 3: (7.6)(B)	3	Lesson 7-3			
	4–5	Lesson 7-4	Obj. 2: (7.3)(A)	12–13	Lesson 6-7
Obj. 3: (7.6)(A)	6–7	Lesson 7-2	Obj. 1: (7.1)(B)	14–16	Lesson 6-2
Obj. 2: (7.5)(A)	8	Lesson 4-6	Obj. 2: (7.3)(B)	17	Lesson 5-3
	9	Lesson 4-3		18	Lesson 5-5

For additional TAKS practice, see the *TAKS Review and Preparation Workbook*.

8 Measurement

Chapter at a Glance

Lesson Titles, Objectives, and Features	Assessment	NCTM Standards	TEKS ★ TAKS
8-1 Estimating Perimeter and Area • To estimate length, perimeter, and area.	Lesson Quiz	3, 4, 6, 7, 8, 9, 10	**TEKS** (7.8)(C), (7.9)(A), (7.14)(A) TAKS **Obj. 3, 4, 6**
8-2a Activity Lab, Hands On: Generating Formulas for Area **8-2 Area of a Parallelogram** • To find the area and perimeter of a parallelogram	Lesson Quiz	3, 4, 6, 7, 8, 9, 10	**TEKS** (7.4)(A), (7.9)(A), (7.14)(A) TAKS **Obj. 2, 4, 6**
8-3 Perimeter and Area of a Triangle • To find the perimeter and area of a triangle	Lesson Quiz	3, 4, 6, 7, 8, 9, 10	**TEKS** (7.4)(A), (7.9)(A) TAKS **Obj. 2, 4**
8-4 Areas of Other Figures • To find the area of a trapezoid and the areas of irregular figures	Lesson Quiz Checkpoint Quiz 1	3, 4, 6, 7, 8, 9, 10	**TEKS** (7.4)(A), (7.9)(A) TAKS **Obj. 2, 4**
8-5a Activity Lab, Hands On: Modeling a Circle **8-5 Circumference and Area of a Circle** • To find the circumference and area of a circle **Guided Problem Solving:** Areas of Irregular Figures	Lesson Quiz	3, 4, 6, 7, 8, 9, 10	**TEKS** (7.4)(A), (7.8)(C), (7.9)(A) TAKS **Obj. 2, 3, 4**
8-6 Square Roots and Irrational Numbers • To find and estimate square roots and to classify numbers as rational or irrational	Lesson Quiz	3, 4, 6, 7, 8, 9, 10	**TEKS** (7.1)(C), (7.14)(A) TAKS **Obj. 1, 6** **TEKS** (7.13)(D)
8-7a Activity Lab, Hands On: Exploring Right Triangles **8-7 The Pythagorean Theorem** • To use the Pythagorean Theorem to solve real-world problems	Lesson Quiz	2, 3, 4, 6, 7, 8, 9, 10	Prepares for **TEKS** (8.9)(A)
8-8a Activity Lab, Hands On: Three Views of an Object **8-8 Three-Dimensional Figures** • To classify and draw three-dimensional figures	Lesson Quiz	3, 4, 6, 7, 8, 9, 10	**TEKS** (7.6)(C), (7.8)(A), (7.8)(C) TAKS **Obj. 3** **TEKS** (7.13)(D)
8-9 Surface Areas of Prisms and Cylinders • To find the surface areas of prisms and cylinders using nets **Extension:** Patterns in Three-Dimensional Figures	Lesson Quiz Checkpoint Quiz 2	3, 4, 6, 7, 8, 9, 10	**TEKS** (7.8)(B) TAKS **Obj. 3;** Prepares for **TEKS** (8.8)(C)
8-10 Volumes of Prisms and Cylinders • To find the volumes of prisms and cylinders **8-10b Activity Lab, Hands On:** Generating Formulas for Volume	Lesson Quiz	3, 4, 6, 7, 8, 9, 10	**TEKS** (7.4)(A), (7.9)(C), (7.14)(A) TAKS **Obj. 2, 4, 6** **TEKS** (7.9)(B)
TAKS **Tune-Up: Cumulative Practice**			

NCTM Standards 2000
1 Number and Operations   **2** Algebra   **3** Geometry   **4** Measurement   **5** Data Analysis and Probability
6 Problem Solving   **7** Reasoning and Proof   **8** Communication   **9** Connections   **10** Representation

Correlations to Standardized Tests

All content for these tests is contained in *Prentice Hall Math,* Course 2. This chart reflects coverage in this chapter only.

	8-1	8-2	8-3	8-4	8-5	8-6	8-7	8-8	8-9	8-10
Terra Nova CAT6 (Level 17)										
Number and Number Relations										
Computation and Numerical Estimation										
Operation Concepts										
Measurement	✔	✔	✔	✔	✔	✔	✔	✔	✔	✔
Geometry and Spatial Sense	✔	✔	✔	✔	✔	✔	✔	✔	✔	✔
Data Analysis, Statistics, and Probability										
Patterns, Functions, Algebra										
Problem Solving and Reasoning	✔	✔	✔	✔	✔	✔	✔	✔	✔	✔
Communication	✔	✔	✔	✔	✔	✔	✔	✔	✔	✔
Decimals, Fractions, Integers, and Percent	✔	✔	✔	✔	✔	✔	✔	✔	✔	✔
Order of Operations										
Terra Nova CTBS (Level 17)										
Decimals, Fractions, Integers, Percents										
Order of Operations, Numeration, Number Theory										
Data Interpretation										
Pre-algebra							✔			
Measurement	✔	✔	✔	✔	✔	✔	✔	✔	✔	✔
Geometry	✔	✔	✔	✔	✔	✔	✔	✔	✔	✔
ITBS (Level 13)										
Number Properties and Operations										
Algebra										
Geometry	✔	✔	✔	✔	✔	✔	✔	✔	✔	✔
Measurement	✔	✔	✔	✔	✔	✔	✔	✔	✔	✔
Probability and Statistics										
Estimation	✔									
SAT10 (Int 3 Level)										
Number Sense and Operations										
Patterns, Relationships, and Algebra										
Data, Statistics, and Probability										
Geometry and Measurement	✔	✔	✔	✔	✔	✔	✔	✔	✔	✔
NAEP										
Number Sense, Properties, and Operations						✔				
Measurement	✔	✔	✔	✔	✔				✔	✔
Geometry and Spatial Sense							✔	✔		
Data Analysis, Statistics, and Probability										
Algebra and Functions										

CAT6 California Achievement Test, 6th Ed.   **CTBS** Comprehensive Test of Basic Skills   **ITBS** Iowa Test of Basic Skills, Form M
SAT10 Stanford Achievement Test, 10th Ed.   **NAEP** National Assessment of Educational Progress 2005 Mathematics Objectives

TEKS Math Background

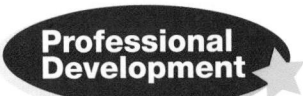
Focus on the TEKS

- At Grade 7, students solve problems involving perimeter, circumference, and area (7.9)(A). Analysis of TAKS results shows that students struggle with this student expectation.

  In Lesson 8-1, students estimate perimeter and area. Students find the area of polygons including parallelograms, triangles, and trapezoids in Lessons 8-2 through 8-4. Students also find the circumference and area of a circle in Lesson 8-5. Place special emphasis on these lessons because they all focus on (7.9)(A).

- New at Grade 7 is connecting models and solving problems involving volume of prisms and cylinders (7.9)(B), (7.9)(C). Students use three-dimensional figures to solve volume problems in Lesson 8-10.

8-1 Estimating Perimeter and Area

TEKS ★ TAKS (7.8)(C), (7.9)(A), (7.14)(A) Obj. 3, 4, 6

Math Understandings

- You can estimate the perimeter of a figure in units and its area in square units.

8-2 Area of Parallelogram
8-3 Perimeter and Area of a Triangle
8-4 Areas of Other Figures

TEKS ★ TAKS (7.4)(A), (7.9)(A) Obj. 2, 4

Math Understandings

- You can find the area of an irregular figure by separating it into familiar figures, finding the area of each smaller figure, and adding the areas together.
- Any side of a parallelogram or triangle can be its base.

Area of a Parallelogram
The area of a parallelogram is equal to the product of any base b and the corresponding height h.

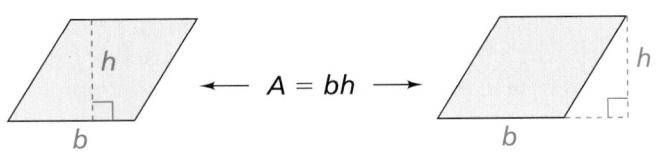

The **height of a parallelogram** is the perpendicular distance from one **base of a parallelogram** to the other. Any side of a triangle can be considered the **base of a triangle**. The **height of a triangle** is the length of the perpendicular segment from a vertex to the base opposite the vertex.

Area of a Triangle	Area of a Trapezoid
The area of a triangle is equal to half the product of any base and the corresponding height.	The area of a trapezoid is one half the product of the height and the sum of the lengths of the bases.
$A = \frac{1}{2}bh$	$A = \frac{1}{2}h(b_1 + b_2)$

The two parallel sides of a trapezoid are the **bases**, with lengths b_1 and b_2. The **height** h is the length of a perpendicular segment connecting the bases.

8-5 Circumference and Area of a Circle

TEKS ★ TAKS (7.8)(C), (7.9)(A) Obj. 3, 4

Math Understandings

- Although π does not equal $\frac{22}{7}$ or 3.14, you can use these numbers as good approximations for the value of π.
- For every circle, the ratio of the circumference to the diameter is the same.
- The circumference of a circle is about three times its diameter or six times its radius.

Circumference is the distance around a circle. *Pi* (π) is a nonterminating, nonrepeating decimal (irrational number), the ratio of the circumference to its diameter.

Circumference of a Circle	Area of a Circle
The circumference of a circle is π times the diameter.	The area of a circle is π times the square of the radius r.
$C = \pi d = 2\pi r$	$A = \pi r^2$

| 8-6 | **Square Roots and Irrational Numbers** |
| 8-7 | **The Pythagorean Theorem** |

TEKS ★ 𝐓𝐀𝐊𝐒 (7.1)(C), (7.14)(A) Obj. 1, 6; (7.13)(D); Prepares for TEKS (8.9)(A)

Math Understandings

- Mathematicians have agreed that the symbol $\sqrt{}$ indicates the nonnegative square root of a number. So, while $x^2 = 9$ has two roots, $+3$ and -3, the symbol $\sqrt{9}$ has only one meaning: $+3$.

A number that is the square of an integer is a **perfect square**. The inverse of squaring a number is finding a **square root**. If a positive integer is not a perfect square, its square root is *irrational*. An **irrational number** is a number that cannot be written as a ratio of two integers. As decimals, irrational numbers neither terminate nor repeat.
In a right triangle, the two shortest sides are **legs**. The side opposite the right angle is the **hypotenuse**.

Pythagorean Theorem
The Pythagorean Theorem states that, in any right triangle, the sum of the squares of the lengths of the legs is equal to the square of the length of the hypotenuse. $\quad a^2 + b^2 = c^2$

8-8	**Three-Dimensional Figures**
8-9	**Surface Areas and Volumes of**
8-10	**Rectangular Prisms and Cylinders**

TEKS ★ 𝐓𝐀𝐊𝐒 (7.6)(C), (7.8)(B), (7.8)(C), (7.9)(C) Obj. 3, 4; (7.9)(B); Prepares for TEKS (8.8)(C)

Math Understandings

- Prisms and pyramids have faces that are flat surfaces. Cones, cylinders, and spheres have at least one surface that is curved.
- One way to find the surface area of a three-dimensional solid is to find the area of its net.

- You can find the volume of a rectangular prism and a cylinder by using the same formula, $V = B \cdot h$, where B is the area of the base and h is height.

A **three-dimensional figure**, or solid, is a figure that does not lie in a plane. A flat surface shaped like a polygon is called a **face**. Each segment formed by the intersection of two faces is an **edge**. A **prism** is a three-dimensional figure with two parallel and congruent polygonal faces, called **bases**. The other faces are rectangles. The **height** of a prism is the length of a perpendicular segment that joins the bases. A **cube** is a rectangular prism with square faces. A **cylinder** has two congruent parallel **bases** that are circles. A cylinder's **height** is the length of a perpendicular segment that joins the bases.

A **pyramid** is a three-dimensional figure with triangular faces that meet at one point, a **vertex**, and a base that is a polygon. A **cone** has one circular **base** and one **vertex**. A **sphere** is the set of all points in space that are the same distance from a **center** point.

A **net** is a two-dimensional pattern that you can fold to form a three-dimensional figure. The **surface area** of a prism is the sum of the areas of its faces. The **volume** of a three-dimensional figure is the number of cubic units needed to fill the space.

Volume of a Rectangular Prism	Volume of a Cylinder
V = area of base • height $\quad = Bh$ $\quad = lwh$	V = area of base • height $\quad = Bh$ $\quad = \pi r^2 h$

Additional Professional Development Opportunities

Math Background Notes for Chapter 8: Every lesson has a Math Background in the PLAN section.

Research Overview, Mathematics Strands
Additional support for these topics and more is in the front of the Teacher's Edition.

LessonLab
LessonLab, a Pearson Education company, offers comprehensive, facilitated professional development designed to help teachers to improve student achievement. To learn more, please visit lessonlab.com.

Texas Chapter 8 Resources

Print Resources

Resource	8-1	8-2	8-3	8-4	8-5	8-6	8-7	8-8	8-9	8-10	For the Chapter
L3 Practice	●	●	●	●	●	●	●	●	●		
L1 Adapted Practice	●	●	●	●	●	●	●	●	●		
L3 Guided Problem Solving	●	●	●	●	●	●	●	●	●		
L2 Reteaching	●	●	●	●	●	●	●	●	●		
L4 Enrichment	●	●	●	●	●	●	●	●	●		
L3 Daily Notetaking Guide	●	●	●	●	●	●	●	●	●		
L1 Adapted Daily Notetaking Guide	●	●	●	●	●	●	●	●	●		
L3 Vocabulary and Study Skills Worksheets	●		●				●		●		●
L3 Daily Puzzles	●	●	●	●	●	●	●	●	●		
L3 Activity Labs	●	●	●	●	●	●	●	●	●		
L3 Checkpoint Quiz				●					●		
L3 Chapter Project											●
L2 Chapter Test											●
L3 Chapter Test											●
L4 Alternative Assessment											●
L3 Cumulative Review											●

Spanish Resources **ELL**

Resource	8-1	8-2	8-3	8-4	8-5	8-6	8-7	8-8	8-9	8-10	For the Chapter
L3 Practice	●	●	●	●	●	●	●	●	●	●	
L3 Vocabulary and Study Skills Worksheets	●		●				●	●	●	●	
L3 Checkpoint Quiz				●					●		
L2 Chapter Test											●
L3 Chapter Test											●
L4 Alternative Assessment											●
L3 Cumulative Review											●

Transparencies

Resource	8-1	8-2	8-3	8-4	8-5	8-6	8-7	8-8	8-9	8-10	For the Chapter
Check Skills You'll Need	●	●	●	●	●	●	●	●	●	●	
Additional Examples	●	●	●	●	●	●	●	●	●	●	
Problem of the Day	●	●	●	●	●	●	●	●	●	●	
TAKS Daily Review	●	●	●	●	●	●	●	●	●	●	
Classroom Aid							●	●			
Student Edition Answers	●	●	●	●	●	●	●	●	●	●	●
Lesson Quiz	●	●	●	●	●	●	●	●	●	●	
TAKS Strategies											●

Technology

Resource	8-1	8-2	8-3	8-4	8-5	8-6	8-7	8-8	8-9	8-10	For the Chapter
Texas Interactive Textbook Online	●	●	●	●	●	●	●	●	●	●	●
Texas StudentExpress CD-ROM	●	●	●	●	●	●	●	●	●	●	●
Success Tracker™ Online Intervention	●	●	●	●	●	●	●	●	●	●	●
TeacherExpress CD-ROM	●	●	●	●	●	●	●	●	●	●	●
PresentationExpress CD-ROM	●	●	●	●	●	●	●	●	●	●	●
Texas ExamView CD-ROM with QuickTake	●	●	●	●	●	●	●	●	●	●	●
MindPoint Quiz Show CD-ROM	●	●	●	●	●	●	●	●	●	●	●
Prentice Hall Web Site: PHSchool.com	●	●	●	●	●	●	●	●	●	●	●

Also available: **TAKS Tune-Up Kit**
- TAKS Daily Review Transparencies
- TAKS Review and Preparation Workbook
- TAKS Strategies with Transparencies
- Texas Progress Monitoring Assessments
- Texas ExamView CD-ROM
- MindPoint Quiz Show CD-ROM

Other Resources
Algebra Readiness Tests
All-in-One Student Workbook
All-in-One Student Workbook, Adapted Version
Multilingual Handbook

Solution Key
Math Notes Study Folder
Spanish Cumulative Assessment

Where You Can Use the Lesson Resources

Here is a suggestion, following the four-step teaching plan, for how you can incorporate Differentiated Instruction resources into your teaching.

	Instructional Resources 〔L3〕	**Differentiated Instruction Resources**
1. Plan		
Preparation Read the Math Background in the Teacher's Edition to connect this lesson with students' previous experience. **Starting Class** **Check Skills You'll Need** Assign these exercises to review prerequisite skills. **TEKS** ★ 〔TAKS〕 Review the full text of the TEKS student expectations and TAKS objectives covered in this lesson. **New Vocabulary** Help students pre-read the lesson by pointing out the new terms introduced in the lesson.	**TEKS Math Background** **Math Understandings** **Transparencies & PresentationExpress CD-ROM** Check Skills You'll Need Problem of the Day TAKS Daily Review **Resources** Vocabulary and Study Skills	**Spanish Support** ELL Vocabulary and Study Skills
2. Teach		
〔L3〕 **Guided Instruction** Use the Activity Labs to build conceptual understanding. Teach each Example. Use the Teacher's Edition side column notes for specific teaching tips, including Error Prevention notes. Use the Additional Examples found in the side column (and on transparency and PowerPoint) as an alternative presentation for the content. After each Example, assign the Quick Check exercise for that Example to get an immediate assessment of student understanding. Use the Closure activity in the Teacher's Edition to help students attain mastery of lesson content.	**Student Edition** Activity Lab **Resources** Daily Notetaking Guide Activity Lab **Transparencies & PresentationExpress CD-ROM** Additional Examples Classroom Aids **Texas ExamView CD-ROM with QuickTake**	**Teacher's Edition** Every lesson includes suggestions for working with students who need special attention. 〔L1〕 Special Needs 〔L2〕 Below Level 〔L4〕 Advanced Learners ELL English Language Learners **Resources** 〔L1〕 Adapted Daily Notetaking Guide **Multilingual Handbook**
3. Practice		

Assignment Guide
Check Your Understanding
Use these questions to check students' understanding before you assign homework.
Homework Exercises
Assign homework from these leveled exercises in the Assignment Guide.
  A Practice by Example
  B Apply Your Skills
  C Challenge
  〔TAKS〕 Tune-Up and Mixed Review
Homework Quick Check
Use these key exercises to quickly check students' homework.
	Transparencies & PresentationExpress CD-ROM
	Student Answers
	Resources
	Practice
	Guided Problem Solving
	Vocabulary and Study Skills
	Activity Lab
	Daily Puzzles
	Texas ExamView CD-ROM with QuickTake
		Spanish Support
		ELL Practice
		ELL Vocabulary and Study Skills
		Resources
		〔L1〕 Adapted Practice
		〔L4〕 Enrichment

4. Assess & Reteach		
Lesson Quiz Assign the Lesson Quiz to assess students' mastery of the lesson content. **Checkpoint Quiz** Use the Checkpoint Quiz to assess student progress over several lessons.	**Transparencies & PresentationExpress CD-ROM** Lesson Quiz **Resources** Checkpoint Quiz	**Resources** 〔L2〕 Reteaching ELL Checkpoint Quiz Success Tracker™ Online Intervention **Texas ExamView CD-ROM with QuickTake**

KEY 〔L1〕 Special Needs   〔L2〕 Below Level   〔L3〕 For All Students   〔L4〕 Advanced, Gifted   ELL English Language Learners

Check Your Readiness

Answers are in the back of the textbook.

For intervention, direct students to:

Multiplying Decimals
Lesson 1-3
Extra Skills and Word
  Problems Practice, Ch. 1

Order of Operations
Lesson 2-1
Extra Skills and Word
  Problems Practice, Ch. 2

Changing Units in the Customary System
Lesson 3-6
Extra Skills and Word
  Problems Practice, Ch. 3

Finding the Measures of Angles in Right Triangles
Lesson 7-3
Extra Skills and Word
  Problems Practice, Ch. 7

CHAPTER 8 **Measurement**

 What You've Learned

TEKS ★ **TAKS**

• **(7.2)(E)** In Chapter 2, you simplified numerical expressions involving order of operations and exponents. **TAKS Obj. 1**

• **(7.4)(A)** In Chapter 5, you generated formulas involving scaling. **TAKS Obj. 2**

• **(7.6)(B)** In Chapter 7, you used properties to classify triangles and quadrilaterals. **TAKS Obj. 3**

 Check Your Readiness

GO for Help

For Exercises	See Lesson
1–2	1-3
3–5	2-1
6–9	3-6
10–12	7-3

Multiplying Decimals

Find each product.

1. $0.25 \cdot 3.14 \cdot 4$ 3.14

2. $3 \cdot 20.5 \cdot 2$ 123

Order of Operations

Simplify.

3. $3^3 \cdot (8 - 6)^2$ 108

4. $(2^3 \cdot 5) - 6^2$ 4

5. $6^2 \cdot 2 + 5^2$ 97

Changing Units in the Customary System

Complete.

6. $3 \text{ c} = \blacksquare \text{ fl oz}$ 24

7. $12 \text{ ft} = \blacksquare \text{ in.}$ 144

8. $48 \text{ oz} = \blacksquare \text{ lb}$ 3

9. $96 \text{ in.} = \blacksquare \text{ ft}$ 8

Finding the Measures of Angles in Triangles

Algebra **Find the value of x in each triangle.**

10.

58°

11. 63°

55° 62°

12. 50°

107° 23°

What You'll Learn Next

TEKS ★ TAKS

- **(7.1)(C)** In this chapter, you will represent squares and square roots using geometric models. **TAKS Obj. 1**

- **(7.4)(A)** You will generate formulas involving perimeter, area, circumference, and volume. **TAKS Obj. 2**

- **(7.6)(C)** You will use properties to classify three-dimensional figures, including pyramids, cones, prisms, and cylinders. **TAKS Obj. 3**

TAKS Tune-Up On pages 431–433, you will review and practice the vocabulary and *TAKS* objectives you have learned.

◀)) Key Vocabulary

- area (p. 375)
- circumference (p. 394)
- cone (p. 411)
- cylinder (p. 410)
- hypotenuse (p. 405)
- irrational number (p. 401)
- net (p. 414)
- perimeter (p. 375)
- prism (p. 410)
- pyramid (p. 410)
- Pythagorean Theorem (p. 405)
- sphere (p. 411)
- square root (p. 400)
- surface area (p. 415)
- three-dimensional figure (p. 410)
- volume (p. 421)

TEKS ★ TAKS for Chapter 8

Number, Operation, and Quantitative Reasoning
TEKS (7.1)(C) TAKS Obj. 1

Patterns, Relationships, and Algebraic Thinking
TEKS (7.4)(A) TAKS Obj. 2

Geometry and Spatial Reasoning
TEKS (7.6)(C), (7.8)(A), (7.8)(C) TAKS Obj. 3

Measurement
TEKS (7.9)(A), (7.9)(C) TAKS Obj. 4;
TEKS (7.9)(B)

Underlying Processes and Mathematical Tools
TEKS (7.14)(A) TAKS Obj. 6;
TEKS (7.13)(D)

Chapter 8 Overview

In this chapter, students build on their knowledge of the geometric concepts from the previous chapter to estimate and find areas of triangles, parallelograms, and other polygons. They also find the circumference and area of circles, as well as the surface area and volume of rectangular prisms and cylinders. In addition, students learn about squares and square roots in preparation for using the Pythagorean Theorem to find lengths of sides of right triangles.

Activating Prior Knowledge

In this chapter, students will build on their knowledge of geometric concepts to compute areas and volumes of geometric figures. They use their understanding of the properties and characteristics of triangles when they apply the Pythagorean Theorem to solve problems.

Ask questions such as:
- *How many right angles are in a right triangle?* one
- *How many acute angles are in a right triangle?* two
- *What is the sum of the measures of the angles of any triangle?* 180°

373

TEKS ★ TAKS

(7.9)(A) To estimate measurements involving perimeter and area **TAKS** Obj. 4
Also Supports
(7.8)(C) **TAKS** Obj. 3
(7.14)(A) **TAKS** Obj. 6

Dana Center TEKS Toolkit Clarifying Activities (7.9)(A), (7.8)(C), (7.14)(A)
Visit: PHSchool.com
Web Code: arq-9045

TEKS Math Background

Estimation is a fundamental number sense skill. A meaningful estimate for measurements, such as length and area, must include a unit label.

More Math Background: p. 372C

Lesson Planning and Resources

See p. 372E for a list of the resources that support this lesson.

Bell Ringer Practice

✓ **Check Skills You'll Need**
Use student page, transparency, or PowerPoint.

TAKS **Daily Review 57**
Use transparency.

8-1 Estimating Perimeter and Area

✓ **Check Skills You'll Need**

1. **Vocabulary Review**
Name four units of length in the *customary system.*
inch, foot, yard, mile
Complete.

2. 6 ft = ■ in. 72

3. 48 in. = ■ ft 4

4. 17 ft = ■ in. 204

GO for Help
Lesson 3-6

TEKS ★ TAKS
• (7.9)(A) To estimate measurements involving perimeter and area **TAKS** Obj. 4
• (7.8)(C) To use geometric concepts in fields such as art **TAKS** Obj. 3
• (7.14)(A) To communicate ideas using appropriate units **TAKS** Obj. 6

🔊 **New Vocabulary** area, perimeter

Why Learn This?

In some situations, an estimate of length or area will be enough to solve a problem. Painters estimate the area of a wall to make sure they buy enough paint.

A measurement must include a unit of measure to make sense. When you estimate, you can use familiar objects whose lengths you know.

 length of a paper clip ≈ 1 inch

length of a textbook ≈ 1 foot

length of a baseball bat ≈ 1 yard

EXAMPLE Choosing Reasonable Estimates

① Choose a reasonable estimate. Explain your choice.

a. the length of a new pencil: 9 in. or 9 ft

A new pencil is about 9 paper clips long. So 9 in. is reasonable.

b. the height of a flagpole: 10 in. or 10 yd

A flagpole is many baseball-bat lengths high. So 10 yd is reasonable.

✓ **Quick Check**

1. Which is a reasonable estimate for the distance between Boston, Massachusetts, and Washington, D.C., 400 ft or 400 mi? Explain.
400 mi; driving distances are usually measured in miles.

Differentiated Instruction Solutions for All Learners

Special Needs L1	**Below Level** L2
In Example 1, ask students to line up some paper clips next to their pencils to see about how many it takes to cover the length of their pencils. Ask them to hold 1 paper clip against a ruler.	Review with students customary and metric measures (p. 148). Encourage students to use these tables for the lesson.
learning style: tactile	learning style: visual

The **perimeter** of a figure is the total distance around the figure.

EXAMPLE Estimating Perimeter

 GO for Help

The formula for perimeter P of a rectangle is
$P = 2\ell + 2w$ or
$P = 2(\ell + w)$.

For a list of formulas, go to p. 673.

② Estimate the perimeter of the rectangle.

Estimate length and width.

The **length** is about 7 units.
The **width** is about 5 units. →

Use the formula for perimeter of a rectangle.

$2(7 + 5) = 24$ ← **Substitute for ℓ and w.**

The perimeter is about 24 units long.

✓ Quick Check

2. Estimate the perimeter of the rectangle.
   Answers may vary. Sample: about 24 units

The **area** of a figure is the number of square units a figure encloses.

EXAMPLE Estimating Area

③ **Geography** Estimate the area of Lake Superior. Each square represents 900 mi^2.

Lake Superior

Count the number of squares filled or almost filled. Then count the number of squares that are about half filled.

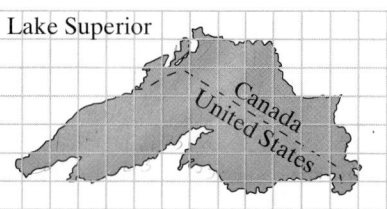

Lake Superior

3	1
5	1
9	0
8	3
6	3
31	8

Add the filled squares and the half-filled squares. The total is $31 + \frac{1}{2}(8)$, or 35. Since each square represents 900 mi^2, multiply 35 by 900 mi^2.

The area is about 31,500 mi^2.

✓ Quick Check

3. Estimate the area of the shaded region. Each square represents 4 yd^2.
   Answers may vary. Sample: about 92 yd^2

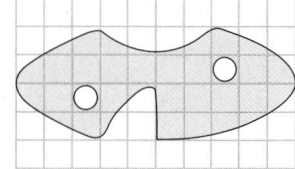

---

2. Teach

Activity Lab

Use before the lesson.

All in One Teaching Resources

Activity Lab 8-1: Estimating Area and Perimeter

Guided Instruction

Example 3
Use plain language to help students understand the notation for square units: ft^2 (square feet), yd^2 (square yards), and so on.

PowerPoint
Additional Examples

① Choose a reasonable estimate for the perimeter of a piece of paper: 40 in. or 40 ft. 40 in.

② Each square represents 1 in^2. Estimate the perimeter of the rectangle.

about 18 inches

③ Each square represents 50 yd^2. Estimate the area of the shaded figure. about 250 yd^2

④ Each square represents 5 ft^2. Estimate the area and perimeter of the figure.

perimeter about 18 ft, area about 82.5 ft^2

Advanced Learners L4
Have students draw three different triangles on graph paper, each having an area of 18 units. Check students' drawings.

English Language Learners ELL
For Example 1, ask students to give alternate reasons for why the estimates are reasonable. For example, ask them to show how long 9 feet might be, and to compare that length to their pencils.

Pre-AP™

learning style: visual

375

Closure

- *How can you estimate an appropriate unit of length?*
  Sample: Identify possible units and choose the best one.
- *How can you estimate the area of an irregular figure?* Count the number of squares that the figure occupies and multiply by the number of square units that each square represents.

 EXAMPLE Using Area and Perimeter

4 **TAKS Multiple Choice** Carl wants to paint a landscape. He will choose one of the four canvases shown below.

| Canvas I | Canvas II | Canvas III | Canvas IV |

Each square on the grid represents 4 square feet. Which canvas has an area of about 48 ft² and a perimeter of about 28 ft?

- **A** Canvas I
- **C** Canvas III
- **B** Canvas II
- **D** Canvas IV

You can estimate each area by counting the number of filled squares. You can estimate each perimeter by finding the sum of the side lengths. Since each square represents 4 ft², the side length of each square is 2 ft.

TAKS Tip

Making a table can help you decide which answer choices to eliminate.

Canvas	Area (ft²)	Perimeter (ft)
I	32 ✗	
II	36 ✗	
III	48 ✔	32 ✗
IV	48 ✔	28 ✔

Since Canvases I and II do not have an area of about 48 ft², you can eliminate them.

Canvas III has an area of about 48 ft², but does not have a perimeter of about 28 ft.

Canvas IV has an area of about 48 ft² and has a perimeter of about 28 ft.

Canvas IV has the correct area and perimeter, so the answer is D.

✓ Quick Check

4. Each square represents 25 square feet.
   Estimate the area and perimeter of the figure.
   Answers may vary. Sample:
   area: about 60 ft²; perimeter: about 90 ft

✓ Check Your Understanding

1. square

2. No; the perimeter is twice the rectangle's length plus twice its width, so the perimeter must be greater than just the length.

1. **Vocabulary** Area is the number of ? units a figure encloses.

2. **Reasoning** Is it possible for the length of a rectangle to be greater than its perimeter? Explain.

Match each item with a reasonable estimate of its length.

3. length of a bowling lane **C**

4. height of a coffee mug **B**

5. length of a car **A**

- **A.** 16 ft
- **B.** 4 in.
- **C.** 20 yd

Homework Exercises

For more exercises, see Extra Skills and Word Problems.

GO for Help

For Exercises	See Examples
6–9	1
10–11	2
12–13	3
14–15	4

8. 10 ft; it is deeper than the height of a person.

14. area: about 135 yd²; perimeter: about 75 yd

15. area: about 198 yd²; perimeter: about 81 yd

16. Answers may vary. Sample: about 21½ ft²

A **Choose a reasonable estimate. Explain your choice.**

6. length of a spoon: 4 in. or 4 ft   4 in.; a spoon is about as long as 4 paperclips.

7. width of your hand: 6 in. or 6 ft   6 in.; it is less than a foot.

8. depth of an in-ground swimming pool: 10 in. or 10 ft   See left.

9. length of a mouse's tail: 2 in. or 2 yd   2 in.; the tail is less than a foot.

Estimate the perimeter of each figure. The length of one side of each square represents 1 ft. 10–15. Answers may vary. Samples are given.

10.

about 24 ft

11.

about 20 ft

Estimate the area of each shaded region. Each square represents 25 mi².

12.

about 625 mi²

13.

about 875 mi²

Estimate the area and perimeter. Each square represents 9 yd².

14.

15.

14–15. See left.

B **GPS** 16. **Guided Problem Solving** In the diagram of the fish pond at the right, each square represents 1 ft². Estimate the area of the pond.   See left.
- The number of full squares in the pond = ▨.
- The number of half squares in the pond = ▨.
- The area of the pond ≅ ▨ + ½ ▨.

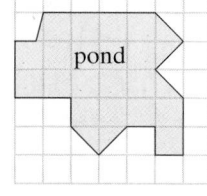
pond

17. Katy painted the window frame at the right. She did not paint the glass inside. If each square represents 1 ft², what is the area of the glass?   about 8 ft²

Glass

Assignment Guide

Check Your Understanding
Go over Exercises 1–5 in class before assigning the Homework Exercises.

Homework Exercises
A Practice by Example   6–15
B Apply Your Skills   16–27
C Challenge   28
TEKS ★ TAKS Tune-Up and Mixed Review   29–34

Homework Quick Check
To check students' understanding of key skills and concepts, go over Exercises 11, 14, 17, 26, and 27.

---

4. Assess & Reteach

PowerPoint

Lesson Quiz

Choose a reasonable estimate for the length of each object.

1. bed: 5 ft or 5 in. **5 ft**

2. soccer field: 100 in. or 100 yd **100 yd**

3. Estimate the perimeter. Each square represents 4 ft². **50 ft**

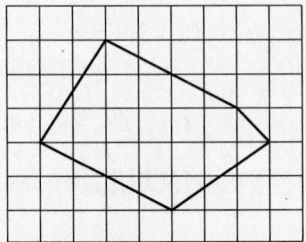

4. Estimate the area. Each square represents 5 cm². **about 75 cm²**

31. 150% increase

32. 75% decrease

33. 44.4% decrease

34. 46.7% increase

378

GO **Online**
Homework Help
Visit: PHSchool.com
Web Code: are-0801

23. Answers may vary. Sample: about 500 yd²

24. Answers may vary. Sample: 2 ft × 5 ft

25. Lay the string around the edge of the puzzle piece. Mark the length and then measure the string.

26.

4
8

27a. about 7,840,000 ft²

Florida

Estimate each length in inches. 1 in.

18. about 2 in.

19. about ½ in.

20. about 1½ in.

21. about 1 in.

22. **Estimation** Measure the length of your shoe.
Use your shoe length to estimate the length of your desk.
Check students' work.

23. A diagram of a golf fairway is shown at the right. Each square represents 20 yd². Estimate the area. **See left.**

hole #7

24. A rectangle has a perimeter of 14 ft. Write whole-number dimensions for another rectangle with the same perimeter. **See left.**

25. **Writing in Math** How could you use a piece of string to estimate the perimeter of the puzzle piece at the right? **See left.**

26. **Open Ended** Draw a rectangle on graph paper with a perimeter of 24 units and an area of 32 units². **See left.**

27. An acre equals 43,560 ft². A theme park covers about 180 acres.
  a. Estimate the number of square feet in the theme park. **See left.**
  b. The area of a football field is 57,600 ft². About how many football fields are equal to the area of the theme park? **about 136**

C 28. **Challenge** In the map at the left, each square represents 5,575 mi². Use the map to estimate the area of Florida. **about 61,325 mi²**

TEKS ★ TAKS Tune-Up and Mixed Review

TAKS Objective 4
TEKS (7.9)(A)

29. The flag of Nepal at the right is not rectangular in shape. If each square on the grid represents 4 square inches, what is the approximate area of the flag shown? **D**

  A 18 in.²   **C** 36 in.²
  B 44 in.²   **D** 70 in.²

TAKS Objective 2
TEKS (7.3)(A)

30. Stewart Middle School has 243 seventh-grade students. About 32% of them attended the high school football game. About how many seventh-grade students attended the football game? **G**

  F Fewer than 75   **H** Between 85 and 100
  G Between 75 and 85   **J** More than 100

GO for Help   Lesson 6-8

Find each percent of increase or decrease. Round to the nearest tenth.
31–34. See margin.
31. 20 to 50   **32.** 32 to 8   **33.** 99 to 55   **34.** 75 to 110

TEKS ★ TAKS Resources

- TAKS Strategies, p. 427
- TAKS Tune-Up, pp. 431–433

TAKS Tune-Up Kit
- TAKS Daily Review Transparencies
- TAKS Review and Preparation Workbook
- TAKS Strategies with Transparencies
- Texas Progress Monitoring Assessments

Alternative Assessment

Each student in a pair draws on graph paper a shaded picture, such as a pond, leaf, or geometric figure. Each designates the measurement that a square unit represents. Then partners estimate the area of each other's figures. Pairs then exchange drawings with other pairs to check their estimates.

Generating Formulas for Area

You can generate the area of a figure by separating or combining the areas of two figures you know.

TEKS ★ **TAKS**
(7.4)(A) To generate formulas involving area
TAKS Obj. 2
(7.14)(A) To communicate mathematical ideas using physical and algebraic models
TAKS Obj. 6

ACTIVITY

1. Using graph paper, draw a parallelogram like the one at the right. When you draw the perpendicular segment, what two polygons are formed? **trapezoid, triangle**

2. Cut out the parallelogram and then cut along the perpendicular segment. **Check students' work.**

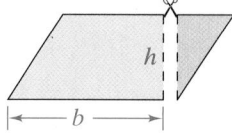

3. Rearrange the pieces to form a rectangle.
   a. What is the area of the rectangle?
   b. What was the area of the parallelogram?

The area of the rectangle and the area of the parallelogram should be the same.

4. How do b and h relate to the length and width of the rectangle? Write a formula for the area of a parallelogram. **The rectangle has length b and height h; $A = bh$.**

ACTIVITY

5–6. Check students' work.

5. Fold a piece of graph paper in half. On one side, draw a right triangle like the one at the right.

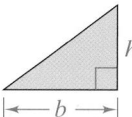

6. Cut out the triangle, cutting through both layers of the folded paper. You now have two congruent triangles.

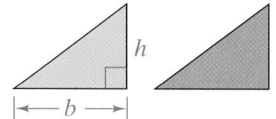

7. Arrange the pieces to form a rectangle.
   a. What is the area of the rectangle?
   b. What is the area of one triangle?

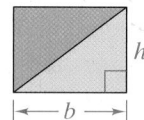

The area of the triangle should be half the area of the rectangle.

8. How do b and h relate to the length and width of the rectangle? Write a formula for the area of a triangle. **The rectangle has length b and height h; $A = \frac{1}{2}bh$.**

Activity Lab   Generating Formulas for Area   **379**

Activity Lab

Generating Formulas for Area

Students learn to find the area of an unfamiliar figure by rearranging its pieces into familiar figures. This will help them understand the formula for area used in Lesson 8-2.

Guided Instruction

Before beginning the Activity, explain to students that any parallelogram can be separated into two pieces and those pieces will form a rectangle. Demonstrate separating a triangle from a parallelogram and attaching it to the other side to form a rectangle.
Ask:
• *What dimension is the same height as the height of the rectangle?* **the height of the triangle**

Activity
Distribute graph paper and work through the Activity as a class. Have volunteers answer the questions in steps 3, 4, 7, and 8. Make sure each student has enough time to complete and understand each step before proceeding to the next step.

Alternative Method
Some students may need to count the squares to verify that the height and base of the parallelogram is the same as that of the rectangle.

TEKS ★ **TAKS** **Resources**

• Activity Lab 8-2: Critical Thinking
• graph paper
• scissors

Dana Center TEKS Toolkit Clarifying Activities (7.4)(A), (7.14)(A)
Visit: PHSchool.com
Web Code: arq-9045

TEKS ★ TAKS

(7.4)(A) To generate formulas involving perimeter and area **TAKS** Obj. 2

(7.9)(A) To solve application problems involving area of polygons **TAKS** Obj. 4

Dana Center TEKS Toolkit Clarifying Activities (7.4)(A), (7.9)(A)
Visit: PHSchool.com
Web Code: arq-9045

TEKS Math Background

A *parallelogram* is a four-sided figure whose opposite sides are parallel. The formula for the area of a parallelogram is $A = b \cdot h$, where b is the base length and h is the height, or perpendicular distance, from one base to the other. Note that any side of a parallelogram can be considered the base.

More Math Background: p. 372C

Lesson Planning and Resources

See p. 372E for a list of the resources that support this lesson.

PowerPoint

Bell Ringer Practice

✓ **Check Skills You'll Need**
Use student page, transparency, or PowerPoint.

TAKS Daily Review 58
Use transparency.

380

✓ Check Skills You'll Need

1. **Vocabulary Review**
State the *Commutative Property of Multiplication.*
See below.
Find each product.

2. 100×4.5 **450**

3. 2.34×12 **28.08**

4. 10.2×5.6 **57.12**

5. 0.6×3.4 **2.04**

GO for Help
Lesson 1-3

Check Skills You'll Need
1. Changing the order of the factors does not change the product.

Vocabulary Tip

Perpendicular segments intersect to form right angles.

GO Online

Video Tutor Help
Visit: PHSchool.com
Web Code: are-0775

TEKS ★ TAKS

- (7.4)(A) To generate formulas involving perimeter and area **TAKS** Obj. 2
- (7.9)(A) To solve application problems involving area of polygons **TAKS** Obj. 4

🔊 **New Vocabulary** height of a parallelogram, base of a parallelogram

Why Learn This?

The floor plan of the building at the right is in the shape of a parallelogram. You can calculate the area of the parallelogram to determine how much office space is available on a given floor of the building.

The **height of a parallelogram** is the length of a perpendicular segment connecting one **base of a parallelogram** to the other.

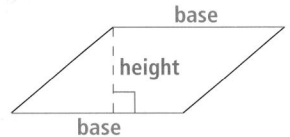

The diagram below relates the formula for the area of a rectangle to the formula for the area of a parallelogram.

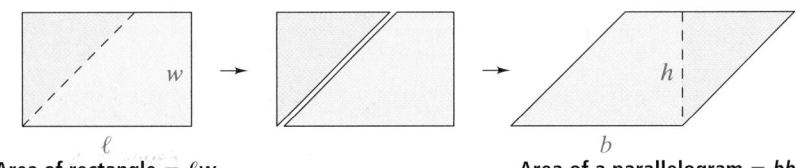

Area of rectangle $= \ell w$ Area of a parallelogram $= bh$

KEY CONCEPTS Area of a Parallelogram

The area of a parallelogram is equal to the product of any base b and the corresponding height h.

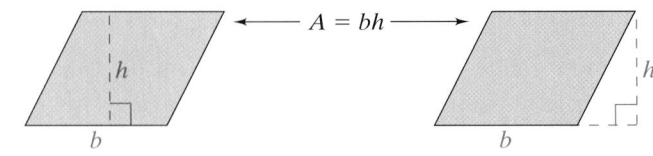

$$A = bh$$

380 Chapter 8 Measurement

Differentiated Instruction Solutions for All Learners

Special Needs L1	**Below Level** L2
Show students that when you mark off the height on both sides of a parallelogram, the resulting interior shape is a rectangle. This will help them understand why *bh* works for both shapes, although we customarily use *lw* for the area of rectangles.	Review with students the meaning of *parallel* and *perpendicular*. Have them identify a vertex in a parallelogram.
learning style: visual	learning style: verbal

EXAMPLE Finding the Area of a Parallelogram

1 Find the area of the parallelogram.

$A = bh$ ← **Use the area formula.**

$\quad = (9)(15)$ ← **Substitute.**

$\quad = 135$ ← **Simplify.**

The area is 135 in.²

✓ Quick Check

1. Find the area of the parallelogram.
90 cm²

You can also use lengths of the sides of a rectangle to find perimeter.

EXAMPLE Relating Perimeter and Area

2 **TAKS Multiple Choice** Melinda wants to plant a rectangular garden and put a fence around it. She has 34 ft of fencing and she wants her garden to be as big as possible. Which dimensions should she use?

  Ⓐ Length of 9 ft and width of 8 ft

  Ⓑ Length of 10 ft and width of 7 ft

  Ⓒ Length of 12 ft and width of 6 ft

  Ⓓ Length of 14 ft and width of 5 ft

Since all answer choices give the length ℓ and width w, you can calculate both the perimeter $2\ell + 2w$ and the area $\ell \times w$.

Perimeter   **Area**

$2(9) + 2(8) \;= 34$ ✔ $9 \times 8 \;= 72$ ← **Perimeter is correct; find the area.**

$2(10) + 2(7) = 34$ ✔ $10 \times 7 = 70$ ← **Perimeter is correct; the area in choice A is greater.**

$2(12) + 2(6) = 36$ ✘   ← **Perimeter is greater than 34 ft.**

$2(14) + 2(5) = 38$ ✘   ← **Perimeter is greater than 34 ft.**

The rectangle with a length of 9 ft and a width of 8 ft will have the correct perimeter and the greatest area. The answer is A.

✓ Quick Check

2. What is the perimeter of the rectangle?
22 cm

★ TAKS Tip

If the first part in an answer choice is incorrect, do not bother to calculate the second part.

8-2 Area of a Parallelogram   **381**

---

2. Teach

Activity Lab

Use before the lesson.
Student Edition Activity Lab, Hands On 8-2a, Generating Formulas for Area, p. 379

All in One Teaching Resources
Activity Lab 8-2: Critical Thinking

Guided Instruction

Error Prevention!

Some students confuse *base* and *height.* Have them cut two strips of paper and tape them together to make an upside-down *T*. Have them label the horizontal strip *base* and the vertical strip *height*. They can tape their "reference charts" in their notebooks.

Example 1

Remind students that the units for area are square units. You can illustrate this by including the units in the calculation.
9 in. × 15 in. = 135 in.² because in. × in. = in.²

PowerPoint
Additional Examples

1 Find the area of the parallelogram. 216 ft²

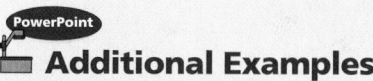

2 A backyard pool has a perimeter of 90 ft and an area of 500 ft². What are the pool's length and width? 25 ft, 20 ft

All in One Teaching Resources
• Daily Notetaking Guide 8-2 **L3**
• Adapted Notetaking 8-2 **L1**

Closure

• *How do you find the area of a parallelogram?* Multiply any base times the corresponding height (perpendicular distance from one base to the other).

Advanced Learners L4
Three identical parallelograms are placed side by side. A diagonal connects opposite corners and forms two triangles with an area of 21 ft² each. What is the area of each parallelogram? 14 ft²

English Language Learners ELL
For Example 2, provide graph paper and have students draw shapes according to the dimensions in each of the choices. Ask them to compare their pictures to their calculations.

Pre-AP™

learning style: visual

381

3. Practice

Assignment Guide

Check Your Understanding
Go over Exercises 1–5 in class before assigning the Homework Exercises.

Homework Exercises
A Practice by Example   6–16
B Apply Your Skills   17–24
C Challenge   25
TEKS ★ *TAKS* Tune-Up and
Mixed Review   26–33

Homework Quick Check
To check students' understanding of key skills and concepts, go over Exercises 6, 13, 22, 23, and 24.

Differentiated Instruction Resources

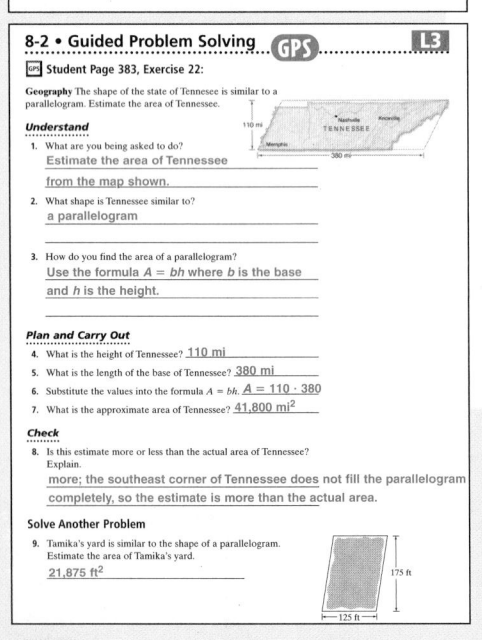

382

Check Your Understanding

2. True; corresponding parts are congruent.

3. True; $A = bh$, so if the bases are equal and the heights are equal, the areas will be equal.

1. **Vocabulary** What kind of angle is formed by perpendicular lines?
    right

Two parallelograms have a base and a height that are equal. Tell whether each statement is true or false. Explain your answer.

2. The two parallelograms must be congruent.

3. The areas of the two parallelograms are equal.

Use the parallelogram at the right. Fill in the blank.

4. The formula for the area is $A = bh = (3)(\blacksquare)$. 4

5. The formula for the perimeter is $P = 2(\blacksquare) + 2(5)$.
    3

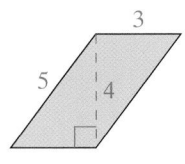

Homework Exercises

For more exercises, see Extra Skills and Word Problems.

A **Find the area of each parallelogram.**

GO for Help

For Exercises	See Examples
6–15	1
16	2

6.

10 m
6 m
60 m²

7.
5 m
5 m
25 m²

8.

9 cm
12 cm
108 cm²

9.
3 ft
4 ft   4.5 ft
12 ft²

10.
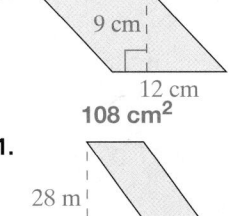
10 in.
15 in.
150 in.²

11.
28 m
14 m
392 m²

Find each area for base b and height h of a parallelogram.

12. $b = 14$ in.
     $h = 6$ in.
     84 in.²

13. $b = 25$ mi
     $h = 25$ mi
     625 mi²

14. $h = 40$ cm
     $b = 0.5$ cm
     20 cm²

15. $h = 1,000$ m
     $b = 20$ m
     20,000 m²

16. A rectangular fish pond is 21 ft² in area. If the owner can surround the pond with a 20-foot fence, what are the dimensions of the pond?
     3 ft by 7 ft

B **GPS** 17. **Guided Problem Solving** The diagram shows a park bounded by streets. The park is in the shape of a parallelogram. Each square is 10 yards on a side. What is the area of the park? 36 units²
     • What are the base and the height of the parallelogram?
     • What formula should you use?

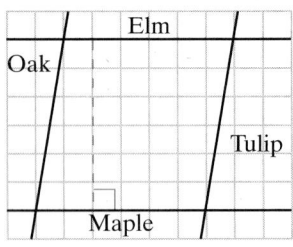

382   Chapter 8   Measurement

29. 2; 2

30. 1.35; $1\frac{7}{20}$

31. 1.52; $1\frac{13}{25}$

32. 0.0003; $\frac{3}{10,000}$

33. 0.0045; $\frac{9}{2,000}$

Find the missing measures for each rectangle.

18.	19.	20.	21.
$\ell = 14$ in.	$\ell = \blacksquare$	$\ell = 7$ ft	$\ell = \blacksquare$
$w = \blacksquare$	$w = 4.2$ m	$w = \blacksquare$	$w = 2$ cm
$A = \blacksquare$	$A = 37.8$ m^2	$A = 18.2$ ft^2	$A = \blacksquare$
$P = 34$ in.	$P = \blacksquare$	$P = \blacksquare$	$P = 25$ cm
3 in.; 42 in.^{2}	9 m; 26.4 m	2.6 ft; 19.2 ft	10.5 cm; 21 cm^2

23. They have the same bases, but the height of the parallelogram must be less than the height of the rectangle because a leg is shorter than the hypotenuse.

22. Geography The shape of the state of Tennessee is similar to a **GPS** parallelogram. Estimate the area of Tennessee. **41,800 mi^2**

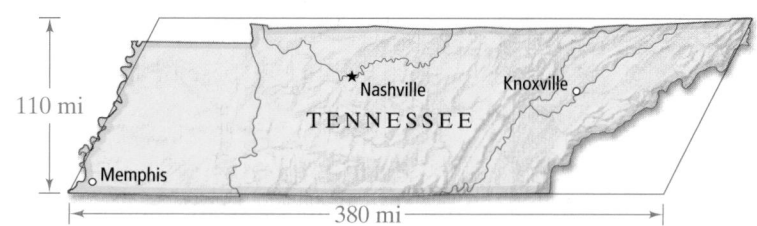

110 mi
Nashville Knoxville
TENNESSEE
Memphis
380 mi

4 m
2 m

4 m
1.6 m   2 m

24. No; the approximate area is 60 m × 70 m or 4,200 m^2.

23. Reasoning The rectangle and the parallelogram at the left have the same perimeter. How do you know that the area of the rectangle is greater than the area of the parallelogram? **See left.**

24. Writing in Math A rectangular lot is 70.2 m long and 59.8 m wide. Is 42,000 m^2 a reasonable estimate for the area of the lot? Explain. **See left.**

C 25. Challenge Find the area and perimeter of the figure at the right.

area = 161 in.^{2};
perimeter = 62 in.

7 in.
5 in.
12 in.
7 in.
7 in.
5 in.
23 in.

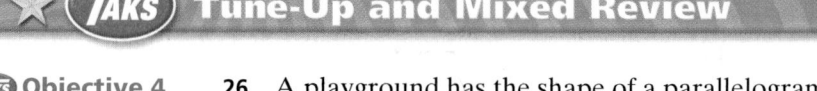
TEKS ★ TAKS Tune-Up and Mixed Review

TAKS Objective 4
TEKS (7.9)(A)

26. A playground has the shape of a parallelogram. If the base is 30 feet, and the corresponding height is 25 feet, what is its area? **D**
Ⓐ 55 ft^2 Ⓑ 187.5 ft^2 Ⓒ 375 ft^2 Ⓓ 750 ft^2

TAKS Objective 2
TEKS (7.4)(A)

27. Which of the following expressions CANNOT be used to find the perimeter of a regular hexagon with sides of length h? **H**
Ⓕ $6h$ Ⓗ $3h \times 3h$
Ⓖ $2h + 2h + 2h$ Ⓙ $6 \times h$

TAKS Objective 1
TEKS (7.1)(B)

28. In Solomon's stamp collection, $\frac{4}{25}$ of the stamps are international. What percent of Solomon's stamps are international? **B**
Ⓐ 4%   Ⓑ 16%   Ⓒ 21%   Ⓓ 29%

GO for Help
Lesson 6-3

Write each percent as a decimal and as a fraction in simplest form.
29–33. See margin.
29. 200%   **30.** 135%   **31.** 152%   **32.** 0.03%   **33.** 0.45%

Alternative Assessment

Each student in a pair draws a parallelogram and labels the base and height. Partners exchange drawings and find the area of each other's figure. If necessary, direct students to find the area to the nearest tenth. Remind students to report area in square units.

TEKS ★ TAKS Resources

• TAKS Strategies, p. 427
• TAKS Tune-Up, pp. 431–433

TAKS Tune-Up Kit

• TAKS Daily Review Transparencies
• TAKS Review and Preparation Workbook
• TAKS Strategies with Transparencies
• Texas Progress Monitoring Assessments

PowerPoint

Lesson Quiz

Find each area.

1. 5 cm
4 cm
12 cm
48 cm^2

2. Find the area and perimeter for a parallelogram with $b = 7$ ft and $h = 4$ ft.
area = 28 ft^2, perimeter = 22 ft

Reteaching 8-2   Area of a Parallelogram

Enrichment 8-2   Area of a Parallelogram

383

Perimeter and Area of a Triangle

(7.4)(A) To generate formulas involving perimeter and area TAKS **Obj. 2**

(7.9)(A) To estimate measurements and solve application problems involving perimeter and area of polygons TAKS **Obj. 4**

Dana Center TEKS Toolkit Clarifying Activities (7.4)(A), (7.9)(A)
Visit: PHSchool.com
Web Code: arq-9045

TEKS Math Background

The perimeter of a triangle is found by adding the lengths of all three sides. The area of a triangle is always one half the area of a parallelogram with the same base and height. To find the formula for the area of a triangle, multiply the formula for the area of a parallelogram, *bh,* by $\frac{1}{2}$. The area of a triangle is $\frac{1}{2}bh$.

More Math Background: p. 372C

Lesson Planning and Resources

See p. 372E for a list of the resources that support this lesson.

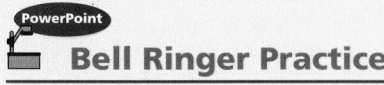

Bell Ringer Practice

☑ **Check Skills You'll Need**
Use student page, transparency, or PowerPoint.

TAKS **Daily Review 59**
Use transparency.

☑ Check Skills You'll Need

1. Vocabulary Review
What is the *reciprocal* of 2? $\frac{1}{2}$

Find each product.

2. $\frac{1}{4} \cdot 12$ 3   **3.** $20 \cdot \frac{1}{10}$ 2

4. $15 \cdot \frac{1}{3}$ 5   **5.** $\frac{1}{2} \cdot 9$ 4.5

GO for Help
Lesson 3-4

TEKS ⭐ TAKS

- **(7.4)(A)** To generate formulas involving perimeter and area TAKS **Obj. 2**
- **(7.9)(A)** To estimate measurements and solve application problems involving perimeter and area of polygons TAKS **Obj. 4**

🔊 **New Vocabulary** base of a triangle, height of a triangle

Why Learn This?

You use perimeter when you solve problems involving borders. You can find perimeter to see if you have enough material to sew a border around the triangular quilt piece at the right.

To find the perimeter of a triangle, you can add the side lengths.

EXAMPLE   Finding the Perimeter of a Triangle

1 Quilting How much material do you need to sew a border around the triangular piece on the quilt above?

Estimate $3.4 + 3.1 + 4.7 \approx 3 + 3 + 5 = 11$

$P = 3.4 + 3.1 + 4.7$ ← Find the perimeter.

$= 11.2$ ← Simplify.

You need 11.2 in. of material to border the triangular piece.

Check for Reasonableness 11.2 is close to 11. The answer is reasonable.

☑ Quick Check

1. **Mental Math** How much fabric do you need to border a triangular quilt piece whose sides are 6 cm, 8 cm, and 10 cm long? **24 cm**

Any side of a triangle can be considered the **base of a triangle.** The **height of a triangle** is the length of the perpendicular segment from a vertex to the base opposite the vertex or to an extension of the base.

  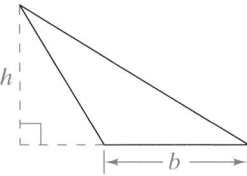

384   Chapter 8   Measurement

Differentiated Instruction Solutions for All Learners

Special Needs L1
To help students see the relationship between parallelograms and triangles, give them a drawing of a parallelogram. Ask them to cut off the triangles.

Below Level L2
Provide students with several triangle cutouts, so they can trace them, label the base and height, and trace the other half of a parallelogram with the same base and height.

learning style: visual

learning style: tactile

The formula for the area of a triangle follows from the formula for the area of a parallelogram.

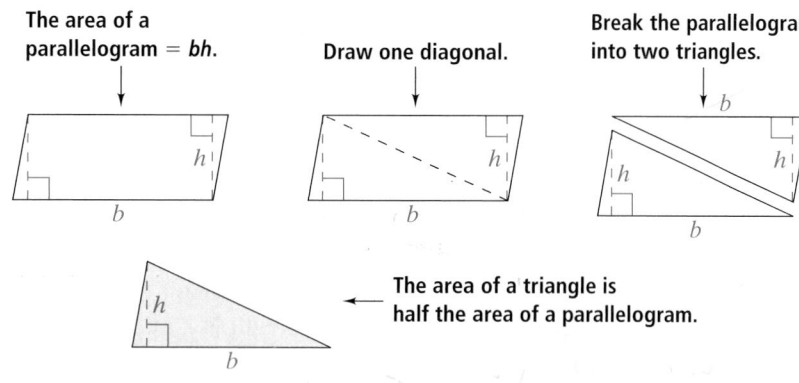

The area of a parallelogram = *bh*.

Draw one diagonal.

Break the parallelogram into two triangles.

← **The area of a triangle is half the area of a parallelogram.**

KEY CONCEPTS **Area of a Triangle**

The area of a triangle is equal to half the product of any base *b* and the corresponding height *h*.
$$A = \frac{1}{2}bh$$

When you find the area of a triangle, remember that you only need the length of the base and the perpendicular height of the triangle.

EXAMPLE **Finding the Area of a Triangle**

② Find the area of each triangle.

a.

5.1 ft 5 ft 8.6 ft 8 ft

b.

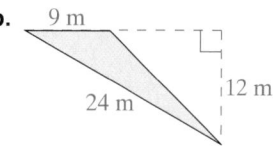
9 m 24 m 12 m

$A = \frac{1}{2}bh$	← Use the area formula. →	$A = \frac{1}{2}bh$
$= \frac{1}{2}(8)(5)$	← Substitute. →	$= \frac{1}{2}(9)(12)$
$= 20$	← Simplify. →	$= 54$

The area is 20 ft².   The area is 54 m².

Vocabulary Tip

Areas are always measured in *square units*.

✓ Quick Check

2. Find the area of each triangle.

a.

26.8 m 12 m 19 m 36 m **216 m²**

b. **48 cm²**

16 cm 4 cm 6 cm 20.9 cm

Advanced Learners **L4**
Jake has a garden shaped like a parallelogram. Its base is 6 m and its height is 4.5 m. If he plants carrots in half of his garden, what is the area of the carrot patch?
13.5 m²

Pre-AP™

English Language Learners **ELL**
Ask students to *restate*, in their own words, what the base and height of a triangle are. Ask them to draw a triangle and label the base and height of it.

learning style: visual

Activity Lab

Use before the lesson.

All in One Teaching Resources

Activity Lab 8-3: Perimeter and Area of Triangles

Guided Instruction

Example 2
Help make the connection that the area of each triangle is one half the area of the related parallelogram. Ask:
• *How many triangles form a parallelogram?* **2**
• *Write an equation to represent this. Use* t *for the area of the triangle and* p *for the area of the parallelogram.* **2t = p**
• *Solve for* t. $t = \frac{p}{2}$ *or* $\frac{1}{2}p$

PowerPoint

▣ Additional Examples

❶ Find the perimeter of the triangle. **31 ft**

7 ft 10 ft 14 ft

❷ A school is creating a triangular playground. Find the area of the playground if the base is 80 yd and the height is 40 yd. **1,600 yd²**

All in One Teaching Resources
• Daily Notetaking Guide 8-2 **L3**
• Adapted Notetaking 8-2 **L1**

Closure

• *How is the formula for the area of a triangle related to the formula for an area of a parallelogram?*
Sample: Both formulas use the base and height of the figure to calculate area. Both have measurements expressed in square units. The formula for the area of a triangle is $A = \frac{1}{2}bh$ or the area is one half that of a parallelogram.

385

3. Practice

Assignment Guide

Check Your Understanding
Go over Exercises 1–7 in class before assigning the Homework Exercises.

Homework Exercises
A Practice by Example   8–17
B Apply Your Skills   18–27
C Challenge   28
TEKS ★ (TAKS) Tune-Up and
     Mixed Review   29–33

Homework Quick Check
To check students' understanding of key skills and concepts, go over Exercises 10, 15, 24, 25, and 26.

✓ Check Your Understanding

1. **Vocabulary** A triangle that has a 90° angle is a(n) __?__ triangle.
   right

Each triangle's perimeter is 15 cm. Find the length of the missing side.

2. 4 cm, 5 cm, ■ **6 cm**   3. 2 cm, 7 cm, ■ **6 cm**   4. 1 cm, 7 cm, ■ **7 cm**

Find the area of each triangle.

5. $b = 4$ cm, $h = 5$ cm **10 cm²**   6. $b = 2$ in., $h = 7$ in. **7 in.²**

7. A carpenter has blueprints for a wooden triangular patio. The base is 5 m and the height is 7 m. What is the area of the patio? **17.5 m²**

Homework Exercises

For more exercises, see Extra Skills and Word Problems.

(A) Find the perimeter of each triangle.

For Exercises	See Examples
8–11	1
12–17	2

8.
4 ft   3 ft
4 ft 6 in.
11 ft 6 in.

9.
5 ft
4 ft
3.5 ft
12.5 ft

10.
5.5 cm
5 cm
2 cm
12.5 cm

11. You bend a drinking straw into the shape of an equilateral triangle. Each side is 4.5 cm long. How long is the straw? **13.5 cm**

Find the area of each triangle.

12.
8 cm
14 cm
56 cm²

13.
60 yd
48 yd
1,440 yd²

14.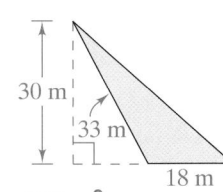
30 m
33 m
18 m
270 m²

15.
12 km
26.8 km
72 km²

16.
18 in.   22 in.
17 in.
24 in.
187 in.²

17.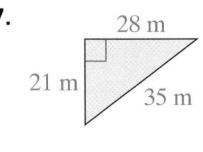
28 m
21 m
35 m
294 m²

(B) GPS 18. **Guided Problem Solving** An equilateral triangle's perimeter is 27 ft. The height of the triangle is 7.8 ft. What is the triangle's area?
   • You can *Draw a Picture* to solve this problem. Sketch and label the triangle. Find the perimeter and then use the area formula.
   35.1 ft²

19. **50,000 yd²**

19. A conservation group plans to buy a triangular plot of land. What is the area of the plot of land in the diagram?
   See left.

200 yd
500 yd

24. The area is doubled. If $b = 3$ and $h = 10$, then the area of the triangle is $A = \frac{1}{2}(3)(10) = 15$. If you double the base, then the area is $A = \frac{1}{2}(6)(10) = 30$.

27. 3 ft; if $b = 4$ and $h =$ the corresponding height, then the area of the triangle is $\frac{1}{2}(4)h$, or $2h$. Since the area is 6 ft², $2h = 6$. So $h = 3$.

Find the area for base *b* and height *h* of each triangle.

20. $b = 4.2$ in.
$h = 6.3$ in.
13.23 in.²

21. $b = 12$ m
$h = 17$ m
102 m²

22. $h = 6.2$ ft
$b = 2.5$ ft
7.75 ft²

23. $h = 100$ km
$b = 200$ km
10,000 km²

24. Writing in Math The base of a triangle is doubled and the height remains the same. Explain how the area changes. Use examples.
See margin.

25. A rescue helicopter receives a distress call from a ship at sea. The diagram at the right displays the search pattern the helicopter will use. Each pass from a central point forms an equilateral triangle. What is the area of one of the triangular regions? **27.68 km²**

Key:
→ First search
- - → Second search

Careers Rescue swimmer is one of the jobs offered in the coast guard.

26. Two equilateral triangles with sides of length 6 inches are joined **GPS** together to form a rhombus. What is the perimeter of the rhombus?
24 in.

27. Reasoning One base of a triangle has a length of 6 ft and a corresponding height of 2 ft. This means that the area of the triangle is $\frac{1}{2}(6$ ft $\cdot 2$ ft$) = 6$ ft². Another base of the same triangle has a length of 4 ft. What is its corresponding height? Explain.
See margin.

C **28. Challenge** The area of an isosceles right triangle is 121 ft². What is the approximate length of each of the two equal sides? **15.6 ft**

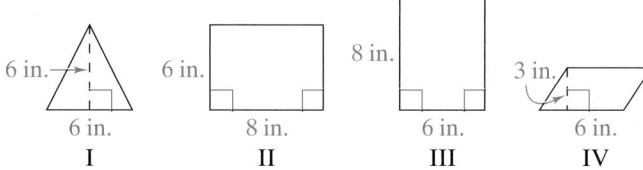

TEKS ★ TAKS **Tune-Up and Mixed Review**

TAKS Objective 4
TEKS (7.9)(A)

29. Which two of the figures shown have the same area? **C**

6 in.
6 in.
6 in.
I

6 in.
8 in.
II

8 in.
6 in.
III

3 in.
6 in.
IV

Ⓐ Figures I and II
Ⓑ Figures I and III
Ⓒ Figures I and IV
Ⓓ Figures II and IV

TAKS Objective 2
TEKS (7.4)(A)

30. A square has a perimeter of *x* feet. What is its area in terms of *x*? **F**

Ⓕ $\frac{x^2}{16}$
Ⓖ $4x^2$
Ⓗ $\frac{x^2}{4}$
Ⓙ $\frac{x}{16}$

Lesson 5-4

Algebra **Solve each proportion using mental math.**

31. $\frac{m}{35} = \frac{4}{5}$ **28**

32. $\frac{55}{99} = \frac{5}{x}$ **9**

33. $\frac{9}{p} = \frac{180}{200}$ **10**

Alternative Assessment

Each student in a pair draws a triangle and labels the base and lengths of each leg. Partners exchange drawings and find the perimeter and area of each other's figure. If necessary, direct students to find the area to the nearest tenth. Remind students to report area in square units.

TEKS ★ TAKS Resources

• TAKS Strategies, p. 427
• TAKS Tune-Up, pp. 431–433

TAKS Tune-Up Kit

• TAKS Daily Review Transparencies
• TAKS Review and Preparation Workbook
• TAKS Strategies with Transparencies
• Texas Progress Monitoring Assessments

---

4. Assess & Reteach

PowerPoint
Lesson Quiz

Use the figure below.

1. Find the perimeter. **21.5 ft**

2. Find the area. **17.5 ft²**

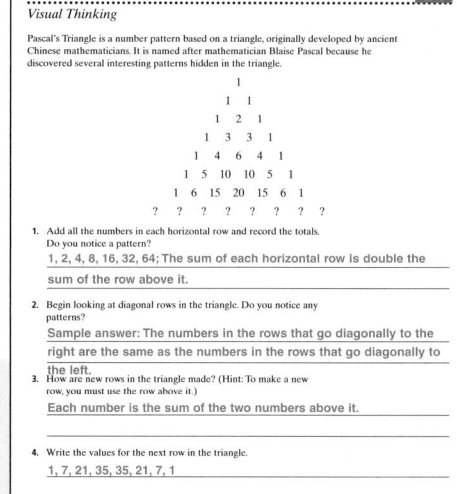

387

Areas of Other Figures

TEKS ★ TAKS

(7.4)(A) To generate formulas involving area TAKS Obj. 2

(7.9)(A) To estimate measurements and solve application problems involving area of polygons and other shapes TAKS Obj. 4

Dana Center TEKS Toolkit Clarifying Activities (7.4)(A), (7.9)(A)
Visit: PHSchool.com
Web Code: arq-9045

TEKS Math Background

A *trapezoid* is a four-sided figure with one pair of parallel sides that form the bases. The height of a trapezoid is the perpendicular distance between bases. Take two identical trapezoids, rotate one, and put their sides together to form a parallelogram. Since the formula for the area of a parallelogram is $A = b \times h$, the formula for the area of a trapezoid is $\frac{1}{2}$ of the height multiplied by the sum of the bases: $A = \frac{1}{2}h(b_1 + b_2)$, read as "area equals one half height times the quantity of base one plus base two."

More Math Background: p. 372C

Lesson Planning and Resources

See p. 372E for a list of the resources that support this lesson.

PowerPoint

Bell Ringer Practice

✓ **Check Skills You'll Need**
Use student page, transparency, or PowerPoint.

TAKS **Daily Review 60**
Use transparency.

✓ Check Skills You'll Need

1. Vocabulary Review
What is the *base of a parallelogram?*
See below.
Find the area of each figure.

2.

10 cm
7.5 cm
75 cm²

3.

15 m
9 m
135 m²

GO for Help
Lesson 8-2

Vocabulary Tip

A *trapezoid* is a quadrilateral that has exactly one pair of parallel sides. Read b_1 as "base 1" and b_2 as "base 2."

Check Skills You'll Need

1. It is one of a pair of opposite sides.

TEKS ★ TAKS

- (7.4)(A) To generate formulas involving area TAKS Obj. 2
- (7.9)(A) To estimate measurements and solve application problems involving area of polygons and other shapes TAKS Obj. 4

🔊 **New Vocabulary** bases of a trapezoid, height of a trapezoid

Why Learn This?

If you know how to find the area of simple figures, you can find the area of an irregular figure, such as the area of a backyard deck.

The formula for the area of a trapezoid follows from the formula for the area of a parallelogram.

base
height
base

The two parallel sides of a trapezoid are the **bases of a trapezoid**, with lengths b_1 and b_2. The **height of a trapezoid** h is the length of a perpendicular segment connecting the bases.

If you put two identical trapezoids together, you get a parallelogram. The area of the parallelogram is $(b_1 + b_2)h$. The area of one trapezoid equals $\frac{1}{2}(b_1 + b_2)h$.

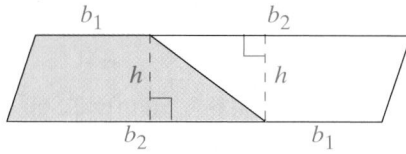
b_1 b_2
h h
b_2 b_1

KEY CONCEPTS   Area of a Trapezoid

The area of a trapezoid is one half the product of the height and the sum of the lengths of the bases.

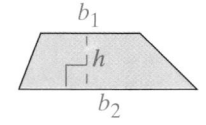
b_1
h
b_2

$$A = \frac{1}{2}h(b_1 + b_2)$$

Differentiated Instruction Solutions for All Learners

Special Needs L1	**Below Level** L2
Ask students to draw a triangle, parallelogram, and trapezoid, one on each of three index cards. Ask them to write the formula for the area of each next to the drawing. Suggest that students refer to the cards as they work through the chapter.	Review with students the Order of Operations and multiplying a number by $\frac{1}{2}$.
learning style: visual	learning style: verbal

EXAMPLE Finding the Area of a Trapezoid

1 Find the area of the trapezoid shown at the right.

15.8 cm
8.5 cm   13.5 cm
15 cm

$A = \frac{1}{2}h(b_1 + b_2)$ ← **Use the area formula for a trapezoid.**

$= \frac{1}{2}(15)(8.5 + 13.5)$ ← **Substitute for h, b_1, and b_2.**

$= \frac{1}{2}(15)(22)$ ← **Add.**

$= 165$ ← **Multiply.**

The area of the trapezoid is 165 cm^2.

✓ Quick Check

1. Find the area of each trapezoid.

a.

6 m
5 m   4.4 m   4.5 m
9.5 m
34.1 m^2

b.

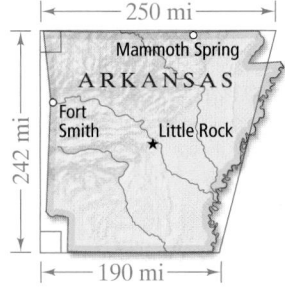
21 m
13.5 m   6 m   6.8 m
6 m
81 m^2

You can estimate the area of states shaped like trapezoids.

EXAMPLE Application: Geography

2 Estimate the area of Arkansas by finding the area of the trapezoid shown.

← 250 mi →
Mammoth Spring
ARKANSAS
Fort Smith   Little Rock ★
242 mi
← 190 mi →

$A = \frac{1}{2}h(b_1 + b_2)$ ← **Use the area formula for a trapezoid.**

$= \frac{1}{2}(242)(250 + 190)$ ← **Substitute for h, b_1, and b_2.**

$= \frac{1}{2}(242)(440)$ ← **Add.**

$= 53,240$ ← **Multiply.**

The area of Arkansas is about 53,240 mi^2.

At Crater of Diamonds State Park in Arkansas, visitors can search for and keep diamonds and other gems.

✓ Quick Check

2. Estimate the area of the figure at the right by finding the area of the trapezoid. **8.75 in.^{2}**

3 in.   2 in.
3.5 in.

Activity Lab

Use before the lesson.

All in One Teaching Resources

Activity Lab 8-4: Extend Your Thinking About Areas

Guided Instruction

Error Prevention!

In Quick Check 1b, students may think that the bases are always the top and bottom sides. Remind them that the bases need to be parallel. If students are used to considering the bases as the top and bottom, have them simply rotate their books.

PowerPoint

Additional Examples

1 Find the area of each trapezoid. **48 cm^2**

6 cm
6 cm   7.2 cm
10 cm

2 Estimate the area of the piece of metal by using the trapezoid shown. **126 cm^2**

10 cm
9 cm
8 cm

Advanced Learners L4

A trapezoid has an area of 96 m^2, a height of 12 m, and one base of 6 m. What is the measure of the other base? **10 m**

Pre-AP™

English Language Learners ELL

Ask students to read the formulas given for each of the shapes they have learned. Make sure they use words for A, $\frac{1}{2}$, b, h, l and w. Ask them to show you, on drawings, where each part is on particular figures.

learning style: verbal

Closure

- *What is a trapezoid?* a four-sided figure in which exactly two sides are parallel
- *How can you calculate the area of a trapezoid?*
  $A = \frac{1}{2}h(b_1 + b_2)$

You can find the area of any figure by separating it into familiar figures.

● More Than One Way

Anna and Ryan are helping their friends build a large wooden deck. What is the area of the deck?

Anna's Method

I'll subtract the area of the triangle from the area of the rectangle.

Area of the rectangle:

$A = bh$
$= (27)(12) = 324$

Area of the triangle:

$A = \frac{1}{2}bh$
$= \frac{1}{2}(12)(9) = 54$

Now I'll subtract the area of the triangle from the area of the rectangle.

$A = 324 - 54 = 270$

The area of the deck is 270 ft^2.

Ryan's Method

I'll add the areas of the rectangle and the trapezoid.

Area of the rectangle:

$A = bh$
$= (15)(12)$
$= 180$

Area of the trapezoid:

$A = \frac{1}{2}h(b_1 + b_2)$
$= \frac{1}{2}(12)(3 + 12)$
$= 90$

Now I'll add the two areas together.

$A = 180 + 90 = 270$

The area of the deck is 270 ft^2.

Choose a Method

Find the area of the figure. **30 m²**

1. **Vocabulary** The perpendicular distance between the two parallel sides of a trapezoid is called the __?__ of the trapezoid. **height**

Identify the bases b_1 and b_2 and height h of each trapezoid below.

2.

$b_1 = 6$ m, $b_2 = 9$ m, $h = 3.6$ m

3.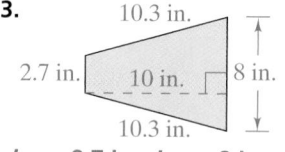

$b_1 = 2.7$ in., $b_2 = 8$ in., $h = 10$ in.

4.

$b_1 = 4$ ft, $b_2 = 7$ ft, $h = 4$ ft

Homework Exercises

For more exercises, see Extra Skills and Word Problems.

GO for Help

For Exercises	See Examples
5–7	1–2

A Find the area of each trapezoid.

5.

144 m²

6.

960 ft²

7. **Engineering** When the Erie Canal opened in 1825, it was hailed as an engineering marvel. Find the area of the trapezoidal cross section of the Erie Canal at the right. **136 ft²**

Not to scale

B GPS 8. **Guided Problem Solving** Estimate the area of Nevada by finding the area of the trapezoid shown at the right. **110,622 mi²**
   - Which measurements in the diagram will you use for the bases and the height?
   - How will you use the bases and height to calculate the area?

9. **Choose a Method** You plan to replace the carpeting in the room shown at the left. What is the area of the room? **198 ft²**

Use familiar figures to find the area of each irregular figure.

10.

847 m²

11.

500 km²

391

PowerPoint

Lesson Quiz

Find the area of each figure.

1. 148.5 cm²

6 cm

18 cm

9 cm

27 cm

2. 240 mm²

16 mm

8 mm

11 mm

12 mm

8 mm

16 mm

Alternative Assessment

Have students work in pairs. Each student draws and labels the bases and height of two trapezoids. Partners exchange drawings and find the areas to the nearest tenth. Then each student draws an irregular figure similar to those in Exercises 18 and 19. Again partners exchange drawings and find the areas.

Enrichment 8-4 **L4**

Reteaching 8-4 Areas of Other **L2**

392

GO Online

Homework Help

Visit: PHSchool.com
Web Code: are-0804

15. $5\frac{3}{4}$ ft²

16. 1 and 5; 2 and 4; 3 and 3
By solving
$3 = \frac{1}{2} \cdot 1(b_1 + b_2)$ for
$b_1 + b_2$, you find the
sum of the numbers
must be 6.

Find the area of each trapezoid, given the bases b_1 and b_2 and height h.

12. $b_1 = 3$ m
$b_2 = 7$ m
$h = 3$ m
15 m²

13. $b_1 = 11$ in.
$b_2 = 16$ in.
$h = 9$ in.
121.5 in.²

14. $b_1 = 5.6$ cm
$b_2 = 8.5$ cm
$h = 6$ cm
42.3 cm²

15. $b_1 = 3\frac{1}{2}$ ft
$b_2 = 2\frac{1}{4}$ ft
$h = 2$ ft
See left.

16. Writing in Math Find the whole-number possibilities for the lengths of the bases of a trapezoid with a height of 1 m and an area of 3 m². Explain how you found your answer. **See left.**

17. Music A hammered dulcimer is shaped like a trapezoid. The top edge is 17 in. long, and the bottom edge is 39 in. long. The distance from the top edge to the bottom edge is 16 in. What is the area of the dulcimer? **448 in.²**

Use familiar figures to find the area and perimeter of each figure.

18.

60 cm
43 cm
30 cm
30 cm
40 cm
43 cm
42 cm
42 cm
3,300 cm²; 260 cm

19.
2.8 m
6 m
8 m
2 m
4 m
8 m
10 m
2.8 m
6 m
14 m
104 m²; 45.6 m

C 20. Challenge A trapezoid has an area of 184 in.². The height is 8 in. and the length of one base is 16 in. Write and solve an equation to find the length of the other base. $184 = \frac{1}{2}(8)(16 + b_2)$; 30 in.

TEKS ★ TAKS Tune-Up and Mixed Review

TAKS Objective 4
TEKS (7.9)(A)

21. The Hernandez family is purchasing tile for the kitchen shown in the diagram. If tile is not needed for the island area, how many square feet of tile will be needed? **C**

4.5 ft
10 ft
Kitchen island
12 ft
6 ft
12 ft

Ⓐ 27 ft²   Ⓒ 105 ft²
Ⓑ 93 ft²   Ⓓ 120 ft²

TAKS Objective 3
TEKS (7.6)(A)

22. A carpenter finds that the measure of an angle formed between a vaulted ceiling and one wall is 67°. How many degrees is the supplement of this angle? **H**

Ⓕ 23°   Ⓖ 103°   Ⓗ 113°   Ⓙ 157°

GO for Help Lesson 6-7

Find each payment.

$52.70

23. $453 with a 6% sales tax **$480.18**   **24.** $49.95 with a 5.5% sales tax

TEKS ★ TAKS Resources

- TAKS Strategies, p. 427
- TAKS Tune-Up, pp. 431–433

TAKS Tune-Up Kit

- TAKS Daily Review Transparencies
- TAKS Review and Preparation Workbook
- TAKS Strategies with Transparencies
- Texas Progress Monitoring Assessments

Checkpoint Quiz 1

Each square below represents 20 km². Estimate the area of each shaded region.

1. 420 km²

2. 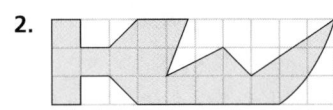 360 km²

Find the area of each figure. Where necessary, use familiar figures.

3. 17.5 m 9 m **54 m²** ⊢—12 m—⊣

4. 12 in. **240 in.²** 20 in.

5. 3 m 6 m 6 m **90 m²** ⊢——18 m——⊣

8-5a Activity Lab

Hands On

Modeling a Circle

When a regular polygon has many sides, it can be a model for a circle.

TEKS ★ TAKS

(7.4)(A) To generate formulas involving circumference
TAKS Obj. 2

ACTIVITY

1. Form a chain of drinking straws by stapling them end to end.

2. Make a regular polygon using a chain of about 15 straws. Use another chain of straws to measure the widest distance across the polygon.

3. Record the number of straws you used in the table at the right. Measure the length of each straw to the nearest centimeter, and calculate the distance around and across each polygon.

Number of Straws		Distance (cm)		Around ÷ Across (cm)
Around	Across	Around	Across	
■	■	■	■	■
■	■	■	■	■

4. Repeat steps 2 and 3 using 20 straws and 30 straws.
 5–6. See margin.

5. Calculate and record the ratio of "distance around ÷ distance across" for each polygon. What pattern do you notice?

6. Suppose a regular polygon of 100 sides has a distance across of 100 cm. What is the distance around the polygon? Explain.

393

---

5. The ratio of distance around ÷ distance across is about 3 for each polygon.

6. About 300 cm; the distance around a regular polygon is about 3 times the distance across.

Checkpoint Quiz

Use this Checkpoint Quiz to check students' understanding of the skills and concepts of Lessons 8-1 through 8-4.

Resources

- All-in-One Teaching Resources Checkpoint Quiz 1
- Texas ExamView CD-ROM
- Success Tracker™ Online Intervention

Activity Lab

Modeling a Circle

Use a model of a polygon with many sides to help to understand the dimensions of a circle and prepare to calculate the circumference and area of a circle in Lesson 8-5.

Guided Instruction

Ask questions such as:
- *Why is it difficult to measure a circle with a ruler?* **It does not have straight sides.**
- *Why is a model with many sides better than a model with fewer sides?* **It more closely approximates a circle.**

Activity
Have students in pairs take turns measuring and recording results, then together answer questions.

Differentiated Instruction

Below Level **L2**
Some students may have difficulty with the straw chain. Provide string for the chain of segments.

TEKS ★ TAKS Resources

- Activity Lab 8-5: Areas of Circles
- straws, stapler, string

Dana Center TEKS Toolkit Clarifying Activities (7.4)(A)
Visit: PHSchool.com
Web Code: arq-9045

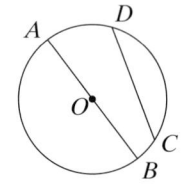
Circumference and Area of a Circle

(7.9)(A) To estimate measurements and solve application problems involving circumference and area of circles TAKS **Obj. 4**

(7.8)(C) To use geometric concepts in fields such as art and architecture TAKS **Obj. 3**

Dana Center TEKS Toolkit Clarifying Activities (7.9)(A), (7.8)(C)
Visit: PHSchool.com
Web Code: arq-9045

TEKS Math Background

Similar to perimeter the *circumference* is the distance around a circle. It is calculated by using the ratio $\pi = \frac{C}{d}$, (*C* is circumference, *d* is diameter, and π is pi). Pi is a constant for all circles and is approximated by $\frac{22}{7}$ or 3.14. So the circumference of a circle is $C = \pi d$. Because the radius of a circle is half its diameter, the circumference can also be expressed as $C = 2\pi r$. The *area* of a circle is $A = \pi r^2$ and is measured in square units.

More Math Background: p. 372C

Lesson Planning and Resources

See p. 372E for a list of the resources that support this lesson.

Bell Ringer Practice

✓ **Check Skills You'll Need**
Use student page, transparency, or PowerPoint.

TAKS **Daily Review 61**
Use transparency.

✓ Check Skills You'll Need

1. Vocabulary Review
What is the name of the segment that connects a circle to its center? radius

Name each segment for circle *O*.

2. radius $\overline{OA}$ or $\overline{OB}$

3. chord $\overline{DC}$ or $\overline{AB}$

4. diameter $\overline{AB}$

GO for Help
Lesson 7-6

- **(7.9)(A)** To estimate measurements and solve application problems involving circumference and area of circles TAKS **Obj. 4**
- **(7.8)(C)** To use geometric concepts in fields such as art and architecture TAKS **Obj. 3**

🔊 **New Vocabulary** circumference, pi

Why Learn This?

If you know how to find the circumference of a circle, you can find how far you must travel to move all the way around the circle.

In the picture below, a Sacagawea dollar rolls along a surface. The distance the dollar rolls is the same as the distance around the edge of the dollar. This distance is the coin's circumference. **Circumference** is the distance around a circle.

C

Pi is the ratio of a circle's circumference *C* to its diameter *d*. Use the symbol π for this ratio. So, $\pi = \frac{C}{d}$. The formula for the circumference comes from this ratio.

KEY CONCEPTS **Circumference of a Circle**

The circumference of a circle is π times the diameter *d*.

$$C = \pi d \text{ or } C = 2\pi r$$

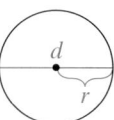

Pi is a nonterminating and nonrepeating decimal. Both $\frac{22}{7}$ and 3.14 are good approximations for π. Many calculators have a key for π and display it to nine decimal places. Your results will vary slightly, depending on which value for π you use.

Differentiated Instruction Solutions for All Learners

Special Needs L1
Ask students to identify which part of the circle has the greatest and least length: radius, diameter, or circumference. Ask them to prove their ideas using a picture of a circle and a piece of string.

learning style: tactile

Below Level L2
Review with students the meaning of *radius, diameter,* and *center of a circle.* Relate circumference of a circle to perimeter of a rectangle.

learning style: verbal

EXAMPLE Finding the Circumference of a Circle

1 **a.** Find the circumference of the the circle using 3.14 for π.

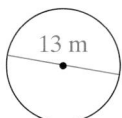
13 m

b. Find the circumference of the circle using a calculator's π key.

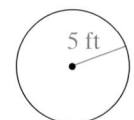
5 ft

$C = \pi d$ ← Use the formula for a circumference. → $C = 2\pi r$

$= 3.14(13)$ ← Substitute. → $= 2\pi(5)$

$= 40.82$ Use a calculator. → ≈ 31.41592654

The circumference is about 40.8 m.

The circumference is about 31.4 ft.

✓ Quick Check

1. Find the circumference of the circle at the right. Round to the nearest tenth. **28.3 m**

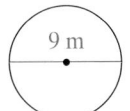
9 m

KEY CONCEPTS Area of a Circle

The area of a circle is the product of π and the square of the radius r.

$A = \pi r^2$

r

EXAMPLE Finding the Area of a Circle

2 A standard circus ring has a diameter of 13 m. What is the area of the ring? Round to the nearest tenth.

$r = \dfrac{13}{2} = 6.5$ ← The radius is half of the diameter.

$A = \pi r^2$ ← Use the formula for the area of a circle.

$= \pi(6.5)^2$ ← Substitute 6.5 for the radius.

$= 132.73328$ ← Use a calculator.

≈ 132.7 ← Round to the nearest tenth.

The area of a standard circus ring is about 132.7 m².

✓ Quick Check

2. Find the area of the circle. Round to the nearest square unit. **452 m²**

12 m

8-5 Circumference and Area of a Circle   **395**

2. Teach

Activity Lab

Use before the lesson.
Student Edition Activity Lab, Hands On 8-5a, Modeling a Circle, p. 393

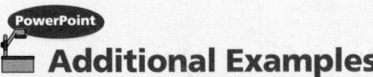 **Teaching Resources**
Activity Lab 8-5: Areas of Circles

Guided Instruction

Error Prevention!

Some students may multiply π times the radius and then square the entire product. Have students rewrite the equation as $A = \pi \times r \times r$ as a reminder that only r should be squared. Students can substitute the value for the radius into this equation.

PowerPoint
Additional Examples

1 Find the circumference.
   a. 9 yd   **b.** 40 cm

    56.5 yd   **125.7 cm**

2 Find the area of the circle to the nearest unit. **227 m²**

8.5 m

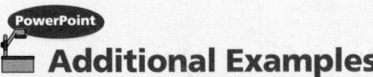 **Teaching Resources**
• Daily Notetaking Guide 8-5 **L3**
• Adapted Notetaking 8-5 **L1**

Closure

• *What is the formula for the circumference of a circle?* $C = 2\pi r$, where r is the radius of the circle and π is 3.14; or $C = \pi d$ where d is the diameter
• *How do you find the area of a circle given its radius?* Use the formula $A = \pi r^2$ (r is the radius).

Advanced Learners **L4**
Solve for the radius of a circle given the area. $r = \sqrt{\dfrac{A}{\pi}}$

Use your equation to find the diameter of a circle with an area of 128.5 m². **about 12.8 m**

Pre-AP™

English Language Learners **ELL**
Have students draw a circle. Ask them to draw an arrow around it, and label it *circumference*. Then have them shade the inside, and label that *area*. Make sure they identify the diameter and the radius. They can write the formulas for area and circumference next to the circle.   **learning style: visual**

Assignment Guide

Check Your Understanding
Go over Exercises 1–5 in class
before assigning the Homework
Exercises.

Homework Exercises

A Practice by Example 6–18
B Apply Your Skills 19–27
C Challenge 28
TEKS ★ (TAKS) Tune-Up and
Mixed Review 29–33

Homework Quick Check
To check students' understanding
of key skills and concepts, go over
Exercises 7, 13, 22, 25, and 27.

Differentiated Instruction **Resources**

Check Your Understanding

1. **Number Sense** Is it possible to write out the exact value of pi as a decimal? Explain. **No; π is nonrepeating and nonterminating.**

Identify the radius, the diameter, and the circumference.

2. 1, 2π, 2
   1; 2; 2π

3. 4π, 4, 2
   2; 4; 4π

4. 7, 3.5, 22
   3.5; 7; 22

5. $\frac{2}{\pi}$, $\frac{1}{\pi}$, 2
   $\frac{1}{\pi}$; $\frac{2}{\pi}$; 2

Homework Exercises

For more exercises, see Extra Skills and Word Problems.

GO for Help

For Exercises	See Examples
6–11	1
12–18	2

Find the circumference of each circle. Round to the nearest tenth.

Ⓐ 6. 157.1 cm   7. 53.4 mm   8. 84.8 m

9. 251.3 in.   10. 44.0 cm   11. 50.3 mi

Find the area of each circle. Round to the nearest square unit.

12. 113 in.²   13. 314 m²   14. 1,963 cm²

15. 707 ft²   16. 380 cm²   17. 177 km²

18. **Social Studies** The circular bases of the traditional tepees of the Sioux and Cheyenne tribes have a diameter of about 15 ft. What is the area of the base? Round to the nearest square unit. **177 ft²**

Ⓑ **GPS** 19. **Guided Problem Solving** A Ferris wheel has a diameter of 135 m. How far does a rider travel in one full revolution of the wheel? Round to the nearest unit. **424 m**
- What is the diameter of the circle?
- What is the formula for circumference, using diameter?

20. In a circle with radius 5 cm, how long can the longest chord be? **10 cm**

Use $\pi \approx \frac{22}{7}$ to estimate the circumference and area for each circle. Where necessary, round to the nearest tenth.

21. $r = 14$ m
88 m; 616 m²

22. $r = \frac{7}{10}$ cm
4.4 cm; 1.54 cm²

23. $d = 22$ in.
69.1 in.; 380.3 in.²

24. $d = 12$ ft
37.7 ft; 113.1 ft²

25. Bicycles The front wheel of a high-wheel bicycle from the late
GPS 1800s was larger than the rear wheel to increase the bicycle's overall speed. The front wheel measured in height up to 60 in. Find the circumference and area of the front wheel of a high-wheel bicycle.
about 188 in.; about 2,827 in.²

26. about 707 m²

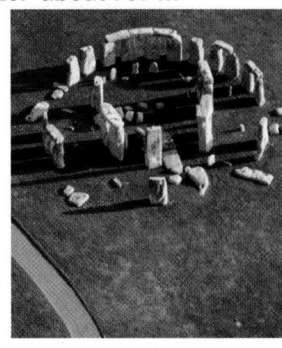

26. Archaeology The large stones of Stonehenge are arranged in a circle about 30 m in diameter. Find the area of the circle. **See left.**

27. Writing in Math Use the π key to calculate the area of the circle at the right to the nearest hundredth. Which is the better estimate, 98 m² or 99 m²? Explain. **99 m²; 98.52 rounds to 99.**

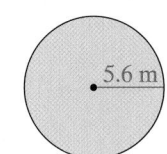
5.6 m

C 28. Challenge The diagram shows a fountain at the center of a circular park. The radius of the circle is 30 ft. The circular region is divided into six equal parts. What is the length of the arc in the shaded region? Round to the nearest tenth. **31.4 ft**

Fountain
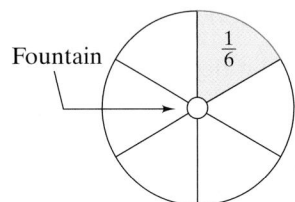
$\frac{1}{6}$

TEKS ★ TAKS Tune-Up and Mixed Review

TAKS Objective 4
TEKS (7.9)(A)

29. Use a centimeter ruler to measure the radius of the button. What is the area of the button to the nearest square centimeter? **B**

Ⓐ 3 cm² Ⓒ 7 cm²
Ⓑ 22 cm² Ⓓ 89 cm²

TAKS Objective 2
TEKS (7.4)(A)

30. A homebuilder wants to use the logo shown on a sign. Which of the following expressions can be used to find the perimeter of the logo? **G**

Ⓕ $2 + 4 + x + y$
Ⓖ $4 + 4 + x + 2y$
Ⓗ $4 + 4 + 2x + 2y$
Ⓙ $2 + 4 + 2x + 4y$

2 cm 4 cm

y
x

Lesson 7-5 $\triangle CAT \cong \triangle DOG$. **Complete each congruence statement.**

31. $\angle A \cong$ ▢ $\angle O$ **32.** $\angle G \cong$ ▢ $\angle T$ **33.** $\overline{CT} \cong$ ▢ $\overline{DG}$

Alternative Assessment

Have students work in pairs. Each student draws four circles, labeling either the radius or diameter in each circle. Partners exchange circles and find the circumference and the area of each circle. Partners must agree on the results.

TEKS ★ TAKS Resources

• TAKS Strategies, p. 427
• TAKS Tune-Up, pp. 431–433

TAKS Tune-Up Kit
• TAKS Daily Review Transparencies
• TAKS Review and Preparation Workbook
• TAKS Strategies with Transparencies
• Texas Progress Monitoring Assessments

4. Assess & Reteach

PowerPoint
Lesson Quiz

Use 3.14 for π. Find the area and the circumference of each circle to the nearest tenth.

1. $r = 10$ m $A = 314$ m²;
$C = 62.8$ m

2. $d = 14$ ft $A = 153.9$ ft²;
$C = 44.0$ ft

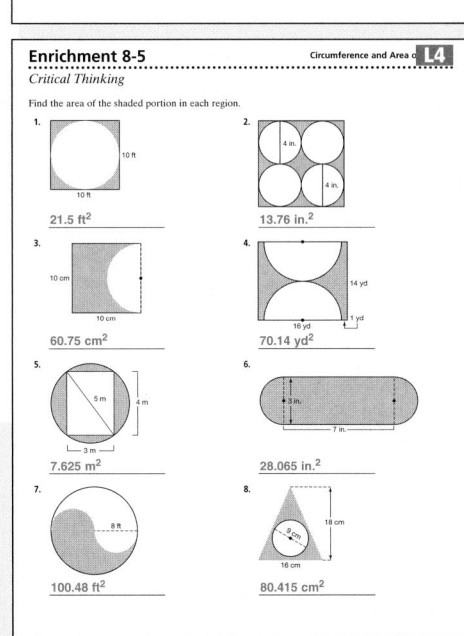

397

GPS **Guided Problem Solving**

Areas of Irregular Figures

In this feature, students work with problems involving area of irregular figures.

Guided Instruction

Discuss with students why it is helpful to know how to calculate the areas of irregular figures. Explain that most objects in everyday life are not in the shape of regular polygons.

Have a volunteer read the problem aloud.

Ask:

• *How can we make finding the area simpler?* Divide the shape into familiar geometric figures.

• *Are there other ways to divide the art into figures? What are they?* Yes. Answers will vary.

• *Why multiply by 1.10?* Erin wants to buy 10% more tiles than the area to be covered. 10% is 0.10 as a decimal. (1 + 0.10) times the total area will give the total amount of tiles to buy.

Areas of Irregular Figures

TEKS ★ TAKS

(7.9)(A) To solve problems involving area of polygons and other shapes TAKS Obj. 4

You can find the area of an irregular-shaped figure by combining basic shapes such as rectangles or triangles, or removing them from an existing figure.

Mosaic Erin is creating a mosaic and needs to buy tiles for her artwork. She wants to buy 10% more than the area to be covered. How many square inches of tile does she need to purchase?

What You Might Think

What do I know?
What am I trying to find out?

How do I solve the problem?

What do I need to calculate?

What is the answer?

What You Might Write

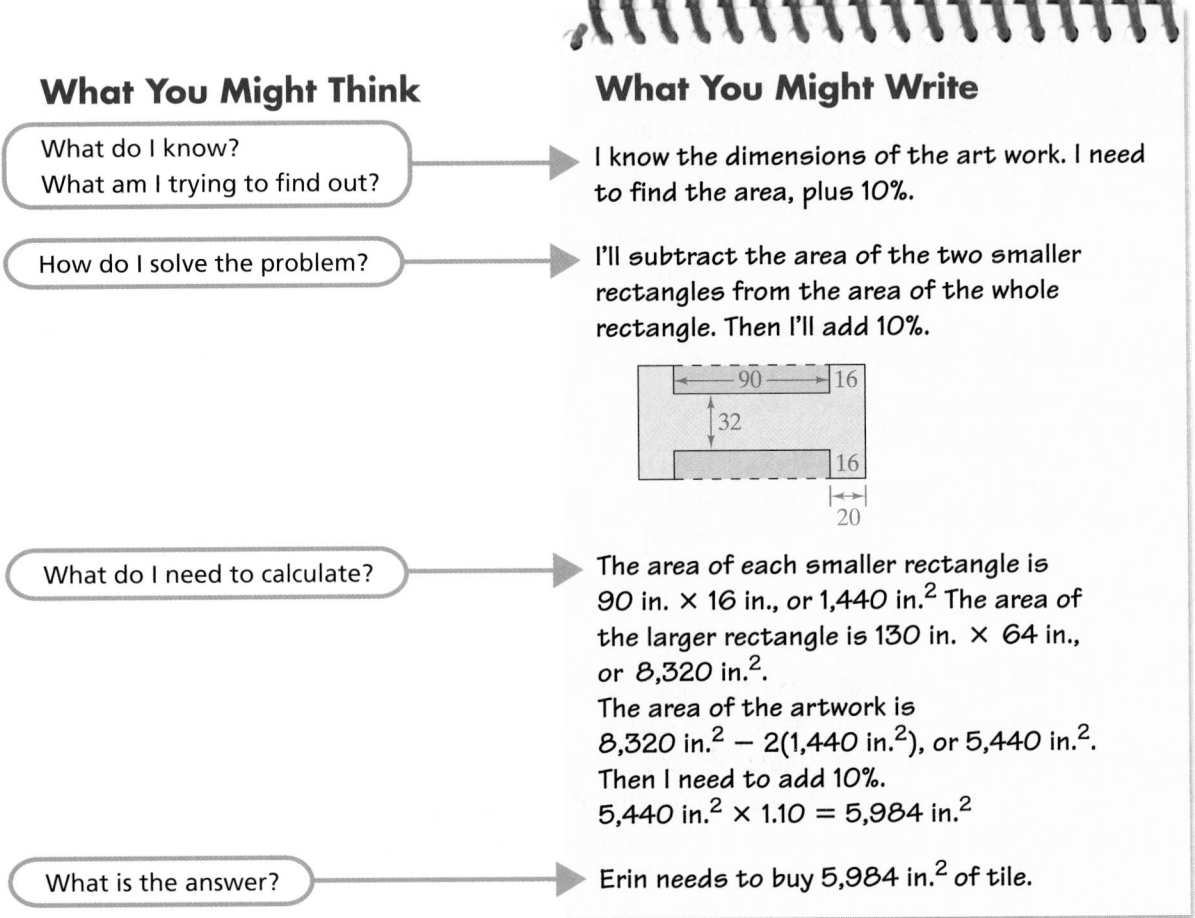

I know the dimensions of the art work. I need to find the area, plus 10%.

I'll subtract the area of the two smaller rectangles from the area of the whole rectangle. Then I'll add 10%.

The area of each smaller rectangle is 90 in. × 16 in., or 1,440 in.^{2} The area of the larger rectangle is 130 in. × 64 in., or 8,320 in.^{2}.
The area of the artwork is 8,320 in.^{2} − 2(1,440 in.^{2}), or 5,440 in.^{2}.
Then I need to add 10%.
5,440 in.^{2} × 1.10 = 5,984 in.^{2}

Erin needs to buy 5,984 in.^{2} of tile.

Think It Through

1. Why does multiplying by 1.1 add 10% to the area? 1.1 is the same as the sum of one whole and 0.1 (10%).

2. Is there a way to find the total area by adding instead of subtracting? Explain. Yes; make three rectangles and add the areas.

TEKS ★ TAKS Resources

Dana Center TEKS Toolkit Clarifying Activities (7.9)(A)
Visit: PHSchool.com
Web Code: arq-9045

Error Prevention!

Some students may multiply by the wrong decimal to find 110% of the area. Make sure students understand that they will find the total amount of tile by adding the amount of tile for the art and 10% more.

Exercises

Have students work independently on the Exercises. Students may compare papers when they have finished and discuss how they arrived at their answers.

Differentiated Instruction

Below Level　　　　　**L2**

Provide students with paper models of the shapes shown in the problems. Allow them to cut the models into pieces to help them understand how to divide shapes into geometric figures whose area they know how to find.

Exercises

Solve the problems. For Exercises 3 and 4, answer the questions first.

3. You plan to replace the carpeting in the room shown below. What is the area of the room?　**575 ft²**

a. What do you know? What do you need to find out?

b. Can you find the answer in two different ways? Explain.

4. Sam wants to paint the wall below. What is the area of the wall to the nearest tenth?　**63.4 ft²**

a. What shapes make up the door?

5. Data from the 2000 U.S. Census for four states are in the table below. Order the states from smallest population per square mile, to greatest. Explain what this means.　**Alaska, Texas, Florida, and New Jersey; New Jersey is the most densely populated.**

State	Population	Area (mi²)
Alaska	626,932	663,267
Florida	15,982,378	65,755
New Jersey	8,414,350	8,721
Texas	20,851,820	268,581

6. Wilma agreed to cut the grass on the infield of the school track for $0.35 /yd² on her riding lawnmower. How much would she make each time she cut the grass?　**about $40.65**

1. Plan

TEKS ★ **TAKS**

(7.1)(C) To represent squares and square roots using geometric models **TAKS** Obj. 1

Also supports
(7.13)(D) **TAKS** Obj. 6
(7.14)(A) **TAKS** Obj. 6

Dana Center TEKS Toolkit Clarifying Activities (7.1)(C), (7.13)(D), (7.14)(A)
Visit: PHSchool.com
Web Code: arq-9045

TEKS Math Background

The number 25 is called a *perfect square* because it is the square of 5, or 5×5. The inverse operation of squaring (multiplying a number by itself) is taking a *square root,* finding the number that is multiplied by itself to make the square. So, the square root of 25 is 5, or $\sqrt{25} = 5$. The symbol $\sqrt{}$ indicates a positive square root. Numbers that are not perfect squares, such as $\sqrt{21}$, are classified as *irrational numbers* because they cannot be stated in the form $\frac{a}{b}$ where a is an integer and b is any nonzero integer.

More Math Background: p. 372D

Lesson Planning and Resources

See p. 372E for a list of the resources that support this lesson.

PowerPoint

Bell Ringer Practice

✓ **Check Skills You'll Need**
Use student page, transparency, or PowerPoint.

TAKS **Daily Review 62**
Use transparency.

✓ **Check Skills You'll Need**

1. Vocabulary Review
How do you find the *square* of a number?
See below.
Simplify.

2. 8^2 64   **3.** 12^2 144

4. 2^2 4   **5.** 7^2 49

GO **for Help**
Lesson 2-1

Check Skills You'll Need

1. Multiply the number by itself.

TAKS **Tip**

You can use the 7-by-7 grid below to represent 7^2 or $\sqrt{49} = 7$.

TEKS ★ **TAKS**

- (7.1)(C) To represent squares and square roots using geometric models **TAKS** Obj. 1
- (7.13)(D) To select mental math and estimation to solve problems
- (7.14)(A) To communicate mathematical ideas using graphical and numerical models **TAKS** Obj. 6

🔊 **New Vocabulary** perfect square, square root, irrational number

Why Learn This?

If you know the area of a square, you can find its square root to find the side lengths. You can use square roots when you install flooring.

A number that is the square of an integer is a **perfect square**. For example, the square of 2 is 4, so 4 is a perfect square.

The inverse of squaring a number is finding a **square root**. The symbol $\sqrt{}$ in this book indicates the positive square root of a number.

EXAMPLE **Finding Square Roots of Perfect Squares**

1 **Mental Math** Simplify $\sqrt{49}$.

Since $7^2 = 49$, $\sqrt{49} = 7$.

✓ **Quick Check**

1. Simplify.

   a. $\sqrt{64}$ 8   **b.** $\sqrt{81}$ 9   **c.** $\sqrt{225}$ 15

If a number is not a perfect square, you can estimate its square root.

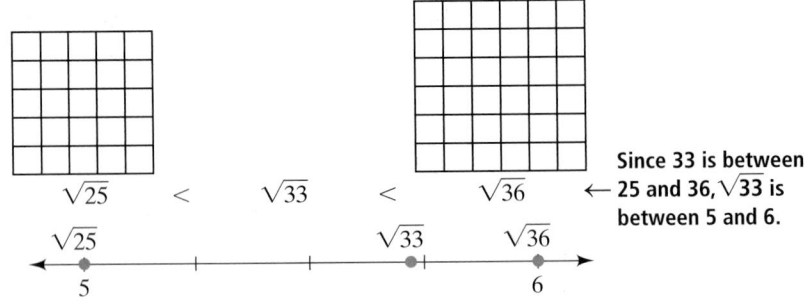

$\sqrt{25} < \sqrt{33} < \sqrt{36}$

Since 33 is between ← 25 and 36, $\sqrt{33}$ is between 5 and 6.

Differentiated Instruction **Solutions for All Learners**

Special Needs **L1**
Given 10, 36, 56, 64, and 100, have students use tiles, equations, or pictures to show whether each number is a perfect square. 36, 64, 100 For each perfect square, they should find the square root. 6, 8, 10

learning style: tactile

Below Level **L2**
Revisit pictures that represent numbers that are perfect squares. For example, provide a list that shows the numbers 1, 4, 9, 16, 25, through 100, along with the squares drawn (1x1, 2x2, and so on.) Ask students to identify the square root for each.

learning style: visual

EXAMPLE Estimating Square Roots

2 **Tiles** Juanita bought 40 tiles on sale. They measured 1 ft² each. What is the largest square bathroom floor she can tile?

$$A = s^2 \qquad \leftarrow \text{Use the formula for the area of a square.}$$
$$40 = s^2 \qquad \leftarrow \text{Substitute 40 for the area.}$$
$$\sqrt{40} = \sqrt{s^2} \qquad \leftarrow \text{Take the square root of each side.}$$
$$\sqrt{40} = s \qquad \leftarrow \text{Simplify.}$$
$$\sqrt{36} < \sqrt{40} < \sqrt{49} \qquad \leftarrow \text{Find the perfect squares close to 40.}$$
$$6 < \sqrt{40} < 7 \qquad \leftarrow \text{Simplify.}$$

$\sqrt{40}$ is between 6 and 7. Since 40 is closer to 36 than to 49, $\sqrt{40}$ is about 6. So the largest floor she can tile is about 6 ft × 6 ft.

✓ **Quick Check**

2. Suppose Juanita bought twice the number of tiles above. Estimate the dimensions of the largest square floor she can tile.
   about 9 ft × 9 ft

GO for Help

For help with terminating decimals and repeating decimals, go to Lesson 2-6, Examples 1 and 2.

An **irrational number** is a number that cannot be written as a ratio of two integers. As decimals, irrational numbers neither terminate nor repeat. The diagram below summarizes these relationships.

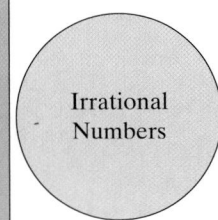

If a positive integer is not a perfect square, its square root is irrational.

Rational → $\sqrt{4}, \sqrt{9}, \sqrt{16}$
Irrational → $\sqrt{2}, \sqrt{3}, \sqrt{27}$

EXAMPLE Classifying Numbers

3 Identify each number as *rational* or *irrational*.

  a. $\sqrt{14}$ irrational   ← 14 is not a perfect square.

  b. 0.323223222 . . . irrational   ← The decimal neither terminates nor repeats.

  c. −0.98   rational   ← It is a terminating decimal.

✓ **Quick Check**

3. Identify each number as *rational* or *irrational*.
  a. $\sqrt{2}$ **b.** $\sqrt{81}$ **c.** $0.\overline{6}$ **d.** $1\frac{2}{7}$
  irrational   rational   rational   rational

8-6   Square Roots and Irrational Numbers   **401**

401

Assignment Guide

Check Your Understanding
Go over Exercises 1–5 in class before assigning the Homework Exercises.

Homework Exercises
A Practice by Example   6–29
B Apply Your Skills   30–45
C Challenge   46
TEKS ★ **(TAKS)** Tune-Up and
     Mixed Review   47–52

Homework Quick Check
To check students' understanding of key skills and concepts, go over Exercises 13, 19, 32, 33, and 35.

Differentiated Instruction Resources

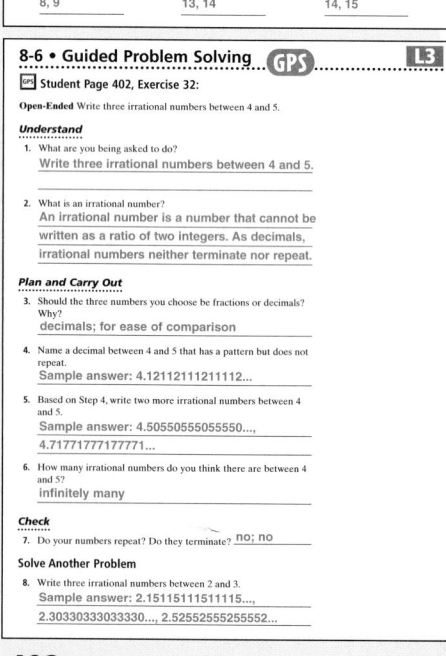

Check Your Understanding

1. **Vocabulary** The square root of the __?__ of a square is the same as the length of one side of the square. **area**

2. **Number Sense** If you double the length of each side of a square, what happens to the area of the square? **It quadruples.**

Determine whether or not each decimal has a repeating pattern.

3. $2.3423423423\ldots$ 4. $0.1234567891011\ldots$ 5. $0.17893624775\ldots$
    yes   no   no

Homework Exercises

For more exercises, see Extra Skills and Word Problems.

GO for Help

For Exercises	See Examples
6–15	1
16–21	2
22–29	3

(A) Simplify each square root.

6. $\sqrt{16}$ 4   7. $\sqrt{100}$ 10   8. $\sqrt{36}$ 6   9. $\sqrt{25}$ 5   10. $\sqrt{81}$ 9

11. $\sqrt{169}$ 13   12. $\sqrt{144}$ 12   13. $\sqrt{121}$ 11   14. $\sqrt{1}$ 1   15. $\sqrt{9}$ 3

Estimate the value of each square root.

16. $\sqrt{18}$ 17. $\sqrt{5}$ 18. $\sqrt{41}$ 19. $\sqrt{54}$ 20. $\sqrt{75}$
  about 4   about 2   about 6   about 7   about 9

21. **Industrial Arts** A square carpet covers an area of 64 ft². What is the length of each side of the carpet?   **8 ft**

Identify each number as *rational* or *irrational*.

22. $\sqrt{99}$ irrational   23. $\sqrt{41}$ irrational   24. $\sqrt{49}$ rational

25. -0.4744 rational   26. $-\frac{3}{2}$ rational   27. $-0.666666\ldots$
                                                      rational

28. $0.12122122212222\ldots$ 29. $0.\overline{35}$
   irrational   rational

(B) (GPS)

30. **Guided Problem Solving** A fence surrounds a square plot of land. The area of the land is 324 yd². Find the length of each side of the fence. **18 yd**

Use the strategy *Systematic Guess and Check*.
- $10 \times 10 = \blacksquare$ The initial guess is (correct, high, low).
- $20 \times 20 = \blacksquare$ This guess is (correct, high, low).
- $\blacksquare \times \blacksquare = 324$ This guess is correct.

31. The area of a square cover for a whirlpool bath is 144 ft². What is the length of each side of the cover? **12 ft**

32. **Open-Ended** Write three irrational numbers between 4 and 5.
   See left.

33. **Writing in Math** What are the square roots of $\frac{1}{4}$ and $\frac{4}{9}$? Write a method of finding the square root of a fraction. **See left.**

32. Answers may vary.
Sample: 4.112123 . . .;
4.535335 . . .;
4.91911 . . .

33. $\frac{1}{2}$; $\frac{2}{3}$; take the square root of both the numerator and denominator.

41–44. See back of book.

34. rational

35. rational

36. rational, whole, integer, natural

37. rational

38. rational

For each number, write all the sets to which it belongs. Choose from *irrational, rational, whole,* **or** *natural numbers,* **or** *integers.*

34. $\frac{3}{5}$ **35.** $0.\overline{23}$ **36.** $\sqrt{36}$ **37.** 4.5 **38.** $\frac{22}{7}$

34–38. See left.

Math in the Media Use the cartoon below for Exercises 39 and 40.

FOXTROT *by Bill Amend.*

39. Does the cartoon suggest that π is *rational* or *irrational*? irrational

40. What rational numbers can you use to approximate π?
Answers may vary. Sample: 3.14; $\frac{22}{7}$

Draw and label a square to model each area. 41–44. See margin.

41. 64 km^2 **42.** 81 m^2 **43.** 121 ft^2 **44.** 4 mi^2

45. Use a calculator to estimate $\sqrt{723}$ to the nearest tenth. about 26.9

Calculator Tip

Press 2nd x^2 7 2 3
) ENTER

C **46.** **Challenge** When an object falls, the distance that it falls is given by the formula $d = 16t^2$, where d is the distance in feet and t is the time in seconds. A stone falls from a bridge 1,600 ft above the water. How long does it take for the stone to reach the water? 10 s

TEKS **TAKS** **Tune-Up and Mixed Review**

TAKS Objective 1
TEKS (7.1)(C)

47. The model represents $\sqrt{36} = 6$. Which arrangement can be used to represent $\sqrt{225}$? C
- Ⓐ 2 rows of 15 small squares
- Ⓑ 2 rows of 25 small squares
- Ⓒ 15 rows of 15 small squares
- Ⓓ 25 rows of 25 small squares

TAKS Objective 2
TEKS (7.4)(A)

48. A standard basketball rim has a circumference of about 56.6 inches. Which expression can be used to find the diameter of the rim? H
- Ⓕ $\frac{56.6}{2\pi}$
- Ⓗ $\frac{56.6}{\pi}$
- Ⓖ $56.6 \times \pi$
- Ⓙ $56.6 \times 2\pi$

GO for Help   **Lesson 6-4**   **Find each answer.**

49. 5% of 40 2   **50.** 60% of 90 54   **51.** 75% of 15 11.25   **52.** 30% of 120 36

Alternative Assessment

Students work with a partner to find and list the perfect squares from 1 to 225 and their square roots. You may wish to have them use calculators. Students can then refer to their lists to complete Exercises 6–15 and 22–29.

TEKS ★ **TAKS** **Resources**

- TAKS Strategies, p. 427
- TAKS Tune-Up, pp. 431–433

TAKS **Tune-Up Kit**
- TAKS Daily Review Transparencies
- TAKS Review and Preparation Workbook
- TAKS Strategies with Transparencies
- Texas Progress Monitoring Assessments

---

4. Assess & Reteach

PowerPoint
Lesson Quiz

Estimate each square root.

1. $\sqrt{6}$ about 2

2. $\sqrt{22}$ about 5

Identify each number as rational or irrational.

3. 0.625 rational

4. $\sqrt{150}$ irrational

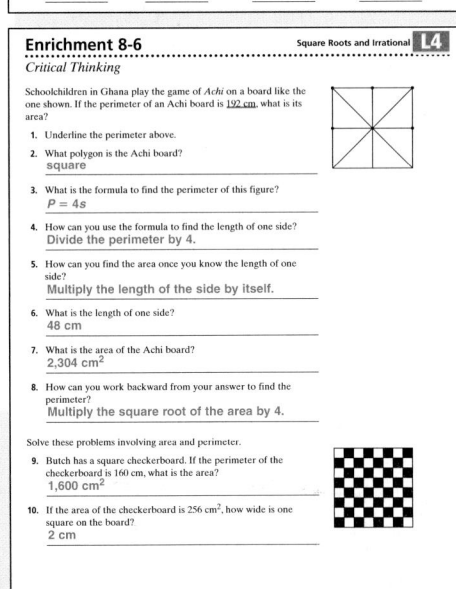

403

Exploring Right Triangles

In this Activity, students explore the relationship between the lengths of the sides of a right triangle by investigating the areas of squares formed from the legs and the hypotenuse of the triangle. Working through this Activity prepares students for exploring and using the Pythagorean Theorem in Lesson 8-7.

Guided Instruction

Before beginning the Activity, discuss the features of triangles with students. You may wish to review the meanings of *leg* and *hypotenuse* at this time.
Ask:
• *What characteristics do all triangles share?* three sides, three angles whose sum is 180°
• *How are right triangles different from other triangles?* A right triangle must contain one 90° angle.

Exercises
Have students work in pairs on the Exercises. Circulate to check students' work.

Alternative Method
You can have some students use a compass and straightedge to construct the squares from the sides of the triangle. Demonstrate or ask a volunteer to demonstrate this procedure.

Resources

• Activity Lab 8-7: Patterns in Geometry
• centimeter graph paper
• straightedge
• compass
• scissors
• Classroom Aid 2

8-7a Activity Lab

Hands On

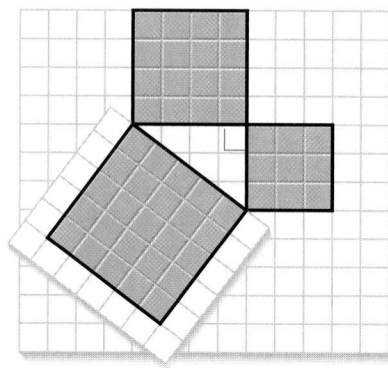

Exploring Right Triangles

Complete this activity to discover a special relationship among the side lengths of right triangles.

ACTIVITY

Step 1 Use centimeter graph paper to draw a right triangle with perpendicular sides that are 3 cm and 4 cm long.

Step 2 Draw squares that have the horizontal and vertical sides of the right triangle as sides.

Step 3 Use another piece of the graph paper to make a square on the side opposite the right angle, as shown at the right.

Exercises

1. What is the length of the side of the square opposite the right angle? **5 cm**

2. What is the area of each of the three squares? **9 cm²; 16 cm²; 25 cm²**

3. Draw a right triangle on graph paper with perpendicular sides that are 8 cm and 15 cm long. Repeat Steps 2 and 3.
   a. What is the length of each side of the square made on the side opposite the right angle? **17 cm**
   b. What is the area of each of the three squares? **64 cm²; 225 cm²; 289 cm²**

4. Construct three squares on the sides of the triangle at the right. What are the areas of the three squares? **36 cm²; 64 cm²; 100 cm²**

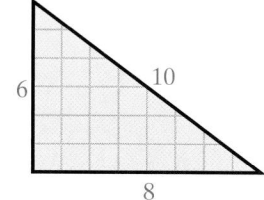

5. a. **Patterns** What seems to be the relationship of the areas of the smaller two squares and the third square made on the sides of a right triangle? **See margin.**
   b. Write an equation for each triangle that compares the areas of its squares. **$3^2 + 4^2 = 5^2$; $8^2 + 15^2 = 17^2$; $6^2 + 8^2 = 10^2$**

6. A rectangular park is shown at the right. The park is 630 yd long and 430 yd wide. How long is the path connecting opposite corners of the park? Round to the nearest tenth. **762.8 yd**

7. **Writing in Math** A triangle has side lengths 6 cm, 10 cm, and 12 cm. Explain why this triangle is not a right triangle. **See margin.**

404 Activity Lab Exploring Right Triangles

5a. The sum of the areas of the two smaller squares is equal to the area of the larger square.

7. It is not a right triangle, because the sum of the squares of the shorter sides does not equal the square of the longest side. 36 + 100 ≠ 144

The Pythagorean Theorem

1. Vocabulary Review
A *perfect square* is the square of what kind of number?
an integer

Simplify each square root.

2. $\sqrt{4}$ **2**   **3.** $\sqrt{16}$ **4**

4. $\sqrt{36}$ **6**   **5.** $\sqrt{49}$ **7**

 for Help
Lesson 8-6

What You'll Learn

To use the Pythagorean Theorem to solve problems

- Prepares for **TEKS (8.9)(A)** To use the Pythagorean Theorem to solve real-life problems

🔊 **New Vocabulary** legs, hypotenuse, Pythagorean Theorem

Why Learn This?

The lengths of the sides of a right triangle are related. When you understand the Pythagorean Theorem, you can use right triangles to find unknown distances.

In a right triangle, the two shortest sides are the **legs**. The side opposite the right angle is the **hypotenuse**.

The **Pythagorean Theorem** states that in any right triangle, the sum of the squares of the lengths of the legs equals the square of the length of the hypotenuse.

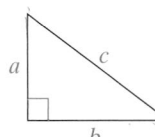

$$a^2 + b^2 = c^2$$

You can find the length of a hypotenuse with the Pythagorean Theorem.

Online active math

For: Triangle Activity
Use: Interactive Textbook, 8-7

EXAMPLE Finding the Length of a Hypotenuse

1 The catcher throws a ball from home plate to second base. How far does the catcher throw?

$c^2 = a^2 + b^2$ ← **Pythagorean Theorem**

$c^2 = 90^2 + 90^2$ ← **Substitute.**

$c^2 = 8{,}100 + 8{,}100$ ← **Simplify.**

$c^2 = 16{,}200$

$\sqrt{c^2} = \sqrt{16{,}200} \approx 127.3$ ← **Take the square root of each side.**

To reach second base from home plate, the catcher throws about 127 ft.

✓ Quick Check

1. Find the length of the hypotenuse in the triangle at the right. **17 in.**

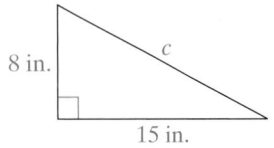

TEKS ⭐ **TAKS**

Prepares for **TEKS (8.9)(A)** To use the Pythegoream Theorem to solve real-life problems

Professional Development

TEKS Math Background

In a right triangle, the two short sides, or legs, form the 90° angle. The longest side, the hypotenuse, is opposite the 90° (and largest) angle. If you know the length of any two sides, you can calculate the "missing" side length by using the Pythagorean Theorem: $a^2 + b^2 = c^2$, where a and b are lengths of the legs and c is the length of the hypotenuse.

More Math Background: p. 372D

Lesson Planning and Resources

See p. 372E for a list of the resources that support this lesson.

PowerPoint
Bell Ringer Practice

✓ **Check Skills You'll Need**
Use student page, transparency, or PowerPoint.

TAKS Daily Review 63
Use transparency.

Differentiated Instruction Solutions for All Learners

Special Needs L1
Give students a picture of a right triangle with side lengths that make it easy to compute square roots. For example, a 3, 4, 5 unit triangle whose hypotenuse is 5 units can help them practice the calculation.

learning style: visual

Below Level L2
Review with students the characteristics of triangles. Elicit the description of a right triangle. Help students identify the legs and the hypotenuse.

learning style: visual

2. Teach

Activity Lab

Use before the lesson.
Student Edition Activity Lab, Hands On 8-7a, Exploring Right Triangles, p. 404

All in One Teaching Resources
Activity Lab 8-7: Patterns in Geometry

Guided Instruction

Example 1
Point out that you can substitute the lengths of the legs into the theorem in either order.

Error Prevention!

In Quick Check 3, students might substitute 60 for the hypotenuse. Point out that this is the height of the tower.

PowerPoint

Additional Examples

1 Find the length of the hypotenuse. **29 in.**

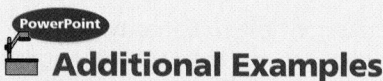
20 in. 21 in.

2 Find the missing leg of the triangle. **20 ft**

15 ft 25 ft

3 A ladder, placed 4 ft from a wall, touches the wall 11.3 ft above the ground. What is the approximate length of the ladder? **about 12 ft**

All in One Teaching Resources
• Daily Notetaking Guide 8-7 **L3**
• Adapted Notetaking 8-7 **L1**

Closure

• *How can you find the length of a leg of a right triangle if one leg and the hypotenuse are known?* Substitute the length of one leg and the hypotenuse in $a^2 + b^2 = c^2$; solve for the missing leg, either a or b.

406

You can use the Pythagorean Theorem to find the length of a leg of a right triangle.

EXAMPLE Finding the Length of a Leg

2 Find the length of the missing leg of the triangle.

$a^2 + b^2 = c^2$ ← Pythagorean Theorem
$a^2 + 8^2 = 10^2$ ← Substitute.
$a^2 + 64 = 100$ ← Simplify.
$a^2 + 64 - 64 = 100 - 64$ ← Subtract 64 from each side.
$a^2 = 36$ ← Simplify.
$\sqrt{a^2} = \sqrt{36}$ ← Take the square root of each side.
$a = 6$

8 m
a
10 m

The length of the leg is 6 m.

✓ Quick Check

2. Find the missing length in the triangle below. **24 mi**

7 mi
25 mi
b

EXAMPLE Application: Recreation

3 A water slide starts 6 m above the water and extends 11 m horizontally. What is the length of the slide to the nearest tenth of a meter?

A sketch shows that the length of the slide is the length of the hypotenuse.

$a^2 + b^2 = c^2$ ← Use the Pythagorean Theorem.
$6^2 + 11^2 = c^2$ ← Substitute.
$157 = c^2$ ← Simplify.
$\sqrt{157} = \sqrt{c^2}$ ← Take the square root of each side.
$c \approx 12.529964$

6 m c
11 m

The slide is about 12.5 m.

✓ Quick Check

3. A support wire is attached to the top of a 60-m tower. It meets the ground 25 m from the base of the tower. How long is the wire? **65 m**

Some water slides are straight, while others have curves.

Advanced Learners L4
A right triangle has an area of 241 cm². The length of one of its legs is 26 cm. What is the length of the hypotenuse? **about 32 cm**

English Language Learners ELL
For most of the practice problems and homework, where triangles are described, ask students to draw the triangles before computing. Then ask them to identify the hypotenuse, and label the lengths they know.

Pre-AP™

learning style: visual

✓ Check Your Understanding

1. hypotenuse

2. No; you are taking the square root of the squares of the numbers, so the length of *t* will increase by less than 2.

1. **Vocabulary** The side opposite the right angle in a triangle is called the __?__.

2. **Number Sense** If the longer leg of the triangle at the right is increased by 2, will the length of *t* increase by 2? Explain.

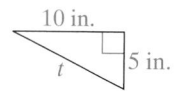

The lengths of two legs of a right triangle are given. Find the length of the hypotenuse to the nearest tenth.

3. 8 m and 11 m
   13.6 m

4. 4 in. and 3 in.
   5 in.

5. 12 ft and 20 ft
   23.3 ft

Homework Exercises

For more exercises, see Extra Skills and Word Problems.

GO for Help

For Exercises	See Examples
6–8	1
9–15	2–3

Ⓐ **Find the length of the hypotenuse of each triangle. Round to the nearest tenth of a unit, if necessary.**

6.
   13 m

7.
   17.5 m

8.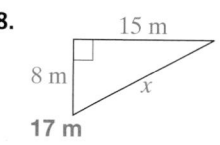
   17 m

Find each missing length. Round to the nearest tenth, if necessary.

9.
   12 ft

10.
    15 in.

11.
    9 m

12.
    51.9 cm

13.
    26.6 in.

14.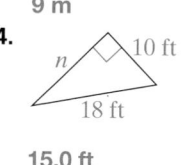
    15.0 ft

15. A tennis court is 78 ft long and 27 ft wide. To the nearest foot, what is the length of the diagonal of a tennis court? **83 ft**

Ⓑ 16. **Guided Problem Solving** A rectangular park is 600 m long and 300 m wide. You walk diagonally across the park from corner to corner. How far do you walk, to the nearest meter? **671 m**
   - You can use the strategy *Draw a Diagram*. Label the diagram. Then use the Pythagorean Theorem.

17. A ladder is 6 m long. How much farther up a wall does the ladder reach when the base of the ladder is 2 m from the wall than when it is 3 m from the wall? Round to the nearest tenth of a meter. **0.5 m**

Assignment Guide

Check Your Understanding
Go over Exercises 1–5 in class before assigning the Homework Exercises.

Homework Exercises
A Practice by Example 6–15
B Apply Your Skills 16–24
C Challenge 25
TEKS ★ (TAKS) Tune-Up and Mixed Review 26–29

Homework Quick Check
To check students' understanding of key skills and concepts, go over Exercises 6, 13, 22, 23, and 24.

Differentiated Instruction Resources

PowerPoint

Lesson Quiz

Find the length of the missing side of each right triangle to the nearest tenth.

1. legs of 4 cm and 6 cm **7.2 cm**

2. leg of 9 m, hypotenuse of 15 m
   12 m

3. leg of 36 ft, hypotenuse of 39 ft **15 ft**

4. legs of 28 cm and 45 cm **53 cm**

28. $n = 0.05 \cdot 225$; **11.25**

29. $n = 0.60 \cdot 40$; **24**

Reteaching 8-7   The Pythagorean **L2**

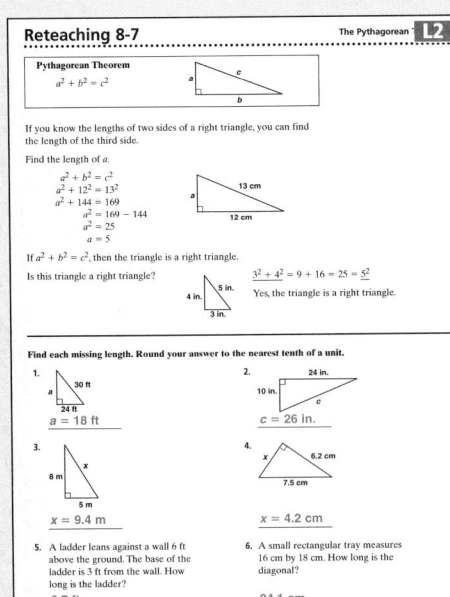

Pythagorean Theorem
$a^2 + b^2 = c^2$

If you know the lengths of two sides of a right triangle, you can find the length of the third side.

Find the length of a.
$a^2 + b^2 = c^2$
$a^2 + 12^2 = 13^2$
$a^2 + 144 = 169$
$a^2 = 169 - 144$
$a^2 = 25$
$a = 5$

If $a^2 + b^2 = c^2$, then the triangle is a right triangle.

Is this triangle a right triangle?
$3^2 + 4^2 = 9 + 16 = 25 = 5^2$
Yes, the triangle is a right triangle.

Find each missing length. Round your answer to the nearest tenth of a unit.

1. $a = 18$ ft
2. $c = 26$ in.
3. $x = 9.4$ m
4. $x = 4.2$ cm

5. A ladder leans against a wall 6 ft above the ground. The base of the ladder is 3 ft from the wall. How long is the ladder?
   6.7 ft
6. A small rectangular tray measures 16 cm by 18 cm. How long is the diagonal?
   24.1 cm

Enrichment 8-7   The Pythagorean **L4**

Patterns in Geometry

Some right triangles have special properties. Use the Pythagorean Theorem to find the missing leg in each triangle below. Use a calculator to check, and round all your answers to the nearest tenth.

1. $a = $ **5.0 cm**
2. $a = $ **12.0 cm**

3. What do you notice about the length of the hypotenuse in each of the 30°-60°-90° triangles above and the length of one of the sides?
   Sample answer: The side opposite the 30° angle is one half the length of the hypotenuse.

Use your observation to give the length to the nearest tenth of a unit of the missing sides below.

4. $a = $ **2.0 cm**
5. $a = $ **3.0 cm**

Find the missing leg in each triangle below.

6. $a = $ **4 cm**
7. $a = $ **7 cm**

8. What do you notice about the length of the hypotenuse in each 45°-45°-90° triangle and the length of one of the sides?
   Sample answer: The hypotenuse is the length of one side times $\sqrt{2}$.

408

GO **O**nline
Homework Help
Visit: PHSchool.com
Web Code: are-0807

24. Check to see if the sum of the squares of the two shortest sides equals the square of the longest side.
    $10^2 + 24^2 \stackrel{?}{=} 26^2$
    $100 + 576 \stackrel{?}{=} 676$
    $676 = 676$
    It is a right triangle.

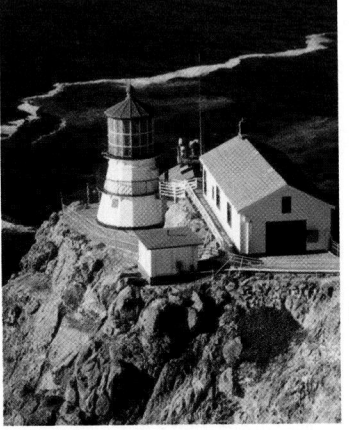

The lengths of two sides of a right triangle are given. Find the length of the third side to the nearest tenth.

18. legs 8 yd and 11 yd
    13.6 yd

19. leg 18 m and hypotenuse 28 m
    21.4 m

20. Find the perimeter and area of the triangle at the right. Round to the nearest tenth. **33.7 in.; 48.3 in.^{2}**

9 in.   14 in.

21. **Camping** A large tent has an adjustable
    GPS center pole. A rope 26 ft long connects the top of the pole to a peg 24 ft from the bottom of the pole. What is the height of the pole? Round to the nearest hundredth if necessary.
    10 ft

22. The rectangular section of fencing at the right is reinforced with wood nailed across the diagonal of the rectangle. What is the length of the diagonal? **10 ft**

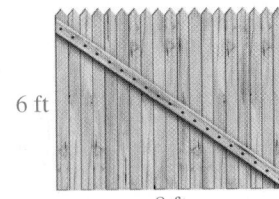
6 ft   8 ft

23. **Navigation** A dock is located 24 km directly east of a lighthouse. A sailboat is directly north of the lighthouse. The sailboat is 25 km from the dock. How far away from the lighthouse is the sailboat? **7 km**

24. **Writing in Math** A triangle has side lengths measuring 10 m, 24 m, and 26 m. Explain how you use the Pythagorean Theorem to determine whether or not the triangle is a right triangle. **See left.**

25. **Challenge** Find x.
    C   **3**

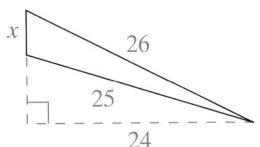
x 26   25   24

TEKS ★ TAKS Tune-Up and Mixed Review

TAKS Objective 6
TEKS (7.14)(A)

26. The hypotenuse of a right triangle is 12 cm long. Another side of the triangle is 8 cm long. Which equation can be used to find n, the length of the third side of the triangle? **D**
    Ⓐ $n = 12^2 + 8^2$ Ⓒ $n = 12^2 - 8^2$
    Ⓑ $n = \sqrt{12^2 + 8^2}$ Ⓓ $n = \sqrt{12^2 - 8^2}$

TAKS Objective 2
TEKS (7.3)(B)

27. Computers are used to design and improve spacesuits. An astronaut's arm is 32 inches long. What is the arm length in the computer image, if the computer image is $\frac{1}{8}$ of the actual length? **G**
    Ⓕ $\frac{1}{8}$ in.   Ⓖ 4 in.   Ⓗ 32 in.   Ⓙ 256 in.

GO **for Help**   Lesson 6-5   **Algebra** **Write and solve an equation to find the part of a whole.**
28–29. See margin.

28. What number is 5% of 225?   29. What number is 60% of 40?

TEKS ★ TAKS Resources

- TAKS Strategies, p. 427
- TAKS Tune-Up, pp. 431–433

TAKS Tune-Up Kit
- TAKS Daily Review Transparencies
- TAKS Review and Preparation Workbook
- TAKS Strategies with Transparencies
- Texas Progress Monitoring Assessments

Alternative Assessment

Have each student in a pair draw a triangle and label two sides. Partners exchange triangles and solve for the missing side length. Partners check each other's results and repeat the activity as time permits.

Three Views of an Object

Three-dimensional objects can be drawn to show length, width, and height. You can make drawings that show the *top view*, *front view*, and the *right side view*.

TEKS ★ **TAKS**

(7.8)(A) To sketch three-dimensional figures when given the top, side, and front views **TAKS** Obj. 3

(7.13)(D) To select tools such as manipulatives to solve problems

EXAMPLE **Drawing Three Views**

Draw the top, front, and right side views of the figure at the right.

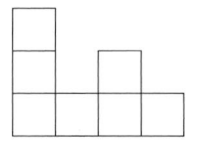 ← Draw the top view as if you are looking down on the blocks.

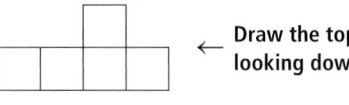 ← Draw the front view as if you are in front of the blocks.

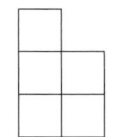 ← Draw the right side view as if you are on the right side of the blocks.

Exercises

Draw the top, front, and right side views of each figure. 1–5. See margin.

1.

2.

3.
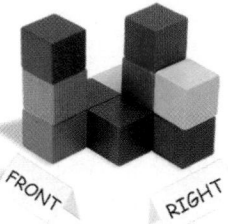

Use the given views to make a three-dimensional figure with blocks.

4.

Top   Front   Right

5.

Top

Front

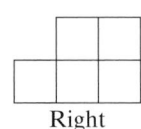
Right

Activity Lab Three Views of an Object **409**

1–5. See back of book.

Activity Lab

Three Views of an Object

The ability to visualize and analyze different views of three-dimensional objects is a valuable life skill. Architects and construction workers are among those who regularly make use of it in a work setting. This Activity Lab prepares students for Lesson 8-8 and addresses the skill of viewing objects from the top, front, and sides.

Guided Instruction

Before beginning the Activity, ask students to describe classroom objects that look different when viewed from different positions. Encourage students to draw one of these objects from different views.
Ask questions such as:
• *Why does each view look different?* because you can see different parts of the object from each view.
• *How can each view help you construct a model of the object?* Each view shows what one side of the model should look like.

Exercises

Have students work in pairs and compare their drawings for each exercise.

Alternative Method

Invite students to use cubes to construct the figures in the Exercises before they make their drawings. Encourage them to build different figures for others to draw from the top, sides, and front.

TEKS ★ TAKS Resources

• Activity Lab 8-8: Three Dimensional Figures
• cubes
• graph paper
• Classroom Aid 2

Dana Center TEKS Toolkit Clarifying Activities (7.8)(A), (7.13)(D)
Visit: PHSchool.com
Web Code: arq-9045

8-8

TEKS ★ TAKS

(7.6)(C) To classify solids, such as pyramids, cones, prisms, and cylinders **TAKS** Obj. 3

(7.8)(C) To use geometric concepts in art and architecture **TAKS** Obj. 3

Dana Center TEKS Toolkit Clarifying Activities (7.6)(C), (7.8)(C)
Visit: PHSchool.com
Web Code: arq-9045

TEKS Math Background

Because a parallelogram has only height and width, it is called *two-dimensional.* Figures with three dimensions do not lie in a plane. A flat surface on a three-dimensional figure is called a *face.* Prisms, cubes, and pyramids are composed of only flat faces. Cones, cylinders, and spheres are all three-dimensional objects that include curved surfaces.

More Math Background: p. 372D

Lesson Planning and Resources

See p. 372E for a list of the resources that support this lesson.

PowerPoint

Bell Ringer Practice

☑ **Check Skills You'll Need**
Use student page, transparency, or PowerPoint.

TAKS **Daily Review 64**
Use transparency.

☑ Check Skills You'll Need

1. Vocabulary Review
A _?_ is a polygon with all sides and angles congruent.
regular polygon

Use dot paper to draw each figure. 2–4. See back of book.
2. rhombus

3. trapezoid

4. rectangle

GO for Help
Lesson 7-4

TEKS ★ TAKS

- (7.6)(C) To classify solids, such as pyramids, cones, prisms, and cylinders **TAKS** Obj. 3
- (7.8)(C) To use geometric concepts in art and architecture **TAKS** Obj. 3

🔊 **New Vocabulary** three-dimensional figure, face, edge, bases, prism, height, cube, cylinder, pyramid, vertex, cone, sphere, center

Why Learn This?

You already know about some three-dimensional figures. You see them in many ordinary objects around you. If you know how to classify three-dimensional figures, you can describe the shapes of the objects you see.

A **three-dimensional figure,** or solid, is a figure that does not lie in a plane. A flat surface of a solid shaped like a polygon is called a **face.** Each segment formed by the intersection of two faces is an **edge.**

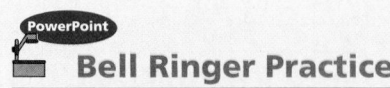

A glass prism can refract, or bend, light.

A **prism** is a three-dimensional figure with two parallel and congruent polygonal faces, called **bases.** The other faces are rectangles. The **height** of a prism is the length of a perpendicular segment that joins the bases. A prism is named for the shape of its bases.

A **cube** is a rectangular prism with faces that are all squares.

A **cylinder** has two congruent parallel **bases** that are circles. The **height** of a cylinder is the length of a perpendicular segment that joins the bases.

A **pyramid** has triangular faces that meet at one point, a **vertex,** and a **base** that is a polygon. A pyramid is named for the shape of its base.

Differentiated Instruction Solutions for All Learners

Special Needs L1
Drawing the figures may be too difficult for some students. If so, provide them nets so that they can form the solids. If that is also difficult, pair them up with students who can do the drawing. They can then check the drawing against the definition.

learning style: tactile

Below Level L2
Students can work in groups to create charts. Charts should have 4 columns: *two-dimensional figures, prisms, pyramids, other three-dimensional objects.* Have them draw at least three figures in each column.

learning style: visual

A **cone** has one circular **base** and one **vertex**.

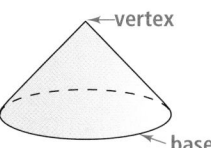

vertex

base

A **sphere** is the set of all points in space that are the same distance from a **center** point.

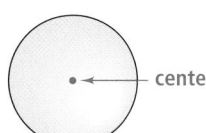

center

EXAMPLE **Naming Figures**

① **Architecture** Look at the architectural blocks. Name Figure 3.

Figure 3 has two parallel, congruent bases that are circles.

Figure 3 is a cylinder.

✓ Quick Check

● **1.** Name Figures 1 and 2. triangular prism; cone

You can use graph paper to draw three-dimensional figures.

EXAMPLE **Drawing Three-Dimensional Figures**

② Draw a hexagonal prism.

Vocabulary Tip

Notice the word hexagon inside *hexagonal.* A hexagon has six sides, so a *hexagonal* prism is a prism with a six-sided base.

2.

Step 1 Draw a hexagon.

Step 2 Draw a second hexagon congruent to the first.

Step 3 Connect the vertices. Use dashed lines for hidden edges.

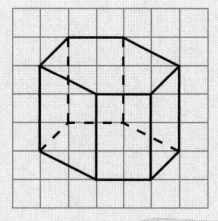

✓ Quick Check

● **2.** Use graph paper to draw a triangular prism. See left.

8-8 Three-Dimensional Figures **411**

---

2. Teach

Activity Lab

Use before the lesson.
Student Edition Activity Lab, Hands On 8-8a, Three Views of an Object, p. 409

 Teaching Resources

Activity Lab 8-8: Three Dimensional Figures

Guided Instruction

Error Prevention!

Students may confuse *prism* and *pyramid.* Have students ask themselves: *Can the figure stand on both of its bases?* If the answer is yes, it's a prism.

PowerPoint
Additional Examples

① Name the geometric figure.
sphere

② Draw a pentagonal prism.

Teaching Resources

- Daily Notetaking Guide 8-8 **L3**
- Adapted Notetaking 8-8 **L1**

Closure

- *What three-dimensional figures are named for their bases?* prisms and pyramids
- *What three-dimensional figures have only flat faces?* cube, prism, pyramid
- *What three-dimensional figures have curved surfaces?* sphere, cone, cylinder

---

Advanced Learners **L4**
True or false? Explain. *Every rectangular prism is a cube.* False; a cube must have four equal sides. *Some pyramids are prisms.* False; pyramids have only one base and prisms have two.

Pre-AP™

English Language Learners **ELL**
Divide the students into three groups and distribute index cards. One group copies the definitions of prisms. One group draws the shapes. The third group writes the names of the shapes. Ask students to correctly find the name, picture, and definition of each shape.

learning style: visual

411

Assignment Guide

Check Your Understanding
Go over Exercises 1–5 in class before assigning the Homework Exercises.

Homework Exercises
A Practice by Example 6–14
B Apply Your Skills 15–24
C Challenge 25
TEKS ★ (TAKS) Tune-Up and Mixed Review 26–29

Homework Quick Check
To check students' understanding of key skills and concepts, go over Exercises 8, 14, 16, 23, and 24.

Differentiated Instruction Resources

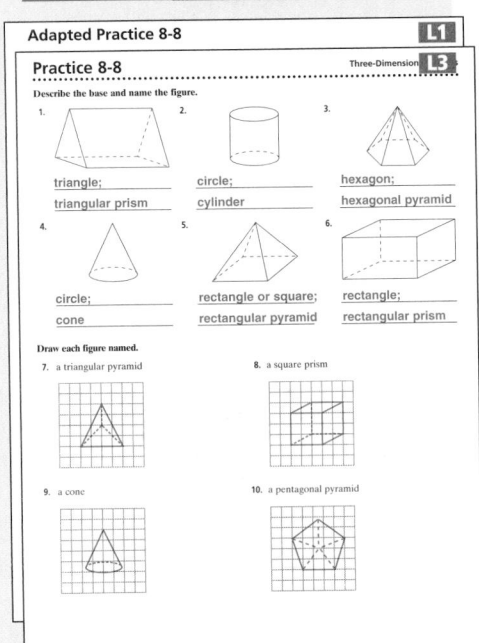

Adapted Practice 8-8 · L1
Practice 8-8 · L3 · Three-Dimension

Describe the base and name the figure.
1. triangle; triangular prism
2. circle; cylinder
3. hexagon; hexagonal pyramid
4. circle; cone
5. rectangle or square; rectangular pyramid
6. rectangle; rectangular prism

Draw each figure named.
7. a triangular pyramid
8. a square prism
9. a cone
10. a pentagonal pyramid

8-8 • Guided Problem Solving · GPS · L3
Student Page 413, Exercise 23:
What are the areas of all the faces of the figure at the right? 3.5 m, 4 m, 2 m, 6 m

Understand
1. What are you being asked to do?
   Find the area of the faces of the figure.
2. How many rectangular faces are there? 3
3. How many triangular faces are there? 2

Plan and Carry Out
4. What is the formula for the area of a rectangle? $A = bh$
5. What is the formula for the area of a triangle? $A = \frac{1}{2}bh$
6. What are the dimensions of the triangular faces? $b = 2$ m; $h = 3.5$ m
7. What is the area of one triangular face? 3.5 m²
8. What is the area of all the triangular faces? 7 m²
9. What are the dimensions of each rectangular face? 2 m × 6 m; 6 m × 4 m; 6 m × 3.5 m
10. What is the area of each rectangular face? 12 m²; 24 m²; 21 m²
11. Find the total area of the base and faces of each figure. 7 m² + 12 m² + 24 m² + 21 m² = 64 m²

Check
12. Did you find the area of each face? How many faces are there? yes; 5

Solve Another Problem
13. A rectangular solid has a base 11 in., height 15 in., and a length of 6 in. Find the total area of all faces.
$A = 2(11 \times 15) + 2(11 \times 6) + 2(15 \times 6)$
$= 642$ in.²

Check Your Understanding

1. **Vocabulary** A ___?___ has two congruent parallel bases that are circles. cylinder

2. Which three-dimensional figure does NOT have a base? D
   Ⓐ cone   Ⓑ prism   Ⓒ pyramid   Ⓓ sphere

Describe each base and name each prism.

3.
rectangle; rectangular prism

4.
triangle; triangular prism

5.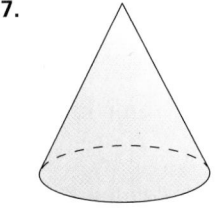
pentagon; pentagonal prism

Homework Exercises

For more exercises, see Extra Skills and Word Problems.

GO for Help

For Exercises	See Examples
6–11	1
12–14	2

Ⓐ **Name each figure.** 6–11. See left.

6. cylinder
7. cone
8. sphere
9. hexagonal pyramid
10. cone
11. rectangular pyramid

6.

7.

8.

9.

10.

11.

Use graph paper to draw each figure. 12–14. See margin.

12. cylinder   13. pentagonal prism   14. square pyramid

Ⓑ **GPS** 15. **Guided Problem Solving** Refer to the three-dimensional figure shown at the right. Which two solids make up the figure? See left.
   • What polygon is the base of the lower portion?
   • What polygon is the base of the upper portion?

15. rectangular prism; triangular prism

16. A solid has a rectangle for its base and four faces that are triangles. What is the solid? rectangular pyramid

12–14. See back of book.

Name the three-dimensional figure in each photograph.

17.

rectangular prism

18.

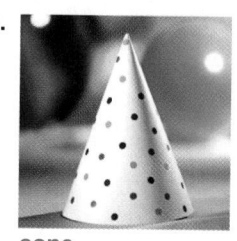

sphere

19.

cone

Use the pentagonal pyramid at the right.

20. Name four edges that intersect $\overline{AB}$. $\overline{MA}$, $\overline{BP}$, $\overline{KA}$, $\overline{KB}$

21. Name any edges that are parallel to $\overline{AB}$. none

22. Name the five edges that are *not* parallel to $\overline{AB}$ and do *not* intersect $\overline{AB}$.
$\overline{MD}$, $\overline{DP}$, $\overline{KP}$, $\overline{KM}$, $\overline{KD}$

24. Yes; the edges are all part of square faces of the same size.

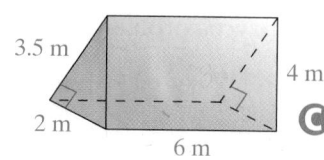

3.5 m
4 m
2 m
6 m

23. What are the areas of all the faces of the figure at the left? 64 m²

GPS **Writing in Math** 24. Are the edges of a cube congruent? Explain. See left.

C 25. **Challenge** Identify the number of faces, edges, and vertices a hexagonal pyramid has. 7 faces; 12 edges; 7 vertices

TEKS ★ TAKS Tune-Up and Mixed Review

TAKS Objective 1
TEKS (7.1)(C)

26. Which model represents 5^2? C

 A B C D

TAKS Objective 6
TEKS (7.15)(B)

27. What is the measure of each angle of an equilateral triangle? H

F 180°, 90°, and 90°, because the sum of the angles in a triangle is 360° and two angles are congruent

G 45°, 45°, and 90°, because the sum of the angles in a triangle is 180° and two angles are congruent

H 60°, 60°, and 60°, because the sum of the angles in a triangle is 180° and all three angles are congruent

J 45°, 45°, and 45°, because the sum of the angles in a triangle is 135° and all three angles are congruent

TAKS Objective 3
TEKS (7.6)(C)

28. Which of the following has two bases that are regular polygons? D
A Pyramid   B Cylinder   C Cone   D Prism

GO for Help Lesson 8-7

29. The hypotenuse of a right triangle is 61 m long. One leg is 60 m long. What is the length of the third side? 11 m

TEKS ★ TAKS Resources

- TAKS Strategies, p. 427
- TAKS Tune-Up, pp. 431–433

TAKS Tune-Up Kit

- TAKS Daily Review Transparencies
- TAKS Review and Preparation Workbook
- TAKS Strategies with Transparencies
- Texas Progress Monitoring Assessments

4. Assess & Reteach

Lesson Quiz

Name each figure.

1. cylinder

2. hexagonal prism

3. Draw a square pyramid.
Sample:

Alternative Assessment

Each student in a pair names one of the three-dimensional figures in this lesson. The partner draws the figure on graph paper or makes a model.

413

TEKS ★ (TAKS)

(7.8)(B) To make a net of the surface area of a three-dimentional figure
(TAKS) Obj. 3

Prepares for TEKS (8.8)(C) To solve application problems involving surface area

Dana Center TEKS Toolkit Clarifying Activities (7.8)(B)
Visit: PHSchool.com
Web Code: arq-9045

TEKS Math Background

A *net* is a two-dimensional pattern that you can fold to form a three-dimensional figure. Nets illustrate the *surface area* of three-dimensional figures. Surface area is the two-dimensional "surface" of a three-dimensional figure. Surface area is measured in square units like the area of any two-dimensional figure. The surface area of three-dimensional figures can be found by finding the area of each face and finding the sum of all these areas. So the surface area of a figure's net is also the surface area of the figure.

More Math Background: p. 372D

Lesson Planning and Resources

See p. 372E for a list of the resources that support this lesson.

Bell Ringer Practice

☑ **Check Skills You'll Need**
Use student page, transparency, or PowerPoint.

(TAKS) **Daily Review 65**
Use transparency.

414

8-9 · Surface Areas of Prisms and Cylinders

☑ Check Skills You'll Need

1. **Vocabulary Review**
   What is the *height of a triangle*?
   See below.
   Find the area of each triangle.

2.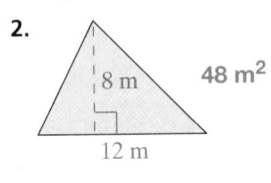
   8 m   48 m²
   12 m

3.
   6.7 ft
   3 ft   3.6 ft
   2 ft   4 ft
   6 ft²

GO for Help
Lesson 8-3

Check Skills You'll Need

1. The height of a triangle is the length of the perpendicular segment from a vertex to the base opposite the vertex or to an extension of the base.

TEKS ★ (TAKS)

• (7.8)(B) To make a net of the surface area of a three-dimensional figure
(TAKS) Obj. 3

Prepares for TEKS (8.8)(C) To solve application problems involving surface area

🔊 **New Vocabulary** net, surface area

Why Learn This?

When you wrap a birthday gift or cover a textbook, you are working with surface area. Surface area tells you how much material you need to cover something. You can use a net to solve surface area problems.

A **net** is a two-dimensional pattern that you can fold to form a three-dimensional figure. You can use nets to design boxes.

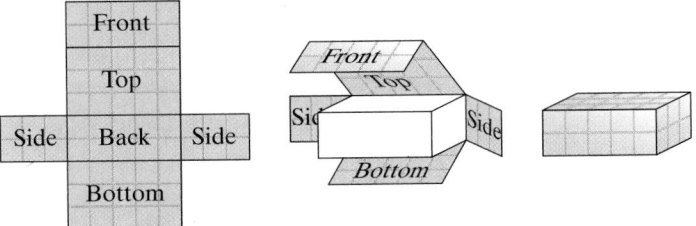

You can draw many different nets for a three-dimensional figure.

EXAMPLE   Drawing a Net

1 Draw a net for the triangular prism at the right.

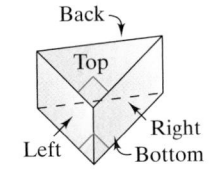

← Begin by labeling the bases and faces.

First draw one base. Then draw one face that connects both bases. Next, draw the → other base. Draw the remaining faces.

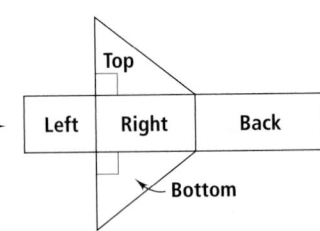

☑ Quick Check
See back of book.

1. Draw a different net for the right triangular prism in Example 1.

Differentiated Instruction   Solutions for All Learners

Special Needs [L1]
Have students label the shape of each face of the different solids. Then ask them to write the formula for the area of each face.

learning style: visual

Below Level [L2]
Display a box and several possible nets for the box. Ask students which net matches the box. Students can trace each possible net, fold along the lines, and see if the net will fit on the box. Continue with other shapes.

learning style: visual

The **surface area** of a prism is the sum of the areas of its faces. You measure surface area of a prism in square units. You can find the surface area by finding the area of its net.

EXAMPLE Finding the Surface Area of a Prism

GO for Help

For help with finding the area of a triangle, go to Lesson 8-3, Example 2.

2 Find the surface area of the triangular prism.

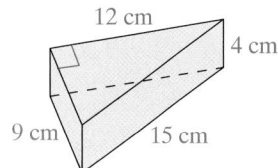

First draw a net for the prism.

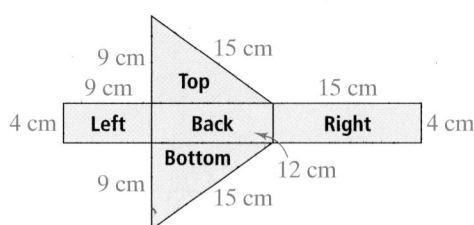

Then find the total area of the five faces.

left side	back	right side	top	bottom
$4(9)$	$+ \quad 4(12)$	$+ \quad 4(15)$	$+ \quad \frac{1}{2}(12)(9)$	$+ \quad \frac{1}{2}(12)(9) = 252$

The surface area of the triangular prism is 252 cm².

Quick Check

2. Find the surface area of the rectangular prism. **328 ft²**

If you cut a label from a can, you will see that the label is a rectangle. The height of the rectangle is about the height of the can. The base length of the rectangle is the circumference of the can.

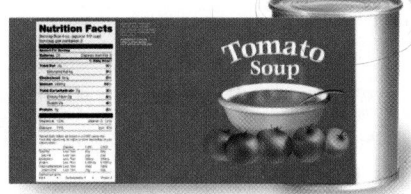

Similarly, if you cut up a cylinder, you get a rectangle and two circles.

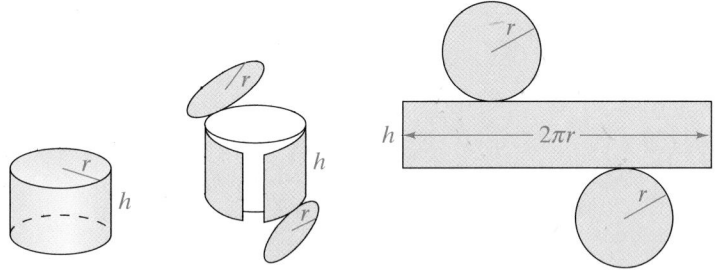

You can use a net of a cylinder to find its surface area.

---

2. Teach

Activity Lab
Use before the lesson.

All in One Teaching Resources
Activity Lab 8-9: Surface Area

Guided Instruction

Example 1
Some students have difficulty visualizing a three-dimensional figure given a net. Use common objects, such as a tissue box, that can be unfolded to make nets.

Error Prevention!

Review the formulas for finding the area of a rectangle ($A = \ell w$ or $A = bh$) and the area of a triangle ($A = \frac{1}{2}bh$).

PowerPoint
Additional Examples

1 Draw a net for the square prism.

2 Find the surface area of the prism. **840 cm²**

3 Find the surface area of the cylinder. Round to the nearest tenth. **94.2 cm²**

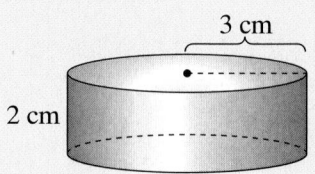

Advanced Learners L4
Explain why the shape of a net for a cylinder can or cannot vary. **Sample: The circles and the rectangle can vary in size, but the shape of the net is always two circles and a rectangle.**

Pre-AP™

English Language Learners ELL
Students often have a difficult time with the term *surface area*, since it appears that the area of a polygon is also surface area. Use solids, cereal boxes, or desks, and ask them to touch all the surfaces. Remind them that the faces are polygons.

learning style: tactile

Closure

- *What is a net?* a two-dimensional pattern that you can fold to form a three-dimensional figure
- *How do you find the surface area of a prism?* Find the area of each face and add the values together.
- *How do you find the surface area of a cylinder?* Find the area of one circle and the area of the rectangle. Add the areas of 2 circles and the rectangle.

EXAMPLE Finding the Surface Area of a Cylinder

3 **Crafts** You plan to make a birthday present for your friend. The first step is to cover a coffee can with construction paper. How much construction paper do you need?

Step 1 Draw a net.

Step 2 Find the area of one circle.

$$A = \pi r^2$$
$$= \pi(5)^2$$
$$= \pi(25)$$
$$\approx 78.54$$

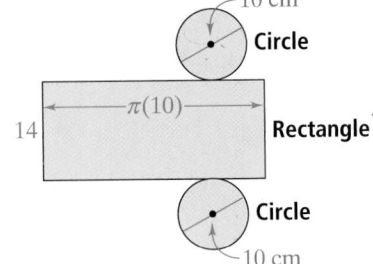

Step 3 Find the area of the rectangle.

$$(\pi d)h = \pi(10)(14)$$
$$= 140\pi$$
$$\approx 439.82$$

Step 4 Add the areas of the two circles and the rectangle.

$$\text{Surface area} = 78.54 + 78.54 + 439.82 = 596.9$$

The amount of construction paper needed is about 597 cm².

✓ Quick Check

3. What is the surface area of the cylinder at the right? Round to the nearest tenth. **3,455.8 m²**

✓ Check Your Understanding

1. **Vocabulary** The $\underset{\text{surface area}}{\underline{\quad?\quad}}$ of a prism is the sum of the areas of its faces.

2. rectangle; the net of a triangular prism consists of 3 rectangles and 2 triangles. The net of a rectangular prism consists of 6 rectangles.

2. **Reasoning** What kind of polygon is included in both a net of a triangular prism and in a net of a rectangular prism? **See left.**

Identify the figure formed by each net. Then find its surface area.

3.

cylinder; about 5,089.4 in.²

4.

cube; 294 cm²

For more exercises, see Extra Skills and Word Problems.

GO for Help

For Exercises	See Examples
5–8	1
9–11	2
12–14	3

A Draw a net for each three-dimensional figure. 5–8. See margin.

5.

6.

7.

8.

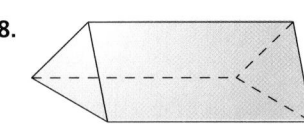

Find the surface area of each prism.

9.

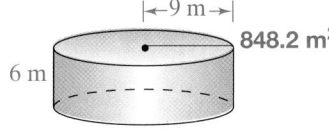

264 m²

10.

6 in.

5 in.

4 in.

148 in.²

11.

6 m

7 m

4 m

188 m²

Vocabulary Tip

Cylindrical means "in the shape of a cylinder."

Find the surface area of each cylinder. Round to the nearest tenth.

12.

|←9 m→|

6 m

848.2 m²

13.

5 cm

20 cm

785.4 cm²

14. The diameter of the base of a cylindrical can is 4 in. The height of the can is 6.5 in. Find the can's surface area to the nearest tenth. 106.8 in.²

B GPS 15. **Guided Problem Solving** The tent at the right is similar to a triangular prism. Calculate the surface area of the tent to find the amount of fabric needed to make the tent. 136 ft²

• A triangular prism has ■ faces.
• Find and add the areas of the faces:
   surface area = ■ + ■ + ■ + ■ . . .

4.75 ft

4 ft

5 ft

8 ft

16. Some cans are cut from a large sheet of metal. Find the amount of metal needed to make a can similar to the one at the right. Round to the nearest tenth. 282.7 cm²

6 cm

12 cm

17. Calculate the surface area of a rectangular prism with a height of 4 in., a width of 16 in., and a length of 10 in. 528 in.²

5–8. See back of book.

3. Practice

Assignment Guide

Check Your Understanding
Go over Exercises 1–4 in class before assigning the Homework Exercises.

Homework Exercises
A Practice by Example 5–14
B Apply Your Skills 15–26
C Challenge 27
TEKS ★ TAKS Tune-Up and Mixed Review 28–32

Homework Quick Check
To check students' understanding of key skills and concepts, go over Exercises 9, 12, 16, 22, and 25.

Differentiated Instruction Resources

417

PowerPoint

Lesson Quiz

1. Draw a net for a triangular prism. **Sample:**

Find the surface area of each. Round to the nearest tenth.

2. rectangular prism: 12 cm by 8 cm by 9 cm. **552 cm²**

3. cylinder: radius 6 cm, height 10 cm **603.2 cm²**

Reteaching 8-9 — Surface Areas of Prisms and C... **L2**

Enrichment 8-9 — Surface Areas of Prisms and **L4**
Critical Thinking

GO Online
Homework Help
Visit: PHSchool.com
Web Code: are-0809

24. You cannot interchange the values of r and h.

14 in.
24 in.

Find the surface area of each cylinder given the base radius and height of the cylinder. Round to the nearest square unit.

18. $r = 3$ cm
$h = 10$ cm
245 cm²

19. $r = 7$ ft
$h = 25$ ft
1,407 ft²

20. $r = 12$ m
$h = 16$ m
2,111 m²

21. $r = 10$ in.
$h = 3$ ft
2,890 in.²

22. A cosmetics company that makes small cylindrical bars of soap **GPS** wraps the bars in plastic prior to shipping. Find the surface area of a bar of soap if the diameter is 5 cm and the height is 2 cm. Round to the nearest tenth. **70.7 cm²**

23. Suppose you wish to make a cylindrical case that will exactly fit the bass drum at the left. What is the surface area of the case to the nearest tenth? **1960.4 in.²**

24. **Error Analysis** A student says the two cylinders at the right have the same surface area. Explain the student's error. **See above left.**

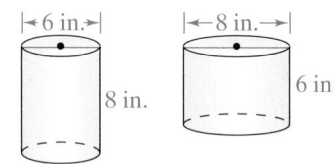
⊢ 6 in. ⊣   ⊢ 8 in. →
8 in.   6 in.

25. **Writing in Math** Which has a greater effect on the surface area of a cylinder—doubling the radius or doubling the height? Explain. See margin.

26. **Open-Ended** Draw a net for a prism that has a surface area of 72 cm². See margin.

27. **Challenge** Find the surface area of the figure at the right. Round to the nearest tenth. **990 ft²**

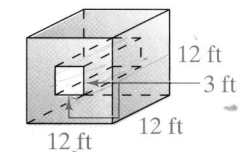
12 ft
3 ft
12 ft
12 ft

TEKS ★ TAKS Tune-Up and Mixed Review

TAKS Objective 3
TEKS (7.8)(B)

28. Which solid can be formed from the net shown at the right? **A**

Ⓐ Triangular prism
Ⓑ Rectangular prism
Ⓒ Triangular pyramid
Ⓓ Rectangular pyramid

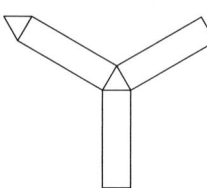

TAKS Objective 6
TEKS (7.15)(A)

29. Chip grows $\frac{3}{4}$ inch in January, $\frac{5}{8}$ inch in February, and $\frac{1}{2}$ inch in March. If the pattern continues, how much will he grow in May? **G**

Ⓕ $\frac{1}{8}$ in.   Ⓗ $\frac{3}{8}$ in.

Ⓖ $\frac{1}{4}$ in.   Ⓙ $\frac{1}{2}$ in.

GO for Help Lesson 8-6

Identify each number as *rational* or *irrational*.

30. $2.22222\ldots$
rational

31. $\sqrt{625}$
rational

32. $\sqrt{18}$
irrational

TEKS ★ TAKS Resources

- TAKS Strategies, p. 427
- TAKS Tune-Up, pp. 431–433

TAKS Tune-Up Kit

- TAKS Daily Review Transparencies
- TAKS Review and Preparation Workbook
- TAKS Strategies with Transparencies
- Texas Progress Monitoring Assessments

Alternative Assessment

Provide pairs of students with graph paper and exercises similar to Exercises 9–13. Partners check each other's work and must agree on the results.

25–26. See back of book.

Patterns in 3-Dimensional Figures

You can explore number patterns using unit cubes.

Suppose you use unit cubes to make a larger cube with two unit cubes on an edge. You paint the outside of the larger cube. You need eight unit cubes to form the larger cube. Each cube has three sides painted.

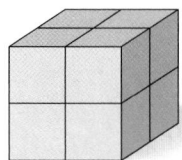

Exercises

Use the table for Exercises 1–3.

Number of Unit Cubes on an Edge	Total Number of Unit Cubes	Total Number Expressed as a Power	Number of Unit Cubes With Given Number of Sides Painted			
			0	1	2	3
2	8	2^3	0	0	0	8
3	▪	▪	▪	▪	▪	▪
4	▪	▪	▪	▪	▪	▪
5	▪	▪	▪	▪	▪	▪
6	▪	▪	▪	▪	▪	▪
7	▪	▪	▪	▪	▪	▪

2a. $(n - 2)^3$; $6(n - 2)^2$; $12(n - 2)$; 8

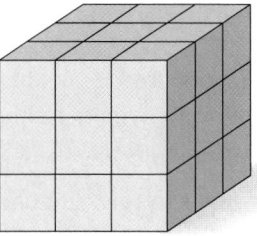

1. Copy and complete the table above. Use the figure at the right to help you fill in the row for 3 unit cubes on an edge.
   See back of book.

2. **a. Patterns** Describe the number pattern you see in each of the last four columns of your table. **See above right.**
   b. Use the number patterns and extend the table for 8 number cubes on an edge. **8, 512, 8^3, 216, 216, 72, 8**

3. **a. Number Sense** What is the total number of unit cubes in a cube with 10 unit cubes on an edge? **1,000**
   b. If there are 15 unit cubes on an edge, how many unit cubes will have no side painted? One side painted? Two sides painted? **2,197; 1,014; 156**
   c. Reasoning If 144 unit cubes have two sides painted, how many unit cubes are on one edge of the cube? **14**

Extension

Patterns in 3-Dimensional Figures

In this Extension of Lesson 8-9, students use unit cubes to explore number patterns in three-dimensional figures.

Guided Instruction

Review the meanings of the terms *edge* and *face* with students. Show examples of each. Have students construct the model in the example with unit cubes. Ask students what they observe about the cube. Ask questions such as:
- *Why one face of the large cube is made of 4 small cube faces?* **The face of a cube is a square. The edge of the cube is 2 units. 2 squared is 4.**
- *What is the total surface area of the large cube?* **24 square units**

Exercises

Have students work with partners. Guide pairs to construct models of the 27-cube larger cube to fill in the table and complete Exercise 2. Encourage tactile and visual learners to make models using the small cubes to complete the exercises.

Teaching Tip

Have students connect their models to formulas for the volume and surface area of rectangular prisms.

Differentiated Instruction

Advanced Learners   L4

Challenge your advanced students to explore with models to see how *removing* one or more unit cubes affects the surface area of the large figures. Have them share their findings.

Resources

- unit cubes
- Student Manipulatives Kit

Use this Checkpoint Quiz to check students' understanding of the skills and concepts of Lessons 8-5 through 8-9.

Resources

- All-in-One Teaching Resources Checkpoint Quiz 2
- Texas ExamView CD-ROM
- Success Tracker™ Online Intervention

Square Root Bingo

This game will help students associate perfect squares with their square roots.

Guided Instruction

Students play in pairs.

Have them read the rules before beginning. Review the definition of *perfect square* and *square root*. Ask for examples of perfect squares.

Differentiated Instruction

English Language Learners **ELL**
Review the terms *diagonally*, *horizontally*, and *vertically*. Ask students to use their hands to show their meanings.

Resources

- 20 index cards with a perfect square of a number from 1–20 under the square root symbol on each

---

Checkpoint Quiz 2

1. Find two consecutive whole numbers that $\sqrt{77}$ falls between. $8 < \sqrt{77} < 9$

2. Find the length of the sides of a square with an area of 324 cm². **18 cm**

Find each missing length.

3. **39 cm**

4. **4 yd**

5. **8 m**

Name each figure.

6. sphere

7. cone

8. rectangular prism

Find the surface area of each figure. Round to the nearest tenth.

9. **36 in.²**

10. **2,884 m²**

MATH GAMES

Square Root Bingo

What You'll Need

- 20 index cards. On each card write one of the first 20 perfect squares (not including 0) under the square root symbol.

How To Play

- All players draw a 16-square playing board. In each square, they write a number from 1–20 without repeats.
- One player shuffles the cards and places them face down.
- The player to the right chooses the top card and places it face up. Players with the matching square root on their board make a mark on the appropriate square.
- The player to the right chooses the next card.
- The winner is the first player who has four marks diagonally, horizontally, or vertically.

420

Volumes of Prisms and Cylinders

Check Skills You'll Need

1. Vocabulary Review
How is π related to the circumference and the diameter of a circle? $\pi = \frac{C}{d}$

Find the area of each circle. Round to the nearest square unit.

2.

12 m   113 m²

3.

15 in.   177 in.²

GO for Help
Lesson 8-5

GO Online

Video Tutor Help
Visit: PHSchool.com
Web Code: are-0775

TEKS ★ TAKS

- **(7.9)(B)** To connect models for volume of prisms and cylinders to formulas of prisms and cylinders
- **(7.9)(C)** To estimate measurements and solve problems involving volume of prisms and cylinders **TAKS** Obj. 4

◀)) **New Vocabulary** volume, cubic unit

Why Learn This?

Many storage silos are shaped like cylinders. You can use volume formulas to find the amount of storage space inside a figure like a silo.

The **volume** of a three-dimensional figure is the number of cubic units needed to fill the space inside the figure.

A **cubic unit** is a cube with edges one unit long. A cubic centimeter is a cube with edges one centimeter long.

1 cm 1 cm 1 cm

Consider filling the rectangular prism below with cubic centimeters.

3 cm   4 cm
10 cm

The bottom layer of the prism contains 10 · 4, or 40, cubes.

3 cm   4 cm
10 cm

Three layers of 40 cubes fit in the prism. 3 · 40 = 120

3 cm   4 cm
10 cm

The volume of the prism is 120 cm³.

TEKS ★ TAKS

(7.9)(B) To connect models for volume of prisms and cylinders to formulas of prisms and cylinders
(7.9)(C) To estimate measurements and solve problems involving volume of prisms and cylinders **TAKS** Obj. 4

Dana Center TEKS Toolkit Clarifying Activities (7.9)(B), (7.9)(C)
Visit: PHSchool.com
Web Code: arq-9045

Professional Development

TEKS Math Background

When you pick up a drinking glass, you are touching its surface (area), which is measured in square units. The capacity or volume of water contained in the glass is measured in cubic units. To calculate the volume of prisms and cylinders, find the area of the base and multiply it by the height. The formula for volume is $V = Bh$ where B is the area of the base and h is the height.

More Math Background: p. 372D

Lesson Planning and Resources

See p. 372E for a list of the resources that support this lesson.

PowerPoint

🔲 **Bell Ringer Practice**

✓ **Check Skills You'll Need**
Use student page, transparency, or PowerPoint.

TAKS **Daily Review 66**
Use transparency.

Differentiated Instruction Solutions for All Learners

Special Needs L1
Have students hold a cube that is formed by smaller linking cubes, or a box with graph paper for sides. Ask them to undo the cube figure (or take out the cubes) and put it back together. Then ask the students how many little cubes formed the solid. That is the volume of the larger cube.

learning style: tactile

Below Level L2
Help students differentiate the concepts of perimeter (distance around), area (surface covered), and volume (space filled).

learning style: verbal

421

Guided Instruction

Example 1
Some students may think of volume as only an amount of liquid and may have trouble thinking of volume in terms of cubic units. Tell them that liquids like juice assume the shape of the container that holds it and could easily be poured into vessels of other shapes, like a juice carton.

Example 3
Point out that volume is expressed in cubic units, or units^3. Ask: Why do you think the volume is 452 in^3 instead of 452 in^2? **Sample: Volume tells how many cubes a container can hold.**

Error Prevention!

Students may multiply π and r and then square the entire product before multiplying by height. Have students write $V = \pi \cdot r \cdot r \cdot h$. Then have them substitute the values into the formula and multiply.

Teaching Tips
- Have students use circular chips to build cylinders and triangular chips to build triangular prisms. Discuss the fact that the total volume is the volume of one chip multiplied by how many chips high the cylinder or triangular prism is.
- Have students use models to show why the formula for the volume of a prism is similar to the formula for the volume of a cylinder.

The previous calculation of volume suggests the following formula.

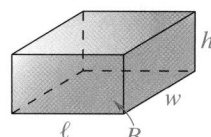

KEY CONCEPTS **Volume of a Rectangular Prism**

$$V = \text{area of base} \cdot \text{height}$$
$$= Bh$$
$$= \ell w h$$

EXAMPLE **Finding Volume of a Rectangular Prism**

1 **TAKS Griddable Item** Mr. Cho is building a craft box like the one shown at the right. What is the volume of the craft box in cubic inches?

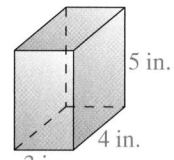

$$V = \ell w h \qquad \leftarrow \text{Use the formula.}$$
$$= (3)(4)(5) \qquad \leftarrow \text{Substitute.}$$
$$= 60 \qquad \leftarrow \text{Multiply.}$$

The volume of the craft box is 60 cubic inches.

✓ Quick Check

1. If the height of the prism above is doubled, what is the volume?

120 in.^{3}

The volume formulas for rectangular and triangular prisms are similar.

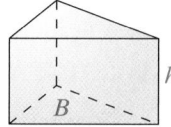

TAKS Tip

When finding volume, remember to calculate the area of the base first.

KEY CONCEPTS **Volume of a Triangular Prism**

$$V = \text{area of base} \cdot \text{height}$$
$$= Bh$$

EXAMPLE **Finding the Volume of a Triangular Prism**

2 Find the volume of the triangular prism.

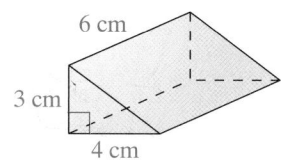

$$V = Bh \qquad \leftarrow \text{Use the formula.}$$
$$= (6)(6) \qquad \leftarrow \text{Substitute: } B = \tfrac{1}{2} \times 3 \times 4 = 6.$$
$$= 36 \qquad \leftarrow \text{Multiply.}$$

The volume of the triangular prism is 36 cm^3.

✓ Quick Check

72 cm^3

2. If the height of the prism above is doubled, what is the volume?

Advanced Learners **L4**
A rectangular prism has two square faces and four rectangular faces. Its longest edge is 9 cm, and its surface area is 230 cm^2. What is its volume? **225 cm^3**

Pre-AP™

English Language Learners **ELL**
Tell students that although volume is measured in cubic units, containers are rarely filled with cubic units. They are filled with various products or items, such as cereal, or popcorn. Remind them that a cubic unit is a standard unit of measure.

learning style: visual

The volume formula for a cylinder is also similar to the volume formula for a prism.

> **KEY CONCEPTS** Volume of a Cylinder
>
> V = area of base · height
> $= Bh$
> $= \pi r^2 h$
>
>

EXAMPLE Finding the Volume of a Cylinder

Online active math

For: Volume Activity
Use: Interactive Textbook, 8-10

3 Painting Estimate the volume of the cylindrical paint can. Then find the volume to the nearest cubic unit.

|← 4 in. →|

9 in.

Estimate

$V = \pi r^2 h$ ← Use the formula.

$\approx (3)(4)^2(9)$ ← Use 3 to estimate π.

$\approx (50)(9)$ ← Use 50 to estimate 48 (3 · 16).

≈ 450

The estimated volume is 450 in.^{3}.

Calculate

$V = \pi r^2 h$ ← Use the formula.

$\approx (\pi)(4)^2(9)$ ← Substitute.

≈ 452.38934 ← Use a calculator.

≈ 452 ← Round to the nearest whole number.

The calculated volume is about 452 in.^{3}.

Check for Reasonableness The calculated volume is close to the estimated volume, so the answer is reasonable.

✓ Quick Check

3. a. Estimate the volume of the cylinder. Then find the volume to the nearest cubic centimeter. about 6,000 cm^3; 6,107 cm^3

24 cm

18 cm

b. Reasoning Suppose you estimate using 20 for 4^2 instead of 16 in Example 3. Will your estimate be reasonable? The estimate will be a little large.

---

1 Find the volume of the rectangular prism. 960 cm^3

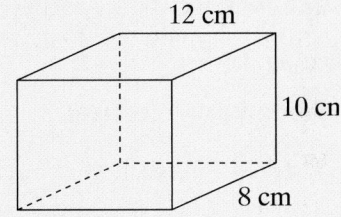

12 cm

10 cm

8 cm

2 Find the volume of the triangular prism. 120 cm^3

4 cm   10 cm   6 cm

3 Find the volume of the cylinder. Round to the nearest cubic centimeter. 113 cm^3

2 cm

9 cm

All in One Teaching Resources

- Daily Notetaking Guide 8-10 **L3**
- Adapted Notetaking 8-10 **L1**

Closure

- *What is volume for a three-dimensional figure?* the number of cubic units needed to fill the space inside the figure
- *How do you find the volume of a rectangular prism?* Use $V = \ell wh$ and write the units^3.
- *How do you find the volume of a cylinder?* Use the formula $V = \pi r^2 h$, where r is the radius and h is the height of the cylinder; write the units^3.

423

Assignment Guide

Check Your Understanding
Go over Exercises 1–4 in class before assigning the Homework Exercises.

Homework Exercises
A Practice by Example   5–13
B Apply Your Skills   14–22
C Challenge   23
TEKS ★ TAKS Tune-Up and
   Mixed Review   24–30

Homework Quick Check
To check students' understanding of key skills and concepts, go over Exercises 7, 12, 18, 19, and 21.

Differentiated Instruction Resources

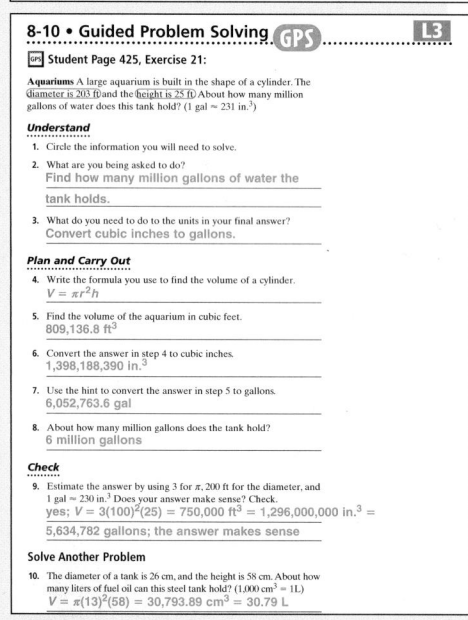

1. **Vocabulary** The number of cubic units needed to fill the space inside a three-dimensional figure is called the __?__. **volume**

2. How does the volume of a cylinder change if the height is doubled? **B**
   - A It does not change.
   - B It doubles.
   - C It quadruples.
   - D It halves.

Find the volume of each figure, given the following dimensions.

3. triangular prism
   $B = 20$ in.^{2}; $h = 3$ in.
   60 in.^{3}

4. cylinder
   $r = 5$ cm; $h = 7$ cm
   549.8 cm^3

Homework Exercises

For more exercises, see Extra Skills and Word Problems.

GO for Help

For Exercises	See Examples
5–7	1
8–10	2
11–13	3

Ⓐ Find the volume of each rectangular prism.

5.

5.5 in.
5.5 in.   5.5 in.
166.375 in.^{3}

6.
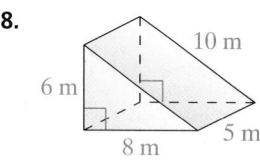
2 cm   6 cm
2 cm
24 cm^3

7.

7.5 ft
7.5 ft
7.5 ft
421.875 ft^3

Find the volume of each triangular prism.

8.

10 m
6 m
8 m   5 m
120 m^3

9.

4.5 in
2 in.   7 in.
31.5 in.^{3}

10.
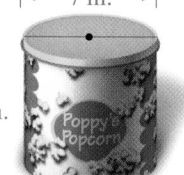
4 ft
4 ft
5 ft
40 ft^3

Packaging Estimate the volume of each cylinder. Then find the volume to the nearest cubic unit.

about 300 in.^{3}; 250 in.^{3}
|←— 7 in.—→|

11.

2 in.
7 in.
Peanut Butter
about 84 in.^{3}; 88 in.^{3}

12.
13 cm
33 cm
Mountain Ground Coffee
about 1,500 cm^3; 17,521 cm^3

13.
6.5 in.
Poppy's Popcorn

Ⓑ **GPS** 14. **Guided Problem Solving** What is the volume of the object shown at the right? **1,759 mm^3**
   - Identify the two familiar solids that make up the object. What are they?
   - What is the volume of each familiar solid?

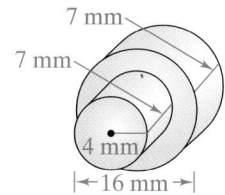
7 mm
7 mm
4 mm
|←16 mm→|

19. Since the volume of a cylinder is $V = \pi r^2 h$, you can substitute the values for V and h.
    $385 = 3.14 \cdot 10r^2$
    $385 = 31.4r^2$
    $12.26 = r^2$
    $3.5 \approx r$
    The radius is about 3.5 in.

23. Yes; the height of the can is less than the height of the case. Since $3(2.5) < 7.6$, 3 cans will fit along the width of the case. Since $4(2.5) < 11$, 4 cans will fit along the length of the case. Then the case can hold 3×4, or 12, cans.

GO Online

Homework Help

Visit: PHSchool.com
Web Code: are-0810

Find the height of each rectangular prism.

15. $V = 455$ cm^3
$\ell = 10$ cm
$w = 7$ cm
6.5 cm

16. $V = 525$ m^3
$\ell = 7.5$ m
$w = 3.5$ m
20 m

17. $V = 5,832$ in.^{3}
$\ell = 18$ in.
$w = 18$ in.
18 in.

18. The cylinder has a volume of 130.7 cm^3. The cube has a volume of 166.4 cm^3. The cylinder is missing the "corners."

18. Reasoning Compare the volumes of the figures. Why are their volumes different? **See left.**

19. Writing in Math Explain how you can find the radius of a cylinder with a height of 10 in. and a volume of 385 in.^{3}. (Use $\pi = 3.14$.) **See margin.**

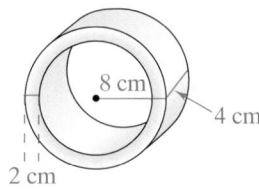

20. Find the volume of the figure at the left to the nearest cubic centimeter. **352 cm^3**

21. Aquariums A large aquarium is built in the shape of a cylinder. **GPS** The diameter is 203 ft and the height is 25 ft. About how many million gallons of water does this tank hold? (1 gal ≈ 231 in.^{3})
about 6 million gal

22. A rectangular prism has a length of 3.1 m, a width of 2.2 m, and a height of 5.6 m. Find the volume to the nearest cubic meter. **38 m^3**

C 23. Challenge A soft-drink can has a height of about 4.8 in. and a diameter of about 2.5 in. Suppose you need to put 12 cans in a rectangular case about 5 in. tall, 11 in. long, and 7.6 in. wide. Will the cans fit in the case? Explain. **See margin.**

TEKS ★ TAKS Tune-Up and Mixed Review

TAKS Objective 4
TEKS (7.9)(C)

24. Mrs. Panosian has a can of concentrated orange juice like the one at the right. What is the volume of the can in cubic centimeters? **308**

TAKS Objective 1
TEKS (7.2)(B)

25. Nina created a project on water conservation. She found that you use 1.6 gallons of water each time you flush a toilet. At this rate, how many gallons of water would you use flushing 7 times? **105**

TAKS Objective 1
TEKS (7.2)(F)

26. Ethan collected five rocks that weighed a total of 43.4 kg. Two of the rocks were identical, and each weighed 13.3 kg. If two of the other rocks weighed 4.7 kg and 5.3 kg, what was the weight of the fifth rock in kilograms? **6.8**

for Help
Lesson 7-2

Find the measures of the complement and supplement of each angle.

27. $m\angle A = 40°$
50°; 140°

28. $m\angle B = 65°$
25°; 115°

29. $m\angle C = 37°$
53°; 143°

30. $m\angle D = 5°$
85°; 175°

Alternative Assessment

Have students work in pairs and take turns completing Exercises 5–13. Suggest that they write each formula at the top of their papers for quick reference. Allow pairs to discuss their methods as they work. You may wish to have them use calculators to aid them in their computations.

TEKS ★ TAKS Resources

- TAKS Strategies, p. 427
- TAKS Tune-Up, pp. 431–433

TAKS Tune-Up Kit

- TAKS Daily Review Transparencies
- TAKS Review and Preparation Workbook
- TAKS Strategies with Transparencies
- Texas Progress Monitoring Assessments

---

4. Assess & Reteach

PowerPoint
Lesson Quiz

Find the volume of each figure to the nearest cubic unit.

1. 2,304 ft^3

2. 187.5 ft^3

3. 8,743 cm^3

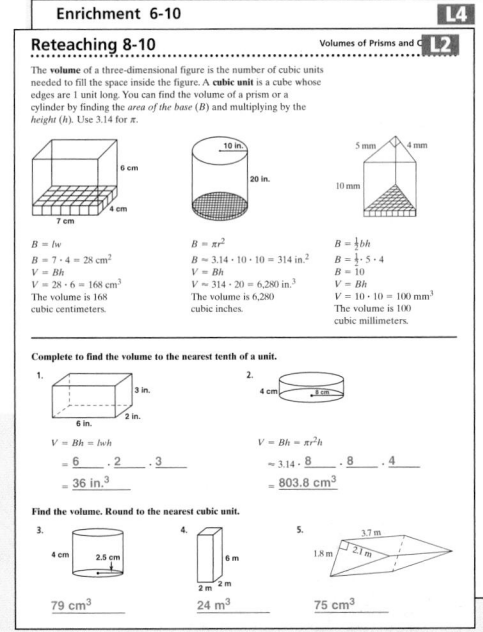

425

Generating Formulas For Volume

Students will relate volumes of pyramids and prisms. This will extend the skills they learned in Lesson 8-10.

Guided Instruction

Before beginning the Activity, ask students to compare different solids and tell which they think has a greater volume.
Ask:

- *Name an example of comparing the volumes of two solids.* Sample: comparing how many small cubes it takes to fill a large rectangular box or prism
- *How can you determine the volume of a large solid?* Find the volume of a smaller solid and find how many times that solid will fit inside the larger solid.

Have students work independently on the Exercises. Then conduct a class discussion about how the volumes of different solids are related.

Differentiated Instruction

Below Level   L2
Provide paper models of the nets of the cone and cylinder in Exercise 2. Allow students to construct the solids and fill them with rice as in the Activity to reinforce the connection between the solids and the formula.

TEKS ★ TAKS Resources

- posterboard
- scissors
- tape
- rice
- paper

Dana Center TEKS Toolkit Clarifying Activities (7.4)(A), (7.14)(A)
Visit: PHSchool.com
Web Code: arq-9045

426

8-10b Activity Lab   Hands On

Generating Formulas for Volume

In this activity, you will relate the volume of a pyramid to the volume of a prism.

TEKS ★ TAKS
(7.4)(A) To generate formulas involving volume **TAKS Obj. 2**
(7.14)(A) To communicate mathematical ideas using physical and algebraic models **TAKS Obj. 6**

ACTIVITY

Step 1 Using poster board, draw and cut out four congruent isosceles triangles like the one below.

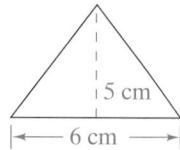

Step 2 Tape the edges of the four triangles to form a pyramid without a base. What is the area of the missing base?

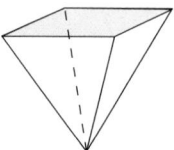

Step 3 Using poster board, draw and cut out four congruent rectangles and one square like the one below.

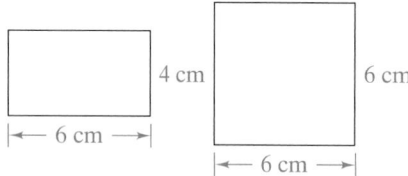

Step 4 Tape the edges of the polygons to form a prism without a base. Compare the areas of the missing base of the prism and the missing base of the pyramid.

Step 5 Place the pyramid and the prism side by side. What do you notice about their heights?

Step 6 Fill the pyramid with rice. Pour the rice from the pyramid into the prism. Repeat until the prism is full.

Exercises

1. **a.** How many pyramids full of rice did you need to fill the prism? **3 pyramids**
   b. How does the volume of the pyramid compare to the volume of the prism? **See margin.**
   c. Make a conjecture about the formula for volume of a pyramid. $A = \frac{1}{3}bh$

2. **Reasoning** To fill a cylinder with base area B and height h, you need 3 cones as shown at the right. Make a conjecture about the formula for volume of a cone. **See margin.**

 + +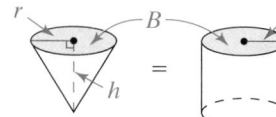

1b. The volume of the pyramid is one third the volume of the prism.

2. $V = \frac{1}{3}Bh$ or $V = \frac{1}{3}\pi r^2 h$

Measuring to Solve

Some test questions ask you to measure with a centimeter ruler before solving a problem.

EXAMPLE

The bottom of a bottle is circular, as shown at the right. Measure the radius of the bottle in centimeters.

Which of the following is closest to the circumference of the bottom of the bottle?

- (A) 6 cm
- (C) 15 cm
- (B) 9 cm
- (D) 19 cm

Use a centimeter ruler to measure the radius of the bottle. Label the radius. To find the circumference of the bottle, use the formula for the circumference of a circle.

$C = 2\pi r$, or πd

$C = 2\pi r = 2 \times \pi \times 3 \approx 18.84955 \ldots$

The circumference of the bottle is about 19 cm. The answer is D.

Exercises

 Objective 3
TEKS (7.8)(C)

1. A vase has a circular base, as shown at the right. Measure the radius of the base in centimeters. Which of the following is the closest to the area of the circular base? **C**
   - (A) 2 cm^2
   - (B) 6 cm^2
   - (C) 12 cm^2
   - (D) 24 cm^2

 Objective 4
TEKS (7.9)(A)

2. Celine bought earrings and made a gift box for them that is 4 cm high. The base of the box is shown at the right. Measure the dimensions of the base in centimeters. Which best represents the volume of the box? **J**
   - (F) 6 cm^3
   - (G) 8 cm^3
   - (H) 12 cm^3
   - (J) 32 cm^3

Measuring to Solve

On some tests, students are asked to measure objects in order to determine an answer. This feature provides practice in measuring test items and using the measurements to answer questions.

Guided Instruction

Explain to students that they may not always be able to measure the dimension in the question, but they can use their ruler and knowledge of formulas to find the answer. Measuring a drawing in a question may also give them information that they need for a formula to answer the question.

Exercises

You may want students to write formulas they need to solve Exercises 1 and 2 before they do the problems.

TEKS ★ **TAKS** Resources

TAKS Strategies with Transparencies
- Transparency 13
- Practice sheet, p. 20

Chapter 8 Review

TEKS ★ TAKS Resources

Student Edition
Extra Skills and Word Problems
    Practice, Ch. 8, p. 644
English/Spanish Glossary, p. 675
Formulas and Properties, p. 673
Tables, p. 670
All in One Teaching Resources
• Vocabulary and Study
  Skills 8F   L3

TAKS Tune-Up Kit
• TAKS Daily Review
  Transparencies
• TAKS Review and Preparation
  Workbook
• TAKS Strategies with
  Transparencies
• Texas Progress Monitoring
  Assessments
• Texas ExamView CD-ROM
• MindPoint Quiz Show CD-ROM

Differentiated Instruction

Spanish Vocabulary Workbook
with Study Skills   ELL

Texas Interactive Textbook
• Audio Glossary

Online Vocabulary Quiz

Success ⊃⊂ Tracker™
Online at PHSchool.com

Vocabulary Review

 area (p. 375)
base(s) (pp. 380, 384, 388, 410, 411)
center (p. 411)
circumference (p. 394)
cone (p. 411)
cube (p. 410)
cubic unit (p. 421)
cylinder (p. 410)
edge (p. 410)

face (p. 410)
height (pp. 380, 384, 388, 410)
hypotenuse (p. 405)
irrational number (p. 401)
legs (p. 405)
net (p. 414)
perfect square (p. 400)
perimeter (p. 375)
pi (p. 394)
prism (p. 410)

pyramid (p. 410)
Pythagorean Theorem (p. 405)
sphere (p. 411)
square root (p. 400)
surface area (p. 415)
three-dimensional figure (p. 410)
vertex (p. 410)
volume (p. 421)

Choose the correct term to complete each sentence.

1. A(n) (edge, vertex) is the intersection of two faces. **edge**

2. The longest side of a right triangle is the (hypotenuse, leg). **hypotenuse**

3. A (prism, pyramid) has two parallel and congruent bases. **prism**

4. The perimeter of a circle is the (area, circumference) of the circle. **circumference**

5. A (cone, cylinder) has one circular base and one vertex. **cone**

Go Online
PHSchool.com
For: Online Vocabulary Quiz
Web Code: arj-0851

Skills and Concepts

TEKS ★ TAKS

Lesson 8-1
(7.9)(A) To estimate
measurements involving
perimeter and area
TAKS Obj. 4

(7.14)(A) To communicate
mathematical ideas using
appropriate units TAKS Obj. 6

The **area** of a figure is the number of square units it encloses.

6. Estimate the area of the shaded region.
   Each square represents 20 in.^{2}. **about 400 in.^{2}**

7. Choose a reasonable estimate for the
   width of a book—7 in. or 7 ft. Explain.
   7 in.; the width is less than a foot.

Lessons 8-2, 8-3, 8-4
(7.4)(A) To generate
formulas involving
perimeter and area
TAKS Obj. 2

(7.9)(A) To estimate
measurements and solve
application problems
involving perimeter and
area of polygons TAKS Obj. 4

8. 10.5 m^2

9. 38 cm^2

10. 160 ft^2

To find the area of an irregular figure, first separate it into familiar
figures and find the area of each piece. Then add the areas.

parallelogram	triangle	trapezoid
$A = bh$	$A = \frac{1}{2}bh$	$A = \frac{1}{2}h(b_1 + b_2)$

Use familiar figures to find the area of each figure. 8–10. See left.

8.

9.

10.
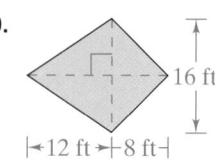

428 Chapter 8 Chapter Review

Lesson 8-5

(7.9)(A) To estimate measurements and solve application problems involving circumference and area of circles **TAKS Obj. 4**

(7.8)(C) To use geometric concepts in fields such as art and architecture **TAKS Obj. 3**

To find the **circumference** of a circle, use the formula $C = \pi d = 2\pi r$. To find the area of a circle, use the formula $A = \pi r^2$.

Find the circumference and area of each circle.

11.

8 in.

25.1 in.; 50.3 in.²

12.

14 mi

44 mi; 153.9 mi²

13.

7 km

22 km; 38.5 km²

Lessons 8-6, 8-7

(7.1)(C) To represent squares and square roots using geometric models **TAKS Obj. 1**

(7.13)(D) To select mental math and estimation to solve problems

Prepares for **TEKS (8.9)(A)** To use the Pythagorean Theorem to solve real-life problems

A **perfect square** is a square of an integer. The opposite of squaring a number is finding its **square root.** Many square roots are **irrational numbers,** or numbers that cannot be written as the ratio of two integers.

The **Pythagorean Theorem,** $a^2 + b^2 = c^2$, relates the lengths of the **legs** of a right triangle to the length of its **hypotenuse.**

14. Art A square piece of glass in a picture frame covers an area of 36 in.². What is the length of each side of the glass? 6 in.

15. A pipeline is placed diagonally across a rectangular field that is 25 yd by 30 yd. How long is the pipeline, to the nearest yard? 39 yd

Lesson 8-8

(7.6)(C) To use properties to classify three-dimensional figures, including pyramids, cones, prisms, and cylinders **TAKS Obj. 3**

(7.8)(C) To use geometric concepts in art and architecture **TAKS Obj. 3**

Some **three-dimensional figures** have only flat surfaces. **Prisms** and **pyramids** are named for the shape of their bases. **Cones** and pyramids have one **vertex.**

Name each figure.

16.

cylinder

17.

rectangular pyramid

18.

pentagonal pyramid

Lessons 8-9, 8-10

(7.8)(B) To make a net of a three-dimensional figure **TAKS Obj. 3**

(7.9)(B) To connect models for volumes of prisms and cylinders to formulas of prisms and cylinders

(7.9)(C) To estimate measurements and solve problems involving volume of prisms and cylinders **TAKS Obj. 4**

To find the **surface area** of a prism or cylinder, draw a **net** and find the area of the net. To find the **volume** of a prism, use the formula $V = Bh$. To find the volume of a cylinder, use the formula $V = \pi r^2 h$.

Find the surface area and volume for each figure.

19.

2 in.
1 in.
3 in.
22 in.²; 6 in.³

20.

9 m   6 m
6 m
288 m²; 324 m

21. 14 yd

10 yd

747.7 yd²; 1,539.4 yd³

Chapter 8 Test

Go Online
PHSchool.com
For: Online chapter test
Web Code: ara-0852

Estimate the area of each shaded region. Each square represents 50 in.²

1.

about 800 in.²

2.
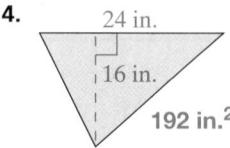
about 650 in.²

Find the area of each figure.

3.
9 cm
108 cm²   12 cm

4.
24 in.
16 in.
192 in.²

5.
5 m
7.5 m
10 m
56.25 m²

6.

12 cm
12 cm
|← 20 cm →|
192 cm²

Find the circumference and area of each circle. Round to the nearest tenth.

7.
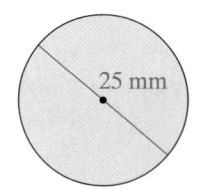
20 cm
62.8 cm; 314.2 cm

8.
25 mm
78.5 mm; 490.9 mm²

Simplify each square root.

9. $\sqrt{9}$ 3   **10.** $\sqrt{25}$ 5   **11.** $\sqrt{49}$ 7   **12.** $\sqrt{100}$ 10

13. $\sqrt{121}$ 11   **14.** $\sqrt{1}$ 1   **15.** $\sqrt{64}$ 8   **16.** $\sqrt{81}$ 9

17. A square plot of land has an area of 100 m². What is the perimeter of the plot? **40 m**

Find two consecutive whole numbers that each number falls between. Then estimate the number's value. 18–21. See margin.

18. $\sqrt{55}$ **19.** $\sqrt{63}$ **20.** $\sqrt{8}$ **21.** $\sqrt{45}$

22. Construction The area of a window is 18 ft². The length of the window is two times the width of the window. What are the dimensions of the window? **3 ft × 6 ft**

Find each missing length to the nearest tenth.

23.
10 cm
w   6 cm
11.7 cm

24.
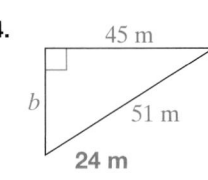
45 m
b   51 m
24 m

25. A ladder 26 ft long is placed 10 ft from the base of a house. How high up the side of the house does the ladder reach? **24 ft**

26. A support cable connects the top of a 30-m pole to an anchor 20 m from the base of the pole. How long is the support cable, to the nearest tenth of a meter? **36.1 m**

Identify each number as *rational* or *irrational*.

27. $\sqrt{30}$ **28.** $3.\overline{7}$ **29.** $\frac{22}{7}$ **30.** π
irrational   rational   rational   irrational

Find the surface area to the nearest whole unit.

31.

12 m   16 m
4 m
20 m
384 m²

32.
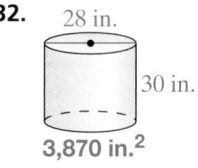
28 in.
30 in.
3,870 in.²

Find the volume to the nearest whole unit.

33.
8 cm
3 cm
6 cm
144 cm³

34.

20 mm
13 mm
4,084 mm³

35. A triangular prism has a volume of 96 m³. The area of the base is 16 m². What is the height of the prism? **6 m**

36. Writing in Math Explain how you would show that a triangle with side lengths 7 in., 24 in., and 25 in. is a right triangle. **See margin.**

37. Measurement The volume of a rectangular prism is 2,058 cm³. The length of the prism is three times the width. The height is 14 cm. Find the other dimensions. length 21 cm, width 7 cm

18. $7 < \sqrt{55} < 8$; about 7

19. $7 < \sqrt{63} < 8$; about 8

20. $2 < \sqrt{8} < 3$; about 3

21. $6 < \sqrt{45} < 7$; about 7

36. Use the Pythagorean Theorem.
$$7^2 + 24^2 = 25^2$$
$$49 + 576 = 625$$
$$625 = 625$$

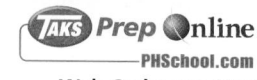

★ TAKS Tips

Some questions on TAKS tests ask you to analyze an object from its top, front, and right-side views.

Below are the top, side, and front views of an object.

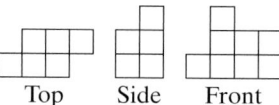

Top   Side   Front

Which solid below matches these three views?

Tip 1
Choose *one* view and see if it matches the answer choices. For example, the top view matches choices A and B.

Tip 2
If an answer choice does not match even one of the views given, you can eliminate it. Since C and D do not match the top view, eliminate them.

Think It Through
Choices A and B match the side view. Looking at the front view, choice B is missing a block on the right side. Therefore, the correct answer is A.

TAKS Review and Preparation Workbook

Texas ExamView CD-ROM
- Instant TAKS Practice Test
- TAKS Practice Items

Differentiated Instruction

Texas Progress Monitoring Assessments
- Benchmark Test 4 **L3**

Spanish Assessment Resources
- Spanish Cumulative Review **ELL**

Texas ExamView CD-ROM
- Special Needs Practice Bank **L1**

Vocabulary Builder

As you solve test items, you must understand the meanings of mathematical terms. Match each term with its mathematical meaning.

A. volume **IV**

B. square root **II**

C. circumference **I**

D. surface area **III**

I. distance around a circle

II. inverse of squaring a number

III. sum of the areas of the faces of a solid

IV. number of cubic units needed to fill the space inside a solid

---

Multiple Choice

Read each question. Then write the letter of the correct answer on your paper.

1. The lens of a pair of glasses is shown. Use a centimeter ruler to measure the radius of the lens.

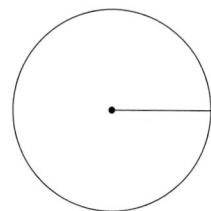

Which of the following is closest to the circumference of the lens? **A**

(A) 9 cm

(B) 3 cm

(C) 7 cm

(D) 2.2 cm

TAKS Daily Review Transparencies

TAKS Daily Review 1   Objective 1: (7.1)(B)
Multiple Choice

The seventh-grade class at Anarene Middle School sold $\frac{1}{20}$ of the Corsicana fruitcakes they bought. Which decimal is equivalent to the fraction sold?

A   65
B   0.65
C   6.5
D   650

Answer: B

TAKS Daily Review 2   Objective 5: (7.12)(A)
Multiple Choice

Shey has been practicing running the 200-meter foot race. Her last 6 times are shown.

23.60 24.15 24.68 28.62 24.25 23.92

What is her mean time?

F   5.02
G   23.92
H   24.21
J   24.87

Answer: J

2. A necklace charm is shown in the diagram below.

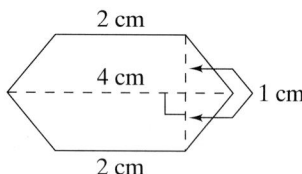

What is the area of the charm? **G**

F. 3 cm²   H. 8 cm²

G. 6 cm²   J. 12 cm²

3. Mrs. Browning made a quilt block in the shape shown below.

Which of the following can be used to find the area of the quilt block? **C**

A. $\frac{1}{2}(3b)$ C. $3b$

B. $4.5b$ D. $\frac{1}{2}(b + 3)$

4. Which of the following CANNOT be used to find the amount of canvas in a sail that is in the shape of a triangle with a height of 12 ft and a width of w feet? **G**

F. $\frac{1}{2}(12w)$ H. $\frac{12w}{2}$

G. $12w$ J. $6w$

5. Mr. McCarrol's garden is shown below.

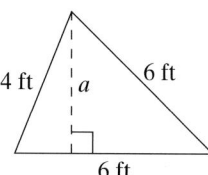

Which of the following expressions can be used to find the area of his garden? **D**

A. $\frac{1}{2}(3a)$ C. $6a$

B. $\frac{a}{2} \times 3$ D. $3a$

6. The model below represents $\sqrt{25} = 5$.

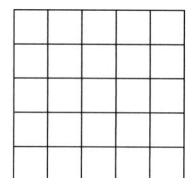

Which arrangement can be used to represent $\sqrt{100}$? **H**

F. 2 rows of 50 small squares

G. 10 rows of 100 small squares

H. 10 row of 10 small squares

J. 50 rows of 2 small squares

7. Which model represents 12^2? **D**

A.

B.

C.

D.

---

8. Which of the following has one base that is a polygon and triangular faces that meet at a vertex? **F**

 F Pyramid   **H** Cylinder

 G Prism   **J** Cone

9. Which of the following statements is NOT true about the figure shown below? **D**

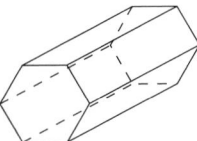

 A It has 18 edges.

 B The bases of the prism are hexagons.

 C It has 6 rectangular faces.

 D It has 10 vertices.

10. Each year the average number of vacation days taken by citizens of the United Kingdom is 28; of Canada, 26 days; of Korea, 25 days; of Japan, 25 days; and of the United States, 13 days. Which measure of the data is 15 days? **J**

 F Mode   **H** Mean

 G Median   **J** Range

11. Texas has 125 state parks, Oklahoma has 51, New Mexico has 31, Arizona has 28, and Louisiana has 30. Which measure of the data given is 53? **C**

 A Mode   **C** Mean

 B Median   **D** Range

Griddable Items

Record your answers in a grid.

12. Regina is making candles. The mold she is using is shown below. Use a centimeter ruler to measure the height of the mold.

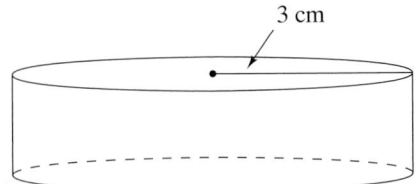

3 cm

To the nearest tenth, how many cubic centimeters of wax does Regina need to fill the mold? **42.4**

13. The diagram shows a glass vase that Mya is filling with water. How many cubic inches of water will Mya need to completely fill the vase? **100**

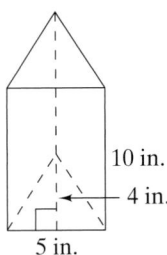

10 in.

4 in.

5 in.

TAKS **GO for Help Guide**

TAKS Objective	Item Number	GO To	TAKS Objective	Item Number	GO To
Obj. 4: (7.9)(A)	1	Lesson 8-5	Obj. 3: (7.6)(C)	8–9	Lesson 8-8
	2	Lesson 8-4	Obj. 5: (7.12)(B)	10–11	Lesson 1-10
Obj. 2: (7.4)(A)	3	Lesson 8-2	Obj. 4: (7.9)(C)	12–13	Lesson 8-10
	4–5	Lesson 8-3			
Obj. 1: (7.1)(C)	6–7	Lesson 8-6			

For additional TAKS practice, see the *TAKS Review and Preparation Workbook.*

9 Patterns and Rules

Chapter at a Glance

Lesson Titles, Objectives, and Features	Assessment	NCTM Standards	TEKS ★ ⒯ⓐⓚⓢ
9-1a Activity Lab, Data Analysis: Choosing Scales and Intervals **9-1 Patterns and Graphs** • To graph data and to use graphs to make predictions	Lesson Quiz	1, 2, 3, 6, 7, 8, 9, 10	**TEKS** (7.4)(B), (7.11)(B) ⒯ⓐⓚⓢ **Obj. 2, 5**
9-2a Activity Lab, Hands On: Finding Patterns **9-2 Number Sequences** • To describe the patterns in arithmetic and geometric sequences and use the patterns to find terms	Lesson Quiz	1, 2, 3, 6, 7, 8, 9, 10	**TEKS** (7.4)(C), (7.15)(A) ⒯ⓐⓚⓢ **Obj. 2, 6**
9-3 Patterns and Tables • To use tables to represent and describe patterns	Lesson Quiz Checkpoint Quiz 1	1, 2, 6, 7, 8, 9, 10	**TEKS** (7.4)(C), (7.15)(A), (7.15)(B) ⒯ⓐⓚⓢ **Obj. 2, 6**
9-4a Activity Lab: Generating Formulas From a Table **9-4 Function Rules** • To write and evaluate functions	Lesson Quiz	1, 2, 6, 7, 8, 9, 10	**TEKS** (7.4)(A), (7.15)(A) ⒯ⓐⓚⓢ **Obj. 2, 6;** Prepares for **TEKS (A.1)(C)**
9-5 Using Tables, Rules, and Graphs • To find solutions to application problems using tables, rules, and graphs **9-5b Activity Lab, Technology:** Three Views of a Function	Lesson Quiz	1, 2, 5, 6, 7, 8, 9, 10	**TEKS** (7.4)(B), (7.5)(B), (7.14)(A) ⒯ⓐⓚⓢ **Obj. 2, 6**
9-6 Interpreting Graphs • To describe and sketch graphs that represent real-world situations **Guided Problem Solving:** Solving Pattern Problems	Lesson Quiz Checkpoint Quiz 2	1, 2, 5, 6, 7, 8, 9, 10	**TEKS** (7.4)(B), (7.13)(C), (7.14)(A), (7.15)(A) ⒯ⓐⓚⓢ **Obj. 2, 6**
9-7 Simple and Compound Interest • To find simple interest and compound interest	Lesson Quiz	1, 2, 6, 7, 8, 9, 10	
9-8 Transforming Formulas • To solve for a variable **9-8b Activity Lab, Algebra Thinking:** More About Formulas	Lesson Quiz	1, 2, 3, 4, 5, 6, 7, 8, 9, 10	**TEKS** (7.13)(A) ⒯ⓐⓚⓢ **Obj. 6**
⒯ⓐⓚⓢ **Tune-Up: Cumulative Practice**			

NCTM Standards 2000
1 Number and Operations   **2** Algebra   **3** Geometry   **4** Measurement   **5** Data Analysis and Probability
6 Problem Solving   **7** Reasoning and Proof   **8** Communication   **9** Connections   **10** Representation

Correlations to Standardized Tests

All content for these tests is contained in *Prentice Hall Math,* Course 2. This chart reflects coverage in this chapter only.

	9-1	9-2	9-3	9-4	9-5	9-6	9-7	9-8
Terra Nova CAT6 (Level 17)								
Number and Number Relations	✔	✔	✔	✔	✔	✔	✔	✔
Computation and Numerical Estimation	✔	✔	✔	✔	✔	✔	✔	✔
Operation Concepts	✔	✔	✔	✔	✔	✔	✔	✔
Measurement								
Geometry and Spatial Sense	✔	✔						✔
Data Analysis, Statistics, and Probability								✔
Patterns, Functions, Algebra	✔	✔	✔	✔	✔	✔	✔	✔
Problem Solving and Reasoning	✔	✔	✔	✔	✔	✔	✔	✔
Communication	✔	✔	✔	✔	✔	✔	✔	✔
Decimals, Fractions, Integers, and Percent	✔	✔	✔	✔	✔	✔	✔	✔
Order of Operations								
Terra Nova CTBS (Level 17)								
Decimals, Fractions, Integers, Percents	✔	✔	✔	✔	✔	✔	✔	✔
Order of Operations, Numeration, Number Theory	✔	✔	✔	✔	✔	✔	✔	✔
Data Interpretation				✔				✔
Pre-abgebra	✔	✔	✔	✔	✔	✔	✔	✔
Measurement								
Geometry	✔	✔						✔
ITBS (Level 13)								
Number Properties and Operations	✔	✔	✔	✔	✔	✔	✔	✔
Algebra	✔	✔	✔	✔	✔	✔	✔	✔
Geometry	✔	✔						✔
Measurement								
Probability and Statistics								
Estimation								
SAT10 (Int 3 Level)								
Number Sense and Operations	✔	✔	✔	✔	✔	✔	✔	✔
Patterns, Relationships, and Algebra	✔	✔	✔	✔	✔	✔	✔	✔
Data, Statistics, and Probability								
Geometry and Measurement	✔	✔						✔
NAEP								
Number Sense, Properties, and Operations	✔		✔	✔	✔		✔	✔
Measurement								
Geometry and Spatial Sense								
Data Analysis, Statistics, and Probability								
Algebra and Functions						✔		

CAT6 California Achievement Test, 6th Ed.　**CTBS** Comprehensive Test of Basic Skills　**ITBS** Iowa Test of Basic Skills, Form M
SAT10 Stanford Achievement Test, 10th Ed.　**NAEP** National Assessment of Educational Progress 2005 Mathematics Objectives

TEKS Math Background

Focus on the TEKS

- At Grade 7, students use words and symbols to describe the relationship between terms in an arithmetic sequence and their positions in the sequence (7.4)(C). Analysis of TAKS results shows that students struggle with this new student expectation.

  In Lesson 9-2, students identify sequences, write rules to describe the sequence, and solve for terms in a sequence. Students use tables to describe and solve for terms in a sequence in Lesson 9-3. Place special emphasis on these lessons because they both focus on (7.4)(C).

- Also new at Grade 7 is formulating an equation when given a problem situation (7.5)(B). Students write function rules to solve real-life problem situations in Lesson 9-5 (7.5)(B).

9-1　Patterns and Graphs

TEKS ★ (TAKS) (7.4)(B), (7.11)(B) Obj. 2, 5

Math Understandings
- You can visually represent the relationship between two or more sets of numbers by drawing a graph.
- The scales on each axis can have different increments and can represent different measures. However, the increments on each axis must be of equal size.
- You can use a graph to make estimates between or beyond data points.

You can use a graph to make a prediction by extending the graph by finding the corresponding value on the appropriate axis.

Example: Graph the data in the table and predict from the graph what the height of the plant will be after 5 weeks.

2.5 in.

Plant Growth	
Age (weeks)	Height (in.)
1	0.5
2	1.0
3	1.5

9-2　Number Sequences

TEKS ★ (TAKS) (7.4)(C), (7.15)(A) Obj. 2, 6

Math Understandings
- You can write a sequence if you know the pattern it follows and the first term.
- In an arithmetic sequence, there is a common difference between successive terms; in a geometric sequence, there is a common ratio between successive terms.
- A conjecture assumes that a given pattern will continue (inductive reasoning).

A **sequence** is a set of numbers that follow a pattern. You can find each term of an **arithmetic sequence** by adding a fixed number to the previous term. In a **geometric sequence,** you find each term by multiplying the previous term by a fixed number. A **conjecture** is a prediction that suggests what you expect will happen.

9-3　Patterns and Tables
9-4　Function Rules

TEKS ★ (TAKS) (7.4)(C), (7.15)(A), (7.15)(B) Obj. 2, 6;
Prepares for TEKS (A.1)(C)

Math Understandings
- You can represent the relationship between two quantities using a table or a rule.
- When the value of one quantity, y, depends on one value of another quantity, x, then y is a function of x.

You can pair the term numbers in a sequence with the values in the sequence. The rule for the relationship in the table below is multiply the term number by 3, or $3n$.

Term number	1	2	3	4
Value	3	6	9	12

A **function** is a relationship that assigns exactly one output value for each input value.

Example: Is the relationship in each table a function?

input	1	2	3	4
output	0	2	0	2

This is a function because each input has exactly one output. Note that two inputs can have the same output.

input	1	1	3	4
output	0	2	0	2

This is NOT a function because one input is associated with two outputs.

9-5 Using Tables, Rules, and Graphs
9-6 Interpreting Graphs

TEKS ★ *TAKS* (7.4)(B), (7.5)(B), (7.14)(A) Obj. 2, 6

Math Understandings

- You can represent the relationship between two quantities using a table, a rule, or a graph.
- The graph of a function shows the relationship between inputs and outputs.

Example: Write and graph the function $y = 8x$ that relates the total amount earned, y, to the number of $8 shirts sold, x.

Make a table of values.

Number of Shirts Sold	1	10	20	30
Total Earned ($)	8	80	160	240

9-7 Simple and Compound Interest

Math Understandings

- Interest is money that you pay to use someone else's money, or money that you earn when someone else uses your money.

Simple Interest Formula	Compound Interest Formula
$I = prt$	$B = p(1 + r)^t$
I is interest, p is principal, r is annual interest rate, and t is time in years.	B is balance, p is principal, r is annual interest rate, and t is time in years.

The original amount you deposit or borrow is the **principal**. Interest calculated on the principal is **simple interest**. In accounts where money is not withdrawn, compound interest is paid on the original principal and on any interest that has been left in the account. The **balance** of an account is the principal plus the interest earned.

9-8 Transforming Formulas

Math Understandings

- When you solve an equation or formula for a variable, you use inverse operations and the properties of equality.

A **formula** is a rule that shows the relationship between two or more quantities. You can use the properties of equality to transform a formula and solve for a variable. When you transform a formula, you rewrite it in an equivalent form so that the variable for which you are solving is isolated on one side of the equation.

Example: Solve the formula $F = \frac{9}{5}C + 32$ for C.

$$F = \frac{9}{5}C + 32$$

$$F - 32 = \frac{9}{5}C \qquad \longleftarrow \text{Subtract 32 from each side.}$$

$$\frac{5}{9}(F - 32) = \frac{5}{9} \cdot \frac{9}{5}C \longleftarrow \text{Multiply each side by } \frac{5}{9}, \text{ the reciprocal of } \frac{9}{5}.$$

$$\frac{5}{9}(F - 32) = C$$

Additional Professional Development Opportunities

Math Background Notes for Chapter 9: Every lesson has a Math Background in the PLAN section.

Research Overview, Mathematics Strands
Additional support for these topics and more is in the front of the Teacher's Edition.

LessonLab
LessonLab, a Pearson Education company, offers comprehensive, facilitated professional development designed to help teachers to improve student achievement. To learn more, please visit lessonlab.com.

Texas Chapter 9 Resources

	9-1	9-2	9-3	9-4	9-5	9-6	9-7	9-8	For the Chapter
Print Resources									
L3 Practice	●	●	●	●	●	●	●	●	
L1 Adapted Practice	●	●	●	●	●	●	●	●	
L3 Guided Problem Solving	●	●	●	●	●	●	●	●	
L2 Reteaching	●	●	●	●	●	●	●	●	
L4 Enrichment	●	●	●	●	●	●	●	●	
L3 Daily Notetaking Guide	●	●	●	●	●	●	●	●	
L1 Adapted Daily Notetaking Guide	●	●	●	●	●	●	●	●	
L3 Vocabulary and Study Skills Worksheet	●		●	●		●		●	●
L3 Daily Puzzles	●	●	●	●	●	●	●	●	
L3 Activity Labs	●	●	●	●	●	●			
L3 Checkpoint Quiz			●			●			
L3 Chapter Project									●
L2 Chapter Test									●
L3 Chapter Test									●
L4 Alternative Assessment									●
L3 Cumulative Review									●
Spanish Resources ELL									
L3 Practice	●	●	●	●	●	●	●	●	●
L3 Vocabulary and Study Skills Worksheets	●		●	●		●		●	●
L3 Checkpoint Quiz			●			●			
L2 Chapter Test									●
L3 Chapter Test									●
L4 Alternative Assessment									●
L3 Cumulative Review									●
Transparencies									
Check Skills You'll Need	●	●	●	●	●	●	●	●	
Additional Examples	●	●	●	●	●	●	●	●	
Problem of the Day	●	●	●	●	●	●	●	●	
TAKS Daily Review	●	●	●	●	●	●	●		
Classroom Aid					●				
Student Edition Answers	●	●	●	●	●	●	●	●	●
Lesson Quiz	●	●	●	●	●	●	●	●	
TAKS Strategies									●
Technology									
Texas Interactive Textbook Online	●	●	●	●	●	●	●	●	
Texas StudentExpress CD-ROM	●	●	●	●	●	●	●	●	●
Success Tracker™ Online Intervention	●	●	●	●	●	●	●	●	●
TeacherExpress CD-ROM	●	●	●	●	●	●	●	●	●
PresentationExpress CD-ROM	●	●	●	●	●	●	●	●	●
Texas ExamView CD-ROM with QuickTake	●	●	●	●	●	●	●	●	●
MindPoint Quiz Show CD-ROM	●	●	●	●	●	●	●	●	●
Prentice Hall Web Site: PHSchool.com	●	●	●	●	●	●	●	●	●

Also available: **TAKS Tune-Up Kit**
- TAKS Daily Review Transparencies
- TAKS Review and Preparation Workbook
- TAKS Strategies with Transparencies
- Texas Progress Monitoring Assessments
- Texas ExamView CD-ROM
- MindPoint Quiz Show CD-ROM

Other Resources
Algebra Readiness Tests
All-in-One Student Workbook
All-in-One Student Workbook, Adapted Version
Multilingual Handbook

Solution Key
Math Notes Study Folder
Spanish Cumulative Assessment

Where You Can Use the Lesson Resources

Here is a suggestion, following the four-step teaching plan, for how you can incorporate Differentiated Instruction Resources into your teaching.

	Instructional Resources L3	**Differentiated Instruction Resources**
1. Plan		
Preparation Read the Math Background in the Teacher's Edition to connect this lesson with students' previous experience. **Starting Class** **Check Skills You'll Need** Assign these exercises to review prerequisite skills. **TEKS** ★ **TAKS** Review the full text of the TEKS student expectations and TAKS objectives covered in this lesson. **New Vocabulary** Help students pre-read the lesson by pointing out the new terms introduced in the lesson.	**TEKS Math Background** **Math Understandings** **Transparencies & PresentationExpress CD-ROM** Check Skills You'll Need Problem of the Day TAKS Daily Review **Resources** Vocabulary and Study Skills	**Spanish Support** ELL Vocabulary and Study Skills
2. Teach		
L3 Guided Instruction Use the Activity Labs to build conceptual understanding. Teach each Example. Use the Teacher's Edition side column notes for specific teaching tips, including Error Prevention notes. Use the Additional Examples found in the side column (and on transparency and PowerPoint) as an alternative presentation for the content. After each Example, assign the Quick Check exercise for that Example to get an immediate assessment of student understanding. Use the Closure activity in the Teacher's Edition to help students attain mastery of lesson content.	**Student Edition** Activity Lab **Resources** Daily Notetaking Guide Activity Lab **Transparencies & PresentationExpress CD-ROM** Additional Examples Classroom Aids **Texas ExamView CD-ROM with QuickTake**	**Teacher's Edition** Every lesson includes suggestions for working with students who need special attention. L1 Special Needs L2 Below Level L4 Advanced Learners ELL English Language Learners **Resources** L1 Adapted Daily Notetaking Guide **Multilingual Handbook**
3. Practice		

Assignment Guide
Check Your Understanding
Use these questions to check students' understanding before you assign homework.
Homework Exercises
Assign homework from these leveled exercises in the Assignment Guide.
  A Practice by Example
  B Apply Your Skills
  C Challenge
  TAKS Tune-Up and Mixed Review
Homework Quick Check
Use these key exercises to quickly check students' homework.
	Transparencies & PresentationExpress CD-ROM
	Student Answers
	Resources
	Practice
	Guided Problem Solving
	Vocabulary and Study Skills
	Activity Lab
	Daily Puzzles
	Texas ExamView CD-ROM with QuickTake
		Spanish Support
		ELL Practice
		ELL Vocabulary and Study Skills
		Resources
		L1 Adapted Practice
		L4 Enrichment

4. Assess & Reteach		
Lesson Quiz Assign the Lesson Quiz to assess students' mastery of the lesson content. **Checkpoint Quiz** Use the Checkpoint Quiz to assess student progress over several lessons.	**Transparencies & PresentationExpress CD-ROM** Lesson Quiz **Resources** Checkpoint Quiz	**Resources** L2 Reteaching ELL Checkpoint Quiz Success Tracker™ Online Intervention **Texas ExamView CD-ROM with QuickTake**

KEY   L1 Special Needs   L2 Below Level   L3 For All Students   L4 Advanced, Gifted   ELL English Language Learners

CHAPTER 9

Patterns and Rules

 Check Your Readiness

Answers are in the back of the textbook.

For intervention, direct students to:

Exponents and Order of Operations
Lesson 2-1
Extra Skills and Word
  Problems Practice, Ch. 2

Evaluating Algebraic Expressions
Lesson 4-1
Extra Skills and Word
  Problems Practice, Ch. 4

Solving Two-Step Equations
Lesson 4-6
Extra Skills and Word
  Problems Practice, Ch. 4

Percents, Fractions, and Decimals
Lesson 6-2
Extra Skills and Word
  Problems Practice, Ch. 6

What You've Learned
TEKS ★ TAKS

- **(7.5)(A)** In Chapter 4, you used concrete and pictorial models to solve equations and used symbols to record the actions. **TAKS Obj. 2**
- **(7.5)(B)** You also formulated problem situations when given a simple equation and formulated an equation when given a problem situation. **TAKS Obj. 2**
- **(7.4)(A)** In Chapter 8, you generated formulas involving perimeter, area, circumference, and volume. **TAKS Obj. 2**

 Check Your Readiness

GO for Help	
For Exercises	**See Lesson**
1–4	2-1
5–8	4-1
9–14	4-6
15–19	6-2

Exponents and Order of Operations

Simplify.

1. $2^3 \cdot 2 - 4^2$ 0

2. $2^3 \cdot (2 - 4)^2$ 32

3. $(3 - 2)^2 - 2^2$ −3

4. $4^3 + 4 \div 4$ 65

Evaluating Algebraic Expressions

Evaluate each expression using $r = 4$, $s = -2$, and $t = 5.1$.

5. $3r - t$ 6.9

6. rst −40.8

7. $8s^2 + rt$ 52.4

8. $1.5(1 + s)^r$ 1.5

Solving Two-Step Equations

Solve each equation.

9. $3x - 1 = 14$ 5

10. $10 + 3n = 25$ 5

11. $4(b - 3) = 7$ $4\frac{3}{4}$

12. $\frac{2}{3}n - 10 = 14$ 36

13. $\frac{x}{7} = 49$ 343

14. $1.5 + \frac{4}{5}a = 21$ $24\frac{3}{8}$

Percents, Fractions, and Decimals

Write each percent as a decimal.

15. 4% 0.04

16. 12% 0.12

17. 3.58% 0.0358

18. 4.05% 0.0405

19. 10.3% 0.103

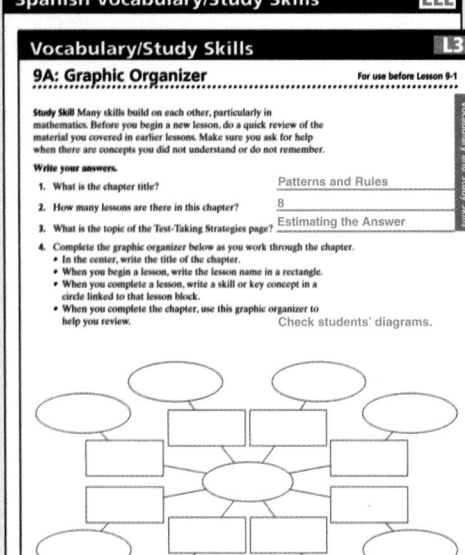

Spanish Vocabulary/Study Skills ELL

Vocabulary/Study Skills L3

9A: Graphic Organizer *For use before Lesson 9-1*

Study Skill Many skills build on each other, particularly in mathematics. Before you begin a new lesson, do a quick review of the material you covered in earlier lessons. Make sure you ask for help when there are concepts you did not understand or do not remember.

Write your answers.

1. What is the chapter title? *Patterns and Rules*
2. How many lessons are there in this chapter? *8*
3. What is the topic of the Test-Taking Strategies page? *Estimating the Answer*
4. Complete the graphic organizer below as you work through the chapter.
   • In the center, write the title of the chapter.
   • When you begin a lesson, write the lesson name in a rectangle.
   • When you complete a lesson, write a skill or key concept in a circle linked to that lesson block.
   • When you complete the chapter, use this graphic organizer to help you review. *Check students' diagrams.*

434

434   Chapter 9

Patterns, Relationships, and Algebraic Reasoning
TEKS (7.4)(A), (7.4)(B), (7.4)(C), (7.5)(B)
TAKS Obj. 2

Probability and Statistics
TEKS (7.11)(B)
TAKS Obj. 5

Underlying Processes and Mathematical Tools
TEKS (7.13)(A), (7.13)(C), (7.14)(A), (7.15)(A), (7.15)(B)
TAKS Obj. 6

Chapter 9 Overview

In this chapter, students study patterns, sequences, and functions as they interpret and use tables, rules, graphs, and formulas. They draw upon their knowledge of percents and decimals to find simple and compound interest.

Activating Prior Knowledge

In this chapter, to find and use patterns to solve problems, students will use their number sense and build on their knowledge of equations, expressions, decimals, fractions, and percents. Ask questions such as:

• *How do you find 20% of a number?* Multiply the number by 0.2 or $\frac{1}{5}$.

• *What is the value of the expression* $y + 3x + 2$ *when* $y = 4$ *and* $x = 12$? 42

What You'll Learn Next
TEKS ⭐ TAKS

• **(7.4)(B)** In this chapter, you will learn to graph data to demonstrate relationships in familiar concepts such as conversions, perimeter, area, circumference, and volume. **TAKS Obj. 2**

• **(7.4)(C)** You will use words and symbols to describe the relationship between the terms in an arithmetic sequence and their positions in the sequence. **TAKS Obj. 2**

• **(7.15)(A)** You will make conjectures from patterns or sets of examples. **TAKS Obj. 6**

TAKS Tune-Up On pages 481–483, you will review and practice the vocabulary and *TAKS* objectives you have learned.

Key Vocabulary

• arithmetic sequence (p. 442)
• balance (p. 469)
• compound interest (p. 469)
• conjecture (p. 443)
• formula (p. 472)
• function (p. 452)
• geometric sequence (p. 442)
• principal (p. 468)
• sequence (p. 442)
• simple interest (p. 468)

Activity Lab

Choosing Scales and Intervals

Students learn to choose appropriate scales and intervals to accurately display data on a graph. This will prepare them to work with graphs in Lesson 9-1.

Guided Instruction

Display a graph and use it to demonstrate the meanings of *scale* and *interval*. Point out that a graph has two scales, horizontal and vertical. Ask questions such as:

• *Why is it important to find the right scale and interval to display data accurately?* A graph with the right scale and intervals shows all the relevant data at a level of detail that makes it easy to see the relationship between sets of data.

• *Why do we divide to find the scale?* to find the number of intervals and how far apart they should be

Exercises

Have students work independently on the Exercises. Have students form small groups and compare graphs when they have finished.

Alternative Method

Some students may find it easier to make the calculations using a calculator. Make sure they are available to students who want them.

TEKS ★ TAKS Resources

• Activity Lab 9-1: Patterns in Data
• graph paper
• calculator

Dana Center TEKS Toolkit Clarifying Activities (7.4)(B)
Visit: PHSchool.com
Web Code: arq-9045

Choosing Scales and Intervals

TEKS ★ TAKS

(7.4)(B) To graph data to demonstrate relationships in familiar concepts **TAKS** Obj. 2

To display data on a graph, you need to choose scales and intervals. A graph includes two *scales*, the horizontal axis and the vertical axis. An *interval* is the difference between the values on a scale.

EXAMPLE

Graph the data in the table at the right.

Step 1 Choose the scales and intervals.
Use the horizontal scale for the amount saved. Use the vertical scale for the interest earned. Start both scales at 0. Graphs that have from 6 to 10 intervals are easy to read. Since the greatest amount saved is $900, the horizontal scale needs to range from $0 to at least $900. Divide 900 by a factor from 6 to 10. Choose 9, since 900 is divisible by 9.

$900 \div 9 = 100$ ← Divide the greatest amount by a compatible number.

Use 9 intervals of $100 for the horizontal scale. Since the greatest interest earned is $36, the vertical scale needs to range from $0 to at least $36. Divide 36 by a factor from 6 to 10.

$36 \div 9 = 4$ ← Divide the greatest amount by a compatible number.

Use 9 intervals of $4 for the vertical scale.

Step 2 Use points to represent the data.
The red dashes show how to plot the point representing interest earned of $14 for an amount saved of $350.

Interest on Savings

Amount Saved ($)	Interest Earned ($)
200	8
350	14
500	20
750	30
900	36

Interest on Savings

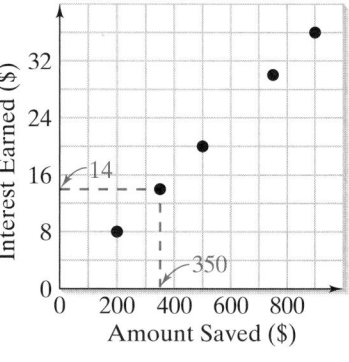

Exercises

1. a. **Number Sense** Use the table at the right. What interval can you use for time? For distance? Answers may vary. Sample:
   b. Graph the data. See margin. 8 intervals of 10; 6 intervals of 10

2. a. Graph the data in the Example using a vertical interval of $5.
   b. **Reasoning** Which interval is easier to use, $4 or $5? Explain.
   2a. See margin.
      b. An interval of $4; more of the numbers are divisible by 4 than by 5.

Travel Speed

Time (min)	Distance (mi)
0	0
20	15
40	30
60	45
80	60

436 Activity Lab Choosing Scales and Intervals

1b. See back of book.
2a. See back of book.

Patterns and Graphs

Check Skills You'll Need

1. Vocabulary Review
Is a *repeating decimal* a rational number? Explain. 1–5.
See back of book.
Graph and label each point.

2. 7   **3.** $3\frac{1}{2}$

4. 2.3   **5.** 0.8

 for Help
Lesson 2-7

TEKS ★ (TAKS)
• **(7.4)(B)** To graph data to demonstrate relationships in familiar concepts such as conversions and perimeter (TAKS) **Obj. 2**
• **(7.11)(B)** To make inferences and convincing arguments based on an analysis of given or collected data (TAKS) **Obj. 5**

Why Learn This?

You may have heard that "a picture is worth a thousand words." Graphs can help you see patterns in data. The table at the right shows the conversion of yards to inches. A graph of the same data can be easier to understand.

Yards and Inches

Number of Yards	Number of Inches
1	36
2	72
3	108
4	144
5	180

EXAMPLE   Graphing Data

1 Graph the data in the table above.

The pattern in the first column of data suggests a horizontal interval of 1.

Graphs that have from 6 to 10 intervals are easy to read. The greatest value in the second column is 180. Divide 180 by a factor from 6 to 10. Choose 9, since 180 is divisible by 9.

$$180 \div 9 = 20 \quad \leftarrow \text{Divide the greatest amount by a compatible number.}$$

Use 9 intervals of 20 for the vertical scale. Use points to represent the data.

Yards and Inches

Quick Check

1. Graph the data in the table below. See back of book.

Yogurt Costs

Amount of Yogurt (c)	Price ($)
50	26
100	49
150	72
200	95

TEKS ★ (TAKS)

(7.4)(B) To graph data to demonstrate relationships in familiar concepts such as conversions and perimeter (TAKS) **Obj. 2**
Also supports
(7.11)(B) (TAKS) **Obj. 5**

Dana Center TEKS Toolkit Clarifying Activities (7.4)(B), (7.11)(B)
Visit: PHSchool.com
Web Code: arq-9045

TEKS Math Background

The key to making a useful graph is choosing appropriate *scales* and *intervals*. The scale is the units used for an axis. The interval is the distance between values on a scale. For instance, a scale for an axis that represents distance might be feet or miles, and its interval might be 5 feet, 20 feet, or 1 mile.

More Math Background: p. 434C

Lesson Planning and Resources

See p. 434E for a list of the resources that support this lesson.

PowerPoint
Bell Ringer Practice

✓ **Check Skills You'll Need**
Use student page, transparency, or PowerPoint.

(TAKS) **Daily Review 67**
Use transparency.

Differentiated Instruction   Solutions for All Learners

Special Needs L1
If students have a difficult time drawing graphs, have them work with a partner. The partner can graph the data while the student makes decisions about interval sizes and checks the graph against the data table.

learning style: visual

Below Level L2
What intervals would you use to graph the following data?

Number of CDs	1	3	7
Cost ($)	4.99	14.97	34.93

Sample: 1 for *x*-axis, $5 for *y*-axis

learning style: visual

Activity Lab

Use before the lesson.
Student Edition Activity Lab, Data
Analysis 9-1a, Choosing Scales and
Intervals, p. 436

 Teaching Resources

Activity Lab 9-1: Patterns in Data

Guided Instruction

Example 3
Students might extend graphs in
the wrong direction. Remind them
that data, such as temperature, can
be extended into quadrants with
negative numbers. Other types of
data, such as height and length,
cannot have negative values.

PowerPoint

Additional Examples

1 Graph the data in the table.
See back of book.

No. of Boxes	20	40	60	80	100
Cost ($)	15	25	35	40	50

Use the graph for Exercises 2–3.

2 A water company charges a set
fee for each gallon of water.
How much do 250 gallons of
water cost? about $10

3 Estimate the cost for 600
gallons of water. about $24

 Teaching Resources
• Daily Notetaking Guide 9-1 **L3**
• Adapted Notetaking 9-1 **L1**

Closure

• Explain how to choose an
appropriate interval for a scale.
Sample: Subtract the smallest
data value from the largest;
divide by the number of
intervals desired and round to a
convenient number.

You can use a graph to make estimates between data points.

> **EXAMPLE** **Estimating on a Graph**

2 **TAKS Multiple Choice** The graph shows the cost of renting a personal
watercraft. Which is the best estimate for the cost of a $3\frac{1}{2}$-hour rental?

  Ⓐ about $200   Ⓒ about $250

  Ⓑ about $225   Ⓓ about $350

Watercraft Rental

Draw lines to locate the value on the
vertical axis that corresponds to $3\frac{1}{2}$ on
the horizontal axis.

The cost is greater than $200, but less
than $250. Estimate the cost as $225.

The cost of a $3\frac{1}{2}$-hour rental is about $225. The correct answer is B.

> ✓ **Quick Check**

2. Use the graph in Example 2 to estimate the cost of a $1\frac{1}{2}$-hour rental.
      about $125

You can use a graph to make a prediction. Extend the graph and find a
corresponding value on the appropriate axis.

> **EXAMPLE** **Making a Prediction**

> ★ **TAKS Tip**
> Make sure the lines you use
> to locate a point are parallel
> to the scales of the graph.

3 The graph shows the relationship between Celsius and Fahrenheit
temperatures. Estimate the Celsius temperature for $160°F$.

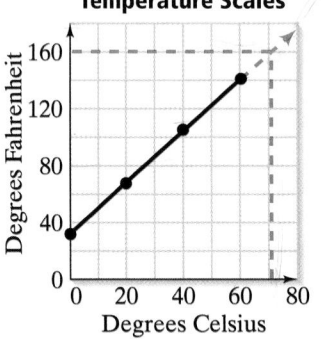

Temperature Scales

← Extend the graph beyond 160°F.

For 160°F, the Celsius temperature
← is slightly more than 70°. Estimate
the answer.

A temperature of $160°F$ is about $71°C$.

> ✓ **Quick Check**

3. Estimate the Fahrenheit temperature for $80°C$. about 175°F

438   Chapter 9   Patterns and Rules

Advanced Learners **L4**
*Given x = −1, 2, and 4 when y = −6, 6, and 14, what
equation describes the pattern?* $y = 4x − 2$

Pre-AP™

English Language Learners ELL
Help students make sense of the choices made in
Example 1. Ask questions like, *Why choose an interval
of one along the horizontal axis?* Data suggests it.
*What would have happened if we had chosen 6 or 10
as a factor to divide 180 by?* different interval sizes

learning style: verbal

Shoveling Snow

Hours Worked	Wages ($)
2	18
4	36
5	45
6	54

1. **Vocabulary** How can a graph help you make a prediction? *A graph shows how the data are changing.*

2. Use the data in the table at the left. If you were to graph wages on the vertical axis, what scale and interval would you use? *Answers may vary. Sample: $0–$54; 6 intervals of $9*

3. If you were to graph hours worked on the horizontal axis, what scale and interval would you use? *Answers may vary. Sample: 0–8; 4 intervals of 2*

Choose a reasonable scale and interval to graph each set of data.
4–5. Answers may vary. Samples are given.

4. 70, 35, 55, 10, 43, 25, 80
0–80; 8 intervals of 10

5. 4,700; 2,000; 3,400; 1,650; 2,800
0–5,000; 10 intervals of 50

Homework Exercises

For more exercises, see Extra Skills and Word Problems.

GO for Help

For Exercises	See Examples
6–7	1
8–9	2
10–12	3

Ⓐ Graph the data in each table. *6–7. See margin.*

6. **Plant Growth**

Age (yr)	Height (cm)
5	90
7	95
9	102
11	110

7. **Used Dirt Bike Prices**

Age (yr)	Price ($)
2	43
4	37
6	30

Estimate using your graphs from Exercises 6 and 7.

8. the height of an 8-year-old plant *about 100 cm*

9. the age of a bike that is sold for $40 *about 3 yr*

Estimate using the graph at the left.

Electricity Charges

10. the cost of 85 kilowatt-hours of electricity *about $7*

11. the cost of 100 kilowatt-hours of electricity *about $8*

12. the number of kilowatt-hours that cost $6.50 *about 81 h*

13. **Writing in Math** Describe what a graph looks like when both sets of values increase. *Answers may vary. Sample: Each point is to the right and above the previous point.*

Ⓑ **GPS** 14. **Guided Problem Solving** Graph the data in the table. Then estimate the missing value. *See margin.*

Hours of Sleep	Math Test Score
9	93
8	85
7	74
6	n

- **Make a Plan** Draw a graph. Extend the graph to locate the missing value.
- **Carry Out the Plan** For a value of 6 on the horizontal scale, the value on the vertical scale is ▦.

6.

7.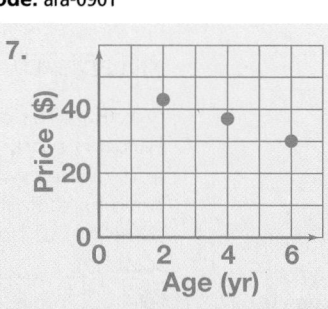

14. See back of book.

PowerPoint

Lesson Quiz

1. Graph the data in the table.

Chain (ft)	15	20	30	40
Cost ($)	36	48	72	96

Chain Length Costs

2. About how much do 25 ft of chain cost? about $60

3. About how much do 5 ft of chain cost? about $12

15–16. See back of book.
17a. See back of book.
18–19b. See back of book.

GO **Online**
Homework Help
Visit: PHSchool.com
Web Code: are-0901

Graph the data. Use the graph to estimate the missing value.
15–16. See margin.

15.

Time (h)	Temp. (°C)
1	12
2	15
5	24
8	n

16.

Gallons	Quarts
2	8
3	n
5	20
6	24

17. a. Geometry Graph the perimeters of squares with side lengths of 1, 2, 3, 4, and 5 in. Use the graph for parts (b) and (c). See margin.
b. Estimate the side length of a square with perimeter 9.6 in. 2.4 in.
c. Estimate the perimeter of a square with side length 3.5 in. 14 in.
d. Calculator Test your estimates with a calculator. Were your estimates correct? Check students' work.

18. Physical Fitness To qualify for the Presidential Physical Fitness Award, girls between the ages of 11 and 14 must be able to run one mile within the times listed. Graph the data. Then estimate the time for a 17-year-old girl. Why might your estimate be inaccurate? See margin.

Age (yr)	Time (min)
11	9.02
12	8.23
13	8.13
14	7.59

C **19. Challenge** Suppose a neighbor will pay you $10 per week to wash windows. Another neighbor will give you $40 plus $7 per week.
a. Make two tables, one for each neighbor, showing the amount you receive from each neighbor for 1, 2, 3, 4, and 5 weeks of work.
b. Graph both sets of data on the same axes. 19a–b. See margin.
c. How much will you receive from each neighbor after 10 weeks? Which job would you prefer? first neighbor: $100; second neighbor: $110; working for the second neighbor

The Presidential Fitness Challenge consists of five fitness tests, including pull-ups.

TEKS ★ TAKS Tune-Up and Mixed Review

TAKS Objective 2
TEKS (7.4)(B)

20. Which of the following relationships is best represented by the data in the graph at the right? **C**

A Conversion of quarts to pints
B Conversion of gallons to cups
C Conversion of cups to fluid ounces
D Conversion of gallons to fluid ounces

TAKS Objective 4
TEKS (7.9)(C)

21. A small box measures 3 inches on each side. A larger box holds 125 of these small boxes. What is the volume of the larger box? **F**
F $3{,}375 \text{ in.}^3$ G $1{,}125 \text{ in.}^3$ H 375 in.^3 J 26 in.^3

GO **for Help**   Lesson 6-2

Write each percent as a decimal.

22. 38% 0.38   **23.** 5% 0.05   **24.** 150% 1.50   **25.** 6.2% 0.062

Enrichment 9-1 **L4**
Reteaching 9-1 Patterns and **L2**

Graphs can help you visualize the relationship between data. A graph includes two scales, one on the horizontal axis and one on the vertical axis. An interval is the distance between the values on a scale.

Graph the data in the table.

Step 1 Choose the scales and intervals.

Graph the data in the first column on the horizontal axis. Graph the data in the second column on the vertical axis.

Choose the interval for the scale on the horizontal axis. The greatest number of hours worked is 9. If each interval is 1 hour, then the number of intervals is 9 ÷ 1 = 9.

Choose the interval for the scale on the vertical axis. The greatest amount of money earned is $74.25. If each interval is $5, then the number of intervals is 74.25 ÷ 5 = 14.85, or 15 intervals.

Step 2 Draw the graph and plot the data. Estimate the position of data points that fall between intervals.

Hours Worked	Money Earned
5	$41.25
6	$49.50
7	$57.75
8	$66.00
9	$74.25

Graph the data in each table.

1.

Hours	Miles Run
2	10
2.8	14
3.2	16
3.6	18

2.

Gallons of Gas	Miles Driven
0.5	13
1.5	39
2.5	65
3	78

TEKS ★ TAKS Resources

• TAKS Strategies, p. 477
• TAKS Tune-Up, pp. 481–483

TAKS Tune-Up Kit
• TAKS Daily Review Transparencies
• TAKS Review and Preparation Workbook
• TAKS Strategies with Transparencies
• Texas Progress Monitoring Assessments

Alternative Assessment

Provide pairs of students with graph paper. Partners work together to complete Exercises 6 and 7. They write a title for their graphs and label both axes. Partners work together to write a summary of how they chose the intervals for both scales.

Finding Patterns

ACTIVITY

Use pattern blocks or draw diagrams.

1. Make the next two figures in the pattern below.

1.

Figure 1   Figure 2   Figure 3

2. How many blocks do you add to each figure to make the next figure in the pattern? 6 blocks

3. Copy and complete the table. See margin.

4. Describe any patterns you notice in your table.
Answers may vary. Sample: Each figure has 6 more blocks than the previous figure.

Figure	1	2	3	4	5	6	7	8
Number of Blocks	1							

Exercises

Use the pattern of cubes pictured below for Exercises 1–4.

1. a. Number Sense How many cubes will be in the fourth prism? 64
   b. Build the fourth prism using colored cubes. Check students' work.

2. a. Number Sense How many cubes will be in the fifth prism? 125
   b. Build the fifth prism using colored cubes. Check students' work.

3. Copy and complete the table at the right. See margin.

4. (Algebra) Write a formula that relates the prism number p to the number of blocks n.
$n = p^3$

Prism	1	2	3	4	5
Number of Blocks	1	8	27		

Activity
3.

Figure	1	2	3	4	5	6	7	8
Number of Blocks	1	7	13	19	25	31	37	43

Exercises
3.

Prism	1	2	3	4	5
Number of Blocks	1	8	27	64	125

Finding Patterns

Students use pattern blocks or drawings to study patterns and draw conclusions. This Activity will help them recognize patterns in number sequences in Lesson 9-2.

Guided Instruction

Before beginning the Activity, discuss patterns they have seen in everyday life. Display a quilt or other item containing a repeating pattern and have students identify the pattern. Ask questions, such as:

- *What is the pattern in the Activity?* one central block plus six new blocks for each new figure
- *What expression would you write to show that pattern?* 1 + 6x or 6x + 1
- *What does the variable stand for?* the number of times the pattern the repeats
- *How many blocks would there be in Figure 10?* 61

Exercises

Have students work independently on the Exercises. When they have finished, have them compare answers with a partner to see if their patterns are the same.

Alternative Method

Some students may be able to see the pattern from the numbers in the table. Have them look at the numbers in the bottom row of the table and ask if they can see the pattern that way.

TEKS ⋆ (TAKS) Resources

- Activity Lab 9-2: Patterns in Geometry
- pattern blocks

Dana Center TEKS Toolkit
Clarifying Activities (7.4)(C), (7.15)(A)
Visit: PHSchool.com
Web Code: arq-9045

TEKS ⋆ (TAKS)
(7.4)(C) To use words and symbols to describe the relationship between terms and their positions in a sequence (TAKS) Obj. 2
(7.15)(A) To make conjectures from patterns or sets of examples (TAKS) Obj. 6

9-2 **Number Sequences**

TEKS

(7.4)(C) To use words and symbols to describe the relationship between terms in an arithmetic sequence and their positions in the sequence **TAKS** Obj. 2
Also supports
(7.15)(A) **TAKS** Obj. 6

Dana Center TEKS Toolkit Clarifying Activities (7.4)(C), (7.15)(A)
Visit: PHSchool.com
Web Code: arq-9045

TEKS Math Background

A *sequence* is a set of numbers that follows a pattern. In an *arithmetic sequence,* each term is derived from the one before it by consistently adding the same amount. In a *geometric sequence,* each term is derived from the one before it by multiplying the term by the same number. A sequence can be arithmetic, geometric, both, or neither.

More Math Background: p. 434C

Lesson Planning and Resources

See p. 434E for a list of the resources that support this lesson.

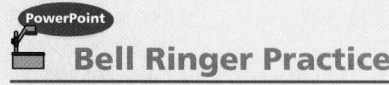

Bell Ringer Practice

☑ **Check Skills You'll Need**
Use student page, transparency, or PowerPoint.

TAKS **Daily Review 68**
Use transparency.

442

☑ **Check Skills You'll Need**

1. Vocabulary Review
The *additive inverse* of −8 is ■. 8

Add.

2. −3 + 3   0

3. −3 + 2   −1

4. −3 + 1   −2

5. −3 + 0   −3

GO **for Help**
Lesson 1-7

Vocabulary Tip

You pronounce *arithmetic sequence* as "ar ith MET ik SEE kwuns."

TEKS
- (7.4)(C) To use words and symbols to describe the relationship between terms in an arithmetic sequence and their positions in the sequence **TAKS** Obj. 2
- (7.15)(A) To make conjectures from patterns **TAKS** Obj. 6

🔊 **New Vocabulary** sequence, arithmetic sequence, geometric sequence, conjecture

Why Learn This?

Some patterns are found in nature. If you can recognize a pattern in a list of numbers, you can make predictions about how the list will continue.

A **sequence** is a set of numbers that follow a pattern. Each number in a sequence is called a *term.* The set of numbers 1, 3, 5, 7, 9, … has a pattern. If you add 2 to any number, you get the next number in the set.

In an **arithmetic sequence,** you find each term by adding a fixed number (called the common difference) to the previous term.

EXAMPLE **Describing an Arithmetic Sequence**

1 Describe the pattern in the sequence below. Then find the next three terms in the sequence.

Position	1	2	3	4
Value of Term	12	7	2	−3

+(−5) +(−5) +(−5)   ← **Find the common difference.**

Start with 12 and add −5 repeatedly.

The next three terms are −8, −13, and −18.

☑ **Quick Check**

1. Describe the pattern in the sequence. Find the next 3 terms.
Start with 44 and add −9 repeatedly; −1, −10, −19.

Position	1	2	3	4	5
Value of Term	44	35	26	17	8

In a **geometric sequence,** you find each term by multiplying the previous term by a fixed number (called the common ratio). In the sequence 2, 7, 24.5, 85.75, … you multiply each term by 3.5 to get the next term.

442 Chapter 9 Patterns and Rules

Differentiated Instruction **Solutions for All Learners**

Special Needs **L1**
Have students draw number lines and trace the common difference with their finger, between one term and the next for some of the arithmetic sequences. They can understand the idea of adding positive or negative numbers to get the next term.

learning style: tactile

Below Level **L2**
Find the next three terms in each sequence and give the rule.

2, 5, 8, 11 14, 17, 20; Rule: +3
1, 10, 100 1,000, 10,000, 100,000; Rule: ×10
10, 9, 8, 7 6, 5, 4; Rule: +(−1)

learning style: verbal

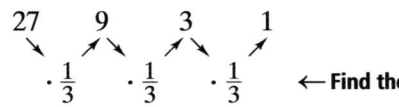 **EXAMPLE** **Describing Geometric Sequences**

② Describe the pattern in 27, 9, 3, 1, . . . Find the next three terms.

$$27 \quad 9 \quad 3 \quad 1$$

$$\cdot \frac{1}{3} \quad \cdot \frac{1}{3} \quad \cdot \frac{1}{3} \quad \leftarrow \text{Find the common ratio.}$$

Start with 27 and multiply by $\frac{1}{3}$ repeatedly.

$$1 \cdot \frac{1}{3} = \frac{1}{3} \qquad \frac{1}{3} \cdot \frac{1}{3} = \frac{1}{9} \qquad \frac{1}{9} \cdot \frac{1}{3} = \frac{1}{27} \quad \leftarrow \text{Find the next three terms.}$$

The next three terms are $\frac{1}{3}$, $\frac{1}{9}$, and $\frac{1}{27}$.

 Tip

Dividing is the same as multiplying by a reciprocal.

✓ **Quick Check**

● **2.** Describe the pattern in 1,000; 100; 10; . . . Find the next 3 terms.
  Start with 1,000 and multiply by $\frac{1}{10}$ repeatedly; 1, $\frac{1}{10}$, $\frac{1}{100}$.

A sequence is neither arithmetic nor geometric if there is no common difference or common ratio.

A **conjecture** is a prediction that suggests what you expect to happen. When you describe a pattern in a sequence, you are using *inductive reasoning*. Check your results whenever possible.

EXAMPLE **Geometry**

③ Describe the pattern to find the number of circles in each figure. Is the resulting sequence *arithmetic, geometric, both,* or *neither*?

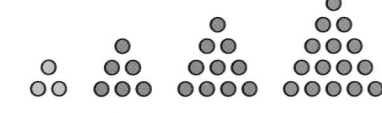

GO for Help

For help with ratios, go to Lesson 5-1, Example 1.

$$3 \quad 6 \quad 10 \quad 15 \ldots \quad \leftarrow \text{number of circles in each figure}$$

$$+3 \quad +4 \quad +5 \quad \leftarrow \text{Look for a common difference or a common ratio.}$$

Start with 3. Add consecutive integers. First add 3, then add 4, and so on.

The sequence is neither arithmetic nor geometric. $\leftarrow$ conjecture

Check Is there a common ratio?

$$3 \quad 6 \quad 10 \quad 15$$

$$\cdot 2 \quad \cdot 1\frac{2}{3} \quad \cdot 1\frac{1}{2}$$

You cannot multiply by or add the same number to each $\leftarrow$ term to find the next term. The sequence is neither arithmetic nor geometric. The conjecture is correct.

✓ **Quick Check**

3. Identify each sequence as *arithmetic, geometric, both,* or *neither*.
  a. 1, 2, 6, 24, . . .   **b.** 2, 3, 6, 11, . . .   **c.** 10, 9, 8, 7, . . .
  neither   neither   arithmetic

9-2 Number Sequences **443**

Advanced Learners **L4**
Have students write a sequence that is both geometric and arithmetic, such as 8, 8, 8, 8, ... Have them give the two rules for each sequence. arithmetic: +0; geometric: ×1

English Language Learners **ELL**
Differentiate between the terms in arithmetic and geometric sequences, and the terms in algebraic expressions. Students have learned that terms have variables in expressions, but that is not always the case in these sequences.

Pre-AP™

learning style: verbal

---

2. Teach

Activity Lab

Use before the lesson.
Student Edition Activity Lab, Hands On 9-2a, Finding Patterns, p. 441

All in One Teaching Resources
Activity Lab 9-2: Patterns in Geometry

Guided Instruction

Example 1
If your school has a long hallway with square tiles, use a section of hall that is at least 55 tiles long. Have students start on one end and place counters on tiles 44, 35, 26, 17, ... Relate the tiles to a number line to help them follow the pattern into negative numbers.

PowerPoint
Additional Examples

① Write a rule for the sequence 100, 93, 86, 79 . . . . Find the next three terms. Start with 100 and add −7 repeatedly. 72, 65, and 58

② Write a rule for the sequence 2, 6, 18, 54 . . . . Find the next three terms. Start with 2 and multiply by 3 repeatedly. 162, 486, and 1,458

③ Identify each sequence as *arithmetic, geometric, both,* or *neither*.
  a. 2, 8, 32, 128, . . . geometric
  b. 15, 16, 18, 21, . . . neither
  c. 40, 37, 34, . . . arithmetic

All in One Teaching Resources
• Daily Notetaking Guide 9-2 **L3**
• Adapted Notetaking 9-2 **L1**

Closure

• *What makes a sequence an arithmetic sequence?* Each term is found by adding the same number to the previous term.

• *What makes a geometric sequence?* Each term is found by multiplying the same number by the previous term.

443

Assignment Guide

Check Your Understanding
Go over Exercises 1–5 in class before assigning the Homework Exercises.

Homework Exercises
A Practice by Example   6–19
B Apply Your Skills   20–30
C Challenge   31
TEKS ★ (TAKS) Tune-Up and
   Mixed Review   32–37

Homework Quick Check
To check students' understanding of key skills and concepts, go over Exercises 10, 18, 21, 26, and 28.

Differentiated Instruction Resources

✓ Check Your Understanding

1. Yes; dividing by −4 is the same as multiplying by $-\frac{1}{4}$.

1. **Vocabulary** A pattern for a sequence is described as *start with 12 and divide by −4 repeatedly*. Is this a geometric sequence? Explain.

2. Can two different arithmetic sequences have the same common difference? Explain.   **Yes; they can begin with different numbers.**

3. What is the common difference in the sequence 35, 29, 23, 17, . . . ?   **−6**

Find the missing term in each sequence.

4. 6, 13, 20, ■, 34, 41   **27**

5. 100, 50, 25, ■, 6.125   **12.5**

Homework Exercises

For more exercises, see Extra Skills and Word Problems.

(A) Describe the pattern for each sequence. Then find the next three terms.
6–13. See margin.

GO for Help

For Exercises	See Examples
6–7	1
8–13	2
14–19	3

6.

Position	1	2	3	4
Value of Term	−8	−1	6	13

7.

Position	1	2	3	4
Value of Term	25	21	17	13

8. 1, 2, 4, 8, . . .

9. 2, −6, 18, −54, . . .

10. 600, −300, 150, . . .

11. $\frac{1}{2}, \frac{1}{4}, \frac{1}{8}, \frac{1}{16}, \ldots$

12. −2, 4, −8, 16, . . .

13. $\frac{1}{4}, \frac{1}{12}, \frac{1}{36}, \frac{1}{108}, \ldots$

Identify each sequence as *arithmetic*, *geometric*, *both*, or *neither*.

14. 2, 5, 10, 17, 26, . . .   **neither**

15. 1, 4, 9, 16, 25, . . .   **neither**

16. 7, 14, 28, 56, . . .   **geometric**

17. −2, −2, −2, . . .   **both**

18. 300, 60, 12, 2.4, . . .   **geometric**

19. 84, 63, 42, 21, . . .   **arithmetic**

(B) (GPS) 20. Guided Problem Solving A female bee has two biological parents—a female and a male. A male bee has only one biological parent, a female. The numbers of ancestors form a number sequence. Is the sequence *arithmetic*, *geometric*, *both*, or *neither*?   **neither**

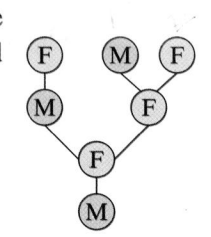

Ancestors
3
2
1

● **Make a Plan** Make a family tree of a male bee's ancestors. Show five generations. Find the number of ancestors in each generation.

21. **Answers may vary. Sample: He may be correct, but he cannot keep decreasing his time by 15 s indefinitely.**

21. **Running** Mario can run a mile in 9 min. After 4 months of training, (GPS) he hopes to run a mile in 8 min. His time decreases by 15 s each month. What would you tell Mario about his conjecture?   See left.

22. A sequence starts with 7. The common difference is *D*. Write expressions for the next three terms in the sequence.

$7 + D, 7 + D + D, 7 + D + D + D$

6–13. See back of book.

27a. 17; 16

b. Blue tiles: start with 1, add 0, 4, 0, 4 and so on; yellow tiles: start with 0, add 4, 0, 4, 0 and so on.

The spiral of a chambered nautilus shell follows the Fibonacci sequence.

28. The sequence is both arithmetic and geometric. You can add 0 repeatedly or multiply by 1 repeatedly to get any term.

29. 123,456 × 9 = 1,111,104

Calculator Make a conjecture about the next term in each sequence. Test your conjecture with a calculator.

23. $2^4 = 16$
$2^3 = 8$
$2^2 = 4$
$2^1 = 2$
$2^0 = $ 1

24. $3^4 = 81$
$3^3 = 27$
$3^2 = 9$
$3^1 = 3$
$3^0 = $ 1

25. $4^4 = 256$
$4^3 = 64$
$4^2 = 16$
$4^1 = 4$
$4^0 = $ 1

26. The Fibonacci sequence 1, 1, 2, 3, 5, 8, ... occurs in nature. Find the ninth and tenth terms in the Fibonacci sequence. Is the Fibonacci sequence *arithmetic, geometric, both,* or *neither?* 34, 55; neither

27. a. How many blue tiles will be in the ninth figure of the pattern? How many yellow tiles will there be?
b. Describe the pattern. 27a–b. See left.

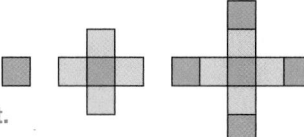

28. **Writing in Math** Every term in a sequence is 1. Is the sequence *arithmetic, geometric, both,* or *neither?* Explain. See left.

29. **Patterns** Look at the pattern below. Make a conjecture about the next term in the sequence. Test your conjecture with a calculator.
$123 \times 9 = 1,107$ $1,234 \times 9 = 11,106$ $12,345 \times 9 = 111,105$ See left.

30. A sequence starts with 2. The common ratio is R. Write expressions for the next three terms in the sequence. $2R$, $2R^2$, $2R^3$

C 31. **Challenge** Make a conjecture about the next term in the sequence, and then find it. −5

Position	1	2	3	4	5	6
Value of Term	1	4	−1	6	−3	8

 TEKS ★ **TAKS** Tune-Up and Mixed Review

TAKS Objective 2
TEKS (7.4)(C)

32. Which sequence follows the rule $3n + 2$, where n is the position of a term in the sequence? D
Ⓐ 3, 9, 27, 81, ...
Ⓑ 5, 7, 9, 11, ...
Ⓒ 3, 6, 9, 12, ...
Ⓓ 5, 8, 11, 14, ...

TAKS Objective 1
TEKS (7.1)(C)

33. Which expression does the model at the right represent? F
Ⓕ 9^2
Ⓖ 9^3
Ⓗ 2^3
Ⓙ 2^9

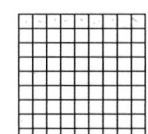

GO for Help Lesson 5-7

The scale on a map is 2 in. : 50 mi. Find the actual distance for each map distance. Round your answer to the nearest tenth of a mile.

34. 3 in. 75 mi   35. $\frac{1}{2}$ in. 12.5 mi   36. $1\frac{3}{4}$ in. 43.8 mi   37. 5 in. 125 mi

---

4. Assess & Reteach

PowerPoint
Lesson Quiz

Identify each sequence as *arithmetic, geometric,* or *neither.* Give the next two terms in each sequence.

1. 2, 6, 18, 54, ... geometric; 162, 486

2. 5, 6, 8, 11, ... neither; 15, 20

3. 42, 37, 32, 27, ... arithmetic; 22, 17

4. 1, 1, 2, 3, 5, 8, ... neither; 13, 21

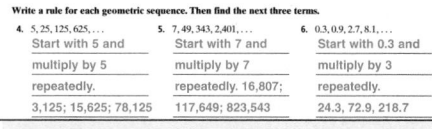

Alternative Assessment

Each student in a pair writes one arithmetic sequence, one geometric sequence, and one sequence that is neither arithmetic nor geometric. Partners exchange papers, write the rules for each other's sequences, and then extend the sequences by three terms.

TEKS ★ **TAKS** Resources

- TAKS Strategies, p. 477
- TAKS Tune-Up, pp. 481–483

TAKS Tune-Up Kit

- TAKS Daily Review Transparencies
- TAKS Review and Preparation Workbook
- TAKS Strategies with Transparencies
- Texas Progress Monitoring Assessments

445

9-3 **Patterns and Tables**

(7.4)(C) To use words and symbols to describe the relationship between the terms in an arithmetic sequence and their positions in the sequence
TAKS Obj. 2
Also supports
(7.15)(A) TAKS Obj. 6
(7.15)(B) TAKS Obj. 6

Dana Center TEKS Toolkit Clarifying Activities (7.4)(C), (7.15)(A), (7.15)(B)
Visit: PHSchool.com
Web Code: arq-9045

TEKS Math Background

In Lesson 9-1, graphs were drawn to illustrate patterns in data. Number patterns can also be represented in tables. You can find values for unknown quantities in a table by applying the rule that describes the relationship between values in the table.

More Math Background: p. 434C

Lesson Planning and Resources

See p. 434E for a list of the resources that support this lesson.

Bell Ringer Practice

☑ **Check Skills You'll Need**
Use student page, transparency, or PowerPoint.

TAKS **Daily Review 69**
Use transparency.

446

☑ **Check Skills You'll Need**

1. Vocabulary Review
The *inverse operation* of subtraction is _?_.
addition
Solve each equation.

2. $x + 4 = -6$ -10

3. $7 + t = 11$ 4

4. $y - 5 = -13$ -8

5. $a - (-3) = 17$ 14

 for Help
Lesson 4-3

TEKS ★ TAKS

- **(7.4)(C)** To use words and symbols to describe the relationship between the terms in an arithmetic sequence and their positions in the sequence TAKS Obj. 2
- **(7.15)(A)** To make conjectures from patterns TAKS Obj. 6
- **(7.15)(B)** To validate conclusions using mathematical properties and relationships TAKS Obj. 6

Why Learn This?

At a market, it is common to display costs for different items. Sometimes making a table is the easiest way to organize data. Often you can make a table as your first step in solving a problem.

You can use a table to represent a pattern.

EXAMPLE **Representing a Pattern**

1 **Groceries** The table below shows the costs for different quantities of fish. Find the cost of 20 lb of fish.

Pounds of Fish	Price ($)	
1	6.50	$= 1 \times 6.5$
2	13.00	$= 2 \times 6.5$
3	19.50	$= 3 \times 6.5$
4	26.00	$= 4 \times 6.5$

← The values in the second column are 6.5 times the values in the first column.

To find the cost of 20 lb of fish, multiply 20 by 6.5.

$$20 \cdot 6.5 = 130$$

The cost of 20 lb of fish is $130.

Check for Reasonableness 20 lb is 10 times 2 lb. The cost for 2 lb is $13. $130 is 10 times $13, so the answer is reasonable.

☑ **Quick Check**

Amount of Gas (gal)	Miles Driven
1	18.1
2	36.2
3	54.3
4	
5	

1. The table at the left shows the number of miles a car can travel using different amounts of gasoline. Copy and complete the table. Find the distance the car can travel using 15 gallons of gasoline. See back of book.

Differentiated Instruction **Solutions for All Learners**

Special Needs L1	**Below Level** L2
If students have a difficult time copying the tables in the Homework Exercises, ask a partner to copy them. Alternatively, provide a copy of the page with the Homework Exercises.	*The first term in a sequence is 4. The rule is* n + 1. *Find the next 3 terms.* 5, 6, 7 *What is the 100th term?* 103
learning style: visual	learning style: verbal

Given a rule, you can find the value of a term using the position.

EXAMPLE Finding the Value of a Term

TAKS Tip

You can eliminate choices as you find each value. Since the first term in the sequence is 2, you can eliminate choices C and D.

② **TAKS Multiple Choice** Which sequence follows the rule $-3n + 5$, where n represents the position of a term in a sequence?

Ⓐ $2, -1, -4, -7 \ldots$ Ⓒ $-3, -6, -9, -12 \ldots$

Ⓑ $2, 1, 4, 7 \ldots$ Ⓓ $8, 11, 14, 17 \ldots$

Position	$-3n + 5$	Value of Term
1	$-3(1) + 5$	2
2	$-3(2) + 5$	-1
3	$-3(3) + 5$	-4
4	$-3(4) + 5$	-7

← Substitute 1, 2, 3, and 4 for *n*.

The correct answer is choice A.

✓ Quick Check

2. Use the rule $2n + 3$, where n represents the position of a term in a sequence. Find the first four terms in the sequence. **5, 7, 9, 11**

A table can help you write a variable expression to describe a sequence.

EXAMPLE Using a Table With a Sequence

Vocabulary Tip

Using a pattern to find any term in a sequence is often referred to as "finding the *n*th term."

③ Write an expression to describe the sequence $8, 16, 24, 32, \ldots$ Then find the 10th term in the sequence.

$$8 \qquad 16 \qquad 24 \qquad 32 \qquad \ldots$$

Position 1   Position 2   Position 3   Position 4   and so on

Make a table that pairs the position of each term with its value.

Position	1	2	3	4	$\cdots$	10
	$\downarrow \cdot 8$	$\downarrow \cdot 8$	$\downarrow \cdot 8$	$\downarrow \cdot 8$	$\downarrow \cdot 8$	$\downarrow \cdot 8$
Value of Term Sequence	8	16	24	32	$\cdots$	�in

The relationship is *Multiply the term number by 8.*

Let n = the term number. You can write the expression $n \cdot 8$, or $8n$.

$n \cdot 8 = 10 \cdot 8 = 80$ ← Substitute 10 for *n* to find the 10th term.

✓ Quick Check

3. Write an expression to describe the sequence $-8, -7, -6, -5, \ldots$ Find the 10th term in the sequence. **$n - 9$; 1**

9-3 Patterns and Tables **447**

---

2. Teach

Activity Lab

Use before the lesson.

All in One Teaching Resources

Activity Lab 9-3: Patterns in Numbers

Guided Instruction

Example 1
Some students may benefit from "reasoning aloud" as they look at the table. Have them look for the common difference.

Example 2
For Quick Check 2, have students make a table to find the first four terms in the sequence. Then discuss how to check the value of the term.

PowerPoint

Additional Examples

❶ Copy and complete this table.

Number of horses	1	3	5	9
Number of horse shoes	4	12	20	36

❷ Find the values of the variables in the table below.
$s = 5, t = 84$

N	2	s	6	12
P	14	35	42	t

❸ Write an expression for the rule for 2, 4, 6, 8, 10 . . . . Find the hundredth term in the sequence. **2n; 200**

All in One Teaching Resources

- Daily Notetaking Guide 9-3 L3
- Adapted Notetaking 9-3 L1

Closure

- Explain how to find values of variables in a table. **Sample: First, figure out the relationship between the quantities in a row by trying out rules for each row. Then use that relationship to find the values of variables.**

447

Assignment Guide

Check Your Understanding
Go over Exercises 1–4 in class before assigning the Homework Exercises.

Homework Exercises
A Practice by Example   5–18
B Apply Your Skills   19–26
C Challenge   27
TEKS ★ *TAKS* Tune-Up and Mixed Review   28–34

Homework Quick Check
To check students' understanding of key skills and concepts, go over Exercises 5, 12, 20, 24, and 26.

Differentiated Instruction **Resources**

Check Your Understanding

1. **Vocabulary** The expression $5n$ describes a sequence. When $n = 10$, the term position is ▦ and the term value is ▦.   **10; 50**

2. **Mental Math** A sequence follows the rule $100n$, where n is the position of a term. Find the 10th term.   **1,000**

Find the next three numbers in each sequence.

3. 4, 12, 36, 108, ▦, ▦, ▦
   324; 972; 2,916

4. 4, 12, 20, 28, ▦, ▦, ▦
   36, 44, 52

Homework Exercises

For more exercises, see Extra Skills and Word Problems.

For Exercises	See Examples
5–6	1
7–12	2
13–18	3

Ⓐ **Copy and complete each table.**   5–6. See margin.

5.

Cans of Soup	Number of Servings
3	9
4	12
5	15
6	▦
7	▦

6.

Dozens of Beads	Cost ($)
1	0.48
2	0.96
3	1.44
4	▦
5	▦

For Exercises 7–12, n represents the position of a term in a sequence. Find the first four terms in each sequence.

7. $n + 3$ 4, 5, 6, 7
8. $4n - 2$ 2, 6, 10, 14
9. $5n$ 5, 10, 15, 20
10. $6n + 1$ 7, 13, 19, 25
11. $n \div 4$ $\frac{1}{4}, \frac{1}{2}, \frac{3}{4}, 1$
12. $n^2 - 3$ −2, 1, 6, 13

Write an expression to describe each sequence. Then find the 10th term.

13. 11, 22, 33, 44, . . . $11n$; 110
14. −19, −18, −17, −16, . . . $n - 20$; −10
15. $\frac{1}{2}, 1, 1\frac{1}{2}, 2, \ldots$ $\frac{n}{2}$; 5
16. −3, −6, −9, −12, . . . $-3n$; −30
17. −18, −36, −54, −72, . . . $-18n$; −180
18. 100, 200, 300, 400, . . . $100n$; 1,000

19.

Gallons of Gas	Price ($)
5	11
10	22
15	33
25	55

Ⓑ **GPS** 19. **Guided Problem Solving** Suppose the average price for regular unleaded gasoline is $2.20 per gallon. Make a table that shows the price for 5, 10, 15, and 25 gallons of regular gasoline. See left.
- *Make a Table* that shows the price for 1, 2, and 3 gallons.
- What is the pattern in the table?

20. **Music** The table shows costs for violin lessons. Copy and complete the table.   See margin.

Time (h)	0.5	1	1.5	2
Cost ($)	12.50	▦	▦	▦

5.

Cans of Soup	Number of Servings
3	9
4	12
5	15
6	18
7	21

6.

Beads (doz)	Cost ($)
1	0.48
2	0.96
3	1.44
4	1.92
5	2.40

20–27a–b. See back of book.

Copy and complete each table. 21–22. See margin.

21.

Miles	Time (h)
10	0.4
20	0.8
30	1.2
40	■
50	■

22.

Change in a Parking Meter ($)	Time Allowed to Park (h)
0.25	0.5
0.50	1
0.75	■
1.25	■

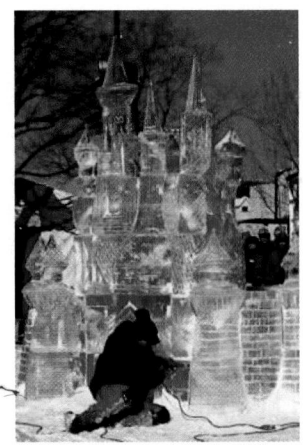

The freezing point of water is 0°C, or 273 K.

23. **Temperature** The relationship between Kelvin (K) and Celsius (C) temperatures is $K = 273 + C$. Make a table of Kelvin temperatures for Celsius temperatures of 0°, 20°, 40°, 80°, and 120°. See margin.

24. **a.** Copy and complete the table.
    b. **Writing in Math** Explain how to find y when you know x.
    24a–b. See margin.

x	0	1	2	3	4	■
y	−1	2	5	8	■	14

25. **Geometry** Use the relationship between side length and area to make a table for the areas of squares with side lengths of 2, 3, 5, 8, 10, and 12 in. See margin.

26. Make a table showing the number of blue and yellow squares in each group. How many blue squares will be in group 10? See margin.

27. **Challenge** Use the relationship $y = \frac{3}{2}x$.
    a. Make a table that shows the values of y for $x = -2, -4, 2,$ and 4.
    b. Find the value of x when $y = 0$. 27a–b. See margin.

TEKS ★ TAKS Tune-Up and Mixed Review

GRIDDABLE ITEMS

TAKS Objective 3
TEKS (7.8)(C)

28. Isabel wants to cover her rectangular dining table with mosaic tiles that are 1 inch on each side. The table measures 3 feet by 4.5 feet. How many tiles does she need to cover the table? 1,944

TAKS Objective 1
TEKS (7.2)(B)

29. Chencha has a part-time job after school. She earns $110.50 for 17 hours of work. How many dollars per hour does she earn? 6.50

TAKS Objective 6
TEKS (7.15)(A)

30. Carlos plans to read every day for 6 days. He reads 9 pages on the first day, 18 pages on the second day, and 27 pages on the third day. If the pattern continues, how many pages will Carlos read on the sixth day? 54

 Lesson 3-4

Find each product.

31. $\frac{1}{4}$ of 28 7   32. $\frac{3}{5} \cdot 25$ 15   33. $\frac{2}{7} \cdot \frac{21}{50}$ $\frac{3}{25}$ 34. $4\frac{2}{3} \cdot 4\frac{1}{2}$ 21

Alternative Assessment

Provide pairs of students with exercises similar to Exercises 13–18. Partners work together to make a table for each exercise and describe the rule. Then students use the expression to find the 20th term, the 50th term, and the 100th term.

TEKS ★ TAKS Resources

• TAKS Strategies, p. 477
• TAKS Tune-Up, pp. 481–483

TAKS Tune-Up Kit

• TAKS Daily Review Transparencies
• TAKS Review and Preparation Workbook
• TAKS Strategies with Transparencies
• Texas Progress Monitoring Assessments

---

4. Assess & Reteach

PowerPoint
Lesson Quiz

Write a variable expression to describe the rule for each sequence. Then find the hundredth term.

1. 3, 6, 9, 12, . . . 3n; 300

2. 14, 15, 16, 17, . . . n + 13; 113

3. 21, 42, 63, 84, . . . 21n; 2,100

4. −10, −9, −8, −7, . . . n − 11; 89

Alternative Method

Have students solve Exercise 26 using the strategy *Work a Simpler Problem*.

449

Resources

- All-in-One Teaching Resources Checkpoint Quiz 1
- Texas ExamView CD-ROM
- Success Tracker™ Online Intervention

MATH AT WORK

Artists

This feature describes how math is used in a career field that may interest many students. It should generate enthusiasm about math among students.

Guided Instruction

Have volunteers read each paragraph. Discuss with students where they may have seen math in art. If possible, display a few pieces of art for examples. Ask questions, such as:
- *How would an artist use math to mix his or her materials?*
- *What other math skills might an artist use?*
- *Have you seen art with patterns in it? Did you like it? Why or why not?*

Checkpoint Quiz 1

Use the table below for Exercises 1–3.

Tablespoons	Teaspoons
1	3
3	9
4	12
6	18

1.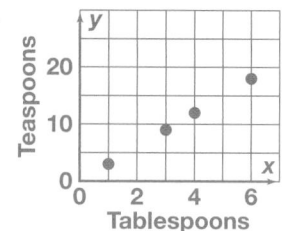

1. Graph the data in the table. **See above.**

2. Use the graph to estimate the number of teaspoons in 10 tablespoons. **30 teaspoons**

3. Use the graph to estimate the number of tablespoons in 20 teaspoons. **3 tablespoons**

Describe the pattern for each sequence. Then find the next three terms.

4. 7, 14, 21, 28, . . . **Start with 7 and add 7 repeatedly; 35, 42, 49.**

5. 250, 220, 190, 160, . . . **Start with 250 and add −30 repeatedly; 130, 100, 70.**

6. 2, 5, 11, 23, . . . **Start with 2, then add 3, 6, 12, 24 and so on; 47, 95, 191.**

7. −4, 12, −36, 108, . . . **Start with −4 and multiply by −3 repeatedly; −324, 972, −2,916.**

8. Identify each sequence in Exercises 4–7 as *arithmetic, geometric, both,* or *neither.* **arithmetic; arithmetic; neither; geometric**

9. Write an expression to describe the sequence 50, 100, 150, 200, . . . Then find the 10th term. **50n; 500**

MATH AT WORK

Artists

Artists use a variety of materials to make images, such as oils, watercolors, plaster, or clay. Recently, many artists have begun to use computers. Graphic artists work for businesses. Fine artists display their works in galleries or museums.

Artists use mathematics when they mix different materials, sell their work, or estimate costs of their materials. Artists also create designs with patterns.

Go Online
PHSchool.com **For:** more information about artists.
Web Code: arb-2031

Generating Formulas From a Table

You can write a formula for the area of a square that is missing its corners.

TEKS ★ TAKS

(7.4)(A) To generate formulas involving area **TAKS** Obj. 2

(7.15)(A) To make conjectures from patterns or sets of examples **TAKS** Obj. 6

ACTIVITY

The corners of each square shown below are shaded.

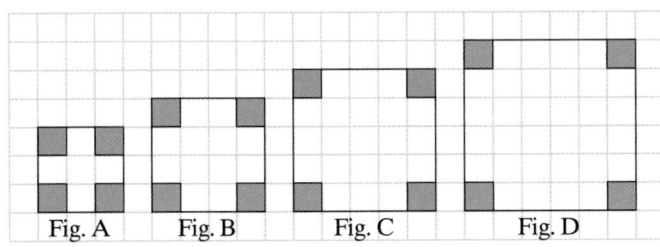

Fig. A   Fig. B   Fig. C   Fig. D

1. Copy and complete the table at the right to find the unshaded area of each square. See margin.

2. For each square, how is the area of the entire square related to the length of a side? $A = s^2$

3. How many corners are shaded in each square? 4 corners

4. What pattern do you notice about the unshaded area of each square? The area of the unshaded area is 4 less than the area of the entire square.

Figure	A	B	C	D
Side Length	3			
Area of Square	9			
Unshaded Area	5			

Exercises

Find the area of a square that is missing its corners for each side length.

1. 7 units 45 units²

2. 8 units 60 units²

3. 10 units 96 units²

4. Suppose a square has a side length of n units and all four corners are shaded. Write a formula for the unshaded area of the square. $n^2 - 4$

Use your formula from Exercise 4 to find the unshaded area of each square with the given side length.

5. 100 units 9,996 units²

6. 500 units 24,996 units²

7. 1,000 units 999,996 units²

1.

Figure	A	B	C	D
Side Length	3	4	5	6
Area of Square	9	16	25	36
Unshaded Area	5	12	21	32

Activity Lab

Generating Formulas From a Table

Students use a table to generate formulas for area. This will prepare them to work with formulas in Lesson 9-4.

Guided Instruction

Before beginning the Activity, review the formula for the area of a square, $A = s^2$. Explain that you can use that formula with a table to find the area of parts of a square.

Ask:
- *How can you find the area of the unshaded area using the formula for area?* Find the area of the square, subtract 4 units.
- *If you shaded 4 squares in each corner, how could you find the area of the unshaded area?* Find the total area, subtract 16.

Exercises

Have students work independently on the Exercises. When they have finished, discuss the answers as a class and come to a conclusion about the area of the unshaded areas.

Alternative Method

Some students may prefer to use algebra tiles. Use different colors for the shaded and unshaded areas and physically remove the "shaded" tiles to help students see the connection

TEKS ★ TAKS Resources

- Activity Lab 9-4: Function Rules
- algebra tiles
- Student Manipulatives Kit

Dana Center TEKS Toolkit Clarifying Activities (7.4)(A), (7.15)(A)
Visit: PHSchool.com
Web Code: arq-9045

451

9-4

9-4

Function Rules

1. Plan

TEKS ★

Prepares for **TEKS (A.1)(C)** To describe functional relationships for given problem situations

TEKS Math Background

A function is a relationship in which an output value (*y*) depends on an input value (*x*) in such a way that only one output is possible for each input. This means that two different input values can have the same output value. But two different output values cannot have the same input value.

More Math Background: p. 434C

Lesson Planning and Resources

See p. 434E for a list of the resources that support this lesson.

PowerPoint

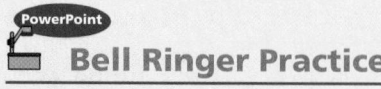

✓ Check Skills You'll Need
Use student page, transparency, or PowerPoint.

TAKS Daily Review 70
Use transparency.

452

✓ Check Skills You'll Need

1. Vocabulary Review
Why is 5 + 2 not an *algebraic expression*?
See below.
Evaluate −4*x* + 1 for each value of *x*.

2. −2 9   **3.** 0 1

4. $\frac{1}{4}$ 0   **5.** $-\frac{1}{4}$ 2

GO for Help
Lesson 4-1

Check Skills You'll Need

1. The expression has no variable.

What You'll Learn

To write and evaluate functions

- Prepares for Algebra 1 **TEKS (A.1)(C)** To describe functional relationships for given problem situations

🔊 **New Vocabulary** function

Why Learn This?

The distance you travel in a car depends on the driving time. When one quantity depends on another, you say that one is a *function* of the other. So distance is a function of time. You can use functions to help you make predictions.

Input (time)

Output (distance)

In the diagram at the right, an input goes through the "function machine" to produce an output.

A **function** is a relationship that assigns exactly one output value for each input value.

EXAMPLE Writing a Function Rule

1 Cars You are traveling in a car at an average speed of 55 mi/h. Write a function rule that describes the relationship between the time and the distance you travel.

You can *make a table* to solve this problem.

Input: time (h)	1	2	3	4
Output: distance (mi)	55	110	165	220

distance in miles = 55 · time in hours ← **Write the function rule in words.**

$d = 55t$ ← **Use variables *d* and *t* for distance and time.**

✓ Quick Check

1. Write a function rule for the relationship between the time and the distance you travel at an average speed of 62 mi/h. $d = 62t$

Differentiated Instruction Solutions for All Learners

Special Needs L1
Provide students with counters or paper tiles to represent the numbers in the function tables. One color should represent the input, while the other represents the output. For example, 2, 3, and 4 red tiles and 4, 5, and 6 blue tiles in a table can represent the function *y* = *x* + 2.
learning style: tactile

Below Level L2
Use each function rule to find y when x = −2, 0, 2, and 4.

y = *x* + 2 0, 2, 4, 6
y = 2*x* −4, 0, 4, 8
learning style: visual

The variables x and y are often used to represent input and output. You can describe the relationship between the values in the table in three ways.

Each output is 3 greater than the input.

$$\text{output} = \text{input} + 3$$
$$y = x + 3$$

Input x	Output y
1	4
2	5
3	6
4	7

EXAMPLE Using Tables to Analyze Functions

2 Write a rule for the function represented by each table.

a.

x	y
0	0
1	-4
2	-8
3	-12

When $x = 0$, $y = 0$.
Each y equals -4 times x.

b.

x	y
0	-3
1	-1
2	1
3	3

When $x = 0$, $y = -3$.
Each y equals 2 times x, plus -3.

The function rule is
$y = -4x + 0$, or $y = -4x$.

The function rule is
$y = 2x + (-3)$, or $y = 2x - 3$.

✓ Quick Check

2. Write a rule for the function represented by the table below.

$y = 4x + 1$

x	0	1	2	3
y	1	5	9	13

Given a function rule, you can evaluate the function for any input value.

EXAMPLE Evaluating Functions

3 Use the function $y = -3x + 5$. Find y for $x = 0, 1, 2,$ and 3. Then make a table for the function.

$y = -3(0) + 5 = 5$ ← Substitute 0, 1, 2, and 3 for x.
$y = -3(1) + 5 = 2$ List the values in a table. →
$y = -3(2) + 5 = -1$
$y = -3(3) + 5 = -4$

x	$y = -3x + 5$
0	5
1	2
2	-1
3	-4

✓ Quick Check

3.

x	y
0	-4
1	-2
2	0
3	2

3. Use the function $y = 2x - 4$. Find y for $x = 0, 1, 2,$ and 3. Then make a table for the function. See left.

Advanced Learners L4
Have students make a table and evaluate the function $y = (x + 1)^2 + 2x$ for 0, positive and negative integers, and positive and negative fractions. Check students' work.

Pre-AP™

English Language Learners ELL
Explicitly state to students that when x and y are used as variables in function tables and equations, x is customarily the input, and y is the output.

learning style: verbal

2. Teach

Activity Lab
Use before the lesson.
Student Edition Activity Lab 9-4a, Generating Formulas From a Table, p. 451

 Teaching Resources
Activity Lab 9-4: Function Rules

Guided Instruction

Example 2
Make sure students understand that the function rule must work for every row in the table. Have students test the rule on each row to help them understand this fact.

PowerPoint
Additional Examples

1 Suppose you can bicycle at an average speed of 10 mi/h. Write a function rule for the relationship between the time and distance you travel.
$d = 10t$

2 Write a rule for the function represented by the table.

x	0	1	2	3	4
y	-2	2	6	10	14

$y = 4x - 2$

3 Use the function $y = 2x - 3$. Find y when $x = -1, 0, 2,$ and 3. Then make a table for the function.

x	-1	0	2	3
y	-5	-3	1	3

All in One **Teaching Resources**
• Daily Notetaking Guide 9-4 L3
• Adapted Notetaking 9-4 L1

Closure

• *What is a function?* a relationship that assigns one output value for each input value
• *How do you evaluate a function?* Substitute a given input value for x and simplify.

3. Practice

Assignment Guide

Check Your Understanding
Go over Exercises 1–4 in class before assigning the Homework Exercises.

Homework Exercises
A	Practice by Example	5–19
B	Apply Your Skills	20–27
C	Challenge	28
TEKS ★ TAKS Tune-Up and Mixed Review		29–32

Homework Quick Check
To check students' understanding of key skills and concepts, go over Exercises 9, 16, 21, 22, and 25.

Differentiated Instruction Resources

454

✓ Check Your Understanding

1. Vocabulary Complete with *at least one* or *exactly one*: Every function pairs ? output value with each input value. **exactly one**

Use the function table at the left for Exercises 2–4.

x	y
0	0
1	5
2	10
3	15

2. What number does the function pair with 3? **15**

3. Describe the pattern in the table using words. **Each output is 5 times the input.**

4. Write a rule for the function represented by the table. **$y = 5x$**

Homework Exercises

For more exercises, see Extra Skills and Word Problems.

GO for Help

For Exercises	See Examples
5–7	1
8–11	2
12–19	3

Ⓐ Write a function rule for each relationship.

5. the time t and distance d you travel at an average speed of 30 mi/h
$d = 30t$

6. the number n of words you type and the time t it takes, if you type at a rate of 32 words/min $n = 32t$

7. the amount c of energy you burn and the time t you spend exercising, if you burn Calories at a rate of 12 Cal/min $c = 12t$

Write a rule for the function represented by each table.

8.
x	y
0	4
1	5
2	6
3	7

$y = x + 4$

9.
x	y
0	5
1	8
2	11
3	14

$y = 3x + 5$

10.
x	y
0	1
1	−8
2	−17
3	−26

$y = -9x + 1$

11.
x	y
0	0
1	−8
2	−16
3	−24

$y = -8x$

Use each function rule. Find y for $x = 0$, 1, 2, and 3. Then make a table for the function. 12–19. See margin.

12. $y = x + 2$

13. $y = 9 - x$

14. $y = 4x$

15. $y = x \div 2$

16. $y = -3x$

17. $y = 2x + 1$

18. $y = 4x - 2$

19. $y = x^2 + 1$

Ⓑ GPS 20. Guided Problem Solving Write a function rule for the number n of inches in f feet. Then find the number of inches in 7 feet.
- How many inches are in 1 foot?
- How many inches are in f feet?

$n = 12f$; 84 in.

21. Money Suppose you put $.50 in a piggy bank on July 1, $1.00 on July 2, $1.50 on July 3, and so on. Use n to represent the date. Write a function rule for the amount you put in for any date in July.

$y = (0.50)n$

454 Chapter 9 Patterns and Rules

12–19. See back of book.

26.
cm³	L
3	0.003
300	0.3
3,000	3

$L = \dfrac{c}{1,000}$

Write a rule for the function represented by each table.

22.

Laundry Loads	Cost ($)
1	2.75
2	5.50
3	8.25
4	11.00

$c = 2.75\ell$

23.

Time (h)	Kangaroo's Distance (km)
2	96
4	192
6	288

$d = 48h$

24. **Reading** A student can read 150 words in one minute.
   a. Write a function rule to represent the relationship between the number of words and the time in which they are read. $w = 150m$
   b. How many words can the student read in 8 minutes? **1,200 words**
   c. How long would it take the student to read 2,850 words? **19 minutes**

25. <u>**Writing in Math**</u> Use the function table at the right. Describe the patterns you notice and explain how to find the function rule. **See left.**

x	y
0	0
1	$\frac{1}{2}$
2	1
3	$1\frac{1}{2}$

26. One cm^3 is equal to 1 mL. Use this relationship to make a table showing the number of liters in 3 cm^3, 300 cm^3, and 3,000 cm^3. Then write a function rule. **See margin.**

27. Use the rule $y = 2x^2 - 4$. Evaluate the function for **See left.** $x = -0.25, -\frac{1}{2}$, and $1\frac{1}{4}$.

Input

$x^2 + x + 2$
Output

(C) 28. **Challenge** Use the function machine at the right to make a table for integer inputs from -5 to 5. Which two input values result in an output of 22? **−5, 4**

25. Answers may vary. Sample: The y-values increase by $\frac{1}{2}$ when the x-values increase by 1.

27. −3.875, −3.5, −0.875

TAKS Objective 2
TEKS (7.4)(C)

29. Which description shows the relationship between a term and n, its position in the sequence? **D**

Position	1	2	3	4	n
Value of Term	6.50	13	19.50	26	▉

   (A) Add 6.50 to n.
   (B) Add 26 to n.
   (C) Multiply n by 26.
   (D) Multiply n by 6.50.

TAKS Objective 3
TEKS (7.6)(B)

30. Which of the following *never* names a quadrilateral with four congruent sides and four congruent angles? **F**
   (F) Trapezoid   (G) Rectangle   (H) Rhombus   (J) Square

for Help   **Lesson 8-1**

Choose a reasonable estimate. Explain your choice.

31. width of a nail: 1 mm or 1 m
   1 mm; it is less than 1 m.

32. length of a car: 4 m or 4 km
   4 m; it is less than 1 km.

Alternative Assessment

Each student in a pair writes a function rule expressed in terms of x and y. Partners exchange papers and make function tables for x = 0, 1, 2, 3, 5, and 10.

TEKS ★ **TAKS** **Resources**

• TAKS Strategies, p. 477
• TAKS Tune-Up, pp. 481–483

TAKS **Tune-Up Kit**

• TAKS Daily Review Transparencies
• TAKS Review and Preparation Workbook
• TAKS Strategies with Transparencies
• Texas Progress Monitoring Assessments

---

4. Assess & Reteach

PowerPoint
Lesson Quiz

1. Make a table for the function $y = 3x - 2$. Find y for $x = 0, 1, 2$, and 3.

x	0	1	2	3
y	−2	1	4	7

2. Write a rule for the function represented in the table.

x	0	1	2	3
y	4	6	8	10

$y = 2x + 4$

Reteaching 9-4

Enrichment 9-4

455

(7.4)(B) To graph data to demonstrate relationships in familiar concepts such as conversions, perimeter, and area **TAKS** Obj. 2

Also supports
(7.5)(B) **TAKS** Obj. 2
(7.14)(A) **TAKS** Obj. 6

Dana Center TEKS Toolkit Clarifying Activities (7.4)(B), (7.5)(B), (7.14)(A)
Visit: PHSchool.com
Web Code: arq-9045

TEKS Math Background

Functions can be represented by equations, word descriptions, tables, and graphs. When graphing functions, the input or independent variable is plotted on the horizontal or *x*-axis.

More Math Background: p. 434D

Lesson Planning and Resources

See p. 434E for a list of the resources that support this lesson.

Bell Ringer Practice

✓ **Check Skills You'll Need**
Use student page, transparency, or PowerPoint.

TAKS Daily Review 71
Use transparency.

 Check Skills You'll Need

1. Vocabulary Review
What is a *sequence*?
See below.
Write an expression to describe each sequence.

2. 5, 10, 15, 20, . . .   *5n*

3. −7, −5, −3, −1, . . .   *2n − 9*

4. 101, 202, 303, . . .   *101n*

 for Help
Lesson 9-3

TEKS ★ **TAKS**
- (7.4)(B) To graph data to demonstrate relationships in familiar concepts such as conversions, perimeter, and area **TAKS** Obj. 2
- (7.5)(B) To formulate an equation when given a problem situation **TAKS** Obj. 2
- (7.14)(A) To communicate mathematical ideas using graphical and algebraic models **TAKS** Obj. 6

Why Learn This?

If you know your height in inches, you can find your height in feet. You can show the relationship between units such as inches and feet using a table, a rule, or a graph.

A graph can show the relationship between inputs and outputs.

EXAMPLE   **Graphing Using a Table**

Number of Inches	Number of Feet
12	1
24	2
36	3
48	4

① The table at the left shows the relationship between the number of inches (input) and the number of feet (output). The rule is $f = \frac{n}{12}$, where f represents the number of feet, and n represents the number of inches. Graph the relationship represented by the table.

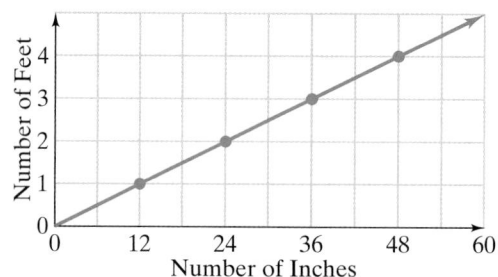

Graph inches on the horizontal axis and feet on the vertical axis.

Draw a line through the points.

Check Skills You'll Need

1. a set of numbers that follow a pattern

✓ **Quick Check**

1. Graph the function represented by the table below.

Input *x*	Output *y*
0	3
1	5
2	7
3	9

1.

Differentiated Instruction   **Solutions for All Learners**

Special Needs **L1**
If students have difficulty drawing the graphs, pair them up with students who can draw the graphs. The pairs can share the task of making a table of values, and coming up with word rules for the relationships.

learning style: visual

Below Level **L2**
Write the ordered pairs that you would graph for the function in the table. (−1, 2), (0, 3), (2, 5), (4, 7)

x	−1	0	2	4
y	2	3	5	7

learning style: visual

Careers Botanists study the life and growth of plants.

EXAMPLE Application: Plants

② A plant grows 1.38 cm for each hour of sunlight it receives. Write and graph a rule to find the growth of the plant when it receives 4 h of sunlight.

Step 1 Write a rule.

Words   growth equals 1.38 times hours of sunlight

Let g = growth in centimeters.

Let s = hours of sunlight.

Equation g = 1.38 · s

Step 2 Make a table of values.

Hours of Sunlight (s)	1.38s	Centimeters of Growth (g)
1	1.38(1)	1.38
2	1.38(2)	2.76
3	1.38(3)	4.14
4	1.38(4)	5.52

Step 3 Make a graph.

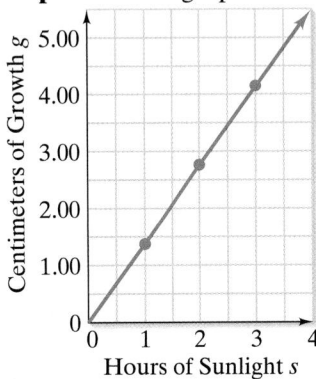

The plant grows 5.52 cm when it receives 4 h of sunlight.

✓ Quick Check

2. A bus travels 60 miles per hour. Write and graph a rule to find the number of miles the bus can travel in 4.5 hours. See back of book.

✓ Check Your Understanding

3.

Output y graph showing points; y-axis labeled 6, 12; x-axis labeled 0, 2, 4, Input x

1. **Vocabulary** What is a table of values? a table showing the relationship between the input and output of a function
2. **Reasoning** Does every relationship have an output of 0 for an input value of 0? Explain. No; any function that involves adding or subtracting from the input will not give you 0 as the output.
3. Graph the relationship represented by the table. See left.

Input x	0	1	2	3
Output y	5	8	11	14

Activity Lab

Use before the lesson.

All in One Teaching Resources
Activity Lab 9-5: Tables and Graphs

Guided Instruction

Error Prevention!

Students may confuse the x-axis and the y-axis. Make sure students are graphing all the values for x on the horizontal axis and all the values for y on the vertical axis.

Example 2
Ask students to evaluate the effectiveness of the rule, table, and graph to communicate the growth of the plant.

PowerPoint
Additional Examples

① Graph the function represented by the table.

Input x	0	1	2	3
Output y	4	6	8	10

See back of book.

② A plant grows 3 in. in one week. The second week, its height is 5 in., and the third week its height is 7 in. Write and evaluate a function rule to find the height of a plant in week 4. Then graph the function.
See back of book.

All in One Teaching Resources
• Daily Notetaking Guide 9-5 **L3**
• Adapted Notetaking 9-5 **L1**

Closure

• *What are some ways you can represent functions?* Sample: You can represent functions with equations, tables, graphs, and word descriptions.

Advanced Learners **L4**
Have students write original functions and make tables based on their functions. Students can graph their functions. Have them use both positive and negative values for x.

Pre-AP™

English Language Learners **ELL**
The most difficult part of this lesson is writing relationships in words that translate easily to tables and functions. Have students work in pairs to develop rules in words.

learning style: verbal

457

Assignment Guide

Check Your Understanding
Go over Exercises 1–3 in class before assigning the Homework Exercises.

Homework Exercises
A Practice by Example   4–7
B Apply Your Skills   8–20
C Challenge   21
TEKS ★ TAKS Tune-Up and
   Mixed Review   22–26

Homework Quick Check
To check students' understanding of key skills and concepts, go over Exercises 4, 6, 9, 13, and 20.

Homework Exercises

For more exercises, see Extra Skills and Word Problems.

Ⓐ Graph the relationship represented by each table.   4–5. See margin.

4.

Side Length of Square *s*	0	1	2	3	4
Perimeter of Square *P*	0	4	8	12	16

5.

Input *x*	Output *y*
0	1
1	4
2	7
3	10

For Exercises 6 and 7, write and graph a function to find the output for an input of 10 h.   6–7. See margin.

6. **Employment** Total earnings *S* depends on the number *t* of hours worked. You earn $6/h.

7. **Air Travel** Total distance depends on the number *t* of hours traveled. Airplane speed averages 320 mi/h.

Ⓑ GPS 8. **Guided Problem Solving** It costs $120 per year to feed a cat. Write and evaluate a rule to find the cost of feeding a cat that lives to the maximum life span of 28 years. $c = 120y$; $3,360
  • **Make a Plan** Write a rule for the cost *c* of feeding a cat during its lifetime *y*.
  • **Carry Out the Plan** Substitute ▩ for *y* to find the cost of feeding a cat that lives to the maximum life span.

9. The number of Calories *c* that are burned by walking depends on *t*, the number of hours spent walking. If you burn 300 Cal/h, how many Calories do you burn in 2.5 hours of walking?   750 Calories

13a–c. Answers may vary. Samples are given.

13a. A table; it can be drawn with only a few values and without a rule.

b. A rule; the rule can represent infinitely many values.

c. A graph; it visually represents the relationship between values.

Match each graph with a rule.

10.
   C

11.
   A

12.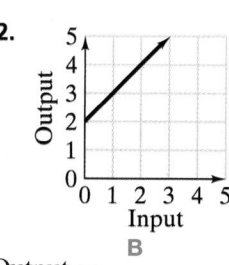
   B

A. Output = $\frac{1}{2}$ · Input

B. Output = Input + 2

C. Output = 2 · Input − 1

13. **Writing in Math** For each situation, which would best represent the relationship—a table, a rule, or a graph? Explain your choice.
  a. You only have a few values or you do not know the rule.
  b. You have many input and output values.   13a–c. See left.
  c. You want to see the relationship between the values.

4–7. See back of book.
14a–18. See back of book.
20a–21. See back of book.

14. a. Make a function table for the graph.
b. Write a rule for the function.
14a–b. See margin.

Graph each rule. Use input values of 1, 2, 3, 4, and 5. 15–18. See margin.

15. $y = 5x$ **16.** $y = 2x + 1$

17. $y = x \div 2$ **18.** $y = x - 3$

19. Open-Ended Choose one rule from Exercises 15–18. Describe a real-world situation that the rule could represent.
Check students' work.

20. Flight Amelia Earhart set several flight
GPS speed records. The table at the right models the relationship between distance and time for a flight at Amelia Earhart's record speed. 20a–d. See margin.

a. Write a rule for the relationship represented by the table.

b. Find the average speed. Justify your answer.

c. Estimate the number of hours it would take to fly 1,890 mi.

d. Graph the rule.

Amelia Earhart's Flight

Time (h)	Distance (mi)
2	362
4	724
6	1,086
8	1,448

In 1928, Amelia Earhart became the first woman to fly across the Atlantic Ocean.

C 21. Challenge The area of an equilateral triangle depends on the side length s. The rule is $A = \frac{\sqrt{3}}{4} s^2$. Evaluate the rule for several values and make a table. Use 0.433 as an approximation of $\frac{\sqrt{3}}{4}$. Then graph the rule. Describe the shape of your graph. See margin.

TEKS ★ TAKS Tune-Up and Mixed Review

TAKS Objective 2
TEKS (7.4)(B)

22. Which of the following relationships is best represented by the data in the graph? **A**
  Ⓐ Conversion of feet to yards
  Ⓑ Conversion of feet to inches
  Ⓒ Conversion of miles to feet
  Ⓓ Conversion of inches to yards

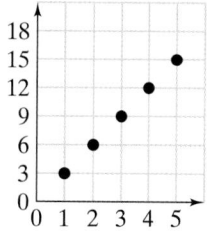

TAKS Objective 2
TEKS (7.4)(A)

23. The circular base of a dome has a diameter of 60 ft. Which expression can be used to find the area of the base? **H**
  Ⓕ $2 \cdot 30 \cdot \pi$ Ⓗ $30 \cdot 30 \cdot \pi$
  Ⓖ $2 \cdot 60 \cdot \pi$ Ⓙ $60 \cdot 60 \cdot \pi$

GO for Help   **Lesson 8-3**   **Find the area of a triangle with the given base and height.**

24. 5 m, 2 m 5 m²   **25.** 10 ft, 3 ft 15 ft²   **26.** 18 cm, 6 cm 54 cm²

Alternative Assessment

Provide graph paper to pairs of students. Partners work together to complete Exercises 6–7. Before they draw each graph, have them discuss appropriate axes labels, scales, and intervals. Have pairs compare their graphs with classmates.

TEKS ★ TAKS Resources

• TAKS Strategies, p. 477
• TAKS Tune-Up, pp. 481–483

TAKS Tune-Up Kit
  • TAKS Daily Review Transparencies
  • TAKS Review and Preparation Workbook
  • TAKS Strategies with Transparencies
  • Texas Progress Monitoring Assessments

4. Assess & Reteach

PowerPoint
Lesson Quiz

A carpenter uses 6 nails for each shelf.

1. Write and evaluate a function to find the number of nails for 14 shelves. $n = 6s$; 84 nails

2. Graph the function using input values of 1, 2, 3, and 4.

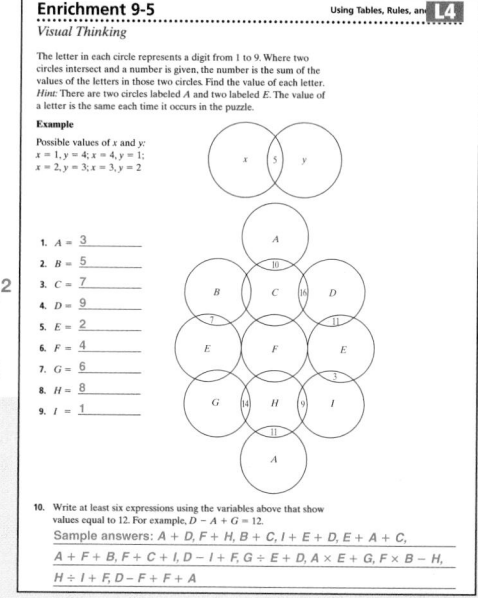

459

Three Views of a Function

In this Activity, students use a graphing calculator to view a graph and a table of values for a function.

Guided Instruction

Technology Tip
Group or pair students who have the same kind of calculator. Provide time for students to become familiar with the way their calculators display tables and graphs. Encourage students to share adjustments they make to complete the steps using their calculator.

Teaching Tip
Work through Steps 1–6 with the class. If you have an overhead calculator, demonstrate each step and the corresponding display. Otherwise, circulate, or have a volunteer show the students what the calculator should display after each step. Make sure students understand what a "range" for a table of values is.

Exercises
Have students work in pairs. Challenge them to predict what the graphs of each of the functions will look like and to explain their reasoning. Invite partners to give each other another function to graph and make a table of values.

Differentiated Instruction

Advanced Learners   L4
Have students write their own functions. They can trade functions with a partner and create the three views of their partner's function.

Resources

- graphing calculator
- Classroom Aid 36

Three Views of a Function

You can use a graphing calculator to graph a function.

EXAMPLE

Graph $y = 9 - x$ and make a table of values.

Step 1 Press WINDOW to set the range.

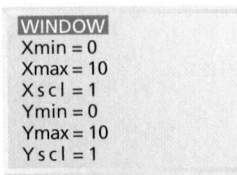

Step 2 Press Y= to enter the function.

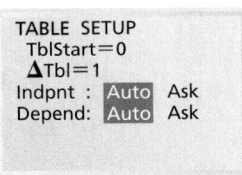

Step 3 Press GRAPH to view the graph.

Step 4 Use the TblSet feature. Set TblStart = 0 and ΔTbl = 1.

TABLE SETUP
TblStart=0
ΔTbl=1
Indpnt : Auto Ask
Depend: Auto Ask

Step 5 Use the TABLE feature to make a table of values.

X	Y₁
0	9
1	8
2	7
3	6
4	5
5	4
6	3

X=0

Step 6 Sketch the graph. Copy the table.

Exercises

Use a graphing calculator. Graph each function and make a table of values. Sketch the graph and copy the table of values. 1–7. See margin.

1. $y = 2x$

2. $y = x - 3$

3. $y = 13 - 2x$

4. $y = x + 1$

5. $y = 3x - 4$

6. $y = 0.5x + 6$

7. Reasoning What values in the WINDOW feature would you use to view the graph of $y = 100x$? Explain.

460 Activity Lab Three Views of a Function

1–7. See back of book.

9-6 Interpreting Graphs

Check Skills You'll Need

1. Vocabulary Review
Give an example of an *input*. Check students' work.
Find the distance for each time. Use $d = rt$ with $r = 40$ mi/h.

2. 2.5 h
100 mi

3. 3.5 h
140 mi

4. $\frac{1}{4}$ h
10 mi

5. $\frac{1}{2}$ h
20 mi

GO for Help
Lesson 9-5

TEKS ★ TAKS

- (7.4)(B) To graph data to demonstrate relationships in familiar concepts TAKS Obj. 2
- (7.14)(A) To communicate mathematical ideas using graphical models TAKS Obj. 6

Why Learn This?

You can see the history of an event by looking at a graph. You can use a graph like the one at the right to show your distance from home when you take a trip or run an errand.

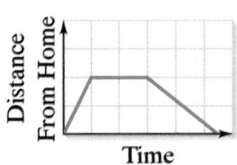

When you graph a relationship, you can see how one quantity changes compared to another.

EXAMPLE Describing a Graph

1 Shopping The graph above relates time and your distance from home. What can you tell about the trip from the steepness of the lines?

A steeper line on the graph shows faster speed. A horizontal line represents a period of no change in distance from home.

Quick Check

1. You walk two blocks at a fast pace and then stop for 12 min. Then you walk 2 blocks at a slower pace and 2 blocks at the faster pace.

1. You live 6 blocks from school. The graph at the right shows your walk home on a sunny day. Describe what the graph shows.
See left.

TEKS ★ TAKS

(7.4)(B) To graph data to demonstrate relationships in familiar concepts TAKS Obj. 2
(7.14)(A) To communicate mathematical ideas using graphical models TAKS Obj. 6

Dana Center TEKS Toolkit Clarifying Activities (7.4)(B), (7.14)(A)
Visit: PHSchool.com
Web Code: arq-9045

Professional Development

TEKS Math Background

A graph can provide a visual description of a situation. Graphs show how one quantity changes in relation to another quantity. A horizontal line shows no change in the variable on the vertical axis of a situation.

More Math Background: p. 434D

Lesson Planning and Resources

See p. 434E for a list of the resources that support this lesson.

PowerPoint
Bell Ringer Practice

✓ Check Skills You'll Need
Use student page, transparency, or PowerPoint.

TAKS Daily Review 72
Use transparency.

Differentiated Instruction Solutions for All Learners

Special Needs L1
Students who have difficulty sketching graphs can work with a partner. The partner can draw the graphs, while the student labels the sections and axes.

learning style: visual

Below Level L2
Should each situation have a graph of points or a line?

no. of visitors each hour **points**
puppy's weight by month **line**
no. of students in each grade **points**

learning style: verbal

461

Guided Instruction

Example 2
Make sure students understand the connection between the slope of the line and the speed of Ciara's travel. The slope for the drive is steeper than the slope for the walk because driving is faster than walking. The slope for time at school is horizontal because her distance did not change. She stayed in the same place.

PowerPoint

Additional Examples

❶ Nancy took a roundtrip walk from home. Describe what the graph shows.
See back of book.

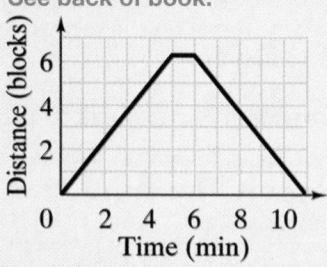

❷ Suppose that after 5 minutes, Nancy ran home. Draw the new graph. See back of book.

❸ Make a graph of this data.

No. Mugs	1	2	3	4
Cost ($)	6	10	15	18

See back of book.

All in One Teaching Resources
• Daily Notetaking Guide 9-6 **L3**
• Adapted Notetaking 9-6 **L1**

Closure

• *What can you learn about a situation from looking at a graph?* Sample: You can learn how one quantity changes relative to another.

462

You can sketch a graph to describe a real-world situation.

EXAMPLE Sketching a Graph

❷ **Transportation** Ciara's mother drove her part of the way to school. Ciara waited for a friend and walked the rest of the way to school. She took a bus home. Sketch a graph to show the distance Ciara traveled compared to time.

✓ Quick Check

2. Sketch a graph of the situation in Example 2 using *Distance from Home* instead of *Distance Traveled* for the vertical axis. See back of book.

When you draw a graph, you may need to consider what is reasonable.

EXAMPLE Graphing Data

❸ The cost to play games at an arcade is given in the table. Make a graph of the cost to play 1, 2, 3, and 4 games at the arcade.

Do not connect the points in the graph.

Number of Games	Cost ($)
1	2.00
2	3.50
3	5.00
4	6.50

Check for Reasonableness Each cost is for playing an entire game. Since you cannot pay for part of a game, connecting the points would not be meaningful.

✓ Quick Check

3. The table shows the number of cans in the cafeteria juice machine over time. Graph the data. See left.

Time	Number of Cans
8 A.M.	30
9 A.M.	20
10 A.M.	19
11 A.M.	19

Online active math

For: Graphing Activity
Use: Interactive Textbook, 9-6

3.

462 Chapter 9 Patterns and Rules

Advanced Learners **L4**
Sketch a graph for this situation: Turtle and Rabbit raced. Rabbit was faster, but slept for 30 minutes. The race ended in a tie. Check students' work.

Pre-AP™

English Language Learners ELL
Have students generate situations, in words, in which they would connect the points on a graph. Have them generate situations in which the points should not be connected. Make sure they understand the difference between graphs of continuous and discrete data.

learning style: verbal

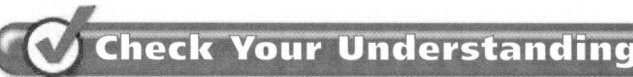

Check Your Understanding

Match each situation with the appropriate graph.

1. height of a person from birth to age 20 **C**

2. air temperature in a 24-hour period starting at midnight **A**

3. distance raced with a fall over a hurdle **B**

A.

Time

B.

Time

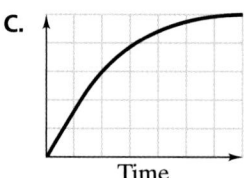

C.

Time

Homework Exercises

For more exercises, see Extra Skills and Word Problems.

GO for Help

For Exercises	See Examples
4–5	1
6	2
7–8	3

Ⓐ **Describe what each graph shows.** 4–5. See left.

4.

Walking Home From School

5.

Distance From Home

4. You walk at a steady pace, traveling 6 blocks in 16 min.

5. You travel at a steady pace for 2 h, stop for $\frac{1}{2}$ h, and then travel at the same steady pace for 2 h.

6. You ride your bike slowly up a steep hill and then quickly down the other side. Sketch a graph for the situation. Label each section and each axis. Show your speed on the bicycle on the vertical axis.
See margin.

Graph the data. Should you connect the points on each graph? Explain.
7–8. See margin.

7.

Lemonade Sales

Cups Sold	Income ($)
1	0.75
2	1.50
3	2.25
4	3.00
5	3.75

8.

Miles From Home

Time (h)	Miles
1	60
2	85
3	120
4	180

Ⓑ **GPS** 9. **Guided Problem Solving** You pay 5 cents a day for overdue library books. Make a graph of the fines for 1–5 days. See margin.
- How can a table help you plot the points on the graph?
- Should you connect the points on your graph?

6–9. See back of book.

PowerPoint

Lesson Quiz

1. Describe what the graph shows.

Sample: Someone walked for 3 blocks then rode for 6 blocks.

2. Graph the data in the table.

No. Copies	1	2	3	4
Cost (¢)	8	16	24	32

10–11c. See back of book.

---

10. Suppose you steadily pour sand into the bowl at the left. Which **GPS** graph below better shows the relationship of the height of the sand over time? Explain. **See margin.**

A.

B.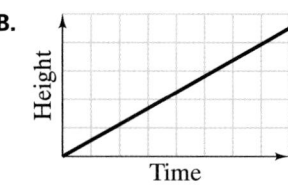

11. The graph shows a 90-m race. One student starts 5 s after the other.
  a. Describe what the graph shows.
  b. Who wins the race?
  c. **Writing in Math** If the lines were parallel, what would the graph tell you about who wins the race?
  11a–c. See margin.

Online
Homework Help
Visit: PHSchool.com
Web Code: are-0906

Estimation **The graph below shows what happens when a ball is thrown in the air.**

12. When does the ball hit the ground? about 2.75 s

13. The ball is 20 ft high on the way up and on the way down. It reaches that height after about 0.4 s and about 2.4 s.

13. Why are there two times when the ball's height is 20 ft? What are they? See left.

14. When the time is 0, the height of the ball is *not* 0. Explain? The ball starts at a height of about 5 ft.

C 15. **Challenge** Describe what might have happened to make the data in the graph. Answers may vary. Sample: A person threw a ball into the air. It left the person's hand 5 feet above the ground and landed on the ground about 2.75 seconds later.

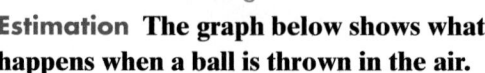

16. Lee is starting his own business by selling personalized photo frames to his class for $19 each. It costs Lee $14 for materials to make one frame. Which equation can be used to find *p*, the amount of profit he makes by selling 25 frames? B
  Ⓐ $p = (25 \times 19) - 14$ Ⓒ $p = 25 \times 19 \times 14$
  Ⓑ $p = 25(19 - 14)$ Ⓓ $p = 14(25 - 19)$

TAKS Objective 6
TEKS (7.14)(A)

TAKS Objective 2
TEKS (7.5)(B)

17. Which problem situation is NOT modeled by $y = 4x$? H
  Ⓕ Cost of a call at $0.04/min   Ⓗ Perimeter of a trapezoid
  Ⓖ Janet's pay after working 4 h   Ⓙ Number of pens in 4 packs

for Help **Lesson 2-4**

Compare. Use <, =, or >.

18. $\frac{7}{9}$ ■ $\frac{3}{4}$ >   **19.** $\frac{5}{14}$ ■ $\frac{2}{6}$ >   **20.** $\frac{7}{30}$ ■ $\frac{1}{3}$ <   **21.** $\frac{8}{24}$ ■ $\frac{2}{6}$ =

TEKS ★ TAKS Resources

• TAKS Strategies, p. 477
• TAKS Tune-Up, pp. 481–483

TAKS Tune-Up Kit

• TAKS Daily Review Transparencies
• TAKS Review and Preparation Workbook
• TAKS Strategies with Transparencies
• Texas Progress Monitoring Assessments

Alternative Assessment

Provide students with graph paper. Partners separately list their activities and the amount of time each takes from the time they leave home in the morning to the time they reach their first class. Students exchange lists and sketch a graph to represent each other's situation.

Write a rule for each table.

1.

x	0	1	2	3
y	0	5	10	15

$y = 5x$

2.

x	0	1	2	3
y	-3	0	3	6

$y = 3x - 3$

3.

x	0	1	2	3
y	9	10	11	12

$y = x + 9$

4. Graph $y = 2x - 4$. See margin.

For Exercises 5–7, use the graph at the right.

5. The graph shows a 50-m race. In this race Edwin had a 15-m head start over Carl. Who won the race?

Edwin

6. By how many seconds did the winner win the race?

1 s

7. You walk for 3 h, eat lunch for 1 h, bike for 1 h, and then do homework for 2 h. Sketch a graph that describes your speed. See margin.

MATH GAMES

Lines in Space

MATH GAMES

Lines in Space

What You'll Need

- 2 players and 2 coordinate grids similar to the one at the right

How To Play

- Without showing each other, Players A and B put three spaceships on their own grids. The lengths of the spaceships are four points, three points, and three points.

- Ships occupy adjacent grid points either left and right, up and down, or diagonally. Players choose whole-number points. They take turns trying to locate each other's ships by calling out function rules.

- If a function rule hits one or more sections of a spaceship, the player must announce a hit. See the table at the right.

- After 7 guesses each, the player who has hit the most sections of the other player's spaceships wins.

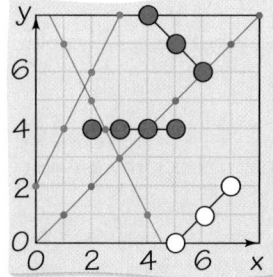

Rule	Result
$y = 2x + 2$?	Miss!
$y = -2x + 9$?	1 Hit!
$y = x$	2 Hits!

465

4.

7.

Solving Pattern Problems

In this feature, students practice solving problems involving patterns. They identify patterns, find the next terms in the pattern, and generate formulas based on the patterns.

Guided Instruction

Review with students the ways of finding patterns they have learned throughout the chapter. Have a volunteer read the problem aloud.
Ask:

- *What is the pattern of the dominoes?* Each row has one more domino than the row preceding it.
- *What is the function for the pattern of dominoes?* $y = x + 1$
- *What kind of number sequence is this?* arithmetic

Solving Pattern Problems

TEKS ★ TAKS
(7.13)(C) To select an appropriate problem-solving strategy, including looking for a pattern TAKS Obj. 6
(7.15)(A) To make conjectures from patterns or sets of examples TAKS Obj. 6

Alondra lines up dominoes to see how many she can knock over by touching only one. She lines them up as shown below. If Alondra makes 20 rows, how many dominoes can she knock over?

What You Might Think

What do I know? What do I want to find out?

How can I show the main idea?

How do I solve the problem?

How can I check my answer?

What You Might Write

I can see one domino in the first row, two in the second, three in the third, and so on. I want to know how many are in 20 rows.

I see a pattern. I see these numbers of dominoes:

1, 2, 3, ... 20. So, add 1 + 2 + 3 + ... + 20.

One way to add the numbers is to make "pairs of 20s," such as 1 + 19 and 2 + 18. I get nine 20s, plus 10 and 20. Since 9 · 20 + 10 + 20 = 210, the answer is 210 dominoes.

I can add the numbers from 1 to 20 in order, using a calculator. I still get 210.

Think It Through

1. Write the numbers from 1 to 20. Show that you have nine pairs that add up to 20, plus 10 and 20.

Answers may vary. Sample:
1 + 19, 2 + 18, 3 + 17, 4 + 16, 5 + 15, 6 + 14, 7 + 13, 8 + 12, 9 + 11, 10, 20

2. If Alondra had made 30 rows, how many dominoes did she use? 465 dominoes

3. **Number Sense** If Alondra had 300 dominoes, how many rows could she make? Explain.
24 rows; since 210 dominoes make 20 rows, you can add row by row until you reach 300.

Word Problem Practice

Exercises

Solve each problem. For Exercises 4 and 5, answer the questions first.

4. William stacked cans of soup as shown below. What is the total number of cans would he need to make the stack 7 rows high? 140 cans

   a. What do you know? What do you want to find out?
   b. Is there a pattern? If so, how can you find the sum?

5. One of the largest passenger jets, the Airbus A380, first flew in 2005. The dimensions of the A380 and the Wright Flyer are shown in the table below. Assume that Wright Flyers can be stacked on top of each other and that they always face the same direction inside a hangar. How many Wright Flyers could fit in a hangar built to house the A380? 480 or 528; answers may vary depending on how planes are stacked.

Plane Dimensions

Plane	Length (ft)	Width (ft)	Height (ft)
Airbus A380	239	262	79
Wright Flyer	21	40	9

   a. A sketch of a box representing the dimensions of the Airbus A380 appears at the right. How can drawing a box that represents the Wright Flyer help you find the answer?

   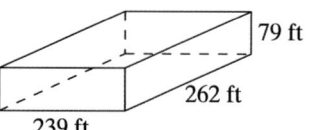

   79 ft
   262 ft
   239 ft

6. A lawnmower engine turns at about 2,500 rpm (revolutions per minute). How many times does the blade turn around every second? How many times does the blade turn around in half an hour? $41\frac{2}{3}$ revolutions per second; 75,000 revolutions per half hour

7. A sheet of notebook paper is about 0.0025 inch thick. It is physically impossible to fold a piece of paper in half 13 times. If you could, how thick would the stack of folded paper be? If you could fold a piece of paper 25 times, how thick would the stack be? 20.48 in.; 83,886.08 in. or about 1.3 mi

Guided Problem Solving Solving Pattern Problems **467**

Error Prevention!

Remind students of the difference between an arithmetic sequence and a geometric sequence. In an arithmetic sequence, they must add the *same* number to each term to get the next term. In a geometric sequence, they must multiply each term by the *same* number to get the next term.

Exercises

Have students work independently on the Exercises. When they have finished, have them form small groups to compare and discuss their answers. Have them elect a representative to report their results and call on different groups to answer each question.

Teaching Tip

For Exercise 4, have students work a simpler problem first. Have them find the total number of cans needed to make a stack 1, 2, 3, and 4 rows high.

Differentiated Instruction

Advanced Learners   L4

Have students write their own similar problems and trade papers with a partner to solve.

Objectives
To find simple interest and compound interest

Examples
1 Finding Simple Interest
2 Graphing Simple Interest
3 Finding Compound Interest

Math Background

Interest is both charged to those who borrow money and paid to those who allow others to use their money. Unlike simple interest, compound interest calculates interest on both the principal and the interest paid. Simple and compound interest can both be calculated with formulas.

More Math Background: p. 434D

Lesson Planning and Resources

See p. 434E for a list of the resources that support this lesson.

Bell Ringer Practice

✓ **Check Skills You'll Need**
Use student page, transparency, or PowerPoint.

Daily Review 73
Use transparency.

468

✓ Check Skills You'll Need

1. Vocabulary Review
What is a *percent*?
See below.
Change each percent to a decimal.

2. 4% 0.04 **3.** 9% 0.09

4. 2.0% 0.020 **5.** 6.5% 0.065

GO for Help
Lesson 6-2

Check Skills You'll Need

1. A percent is a ratio that compares a number to 100.

GO Online

Video Tutor Help
Visit: PHSchool.com
Web Code: are-0775

What You'll Learn

To find simple interest and compound interest

🔊 **New Vocabulary** principal, simple interest, compound interest, balance

Why Learn This?

Money may not grow on trees, but it can grow in a bank. When you deposit money, you earn money called interest. When you borrow money, you pay interest on your loan.

The original amount you deposit or borrow is the **principal.** Interest earned only on the principal is **simple interest.**

You can use a formula to calculate simple interest.

KEY CONCEPTS **Simple Interest Formula**

$$I = prt$$

I is the interest earned, p is the principal, r is the interest rate per year, and t is the time in years.

EXAMPLE Finding Simple Interest

❶ **Griddable Item** You borrow $300 for 5 years at an annual interest rate of 4%. What is the simple interest you pay in dollars?

$I = prt$ ← Write the formula.
$I = (300)(0.04)(5) = 60$ ← Substitute. Use 0.04 for 4%.

The interest is $60.

✓ Quick Check

1. Find the simple interest you pay on a $220 loan at a 5% annual interest rate for 4 years. $44.00

468 Chapter 9 Patterns and Rules

Differentiated Instruction Solutions for All Learners

Special Needs L1
When students use the simple and compound interest formulas, have them label the numbers that correspond to the time, the principal, interest rate, and balance. You can also encourage them to color code the numbers in their formulas.

learning style: visual

Below Level L2
Remind students to change percents to hundredths. 4%, for instance, is 0.04. *Find the simple interest on $400 borrowed for 3 years at a 5% annual interest rate.* $60

learning style: visual

A graph can show the increase in interest earned over time.

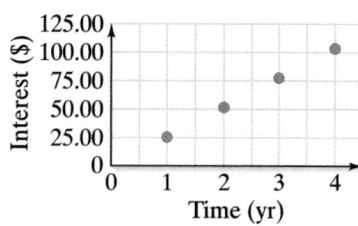

For: Interest Activity
Use: Interactive
Textbook, 9-7

EXAMPLE   Graphing Simple Interest

2 You have $500 in an account that earns an annual rate of 5.1%. At the end of each year, you withdraw the interest you have earned. Graph the total interest you earn after 1, 2, 3, and 4 years.

Step 1 Make a table.

Time (yr)	Interest ($)
1	25.50
2	51.00
3	76.50
4	102.00

Step 2 Draw a graph.

✓ Quick Check

2. Graph the simple interest earned on $950 at an annual rate of 4.2%.
See left.

Compound interest is interest that is paid on the original principal and on any interest that has been left in the account. The **balance** of an account is the principal plus the interest earned.

> ### KEY CONCEPTS   Compound Interest Formula
>
> $$B = p(1 + r)^t$$
>
> B is the balance, p is the principal, r is the annual interest rate, and t is the time in years.

EXAMPLE   Finding Compound Interest

GO for Help

For help using the order of operations with exponents, go to Lesson 2-1, Example 3.

3 **Banking** You deposit $5,000 in a bank account that pays 3.75% compound interest. What is your balance after 9 years?

$B = p(1 + r)^t$ ← **Write the formula.**

$\quad = 5,000(1 + 0.0375)^9$ ← **Substitute. Use 0.0375 for 3.75%.**

$\quad \approx 5,000(1.392813439)$ ← **Use a calculator to simplify the power.**

$\quad = 6,964.07$ ← **Round to the nearest cent.**

The balance after 9 years is $6,964.07.

✓ Quick Check

3. You deposit $3,000 in a bank account that pays 4.25% compound interest. What is your balance after 12 years? $4,943.49

9-7 Simple and Compound Interest   **469**

469

3. Practice

Assignment Guide

Check Your Understanding
Go over Exercises 1–4 in class before assigning the Homework Exercises.

Homework Exercises
A Practice by Example   5–19
B Apply Your Skills   20–29
C Challenge   30
TEKS ★ TAKS Tune-Up and
   Mixed Review   31–35

Homework Quick Check
To check students' understanding of key skills and concepts, go over Exercises 7, 13, 21, 23, and 29.

Differentiated Instruction Resources

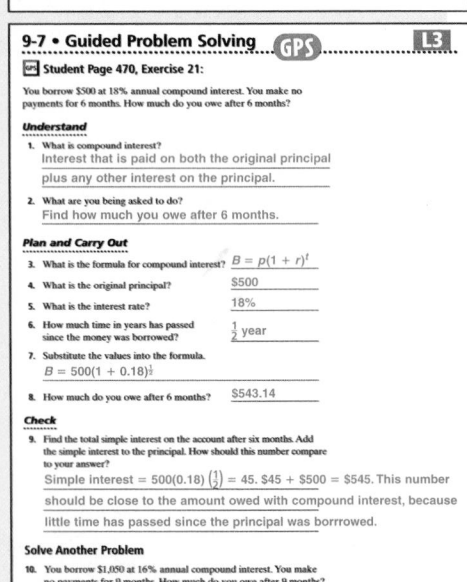

470

---

1. Simple interest is calculated only on the principal. Compound interest is calculated on the principal and any interest left in the account.

1. **Vocabulary** How do simple interest and compound interest differ?

2. Find the simple interest earned on $2000 at 10% for 6 years. **$1,200**

3. Find the compound interest earned on $2000 at 10% for 6 years.
   $1,543.12

4. True or False: Doubling the principal will double the balance. **True**

Homework Exercises

For more exercises, see Extra Skills and Word Problems.

GO for Help

For Exercises	See Examples
5–8	1
9–14	2
15–19	3

Ⓐ **Find the simple interest on a $340 loan at each rate.**

5. 7% annual interest, 3 years
   $71.40
6. 12% annual interest, 5 years
   $204.00
7. 15% annual interest, 1 year
   $51.00
8. 4.6% annual interest, 6 years
   $93.84

Graph the total simple interest earned for each amount over 4 years.
9–14. See margin.

9. $500 at 4.5%
10. $1,200 at 6.5%
11. $375 at 5.75%
12. $200 at 5.0%
13. $2,000 at 10%
14. $2,000 at 0.5%

Find the balance in each compound interest account.

15. $1,400 after 3 years at 5.5%
    $1,643.94
16. $1,800 after 11 years at 6.0%
    $3,416.94
17. $900 after 10 years at 4.62%
    $1,413.81
18. $2,500 after 50 years at 2.2%
    $7,421.38

19. You deposit $1,000 in a certificate of deposit that pays 5.9% compound interest. What is your balance after 3 years? **$1,187.65**

Ⓑ **GPS** 20. **Guided Problem Solving** You have $7,500 in a college savings account that earns 4.25% compound interest. What will the account balance be at the end of 12 years? **$12,358.74**
   • What is 4.25% expressed as a decimal?
   • What value do you substitute for each variable in the formula $B = p(1 + r)^t$?

21. You borrow $500 at 18% annual compound interest. You make no
GPS payments for 6 months. How much do you owe after 6 months?
   $543.14

22. Suppose you invest $2,000 for 5 years at 4% compounded annually. Which would increase your balance in 5 years the most? **A**
   Ⓐ Doubling the starting amount from $2,000 to $4,000
   Ⓑ Doubling the interest rate to 8% annual interest
   Ⓒ Doubling the time from 5 years to 10 years

23. **Writing in Math** Would you prefer $2,000 at 6% compound interest for 5 years or $2,000 at 5% compound interest for 6 years? Explain.
   See margin.

9–14. See back of book.
23. Answers may vary. Sample: I prefer $2,000 at 5% compound interest for 6 years because I will eventually make more money.
34–35. See back of book.

The spreadsheet shows calculations using the compound interest formula. State which column corresponds to each variable.

	A	B	C	D	E
1	Year	Balance at Start of Year	Rate	Interest	Balance at End of Year
2	1st	$3,000.00	0.04	$120.00	$3,120.00
3	2nd	$3,120.00	0.04	$124.80	$3,244.80
4	3rd	$3,244.80	0.04	$129.79	$3,374.59

24. p B **25.** r C **26.** t A **27.** B E

28. Show how to calculate the amount in E4 in the spreadsheet above.
E4 = B4 + D4

29. Calculator You invest $4,000 at 3% compound interest. What is the balance after 3 years? $4,370.91

C **30. Challenge** You invest $2,000 in a simple interest account. The balance after 8 years is $2,720. What is the interest rate? 4.5%

TEKS ★ TAKS Tune-Up and Mixed Review

TAKS Objective 6
TEKS (7.13)(A)

31. When a principal p has a compound interest rate r for t years, the balance B is given by $B = p(1 + r)^t$. Which expression represents the balance for $200 invested for 6 years at a 5% compound interest rate? C
- Ⓐ $200(1.06)^5$
- Ⓒ $200(1.05)^6$
- Ⓑ $200(0.06)(5)$
- Ⓓ $200(1.05)(6)$

TAKS Objective 5
TEKS (7.11)(B)

32. Which situation is best represented by the graph of babies born in Texas?
- Ⓕ About 85 babies were born every hour.
- Ⓖ About 85 babies were born every 2 hours. G
- Ⓗ About 85 babies were born every 3 hours.
- Ⓙ About 85 babies were born every 4 hours.

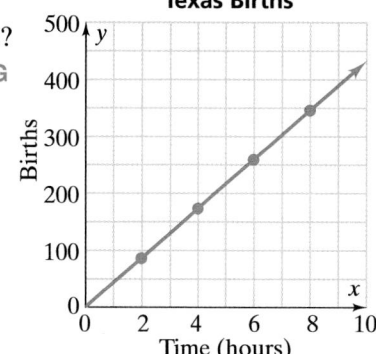
Texas Births

TAKS Objective 3
TEKS (7.6)(A)

33. $\angle A$ and $\angle B$ are supplementary. The measure of $\angle A$ is 24°. What is the measure of $\angle B$? C
- Ⓐ 24°
- Ⓑ 66°
- Ⓒ 156°
- Ⓓ 336°

GO for Help
Lesson 8-8

Use graph paper to draw each figure. 34–35. See margin.

34. triangular prism **35.** pentagonal pyramid

Alternative Assessment

Provide pairs of students with index cards. One student writes a percent less than 10% on each card while the partner writes different whole-dollar amounts on each card. Students place the cards facedown in separate stacks. They choose a card from each stack and use the percents as rates to find the simple interest on the dollar amount.

TEKS ★ TAKS Resources

- TAKS Strategies, p. 477
- TAKS Tune-Up, pp. 481–483

TAKS Tune-Up Kit
- TAKS Daily Review Transparencies
- TAKS Review and Preparation Workbook
- TAKS Strategies with Transparencies
- Texas Progress Monitoring Assessments

---

4. Assess & Reteach

PowerPoint
Lesson Quiz

Krista opened a savings account with $100.

1. Find the simple interest earned at a 6% annual rate for 5 years. $30

2. Find the balance at 6% interest compounded annually for 5 years. $133.82

Reteaching 9-7 Simple and Compound **L2**

When you deposit money in a bank, the bank pays interest. **Simple interest** is interest paid only on the amount you deposited, called the **principal**. **Compound interest** is paid on the original principal and on any interest that has been left in the account.

Simple Interest
To find simple interest, use this formula.
Interest = principal · rate · time in years
$I = p \cdot r \cdot t$
Find the simple interest on $1,800 invested at 5% annual interest for 3 years.
$I = p \cdot r \cdot t$
= 1,800 · 0.05 · 3 ← Use 0.05 for 5%.
= 270
The interest is $270. (The balance will be $1,800 + $270, or $2,070.)

Compound Interest
To find compound interest, use this formula.
Balance = principal · (1 + rate)^time in years
$B = p \cdot (1 + r)^t$
You put $1,800 in the bank. The interest rate is 5% compounded annually. How much will be in the account after 3 years?
$B = p \cdot (1 + r)^t$
= 1,800(1 + 0.05)³ ← Use 0.05 for 5%.
= 1,800 · (1.05)³
≈ 2,083.73
The balance is $2,083.73.

Find the simple interest earned by each account.
1. $800 principal, 4% interest rate, 5 years
$I = p \cdot r \cdot t$
= 800 · 0.04 · 5
= $160
2. $800 principal, 3% interest, 4 years
$96
3. $1,900 principal, 4.5% interest, 20 years
$1,710
4. $20,000 principal, 3.5% interest, 15 years
$10,500

Find the balance of each account earning compound interest.
5. $600 principal, 6% interest rate, 3 years
$B = p(1 + r)^t$
= 600 (1 + 0.06)³
= $714.61
6. $9,000 principal, 5% interest rate, 4 years
$B = p(1 + r)^t$
= 9,000 (1 + 0.05)⁴
= $10,939.56

Enrichment 9-7 Simple and Compound **L4**
Critical Thinking

Solve each problem by writing an equation.

1. You have $3,200 to invest. You decide to put some of your money in a money market fund that makes 8% simple interest and the rest in a bond that makes 5% interest. How much did you invest in each account if after 1 year you earned $220 in interest?
$2,000 at 8% and $1,200 at 5%

2. You have 2 options for saving $12,000 in a bank. You can put it in a savings account that earns 6% simple interest for 1 year or in another account that earns 2% simple interest for 3 years. Which account earns you the most interest?
the 2% compound interest account

3. Your parents invested $5,000 in one account for 6 years and $3,000 in another account for 4 years. If the $5,000 account earned $1,080 more in simple interest and both accounts have the same interest rate, what is the interest rate?
6%

4. Your grandparents invest $4,200 in an account for 3 years that earns 2.5% compound interest. Your aunt earns the same amount of interest as your grandparents, but invests $3,500 in an account for 2 years earning compound interest. What is the interest rate on your aunt's account?
4.5%

5. Your uncle has $2,500 to invest at 3.2% compound interest, but he can only invest for 6 months. Write an equation using the formula for compound interest to show the balance.
$B = 2,500(1 + 0.032)^{0.5}$ or $B = 2,500(1 + 0.032)^{\frac{1}{2}}$

6. If an exponent of 2 means you "square" the base, what does an exponent of the multiplicative inverse of 2, or ½, mean?
to find the square root of the base

7. Simplify the equation you wrote in exercise 5 to find the balance.
$2,539.69

8. Suppose you deposit $12,000 in a bank account that pays 2.75% interest compounded annually. What is your balance after 6 months?
$12,163.88

471

Objectives

To solve for a variable

Examples

1. Transforming a Formula
2. Application: Savings

Math Background

A *formula* is a rule that shows the relationship between two or more quantities. The formula for the area of a rectangle, for instance, is $A = \ell \cdot w$, where A is area, ℓ is length, and w is width. But what if the area and length are known and the width is unknown? The formula has to be transformed. First, solve for the unknown value by using the properties of equality: $w = \frac{A}{\ell}$. Then substitute the values you know and simplify.

More Math Background: p. 434D

Lesson Planning and Resources

See p. 434E for a list of the resources that support this lesson.

Bell Ringer Practice

✓ **Check Skills You'll Need**
Use student page, transparency, or PowerPoint.

(TAKS) **Daily Review 74**
Use transparency.

472

✓ Check Skills You'll Need

1. **Vocabulary Review**
What is the *Division Property of Equality*?
See below.
Solve each equation.

2. $5a = 9$ $\frac{9}{5}$

3. $12 = 4.5t$ $2\frac{2}{3}$

4. $\frac{p}{4} = -8$ -32

GO for Help
Lesson 4-4

Check Skills You'll Need

1. If you divide each side of an equation by the same nonzero number, the two sides remain equal.

⭐ (TAKS) **Tip**

To solve a formula for a variable, you have to get the variable alone on one side of the equation.

What You'll Learn

To solve for a variable

◄)) **New Vocabulary** formula

Why Learn This?

Albert Einstein discovered the relationship between mass, energy, and the speed of light. The formula $E = mc^2$ shows this relationship.

A **formula** is a rule that shows the relationship between two or more quantities.

You can use the properties of equality to transform a formula and solve for a variable.

EXAMPLE Transforming a Formula

1. The formula for the perimeter of a rectangle is $P = 2\ell + 2w$. Solve the formula for ℓ.

$$P = 2\ell + 2w \quad \leftarrow \text{Write the formula.}$$

$$P - 2w = 2\ell \quad \leftarrow \text{Use the Subtraction Property of Equality.}$$

$$\frac{P - 2w}{2} = \frac{2\ell}{2} \quad \leftarrow \text{Use the Division Property of Equality.}$$

$$\frac{P - 2w}{2} = \ell \quad \leftarrow \text{Simplify.}$$

✓ Quick Check

1. Solve each equation for x.

   a. $y = 2x - 4$
   b. $y = x + 3$
   c. $4y = 2x + 10$

   a. $x = \frac{y + 4}{2}$ b. $x = y - 3$ c. $x = 2y - 5$

You can transform formulas to solve real-world problems. First solve for the desired variable. Then substitute the values you know.

472 Chapter 9 Patterns and Rules

Differentiated Instruction Solutions for All Learners

Special Needs L1
Have students draw a rectangle and assign length measures to the sides. Have them label *l* and *w*, and substitute their numbers in the transformed formula in Example 1. This will help them see how the formulas work.

learning style: visual

Below Level L2
Give students practice transforming simple equations.
Solve each equation for x.

| $y = x + 3$ | $y = 4x$ | $y = 3x + 2$ |
| $x = y - 3$ | $x = \frac{y}{4}$ | $x = \frac{y - 2}{3}$ |

learning style: visual

Video Tutor Help

Visit: PHSchool.com
Web Code: are-0775

EXAMPLE Application: Savings

② Your bank account has an annual interest rate of 5.7%. How much should you invest in order to earn $100 in interest each year?

$$\frac{I}{rt} = p \quad \leftarrow \text{Use the simple interest formula } I = prt \text{ and solve for } p.$$

$$\frac{100}{(0.057)(1)} = p \quad \leftarrow \text{Substitute 100 for } I, 0.057 \text{ for } r, \text{ and 1 for } t.$$

$$1{,}754.39 \approx p \quad \leftarrow \text{Simplify.}$$

You should invest about $1,755.

✓ Quick Check

2. Find the interest rate that yields $120 interest each year on $2,000.
6%

● More Than One Way

Your first four test scores were 85, 98, 79, and 92. To get an average score of at least 90, what minimum score do you need on the fifth test?

Will's Method

I'll use a variable for each score and let z be the missing score.

Formula for mean → $\quad 90 = \dfrac{v + w + x + y + z}{5}$

Mult. Prop. of Equality → $\quad 5(90) = v + w + x + y + z$

$5(90) - (v + w + x + y) = z \qquad \leftarrow$ Subtraction Prop. of Equality

$5(90) - (85 + 98 + 79 + 92) = z = 96 \quad \leftarrow$ Substitute and simplify.

I need a minimum score of 96 on the fifth test.

Sarah's Method

I'll work backward. The sum of the 5 scores divided by the number of scores is 90. Since $5 \cdot 90 = 450$, the sum is 450.

The sum of the first scores is $85 + 98 + 79 + 92$, or 354. So, for a total of 450, I need a score on the fifth test of $450 - 354$, or 96.

Choose a Method

Your scores on three tests are 95, 89, and 75. You can replace your lowest score with the mean of that score and a retest. For an average score of 90, what is the minimum you must score on the retest?
The minimum score must be 97.

9-8 Transforming Formulas **473**

---

2. Teach

Activity Lab
Use before the lesson.

All in One Teaching Resources
Activity Lab 9-8: Critical Thinking with Formulas

Guided Instruction

Example 1
Students may benefit from a quick review of inverse operations and solving two-step equations (see Lessons 4-3, 4-4, and 4-6). Remind students to begin with undoing addition or subtraction, and then undoing multiplication or division.

Example 2
Help students transform the equation $I = prt$ by undoing each variable with its own step. For instance, first divide each side of the equation by r and then divide each side by t.

PowerPoint
▲ Additional Examples

① Solve $a = \dfrac{F}{m}$ for F. $F = ma$

② Use $I = prt$. You earn $60 interest for one year on a principal of $1,500. What is the interest rate? 4%

All in One Teaching Resources
• Daily Notetaking Guide 9-8 **L3**
• Adapted Notetaking 9-8 **L1**

Closure

• *How can you transform a formula to solve a problem?*
Sample: Use the properties of equality to solve the formula for the unknown variable. Then substitute the values you know and simplify.

Advanced Learners **L4**
The formula for Celsius temperature given Fahrenheit temperature is $C = \frac{5}{9}(F - 32)$. Solve the formula for F. $F = \frac{9}{5}C + 32$

(Pre-AP™)

English Language Learners **ELL**
The More Than One Way problem may be difficult linguistically. Review what an *average* or *mean* is, and have students discuss in pairs to compare Will's and Sarah's methods for solving the problem.

learning style: verbal

473

3. Practice

Assignment Guide

Check Your Understanding
Go over Exercises 1–6 in class before assigning the Homework Exercises.

Homework Exercises
A Practice by Example   7–18
B Apply Your Skills   19–28
C Challenge   29
TEKS ★ *TAKS* Tune-Up and
Mixed Review   30–34

Homework Quick Check
To check students' understanding of key skills and concepts, go over Exercises 12, 17, 23, 27, and 28.

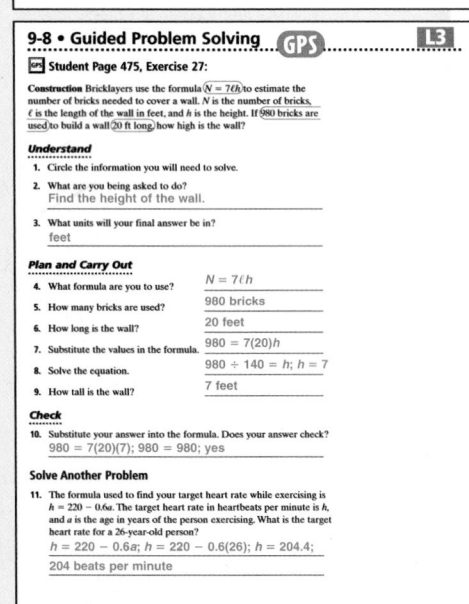

Check Your Understanding

1. No; it cannot be used to show the relationship between two quantities.

2. Yes; it can be used to show the relationship between t and u.

Reasoning Could the equation be a formula? Explain.   1–2. See left.

1. $3 + 4 = 7$ 2. $3t + 4u = 7$ 3. $3 + 4 = 7v$

3. No; it cannot be used to show the relationship between two quantities.

Which operation must you use to solve each equation for x?

4. $1 + x = 13$ 5. $x \div 4 = 52$ 6. $7x = 35$
   subtraction   multiplication   division

Homework Exercises

For more exercises, see Extra Skills and Word Problems.

GO for Help

For Exercises	See Examples
7–15	1
16–18	2

Ⓐ **Solve each equation for the variable in red.** $r = \frac{p + 5}{3}$

7. $x = yz$ $y = \frac{x}{z}$ 8. $t = \frac{u + v}{2}$ $u = 2t - v$ 9. $p = 3r - 5$

10. $P = 4s$ $s = \frac{P}{4}$ 11. $q = \frac{p}{r}$ $p = qr$ 12. $p = s - c$
                                                                                  $s = p + c$

13. $A = \frac{1}{2}bh$ $h = \frac{2A}{b}$ 14. $h = \frac{k}{j}$ $k = hj$ 15. $I = prt$ $t = \frac{I}{pr}$

16. How long would it take to earn $6,000 in interest on a principal of $9,000 at an annual simple interest rate of 4.1%? a little longer than 16.26 years

17. You earn $1,400 simple interest on a principal of $12,500 in 4 years. What is the interest rate on your account? 2.8%

18. Suppose you borrow money for a year at a simple interest rate of 7.2%. You pay $86.40 in interest. How much have you borrowed?
    $1,200

Ⓑ **GPS** 19. **Guided Problem Solving** A real estate agent sells a house and earns 7% commission, or $8,400. Find the selling price of the house.
  • What is a formula for the agent's commission? Let c represent the commission. Let s represent the selling price. $120,000
  • For which variable should you solve?

20. **Geometry** Find the radius of the circle at the right.
    about 4 cm

$C = 25.12$ cm r

21. The formula for converting F degrees Fahrenheit to C degrees Celsius is $C = \frac{5}{9}(F - 32)$. Solve the equation for F to generate the formula for converting C degrees Celsius into F degrees Fahrenheit. $F = \frac{9}{5}C + 32$

22. **Choose a Method** During a 3-day premiere, a theater must sell an average of 200 tickets per night to make a profit. For the first two nights, 206 and 185 tickets were sold. How many tickets must be sold for the third night for the theater to make a profit? 209 tickets

23. **Writing in Math** Solve the formula $V = \ell wh$ for w. Then write and solve a problem involving the transformed version of the formula.
    $w = \frac{V}{\ell \cdot h}$; check students' work.

GO Online
Homework Help
Visit: PHSchool.com
Web Code: are-0908

Solve each equation for the variable in red.

24. $x = 3y + 6$
$y = \frac{1}{3}x - 2$

25. $t = \frac{1}{2}r$
$r = 2t$

26. $w = 3n + 5m$
$n = \frac{w - 5m}{3}$

27. Construction Bricklayers use the formula $N = 7\ell h$ to estimate the number of bricks needed to cover a wall. N is the number of bricks, ℓ is the length of the wall in feet, and h is the height. If 980 bricks are used to build a wall 20 feet long, how high is the wall? **7 ft**

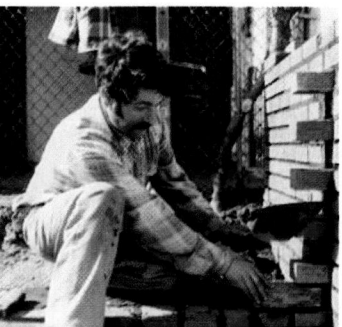

28. Weekly pay w is given by the formula $w = rh + 1.5rv$, where r is the regular hourly wage for a 40-h week, h is the number of regular hours you work, and v is the number of overtime hours you work beyond 40. Suppose your regular wage is \$9/h.
   a. If you work 45 hours in one week, what do you earn? **\$427.50**
   b. For weekly pay of \$468, how many overtime hours do you work? **8 h**

C 29. Challenge The surface area S of a cube with side e is $S = 6e^2$. Find the side length of a cube with a surface area of 150 cm². **5 cm**

TEKS ★ TAKS Tune-Up and Mixed Review

TAKS Objective 3
TEKS (7.8)(C)

30. You want to paint a wall of the playhouse but not the door in the wall. How many square feet of wall do you need to paint? **B**
   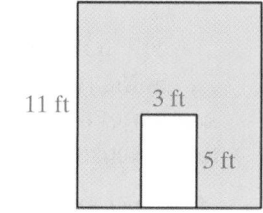
   Ⓐ 15 ft²
   Ⓑ 95 ft²
   Ⓒ 110 ft²
   Ⓓ 125 ft²

TAKS Objective 1
TEKS (7.2)(D)

31. Ezra can swim 50 meters in 30 seconds. About how many seconds will it take him to swim a 200-meter race? **H**
   Ⓕ 60 sec   Ⓖ 80 sec   Ⓗ 120 sec   Ⓙ 150 sec

TAKS Objective 2
TEKS (7.4)(C)

32. Which description shows the relationship between a term and n, its position in the sequence? **A**

Term Number	1	2	3	4	5	n
Value of Term	12	24	36	48	60	■

   Ⓐ Multiply n by 12.
   Ⓑ Divide n by 12.
   Ⓒ Add 12 to n.
   Ⓓ Subtract 12 from n.

GO for Help
Lesson 8-7

Find the missing side length. Round your answer to the nearest tenth.

33.
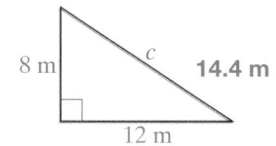
8 m c 14.4 m
12 m

34.

25 in.   28 in. x 12.6 in.

Online lesson quiz, PHSchool.com, Web Code: ara-0908

9-8 Transforming Formulas **475**

PowerPoint
Lesson Quiz

1. Solve $P = 2RT$ for T. $T = \frac{P}{2R}$

2. Use $I = prt$. You earn \$50 interest for one year with an interest rate of 2.5%. What is the principal? \$2,000

Reteaching 9-8   Transforming **L2**

A **formula** such as $I = prt$ states the relationship among unknown quantities represented by the variables I, p, r, and t. It means that interest equals the principal times the rate times the time.

You can use a formula by **substituting** values for the variables. Some formulas have numbers that do not vary, such as this formula for finding the perimeter of a square: $P = 4s$. The number 4 is a **constant**.

A Boeing 747 airplane traveled at 600 mph. At this speed how many hours did it take to travel 2,100 miles?

$d = r \cdot t$ Use the formula $d = rt$.
$2,100 = 600 \cdot t$ Substitute the known values.
$3.5 = t$ Divide to find the unknown value.

The Boeing 747 airplane traveled 2,100 miles in 3.5 hours.

1. Lisa rides her bike for 2 hours and travels 12 miles. Find her rate of speed.
   a. Which formula should you use to find the rate? $r = \frac{d}{t}$
   b. What is the rate of speed? 6 mi/hr

Solve each formula for the values given.

2. $A = lw$ for A, given $l = 35$ m and $w = 22$ m
   $A = 770$ m²

3. $P = 2l + 2w$ for l given $P = 30$ in. and $w = 7$ in.
   $l = 8$ in.

4. $V = lwh$ for l given $V = 60$ ft³, $w = 3$ ft, and $h = 5$ ft
   $l = 4$ ft

5. $I = prt$ for $p = \$100$, $r = 0.05$, and $t = 2$ years
   $I = \$10$

Enrichment 9-8   Transforming **L4**
Critical Thinking

The equation $d = r \times t$ relates rate (r), time (t), and distance (d).

1. If you are traveling at 55 mph, what formula would you use to find the distance you will travel over various lengths of time?
   $d = 55 \times t$

2. Sometimes you are given distances and need to know how long it would take to travel at various rates. Complete the table to find the time it would take to travel 500 miles at speeds of 40, 55, 60, 65, and 70 mph. Round your times to the nearest quarter hour, if necessary.

Rate (mph)	40	55	60	65	70
Time (hours)	$12\frac{1}{2}$	9	$8\frac{1}{4}$	$7\frac{3}{4}$	$7\frac{1}{4}$
Distance (miles)	500	500	500	500	500

3. What operation did you use to find the time? Rewrite the equation so that t stands alone on one side of the equal sign.
   Division: $t = \frac{d}{r}$

4. Rewrite the equation so that r stands alone on one side of the equal sign. Explain your reasoning.
   $r = \frac{d}{t}$; Sample answer: To find the rate, divide the distance by the time.

5. How is rewriting an equation like solving an equation?
   Sample answer: You use inverse operations to isolate the variable.

6. Why would you want to rewrite an equation?
   Sample answer: to find many solutions using the same equation; it would be faster to isolate the variable before doing each calculation.

7. The equation to find the perimeter of a regular polygon can be written as $P = n \times s$ where P is the perimeter, n is the number of sides, and s is the length of each side. How could you rewrite the equation to find the length of a side?
   $s = \frac{P}{n}$

Alternative Assessment

Each student in a pair writes a word problem modeled on Example 2 in this lesson. Partners exchange papers and write a function rule to solve each other's problem. Partners explain their function rules to each other.

TEKS ★ TAKS Resources

• TAKS Strategies, p. 477
• TAKS Tune-Up, pp. 481–483

TAKS Tune-Up Kit

• TAKS Daily Review Transparencies
• TAKS Review and Preparation Workbook
• TAKS Strategies with Transparencies
• Texas Progress Monitoring Assessments

475

9-8b Activity Lab

Algebra Thinking

x = ?

More About Formulas

There are some formulas that are not just interesting mathematically, but are also part of your life. Consider the formulas below.

TEKS ★ TAKS
(7.13)(A) To apply mathematics to everyday experiences, to activities in and outside of school, with other disciplines, and with other mathematical topics
TAKS Obj. 6

ACTIVITY

Use the graph at the right for Exercises 1–3.

1. Gold is measured in karats. The formula $P = \frac{25k}{6}$ gives you the percent of gold in k karats. Graph the percents of gold for 10, 12, 14, and 18 karats. Use the graph started at the right. See margin.

2. Extend the graph until you reach 100% gold. Which karat value corresponds to 100% gold? 24 karat

3. Transform the formula $P = \frac{25k}{6}$ by solving for k. Which karat value corresponds to 100% gold?
$k = \frac{6P}{25}$; 24 karat

Gold

The SPF number of sunscreen s tells you how long you can stay in the sun safely. The formula $t = sn$ represents the amount of time t it takes skin to burn with sunscreen. The amount of time n represents how long it takes skin to burn without sunscreen.

4. Transform the formula above by solving for s. $s = \frac{t}{n}$

5. A summer pool party might last 3 hours. Use the transformed formula to find what SPF number you should apply for $n = 15$ min. SPF 12

Data Analysis Peter Brancazio developed the formula $v = 126 - \frac{5}{4}h$. This formula determines the vertical leap v needed for people of different heights h to slam-dunk a basketball. Both v and h are in inches. 6–9. See margin.

6. Use the graph started at the right. Graph the results of this formula for heights of 5 ft, 5 ft 6 in., 6 ft, 6 ft 6 in., and 7 ft.

7. What do you think 126 represents in the formula? Most basketball hoops are about 10 ft high.

8. **Reasoning** Explain why the formula uses $\frac{5}{4}$ of height instead of exact height.

9. Transform the formula above to solve for h.

Slam Dunk

1. See back of book.
6–9. See back of book.

Estimating the Answer

Using estimation can help you find an answer, check an answer, or eliminate one or more answer choices.

EXAMPLES

1 A store is having a 30%-off sale on all of its cross-training sneakers. What is the sale price on a pair of sneakers that regularly costs $84.99?

   Ⓐ $25.50   Ⓑ $51.99   Ⓒ $59.49   Ⓓ $79.99

You can estimate by changing $84.99 to a number that is easy to multiply in your head, such as $90. A 30% discount will result in a sale price that is 70% of the regular price.

$s = 0.7c$ ← Write a function rule for sale price. Let s = sale price. Let c = regular cost.

$\approx 0.7(90)$ ← Substitute the estimated value.

$= 63$ ← Use mental math.

The sale price will be a little less than $63. The answer is choice C.

2 The formula for converting Celsius temperatures to Fahrenheit temperatures is $F = \frac{9}{5}C + 32$. Sterling silver melts at approximately 893°C. What is the approximate Fahrenheit temperature?

   Ⓕ 998°F   Ⓖ 1,422°F   Ⓗ 1,639°F   Ⓙ 1,995°F

$F = \frac{9}{5}(893) + 32$ ← Substitute into the formula.

$\approx 2(900) + 32$ ← Estimate. $\frac{9}{5} \approx \frac{10}{5}$, or 2, and 893 ≈ 900.

$= 1,832$ ← This is an overestimate, since 900 > 893 and 2 > $\frac{9}{5}$.

According to your estimate, choices F and G are too low. Since 1,832 is an overestimate, you can eliminate choice J. The correct answer is choice H.

Exercises

Objective 2
TEKS (7.3)(A)

1. A salon is offering a 20% discount on all haircuts. What is the discount price of a cut that regularly costs $23.50? **C**

   Ⓐ $12.50   Ⓑ $14.75   Ⓒ $18.80   Ⓓ $22.00

Objective 6
TEKS (7.13)(C)

2. The melting point of pure gold is 1,945°F. What is the approximate melting point in Celsius using the formula $C = \frac{5}{9}(F - 32)$? **F**

   Ⓕ 1,063°C   Ⓖ 1,159°C   Ⓗ 1,205°C   Ⓙ 1,495°C

TAKS Strategies   Estimating the Answer   **477**

TAKS Strategies

Estimating the Answers

This feature presents the valuable test-taking strategy of using estimation to find answers, eliminate answers, or check answers.

Guided Instruction

Present another way to estimate 30% of $84.99: *Think:* 30% is a little less than one third; $84 is a little less than $90. Using the estimating strategy of compatible numbers, find one third of 90, or 30. So, the answer must be about $90 − $30, or $60. Or point out how to use percent number sense to rule out choices A and D—the former is far too low and the latter, far too high.

Teaching Tip

Emphasize that eliminating answer choices is a powerful test-taking strategy.

TEKS ★ **TAKS** Resources

TAKS Strategies with Transparencies
• Transparency 10
• Practice Sheet, p. 21

TAKS **Strategies with Transparencies**

Test-Taking Strategies: Estimating the Answer

Sometimes you can estimate to find the answer.

Example Find the sum: 0.75 + 8.23 + 5.5
A. 15.53   B. 14.48   C. 9.53   D. 21.23
Estimate: Round to the nearest whole number.
0.75 + 8.23 + 5.5
1 + 8 + 6 = 15
Both A and B are near 15, so round to the nearest tenth.
0.8 + 8.2 + 5.5 must be less than 15.
The answer is 14.48, or choice B.

Estimate to find the answer. Explain your reasoning.

1. The area of a square with side 2.7 cm is

   A. 5.4 cm².   B. 7.29 cm².   C. 54 cm².   D. 72.9 cm².

2. Reese went grocery shopping to buy spaghetti sauce, spaghetti noodles, and a loaf of french bread. These items cost $1.59, $1.79, and $1.89. About how much should Reese's grocery bill be?

   F. less than $5   G. between $5 and $6
   H. between $6 and $7   J. more than $7

Chapter 9 Review

Vocabulary Review

 arithmetic sequence (p. 442)
balance (p. 469)
compound interest (p. 469)
conjecture (p. 443)

formula (p. 472)
function (p. 452)
geometric sequence (p. 442)

principal (p. 468)
sequence (p. 442)
simple interest (p. 468)

Go Online
PHSchool.com
For: Vocabulary Quiz
Web Code: arj-0951

Choose the correct term to complete each sentence.

1. A sequence is (arithmetic, geometric) if each term is found by adding the same number to the previous term. **arithmetic**

2. A (formula, function) has only 1 output value for each input value. **function**

3. (Balance, Principal) is an amount deposited or borrowed. **principal**

4. Interest paid on an original deposit and on any interest that has been left in an account is (compound, simple) interest. **compound**

5. A (conjecture, formula) is a prediction. **conjecture**

Skills and Concepts   TEKS ★ TAKS

Lesson 9-1

(7.4)(B) To graph data to demonstrate relationships in familiar concepts such as conversions and perimeter **TAKS Obj. 2**

(7.11)(B) To make inferences and convincing arguments based on an analysis of given or collected data **TAKS Obj. 5**

Graphs can help you visualize the relationship between data. Graphs have horizontal and vertical scales. Each scale is divided into intervals.

Graph the data in each table. 6–7. See margin.

6.

Servings	1	2	3
Calories	280	560	840

7.

Time (days)	2	4	6
Pay ($)	15	30	45

8. Use your graph from Exercise 7 to estimate the pay for 11 days. $82.50

Lessons 9-2, 9-3

(7.4)(C) To use words and symbols to describe the relationship between terms in an arithmetic sequence and their positions in the sequence **TAKS Obj. 2**

(7.15)(A) To make conjectures from patterns **TAKS Obj. 6**

(7.15)(B) To validate conclusions using properties and relationships **TAKS Obj. 6**

A **sequence** is a set of numbers that follow a pattern. Find each term of an **arithmetic sequence** by adding a common difference to each term. Find each term of a **geometric sequence** by multiplying each term by a common ratio. Use a table to show patterns and find unknown quantities.

Identify each sequence as *arithmetic, geometric, both,* or *neither*.

9. 2, 10, 18, 26, . . .   10. 48, 4, $\frac{1}{3}$, . . .   11. 0, 1, 4, 13, 40, . . .
    arithmetic   geometric   neither

12. Write a variable expression to describe the sequence
    $-6, -12, -18, -24, . . .$ Then find the 10th term. $-6n$; -60

478

6.

7.

Lessons 9-4, 9-5

(7.4)(B) To graph data to demonstrate relationships in familiar concepts such as conversions, perimeter, and area ⓣᴬᴷˢ Obj. 2

(7.5)(B) To formulate an equation when given a problem situation ⓣᴬᴷˢ Obj. 2

(7.14)(A) To communicate mathematical ideas using graphical and algebraic models ⓣᴬᴷˢ Obj. 6

Prepares for Algebra 1 TEKS (A.1)(C) To describe functional relationships for given problem situations

A **function** is a relationship that assigns one output value for each input value. Write a function rule by looking for patterns in a table. A graph can show the relationship between inputs and outputs.

Use the graph for Exercises 13–14 and the table for Exercises 15–16.

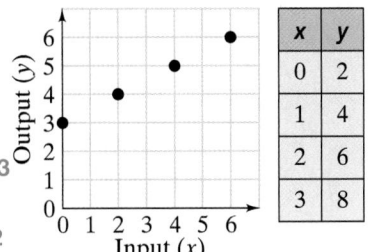

x	y
0	2
1	4
2	6
3	8

13. Make a table for the graph. **See margin.**

14. Write a rule for the graph. $y = \frac{1}{2}x + 3$

15. Write a rule for the relationship represented by the table. $y = 2x + 2$

16. Graph the rule represented by the table. **See margin.**

17. Evaluate $y = -2x + 5$ for x-values $-1, 0, 1, 2,$ and 3. **7, 5, 3, 1, −1**

Lesson 9-6

(7.4)(B) To graph data to demonstrate relationships in familiar concepts ⓣᴬᴷˢ Obj. 2

(7.14)(A) To communicate mathematical ideas using graphical models ⓣᴬᴷˢ Obj. 6

A graph shows how one quantity changes relative to another. In a real-world context, you need to consider what is reasonable.

18. Describe a situation that the graph at the right might represent. **See margin.**

19. You walk at a rate of 3 mi/h for 3 h. You rest for 1 h and then walk 3 mi/h for an hour. Sketch a graph that shows the distance you travel over time. **See margin.**

Lesson 9-7

• To find simple interest and compound interest

Use the formula $I = prt$ to find **simple interest.** Use the formula $B = p(1 + r)^t$ to find the account **balance** with **compound interest.**

20. You deposit $1,500 in an account that earns 6% simple interest. How much interest do you earn in five years? **$450.00**

21. You deposit $2,500 in an account that pays 5.7% interest compounded annually. What is the balance after five years? **$3,298.49**

Lesson 9-8

• To solve for a variable

A **formula** is a rule that shows the relationship between quantities. Use properties of equality to solve for any variable in a formula.

Solve each formula for x.

$x = 9\left(\frac{z}{3} + 4\right)$, or $x = 3z + 36$

22. $z = 3x + y$

$x = \frac{z - y}{3}$

23. $k = -4xyz$

$x = -\frac{k}{4yz}$

24. $\frac{1}{9}x - 4 = \frac{z}{3}$

25. You borrow $200 at a 3% simple interest rate. About how much interest will you owe in 18 months? **$9.00**

---

13. See back of book.
16. See back of book.
18. Answers may vary. Sample: You travel for 2 h at a constant rate of 50 mi/h. You stop for 4 h, and then return to your starting place at a constant rate of 50 mi/h.

19.

Chapter 9 Test

Go Online **For:** Online chapter test
PHSchool.com **Web Code:** ara-0952

Describe the pattern in each sequence. Find the next three terms. 1–6. See margin.

1. 1, 3, 9, 27, . . .   **2.** 4, 9, 14, 19, . . .

3. 3, 4, 6, 9, . . .   **4.** 10, 8, 6, 4, . . .

5. −23, −19, −15, . . .   **6.** 6, 3, 1.5, 0.75, . . .

7. Identify each sequence in Exercises 1–6 as *arithmetic, geometric, both,* or *neither.* See margin.

8. a. Graph the data. See margin.

Picture Framing

Photo Width (in.)	Framed Width (in.)
5	4.17
8	6.67
12	10

b. Estimate the framed width for a photo that is 9.5 in. wide. about 8 in.

c. Estimate the framed width for a photo 18 in. wide. about 15 in.

Make a function table for each function.
9–10. See margin.
9. the cost of 1 to 5 books at $2.95 each

10. the perimeters of squares with sides of 5, 6, 7, 8, and 9 in.

Write a rule for each table. 11–13. See margin.

11.

x	y
0	−2
1	−7
2	−12
3	−17

12.

x	y
0	1
1	3
2	5
3	7

13.

x	y
0	0
1	3
2	6
3	9

14. Graph the rules in Exercises 12 and 13. See margin.

Evaluate for $x = -2$, 0, and 5.

15. $y = x - 5$ −7, −5, 0   **16.** $y = 9 + x$ 7, 9, 14

17. $y = 2x + 1$ −3, 1, 11   **18.** $y = x^2 - 1$ 3, −1, 24

19. Which is not an output for $y = 2x^2 - 5$? D
 A. −3   **B.** 45   **C.** 27   **D.** −8

Use the graph at the right.

20. Make a table for the graph. See margin.

21. Write a rule for the relationship. $s = \frac{1}{5}e$

22. Predict the amount saved when $100 is earned. $20

23. Sports You dribble a basketball five times, pause briefly, and then shoot it into the basket. Sketch a graph that describes the ball's height as a function of time. See margin.

24. Describe what the graph below shows.
See margin.

25. Suppose you borrow $500 from a bank that charges 14.5% compound interest. What do you owe after 4 years? $859.39

Solve each formula for *n*.
26. $n = \frac{6m + p}{3}$, or $n = 2m + \frac{1}{3}p$

26. $3n - p = 6m$ **27.** $PV = nRT$ $n = \frac{PV}{RT}$

28. $s = (n - 2)180$
$n = \frac{s}{180} + 2$ **29.** $(m + 1)n = b$
$n = \frac{b}{m + 1}$

30. Home Repairs A plumber charges customers using the formula $C = 30t + 65$, where C is the amount he charges, and t is the number of hours he works. How many hours does he work when he charges $185?
4 h

31. Science Density is found using the formula $D = \frac{m}{V}$, where m is mass in grams (g), and V is volume in cubic centimeters (cm^3). What is the volume of a pearl with a density of 2.72 g/cm^3 and a mass of 1.768 g? 0.65 cm^3

1–8a. See back of book.
9–14. See back of book.
20. See back of book.
23–24. See back of book.

Tips

Some TAKS test questions ask you to study a graph and determine information about data, such as distance and time.

The graph below shows the number of miles that Marsha rides her bicycle each hour. About how many miles per hour does she ride?

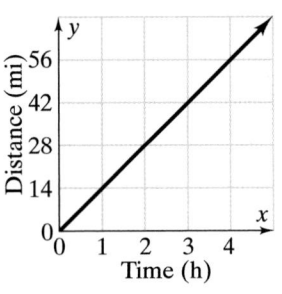

Ⓐ 2   Ⓒ 10
Ⓑ 16   Ⓓ 14

Tip 1
Read the question. The answer will be the miles she can ride in one hour.

Tip 2
Estimate the distance she can ride in an hour. The distance is greater than 10 miles.

Think It Through
The distance she travels per hour is the corresponding y-value when the x-value is 1. At $x = 1$, $y = 14$. This means that Marsha travels about 14 miles each hour. The correct answer is choice D.

Vocabulary Builder

As you solve test items, you must understand the meanings of mathematical terms. Choose the term that correctly completes each sentence.

A. You can find each term in a(n) (arithmetic, geometric) sequence by adding a fixed number to the previous term.   **arithmetic**

B. The (principal, balance) of an investment is the amount you start with.   **principal**

C. A (formula, conjecture) shows the relationship of two or more quantities.   **formula**

Multiple Choice

Read each question. Then write the letter of the correct answer on your paper.

1. Which relationship is best represented by the graph below?   **B**

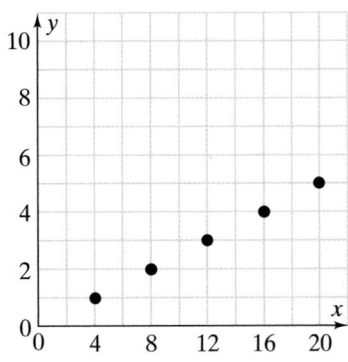

Ⓐ Conversion of pints to cups
Ⓑ Conversion of quarts to gallons
Ⓒ Conversion of pints to quarts
Ⓓ Conversion of fluid ounces to cups

TEKS ★ TAKS Resources

TAKS Review and Preparation Workbook

Texas ExamView CD-ROM
• Instant TAKS Practice Test
• TAKS Practice Items

Differentiated Instruction

Texas Progress Monitoring Assessments
• Quarter 3 Test
  • Forms A & B   **L3**
  • Forms D & E   **L2**

Spanish Assessment Resources
• Spanish Cumulative Review   **ELL**
• Spanish Quarter 3 Test
  • Forms A & B   **L3**

Texas ExamView CD-ROM
• Special Needs Practice Bank   **L1**

TAKS Daily Review Transparencies

TAKS Daily Review 1   Objective 1: (7.1)(B)
Multiple Choice

The seventh-grade class at Anarene Middle School sold ⅔ of the Corsicana fruitcakes they bought. Which decimal is equivalent to the fraction sold?

A 65
B 0.65
C 6.5
D 650

Answer: B

TAKS Daily Review 2   Objective 5: (7.12)(A)
Multiple Choice

Shey has been practicing running the 200-meter foot race. Her last 6 times are shown.

23.60 24.15 24.68 28.62 24.25 23.92

What is her mean time?

F 5.02
G 23.92
H 24.21
J 24.87

Answer: J

2. The graph below shows the maximum speed of Japan's bullet train, called the Shinkansen. Which table best represents the data in the graph? **J**

The Shinkansen

Ⓕ

Time (min)	Distance (mi)
3	1
9	3
12	4
18	6

Ⓗ

Time (min)	Distance (mi)
1	30
3	90
4	120
6	180

Ⓖ

Time (min)	Distance (mi)
1	1
3	3
4	4
6	6

Ⓙ

Time (min)	Distance (mi)
1	3
3	9
4	12
6	18

3. Which sequence follows the rule $5n - 1$, where n represents the position of a term in the sequence? **A**

Ⓐ $4, 9, 14, 19, 24, \ldots$

Ⓑ $4, 8, 12, 16, 20, \ldots$

Ⓒ $5, 10, 15, 20, 25, \ldots$

Ⓓ $4, 8, 16, 32, 64, \ldots$

4. Which rule generates the sequence below?
$7, 11, 15, 19, 23, \ldots$ **H**

Ⓕ $7n + 1$

Ⓖ $4n + 7$

Ⓗ $4n + 3$

Ⓙ $3n + 4$

5. Which description shows the relationship between a term and n, its position in the sequence? **C**

Term Number	1	2	3	4	n
Value of Term	$\frac{3}{4}$	$1\frac{3}{4}$	$2\frac{3}{4}$	$3\frac{3}{4}$	■

Ⓐ Multiply n by $\frac{3}{4}$.

Ⓑ Divide n by $\frac{3}{4}$.

Ⓒ Subtract $\frac{1}{4}$ from n.

Ⓓ Add $\frac{1}{4}$ to n.

6. Which of the following CANNOT be used to find the area of a triangle with base length b and height h? **G**

Ⓕ $\frac{1}{2}(b \cdot h)$

Ⓗ $\frac{b}{2} \cdot h$

Ⓖ $\frac{1}{2}b + h$

Ⓙ $b \cdot \frac{h}{2}$

7. Martha has a circular carpet with a circumference of 44 ft. Which expression could be used to find the radius of the carpet? **C**

Ⓐ $44 - 2\pi$

Ⓒ $\frac{44}{2\pi}$

Ⓑ $44 + 2\pi$

Ⓓ $\frac{44}{\pi}$

8. Shares of stock for a computer company cost $18.75 each. Which is the best estimate of the number of shares Eduardo can buy with $1,950? **H**

Ⓕ From 10 to 50

Ⓗ From 75 to 125

Ⓖ From 50 to 75

Ⓙ From 125 to 175

9. A real estate agent earns a 6% commission. She earns $5,340 for selling a home. Which equation can be used to find p, the selling price of the home? **B**

Ⓐ $p = \frac{6}{100} \cdot 5,340$

Ⓒ $\frac{6}{100} = \frac{p}{5,340}$

Ⓑ $\frac{6}{100} = \frac{5,340}{p}$

Ⓓ $\frac{100}{p} = \frac{5,340}{p}$

Spanish Cumulative Review ELL

Cumulative Review L3

Cumulative Review
Chapter 1–9

Multiple Choice. Choose the letter of the best answer.

1. A shirt, originally priced at $40, is marked down to $26. What is the percent of decrease?
   Ⓐ 35%   B. 54%
   C. 65%   D. not here

2. What is the volume of a cylinder with a base area of 24 m² and a height of 6 m?
   F. 36 m³   G. 48 m³
   H. 72 m³   Ⓙ 144 m³

3. Find the circumference of a circle with a radius of 4 ft. Use 3.14 for π.
   A. 6.28 ft   B. 12.56 ft
   Ⓒ 25.12 ft   D. 31.4 ft

4. Which lengths could be side lengths of a right triangle?
   F. 6, 6, 5   G. 8, 9, 10
   H. 7, 7, 7   Ⓙ 5, 12, 13

5. Find the mean, median, and mode for the data 10, 7, 10, 15, 21, 5, 32, 18, 26.
   A. 20, 21, 10   Ⓑ 16, 15, 10
   C. 15, 21, 5   D. 27, 21, 10

6. Which number has the same value as $|-13|$?
   F. $-|-13|$ G. $-|13|$
   Ⓗ 13   J. -13

7. Order $-5, 6, 0, -2,$ and 1 from least to greatest.
   A. $0, 1, -2, -5, 6$ B. $6, 1, 0, -2, -5$
   C. $-2, -5, 0, 1, 6$ Ⓓ $-5, -2, 0, 1, 6$

8. Which choice is equivalent to the sum of -43 and 18?
   Ⓕ $18 + (-43)$ G. $-43 + (-18)$
   H. $-18 + 43$ J. $43 + (-18)$

9. Which number is the best estimate of $-210 \div 29$?
   A. -10 B. 9
   C. 8   Ⓓ -7

10. Which equation is equivalent to $\frac{x}{6} - 12 = -6$?
    F. $\frac{x}{6} = 18$ G. $6x = 6$
    Ⓗ $x = 36$ J. $x - 12 = 1$

11. Which rule could you use to find the next number in this sequence?
    $-3, -1, 1, 3, 5, \ldots$
    A. add -1 B. subtract 2
    Ⓒ add 2   D. subtract -2

12. The rule for one function is $y = 2x - 4$. The rule for a second function is $y = 4x - 2$. For which value of x are the output values opposites?
    Ⓔ $x = 1$ G. $x = -1$
    H. $x = 2$ J. $x = -2$

13. Evaluate $(-1)^{45}$.
    A. -145 B. -45
    Ⓒ -1 D. 1

482

10. A pair of blue jeans that originally cost $32.50 is marked 25% off. Which equation can be used to find p, an estimate of the sale price? **G**

(F) $p = \frac{1}{4} \cdot 32$ (H) $p = \frac{1}{3} \cdot 33$

(G) $p = \frac{3}{4} \cdot 32$ (J) $p = \frac{2}{3} \cdot 33$

11. In the figure below, trapezoids $ABCD$ and $QRST$ are similar. Which segment corresponds to $\overline{CD}$? **C**

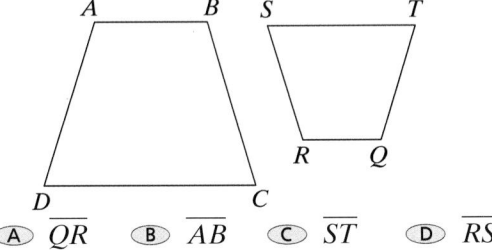

(A) $\overline{QR}$ (B) $\overline{AB}$ (C) $\overline{ST}$ (D) $\overline{RS}$

12. Which of the following statements is NOT true about similar triangles? **H**

(F) If $\triangle ABC$ is similar to a right triangle, then $\triangle ABC$ must be a right triangle.

(G) If $\triangle ABC$ is similar to $\triangle DEF$, then corresponding angles in the two triangles must be congruent.

(H) If $\triangle ABC$ is similar to $\triangle DEF$, then corresponding sides in the two triangles must be congruent.

(J) If $\triangle ABC$ is similar to $\triangle DEF$, then the two triangles have the same shape.

13. $ABCD$ and $QRST$ are squares. Which statement does NOT support the conclusion that $ABCD$ must be similar to $QRST$?

(A) All squares are the same size. **A**

(B) All squares are the same shape.

(C) Since all the angles in both figures are right angles, the corresponding angles are congruent.

(D) Since all four sides of each square are congruent, $\frac{AB}{QR} = \frac{BC}{RS} = \frac{CD}{ST} = \frac{DA}{TQ}$.

14. The expression $6{,}000(1.045)^3$ shows the balance when $6,000 is invested for 3 years at a 4.5% compound interest rate. What is the balance rounded to the nearest dollar? **G**

(F) $18,810   (H) $18,292

(G) $6,847   (J) $24,649

Griddable Items
Record your answer in a grid.

15. What is the value of the expression $2 \cdot 8 - 4 \cdot 5 \div (6 - 4)^2$? **11**

16. The volume of a grain silo can be approximated by the expression $5(3.14)(2)^2 + 0.5(1.33)(3.14)(2)^3$. What is the value of this expression? Round to the nearest tenth. **79.5**

TAKS GO for Help Guide

TAKS Objective	Item Number	GO To
Obj. 2: (7.4)(B)	1 2	Lesson 9-1 Lesson 9-5
Obj. 2: (7.4)(C)	3–4 5	Lesson 9-3 Lesson 9-2
Obj. 2: (7.4)(A)	6 7	Lesson 8-3 Lesson 8-5

TAKS Objective	Item Number	GO To
Obj. 6: (7.13)(A)	8 9–10	Lesson 1-1 Lesson 6-7
Obj. 3: (7.6)(D)	11–13	Lesson 5-5
Obj. 1: (7.2)(E)	14 15–16	Lesson 9-7 Lesson 2-1

For additional TAKS practice, see the *TAKS Review and Preparation Workbook*.

10 Graphing in the Coordinate Plane

Chapter at a Glance

Lesson Titles, Objectives, and Features	Assessment	NCTM Standards	TEKS ★ (TAKS)
10-1 Graphing Points in Four Quadrants • To name and graph points on a coordinate plane **10-1b Activity Lab:** Geometry in the Coordinate Plane	Lesson Quiz	1, 2, 3, 6, 7, 8, 9, 10	**TEKS** (7.7)(A), (7.9)(A) (TAKS) **Obj. 3, 4**
10-2 Graphing Linear Equations • To find solutions of linear equations and to graph linear equations **10-2b Activity Lab, Data Analysis:** Representing Data **Guided Problem Solving:** Practice Solving Problems	Lesson Quiz	1, 2, 3, 6, 7, 8, 9, 10	**TEKS** (7.4)(B), (7.11)(B), (7.13)(A) (TAKS) **Obj. 2, 5, 6**
10-3 Finding the Slope of a Line • To find the slope of a line and use it to solve problems **10-3b Activity Lab, Technology:** Exploring Slope	Lesson Quiz Checkpoint Quiz 1	1, 2, 3, 6, 7, 8, 9, 10	
10-4 Graphing NonLinear Relationships • To graph nonlinear relationships **Vocabulary Builder:** High-Use Academic Words	Lesson Quiz	1, 2, 3, 6, 7, 8, 9, 10	**TEKS** (7.4)(B), (7.14)(A) (TAKS) **Obj. 2, 6**
10-5a Activity Lab: Slides, Flips, and Turns **10-5 Translations** • To graph and write rules for translations	Lesson Quiz	1, 2, 3, 6, 7, 8, 9, 10	**TEKS** (7.7)(A), (7.7)(B), (7.14)(A) (TAKS) **Obj. 3, 6;** Prepares for **TEKS** (7.7)(B)
10-6 Line Symmetry and Reflections • To identigy lines of symmetry and to graph reflections **Extension:** Exploring Tessellations	Lesson Quiz Checkpoint Quiz 2	1, 2, 3, 6, 7, 8, 9, 10	**TEKS** (7.7)(A), (7.7)(B) (TAKS) **Obj. 3**
10-7 Rotational Symmetry and Rotations • To identify rotational symmetry and to rotate a figure about a point	Lesson Quiz	1, 2, 3, 6, 7, 8, 9, 10	
(TAKS) **Tune-Up: Cumulative Practice**			

NCTM Standards 2000
1 Number and Operations	**2** Algebra	**3** Geometry	**4** Measurement	**5** Data Analysis and Probability
6 Problem Solving	**7** Reasoning and Proof	**8** Communication	**9** Connections	**10** Representation

Correlations to Standardized Tests

All content for these tests is contained in *Prentice Hall Math,* Course 2. This chart reflects coverage in this chapter only.

	10-1	10-2	10-3	10-4	10-5	10-6	10-7
Terra Nova CAT6 (Level 17)							
Number and Number Relations							
Computation and Numerical Estimation							
Operation Concepts							
Measurement							
Geometry and Spatial Sense	✔	✔	✔	✔	✔	✔	✔
Data Analysis, Statistics, and Probability							
Patterns, Functions, Algebra	✔	✔	✔	✔	✔	✔	✔
Problem Solving and Reasoning	✔	✔	✔	✔	✔	✔	✔
Communication	✔	✔	✔	✔	✔	✔	✔
Decimals, Fractions, Integers, and Percent							
Order of Operations							
Terra Nova CTBS (Level 17)							
Decimals, Fractions, Integers, Percents							
Order of Operations, Numeration, Number Theory							
Data Interpretation							
Pre-algebra	✔	✔	✔	✔	✔	✔	✔
Measurement							
Geometry	✔	✔	✔	✔	✔	✔	✔
ITBS (Level 13)							
Number Properties and Operations							
Algebra	✔	✔	✔	✔	✔	✔	✔
Geometry	✔	✔	✔	✔	✔	✔	✔
Measurement							
Probability and Statistics							
Estimation							
SAT10 (Int 3 Level)							
Number Sense and Operations							
Patterns, Relationships, and Algebra	✔	✔	✔	✔	✔	✔	✔
Data, Statistics, and Probability							
Geometry and Measurement	✔	✔	✔	✔	✔	✔	✔
NAEP							
Number Sense, Properties, and Operations							
Measurement							
Geometry and Spatial Sense					✔	✔	✔
Data Analysis, Statistics, and Probability							
Algebra and Functions	✔	✔	✔	✔			

CAT6 California Achievement Test, 6th Ed.   **CTBS** Comprehensive Test of Basic Skills   **ITBS** Iowa Test of Basic Skills, Form M
SAT10 Stanford Achievement Test, 10th Ed.   **NAEP** National Assessment of Educational Progress 2005 Mathematics Objectives

TEKS Math Background

Focus on the TEKS

- At Grade 7, students extend Grade 6 skills to locate and name points on a coordinate plane using ordered pairs of integers (7.7)(A). Analysis of TAKS results shows that students should review this student expectation.

  In Lesson 10-1, students are introduced to graphing points in all four quadrants and identify horizontal and vertical lines. Place special emphasis on this lesson because it focuses on (7.7)(A).

- New at Grade 7 is graphing reflections across the horizontal or vertical axis and graphing translations on a coordinate plane (7.7)(B). Students first translate points and figures in Lesson 10-5. Then after reviewing symmetry, students reflect a point and a figure over an axis in Lesson 10-6 (7.7)(B).

10-1 Graphing Points in Four Quadrants

TEKS ★ (TAKS) (7.7)(A) Obj. 3

Math Understandings

- You can name any point on a Cartesian coordinate plane by an ordered pair, and you can graph any ordered pair of real numbers as a point on the plane.
- In a coordinate plane, the interval for the negative half of each axis is the same as the corresponding positive half. However, the x-axis and the y-axis may use different intervals.

A **coordinate plane** is a grid formed by a **horizontal** number line called the **x-axis** and a **vertical** number line called the **y-axis**. An **ordered pair** gives the coordinates of the location of a point. The ordered pair (0, 0) indicates the **origin** 0, where the axes intersect. The first number in an ordered pair is the **x-coordinate**, which tells the number of horizontal units a point is from 0. The second number is the **y-coordinate**, which tells the number of vertical units a point is from 0.

Lines that are parallel to the x-axis are **horizontal lines**. Lines that are parallel to the y-axis are **vertical lines**. The x-axis and y-axis divide the coordinate plane into four **quadrants.**

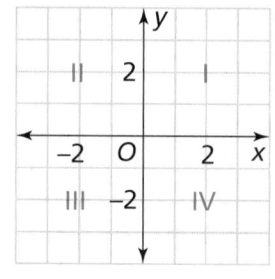

10-2 Graphing Linear Equations

Math Understandings

- Every point on the graph of a linear equation represents a solution, and every solution to the equation represents a point on the graph.
- Although you usually graph points where both values are integers, a linear equation can have infinitely many solutions that are not integers and could be used to graph the equation.

Any ordered pair that makes an equation true is a solution of the equation. The **graph of an equation** is the graph of all the points with coordinates that are solutions of the equation. An equation is a **linear equation** when the graph of its solutions is a line.

10-3 Finding the Slope of a Line

Math Understandings

- The graph of a linear equation has a constant slope.
- To determine the slope, use any pair of points on a line.
- When you move from left to right along a line, if it goes upward, the slope is positive; if it goes downward, the slope is negative.

$$\text{slope} = \frac{\text{rise}}{\text{run}}$$

Slope is a ratio that describes the steepness of a line. The slope is the ratio between the vertical change **(rise)** and the horizontal change **(run)**. A line parallel to the y-axis is infinitely steep and has no slope. A line parallel to the x-axis is level and has a slope of zero.

10-4 Graphing Nonlinear Relationships

TEKS ★ (TAKS) (7.4)(B), (7.14)(A) Obj. 2, 6

Math Understandings

- A graph that is not a straight line may be represented by a nonlinear equation.

A **nonlinear equation** is an equation with a graph that is not a straight line.

10-5 Translations

TEKS ★ TAKS (7.7)(A), (7.7)(B) Obj. 3

Math Understandings

- Translations, reflections, and rotations are called rigid motion transformations because they affect only position and leave shape and size unchanged.

A **transformation** is a change of the position, shape, or size of a figure. Three types of transformations that change position only are slides (translations), flips (reflections), and turns (rotations).

A **translation** is a transformation that moves every point of a figure the same distance and in the same direction. The figure you get after a translation is the **image** of the original. You use prime notation (A′, said as "A prime") to identify an image point. ABC has been translated 2 units right and 4 units down. The rule for this translation is $(x, y) \rightarrow (x + 2, y - 4)$.

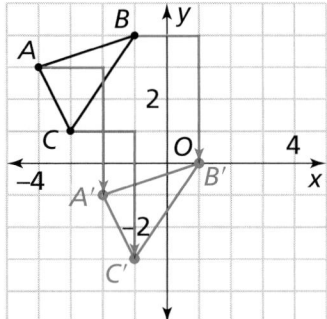

10-6 Line Symmetry and Reflections

TEKS ★ TAKS (7.7)(A), (7.7)(B) Obj. 3

Math Understandings

- To reflect a figure, you need to know the line of reflection.

A figure has **line symmetry** if a line can be drawn through the figure so that one side is a mirror image of the other. A **line of symmetry,** such as the dashed lines in this figure, divides a figure into mirror images.

If you fold along a line of symmetry, one side of the figure fits exactly onto the other side. As shown in this figure, some figures have more than one line of symmetry.

A **reflection** is a transformation that flips a figure over a **line of reflection**. When a figure is reflected, the image is congruent to the original.

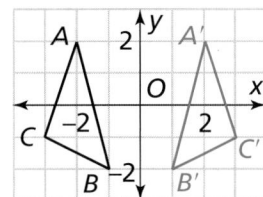

10-7 Rotational Symmetry and Rotations

Math Understandings

- To rotate a figure, you need to know the center of rotation and the angle of rotation.

A **rotation** is a transformation that turns a figure about a fixed point called the **center of rotation**. In this text, all rotations are counterclockwise. A figure has **rotational symmetry** if it can be rotated 180° or less and match the original figure. When a figure has rotational symmetry, the angle measure that it rotates is the **angle of rotation**.

Example: Does this figure have rotational symmetry? Yes. Its angle of rotation is 360° ÷ 2, or 180°.

Additional Professional Development Opportunities

Math Background Notes for Chapter 10: Every lesson has a Math Background in the PLAN section.

Research Overview, Mathematics Strands Additional support for these topics and more is in the front of the Teacher's Edition.

LessonLab
LessonLab, a Pearson Education company, offers comprehensive, facilitated professional development designed to help teachers to improve student achievement. To learn more, please visit lessonlab.com.

Texas Chapter 10 Resources

	10-1	10-2	10-3	10-4	10-5	10-6	10-7	For the Chapter
Print Resources								
L3 Practice	●	●	●	●	●	●	●	
L1 Adapted Practice	●	●	●	●	●	●	●	
L3 Guided Problem Solving	●	●	●	●	●	●	●	
L2 Reteaching	●	●	●	●	●	●	●	
L4 Enrichment	●	●	●	●	●	●	●	
L3 Daily Notetaking Guide	●	●	●	●	●	●	●	
L1 Adapted Daily Notetaking Guide	●	●	●	●	●	●	●	
L3 Vocabulary and Study Skills Worksheets	●	●	●	●	●	●	●	●
L3 Daily Puzzles	●	●	●	●	●	●	●	
L3 Activity Labs	●	●	●	●	●	●	●	
L3 Checkpoint Quiz			●			●		
L3 Chapter Project								●
L2 Chapter Test								●
L3 Chapter Test								●
L4 Alternative Assessment								●
L3 Cumulative Review								●
Spanish Resources ELL								
L3 Practice	●	●	●	●	●	●	●	●
L3 Vocabulary and Study Skills Worksheets	●		●	●	●		●	
L3 Checkpoint Quiz			●			●		
L2 Chapter Test								●
L3 Chapter Test								●
L4 Alternative Assessment								●
L3 Cumulative Review								●
Transparencies								
Check Skills You'll Need	●	●	●	●	●	●	●	
Additional Examples	●	●	●	●	●	●	●	
Problem of the Day	●	●	●	●	●	●	●	
TAKS Daily Review	●	●	●	●	●	●	●	
Classroom Aid			●					
Student Edition Answers	●	●	●	●	●	●	●	●
Lesson Quiz	●	●	●	●	●	●	●	
TAKS Strategies								●
Technology								
Texas Interactive Textbook Online	●	●	●	●	●	●	●	●
Texas StudentExpress CD-ROM	●	●	●	●	●	●	●	●
Success Tracker™ Online Intervention	●	●	●	●	●	●	●	●
TeacherExpress CD-ROM	●	●	●	●	●	●	●	●
PresentationExpress CD-ROM	●	●	●	●	●	●	●	●
Texas ExamView CD-ROM with QuickTake	●	●	●	●	●	●	●	●
MindPoint Quiz Show CD-ROM	●	●	●	●	●	●	●	●
Prentice Hall Web Site: PHSchool.com	●	●	●	●	●	●	●	●

Also available: TAKS Tune-Up Kit
- TAKS Daily Review Transparencies
- TAKS Review and Preparation Workbook
- TAKS Strategies with Transparencies
- Texas Progress Monitoring Assessments
- Texas ExamView CD-ROM
- MindPoint Quiz Show CD-ROM

Other Resources
Algebra Readiness Tests
All-in-One Student Workbook
All-in-One Student Workbook, Adapted Version
Multilingual Handbook

Solution Key
Math Notes Study Folder
Spanish Cumulative Assessment

Where You Can Use the Lesson Resources

Here is a suggestion, following the four-step teaching plan, for how you can incorporate Differentiated Instruction Resources into your teaching.

	Instructional Resources **L3**	**Differentiated** Instruction Resources
1. Plan		
Preparation Read the Math Background in the Teacher's Edition to connect this lesson with students' previous experience. **Starting Class** **Check Skills You'll Need** Assign these exercises to review prerequisite skills. **TEKS ★ (TAKS)** Review the full text of the TEKS student expectations and TAKS objectives covered in this lesson. **New Vocabulary** Help students pre-read the lesson by pointing out the new terms introduced in the lesson.	**TEKS Math Background** **Math Understandings** **Transparencies & PresentationExpress CD-ROM** Check Skills You'll Need Problem of the Day TAKS Daily Review **Resources** Vocabulary and Study Skills	**Spanish Support** **ELL** Vocabulary and Study Skills
2. Teach		
L3 Guided Instruction Use the Activity Labs to build conceptual understanding. Teach each Example. Use the Teacher's Edition side column notes for specific teaching tips, including Error Prevention notes. Use the Additional Examples found in the side column (and on transparency and PowerPoint) as an alternative presentation for the content. After each Example, assign the Quick Check exercise for that Example to get an immediate assessment of student understanding. Use the Closure activity in the Teacher's Edition to help students attain mastery of lesson content.	**Student Edition** Activity Lab **Resources** Daily Notetaking Guide Activity Lab **Transparencies & PresentationExpress CD-ROM** Additional Examples Classroom Aids **Texas ExamView CD-ROM with QuickTake**	**Teacher's Edition** Every lesson includes suggestions for working with students who need special attention. **L1** Special Needs **L2** Below Level **L4** Advanced Learners **ELL** English Language Learners **Resources** **L1** Adapted Daily Notetaking Guide **Multilingual Handbook**
3. Practice		

Assignment Guide
Check Your Understanding
Use these questions to check students' understanding before you assign homework.
Homework Exercises
Assign homework from these leveled exercises in the Assignment Guide.
  A Practice by Example
  B Apply Your Skills
  C Challenge
  (TAKS) Tune-Up and Mixed Review
Homework Quick Check
Use these key exercises to quickly check students' homework.
	Transparencies & PresentationExpress CD-ROM
	Student Answers
	Resources
	Practice
	Guided Problem Solving
	Vocabulary and Study Skills
	Activity Lab
	Daily Puzzles
	Texas ExamView CD-ROM with QuickTake
		Spanish Support
		ELL Practice
		ELL Vocabulary and Study Skills
		Resources
		L1 Adapted Practice
		L4 Enrichment

4. Assess & Reteach		
Lesson Quiz Assign the Lesson Quiz to assess students' mastery of the lesson content. **Checkpoint Quiz** Use the Checkpoint Quiz to assess student progress over several lessons.	**Transparencies & PresentationExpress CD-ROM** Lesson Quiz **Resources** Checkpoint Quiz	**Resources** **L2** Reteaching **ELL** Checkpoint Quiz Success Tracker™ Online Intervention **Texas ExamView CD-ROM with QuickTake**

KEY   **L1** Special Needs   **L2** Below Level   **L3** For All Students   **L4** Advanced, Gifted   **ELL** English Language Learners

CHAPTER 10

Graphing in the Coordinate Plane

CHAPTER 10 **Graphing in the Coordinate Plane**

Check Your Readiness

Answers are in the back of the textbook.

For intervention, direct students to:

Graphing Integers
Lesson 1-6
Extra Skills and Word
Problems Practice, Ch. 1

Evaluating Algebraic Expressions
Lesson 4-1
Extra Skills and Word
Problems Practice, Ch. 4

Using Exponents
Lesson 2-1
Extra Skills and Word
Problems Practice, Ch. 2

Classifying Angles
Lesson 7-2
Extra Skills and Word
Problems Practice, Ch. 7

What You've Learned

TEKS ★ **TAKS**

- **(7.2)(C)** In Chapter 1, you used models, such as number lines, to add, subtract, multiply, and divide integers. **TAKS** Obj. 1
- **(7.4)(A)** In Chapter 8, you generated formulas involving perimeter, area, circumference, and volme. **TAKS** Obj. 2

Check Your Readiness

GO for Help

For Exercises	See Lesson
1–4	1-6
5–8	4-1
9–12	2-1
13–18	7-2

Graphing Integers

Algebra **Graph each integer and its opposite.**

1. 7   1–4. See margin.   **2.** -5

3. -3 **4.** 6

Evaluating Algebraic Expressions

Evaluate each expression using the values $a = 5$, $c = 2$, **and** $g = 7$.

5. $9g$ 63   **6.** $-2a$ -10 **7.** $8c - 10$ 6   **8.** $2a - 5c$ 0

Using Exponents

Simplify each expression.

9. 5^3 125   **10.** $(-2)^6$ 64   **11.** 11^3 1,331   **12.** $(-10)^4$ 10,000

Classifying Angles

Classify each angle as *acute,* *right,* *obtuse,* **or** *straight.*

13. $m\angle A = 43°$ acute   **14.** $m\angle B = 90°$ right   **15.** $m\angle C = 148°$ obtuse

16. $m\angle D = 180°$ **17.** $m\angle E = 167°$ **18.** $m\angle F = 79°$ acute
straight   obtuse

484   **Chapter 10**

1. ![number line -8 to 8 with points at -7 and 7]
   $-8\ -6\ -4\ -2\ \ 0\ \ 2\ \ 4\ \ 6\ \ 8$

2. ![number line -8 to 8 with points at -5 and 5]
   $-8\ -6\ -4\ -2\ \ 0\ \ 2\ \ 4\ \ 6\ \ 8$

3. ![number line -4 to 4 with points at -3 and 3]
   $-4\ -3\ -2\ -1\ \ 0\ \ 1\ \ 2\ \ 3\ \ 4$

4. ![number line -8 to 8 with points at -6 and 6]
   $-8\ -6\ -4\ -2\ \ 0\ \ 2\ \ 4\ \ 6\ \ 8$

Patterns, Relationships, and Algebraic Reasoning
TEKS (7.4)(B) **TAKS** Obj. 2

Geometry and Spatial Reasoning
TEKS (7.7)(A), (7.7)(B)
TAKS Obj. 3

Measurment
TEKS (7.9)(A) **TAKS** Obj. 4

Probability and Statistics
TEKS (7.11)(B) **TAKS** Obj. 5

Underlying Processes and Mathematical Tools
TEKS (7.13)(A), (7.14)(A)
TAKS Obj. 6

Chapter 10 Overview

In this chapter, students study graphing in the coordinate plane. They explore linear relationships and the concept of slope as they graph points and lines in all four quadrants. They also investigate nonlinear relationships, translations, reflections, rotations, and symmetry.

Activating Prior Knowledge

In this chapter, students will build on their knowledge of coordinates and ordered pairs, graphing, and using patterns and tables. They will graph and explore relationships of points on the coordinate plane.
Ask questions such as:
• *How can you describe the line formed by connecting points (3,1), (3,2), and (3,3)?* vertical line; line parallel to *y*-axis

• *Using the formula* d = rt, *what related formula can you write to solve for* r? $r = \frac{d}{t}$

• *What is the next point in this sequence: (2,3), (3,4), (4,5)?* (5,6)

What You'll Learn Next
TEKS ★ TAKS

• **(7.7)(A)** In this chapter, you will locate and name points on a coordinate plane using ordered pairs of integers. **TAKS** **Obj. 3**

• **(7.7)(B)** You will graph reflections across the horizontal or vertical axis and graph translations on a coordinate plane. **TAKS** **Obj. 3**

• **(7.4)(B)** You will graph data to demonstrate relationships such as area, circumference, and volume. **TAKS** **Obj. 2**

TAKS Tune-Up On pages 527–529, you will review and practice the vocabulary and *TAKS* objectives you have learned.

🔊 Key Vocabulary

• coordinate plane (p. 486)
• image (p. 510)
• linear equation (p. 492)
• line symmetry (p. 514)
• nonlinear equation (p. 504)
• ordered pair (p. 486)
• reflection (p. 515)
• rotation (p. 519)
• rotational symmetry (p. 519)
• transformation (p. 510)
• translation (p. 510)
• *x*-axis (p. 486)
• *x*-coordinate (p. 486)
• *y*-axis (p. 486)
• *y*-coordinate (p. 486)

Chapter 10 **485**

Graphing Points in Four Quadrants

1. Plan

TEKS ★ **TAKS**

(7.7)(A) To locate and name points on a coordinate plane using ordered pairs of integers **TAKS** Obj. 3

Dana Center TEKS Toolkit Clarifying Activities (7.7)(A)
Visit: PHSchool.com
Web Code: arq-9045

TEKS Math Background

Maps allow users to find the locations of places. A coordinate plane, such as a map, allows users to identify the locations of points. The plane is formed by a horizontal number line (*x*-axis) and a vertical number line (*y*-axis). A point on the plane is described by coordinates, which give the position of the point in relation to the origin. The coordinates are identified by an ordered pair. The first number of the pair describes a point's location to the left or right of the origin. The second number describes a point's location up or down.

More Math Background: p. 484C

Lesson Planning and Resources

See p. 484E for a list of the resources that support this lesson.

PowerPoint
 Bell Ringer Practice

☑ Check Skills You'll Need
Use student page, transparency, or PowerPoint.

TAKS Daily Review 75
Use transparency.

486

☑ Check Skills You'll Need

1. Vocabulary Review
How can you use a number line to show that 4 and −4 are *opposites*?
1–7. See back of book.
Graph each number and its opposite on a number line.

2. 5   **3.** −3

4. 1   **5.** −10

6. 12   **7.** 8

 for Help
Lesson 1-6

TEKS ★ **TAKS**

- (7.7)(A) To locate and name points on a coordinate plane using ordered pairs of integers **TAKS** Obj. 3

New Vocabulary coordinate plane, *x*-axis, *y*-axis, ordered pair, quadrants, origin, *x*-coordinate, *y*-coordinate

Why Learn This?

Maps use coordinates to help you locate streets and buildings. You can use coordinates to describe the location of a point on a grid.

A **coordinate plane** is a grid formed by a horizontal number line called the **x-axis** and a vertical number line called the **y-axis**.

An **ordered pair** (x, y) gives the location of a point.

The axes divide the plane into four **quadrants**.

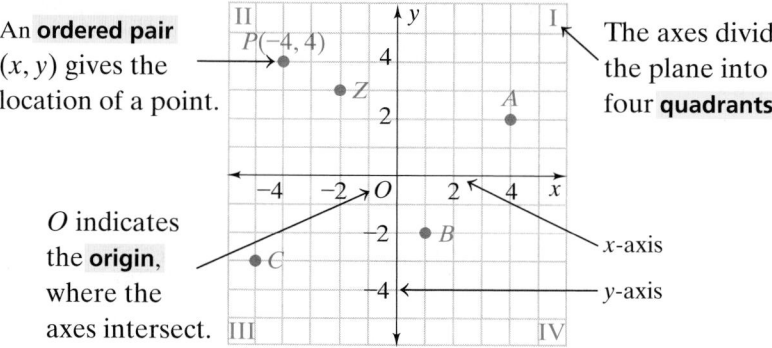

O indicates the **origin**, where the axes intersect.

The first number of an ordered pair is the **x-coordinate**. It tells the number of horizontal units a point is from *O*. The second number is the **y-coordinate**. It tells the number of vertical units a point is from *O*.

★ TAKS Tip

You can remember that the *x*-coordinate is first in an ordered pair because *x* comes before *y* in the alphabet.

EXAMPLE   Naming Coordinates

1 **TAKS Multiple Choice** Name the coordinates of point *Z* in the graph above.

Ⓐ (2, 3)   Ⓑ (−2, −3)   Ⓒ (−2, 3)   Ⓓ (2, −3)

Point *Z* is 2 units to the left of the *y*-axis, so the *x*-coordinate is −2. Point *Z* is 3 units up from the *x*-axis, so the *y*-coordinate is 3.

The coordinates of point *Z* are (−2, 3). The correct answer is C.

☑ Quick Check

(4, 2), (1, −2), (−5, −3)

1. Name the coordinates of *A*, *B*, and *C* in the graph above.

486   Chapter 10   Graphing in the Coordinate Plane

Differentiated Instruction   Solutions for All Learners

Special Needs **L1**
For Example 1, have students run their finger along the *x*-axis. Have them run their finger along the *y*-axis. Have students point to quadrant 1, 2, 3, and 4 when you name them.

learning style: tactile

Below Level **L2**
Draw a coordinate plane on the board. Call out ordered pairs for students to point out and graph. Turn the activity into a game in which students gain points for plotting ordered pairs correctly.

learning style: tactile

You can use an ordered pair to graph a point in a coordinate plane.

EXAMPLE Graphing Points

② Graph point $A(3, -5)$ in a coordinate plane. In which quadrant does the point lie?

Step 1
Start at the origin.

Step 2
Move 3 units to the right.

Step 3
Then move 5 units down. Draw a dot. Label it A.

The point $A(3, -5)$ lies in quadrant IV.

✓ Quick Check

2. Graph point $R(-3, 5)$. In which quadrant does the point lie?
   See left.

2.

Quadrant II

When you graph a polygon in a coordinate plane, first graph each vertex. Then draw line segments to connect adjacent vertices.

EXAMPLE Graphing Polygons

③ **Archaeology** Archaeologists record the location of objects they find by making a grid. Suppose you use graph paper to represent a rectangular dig that measures 9 ft by 6 ft. Draw a rectangle in a coordinate plane. Use $(0, 0)$ as one vertex and label all vertices.

Mark $(0, 0)$ as one vertex.

From the origin, count 9 units right and mark a vertex at $(9, 0)$.

From the origin, count 6 units up and mark a vertex at $(0, 6)$.

Mark the fourth vertex at $(9, 6)$.

Draw the sides of the rectangle.

Careers Archaeologists excavate artifacts to study how people lived in past cultures.

✓ Quick Check

3. In a coordinate plane, draw a different rectangle for the dig described above. Use $(0, 0)$ as one vertex and label all vertices.
   See back of book.

10-1 Graphing Points in Four Quadrants **487**

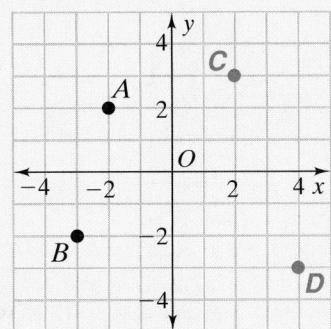

Assignment Guide

Check Your Understanding
Go over Exercises 1–6 in class before assigning the Homework Exercises.

Homework Exercises

A	Practice by Example	7–26
B	Apply Your Skills	27–36
C	Challenge	37
TEKS ★ **TAKS**	Tune-Up and Mixed Review	38–40

Homework Quick Check
To check students' understanding of key skills and concepts, go over Exercises 13, 20, 33, 34, and 35.

Differentiated Instruction Resources

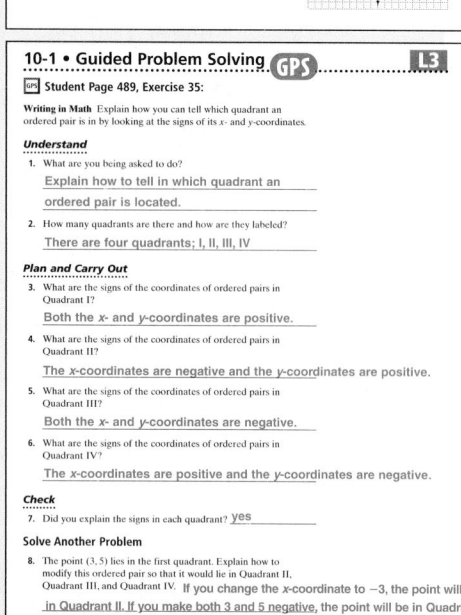

488

✓ Check Your Understanding

1. **Vocabulary** Name the coordinates of the origin. (0, 0)

Match each point with its coordinates.

2. J **B**

3. K **A**

4. L **C**

5. M **D**

A. $(3, 4)$
B. $(-3, 4)$
C. $(3, -4)$
D. $(-3, -4)$

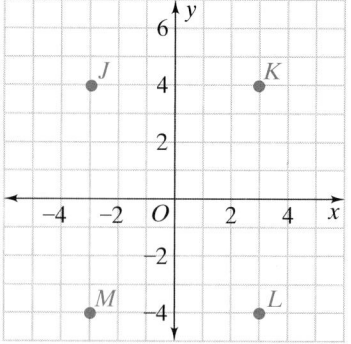

6. Which axis in a coordinate plane is vertical? Which axis is horizontal? *y*-axis; *x*-axis

---

Homework Exercises

For more exercises, see Extra Skills and Word Problems.

GO for Help

For Exercises	See Examples
7–14	1
15–22	2
23–26	3

Ⓐ Name the coordinates of each point.

7. G $(-2, 2)$
8. H $(2, -3)$
9. J $(3, 0)$
10. K $(4, 4)$
11. L $(-3, -4)$
12. M $(-4, 1)$
13. N $(1, 3)$
14. P $(0, -2)$

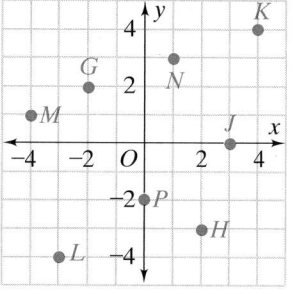

Graph each point on the same coordinate plane. Name the quadrant in which each point lies. See margin for graph.

15. $Q(1, -4)$ IV
16. $R(-5, 3)$ II
17. $S(-3, -2)$ III
18. $T(-6, 2)$ II
19. $U(5, -3)$ IV
20. $V(2, 6)$ I
21. $W(6, 2)$ I
22. $Z(-4, -4)$ III

Graph each polygon. Use (0, 0) as one vertex. Label all vertices.
23–26. See margin.

23. a square with side 3 units long
24. a square with side 6 units long
25. a rectangle with horizontal length 4 units and vertical length 2 units
26. a rectangle with horizontal length 2 units and vertical length 4 units

Ⓑ GPS 27. **Guided Problem Solving** Three vertices of a square are $(-2, -4)$, $(3, -4)$, and $(3, 1)$. What are the coordinates of the fourth vertex?
  • *Draw a Picture* by graphing the three vertices and drawing the two sides of the square. $(-2, 1)$
  • Graph the fourth vertex of the square. What are its coordinates?

15–22. See back of book.

23–26. See back of book.

31–33. See back of book.

35–36. See back of book.

GO Online
Homework Help
Visit: PHSchool.com
Web Code: are-1001

Without graphing, name the quadrant in which each point (x, y) lies.

28. $x < 0$ and $y < 0$ **29.** $x > 0$ and $y < 0$ **30.** $x < 0$ and $y > 0$
     III   IV   II

31. Geometry Graph a triangle with vertices $(2, 5), (8, 3),$ and $(2, 1)$. Classify the triangle by its angles and by its sides. **See margin.**

32. Science A bee's wings move at a rate of about 150 beats per second. The expression $150x$ gives the number of beats in x seconds. Graph the ordered pairs $(x, 150x)$ for $x = 1$, $x = 2$, and $x = 3$. **See margin.**

33. Reasoning List the coordinates of three points on the red line. If the x-coordinate of a point on the line is 37, what is the y-coordinate? Explain. **See margin.**

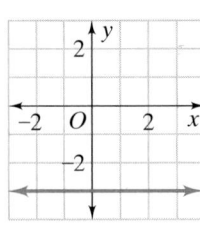

34. A scale drawing of a rectangular board shows three vertices at $(-3, -2)$, $(-3, 2)$, and $(3, 2)$. Each unit represents 2 ft. Find the board's dimensions. **12 ft by 8 ft**

GPS 35. Writing in Math Explain how you can tell which quadrant an ordered pair is in by looking at the signs of its x- and y-coordinates. **See margin.**

36. Open-Ended Graph a parallelogram in a coordinate plane so that each vertex is in a different quadrant. Label all vertices. **See margin.**

37. Answers may vary.
Sample: $(-6, -2) \rightarrow$
$(-6, -4) \rightarrow (-2, -4) \rightarrow$
$(-2, 0) \rightarrow (-6, 0) \rightarrow$
$(-6, 6) \rightarrow (-3, 6) \rightarrow$
$(-3, 4)$

C 37. Challenge A robot arm must move the black peg in the diagram at the right onto the white square. The peg must be moved around—not over—the red walls. List the coordinates of the vertices of a path the robot arm might follow to move the peg. **See left.**

TAKS Objective 3
TEKS (7.7)(A)

38. Which point has the coordinates $(-3, 5)$ in the graph at the right? **C**
   Ⓐ Point L Ⓒ Point N
   Ⓑ Point M Ⓓ Point P

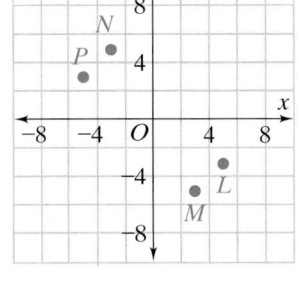

TAKS Objective 3
TEKS (7.6)(C)

39. Which three-dimensional figure has only squares as faces? **H**
   Ⓕ Pyramid   Ⓗ Cube
   Ⓖ Cone   Ⓙ Cylinder

GO for Help
Lesson 8-5

40. The radius of a circle is 11 cm long. Find the area of the circle to the nearest tenth. **380.1 cm²**

Alternative Assessment

Partners take turns. One partner gives the coordinates for a point, and the other graphs it. The partner graphing the point verbalizes how the point is being placed, such as, "right four, down two" for $(4, -2)$.

TEKS ★ TAKS Resources

- TAKS Strategies, p. 523
- TAKS Tune Up, pp. 527–529

TAKS Tune-Up Kit
- TAKS Daily Review Transparencies
- TAKS Review and Preparation Workbook
- TAKS Strategies with Transparencies
- Texas Progress Monitoring Assessments

PowerPoint
Lesson Quiz

Write the coordinates of each point.

1. $A(-2, -3)$ **2.** $B(3, 0)$

Graph each point on the same coordinate plane. **See above.**

3. $C(-3, 1)$ **4.** $D(2, -1)$

Name the coordinates necessary to complete the figure named.

5. Square with 4 unit sides, one vertex at (6, 6) **Sample: (2, 2), (6, 2), (2, 6)**

6. Rectangle 3 units by 5 units, one vertex at (−5, 3) **Sample: (−5, 6), (0, 3), (0, 6)**

Geometry in the Coordinate Plane

This Activity extends Lesson 10-1 to show students how to use a coordinate plane to find the lengths of sides and the areas of geometric figures.

Guided Instruction

Have students draw and label an *x*-axis and a *y*-axis on graph paper to create a coordinate plane. They should plot and then connect the vertices to form △*LMN*, as you do the same on an overhead transparency. Review, as needed, the meanings of *base* and *height* of a triangle. Discuss how to identify the height of any triangle.

Exercises

Have students work independently on the Exercises. When they are finished have them compare answers with a partner to check that their answers are the same.

Differentiated Instruction

Advanced Learners   **L4**
Have students use the Pythagorean Theorem to find the length of the hypotenuse of △*LMN*.

TEKS ☆ 〔TAKS〕 Resources

- graph paper
- straightedge
- Classroom Aids 2, 3

Dana Center TEKS Toolkit Clarifying Activities (7.9)(A), (7.7)(A)
Visit: PHSchool.com
Web Code: arq-9045

490

10-1b Activity Lab

Geometry in the Coordinate Plane

Graphing a figure in a coordinate plane can help you find the figure's perimeter or area.

TEKS ☆ 〔TAKS〕
(7.9)(A) To solve problems involving perimeter and area of polygons 〔TAKS〕 Obj. 4
(7.7)(A) To locate points on a coordinate plane using ordered pairs of integers 〔TAKS〕 Obj. 3

EXAMPLES Finding Perimeter and Area

1 A map has a coordinate plane printed over it. Town Hall *T* is at the origin. Julio rides his bike from home *H* to school *S*. After school, Julio rides to the library *L* and then to his friend's house *F*. Finally, he rides back home. Each unit in the graph represents 1 kilometer. Use the graph to find the number of kilometers Julio rides.

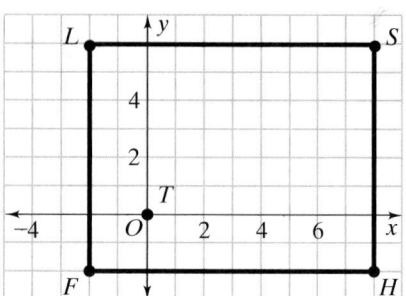

The perimeter of the rectangle represents the distance Julio rides. Since $8 + 10 + 8 + 10$ is 36, Julio rides 36 km.

2 Connect the points $L(-3, -2)$, $M(-1, 3)$, and $N(4, -2)$ to form △*LMN*. Find the area of the triangle using the formula $A = \frac{1}{2}bh$.

The base of the triangle is 7 units. The distance from point *M* to the base is 5 units, so the height of the triangle is 5 units.

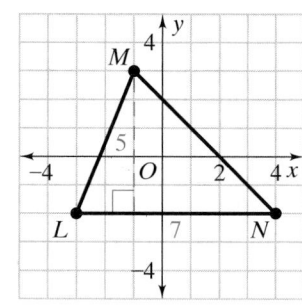

$$A = \frac{1}{2}bh$$
$$= \frac{1}{2} \cdot 7 \cdot 5 \quad \leftarrow \text{Substitute.}$$
$$= 17.5 \quad\quad \leftarrow \text{Simplify.}$$

The area of the triangle is 17.5 units^2.

Exercises

1. Yvonne walks from her house $(0, 0)$ to her aunt's house $(4, 0)$. She then walks to a park $(4, 2)$. From the park, she walks to the store $(0, 2)$ and then returns home. Graph and connect the points. If each unit in the graph represents 1 kilometer, how many kilometers does Yvonne walk in all?

1.
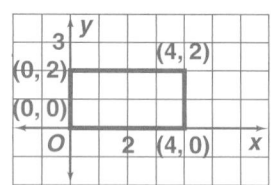

12 km

2. Connect the points $A(4, -4)$, $B(4, 4)$, and $C(-2, 3)$ to form △*ABC*. Find the area of the triangle. **See margin.**

3. Use graphing to find the area of a pentagon with vertices at $(-3, 4)$, $(-3, -9)$, $(6, -4)$, $(8, 0)$ and $(6, 9)$. **See margin.**

2–3. See back of book.

10-2 Graphing Linear Equations

✓ Check Skills You'll Need

1. Vocabulary Review
What does an *equation* have that an *expression* does not have?
an equal sign
Evaluate each expression for $p = 2$.

2. $p + 7$ 9   **3.** $3p$ 6

4. $p - 1$ 1   **5.** $12 - p$ 10

GO for Help
Lesson 4-1

What You'll Learn

To find solutions of linear equations and to graph linear equations

🔊 **New Vocabulary** graph of an equation, linear equation

Why Learn This?

Sometimes you can use an equation to describe a relationship between two quantities. Graphing the equation can make the relationship easier to see.

To make a swing, you need enough rope to reach the branch plus 5 feet to tie the rope. You can use $y = x + 5$ to describe the relationship between the number of feet x the tire hangs below the branch and the number of feet y of rope you need.

A solution of a linear equation is any ordered pair (x, y) that makes the equation true. To find a solution, choose a value of x and substitute it into the equation. Then find the corresponding value of y.

EXAMPLE Finding Solutions

1 Find three solutions of $y = x + 5$. Organize your solutions in a table.

x	x + 5	y	Solution (x, y)	Interpretation
6	6 + 5	11	(6, 11)	If the tire hangs 6 ft below the branch, you need 11 ft of rope.
7	7 + 5	12	(7, 12)	If the tire hangs 7 ft below the branch, you need 12 ft of rope.
10	10 + 5	15	(10, 15)	If the tire hangs 10 ft below the branch, you need 15 ft of rope.

1a. (−2, 6), (0, 8), (2, 10)

b. (−2, −3), (0, −1), (2, 1)

c. (−2, 4), (0, 0), (2, −4)

✓ Quick Check

1a–c. See left.

1. Find three solutions of each equation. Use $x = -2$, $x = 0$, and $x = 2$.

a. $y = x + 8$ **b.** $y = x - 1$ **c.** $y = -2x$

Objectives

To find solutions of linear equations and to graph linear equations

Examples

1 Finding Solutions
2 Graphing to Test Solutions
3 Graphing a Linear Equation

Professional Development

Math Background

In an equation such as $y = x + 4$, any ordered pair (x, y) that makes the equation true is a *solution* of the equation. Such ordered pairs can be graphed on a coordinate plane. So the *graph of an equation* is the graph of all the points with coordinates that are solutions of that equation. If the graph of solutions is a line, the equation is a *linear equation*. Linear equations have an infinite number of possible solutions, comparable to lines that are composed of an infinite number of points.

More Math Background: p. 484C

Lesson Planning and Resources

See p. 484E for a list of the resources that support this lesson.

PowerPoint

Bell Ringer Practice

✓ **Check Skills You'll Need**
Use student page, transparency, or PowerPoint.

TAKS Daily Review 76
Use transparency.

Differentiated Instruction Solutions for All Learners

Special Needs L1
Some students may have a difficult time graphing ordered pairs. Have them work with a partner who can graph the points as they give the coordinates. They can also check and test the solutions.

learning style: visual

Below Level L2
Tell whether each ordered pair is a solution of each equation.
$y = 3x$ (0, 3) **no** (2, 6) **yes** (3, 3) **no**
$y = x - 2$ (4, 2) **yes** (0, 2) **no** (0, −2) **yes**

learning style: verbal

Activity Lab

Use before the lesson.

All in One Teaching Resources

Activity Lab 10-2: Graphing Linear Equations

Guided Instruction

Example 2
Graphing calculators allow for graphing equations expressed in the $y =$ format.

PowerPoint

Additional Examples

1 Find three solutions of $y = x - 5$. **Sample:** (5, 0), (6, 1), (0, −5)

2 Determine whether each ordered pair is a solution of $y = x - 7$.

a. (−2, 5) **no** **b.** (8, 1) **yes**

3 Graph the linear equation $y = x - 1$.

All in One Teaching Resources

• Daily Notetaking Guide 10-2 **L3**
• Adapted Notetaking 10-2 **L1**

Closure

• *How can you find solutions for equations with two variables?* **Sample: Choose values for *x* and make a table. Substitute for *x* to find the corresponding *y*-values. Write the ordered pairs.**

• *How can you tell from a graph whether an equation is linear?* **The graph of a linear equation is a straight line.**

Vocabulary Tip

Notice the word *line* in the word *linear*. A linear equation has a graph that is a line.

GO Online

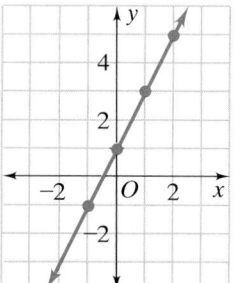

Video Tutor Help
Visit: PHSchool.com
Web Code: are-0775

The **graph of an equation** is the graph of all the points with coordinates that are solutions of the equation. An equation is a **linear equation** when the graph of its solutions lies on a line.

EXAMPLE Graphing to Test Solutions

2 Use the solutions from Example 1 to graph the equation $y = x + 5$. Use the graph to test whether (9, 13) is a solution to the equation.

Step 1 Plot the three ordered-pair solutions.

Step 2 Draw a line through the points.

Step 3 Test (9, 13) by plotting the point in the same coordinate plane. Look to see if the point lies on the line of the graph of the equation.

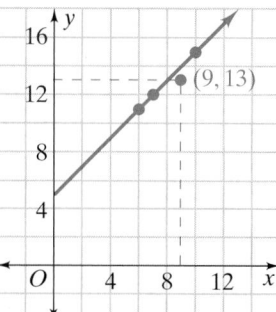

Since (9, 13) is not on the line, (9, 13) is not a solution of $y = x + 5$. For the tire to hang 9 ft below the branch, you need 14 ft of rope.

Quick Check

2. Tell whether (7, 12) is a solution of $y = 3x - 1$. **no**

Linear equations may have negative values in their solutions. You can graph linear equations using positive values, negative values, and zero.

EXAMPLE Graphing a Linear Equation

3 Graph the linear equation $y = 2x + 1$.

Step 1 Make a table of solutions. Use zero as well as positive and negative values for *x*.

Step 2 Graph the points. Draw a line through the points.

x	y = 2x + 1	y	(x, y)
−1	$y = 2(-1) + 1$	−1	(−1, −1)
0	$y = 2(0) + 1$	1	(0, 1)
1	$y = 2(1) + 1$	3	(1, 3)
2	$y = 2(2) + 1$	5	(2, 5)

Quick Check

3. Graph each linear equation. **3a–c. See back of book.**

a. $y = x + 4$ **b.** $y = \frac{1}{2}x$ **c.** $y = -x$

Differentiated Instruction Solutions for All Learners

Advanced Learners **L4**
Write equations for lines that pass through the following quadrants. **Samples:**

Quadrants I and II $y = 1$
Quadrants I and III $y = \frac{3}{2}x$

Pre-AP™

English Language Learners **ELL**
Help students make a connection between the term *ordered pair*, and the order in which they find the point named by two coordinates. Let them know the first number is always the *x*-coordinate, and the second is always the *y*-coordinate. Order matters.

learning style: verbal

1. **Vocabulary** What does the graph of the solution of a linear equation look like? **a line**

Use the equation $y = x - 7$ for Exercises 2–5.

x	x − 7	y	(x, y)
0	■	■	■
−3	■	■	■
10	■	■	■

2. Copy and complete the table at the left to find three solutions of the equation. **See margin.**

3. Graph the equation. **See margin.**

4. Is $(-1, -6)$ a solution of the equation? **no**

5. How does a graph of the equation show that $(5, -2)$ is a solution? **The point (5, −2) lies on the line.**

Homework Exercises

For more exercises, see Extra Skills and Word Problems.

GO for Help

For Exercises	See Examples
6–13	1
14–21	2
22–33	3

Ⓐ **Find three solutions of each equation.** 6–13. See margin.

6. $y = x - 2$ 7. $y = x + 9$ 8. $y = x$ 9. $y = -x + 4$

10. $y = 5x$ 11. $y = -8x$ 12. $y = 3x + 1$ 13. $y = 4x - 5$

Tell whether each ordered pair is a solution of $y = x + 12$.

14. $(-12, 24)$ no   15. $(12, 24)$ yes   16. $(0, -12)$ no   17. $(-12, 0)$ yes

18. $(7, 19)$ yes   19. $(24, 12)$ no   20. $(6, 15)$ no   21. $(9, 21)$ yes

Graph each linear equation. 22–33. See margin.

22. $y = x - 1$ 23. $y = x - 3$ 24. $y = 3x$ 25. $y = 5 + x$

26. $y = x + 4$ 27. $y = -5x$ 28. $y = 2 - x$ 29. $y = 4 - x$

30. $y = -x - 5$ 31. $y = \frac{1}{3}x$ 32. $y = 2x - 1$ 33. $y = \frac{1}{2}x + 4$

Ⓑ GPS 34. **Guided Problem Solving** A shipping company charges $10 for delivery and $5 per pound shipped. The linear equation $y = 5x + 10$ models the cost of shipping an object that weighs x pounds. Graph the equation to find the cost to ship a vase that weighs 4 pounds. **See margin.**
   - Make a table of solutions using the ordered pair (x, y).
   - Graph the equation.
   - Which point on your graph shows the cost for a 4-lb vase?

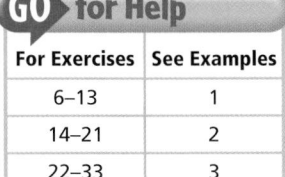

35. **Pets** You are building a fence around a square pen for your pig. You want to use 46 ft of fencing, which accounts for a 2-ft opening. Graph the equation $P = 4s - 2$. Use your graph to find the length of each side of the pen. **See margin.**

2–3. See back of book.
6–13. See back of book.
22–35. See back of book.

Assignment Guide

Check Your Understanding
Go over Exercises 1–5 in class before assigning the Homework Exercises.

Homework Exercises
A	Practice by Example	6–33
B	Apply Your Skills	34–42
C	Challenge	43

TEKS ★ TAKS Tune-Up and
Mixed Review   44–45

Homework Quick Check
To check students' understanding of key skills and concepts, go over Exercises 15, 28, 39, 41, and 42.

Differentiated Instruction Resources

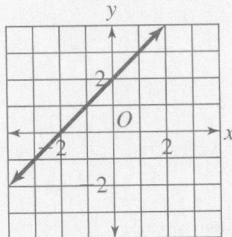

PowerPoint

Lesson Quiz

1. Is $(-3, 5)$ a solution for $y = x - 7$? **no**

2. Find three solutions of $y = -2x$
Sample: $(-1, 2), (0, 0), (1, -2)$

3. Graph the equation $y = x + 2$.
Is it a linear equation? **yes**

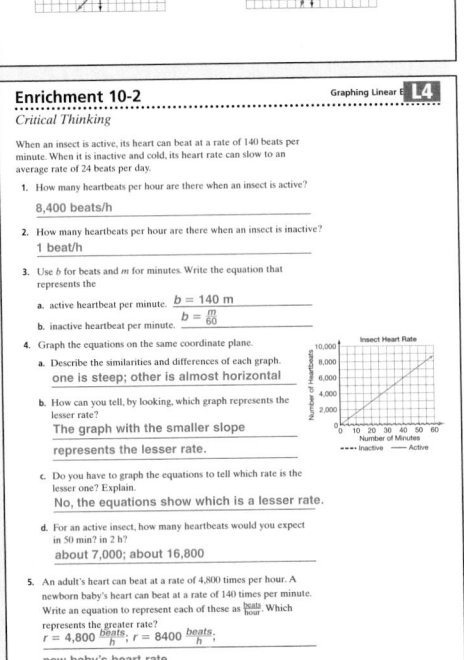

GO Online
Homework Help
Visit: PHSchool.com
Web Code: are-1002

On which of the following lines does each point lie? A point may lie on more than one line.

36. $(0, 0)$ none
37. $(3, 9)$ I, III
38. $(-2, -1)$ III

I. $y = x + 6$
II. $y = x - 6$
III. $y = 2x + 3$

39. Error Analysis A student says that $(-1, -5)$ is a solution of $y = -3x - 2$. What error do you think the student made?
The student thought the product of -3 and -1 was -3; it is 3.

40. Honey bees produce about 50 lb of honey per hive each year. This situation can be represented by $y = 50x$, where x is the number of hives and y is the amount of honey in pounds. Make a table. Can 800 lb of honey be produced in one year with 16 hives? **See margin.**

41. Writing in Math Why is it a good idea to plot at least three points when you graph a linear equation? Answers may vary. Sample: Plotting three points will help you check whether the graph is correct.

42. Measurement Graph the equations $y = 12x$ and $y = \frac{1}{12}x$ on the same coordinate plane. Which of these equations models the conversion of x inches to y feet? **See margin.**

C 43. Challenge Tell whether the graph of $y = x - 5$ passes through the second quadrant. Explain how you know. No; for $x < 0$, the y-values are negative.

TEKS ★ TAKS Tune-Up and Mixed Review

TAKS Objective 2
TEKS (7.4)(B)

44. The data in the table at the left show the relationship between x, the diameter of a circle, and y, the radius of a circle. Which graph best represents the data? **D**

Diameter, x (cm)	Radius, y (cm)
0	0
2	1
4	2
6	3

GO for Help
Lesson 9-7

45. You have $480 in an account that pays 8% simple interest annually. What is your balance after 3 years? **$604.66**

Alternative Assessment

Provide pairs of students with blank coordinate grids. Have partners work together to make a table of values and graph the linear equations in Exercises 22–33. Ask pairs to compare their graphs with other groups and resolve any discrepancies.

40. See back of book.
42. See back of book.

Representing Data

A table is an organized way to represent data. Sometimes it is helpful to visualize the data by creating a graph.

TEKS ★ TAKS

(7.4)(B) To graph data to demonstrate relationships in familiar concepts such as circumference **TAKS** Obj. 2

EXAMPLE

The data in the table show the relationship between the diameter d and the circumference C of a circle.

Which graph best represents the data in the table at the right?

Diameter d (cm)	2	4	6	8
Circumference C (cm)	6.3	12.6	18.8	25.1

(A)

(C)

(B)

(D)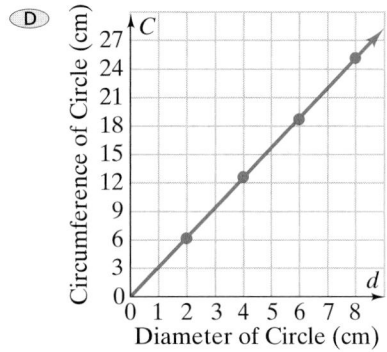

According to the data in the table and what you know to be true about circles, the circumference increases as the diameter increases.

Choice B shows the circumference *decreasing* as the diameter increases. Eliminate choice B.

Choice C shows a vertical line, which means the diameter is constant. A circle with one diameter cannot have several different circumferences. Eliminate choice C.

The first ordered pair is (2, 6.3). In the remaining graphs, this point appears only in choice D. The correct answer is choice D.

Activity Lab

Representing Data

Students extend their graphing skills from Lesson 10-2 by using graphs to represent data from tables.

Guided Instruction

Explain to students that there is often a relationship between data in a table and that sometimes graphing that data makes the relationship easier to see. Ask questions, such as:

- *How do we know the line in Choice B shows an inverse relationship?* as one set of coordinates increases, the other decreases
- *What does the vertical line in Choice C mean?* There is no change in the x-coordinate as the y-coordinate moves up or down.
- *What general conclusion can you draw from these graphs?* You can tell the relationship between two sets of data based on the direction and angle of the line.

Differentiated Instruction

Below Level **L2**

Allow students to create their own graph of the data in the table to help them connect the relationship between two sets of data and the appearance of the graph.

TEKS ★ TAKS Resources

Dana Center TEKS Toolkit Clarifying Activities (7.4)(B)
Visit: PHSchool.com
Web Code: arq-9045

Practice Solving Problems

In this feature, students graph information to help them solve problems. They write an equation and then solve the equation for different values in order to graph the equation.

Guided Instruction

Explain to students that they can find additional information by graphing information from a problem. Tell them they can use information from a problem to create an equation that will allow them to graph.
Ask:

- *Why do we add $3 to the amount Mandy earns per hour?* She gets a $3-dollar transportation fee per job, plus her hourly rate.
- *Why should we solve the equation for h = 1 and h = 5?* to find out how much money, *m*, Mandy makes for a 1-hour job and a 5-hour job
- *What would the equation look like if Mandy charged $5 for transportation and $4.50 per hour? How much would she earn for a 4-hour babysitting job?* $m = 4.5h + 5$; $23
- *What are the steps required to solve the problem?* find the important information, write an equation, solve the equation for different values, graph the equation

TEKS ★ TAKS Resources

Dana Center TEKS Toolkit Clarifying Activities (7.11)(B), (7.13)(A)
Visit: PHSchool.com
Web Code: asq-9045

GPS Guided Problem Solving

Practice Solving Problems

Jobs Mandy earns $6 per hour babysitting, plus $3 for transportation. How much will she earn for a 1-hour job and a 5-hour job this weekend?

TEKS ★ TAKS
(7.11)(B) To make inferences based on an analysis of given data **TAKS** Obj. 5
(7.13)(A) To apply mathematics to activities outside of school **TAKS** Obj. 6

What You Might Think

What do I know?
What am I trying to find out?

How do I show the main idea?

What does the graph look like?

What is the answer?

What You Might Write

Mandy gets $3 to start and earns $6 per hour. I want to find out how much she will earn for a 1-hour job and for a 5-hour job.

I will graph $m = 6h + 3$ to show how much money m she earns after h hours of work.

Solve for $h = 1$ and $h = 5$.
If $h = 1$, then $m = 6(1) + 3$, or 9.
If $h = 5$, then $m = 6(5) + 3$, or 33.
Graph (1, 9) and (5, 33). I can connect the points with a solid line because Mandy can get paid for working part of an hour.

Mandy will earn $9 for the 1-hour job and $33 for the 5-hour job.

Think It Through

The $3 transportation fee does not change, but Mandy earns $6 for every hour h she works.

1. How does the equation $m = 6h + 3$ represent the amount of money m Mandy earns for h hours of work? Explain.

2. How much does Mandy earn for 2 hours, $3\frac{1}{2}$ hours, 4 hours, and $6\frac{1}{4}$ hours of work? $15; $24; $27; $40.50

Exercises

Solve each problem. For Exercises 3 and 4, answer the questions first.

3. Fingernails grow an average of 1.5 in. per year. Suppose your nails are $\frac{1}{2}$ in. long on your tenth birthday. If you do not cut your nails, how long will they be on your sixteenth birthday? $9\frac{1}{2}$ **in.**
   a. What do you know? What do you want to find out?
   b. What equation can you write to find the length of your fingernails at age 10 and age 16?
   c. How does graphing the equation give you additional information?

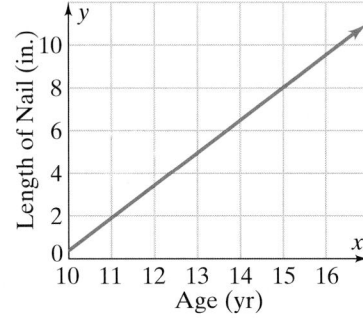

4. Romesh Sharma of India set a record for the longest fingernails. He had five fingernails on his left hand that had a total length of 33 ft. If his nails grew $\frac{1}{8}$ in. each month, about how long did it take to grow those nails? Assume that he started when he was born and never cut his fingernails. **almost 53 years**
   a. If the five nails were about the same length, about how long was each nail?
   b. How does the diagram below help you decide what to do?

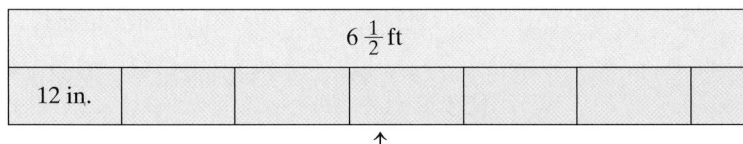

How many inches are in $6\frac{1}{2}$ feet?

5. In 1982, Larry Walters tied 42 helium balloons to an aluminum lawn chair. He floated above Los Angeles International Airport in his chair for 45 min. If Larry and all his equipment weighed 168 lb, how much did each balloon lift on average? **4 lb**

10-3 ★ Finding the Slope of a Line

Objectives
To find the slope of a line and use it to solve problems

Examples
1 Finding Slope
2 Application: Avalanches
3 Drawing Lines on a Graph

Math Background

A ratio expresses the relationship between two values. For a line in the coordinate plane, the steepness of the line is expressed by a ratio. The ratio of the line's rise (the vertical change in a line) to its run (its horizontal change) is called *slope*. The slope for any given line is constant. To find the slope of a line, divide the line's rise by its run. Given a value for slope, you can draw a line with that slope through a given point.

More Math Background: p. 484C

Lesson Planning and Resources

See p. 484E for a list of the resources that support this lesson.

498

✓ Check Skills You'll Need

1. Vocabulary Review
What does it mean to say that the fraction $\frac{5}{9}$ is written in *simplest form*? See below.
Write each fraction in simplest form.

2. $\frac{6}{8}$ $\frac{3}{4}$ **3.** $\frac{8}{-12}$ $-\frac{2}{3}$

4. $\frac{-4}{-12}$ $\frac{1}{3}$ **5.** $\frac{-15}{3}$ -5

for Help
Lesson 2-3

Check Skills You'll Need

1. The numerator and denominator have no common factors other than 1.

Online
active math

For: Slope Activity
Use: Interactive Textbook, 10-5

What You'll Learn
To find the slope of a line and use it to solve problems

 New Vocabulary slope, rise, run

Why Learn This?
Elephants will not climb a ramp with more than a 33-degree slope. When ramps are constructed, they must meet safety standards that ensure they are not too steep. You can understand what factors affect steepness when you understand slope.

Slope is a ratio that describes the steepness of a line. Slope compares the vertical change in a line, called the **rise,** to the horizontal change, called the **run.** For any two points on a line, the ratio of rise to run is the same.

$$\text{slope} = \frac{\text{rise}}{\text{run}}$$

EXAMPLE   Finding Slope

1 Find the slope of the line.

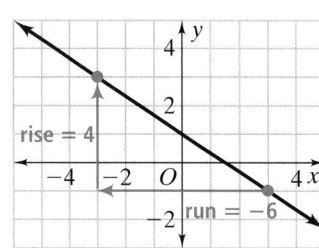

$$\text{slope} = \frac{\text{rise}}{\text{run}}$$

$$= \frac{4}{-6} \quad \leftarrow \text{Substitute rise and run.}$$

$$= -\frac{2}{3} \quad \leftarrow \text{Simplify.}$$

The slope of the line is $-\frac{2}{3}$.

✓ Quick Check

● **1.** Find the slope of the line at the right.

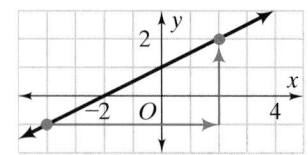

Differentiated Instruction **Solutions for All Learners**

Special Needs L1
Assist students, as needed, to draw and connect points. If they have difficulty, give them a straightedge, and pair them up with a student who can help plot the points and hold the straightedge as they connect the points.

learning style: visual

Below Level L2
Review the rules for subtraction of positive and negative integers. Have students find the rise and run with simple pairs of coordinates, such as (0, 2) and (4, 6). **rise: 4, run: 4**

learning style: visual

The slope of a line can be positive, negative, zero, or undefined. A line that goes upward from left to right has positive slope. A line that goes downward has negative slope. A horizontal line has a slope of 0. The slope of a vertical line is undefined because you cannot divide by 0.

  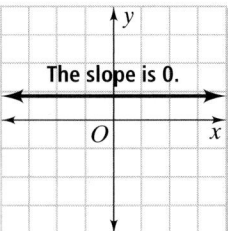

EXAMPLE Application: Avalanches

2. Avalanches are likely to occur on trails where the absolute value of the slope is between 0.5 and 1. Find the slope of the trail and determine whether an avalanche is likely.

From point *A* to point *B*, the rise is 4 and the run is 7.

$$\text{slope} = \frac{\text{rise}}{\text{run}} = \frac{4}{7} \approx 0.57$$

The slope is about 0.57, so an avalanche is likely.

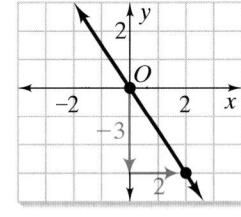

Quick Check

2. Slope is used to find the pitch, or steepness, of a roof. Roof *A* has a pitch of 3 to 12, which means it rises 3 in. for every 12 in. of run. What is the slope of Roof *A*? $\frac{1}{4}$

You can use slope to graph a line if you know a point on the line.

EXAMPLE Drawing Lines on a Graph

3. Draw a line through the origin with a slope of $-\frac{3}{2}$.

Step 1 Graph a point at $(0, 0)$.

Step 2 Move 3 units down and 2 units to the right. Graph a second point.

Step 3 Connect the points to draw a line.

Quick Check

3. Draw a line through $P(2, 1)$ with a slope of $\frac{4}{3}$. See above left.

Guided Instruction

Example 3
Students may forget to write the negative sign for a line with a negative slope. Remind them that if a line goes downward from left to right, its slope is negative. If a line goes upward from left to right, its slope is positive. Draw both a positive slope line and a negative slope line on the board. Write "+" and "−" to indicate each lines' slope.

PowerPoint
Additional Examples

1 Find the slope of the line. -2

2 Find the slope of the roof. $\frac{4}{3}$

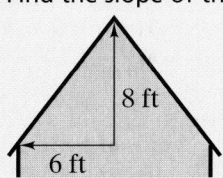

3 Draw a line through the origin with a slope of $\frac{-5}{4}$. See back of book for graph.

All in One Teaching Resources
• Daily Notetaking Guide 10-3 **L3**
• Adapted Notetaking 10-3 **L1**

Closure

• *What is the slope of a line?* Sample: Slope is the ratio of the vertical change to horizontal change, or rise over run.
• *What is the rise of a line?* The rise is its vertical change.
• *What is the run of a line?* The run is its horizontal change.

Vocabulary Tip
Snowboarders and skiers often use the word *slope* to refer to the side of a mountain.

3.
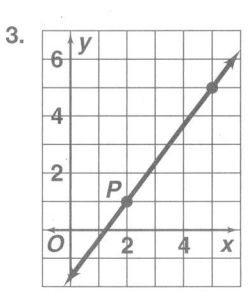

TAKS Tip
You can also move 2 units to the left and 3 units up.

Advanced Learners **L4**
Challenge students to think of relationships that would yield lines with positive slopes (increasing speed and distance), and negative slopes (value depreciation).

Pre-AP™

English Language Learners **ELL**
Have students use index cards to draw and label examples of a positive, negative, zero, and undefined slope. They might also draw and label examples for the terms *rise* and *run*.

learning style: visual

499

3. Practice

Assignment Guide

Check Your Understanding
Go over Exercises 1–4 in class before assigning the Homework Exercises.

Homework Exercises
A Practice by Example   5–11
B Apply Your Skills   12–21
C Challenge   22
TEKS ★ (TAKS) Tune-Up and
Mixed Review   23–25

Homework Quick Check
To check students' understanding of key skills and concepts, go over Exercises 6, 10, 19, 20, and 21.

Differentiated Instruction Resources

Check Your Understanding

1. **Vocabulary** The vertical change between two points on a line is called __?__, and the horizontal change is called __?__.   rise; run

For Exercises 2–4, use the graph at the left.

2. Is the slope of the line positive or negative?   negative

3. Use points A and D to find the slope of the line.   −2

4. **Reasoning** Use points B and C to find the slope of the line. Does using different points affect the slope? Explain.   −2; the slope is the same because the ratio is always the same.

Homework Exercises

For more exercises, see Extra Skills and Word Problems.

GO for Help

For Exercises	See Examples
5–7	1
8–9	2
10–11	3

Ⓐ Find the slope of each line.   5. −1   6. $-\frac{1}{3}$ 7. 2

5.

6.

7.

8.

9.

10.

11.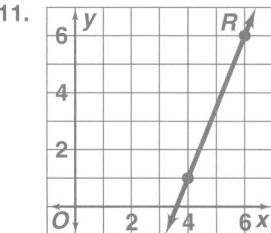

Draw a line with the given slope through the given point.
10–11. See left.

10. $P(0, 0)$, slope = −3

11. $R(6, 6)$, slope = $\frac{5}{2}$

Ⓑ **GPS**

12. **Guided Problem Solving** Some skiers prefer steep trails. Which trails would you recommend to those skiers? Explain.   See left.
- What is the slope of each trail?
- Which trails are the steepest?

12. Diamond and Bear; their slopes are $\frac{1}{2}$ and $\frac{2}{5}$, which are steeper than the other trails, whose slopes are $\frac{1}{4}$.

Ski Trail	Total Rise	Total Run
Alpine	1,800 ft	7,200 ft
Diamond	1,840 ft	3,680 ft
Bear	1,900 ft	4,750 ft
Donner	750 ft	3,000 ft

13. **Reasoning** Draw a horizontal line through $(1, 3)$. Use two points on the line to explain why the slope of the line equals 0.   See margin.

500   Chapter 10   Graphing in the Coordinate Plane

13. See back of book.
17–18. See back of book.
25. See back of book.

Graph the given points. Find the slope of the line through the points.

14. $(4, 8), (5, 10)$ **2**   **15.** $(4, -1), (-4, 1)$ $-\frac{1}{4}$ **16.** $(2, 7), (3, -1)$ -8

17. Roof A has a rise of 5 and a run of 3. Roof B has a rise of 3 and a run of 5. Which roof is steeper? Explain. **See margin.**

18. Ramps Guidelines for a wheelchair ramp allow a maximum of 1 in. of rise for every 12 in. of run. The ramp at the left runs 6 ft 8 in. and rises 2 ft 9 in. Does the ramp meet the guidelines? Explain. **See margin.**

19. Cars The graph shows the value of a car for the first seven years of ownership.
  a. What was the value of the car when it was new? **$24,000**
  b. What is the slope of the graph? -2
  c. What does the slope tell you about the relationship between the age of the car and its value? **Every year, the value of the car decreases $2,000.**

Car's Value (thousands) vs. Car's Age (years)

20. The line slants down from left to right, so the slope should be negative 3.

20. Error Analysis Your classmate graphs **GPS** a line through $(4, 2)$ and $(5, -1)$ and finds that the slope equals 3. Explain why your classmate is incorrect.

21. It would be more difficult, because a slope of $\frac{1}{2}$ is steeper than a slope of $\frac{1}{6}$.

21. Writing in Math Explain why it is more difficult to run up a hill with a slope of $\frac{1}{2}$ than a hill with a slope of $\frac{1}{6}$.

C **22. Challenge** On the same coordinate plane, graph line r through points $(0, 4)$ and $(3, -3)$ and line s through points $(1, 7)$ and $(4, 0)$. Find the slopes of r and s. What are lines with equal slopes called?
$-\frac{7}{3}; -\frac{7}{3};$ **parallel lines**

TEKS ★ TAKS Tune-Up and Mixed Review

TAKS Objective 3
TEKS (7.7)(A)

23. Which line in the graph at the right contains the ordered pair $(0, -4)$? **C**
  Ⓐ Line j Ⓒ Line l
  Ⓑ Line k Ⓓ Line m

TAKS Objective 1
TEKS (7.2)(C)

24. The lowest point in a city is 8 ft below sea level, or -8 ft. A building in that city has 5 stories, and each story is 15 ft high. What is the elevation of the top of the building? **H**
  Ⓕ 12 ft   Ⓖ 20 ft   Ⓗ 67 ft   Ⓙ 75 ft

GO for Help **Lesson 7-5**

25. $\triangle ABC$ is an isosceles triangle. $\triangle XYZ$ has angle measures $45°$, $70°$, and $65°$. Are the two triangles congruent? Explain. **See margin.**

Alternative Assessment

Have students work in pairs to complete Exercises 5–9. Partners work together to copy each line on graph paper. Students then use red pencil to draw and label the run and blue pencil to draw and label the rise. They then express the slope as a fraction in simplest form.

TEKS ★ TAKS Resources

• TAKS Strategies, p. 523
• TAKS Tune Up, pp. 527–529

TAKS Tune-Up Kit
• TAKS Daily Review Transparencies
• TAKS Review and Preparation Workbook
• TAKS Strategies with Transparencies
• Texas Progress Monitoring Assessments

---

4. Assess & Reteach

PowerPoint
Lesson Quiz

1. Find the slope of the line. **2**

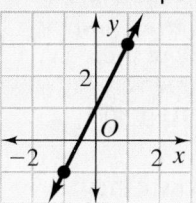

2. $(1, 3)$ and $(2, 6)$ **3**

3. $(-3, 4)$ and $(3, -5)$ $-\frac{3}{2}$

Reteaching 10-3 — Finding the Slope

Enrichment 10-3 — Finding the Slope
Patterns in Algebra

501

Exploring Slope

In Lesson 10-3, students found and used the slope of a line. In this activity, they use a graphing calculator to explore the relationship between an equation and the slope of its graph.

Guided Instruction

Revisit the meaning of *linear equation* and *slope*, and *rise* and *run*. Review the steps for finding the slope of a line.

Error Prevention!

Exercises 1–4
When students use a graphing calculator, they may confuse the steps involved in finding slope. To help, pair students and guide them to use the five steps presented for the Example. In addition, you can have students write the keystrokes they will use to find the slope in each exercise.

Exercises 6–9
Have students share their methods for finding the slopes of the linear equations. Ask: *What are the features all of these forms of equations have in common?* Sample: Each has the $y = mx + b$ form; each equation provides the slope and y-intercept of its graph.

Differentiated Instruction

Below Level   L2
Students may have trouble using the graphing calculator. Have students complete each step by hand and by calculator before going onto the next step.

Resources

- graphing calculator
- Classroom Aid 36

10-3b Activity Lab   Technology

Exploring Slope

You can use a graphing calculator to explore the relationship between an equation and the slope of its graph.

EXAMPLE

Use a graphing calculator to find the slope of $y = 2x + 1$.

Step 1 Use [Y=] to enter the equation.

Step 2 Press [ZOOM] 0 [ENTER] for the integer mode.

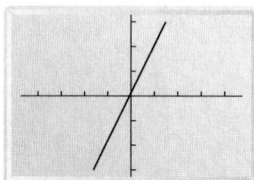

Step 3 Press [TRACE]. The x-coordinate is 0, and the y-coordinate is 1.

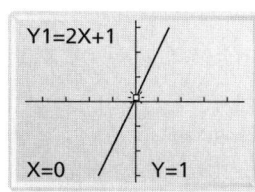

Step 4 Use [▶] to move the cursor to the right 1 unit.

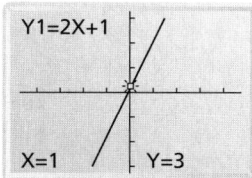

Step 5 Repeat step 4 and examine how the coordinates change. As the x-coordinate increases 1 unit, the y-coordinate increases 2 units. Another way to say this is that for every 1 unit of run, there are 2 units of rise.

slope $= \dfrac{\text{rise}}{\text{run}} = \dfrac{2}{1}$, or 2.

Exercises

Use a graphing calculator to find the slope of each equation.

1. $y = 2x - 3$ 2
2. $y = x + 3$ 1
3. $y = \frac{1}{3}x + 2$ $\frac{1}{3}$
4. $y = -3x$ -3

5. **Reasoning** Look at each slope you found. How is the slope of a line represented in each equation? It is the coefficient of x.

Without graphing, find the slope of each line.

6. $y = 8x + 3$ 8
7. $y = -x - 1$ -1
8. $y = \frac{1}{2}x + 9$ $\frac{1}{2}$
9. $y = \frac{5}{2}x - 3$ $\frac{5}{2}$

Graph each point in the same coordinate plane. Identify the quadrant in which the point lies. See margin for graph.

1. $K(-2, -5)$ III

2. $Q(-3, 4)$ II

3. $D(2, 1)$ I

Graph each linear equation.   4–6. See margin.

4. $y = x + 7$

5. $y = -3x + 2$

6. $y = x - 3$

7. A dragonfly can reach a speed of 50 km/h. The dragonfly's speed can be represented using $d = 50t$, where d represents the distance in kilometers and t represents the time in hours. Graph this equation. See margin.

8. Find the slope of the line on the coordinate plane at the right. $-\frac{3}{2}$

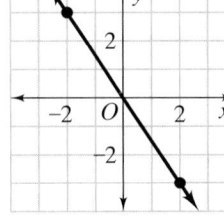

Draw a line with the given slope through the given point. 9–10. See margin.

9. $P(-2, 0)$, slope $= 3$

10. $A(0, -3)$, slope $= \frac{1}{2}$

MATH GAMES

Hide and Seek

What You'll Need

- 2 players, two sheets of graph paper

How To Play

- Using graph paper, draw the first quadrant of the coordinate plane. Label the x- and y-axes from 0 to 10.
- Draw a triangle or rectangle on your graph. The ordered pairs for each vertex must be whole numbers.
- You and your opponent take turns trying to locate each vertex of the other's shape by calling out ordered pairs that are whole numbers.
- If your opponent's guess falls inside your figure, you say "inside." If it falls outside your figure, you say "outside." If it is on the border, you say "border." If the guess falls on a vertex, you must say "bingo."
- The first player to name all the vertices of the opponent's figure wins.

Use this Checkpoint Quiz to check students' understanding of the skills and concepts of Lessons 10-1 through 10-3.

Resources

- All-in-One Teaching Resources Checkpoint Quiz 1
- Texas ExamView CD-ROM
- Success Tracker™ Online Intervention

MATH GAMES

Hide and Seek

In this game, students become more familiar with the locations of ordered pairs on a graph. Players draw a figure on a graph, then take turns trying to guess the coordinates of the vertices of the other player's figure.

Guided Instruction

Have a volunteer read the rules of the game. Explain that it may help students keep track of their guesses by recording them on a graph and marking them inside, outside, border, or "bingo."

Resources

- graph paper

1–7. See back of book.
9–10. See back of book.

1. Plan

TEKS ★ **TAKS**

(7.4)(B) To graph data to demonstrate relationships in familiar concepts such as area and volume **TAKS** Obj. 2

(7.14)(A) To communicate mathematical ideas using graphical and algebraic models **TAKS** Obj. 6

Dana Center TEKS Toolkit Clarifying Activities (7.4)(B), (7.14)(A)
Visit: PHSchool.com
Web Code: arq-9045

TEKS Math Background

The graph of every linear equation is a straight line. The graph of every *nonlinear* equation is not a straight line, although it can be a combination of straight lines as well as curves. This lesson introduces two nonlinear equations: a parabola, or U-shaped curve; and an absolute-value equation, which is V-shaped.

More Math Background: p. 484C

Lesson Planning and Resources

See p. 484E for a list of the resources that support this lesson.

PowerPoint

Bell Ringer Practice

✓ **Check Skills You'll Need**
Use student page, transparency, or PowerPoint.

TAKS **Daily Review 78**
Use transparency.

504

10-4 Graphing Nonlinear Relationships

10-4

✓ **Check Skills You'll Need**

1. **Vocabulary Review**
   What is a *linear equation*? 1–4. See back of book.
   Find three solutions of each equation.

2. $y = x + 12$

3. $y = x - 20$

4. $y = 15x$

GO for Help
Lesson 10-2

TEKS ★ **TAKS**
• **(7.4)(B)** To graph data to demonstrate relationships in familiar concepts such as area and volume **TAKS** Obj. 2
• **(7.14)(A)** To communicate mathematical ideas using graphical and algebraic models **TAKS** Obj. 6

🔊 **New Vocabulary** nonlinear equation

Why Learn This?

When you kick a ball in the air, the path the ball follows is a curve called a parabola. A parabola is a sign of a relationship that is not a linear.

A **nonlinear equation** is an equation whose graph is not a line.

EXAMPLE **Graphing a Nonlinear Equation**

★ **TAKS** Tip

When substituting a value for *x* in $-x^2$, make sure you square the value *before* finding its opposite.

1. Graph $y = -x^2$ using integer values of *x* from −3 to 3.

Step 1 Make a table of solutions.

x	$-x^2$	y	(x, y)
−3	$-(-3)^2$	−9	(−3, −9)
−2	$-(-2)^2$	−4	(−2, −4)
−1	$-(-1)^2$	−1	(−1, −1)
0	$-(0)^2$	0	(0, 0)
1	$-(1)^2$	−1	(1, −1)
2	$-(2)^2$	−4	(2, −4)
3	$-(3)^2$	−9	(3, −9)

Step 2 Use each solution (x, y) to graph a point. Draw a curve through the points.

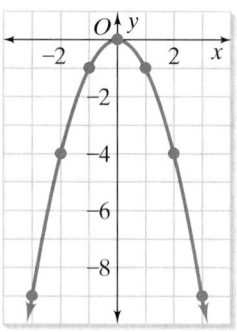

✓ **Quick Check**

● 1. Graph $y = 2x^2$ using integer values of *x* from −3 to 3.

See back of book.

504 Chapter 10 Graphing in the Coordinate Plane

Differentiated Instruction Solutions for All Learners

Special Needs **L1**
For some exercises, students who have difficulty graphing can make a table of solutions. Pair them up with a student who can graph, then use the table of solutions to graph.

learning style: visual

Below Level **L2**
Make a table for each equation for integer values of *x* from −3 to 3.

$y = 2x$ −6, −4, −2, 0, 2, 4, 6
$y = x − 2$ −5, −4, −3, −2, −1, 0, 1

learning style: visual

Video Tutor Help
Visit: PHSchool.com
Web Code: are-0775

EXAMPLE **Graphing Absolute Value Equations**

2 Graph $y = |x|$ using integer values of x from -2 to 2.

x	|x|	y	(x, y)
-2	$|-2|$	2	$(-2, 2)$
-1	$|-1|$	1	$(-1, 1)$
0	$|0|$	0	$(0, 0)$
1	$|1|$	1	$(1, 1)$
2	$|2|$	2	$(2, 2)$

← Make a table
of values.

Graph the
ordered pairs.
Then connect →
the points.

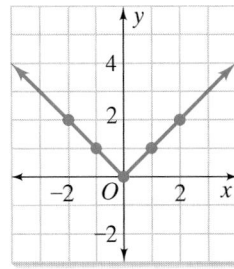

2.

x	-2	-1	0	1	2
y	4	2	0	2	4

✓ **Quick Check**

2. Graph $y = 2|x|$ using integer values of x from -2 to 2. **See left.**

More Than One Way

The equation $y = x^3$ shows the nonlinear relationship between edge length x and volume y of a cube. Determine whether $(3, 12)$ is a solution of $y = x^3$.

Kayla's Method

I will use my graphing calculator. I press **Y=** and enter $y = x^3$. Then I select the integer mode under **ZOOM**. I can use the **TRACE** feature to get the screen at the right.

At $x = 3$, $y = 27$, so $(3, 12)$ is not a solution.

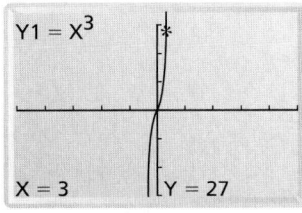

Y1 = X³

X = 3   Y = 27

**Answers may vary.
Sample:** No; by
substituting $(-3, 10)$ into
the equation, you can
determine that $(-3, 10)$ is
not a solution of
$y = x^2 + 2$.

Carlos's Method

I will substitute 3 for x and 12 for y in the equation.

$y = x^3$
$12 \stackrel{?}{=} 3^3$ ← Substitute.
$12 \stackrel{?}{=} 27$ ← Simplify.
$12 \neq 27$

The equation is not true, so $(3, 12)$ is not a solution.

Choose a Method
Determine whether $(-3, 10)$ is a solution of $y = x^2 + 2$. Describe your method and explain why you chose it.

Advanced Learners L4
Write an equation whose solutions include each set of ordered pairs.
$(-4, 2), (-3, 1), (-1, 1), (3, 5)$ $y = |x + 2|$
$(-3, 25), (-1, 9), (0, 4), (2, 0)$ $y = (x - 2)^2$

Pre-AP™

English Language Learners ELL
Write "linear" and "nonlinear" on the board. Write "line" and "not a line" under each, respectively. Show students that the prefix *non* often refers to the word *not*.

learning style: verbal

---

2. Teach

Activity Lab
Use before the lesson.

All in One Teaching Resources
Activity Lab 10-4: Critical Thinking

Guided Instruction

Example 1
For Quick Check 1, remind students to square the value of x *before* multiplying by 2. Draw a table on the board and record the values of x and y as students supply the y-values.

Example 2
Have students use their arms to model basic shapes of functions. As you read equations aloud, students can hold their arms in U shapes or V shapes to indicate the shape of the function. For instance: $y = 3x^2$ U-shaped
$y = x^2 + 3$ U-shaped
$y = |x| + 3$ V-shaped

PowerPoint
Additional Examples

Graph each equation using integer values of x from -3 to 3.

1 $y = x^2 - 2$

2 $y = |x| + 2$

$y = x^2 - 2$

All in One Teaching Resources
• Daily Notetaking Guide 10-4 L3
• Adapted Notetaking 10-4 L1

Closure

• Describe the graph of a parabola. **a U-shaped curve**
• Describe the graph of an absolute-value equation. **a V-shaped curve**

Quick Check
1. **See back of book.**

505

Assignment Guide

Check Your Understanding
Go over Exercises 1–7 in class before assigning the Homework Exercises.

Homework Exercises

A Practice by Example   8–22
B Apply Your Skills   23–31
C Challenge   32
TEKS ★ (TAKS) Tune-Up and
   Mixed Review   33–35

Homework Quick Check
To check students' understanding of key skills and concepts, go over Exercises 13, 21, 24, 25, and 30.

Differentiated Instruction **Resources**

Check Your Understanding

1. **Vocabulary** How can you tell whether an equation is linear or nonlinear? *If the solutions of an equation form a line, it is linear. If the graph of the solutions is not a line, it is nonlinear.*

Graph each equation using integer values of x from −3 to 3.
2–4. See margin.

2. $y = x^2$ 3. $y = |x|$ 4. $y = -x^3$

5. **Answers may vary.**
Sample: Squaring a positive or a negative number always results in a positive number. So for all values of x, x^2 is positive, and y is always positive.

5. **Number Sense** Why does the graph of the equation $y = x^2$ not fall in Quadrant III or Quadrant IV? *See left.*

6. Describe the shape of the graph of the absolute value equation $y = |x|$. *It is V-shaped and opens upward.*

7. **Mental Math** Is $P(1, -3)$ a solution of the equation $y = -x^3$? *no*

Homework Exercises

For more exercises, see Extra Skills and Word Problems.

GO for Help

For Exercises	See Examples
8–16	1
17–22	2

A **Graph each equation using integer values of x from −3 to 3.**
8–16. See margin.

8. $y = 4x^2$ 9. $y = -3x^2$ 10. $y = \frac{1}{2}x^2$

11. $y = x^2 - 2$ 12. $y = x^2 + 2$ 13. $y = -x^2 + 3$

14. $y = -x^2 - 4$ 15. $y = (x + 1)^2$ 16. $y = (x - 1)^2$

Graph each equation using integer values of x from −3 to 3.
17–22. See margin.

17. $y = 2|x|$ 18. $y = \frac{1}{3}|x|$ 19. $y = -|x|$

20. $y = -|x| + 2$ 21. $y = |x - 1|$ 22. $y = |x + 1|$

B **GPS** 23. **Guided Problem Solving** According to legend, Galileo dropped two different objects from the Tower of Pisa to prove that they would fall at the same rate. The equation $d = 16t^2$ can be used to find the distance d, in feet, that the objects fall in t seconds. Graph the equation showing how far the objects fall between 0 and 5 seconds. *See margin.*
  - Make a table of solutions. What values of t will you use?
  - Graph the points. What is the greatest value of d in your graph?

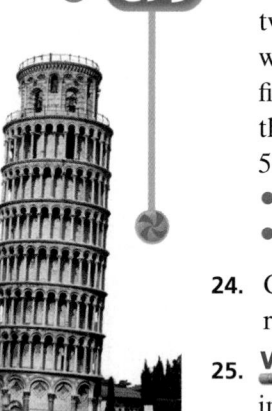

24. Graph the equation $A = \pi r^2$ to show the relationship between radius r and area A of a circle. Use 3.14 as an approximation for π. *See margin.*

25. **Writing in Math** Explain why the graph of $y = -|x|$ has no points in Quadrant I or Quadrant II. *See margin.*

26. Use integer values of −3 to 3 to graph $y = 3|x| + 5$. *See margin.*

2–4. See back of book.
8–26. See back of book.
30a–30b. See back of book.
32. See back of book.

Match each graph with an equation.

27.
A

28.
B

29.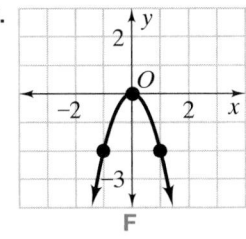
F

A. $y = |x + 1|$ **B.** $y = \frac{1}{3}x^2$ **C.** $y = \frac{1}{2}x^2$

D. $y = |x| - 1$ **E.** $y = 2x^2$ **F.** $y = -2x^2$

30. **Skydiving** Suppose a skydiver leaps from a plane at an altitude of
    GPS 12,000 ft. The equation $h = -16t^2 + 12,000$ models the skydiver's
    height above the ground, in feet, at t seconds.   30a–b. See margin.
    a. Make a table to find the height at 0, 5, 10, and 20 seconds.
    b. Graph the equation. Use the graph to find the height at 12 s.

31. **Choose a Method** The equation $A = s^2$ shows the nonlinear
    relationship between side length s and area A of a square.
    Determine whether (6.5, 42.25) is a solution of $A = s^2$.
    yes; $6.5^2 = 42.25$

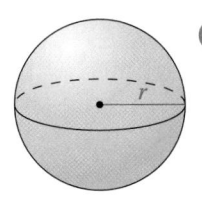

C **32. Challenge** The equation $S = 4\pi r^2$ gives the surface area S of a
    sphere with radius r. The equation $V = \frac{4}{3}\pi r^3$ gives the volume V
    of a sphere with radius r. For each equation, make a table of values
    using integer values of r from 0 to 5. Use 3 as an approximation
    for π. For what value of r will the graphs of the equations intersect?
    See margin.

TEKS ★ **TAKS** **Tune-Up and Mixed Review**

TAKS Objective 2
TEKS (7.4)(B)

33. Which of the following relationships is
    represented in the graph?   A
    Ⓐ The relationship between the edge length
       and the volume of a cube
    Ⓑ The relationship between the side length
       and the surface area of a cube
    Ⓒ The relationship between the side length
       and the area of a square
    Ⓓ The relationship between the radius and
       the area of a circle

TAKS Objective 1
TEKS (7.1)(B)

34. On Monday, $\frac{4}{7}$ of the students at school bought a hot lunch. About
    what percent of the students did NOT buy a hot lunch?   G
    Ⓕ 37%   Ⓖ 43%   Ⓗ 57%   Ⓙ 62%

for Help   Lesson 8-10

35. Find the height of a rectangular prism with a volume of 357 cm³, a
    length of 6 cm, and a width of 8.5 cm.   7 cm

Alternative Assessment

Have pairs of students work together to complete
Exercises 8–19. Have partners alternate roles of
making a table and graphing the equation.

TEKS ★ **TAKS** **Resources**

• TAKS Strategies, p. 523
• TAKS Tune Up, pp. 527–529

TAKS Tune-Up Kit
• TAKS Daily Review Transparencies
• TAKS Review and Preparation Workbook
• TAKS Strategies with Transparencies
• Texas Progress Monitoring Assessments

---

4. Assess & Reteach

PowerPoint
Lesson Quiz

Make a table of values. Then
graph each equation.

1. $y = x^2 + 1$ **2.** $y = 5|x|$

Reteaching 10-4   Graphing Nonlinear Rela... **L2**

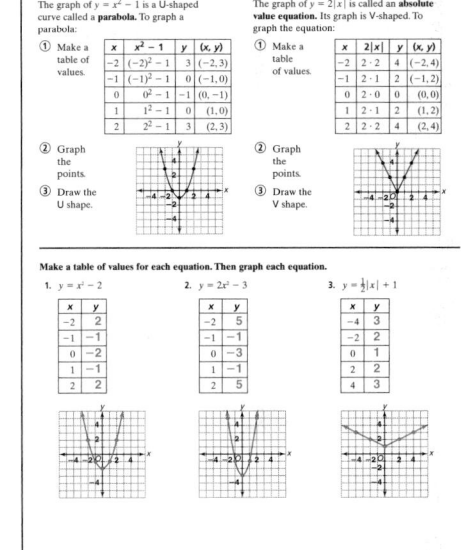

Enrichment 10-4   Graphing Nonlinear Rela... **L4**

507

Vocabulary Builder

High-Use Academic Words

In this feature, students become familiar with the definitions and uses of words that are not strictly mathematical terms but do occur frequently in their texts.

Guided Instruction

Explain to students that some words have multiple meanings, some of which apply to math and others that do not. Have volunteers read each word and its definition aloud. Then ask questions, such as:

- *What is another way to say "Make a diagram using the following coordinates."?* Draw a diagram using the following coordinates.
- *How do we use* predict *when graphing lines?* We can use the slope to *predict* where other points will fall on the line.
- *How can you use* compare *to describe two lines on a graph?* You can *compare* the slopes to see which is greater.

Differentiated Instruction

Advanced Learners **L4**
Have students create their own math problems using the vocabulary words. Then have them trade problems with a partner and solve.

TEKS ★ **TAKS Resources**

Dana Center TEKS Toolkit Clarifying Activities (7.14)(A)
Visit: PHSchool.com
Web Code: arq-9045

508

Vocabulary Builder

TEKS ★ **TAKS**
(7.14)(A) To communicate mathematical ideas using language **TAKS** Obj. 6

High-Use Academic Words

High-use academic words are words that you will see often in textbooks and on tests. These words are not math vocabulary terms, but knowing them will help you to succeed in mathematics.

Direction Words

Some words tell what to do in a problem. I need to understand what these words are asking so that I give the correct answer.

Word	Meaning
Represent	To replace with other words or symbols
Predict	To say in advance the outcomes or effects
Compare	To say how two things are similar or different

Exercises

1–3. Check students' work.
1. Draw a picture to represent the weather outside today.

2. Predict the weather tomorrow.

3. Compare the weather today with the weather six months ago.

4. A puppy weighed about 24 lb. She then gained about 12 lb per month, for x months. Which equation represents her growth? **B**

    Ⓐ $y = 24x + 12$ Ⓑ $y = 12x + 24$ Ⓒ $y = 24x - 12$ Ⓓ $y = 12x - 24$

5. Use the graph at the right. Predict the value of y when x is 10. **800**

6. Compare the slope of the line that goes through $(0, 0)$ and $(5, 2)$ with the slope of the line that goes through $(1, 1)$ and $(2, 5)$. Which slope is greater? See above right.

7. **Word Knowledge** Think about the word *conclude*.
   a. Choose the letter for how well you know the word. 7a–c. Check students' work.
      A. I know its meaning.
      B. I've seen it, but I don't know its meaning.
      C. I don't know it.
   b. **Research** Look up and write the definition of *conclude*.
   c. Use the word *conclude* in a sentence involving mathematics.

6. The slope of the line through $(0, 0)$ and $(5, 2)$ is $\frac{2}{5}$. The slope of the line through $(1, 1)$ and $(2, 5)$ is 4, so this is the greater slope.

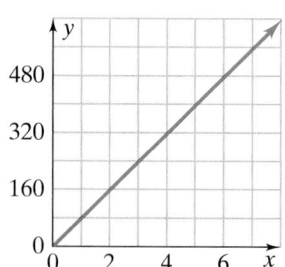

Slides, Flips, and Turns

To change the position of a geometric figure, you can use slides, flips, and turns.

TEKS ★ **TAKS**

(7.14)(A) To communicate mathematical ideas using graphical models **TAKS** Obj. 6

Prepares for **TEKS (7.7)(B)** To graph reflections across the horizontal or vertical axis and to graph translations on a coordinate plane

A *slide* moves a figure so that every point moves the same direction and the same distance.

A *flip* reflects a figure over a line.

A *turn* rotates a figure around a point.

4. Answers may vary. Sample: By flipping a figure twice, you have moved it to a new position, which is a slide.

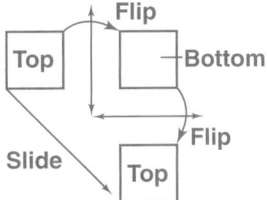

Describe each transformation as a *slide*, *flip*, or *turn*.

1.
   turn

2.
   slide

3.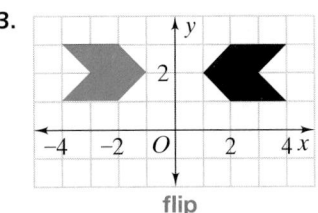
   flip

4. **Writing in Math** Describe how two flips can have the same effect as one slide. Include a drawing to illustrate your example. See above.

5. **Open-Ended** Give an example that involves a slide, a flip, or a turn. Check students' work.

Activity Lab

Slides, Flips, and Turns

Students investigate the transformation of figures. They begin here to explore translations (slides), reflections (flips), and rotations (turns).

Guided Instruction

Explain that figures can change position—move, or *transform*. To identify the three kinds of rigid motion in the transformations presented, draw two congruent irregular figures on the board in different positions (perhaps rotated). Label the vertices (corners) of each. Have students identify the corresponding vertices.

Guide students to see the distinction between *slides, flips,* and *turns* as you discuss the transformations. Provide examples on the board. Ask: *Are transformed figures congruent with the original figures? Explain.* Yes; the figures change in position and orientation only and not in their size and shape.

Exercises

Have students work on the Exercises. When they have finished, they may discuss their answers with a partner and correct their work, if necessary.

Alternative Method

Have student pairs work on the Exercises. Provide pattern blocks to explore transformations. Encourage them to use these manipulatives to model the movements of the figures.

TEKS ★ TAKS Resources

- Activity Lab 10-5: Translations
- pattern blocks

Dana Center TEKS Toolkit Clarifying Activities (7.14)(A)
Visit: PHSchool.com
Web Code: arq-9045

10-5

TEKS ★ TAKS

(7.7)(B) To graph translations on a coordinate plane TAKS **Obj. 3**

(7.7)(A) To locate and name points on a coordinated plane using ordered pairs of integers TAKS **Obj. 3**

Dana Center TEKS Toolkit Clarifying Activities (7.7)(B), (7.7)(A)
Visit: PHSchool.com
Web Code: arq-9045

TEKS Math Background

A *translation* moves each point in a figure the same distance and direction. The *image* of the original figure is the figure you get after a translation. The image does not change in its size or shape—it is a copy of the original figure that has simply moved. Use *prime notation* to identify an image point. Read *A'* as "A prime." A translation that moves each point in a figure 1 unit right and 2 units up can be expressed as

$(x, y) \rightarrow (x + 1, y + 2)$. So, point $B(3, -5)$ becomes the image point $B'(3 + 1, -5 + 2)$, or $B'(4, -3)$.

More Math Background: p. 484D

Lesson Planning and Resources

See p. 484E for a list of the resources that support this lesson.

PowerPoint
Bell Ringer Practice

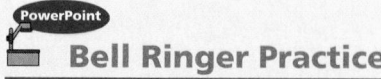

✓ Check Skills You'll Need
Use student page, transparency, or PowerPoint.

TAKS **Daily Review 79**
Use transparency.

10-5 Translations

TEKS ★ TAKS
- **(7.7)(B)** To graph graph translations on a coordinate plane TAKS **Obj. 3**
- **(7.7)(A)** To locate and name points on a coordinate plane using ordered pairs of integers TAKS **Obj. 3**

🔊 **New Vocabulary** transformation, translation, image, prime notation

✓ Check Skills You'll Need

1. Vocabulary Review
Name the *x-coordinate* and the *y-coordinate* of point $A(2, -5)$.
1–5. See back of book. Graph each point on the same coordinate plane.

2. $E(3, 1)$

3. $R(1, 0)$

4. $G(-3, -1)$

5. $S(2, -2)$

GO for Help
Lesson 10-1

Why Learn This?

Patterns like the one at the right use translations. You can describe translations mathematically by graphing in a coordinate plane.

A **transformation** is a change in the position, shape, or size of a figure. Three types of transformations that change only the position are slides, flips, and turns. A slide is also known as a translation. A **translation** is a transformation that moves each point of a figure the same distance and in the same direction.

The result of a transformation is the **image** of the original. **Prime notation** is the way to name an image point. A' is read as "*A* prime."

★ TAKS Tip
Graphing helps you visualize a translation.

EXAMPLE   Translating a Point

1 TAKS **Multiple Choice** Translate point $F(4, 1)$ left 3 units and up 2 units. What are the coordinates of the image F'?

  Ⓐ $(1, -1)$ Ⓑ $(1, 3)$ Ⓒ $(7, -1)$ Ⓓ $(7, 3)$

Locate point F at $(4, 1)$.

From point F, move 3 units left and 2 units up. Graph the image point F'.

The coordinates of F' are $(1, 3)$. The answer is B.

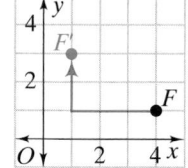

✓ Quick Check

1. Translate point $G(-4, 1)$ right 1 unit and down 4 units. What are the coordinates of the image G'? $(-3, -3)$

To show a translation, you can use arrow notation. For the translation of F to F' in Example 1, you write $F(4, 1) \rightarrow F'(1, 3)$.

Differentiated Instruction **Solutions for All Learners**

Special Needs L1
Pair students who have difficulty drawing on the grid with students who have facility. One can draw while the other writes the arrow notation to show the translation.

learning style: visual

Below Level L2
Have students draw horizontal and vertical arrows along their graphs to show the horizontal and vertical translations for each point.

learning style: visual

Vocabulary Tip

A vertex is the point of intersection of two sides of a figure.

To translate a geometric figure, first translate each vertex of the figure. Then connect the image points. When a geometric figure is translated, the image is congruent to the original figure.

EXAMPLE Translating a Figure

❷ The vertices of △ABC are A(−4, 3), B(−1, 4), and C(−3, 1). Translate △ABC right 2 units and down 4 units. Use arrow notation to describe the translation.

Graph and label vertices A, B, and C. Draw △ABC.

From each vertex, move right 2 units and down 4 units, and then draw an image point.

Label A′, B′, and C′. Draw △A′B′C′.

Use arrow notation:

A(−4, 3), B(−1, 4), C(−3, 1) → A′(−2, −1), B′(1, 0), C′(−1, −3)

✓ **Quick Check**

2. Graph △ABC from Example 2. Translate it left 3 units and up 1 unit. Use arrow notation to describe the translation. **See back of book.**

You can also use arrow notation to write a rule for a translation.

EXAMPLE Writing a Rule for a Translation

❸ **Animation** Computer animators use translations to move objects to new positions on the computer screen. Write a rule for the translation of spaceship A that a computer could apply to the other spaceships.

The horizontal change from A to A′ is 6 units right, so $x \rightarrow x + 6$.

The vertical change from A to A′ is 3 units down, so $y \rightarrow y - 3$.

The rule for the translation is $(x, y) \rightarrow (x + 6, y - 3)$.

Check Apply the rule to point B.
$(x, y) \rightarrow (x + 6, y - 3)$

$B(-4, 1) \rightarrow B'(-4 + 6, 1 - 3) = B'(2, -2)$ ✔ The answer checks.

✓ **Quick Check**

3. Write a rule for the translation of spaceship A to (4, 3).
$(x, y) \rightarrow (x + 6, y + 1)$

10-5 Translations **511**

Activity Lab

Use before the lesson.
Student Edition Activity Lab 10-5a, Slides, Flips, and Turns, p. 509

 Teaching Resources
Activity Lab 10-5: Translations

Guided Instruction

Example 2
Have students shade each vertex a different color. Have them use the same color to trace the path of translation.

PowerPoint
Additional Examples

❶ Translate point A(−3, −1) left 2 units and up 5 units. What are the coordinates of image A′? (−5, 4)

❷ The vertices of △ABC are A(−4, −3), B(−3, 1), C(−1, −2). Graph △ABC and translate it right 5 and down 2. Use arrow notation to show the translation. **See back of book.**

❸ Write a rule for the translation. $(x, y) \rightarrow (x + 3, y - 2)$

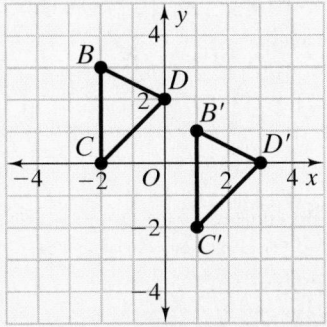

Teaching Resources
• Daily Notetaking Guide 10-5 **L3**
• Adapted Notetaking 10-5 **L1**

Closure

• *What is a transformation?* a change of the position, shape, or size of a figure
• *What is a translation?* a transformation that moves each point in a figure the same distance and same direction

---

Advanced Learners **L4**
Have students find how the translation rule for moving an image back to the original relates to the original rule. **The rules are opposites.**

English Language Learners **ELL**
Help students make a connection between the translations in this lesson to translations of language. The translated images only change location, not shape. Translated words change language, not meaning.

Pre-AP™

learning style: verbal

3. Practice

Assignment Guide

Check Your Understanding
Go over Exercises 1–4 in class before assigning the Homework Exercises.

Homework Exercises
A Practice by Example   5–16
B Apply Your Skills   17–26
C Challenge   27
TEKS ★ TAKS Tune-Up and
   Mixed Review   28–33

Homework Quick Check
To check students' understanding of key skills and concepts, go over Exercises 12, 16, 18, 22, and 26.

✓ Check Your Understanding

3. $P(-3, -3) \rightarrow P'(1, 1)$
    $Q(-1, -1) \rightarrow Q'(3, 3)$
    $R(-1, -3) \rightarrow R'(3, 1)$

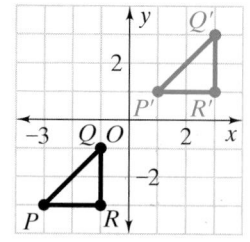

1. **Vocabulary** A translation is a type of ? . **transformation**

2. **Mental Math** Translate the origin $(0, 0)$ left 3 units and up 2 units. What are the coordinates of the image? **(−3, 2)**

For Exercises 3–4, use the graph at the left.

3. Use arrow notation to show the translation. **See left.**
    $P(\blacksquare, \blacksquare), Q(\blacksquare, \blacksquare), R(\blacksquare, \blacksquare) \rightarrow P'(\blacksquare, \blacksquare), Q'(\blacksquare, \blacksquare), R'(\blacksquare, \blacksquare)$

4. Use words to describe the translation. Each point moves ? 4 units and ? 4 units. **right; up**

Homework Exercises

For more exercises, see Extra Skills and Word Problems.

GO for Help

For Exercises	See Examples
5–9	1
10–14	2
15–16	3

Ⓐ **Translate each point left 2 units and down 5 units. Write the coordinates of the image point.**

5. $(3, 3)$ $(1, -2)$
6. $(0, 0)$ $(-2, -5)$
7. $(-3, 2)$ $(-5, -3)$
8. $(-6, -1)$ $(-8, -6)$
9. $(6, -1)$ $(4, -6)$

Graph each translation of $\triangle ABC$. Use arrow notation to show the translation. **10–14. See margin.**

10. left 4 units
11. up 2 units
12. right 6 units, up 1 unit
13. down 2 units
14. left 3 units, up 3 units

Write a rule for the translation shown in each graph.

15.
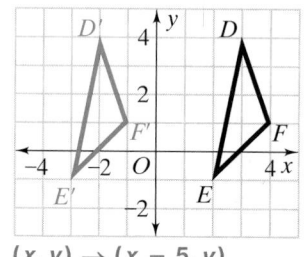
$(x, y) \rightarrow (x - 5, y)$

16.
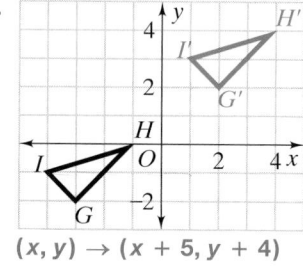
$(x, y) \rightarrow (x + 5, y + 4)$

17. $(x, y) \rightarrow (x + 2, y - 4);$
     $(x, y) \rightarrow (x + 3, y)$

Ⓑ GPS 17. **Guided Problem Solving** Refer to the graph at the right. A graphics animator wants a plane to land on the runway and then move forward. Write two translations to complete the tasks.
   ● What are the plane's coordinates? **See left.**
   ● What are the runway's coordinates?
   ● What translation will move the plane horizontally?

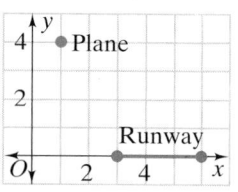

10–14. See back of book.
18–22. See back of book.
26. See back of book.

Graph each point and its image. Use words to describe the translation.
18–21. See margin.

18. $M(3, 5) \rightarrow M'(6, 4)$

19. $G(-1, 6) \rightarrow G'(3, 7)$

20. $H(-2, -5) \rightarrow H'(-1, -3)$

21. $J(4, 0) \rightarrow J'(3, 4)$

22. **Aviation** Three airplanes are flying in a **GPS** triangular formation. After 1 min, airplane P moves to P'. Give the new coordinates of each airplane and write a rule to describe the direction that the airplanes move.
See margin.

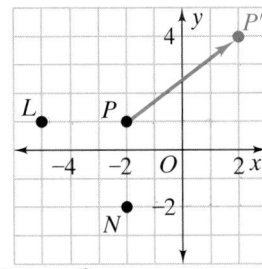

Write a rule for the translation described.

23. right 3 units and down 1 unit $(x, y) \rightarrow (x + 3, y - 1)$

24. right 4 units and up 1 unit $(x, y) \rightarrow (x + 4, y + 1)$

25. left 1 unit and up 4 units $(x, y) \rightarrow (x - 1, y + 4)$

26. **Writing in Math** Why is it helpful to describe a translation by stating the horizontal change first? See margin.

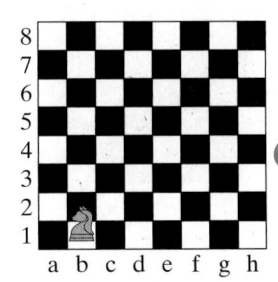

C 27. **Challenge** Translations are used to move pieces on a chess board. A knight moves in an L shape: two vertical spaces and one horizontal space, or two horizontal spaces and one vertical space. What series of translations will move the knight from b1 to h7?
Answers may vary. Sample: up 2, right 1; right 2, up 1; up 2, right 1; right 2, up 1

TEKS ★ TAKS Tune-Up and Mixed Review

TAKS Objective 3
TEKS (7.7)(B)

28. If the quadrilateral shown at the right is translated 3 units to the left and 4 units down, what will be the new coordinates of point A? C

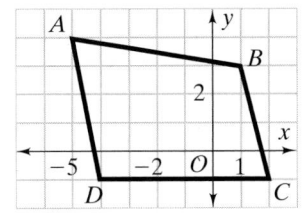

Ⓐ $(-2, 0)$ Ⓒ $(-8, 0)$
Ⓑ $(-5, 4)$ Ⓓ $(-8, 8)$

TAKS Objective 2
TEKS (7.5)(B)

29. A container of juice holds 64 ounces. Which equation shows the remaining amount of juice j after you drink d ounces? G

Ⓕ $\dfrac{64}{d} = j$ Ⓖ $64 - d = j$ Ⓗ $64 + d = j$ Ⓙ $64d = j$

TAKS Objective 1
TEKS (7.2)(G)

30. Jaleel spent $39.95 on a pair of shoes. The sales tax was 8.5%. About how much did Jaleel pay for the shoes, including tax? B

Ⓐ Less than $42   Ⓒ Between $45 and $48
Ⓑ Between $42 and $45   Ⓓ More than $48

GO for Help **Lesson 10-2**   (Algebra) **Find three solutions of each equation.**

31. $y = 4x - 2$
(−1, −6); (0, −2); (1, 2)

32. $y = -3x - 6$
(−1, −3); (0, −6); (1, −9)

33. $y = 5x + 4$
(−1, −1); (0, 4); (1, 9)

1. Graph $K(-1, 4)$ and translate it right 2 units and down 3 units. Write a rule to describe the translation.

$K'(1, 1)$; $(x, y) \rightarrow (x + 2, y - 3)$

2. Translate point $M(3, -4)$ left 5 units and down 2 units. What are the coordinates of image M'? $M'(-2, -6)$

3. A figure is translated to the right 3 units and up 6 units. Write the general rule to show how to find the image.
$(x, y) \rightarrow (x + 3, y + 6)$

Enrichment 10-5 L4

Reteaching 10-5 Tran L2
Movements of figures on a plane are called **transformations**. A translation, or slide, moves all points the same distance and direction.

The translation $(x, y) \rightarrow (x + 4, y - 1)$ moves *each* point to the right 4 units and down 1 unit.

$A(-3, 1)$ moves to $(-3 + 4, 1 - 1)$, where point $A'(1, 0)$ is its **image**.

The square $ABCD$ moves to its image square $A'B'C'D'$.

Complete the following for the figure above.
1. $B(-5, 5) \rightarrow B'(\underline{-1}, \underline{4})$
2. $C(-1, 7) \rightarrow C'(\underline{3}, \underline{6})$
3. $D(\underline{1}, \underline{3}) \rightarrow D'(\underline{5}, \underline{2})$

Graph each translation of figure *PRST*.
4. right 2 units   5. left 2 units, down 2 units   6. right 1 unit, up 3 units

Complete the rule for each translation.
7. right 3 units, up 1 unit   8. left 4 units, up 5 units   9. left 1 unit, down 9 units
$(x, y) \rightarrow (x + 3, y + 1)$ $(x, y) \rightarrow (x - 4, y + 5)$ $(x, y) \rightarrow (x - 1, y - 9)$

Write a rule for the translation.
10. left 1 unit, down 3 units   11. right 1 unit, up 2 units   12. left 3 units, up 2 units
$(x, y) \rightarrow (x - 1, y - 3)$ $(x, y) \rightarrow (x + 1, y + 2)$ $(x, y) \rightarrow (x - 3, y + 2)$

Alternative Assessment

Each student in a pair draws a translation that gives the coordinates of the original and image vertices.

TEKS ★ TAKS Resources
• TAKS Strategies, p. 523
• TAKS Tune Up, pp. 527–529

(TAKS) **Tune-Up Kit**
• TAKS Daily Review Transparencies
• TAKS Review and Preparation Workbook
• TAKS Strategies with Transparencies
• Texas Progress Monitoring Assessments

513

TEKS ★ _TAKS_

(7.7)(B) To graph reflections across the horizontal or vertical axis _TAKS_ **Obj. 3**
Also supports (7.7)(A) _TAKS_ **Obj. 3**

Dana Center TEKS Toolkit Clarifying Activities (7.7)(B), (7.7)(A)
Visit: PHSchool.com
Web Code: arq-9045

TEKS Math Background

A figure has _line symmetry_ when one or more sides of the figure are mirror images of the other. A _line of symmetry_ divides a figure into two mirror images. A _reflection_ is a transformation of an entire figure that is flipped over a line called the _line of reflection_.

More Math Background: p. 484D

Lesson Planning and Resources

See p. 484E for a list of the resources that support this lesson.

Bell Ringer Practice

✓ **Check Skills You'll Need**
Use student page, transparency, or PowerPoint.

TAKS **Daily Review 80**
Use transparency.

✓ **Check Skills You'll Need**

1. Vocabulary Review When you translate a point, what do you call the new point?

Translate point _P_(1, 3) as described. Write the coordinates of _P′_.

2. 4 units left (−3, 3)

3. 2 units up (1, 5)

4. 4 units left and 2 units up (−3, 5)

GO for Help
Lesson 10-5

TEKS ★ _TAKS_
- (7.7)(B) To graph reflections across the horizontal or vertical axis _TAKS_ **Obj. 3**
- (7.7)(A) To locate and name points on a coordinate plane using ordered pairs of integers _TAKS_ **Obj. 3**

🔊 **New Vocabulary** line symmetry, line of symmetry, reflection, line of reflection

Why Learn This?

Symmetry is often seen in nature. A snowflake forms when water vapor freezes. Most snowflakes have line symmetry and rotational symmetry. The red line drawn on the snowflake divides it in half, and the two halves are mirror images of each other.

A figure has **line symmetry** if a line, called a **line of symmetry,** can be drawn through the figure so that one side is a mirror image of the other. If you fold along the red line of symmetry drawn on the snowflake, the right side of the snowflake fits exactly onto the left side.

EXAMPLE **Identifying Lines of Symmetry**

1 _TAKS_ **Griddable Item** How many lines of symmetry does the flower have?

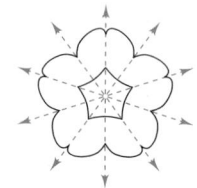

The flower has 5 lines of symmetry, so grid the answer 5 as shown.

✓ **Quick Check**

1. **Art** Sketch the mask and draw the line(s) of symmetry. Does the mask have line symmetry?
   See back of book.

Differentiated Instruction Solutions for All Learners

Special Needs L1
Pair students who have difficulty drawing a reflection with a partner who can draw. After their partner draws, have them identify and check the axis of the drawn reflected image and its coordinates.

learning style: visual

Below Level L2
Have students reflect a letter such as Z or R in a mirror. Elicit the fact that the image is reversed.

learning style: tactile

A **reflection** is a transformation that flips a figure over a line called a **line of reflection**.

TAKS Tip

When a point is reflected over the *x*-axis, the *y*-coordinate changes. When a point is reflected over the *y*-axis, the *x*-coordinate changes.

EXAMPLE Reflecting a Point

2 Graph the point $A(3, -2)$ and its reflection over the indicated axis. Write the coordinates of the image.

a. *y*-axis

b. *x*-axis

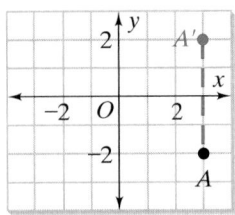

A is 3 units to the right of the *y*-axis, so *A'* is 3 units to the left of the *y*-axis.

A' has coordinates $(-3, -2)$.

A is 2 units below the *x*-axis, so *A'* is 2 units above the *x*-axis.

A' has coordinates $(3, 2)$.

✓ Quick Check

2. Graph the point $P(-4, 1)$ and its reflection over the indicated axis. Write the coordinates of the image. **2a–b. See back of book.**

   a. *y*-axis
   b. *x*-axis

When a figure is reflected, the image is congruent to the original figure.

EXAMPLE Reflecting a Figure

3 Draw the image of $\triangle ABC$ reflected over the *y*-axis. Use arrow notation to describe the original triangle and its image.

A is 1 unit to the left of the *y*-axis, so *A'* is 1 unit to the right of the *y*-axis.

B is 4 units to the left of the *y*-axis, so *B'* is 4 units to the right of the *y*-axis.

C is 2 units to the left of the *y*-axis, so *C'* is 2 units to the right of the *y*-axis.

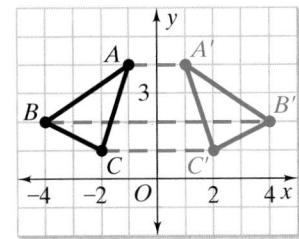

Draw $\triangle A'B'C'$ and use arrow notation:
$A(-1, 4), B(-4, 2), C(-2, 1) \rightarrow A'(1, 4), B'(4, 2), C'(2, 1)$

✓ Quick Check

3. Graph $\triangle ABC$ and its reflection over the *x*-axis. Use arrow notation to describe the original triangle and its image. See back of book.

10-6 Line Symmetry and Reflections **515**

515

Assignment Guide

Check Your Understanding
Go over Exercises 1–5 in class before assigning the Homework Exercises.

Homework Exercises
A Practice by Example   6–18
B Apply Your Skills   19–28
C Challenge   29
TEKS ★ TAKS Tune-Up and
       Mixed Review   30–35

Homework Quick Check
To check students' understanding of key skills and concepts, go over Exercises 9, 16, 21, 25, and 27.

Differentiated Instruction Resources

Check Your Understanding

1. A line of reflection produces a mirror image of the figure, and a line of symmetry divides a figure into mirror images.

3. $A(-1, 1)$, $B(-3, 4)$, $C(-5, -2) \rightarrow A'(1, 1)$, $B'(3, 4)$, $C'(5, -2)$

1. **Vocabulary** How is a line of reflection like a line of symmetry?

2. How many lines of symmetry does an equilateral triangle have?   **three**

Use the graph at the right.

3. Use arrow notation to show the reflection.   **See left.**

$A(\blacksquare, \blacksquare)$, $B(\blacksquare, \blacksquare)$, $C(\blacksquare, \blacksquare) \rightarrow$
$A'(\blacksquare, \blacksquare)$, $B'(\blacksquare, \blacksquare)$, $C'(\blacksquare, \blacksquare)$

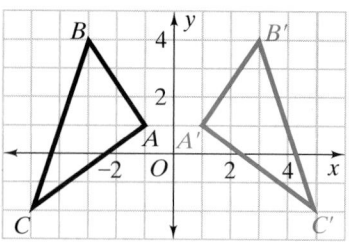

4. $\triangle ABC$ is reflected over the __?__ -axis.   **y-axis**

5. Compare the coordinate pair of each vertex of $\triangle ABC$ and its image.   **The x-coordinates are opposites; the y-coordinates are the same.**

Homework Exercises

For more exercises, see Extra Skills and Word Problems.

GO for Help

For Exercises	See Examples
6–9	1
10–15	2
16–18	3

Ⓐ **Trace each figure and draw the line(s) of symmetry. If there are no lines of symmetry, write *none*.**   **6–9 See margin.**

6.

7.

8.

9.

Graph each point and its reflection over the indicated axis. Write the coordinates of the image.   **10. (4, −2)   11. (1, 5)   12. (3, −2)**

10. $D(4, 2)$, x-axis   11. $F(-1, 5)$, y-axis   12. $G(-3, -2)$, y-axis

13. $H(2, -6)$, x-axis   14. $J(0, 3)$, x-axis   15. $K(-4, 0)$, y-axis
    (2, 6)   **(0, −3)**   **(4, 0)**

The vertices of a triangle are given. Graph the triangle, its reflection over the x-axis, and its reflection over the y-axis.   **16–17. See margin.**

16. $P(1, 6)$, $Q(6, 2)$, $R(2, 0)$ 17. $S(-5, 1)$, $T(-3, 5)$, $V(-3, 1)$

18. The vertices of rectangle $ABCD$ are $A(-3, 3)$, $B(-1, 3)$, $C(-1, -1)$, and $D(-3, -1)$. Use arrow notation to describe the original rectangle and its reflection over the y-axis. **See margin.**

Ⓑ **GPS** 19. **Guided Problem Solving** A figure is a parallelogram but not a rectangle. It has two lines of symmetry. What type of figure is it?
- *Act It Out* by drawing and cutting out several parallelograms.
- Check for symmetry by folding.   **rhombus**

6–9. See back of book.
16–18. See back of book.

Mental Math Without graphing, name the coordinates of the point's image after it is reflected over the *x*-axis and over the *y*-axis.

20. $(6, -1)$ **21.** $(-3, -4)$ **22.** $(-5, 8)$ **23.** $(7, 2)$
$(6, 1), (-6, -1)$ $(-3, 4), (3, -4)$ $(-5, -8), (5, 8)$ $(7, -2), (-7, 2)$

24. Geometry How many lines of symmetry does an isosceles right triangle have? **1**

25. <u>**Writing in Math**</u> $\triangle WXY$ has vertices $W(-4, -2)$, $X(4, 2)$, and **GPS** $Y(1, -4)$. Its image $\triangle W'X'Y'$ has vertices $W'(-4, 2)$, $X'(4, -2)$, and $Y'(1, 4)$. Over which axis is $\triangle WXY$ reflected? Explain. **Over the x-axis; the y-coordinates are opposite.**

26. Natural Science Give an example (other than a butterfly) of line symmetry seen in a plant or animal. Describe the line symmetry. **Check students' work.**

Use words and arrow notation to describe the transformation.
27–28. See left.

27.

28.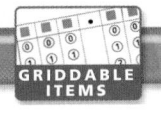

27. reflection over the *y*-axis; $(x, y) \rightarrow (-x, y)$

28. translation 5 units left and 3 units down; $(x, y) \rightarrow (x - 5, y - 3)$

C **29. Challenge** $L(0, 0)$, $M(0, 5)$, and $N(4, 0)$ are vertices of $\triangle LMN$. Graph $\triangle LMN$ in a coordinate plane. Reflect $\triangle LMN$ over the *x*-axis to form a larger triangle. Reflect the larger triangle over the *y*-axis to form a quadrilateral. What type of quadrilateral is formed? **See margin.**

  TEKS ★ **TAKS** **Tune-Up and Mixed Review**

TAKS Objective 3 **TEKS (7.7)(B)**

30. $\triangle BCD$ has vertices $B(4, 3)$, $C(6, 3)$, and $D(1, 4)$. What is the *x*-coordinate of B' after $\triangle BCD$ is reflected over the *x*-axis? **4**

TAKS Objective 5 **TEKS (7.12)(A)**

31. A farmer has eight cows. Two are 3 years old, two are 5 years old, one is 6 years old, one is 7 years old, and one is 9 years old. The mean age of the farmer's eight cows is 5 years. What is the age in years of the remaining cow? **2**

TAKS Objective 3 **TEKS (7.6)(A)**

32. If $\angle B$ and $\angle C$ are complementary, and the measure of $\angle B$ is $27°$, what is the measure of $\angle C$ in degrees? **63**

GO for Help **Lesson 9-3** (**Algebra**) **Find the first four terms in each sequence.** 33–35. See margin.

33. $3n + 2$ **34.** $-n + 4$ **35.** $-2n - 1$

29. See back of book.
33–35. See back of book.

TEKS ★ **TAKS** **Resources**

• TAKS Strategies, p. 523
• TAKS Tune Up, pp. 527–529
TAKS Tune-Up Kit
• TAKS Daily Review Transparencies
• TAKS Review and Preparation Workbook
• TAKS Strategies with Transparencies
• Texas Progress Monitoring Assessments

---

 4. Assess & Reteach

PowerPoint
Lesson Quiz

1. Draw the lines of symmetry of a regular hexagon.

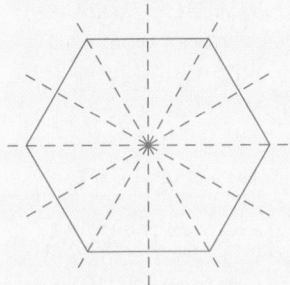

2. $\triangle ABC$ has vertices at $A(1, 4)$, $B(4, 3)$, and $C(3, 1)$. Find the vertices of its reflection over the *y*-axis.
$A'(-1, 4)$, $B'(-4, 3)$, $C'(-3, 1)$

Alternative Assessment

Without marking the lines of symmetry, each student in a pair draws four figures: one with no lines of symmetry, one with one line of symmetry, one with two lines of symmetry, and one with more than two lines of symmetry. Partners exchange drawings and mark the lines of symmetry on each other's figures.

517

Exploring Tessellations

In this feature, students learn about a special kind of translation called a tessellation, which is a repeating pattern of figures with no overlaps or gaps.

Guided Instruction

Define *tessellation* for students and discuss the differences and similarities between tessellations and translations. Point out that all tessellations are translations, but not all translations are tessellations. If you have it available, display some famous tessellations such as the artwork of M. C. Escher.

Activity

Work on the activity as a class. Have each student draw his or her own figure as you display one on the board or on a transparency.

Checkpoint Quiz

Use this Checkpoint Quiz to check students' understanding of the skills and concepts of Lessons 10-4 through 10-6.

Resources

- All-in-One Teaching Resources Checkpoint Quiz 2
- Texas ExamView CD-ROM
- Success Tracker™ Online Intervention

1.

2.

Exploring Tessellations

A *tessellation* is a repeating pattern of figures that has no gaps or overlaps. Tessellations are made using transformations. An example of a tessellation is shown at the right.

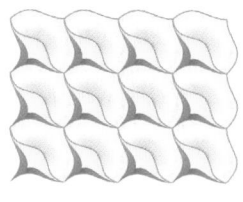

Use a square piece of cardboard.
1–5. Check students' work.

1. Draw a curve from one vertex of the square to a neighboring vertex, as shown at the right.

2. Cut along the curve you drew. Translate the cutout piece to the opposite side of the square, and tape it down.

3. Draw the same curve on the bottom and repeat the process.

4. Trace around your figure on a piece of paper. Carefully translate the figure to the right so that the edges touch.

5. After you have covered a row, translate your figure downward to start a new row. Continue tracing until you have covered the paper.

6. **Reasoning** Can you make a tessellation with your figure using reflections? Explain. **No; any pattern made by reflecting the figure will have gaps.**

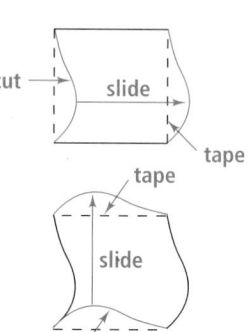

Checkpoint Quiz 2   **Lessons 10-4 through 10-6**

Graph each equation. 1–4. See margin.

1. $y = 3x^2$ 2. $y = |x| - 2$ 3. $y = 2x^2 + 3$ 4. $y = x - 1$

5. Is $(3, -5)$ a solution of $y = x^2 - 4$? Explain. **No; $3^2 - 4 \neq -5$.**

Translate each point right 3 units and up 7 units. Write the new coordinates.

6. $(-6, 2)$ **(-3, 9)**   7. $(9, -1)$ **(12, 6)**   8. $(0, -7)$ **(3, 0)**   9. $(-2, -3)$ **(1, 4)**

10. Which of the following digits have lines of symmetry: 2, 3, 6, 8? Draw the lines of symmetry. **See margin.**

3.

4.

10. See back of book.

Rotational Symmetry and Rotations

Check Skills You'll Need

1. Vocabulary Review
What is the measure of any *right angle*? 90°

Draw an angle for each measure. Then classify each angle as *acute, right, obtuse,* or *straight.* 2–5. See back of book.

2. 60°   **3.** 120°

4. 90°   **5.** 180°

 for Help
Lesson 7-2

Vocabulary Tip

Counterclockwise means the opposite of the direction in which a clock's hands move.

1a. Yes; it looks the same as you move each point to another point.

b. No; it does not match the original figure after any rotation of 180° or less.

c. Yes; it looks the same as the original when it is rotated 180°.

What You'll Learn

To identify rotational symmetry and to rotate a figure about a point

🔊 **New Vocabulary** rotation, center of rotation, rotational symmetry, angle of rotation

Why Learn This?

Some objects rotate, which means to move in a circular manner. When you ride a unicycle, the wheel rotates, and you move!

A **rotation** is a transformation that turns a figure about a fixed point called the **center of rotation.** You describe a rotation by its angle measure and its direction.

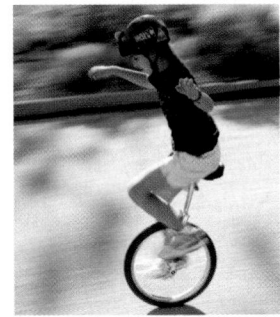

The direction of every rotation in this book is counterclockwise unless noted as clockwise. If a figure can be rotated 180° or less and match the original figure, it has **rotational symmetry.**

EXAMPLE   Identifying Rotational Symmetry

① **Windmills** Do the sails of the windmill have rotational symmetry? Use points *O*, *A*, *A'*, *A"*, and *A'''* to explain.

Yes, the sails have rotational symmetry. The center of rotation is *O*.

If *A* is rotated 90°, the image is *A'*.
If *A* is rotated 180°, the image is *A"*.
If *A* is rotated 270°, the image is *A'''*.
If *A* is rotated 360°, it returns to its original position.

✔ Quick Check

1. Does the figure have rotational symmetry? Explain.   1a–c. See left.

a.   b.   c.

Objectives

To identify rotational symmetry and to rotate a figure about a point

Examples
1 Identifying Rotational Symmetry
2 Finding an Angle of Rotation
3 Rotating a Figure

Math Background

A *rotation* is a transformation that turns a figure about a fixed point called a *center of rotation*. If a figure can be rotated 180° or less and fit exactly on top of the original figure, then that figure has *rotational symmetry*. The angle of rotation is measured in a counterclockwise direction.

More Math Background: p. 484D

Lesson Planning and Resources

See p. 484E for a list of the resources that support this lesson.

Bell Ringer Practice

✔ **Check Skills You'll Need**
Use student page, transparency, or PowerPoint.

Daily Review 81
Use transparency.

Differentiated Instruction   Solutions for All Learners

Special Needs L1
Pair students who have difficulty graphing the images with a partner who can draw them. Provide tracing paper to the student who has difficulty. Have them trace the original and rotated image to check the accuracy of the transformation.

learning style: visual

Below Level L2
Review angle measures and the meaning of counterclockwise. Then have students rotate a point such as (3, 4) about the origin for 90°, 180°, and 270°.

learning style: visual

Activity Lab

Use before the lesson.

All in One Teaching Resources

Activity Lab 10-7: Rotational Symmetry and Rotations

Guided Instruction

Example 1
Discuss the meaning of *rotate*. Show things that rotate (fan blades, hands on a clock) and elicit suggestions from students.

Example 3
Have students trace the figure on their own papers. They can then rotate their figures by holding their pencil tips on point *O*.

PowerPoint

Additional Examples

① Do the letters "H" and "N" have rotational symmetry? Explain. **Yes, both letters look the same when rotated 180°.**

② Does ☀ have rotational symmetry? If it does, find the angle of rotation. **yes, 45°**

③ Choose a nonsymmetrical letter of the alphabet, such as P, and use it to illustrate a rotation of 90°, 180°, and 270° about its center.

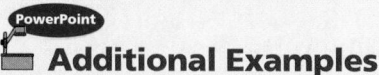

90°   180°   270°

All in One Teaching Resources
- Daily Notetaking Guide 10-7 **L3**
- Adapted Notetaking 10-7 **L1**

Closure

- *What is a rotation?* A transformation that turns a figure around a fixed point is called a rotation.
- Define *rotational symmetry*. A figure with rotational symmetry can be rotated 180° or less and match the original figure.

The number of degrees a figure rotates is the **angle of rotation**. When a figure has rotational symmetry, the angle of rotation is the angle measure the figure must rotate to match the original figure.

EXAMPLE **Finding an Angle of Rotation**

② The wheel below has rotational symmetry. Find the angle of rotation.

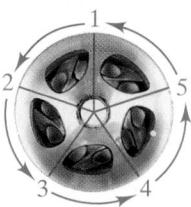

The wheel matches itself in 5 positions. The angle of rotation is 360° ÷ 5, or 72°.

✓ Quick Check

2. Find the angle of rotation of the flower at the left. **60°**

You can rotate a figure in a coordinate plane. Use the center of rotation and an angle.

EXAMPLE **Rotating a Figure**

③ Graph rectangle *ABCD* with vertices *A*(0, 0), *B*(0, 2), *C*(4, 2), and *D*(4, 0). Rotate the rectangle as described. Write the coordinates of the vertices of the image.

a. 180° about point *A*

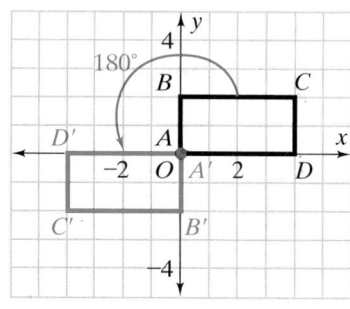

A′(0, 0), *B*′(0, −2), *C*′(−4, −2), and *D*′(−4, 0)

b. 90° about its center, (2, 1).

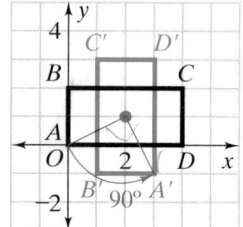

A′(3, −1), *B*′(1, −1), *C*′(1, 3), and *D*′(3, 3)

✓ Quick Check

See back of book.

3. Graph △*TRG* with vertices *T*(0, 0), *R*(3, 3), and *G*(5, 1). Rotate △*TRG* 180° about *T*. Write the coordinates of *T*′, *R*′, and *G*′.

Online active math

For: Transformations Activity
Use: Interactive Textbook, 10-7

Advanced Learners **L4**
What letters of the alphabet have *both* line symmetry and rotational symmetry? **H, I, O, N, S, X, Z**

English Language Learners **ELL**
Provide students with a paper square. Have them place the tip of their pencil in the center, and turn it 90 degrees. Ask: *Does it still look like a square?* **Yes.** Do it again several times. Let them know the square has rotational symmetry, and the pencil point was on the center of rotation.

learning style: tactile

Pre-AP™

Check Your Understanding

1. **Vocabulary** Name two types of symmetry.
   line symmetry and rotational symmetry
2. Name three types of transformations.
   translation, reflection, and rotation
3. Does the figure at the right have rotational symmetry? If so, find the angle of rotation.
   yes; 120°

Estimation Estimate the angle measure of the rotation of △RSO.

4.

270°

5.

90°

6.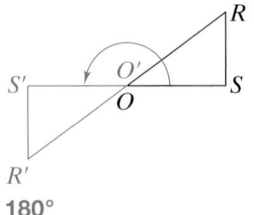

180°

Assignment Guide

Check Your Understanding
Go over Exercises 1–6 in class before assigning the Homework Exercises.

Homework Exercises
A Practice by Example   7–16
B Apply Your Skills   17–26
C Challenge   27
TEKS ★ TAKS Tune-Up and
     Mixed Review   28–33

Homework Quick Check
To check students' understanding of key skills and concepts, go over Exercises 11, 15, 23, 25, and 26.

Differentiated Instruction Resources

Homework Exercises

For more exercises, see Extra Skills and Word Problems.

GO for Help	
For Exercises	**See Examples**
7–9	1
10–12	2
13–16	3

7. No; it does not match the original figure after any rotation of 180° or less.

8. Yes; when the figure is rotated 180°, it looks the same.

9. Yes; the figure looks the same after being rotated 90°, 180°, or 270°.

A Does the figure have rotational symmetry? Explain.   7–9. See left.

7.

8.

9.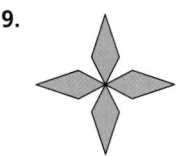

Each figure has rotational symmetry. Find the angle of rotation.

10.

90°

11.

180°

12.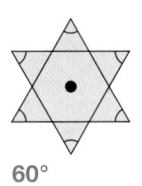

60°

Graph rectangle *PQRS* with vertices *P*(0, 0), *Q*(2, 0), *R*(2, 6), and *S*(0, 6). Rotate the rectangle as described. Write the new coordinates.
13–16. See margin.

13. 180° about point *P*
14. 90° about its center, (1, 3)
15. 180° about its center, (1, 3)
16. 270° about its center, (1, 3)

B GPS 17. **Guided Problem Solving** What is the clockwise angle of rotation of the hour hand on a clock as it moves from 4:00 to 5:00?   30°
   • To which number does the hour hand point at 4:00? At 5:00?
   • How many degrees does the hour hand rotate in a full circle?

Online lesson quiz, PHSchool.com, **Web Code:** ara-1007

13–16. See back of book.

Lesson Quiz

1. Which of the following math symbols have rotational symmetry?

   a. >   b. ÷   c. %
   b and c

2. Graph △XYZ with vertices of X(0, 0), Y(3, 4), and Z(4, 0). Then draw the three images formed by rotating the triangle 90°, 180°, and 270° about point X.

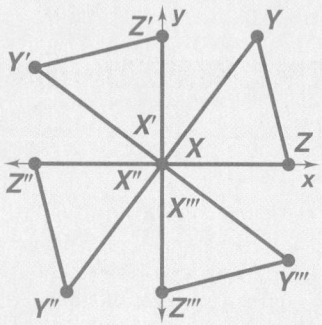

Alternative Assessment

Each student in a pair draws and cuts out two or three geometric figures. Partners exchange figures and determine whether they have rotational symmetry. On each figure that has rotational symmetry, students write the angle of rotation.

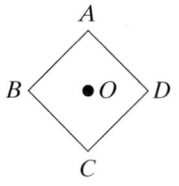

23a. 90°; 180°; 270°

b. Yes; the image stays the same after rotation.

Mental Math A triangle lies entirely in Quadrant I. In which quadrant will the triangle lie after each rotation about (0, 0)?

18. 90°   II   **19.** 180°   III   **20.** 270°   IV   **21.** 360°   I

22. Open-Ended Draw a capital letter of the alphabet that has rotational symmetry. Mark a point at the center of rotation.
Check students' work.

23. **a.** What rotation will move point A to point B? Point A to point C? Point A to point D?
   b. Does the square have rotational symmetry? Explain.
   23a–b. See left.

24. Clocks The second hand of a clock moves clockwise. It makes a full revolution once every minute. What is its clockwise angle of rotation after 20 seconds? After 45 seconds? **120°; 270°**

25. Writing in Math Describe an object in your classroom that has rotational symmetry. Explain how it shows rotational symmetry.
Check students' work.

26. The arrow notation given shows how the vertices of a triangle are moved. Name the type of transformation and describe it with words. $A(2, 4) \rightarrow A'(4, -4)$, $B(4, 4) \rightarrow B'(2, -4)$, and $C(3, 0) \rightarrow C'(3, 0)$ **Rotation; it has been rotated 180° around point C.**

C 27. Challenge Graph the point $E(-6, -2)$ and its three images after 90°, 180°, and 270° rotations about the origin. Connect the four points. What type of quadrilateral is formed? **See margin.**

TEKS ★ TAKS Tune-Up and Mixed Review

TAKS Objective 3
TEKS (7.7)(A)

28. If $\overline{MN}$ is translated 5 units to the right and 2 units up, what will be the coordinates of point M? **A**
   (A) $(1, 1)$ (C) $(-11, 1)$
   (B) $(7, 7)$ (D) $(11, -1)$

TAKS Objective 1
TEKS (7.2)(A)

29. Which expression does the model best represent? **F**
   (F) $1\frac{3}{4} \div \frac{1}{2}$ (H) $1.5 \div \frac{1}{2}$
   (G) $1\frac{3}{4} \times \frac{1}{2}$ (J) $7 \times 3\frac{1}{2}$

TAKS Objective 1
TEKS (7.2)(E)

30. What is the value of the expression $(4 + 2)^2 \times 2 + 9 \div 3$? **D**
   (A) 7   (B) 27   (C) 42   (D) 75

GO for Help   Lesson 7-3

Algebra Suppose the sides of a triangle have the given measures. Classify each triangle by its sides.

31. $4s, 4s, 4s$
equilateral

32. $2.2y, 1.5y, 2.2y$
isoceles

33. $3k, 4k, 5k$
right

TEKS ★ TAKS Resources

27. See back of book.

- TAKS Strategies, p. 523
- TAKS Tune Up, pp. 527–529

TAKS Tune-Up Kit
- TAKS Daily Review Transparencies
- TAKS Review and Preparation Workbook
- TAKS Strategies with Transparencies
- Texas Progress Monitoring Assessments

Answering the Question Asked

When answering a question, be sure to answer the question that is asked. Read the question carefully and identify the information you need to find. Eliminate answer choices that are not related to the question that is asked.

EXAMPLE

Point *M* is translated 3 units to the right and 2 units down.

What are the coordinates of *M'*?

A (4, 3)   C (4, −1)

B (−2, −1)   D (3, −2)

Choice A translates point *M* 3 units to the right and 2 units *up*. Choice B translates *M* 3 units to the *left* and 2 units down. Choice C translates *M* 3 units to the right and 2 units down. Choice D translates *M* 2 units to the right and *3 units* down. The correct answer is C.

Exercises

TAKS Objective 3
TEKS (7.7)(A)

1. Which line contains the ordered pair (−1, −3)? **D**

   A Line *a*

   B Line *b*

   C Line *c*

   D Line *d*

Chapter 10 Review

Vocabulary Review

Choose the correct term to complete each sentence.

1. A flip over a line is a (translation, reflection).   reflection

2. A rotation turns a figure about a fixed point called the (center of
   rotation, angle of rotation).   center of rotation

3. (Rotation, Slope) compares the vertical change, called the rise, to
   the horizontal change, called the run.   slope

4. The second number in a(n) (coordinate plane, ordered pair)
   is the y-coordinate.   ordered pair

5. If a graph of the solutions of an equation is a line, then the equation
   is a (linear equation, nonlinear equation).   linear equation

Go **Online**
PHSchool.com
For: Vocabulary Quiz
Web Code: arj-1051

Skills and Concepts   TEKS ★ (TAKS)

Lessons 10-1, 10-2

(7.7)(A) To locate and name
points on a coordinate plane
using ordered pairs of
integers (TAKS) **Obj. 3**

An **ordered pair** (x, y) gives the coordinates of a point. Any ordered
pair that makes an equation true is a solution of the equation. The
graph of an equation is the graph of coordinates that are solutions of
the equation.

**Graph each point on the same coordinate plane. Name the quadrant in
which each point lies.**   See margin for graph.

6. $A(1, -5)$ IV   7. $B(-3, -4)$ III   8. $C(-2, 3)$ II

Find three solutions of each equation.   9–12. Answers may vary. Samples
                                              are given.

9. $y = x + 3$ 10. $y = x - 5$
   $(0, 3), (-2, 1), (5, 8)$ $(0, -5), (5, 0), (-1, -6)$
11. $y = 2x + 1$ 12. $y = -x - 2$
   $(0, 1), (2, 5), (-3, -5)$ $(0, -2), (4, -6), (-3, 1)$

6–8. See back of book.
13–22. See back of book.

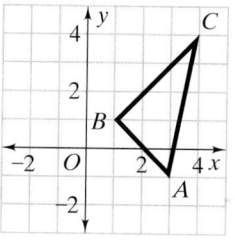
Lessons 10-3, 10-4

(7.4)(B) To graph data to demonstrate relationships in familiar concepts such as area and volume **TAKS** Obj. 2

(7.14)(A) To communicate mathematical ideas using graphical and algebraic models **TAKS** Obj. 6

Slope is a ratio that describes the steepness of a line.

$$\text{slope} = \frac{\text{rise}}{\text{run}}$$

A **nonlinear equation** is an equation with a graph that is not a straight line.

13–14. See margin.

Draw a line with the given slope through the given point.

13. $B(2, 4)$, slope $= 2$

14. $R(-1, 2)$, slope $= \frac{1}{3}$

Make a table of values for each equation. Use integer values of x from -3 to 3. Then graph the equation. 15–18. See margin.

15. $y = x^2 - 1$ 16. $y = |x| + 1$ 17. $y = 2x^2 - 2$ 18. $y = 4|x|$

Lessons 10-5, 10-6

(7.7)(B) To graph reflections across the horizontal or vertical axis and graph translations on a coordinate plane **TAKS** Obj. 3

(7.7)(A) To locate and name points on a coordinate plane using ordered pairs of integers **TAKS** Obj. 3

A **transformation** is the change of the position, shape, or size of a figure. A **translation** is a transformation that moves every point of a figure the same distance and in the same direction.

A figure has **line symmetry** when one side of the figure is a mirror image of the other side. A **reflection** is a transformation that flips a figure over a line.

Graph each transformation of $\triangle ABC$. Use arrow notation to show the translation. 19–22. See margin.

19. down 2 units

20. left 3 units

21. right 3 units and down 5 units

22. Graph $\triangle ABC$ from Exercises 19–21. Then graph its reflection over the x-axis. Use arrow notation to describe the transformation.

Lesson 10-7

• To identify rotational symmetry and to rotate a figure about a point

A **rotation** is a transformation that turns a figure about a fixed point.

Does each figure have rotational symmetry? If it does, find the angle of rotation.

23. yes; 90°

24. 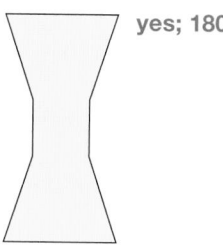 yes; 180°

Chapter 10 Test

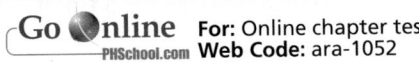 Go Online **For:** Online chapter test
PHSchool.com **Web Code:** ara-1052

Graph each point on the same coordinate plane.
1–4. See margin.

1. $A(1, 4)$
2. $B(-2, -1)$
3. $C(3, -2)$
4. $D(-3, 2)$

Graph each polygon. Use (0, 0) as one vertex and label all vertices. 5–6. See margin.

5. a square with side 4 units long

6. a rectangle with horizontal length 3 units and vertical length 5 units.

Determine whether each ordered pair is a solution of $y = -2x + 5$.

7. $(3, -5)$ no
8. $(2.5, 0)$ yes
9. $(4, -3)$ yes
10. $(0, 5)$ yes

Graph each linear equation. 11–14. See margin.

11. $y = x - 3$
12. $y = 3x + 1$
13. $y = -x + 2$
14. $y = 2x - 4$

Graph each pair of points. Determine the slope of the line through the points. 15. $-\frac{1}{5}$ 16. -3

15. $E(7, 1)$, $F(-3, 3)$
16. $G(-2, 6)$, $H(0, 0)$
17. $L(-4, 0)$, $M(0, 2)$ $\frac{1}{2}$
18. $S(8, 5)$, $T(1, -1)$ $\frac{6}{7}$

Draw a line with the given slope through the given point. 19–20. See margin.

19. $P(-2, -1)$, slope $\frac{1}{4}$
20. $R(2, 4)$, slope $-\frac{2}{3}$

Graph each equation for integer values of x from -3 to 3. 21–22. See margin.

21. $y = x^2 - 2$
22. $y = 2|x| + 1$

23. **Advertising** To advertise in the classified section of a local paper costs $2 plus $.25 for each word. Make a table to graph the equation $y = 0.25x + 2$, where x is the number of words and y is the total cost. See margin.

24. Draw the images of the triangle after rotations of 90°, 180°, and 270° about O. See margin.

The graph of $\triangle ABC$ has vertices at $A(1, 3)$, $B(5, 8)$, and $C(7, 1)$. Graph each image of $\triangle ABC$ for each transformation described. Use arrow notation to show the transformation. 25–27. See margin.

25. translated right 1 unit and down 3 units
26. translated left 3 units and up 2 units
27. reflected over the y-axis

Write a rule for the translation shown in each graph. $(x, y) \rightarrow (x - 3, y - 2)$

28. 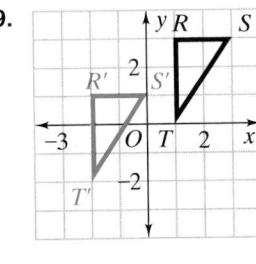 29.

$(x, y) \rightarrow (x + 1, y + 4)$

Use the two figures below for Exercises 30 and 31.

30. Trace each figure and draw the line(s) of symmetry. If there are no lines of symmetry, write *none*. See margin.

31. Does each figure have rotational symmetry? If so, what is the angle of rotation?
   yes, 90°; no

32. **Writing in Math** Give an example of a rotation, a reflection, and a translation you might see in the real world. Check students' work.

1–6. See back of book.
11–14. See back of book.
19–27. See back of book.
30. See back of book.

Prep Online
PHSchool.com
Web Code: arq-1056

Tune-Up

TEKS ★ Resources

TAKS Review and Preparation Workbook

Texas ExamView CD-ROM
- Instant TAKS Practice Test
- TAKS Practice Items

Differentiated Instruction

Texas Progress Monitoring Assessments
- Benchmark Test 5   **L3**

Spanish Assessment Resources
- Spanish Cumulative Review **ELL**

Texas ExamView CD-ROM
- Special Needs Practice Bank   **L1**

★ Tips

Some TAKS tests ask you to identify relationships of units from a graph. This question asks what conversion the data in the graph represents.

Tip 2
Use the Mathematics Chart. Be sure to use the correct system of measurement.

Which of the following conversions is best represented by the data in the graph?

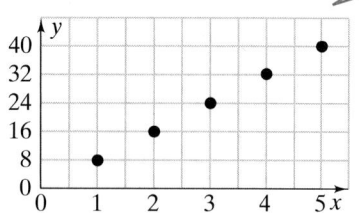

Tip 1
Check the y-value for the x-value of 1. Then check possible conversions from the Mathematics Chart.

- F Gallons to quarts
- G Gallons to ounces
- H Pints to cups
- J Cups to ounces

Think It Through
Note that the y-coordinate is 8 for $x = 1$. Use the Mathematics Chart to identify a relationship that involves 1 of a given unit and 8 of another unit. The only possible relationship is 1 cup = 8 ounces. The correct answer is J.

Vocabulary Builder

As you solve test items, you must understand the meanings of mathematical terms. Match each term with its mathematical meaning.

A. reflection III

B. translation II

C. image I

I. the figure you get after a transformation

II. a transformation that moves a figure a given distance and in a given direction.

III. a transformation that flips a figure

Multiple Choice

Read each question. Then write the letter of the correct answer on your paper.

1. After being moved 6 units down and 4 units to the left, a point is at $(-2, -2)$. What were the original coordinates of the point? **A**
   - A $(2, 4)$
   - B $(-8, -6)$
   - C $(4, 2)$
   - D $(-6, 4)$

2. Which triangle is a translation image of $\triangle XYZ$? **F**

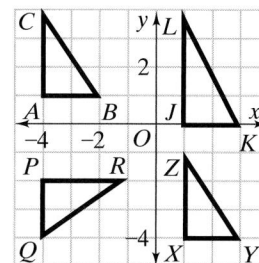

   - F $\triangle ABC$
   - G $\triangle JKL$
   - H $\triangle XYZ$
   - J $\triangle PQR$

527

3. What is the transformation shown at the right? **D**

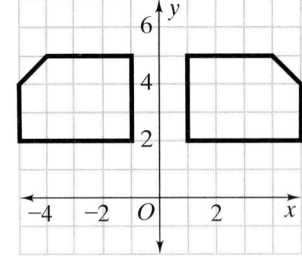

- Ⓐ Translation
- Ⓑ Tessellation
- Ⓒ Rotation
- Ⓓ Reflection

4. The table represents the approximate relationship between the radius x of a circle and the area y of the circle.

Length of Radius, x (in.)	1	2	3	4
Area of Circle, y (in.^{2})	3	13	28	50

Which graph best represents the data in the table above? **F**

Ⓕ   Ⓗ

Ⓖ   Ⓙ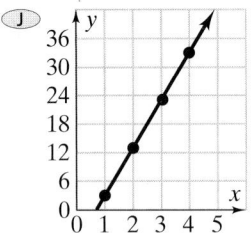

5. Which of the following relationships is best represented by the data in the graph at the right? **B**

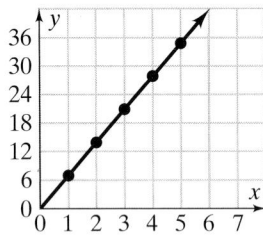

- Ⓐ Conversion of years to months
- Ⓑ Conversion of weeks to days
- Ⓒ Conversion of decades to years
- Ⓓ Conversion of days to hours

6. The data in the table below show the growth in the number of bacteria over time.

Time (min)	0	20	40	60	80
Number of Bacteria	5	10	15	20	25

Which graph best represents the data in the table above? **J**

Ⓕ   Ⓗ

Ⓖ   Ⓙ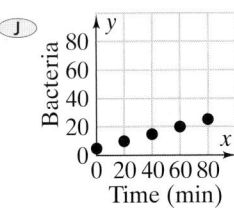

7. Which description shows the relationship between a term and n, its position in the sequence? **B**

Position	1	2	3	4	5	n
Value of Term	3	5	7	9	11	

- Ⓐ Add 2 to n.
- Ⓑ Multiply n by 2 and then add 1.
- Ⓒ Multiply n by 3.
- Ⓓ Multiply n by 3 and then subtract 1.

8. Which sequence follows the rule $3n + 2$, where n is the position of the term in the sequence? **G**

- Ⓕ 5, 7, 8, 9, 10, …
- Ⓖ 5, 8, 11, 14, 17, …
- Ⓗ 2, 5, 8, 11, 14, …
- Ⓙ 2, 5, 8, 12, 16, …

9. Use a centimeter ruler. Measure the length and width of the figure shown.

Which of the following is closest to the area of the figure? **D**

- (A) 2 cm²
- (B) 4 cm²
- (C) 8 cm²
- (D) 16 cm²

10. A game is played on a rectangular field 80 yards wide. The perimeter of the field is 440 yards. What is the area of the field? **F**

- (F) 11,200 yd²
- (G) 22,400 yd²
- (H) 35,200 yd²
- (J) 61,600 yd²

11. The circumference of a small drum's surface is 17 inches. Which of the following is closest to the area of the drum's surface? **C**

- (A) 8.4 in.²
- (B) 17.3 in.²
- (C) 23 in.²
- (D) 91.6 in.²

12. Potatoes cost $3.45 for five pounds. How much do two pounds of potatoes cost? **G**

- (F) $0.89
- (G) $1.38
- (H) $1.73
- (J) $2.14

13. Happy Day Preschool has a teacher-to-student ratio of 2 : 5. Which ratio forms a proportion with this ratio? **D**

- (A) 7 : 1
- (B) 5 : 2
- (C) 10 : 4
- (D) 4 : 10

14. A survey of 1,500 users of an Internet service shows that 850 are very happy with their Internet service provider. There are a total of 30,000 users. Predict the total number of people who are very happy with their Internet service. **J**

- (F) 4,250 users
- (G) 5,667 users
- (H) 13,000 users
- (J) 17,000 users

15. Which two angles are NOT complementary? **A**

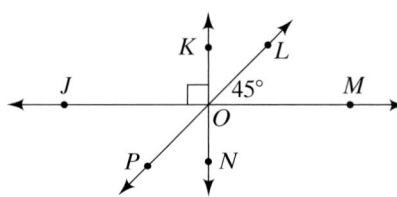

- (A) ∠JOK and ∠KOM
- (B) ∠LOM and ∠KOL
- (C) ∠LOM and ∠NOP
- (D) ∠JOP and ∠LOM

Griddable Items

Record your answer in a grid.

16. A farmer finds that 2 rows of crops meet to form a 35° angle. What is the measure, in degrees, of the complement of this angle? **55**

17. An architect draws two lines, $\overline{AB}$ and $\overline{CD}$, that intersect at point E. The measure of ∠AEC is 40°. What is the measure, in degrees, of ∠BEC? **140**

TAKS GO for Help Guide

TAKS Objective	Item Numbers	GO To	TAKS Objective	Item Numbers	GO To
Obj. 3: (7.7)(B)	1–2	Lesson 10-5	Obj. 4: (7.9)(A)	9–10	Lesson 8-2
	3	Lesson 10-6		11	Lesson 8-5
Obj. 2: (7.4)(B)	4	Lesson 10-4	Obj. 1: (7.2)(D)	12–13	Lesson 5-5
	5–6	Lesson 9-1		14	Lesson 5-4
Obj. 2: (7.4)(C)	7–8	Lesson 9-2	Obj. 3: (7.6)(A)	15–17	Lesson 7-2

For additional TAKS practice, see the *TAKS Review and Preparation Workbook*.

11 · Displaying and Analyzing Data

Chapter at a Glance

Lesson Titles, Objectives, and Features	Assessment	NCTM Standards	TEKS ★ 〈TAKS〉
11-1 Reporting Frequency • To represent data using frequency tables, line plots, and histograms **11-1b Activity Lab:** Venn Diagrams	Lesson Quiz	1, 5, 6, 7, 8, 9, 10	**TEKS** (7.11)(A), (7.11)(B) 〈TAKS〉 **Obj. 5** **TEKS** (7.14)(A)
11-2 Spreadsheets and Data Displays • To interpret spreadsheets, double bar graphs, and double line graphs **11-2b Activity Lab, Technology:** Graphing Using Spreadsheets Software	Lesson Quiz	1, 2, 5, 6, 7, 8, 9, 10	**TEKS** (7.11)(A), (7.11)(B) 〈TAKS〉 **Obj. 5** **TEKS** (7.13)(D), (7.14)(B)
11-3 Stem-and-Leaf Plots • To represent and interpret data using stem-and-leaf plots **11-3b Activity Lab, Data Analysis:** Choosing the Best Display	Lesson Quiz Checkpoint Quiz 1	1, 2, 5, 6, 7, 8, 9, 10	**TEKS** (7.11)(A), (7.11)(B), (7.12)(A) 〈TAKS〉 **Obj. 5**
11-4a Activity Lab, Data Collection: Writing Survey Questions **11-4 Random Samples and Surveys** • To identify a random sample and to write a survey question	Lesson Quiz	5, 6, 7, 8, 9, 10	
11-5 Estimating Population Size • To estimate population size using proportions **Guided Problem Solving:** Describing Data **11-5b Activity Lab, Data Analysis:** Graphing Population Data	Lesson Quiz	1, 2, 4, 5, 6, 7, 8, 9, 10	**TEKS** (7.3)(B), (7.11)(A), (7.11)(B), (7.12)(B) 〈TAKS〉 **Obj. 2, 5**
11-6 Using Data to Persuade • To identify misleading graphs and statistics	Lesson Quiz Checkpoint Quiz 2	1, 5, 6, 7, 8, 9, 10	**TEKS** (7.11)(A), (7.11)(B), (7.12)(A) 〈TAKS〉 **Obj. 5**
11-7a Activity Lab, Data Collection: Two-Variable Data Collection **11-7 Exploring Scatter Plots** • To draw and interpret scatter plots	Lesson Quiz	1, 2, 5, 6, 7, 8, 9, 10	**TEKS** (7.11)(A), (7.11)(B) 〈TAKS〉 **Obj. 5;** Prepares for TEKS (8.12)(B)
〈TAKS〉 **Tune-Up: Cumulative Practice**			

NCTM Standards 2000
1 Number and Operations	**2** Algebra	**3** Geometry	**4** Measurement	**5** Data Analysis and Probability
6 Problem Solving	**7** Reasoning and Proof	**8** Communication	**9** Connections	**10** Representation

Correlations to Standardized Tests

All content for these tests is contained in *Prentice Hall Math,* Course 2. This chart reflects coverage in this chapter only.

	11-1	11-2	11-3	11-4	11-5	11-6	11-7
Terra Nova CAT6 (Level 17)							
Number and Number Relations	✔	✔	✔	✔	✔	✔	✔
Computation and Numerical Estimation	✔	✔	✔	✔	✔	✔	✔
Operation Concepts	✔	✔	✔	✔	✔	✔	✔
Measurement							
Geometry and Spatial Sense							
Data Analysis, Statistics, and Probability	✔	✔	✔	✔	✔	✔	✔
Patterns, Functions, Algebra	✔	✔	✔	✔	✔	✔	✔
Problem Solving and Reasoning	✔	✔	✔	✔	✔	✔	✔
Communication	✔	✔	✔	✔	✔	✔	✔
Decimals, Fractions, Integers, and Percent	✔	✔	✔	✔	✔	✔	✔
Order of Operations							
Terra Nova CTBS (Level 17)							
Decimals, Fractions, Integers, Percents	✔	✔	✔	✔	✔	✔	✔
Order of Operations, Numeration, Number Theory	✔	✔	✔	✔	✔	✔	✔
Data Interpretation	✔	✔	✔	✔	✔	✔	✔
Pre-algrbra		✔	✔		✔		✔
Measurement							
Geometry							
ITBS (Level 13)							
Number Properties and Operations	✔	✔	✔	✔	✔	✔	✔
Algebra	✔	✔	✔	✔	✔	✔	✔
Geometry							
Measurement							
Probability and Statistics	✔	✔	✔	✔	✔	✔	✔
Estimation							
SAT10 (Int 3 Level)							
Number Sense and Operations	✔	✔	✔	✔	✔	✔	✔
Patterns, Relationships, and Algebra	✔	✔	✔	✔	✔	✔	✔
Data, Statistics, and Probability	✔	✔	✔	✔	✔	✔	✔
Geometry and Measurement							
NAEP							
Number Sense, Properties, and Operations					✔		
Measurement							
Geometry and Spatial Sense							
Data Analysis, Statistics, and Probability	✔	✔	✔	✔		✔	✔
Algebra and Functions							

CAT6 California Achievement Test, 6th Ed.   **CTBS** Comprehensive Test of Basic Skills   **ITBS** Iowa Test of Basic Skills, Form M
SAT10 Stanford Achievement Test, 10th Ed.   **NAEP** National Assessment of Educational Progress 2005 Mathematics Objectives

TEKS Math Background

Focus on the TEKS

- At Grade 7, students make inferences and convincing arguments based on analysis of given or collected data (7.11)(B). Analysis of TAKS results shows that students struggle with this student expectation.

  In Lessons 11-1 through 11-3, students analyze data presented in data displays. In Lessons 11-5 through 11-7, students use data and discover the effects of data interpretation. Place special emphasis on these lessons because they all focus on (7.11)(B).

- New at Grade 7 is selecting and using an appropriate representation for presenting and displaying relationships among collected data (7.11)(A). Students work with data displays in Lessons 11-1 through 11-3 and in Lessons 11-5 through 11-7 (7.11)(A).

11-1 Reporting Frequency

TEKS ★ *TAKS* (7.11)(A), (7.11)(B) Obj. 5; (7.14)(B)

Math Understandings

- A frequency table shows how often each data value occurs.
- A line plot visually represents a frequency table on a number line and is best used for a small number of data values.
- A histogram can help you make a clear visual comparison of frequency by grouping many data points into bars of equal width.

A **frequency table** is a table that lists each item in a data set with the number of times the item occurs. A **line plot** is a graph that shows the shape of a data set by stacking X's above each data value on a number line. A **histogram** is a bar graph with no spaces between the bars. The height of each bar shows the frequency of data within that interval. The intervals of a histogram are of equal size and do not overlap.

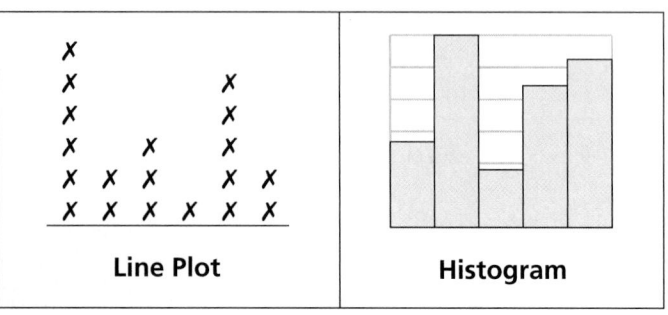

| Line Plot | Histogram |

11-2 Spreadsheets and Data Displays

TEKS ★ *TAKS* (7.11)(A), (7.11)(B) Obj. 5

Math Understandings

- A spreadsheet is an electronic workspace that organizes information in cells that can be used in calculations and graphs.
- You can use a double bar graph or a double line graph to compare two sets of data.

A **spreadsheet** is a tool for organizing and analyzing data. Spreadsheets are arranged in numbered rows and lettered columns. A **cell** is a box where a row and column meet. For example, B6 represents the cell at the intersection of column B and row 6. A bar graph uses vertical or horizontal bars to display numerical information. A **double bar graph** uses bars to compare two sets of data. The **legend,** or key, identifies the data that are compared. A line graph uses a series of line segments to show changes in data over time. A **double line graph** compares changes in two sets of data over time.

11-3 Stem-and-Leaf Plots

TEKS ★ *TAKS* (7.11)(A), (7.11)(B), (7.12)(A) Obj. 5

Math Understandings

- A stem-and-leaf plot can quickly show the distribution of a data set by retaining each data value.

A **stem-and-leaf plot** is a graph that uses the digits of each number to show the shape of the data set. Each data value is broken into a "stem" (digit or digits on the left) and a "leaf" (digit or digits on the right). A back-to-back stem-and-leaf plot compares two sets of data.

11-4 Random Samples and Surveys

Math Understandings

- In most situations, it is extremely difficult and costly to survey every member of a population. You can select a random sample to accurately represent the entire population.
- A survey question should not influence responses by making one answer appear more attractive.

A **population** is a group of objects or people. Pollsters select a **sample,** or part of the population. In a **random sample,** each member of population has an equal chance of being selected for the sample. A **biased question** is a question that makes an unjustified assumption or makes one answer appear better than another.

Example: Is the following question biased or fair? Explain.

Do you prefer bright lighting or gentle lighting?

This question may be biased because "bright" and "gentle" are not clearly defined and may influence responses.

11-5 Estimating Population Size

TEKS ★ (TAKS) (7.3)(B), (7.11)(B) Obj. 2, 5

Math Understandings

- The validity of the capture/recapture method depends on how well both the first and second samples accurately represent the population.

The capture/recapture method is frequently used to estimate animals populations. Researchers collect and mark a sample of animals and release them back in the population. Then, they again capture a sample and count the number of marked animals. Finally, they use a proportion to estimate the animal population.

$$\frac{\text{number of marked animals counted}}{\text{total number of animals counted}} = \frac{\text{number of animals marked}}{\text{estimate of animal population}}$$

11-6 Using Data to Persuade

TEKS ★ (TAKS) (7.11)(A), (7.11)(B), (7.12)(B) Obj. 5

Math Understandings

- Choices you make about the labels, scale intervals, and style of a graph can mislead the viewer of the information.

To evaluate a graph, check to see whether both scales start at zero, or whether the axes have breaks. Examine the intervals to see if they have equal intervals.

11-7 Exploring Scatter Plots

TEKS ★ (TAKS) Prepares for TEKS (8.12)(B)

Math Understandings

- A scatter plot may show a relationship that is not obvious from looking at the numerical data.

A **scatter plot** is a graph that relates two sets of data. When a scatter plot shows a **positive trend,** one set of values increases as the other set tends to increase. When a scatter plot shows a **negative trend,** one set of values increases as the other tends to decrease. When the points in a scatter plot do not cluster along a trend line, the points show no relationship and **no trend.**

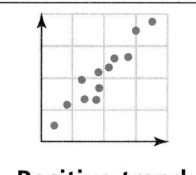

Positive trend

As one set of values increases, the other set tends to increase.

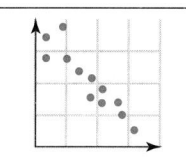

Negative trend

As one set of values increases, the other set tends to decrease.

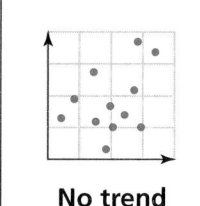

No trend

The points show no relationship.

Additional Professional Development Opportunities

Math Background Notes for Chapter 11: Every lesson has a Math Background in the PLAN section.

Research Overview, Mathematics Strands Additional support for these topics and more is in the front of the Teacher's Edition.

LessonLab
LessonLab, a Pearson Education company, offers comprehensive, facilitated professional development designed to help teachers to improve student achievement. To learn more, please visit lessonlab.com.

Texas Chapter 11 Resources

	11-1	11-2	11-3	11-4	11-5	11-6	11-7	For the Chapter
Print Resources								
L3 Practice	●	●	●	●	●	●	●	
L1 Adapted Practice	●	●	●	●	●	●	●	
L3 Guided Problem Solving	●	●	●	●	●	●	●	
L2 Reteaching	●	●	●	●	●	●	●	
L4 Enrichment	●	●	●	●	●	●		
L3 Daily Notetaking Guide	●	●	●	●	●	●	●	
L1 Adapted Daily Notetaking Guide	●	●	●	●	●	●	●	
L3 Vocabulary and Study Skills Worksheets			●	●	●		●	●
L3 Daily Puzzles	●	●	●	●	●	●	●	
L3 Activity Labs	●	●	●	●	●	●	●	
L3 Checkpoint Quiz			●			●		
L3 Chapter Project								●
L2 Chapter Test								●
L3 Chapter Test								●
L4 Alternative Assessment								●
L3 Cumulative Review								●
Spanish Resources ELL								
L3 Practice	●	●	●	●	●	●	●	
L3 Vocabulary and Study Skills Worksheets	●		●	●	●	●		
L3 Checkpoint Quiz			●			●		
L2 Chapter Test								●
L3 Chapter Test								●
L4 Alternative Assessment								●
L3 Cumulative Review								●
Transparencies								
Check Skills You'll Need	●	●	●	●	●	●	●	
Additional Examples	●	●	●	●	●	●	●	
Problem of the Day	●	●	●	●	●	●	●	
(TAKS) Daily Review	●	●	●	●	●	●	●	
Classroom Aid								
Student Edition Answers	●	●	●	●	●	●	●	●
Lesson Quiz	●	●	●	●	●	●	●	
(TAKS) Strategies								●
Technology								
Texas Interactive Textbook Online	●	●	●	●	●	●	●	●
Texas StudentExpress CD-ROM	●	●	●	●	●	●	●	●
Success Tracker™ Online Intervention	●	●	●	●	●	●	●	●
TeacherExpress CD-ROM	●	●	●	●	●	●	●	●
PresentationExpress CD-ROM	●	●	●	●	●	●	●	●
Texas ExamView CD-ROM with QuickTake	●	●	●	●	●	●	●	●
MindPoint Quiz Show CD-ROM	●	●	●	●	●	●	●	●
Prentice Hall Web Site: PHSchool.com	●	●	●	●	●	●	●	●

Also available: **(TAKS) Tune-Up Kit**
- TAKS Daily Review Transparencies
- TAKS Review and Preparation Workbook
- TAKS Strategies with Transparencies
- Texas Progress Monitoring Assessments
- Texas ExamView CD-ROM
- MindPoint Quiz Show CD-ROM

Other Resources
Algebra Readiness Tests
All-in-One Student Workbook
All-in-One Student Workbook, Adapted Version
Multilingual Handbook

Solution Key
Math Notes Study Folder
Spanish Cumulative Assessment

Where You Can Use the Lesson Resources

Here is a suggestion, following the four-step teaching plan, for how you can incorporate Differentiated Instruction Resources into your teaching.

	Instructional Resources **L3**	Differentiated Instruction Resources
1. Plan		
Preparation Read the Math Background in the Teacher's Edition to connect this lesson with students' previous experience. **Starting Class** **Check Skills You'll Need** Assign these exercises to review prerequisite skills. **TEKS** ★ **TAKS** Review the full text of the TEKS student expectations and TAKS objectives covered in this lesson. **New Vocabulary** Help students pre-read the lesson by pointing out the new terms introduced in the lesson.	**TEKS Math Background** **Math Understandings** **Transparencies & PresentationExpress CD-ROM** Check Skills You'll Need Problem of the Day TAKS Daily Review **Resources** Vocabulary and Study Skills	**Spanish Support** ELL Vocabulary and Study Skills
2. Teach		
L3 Guided Instruction Use the Activity Labs to build conceptual understanding. Teach each Example. Use the Teacher's Edition side column notes for specific teaching tips, including Error Prevention notes. Use the Additional Examples found in the side column (and on transparency and PowerPoint) as an alternative presentation for the content. After each Example, assign the Quick Check exercise for that Example to get an immediate assessment of student understanding. Use the Closure activity in the Teacher's Edition to help students attain mastery of lesson content.	**Student Edition** Activity Lab **Resources** Daily Notetaking Guide Activity Lab **Transparencies & PresentationExpress CD-ROM** Additional Examples Classroom Aids **Texas ExamView CD-ROM with QuickTake**	**Teacher's Edition** Every lesson includes suggestions for working with students who need special attention. **L1** Special Needs **L2** Below Level **L4** Advanced Learners ELL English Language Learners **Resources** **L1** Adapted Daily Notetaking Guide **Multilingual Handbook**
3. Practice		

Assignment Guide
Check Your Understanding
Use these questions to check students' understanding before you assign homework.
Homework Exercises
Assign homework from these leveled exercises in the Assignment Guide.
  A Practice by Example
  B Apply Your Skills
  C Challenge
  TAKS Tune-Up and Mixed Review
Homework Quick Check
Use these key exercises to quickly check students' homework.
	Transparencies & PresentationExpress CD-ROM
	Student Answers
	Resources
	Practice
	Guided Problem Solving
	Vocabulary and Study Skills
	Activity Lab
	Daily Puzzles
	Texas ExamView CD-ROM with QuickTake
		Spanish Support
		ELL Practice
		ELL Vocabulary and Study Skills
		Resources
		L1 Adapted Practice
		L4 Enrichment

4. Assess & Reteach		
Lesson Quiz Assign the Lesson Quiz to assess students' mastery of the lesson content. **Checkpoint Quiz** Use the Checkpoint Quiz to assess student progress over several lessons.	**Transparencies & PresentationExpress CD-ROM** Lesson Quiz **Resources** Checkpoint Quiz	**Resources** **L2** Reteaching ELL Checkpoint Quiz Success Tracker™ Online Intervention **Texas ExamView CD-ROM with QuickTake**

KEY   **L1** Special Needs   **L2** Below Level   **L3** For All Students   **L4** Advanced, Gifted   ELL English Language Learners

CHAPTER 11

Displaying and Analyzing Data

Check Your Readiness

Answers are in the back of the textbook.

For intervention, direct students to:

Comparing Numbers
Lesson 1-6
Extra Skills and Word
Problems Practice, Ch. 1

Finding the Median
Lesson 1-10
Extra Skills and Word
Problems Practice, Ch. 1

Solving Proportions
Lesson 5-4
Extra Skills and Word
Problems Practice, Ch. 5

Graphing on the Coordinate Plane
Lesson 10-1
Extra Skills and Word
Problems Practice, Ch. 10

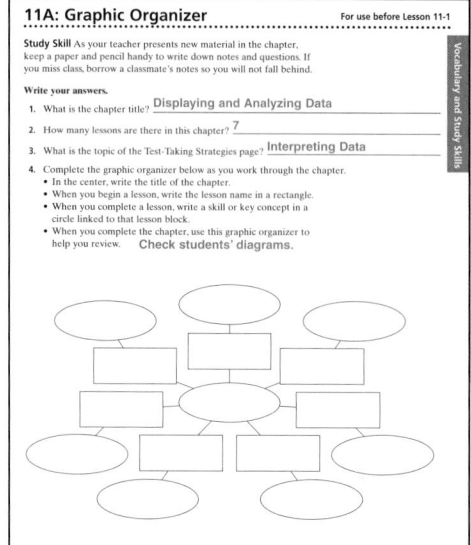
530

CHAPTER 11 · Displaying and Analyzing Data

What You've Learned

TEKS ★ TAKS

- **(7.12)(A)** In Chapter 1, you described a set of data using mean, median, mode, and range. **TAKS** Obj. 5

- **(7.4)(B)** In Chapter 9, you graphed data to demonstrate relationships in familiar concepts such as conversions, perimeter, and area. **TAKS** Obj. 2

- **(7.7)(A)** In Chapter 10, you located and named points on a coordinate plane using ordered pairs of integers. **TAKS** Obj. 3

Check Your Readiness

For Exercises	See Lesson
1–2	1-6
3–6	1-10
7–10	5-4
11–14	10-1

Comparing Numbers

Order the numbers from least to greatest.

1. 32, −31, 34, −30, 13, 33   −31, −30, 13, 32, 33, 34

2. 11.1, 10.9, 11.3, 11.5, 10.2
   10.2, 10.9, 11.1, 11.3, 11.5

Finding the Median

Find the median of each set of data.

3. 15, 9, 16, 12, 8, 10, 13   12   4. 27, 35, 24, 56, 29, 37   32

5. 55, 69, 112, 67, 32, 123, 45   67   6. 8.9, 8.5, 7.6, 8.4, 9.1, 8.5   8.5

Solving Proportions

(**Algebra**) **Solve each proportion.**

7. $\frac{3}{4} = \frac{a}{24}$ 18   8. $\frac{2}{b} = \frac{3}{21}$ 14   9. $\frac{n}{52} = \frac{17}{13}$ 68   10. $\frac{12}{5} = \frac{a}{45}$ 108

Graphing on the Coordinate Plane

Graph each point on the same coordinate plane. Name the quadrant in which each point lies or the axis on which the point lies. 11–14. See margin.

11. $(-4, 7)$ 12. $(0, -5)$ 13. $(6, 3)$ 14. $(2, 0)$

11–14.

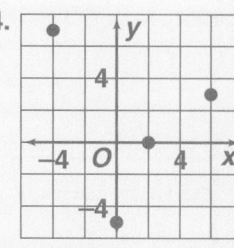

11. II

12. y-axis

13. I

14. x-axis

Patterns, Relationships, and Algebraic Thinking
TEKS (7.3)(B) **TAKS** Obj. 2

Probability and Statistics
TEKS (7.11)(A), (7.11)(B), (7.12)(A), (7.12)(B) **TAKS** Obj. 5

Underlying Processes and Mathematical Tools
TEKS (7.13)(D), (7.14)(B)

Chapter 11 Overview

In this chapter, students build on their knowledge of graphing and statistics as they investigate different ways of obtaining and displaying data. They work with frequency tables and data displays like spreadsheets, histograms, stem-and-leaf plots, and scatter plots. They learn about sampling, surveys, and how to use data to make predictions.

Activating Prior Knowledge

In this chapter, to make and use different kinds of data displays, students will build on their knowledge of graphs, ordered pairs, and measures of central tendency. They will draw upon their understanding of ratios and proportions to estimate populations. Ask questions such as:

- *What is the median of a set of numbers?* The middle value when the data values are arranged in numerical order.
- *What is the mode of this set of data: 2, 4, 4, 8, 9, 12?* 4
- *A model airplane is built using the scale 1 in. = 12 ft. If the wingspan of the model is 6 inches, what is the wingspan of the plane?* 72 ft

What You'll Learn Next
TEKS ✦ TAKS

- **(7.11)(A)** In this chapter, you will select and use an appropriate representation for displaying data, including line plot, line graph, bar graph, stem-and-leaf plot, and Venn diagrams, and justify the selection. **TAKS** Obj. 5

- **(7.11)(B)** You will make inferences and convincing arguments based on analysis of data. **TAKS** Obj. 5

- **(7.12)(B)** You will choose among mean, median, mode, or range to describe a set of data and justify the choice. **TAKS** Obj. 5

> **TAKS Tune-Up** On pages 575–577, you will review and practice the vocabulary and *TAKS* objectives you have learned.

🔊 Key Vocabulary

- biased question (p. 551)
- cell (p. 538)
- double bar graph (p. 539)
- double line graph (p. 539)
- frequency table (p. 532)
- histogram (p. 533)
- legend (p. 539)
- line plot (p. 533)
- negative trend (p. 568)
- no trend (p. 568)
- population (p. 550)
- positive trend (p. 568)
- random sample (p. 550)
- sample (p. 550)
- scatter plot (p. 567)
- spreadsheet (p. 538)
- stem-and-leaf plot (p. 544)

Chapter 11 **531**

11-1 Reporting Frequency

TEKS ⭐ TAKS

(7.11)(A) To select and use an appropriate representation for data, including line plot and bar graph, and justify the selection *TAKS* Obj. 5

Also supports
(7.11)(B) *TAKS* Obj. 5
(7.14)(B)

Dana Center TEKS Toolkit Clarifying Activities (7.11)(A), (7.11)(B), (7.14)(B)
Visit: PHSchool.com
Web Code: arq-9045

Professional Development

TEKS Math Background

Frequency refers to how often something happens. A *frequency table* organizes each item in a data set by how often it occurs. A *line plot* is a quick way to visualize the frequency distribution of a data set using Xs on a number line.

A *histogram* is a bar graph that uses equal intervals to illustrate the frequency distribution of a data set. No spaces are used between consecutive bars because the intervals are continuous (and non-overlapping).

More Math Background: p. 530C

Lesson Planning and Resources

See p. 530E for a list of the resources that support this lesson.

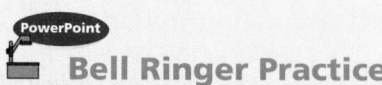
Bell Ringer Practice

✔ **Check Skills You'll Need**
Use student page, transparency, or PowerPoint.

TAKS **Daily Review 82**
Use transparency.

532

✔ Check Skills You'll Need

1. Vocabulary Review
What is an *integer*?
1–3. See below.
Order the numbers from least to greatest.

2. 23, 45, 61, 87, 91, 16, 22, 52

3. −41, 42, −43, 45, 43, −47

 for Help
Lesson 1-6

Check Skills You'll Need

1. An integer is a positive or negative whole number, or 0.

2. 16, 22, 23, 45, 52, 61, 87, 91

3. −47, −43, −41, 42, 43, 45

11-1 Reporting Frequency

TEKS ⭐ TAKS

- (7.11)(A) To select and use an appropriate representation for data, including line plot and bar graph, and justify the selection *TAKS* Obj. 5
- (7.11)(B) To make inferences based on analysis of given data *TAKS* Obj. 5
- (7.14)(B) To evaluate the effectiveness of different representations

🔊 **New Vocabulary** frequency table, line plot, histogram

Why Learn This?

When you count the number of times a particular event or item occurs, you measure frequency. You can use frequency to analyze events such as extreme weather events.

A **frequency table** is a table that lists each item in a data set and the number of times each item occurs.

EXAMPLE **Making a Frequency Table**

1 **Hurricanes** The data below show the number of hurricanes in the Atlantic Ocean each year for a period of 30 years. Make a frequency table of the data.

7 4 9 8 8 10 3 9 11 3 4 4 4 8 7
5 3 4 7 5 2 2 7 9 5 5 5 6 6 4

Atlantic Ocean Hurricanes

Number	2	3	4	5	6	7	8	9	10	11
Tally	II	III	ⅢⅢ I	ⅢⅢ	II	IIII	III	III	I	I
Frequency	2	3	6	5	2	4	3	3	1	1

✔ Quick Check

1. The data below show the number of U.S. Representatives for 22 states. Make a frequency table of the data. **See back of book.**

4 3 1 2 1 5 4 1 7 2 8 1 3 8 5 9 3 5 7 3 1 9

Differentiated Instruction **Solutions for All Learners**

Special Needs L1
Help students keep track of the Xs they draw in line plots, and keep track of the data in their frequency tables. Provide them with graph paper so that they can use the grid squares for orientation.

learning style: visual

Below Level L2
Have students make a histogram using birth dates of students in the class as the data and using the months as the intervals.

learning style: visual

A **line plot** is a graph that shows the shape of a data set by stacking **✗**'s above each data value on a number line.

EXAMPLE Making a Line Plot

② Make a line plot of the data in Example 1.

Step 1 Draw a number line from the least to the greatest value (from 2 to 11).

Step 2 Write an **✗** above each value for each time the value occurs in the data.

Atlantic Ocean Hurricanes

```
        ✗
        ✗  ✗
        ✗  ✗     ✗
     ✗  ✗  ✗     ✗  ✗  ✗
  ✗  ✗  ✗  ✗  ✗  ✗  ✗  ✗
  ✗  ✗  ✗  ✗  ✗  ✗  ✗  ✗  ✗  ✗
  2  3  4  5  6  7  8  9  10  11
```

✓ Quick Check

2. Make a line plot of the number of students in math classes: 24 27
21 25 25 28 22 23 25 25 28 22 23 25 22 24 25 28 27 22.
See back of book.

Vocabulary Tip

The *histo* in histogram is short for *history*.

A **histogram** is a bar graph with no spaces between the bars. The height of each bar shows the frequency of data within that interval. The intervals of a histogram are of equal size and do not overlap.

EXAMPLE Making a Histogram

③ Make a histogram of the data in Example 1.

Make a frequency table. Use the equal-sized intervals 2–3, 4–5, 6–7, 8–9, and 10–11. Then make a histogram.

Atlantic Ocean Hurricanes

Number	Frequency
2–3	丗
4–5	丗 丗 丨
6–7	丗 丨
8–9	丗 丨
10–11	丨丨

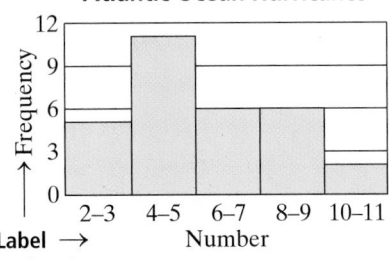

Atlantic Ocean Hurricanes

Label → each axis.

✓ Quick Check

3. Make a histogram of the ages of employees at a retail store: 28 20
44 72 65 40 59 29 22 36 28 61 30 27 33 55 48 24 28 32.
See back of book.

Advanced Learners L4
What happens to a histogram as the number of intervals is reduced? the histogram is narrow and high *as the number of intervals is increased?* the histogram is wider and flatter

Pre-AP™

English Language Learners ELL
Have students describe the parts of a histogram and a line plot. Have them work in pairs to come up with a list of similarities and differences between the two displays of data.

learning style: verbal

---

2. Teach

Activity Lab
Use before the lesson.

All in One Teaching Resources
Activity Lab 11-1: Reporting Frequency

Guided Instruction

Example 2
Have students examine the line plot. Ask:
• *Which number of hurricanes occurs most often?* 4
• *Which number of hurricanes occurs least often?* 10 or 11

Error Prevention!

Help students make a clear distinction between histograms and bar graphs. A histogram has no space between bars because the intervals are continuous. The height of a histogram's bars show frequency instead of amounts.

PowerPoint Additional Examples

① The numbers below represent the ages of the students in a karate class. Make a frequency table of the data.
11 5 9 13 8 9 9 11 10 8 6 7
12 11 13 12 7 6 11 12 10 8

Age	5	6	7	8	9
Tally	I	II	II	III	III
Freq.	1	2	2	3	3

Age	10	11	12	13
Tally	II	IIII	III	II
Freq.	2	4	3	2

② Make a line plot of the data in Exercise 1.

Ages of Students in a Karate Class

```
                 ✗
        ✗  ✗        ✗  ✗
     ✗  ✗  ✗  ✗  ✗  ✗  ✗
     ✗  ✗  ✗  ✗  ✗  ✗  ✗  ✗
     5  6  7  8  9  10  11  12  13
```

533

3 Make a histogram of the data below.

Hours Spent on the Internet

Hours	Tally	Hours	Tally
1	I	11	III
2		12	I
3	II	13	II
4	IIII	14	
5	III	15	I
6	III	16	II
7	IIII	17	III
8	I	18	IIII
9		19	II
10	IIII	20	I

AllinOne Teaching Resources
- Daily Notetaking Guide 11-1 **L3**
- Adapted Notetaking 11-1 **L1**

Closure

- *What is a frequency table?*
  a table that lists each item in a data set with the number of times the item occurs
- *What do histograms and line plots illustrate?* the shape of a data set

534

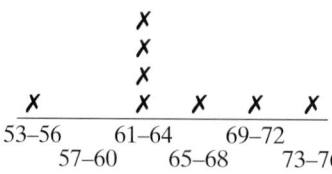

Voting-Age Population Registered to Vote (percent)

State	Percent
Calif.	54
Fla.	63
Ga.	62
Ind.	67
N.C.	69
Ore.	75
Tex.	61
Va.	64

● More Than One Way

Use the table at the left to make a data display.

Anna's Method

I can make a line plot. I'll use six intervals of 4.

Voting-Age Population Registered to Vote (percent)

```
              X
              X
              X
  X           X    X    X    X
  53–56      61–64     69–72
      57–60      65–68     73–76
```

Ryan's Method

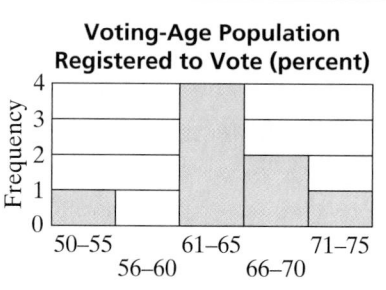

I can make a histogram. I'll use five intervals of 5.

Voting-Age Population Registered to Vote (percent)

(histogram with Frequency axis 0–4, intervals 50–55, 56–60, 61–65, 66–70, 71–75)

Choose a Method

Display the data in the table. Explain your choice of data display.

Number of Hours Worked per Week

Number	35	36	37	38	39	40	41	42	43	44
Tally	THL	III	THL II	THL II	THL I	THL THL	III	THL		I

See margin.

✓ Check Your Understanding

Use the data in the frequency table below. **1–2. See margin.**

Number	15	16	17	18	19	20	21	22	23	24
Tally	THL I	I	III		II	III	I	IIII	THL	II

1. Make a line plot of the data.   **2.** Make a histogram of the data.

More Than One Way. See back of book.

1.

```
        X
        X                   X
        X              X    X
        X    X         X    X X
        X    X    X X  X    X X X
        X X X      X X X X  X X X
        14   16   18   20   22   24
```

For more exercises, see Extra Skills and Word Problems.

GO for Help

For Exercises	See Examples
3–5	1
6–8	2
9–10	3

Ⓐ Make a frequency table of the data. 3–5. See margin.

3. tickets sold: 45 48 51 53 50 46 46 50 51 48 46 45 50 49 46

4. number of TVs: 1 3 2 2 1 4 1 2 2 1 3 1 3 3 2 2 3 1

5. student ages:
13 12 14 12 11 12 13 14 13 13 14 11 12 12 13 11 11

Make a line plot of the data. 6–8. See margin.

6. number of plants sold per person:
5 10 11 8 7 11 9 8 6 7 12 10 10 9 8 7 6

7. miles from home to shopping center:
2 4 10 5 4 6 7 9 5 5 3 1 10 8 6 4 3

8. blocks walked from home to school:
2 8 10 1 2 9 8 7 6 8 4 3 8 9 1 3 10 12 6 4 8

Make a histogram of the data. 9–10. See margin.

9.
How Many Amusement Parks Did You Visit Last Year?

Number of Parks	0–2	3–5	6–8	9–11
Frequency	10	4	3	1

10.
How Many Hours Do You Sleep Each Night?

Number of Hours	5–6	7–8	9–10	11–12
Frequency	4	12	9	1

Ⓑ GPS

11. Guided Problem Solving At the right are the times at which 16 people get up each morning. Display the data to show the most common half-hour interval.

5:30	6:45	5:45	6:15
6:25	6:20	7:15	7:45
8:00	7:00	8:00	7:30
6:00	7:10	7:50	6:10

- What type of display will you use?
- Use the interval 5:30–5:59 first. What are the other intervals?
  See margin.

Use the graph at the right.

12. Books The line plot shows the **GPS** number of books each bookstore customer bought. How many customers bought more than three books? **4 customers**

Number of Books Purchased

```
              X
     X        X
     X        X        X
     X        X        X                           X
     X        X        X        X        X        X
  _____
     1        2        3        4        5        6
```

13. How many customers bought an even number of books?
8 customers

2–11. See back of book.

3. Practice

Assignment Guide

Check Your Understanding
Go over Exercises 1–2 in class before assigning the Homework Exercises.

Homework Exercises
A Practice by Example   3–10
B Apply Your Skills   11–17
C Challenge   18
TEKS ★ TAKS Tune-Up and
Mixed Review   19–24

Homework Quick Check
To check students' understanding of key skills and concepts, go over Exercises 6, 10, 12, 15, and 16.

Differentiated Instruction Resources

PowerPoint

Lesson Quiz

1. Make a frequency table and a line plot for the number of students in each class:

25 24 25 23 24 23 24 24 23

Students	23	24	25
Class	3	4	2

```
        X
    X   X
    X   X   X
    X   X   X
   +---+---+---+
   23  24  25
```

2. The data table below shows how many hours of TV different people watch each week. Make a histogram of the data.

Hours	0–5	6–10	11–15
Frequency	3	5	10

Hours	16–20	21–25
Frequency	24	15

17–18. See back of book.
22–24. See back of book.

536

GO **Online**
Homework Help
Visit: PHSchool.com
Web Code: are-1101

14. about 12 people

15. Find the frequency of each interval and add them all together.

16. No; about 9 people saw either 6 or 7 movies.

Use the histogram for Exercises 14–16.

14. **Movies** About how many people saw fewer than two movies? See left.

15. **Writing in Math** How can you find the number of people who answered the survey? Explain. See left.

16. **Reasoning** Can you tell how many people saw exactly 7 movies? Explain. See left.

How Many Movies Did You See in a Theater Last Summer?

17. **Choose a Method** Display the data below, which give 26 responses to the question, "How many siblings do you have?"
1 3 4 2 2 1 3 1 0 2 0 1 3 4 2 1 0 1 2 0 3 4 2 5 2 6. See margin.

C 18. **Challenge** The table shows home prices. Draw two histograms for the data, one with 4 intervals and one with 8. See margin.

$129,000	$132,000	$121,000	$115,000
$138,000	$152,000	$147,000	$136,000
$137,000	$148,000	$175,000	$127,000
$192,000	$133,000	$167,000	$154,000

TEKS ★ TAKS Tune-Up and Mixed Review

TAKS Objective 5
TEKS (7.11)(A)

19. The line plot shows the number of children of each of 12 recent U.S. presidents. Which set of data does the line plot show? **B**

   A 1 6 2 2 4 4 2 2 3 2 2 6
   B 1 6 2 2 6 4 2 3 1 2 4 4
   C 1 6 2 2 2 4 2 3 3 2 4 4
   D 1 5 6 2 2 4 2 3 2 2 4 4

Number of Children of U.S. Presidents

```
        X
        X           X
   X    X      X     X            X
   X    X  X   X                  X
  +--+---+---+---+---+---+
   1   2   3   4   5   6
```

TAKS Objective 4
TEKS (7.9)(A)

20. A square park measures 45 m on each side. The sidewalk around the park's edge encloses a square area of grass that is 42 m on each side. What is the area of the sidewalk? **F**

   F 261 m^2 G 1,764 m^2 H 1,890 m^2 J 2,025 m^2

TAKS Objective 2
TEKS (7.4)(A)

21. Which expression can be used to find the perimeter of a rectangular trampoline with a length of 16 feet and width w? **B**

   A $16 + 2w$ B $32 + 2w$ C $16w$ D $32 + w$

GO for Help   Lesson 10-4

Algebra Make a table of values for each equation. Use integer values of x from -3 to 3. Then graph each parabola. 22–24. See margin.

22. $y = x^2 - 1$ 23. $y = 3x^2$ 24. $y = -3x^2$

TEKS ★ TAKS Resources

- TAKS Strategies, p. 571
- TAKS Tune-Up, pp. 575–577

TAKS Tune-Up Kit
- TAKS Daily Review Transparencies
- TAKS Review and Preparation Workbook
- TAKS Strategies with Transparencies
- Texas Progress Monitoring Assessments

Alternative Assessment

Students work in pairs to collect or make up data of their choosing, such as how many classmates participate in various sports. Together the partners make a table of the data and a histogram. Students can share their findings with the class.

Venn Diagrams

A Venn diagram shows relationships between sets of items. Each set is represented separately. Items that belong to both sets are represented by the intersection.

> **TEKS ★ TAKS**
>
> **(7.11)(A)** To use an appropriate representation for displaying data, including Venn diagrams **TAKS** Obj. 5
>
> **(7.11)(B)** To make inferences based on an analysis of given data **TAKS** Obj. 5

EXAMPLE   Using a Venn Diagram

Geography There are 22 states that are all or partly in the eastern time zone, and 15 states that are all or partly in the central time zone. This includes the 5 states that are in both the eastern and central time zones. How many states are in at least one of the two time zones?

Draw a Venn diagram.

There are $17 + 5 + 10$, or 32 states in either or both the eastern and central time zones.

Eastern Time Zone States $22 - 5 = 17$ | 5 | Central Time Zone States $15 - 5 = 10$

1.

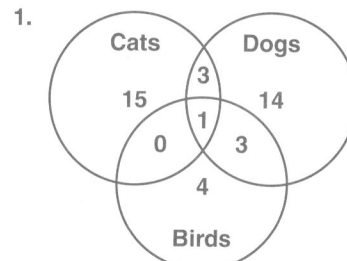

Exercises

Forty students have pets. Thirty-two students have cats or dogs or both, but no birds. Eight students have birds. One student has all three kinds of pets.

1. Copy and complete the Venn diagram. **See above right.**
2. How many students have only dogs and birds? Only dogs and cats?
   3 students; 3 students
3. **Reasoning** A new student who has only fish joins the class. How many of the existing sets would this new set overlap? **none**
4. **Geography** There are 10 states that are completely in the central time zone, and 6 states that are completely in the mountain time zone. There are 21 states that are completely in one of the time zones, or in both. Use a Venn diagram to find how many states are in both time zones.

4.

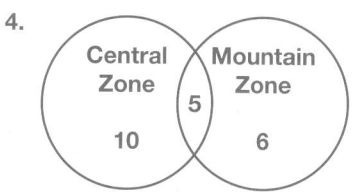

5. **Data Collection** Conduct a survey of your class. Ask students whether they have brothers, sisters, both, or neither. Use a Venn diagram to display the results. **Check students' work.**

Activity Lab

Venn Diagrams

Students learn to use Venn diagrams to represent the relationship between sets of data. This will extend the skills they used in Lesson 11-1.

Guided Instruction

To work with intersecting sets, write two lists of numbers on the board: the whole numbers 1–11 and the even numbers 2–12. Ask:
- *Which numbers are common to both lists?* **2, 4, 6, 8, 10**
- *Which are in the first list only?* **1, 3, 5, 7, 9, 11**
- *Which are in the second list only?* **12**

Example
Discuss the information the Venn diagram illustrates.
Ask:
- *What do the overlapping circles represent?* **states in both time zones**
- *How can you find the number of states only in the eastern time zone or only in the central time zone?* **Subtract from each total the 5 states in both time zones (the intersection of the sets).**

English Language Learners   ELL
Review the distinction between eastern and central time zones. Discuss the time zone you are in and identify the time zones of familiar cities and states.

Exercises
Pair or group students with varying degrees of proficiency in logical reasoning. Have them work together helping one another to use Venn Diagrams to organize the data logically.

TEKS ★ TAKS Resources

- circle manipulatives

Dana Center TEKS Toolkit
  Clarifying Activities (7.11)(A), (7.11)(B)
Visit: PHSchool.com
Web Code: arq-9045

Spreadsheets and Data Displays

TEKS ★ TAKS

(7.11)(A) To select and use an appropriate representation for displaying relationships among data, including bar graph and line graph

Also supports
(7.11)(B) TAKS Obj. 5

Dana Center TEKS Toolkit Clarifying Activities (7.11)(A), (7.11)(B)
Visit: PHSchool.com
Web Code: arq-9045

TEKS Math Background

A *spreadsheet* is an electronic worksheet that organizes data in columns and rows. Spreadsheets can perform calculations and graph data using different types of graphs. Line graphs show trends over time. A *double line graph* compares two lines on the same set of axes. A bar graph allows you to show the relative size of different categories. A *double bar graph* compares the relative sizes of two sets of data. When more than one set of data is graphed, *a legend* identifies the different data sets, or series.

More Math Background: p. 530C

Lesson Planning and Resources

See p. 530E for a list of the resources that support this lesson.

PowerPoint
Bell Ringer Practice

✓ **Check Skills You'll Need**
Use student page, transparency, or PowerPoint.

TAKS Daily Review 83
Use transparency.

✓ **Check Skills You'll Need**

1. Vocabulary Review
A(n) _?_ is the difference between values on a scale.
interval
Graph the data.

2.

Age (yr)	Height (in.)
1	29
2	33
3	36
4	39

See back of book.

GO for Help
Lesson 9-1

TEKS ★ TAKS

• (7.11)(A) To select and use an appropriate representation for displaying relationships among data, including bar graph and line graph **TAKS Obj. 5**
• (7.11)(B) To make inferences based on an analysis of data **TAKS Obj. 5**

🔊 **New Vocabulary** spreadsheet, cell, double bar graph, legend, double line graph

Why Learn This?

You can use spreadsheets to draw graphs and compare data, such as the number of households with VCRs or DVD players.

A **spreadsheet** is a tool for organizing and analyzing data. Spreadsheets are arranged in lettered columns and numbered rows.

A **cell** is a box where a column and a row of a spreadsheet meet. You use a letter and a number to identify each cell.

EXAMPLE Using a Spreadsheet

1 **Electronics** The spreadsheet below shows the number of U.S. households with VCRs and the number with DVD players.

a. What value is in cell C3? What does the value represent?

Column C and row 3 meet at cell C3. The value is 6. The value represents the number of U.S. households, in millions, with DVD players in 2000.

b. How many U.S. households had VCRs in 2004?

Cell B7 shows that 97 million U.S. households had VCRs in 2004.

U.S. Households (millions)

	A	B	C
1	Year	VCRs	DVDs
2	1999	89	2
3	2000	92	6
4	2001	95	15
5	2002	96	28
6	2003	96	42
7	2004	97	62

✓ **Quick Check**

95; 95 million households with VCRs in 2001

1. a. What value is in cell B4? What does the value represent?
   b. Which cell shows the number of DVD players in 2003? C6

Differentiated Instruction Solutions for All Learners

Special Needs L1
Show students how to run their fingers across the columns and rows of a spreadsheet to meet at a cell. Make a connection between this intersection, and locating points on a coordinate grid.

learning style: tactile

Below Level L2
Review simple bar and line graphs. Help students correlate the height of a bar with a number from the vertical axis. Help students find vertical axis values for specific points on a line graph.

learning style: visual

A **double bar graph** is a graph that uses bars to compare two sets of data. The **legend,** or key, identifies the data that are compared.

EXAMPLE Using a Double Bar Graph

Technology Tip

Using a spreadsheet, you can choose the data you want to graph. Then you can select the type of graph for the data.

2 In which year did the number of households with DVD players first exceed 50 million?

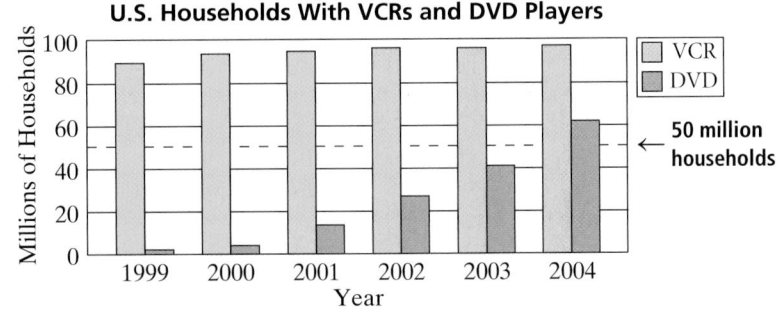

U.S. Households With VCRs and DVD Players

← 50 million households

U.S. households with DVD players first exceeded 50 million in 2004.

✓ Quick Check

2. In which year did the number of U.S. households with DVD players first exceed 10 million? **2001**

A **double line graph** is a graph that compares changes in two sets of data over time.

EXAMPLE Predicting With a Double Line Graph

3 **Estimation** Use the graph to estimate the year in which the number of households with DVD players equals the number of households with VCRs.

The two lines appear to intersect in 2005.

You can estimate that the number of households with DVD players equals the number with VCRs in 2005.

U.S. Households With VCRs and DVD Players

✓ Quick Check

3. Copy and extend the graph. Estimate the number of DVD players in U.S. households in 2006. **Answers may vary. Sample: about 130 million**

---

2. Teach

Activity Lab

Use before the lesson.

All in One Teaching Resources
Activity Lab 11-2: Spreadsheets and Data Displays

Guided Instruction

Example 1
Have students trace down column C and across row 3 with their index fingers so that they intersect at C3.

Example 3
Students may confuse the use of bar graphs and line graphs. Bar graphs are used to compare amounts, while line graphs show changes over time. A double bar graph compares two sets of data. A double line graph compares the trends of two sets of data.

PowerPoint
Additional Examples

1 The spreadsheet below shows the number of graduates in dentistry and medicine.

a. Find the value in cell B5. **43**

b. In what year were the number of graduates from both schools the same? **1996**

	A	B	C
1	Year	Dentistry	Medicine
2	1996	48	48
3	1997	36	51
4	1998	40	56
5	1999	43	42
6	2000	65	38
7	2001	61	46

Advanced Learners L4
Explain when a triple bar graph might be used. **when comparing three sets of data**
Have students construct a triple bar graph for a topic of their choice.

Pre-AP™

English Language Learners ELL
Make sure that students understand the difference between columns and rows. Show them pictures of columns in front of homes, and point out that columns are vertical. Show them rows of chairs or tables, and point out that rows are horizontal.

learning style: visual

2 When did more people first obtain news from the radio than the newspaper? **1990**

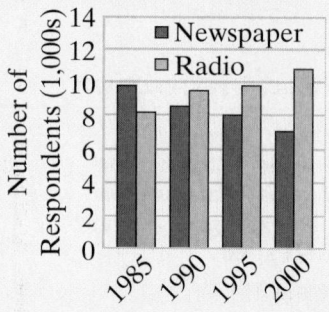

Source of News

3 During what period of time did whole milk consumption decrease the most? **between 1980 and 1985**

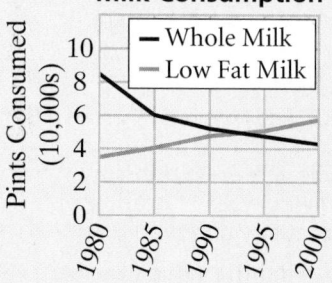

Milk Consumption

All in One Teaching Resources
- Daily Notetaking Guide 11-2 **L3**
- Adapted Notetaking 11-2 **L1**

Closure

- *What is a spreadsheet?* **an electronic tool for organizing and analyzing data**
- *How does a legend help you interpret a double bar graph or a double line graph?* **A legend identifies each set of data.**

Check Your Understanding

Use the data in the spreadsheet.

1. How did Abby earn $50 in June?
   lawn mowing
2. How much money did Abby earn babysitting in July? **$62**
3. Abby's goal was to earn $250 during the summer for a new bicycle. Did she reach her goal? **yes**

Abby's Summer Earnings ($)

	A	B	C
1	Month	Babysitting	Lawn Mowing
2	June	36	50
3	July	62	40
4	August	55	40

Homework Exercises

For more exercises, see Extra Skills and Word Problems.

GO for Help

For Exercises	See Examples
4–12	1
13–17	2
18–21	3

A Give the content or value of each cell.

4. A2 **dog**   5. D2 **26**
6. B3 **46**   7. C2 **37**

Nutrition in One Brand's Dog and Cat Foods
(Calories per 100 Calories)

	A	B	C	D
1	Animal	Fat	Carbohydrates	Protein
2	Dog	37	37	26
3	Cat	46	26	28

Which cell contains the given word or value?

8. Protein **D1** 9. Animal **A1** 10. 28 **D3**   11. 46 **B3**   12. Cat **A3**

Libraries Use the double bar graph below for Exercises 13–17.

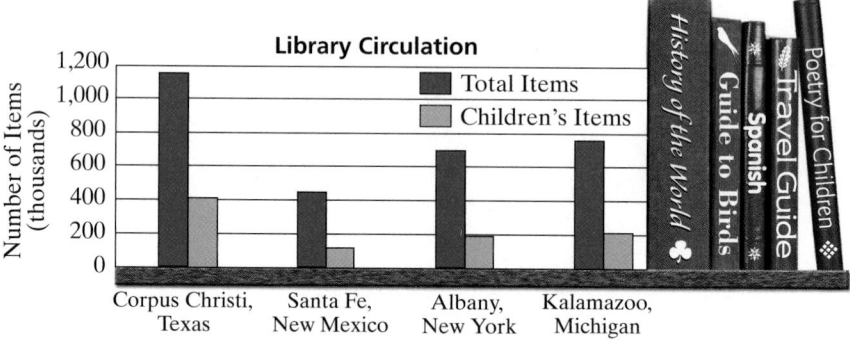

16. Corpus Christi, Texas; Albany, New York; and Kalamazoo, Michigan

17. Albany, New York, and Kalamazoo, Michigan

13. Which library circulated the most children's items?
    Corpus Christi, Texas
14. Which library had the greatest total circulation?
    Corpus Christi, Texas
15. Which libraries circulated fewer than 600,000 children's items?
    all of them
16. Which libraries circulated more than 500,000 total items?
    16–17. See left.
17. **Estimation** Which two libraries had about the same circulation?

Industry Use the double line graph below for Exercises 18–21.

18. About how many bikes were produced in 1960? **about 20 million**

19. In which years did automobile production exceed 23 million? **1975–2000**

20. **Reasoning** The two lines begin to separate widely after 1967. Why might this be? **See left.**

21. **Estimation** About what year was bicycle production closest to automobile production? **1965**

20. Answers may vary. Sample: Because of gas shortages in the 1970s, more people may have started riding bikes.

Worldwide Bicycle and Automobile Production

Year

SOURCE: Worldwatch Institute

(B) GPS 22. Guided Problem Solving Use the graph. Estimate the total population increase of the four states from 1990 to 2000.

22. about 2,300,000

- The 1990 total population of the four states was ▓.
- The 2000 total population of the four states was ▓.
- Find the population increase.

State Populations

SOURCE: U.S. Census Bureau. Go to PHSchool.com for a data update. Web Code: arg-9041

23. **Writing in Math** Describe how you would display measurements of a pet's growth over several years. What measurements would you use? How would you display them? **See margin.**

Sacajawea Middle School Enrollment

Grade	Girls	Boys
Grade 6	37	48
Grade 7	50	44
Grade 8	45	40

24. **Multiple Choice** Which graph best represents the data at the left? **A**

Ⓐ Sacajawea Middle School Enrollment

Ⓒ Sacajawea Middle School Enrollment

Ⓑ Sacajawea Middle School Enrollment

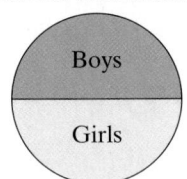

Ⓓ Sacajawea Middle School Enrollment

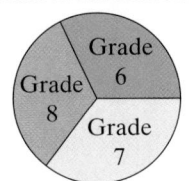

Online lesson quiz, PHSchool.com, Web Code: ara-1102   11-2 Spreadsheets and Data Displays   **541**

23. Answers may vary. Sample: I would use the measurement of my pet every six months and display the data on a line graph.

3. Practice

Assignment Guide

Check Your Understanding
Go over Exercises 1–3 in class before assigning the Homework Exercises.

Homework Exercises
A Practice by Example   4–21
B Apply Your Skills   22–26
C Challenge   27
TEKS ★ TAKS Tune-Up and Mixed Review   28–32

Homework Quick Check
To check students' understanding of key skills and concepts, go over Exercises 15, 21, 23, 24, and 25.

Differentiated Instruction Resources

PowerPoint

Lesson Quiz

	A	B	C
1	Date	Key West	Juneau
2	9/1	71	70
3	9/2	69	69
4	9/3	70	69
5	9/4	70	71
6	9/5	71	72

1. What value is in cell B4? **70**

2. In which cell is the value 72? **C6**

3. Make a double bar graph to display the data contained in the spreadsheet.

27a–b. See back of book.

30. 216 in.^{2}

31. 1,332 m^2

32. 1,536 ft^2

---

25. Double line graph; line graphs are best for showing change over time.

25. Reasoning You want to show grade averages in English and math every month throughout the year. Should you use a double bar or a double line graph? Explain.

26. Data Collection Find the number of students in several grades of your school last year. Find the number of students in those same grades this year. Record your data in a spreadsheet. **Check students' work.**

27. Challenge Make a double line graph of the data in the spreadsheet. Data points are (x_1, y_1) and (x_2, y_2).
  a. From the graph, find the missing y-values in the spreadsheet.
  b. Estimation Estimate the coordinates of the point of intersection of the lines.
  27a–b. See margin.

GO for Help

For help finding the intersection of two lines, go to Lesson 7-1, Example 2.

	A	B	C	D
1	x_1	y_1	x_2	y_2
2	0	1	0	4
3	1	?	1	5
4	2	?	2	?
5	3	10	3	?
6	4	13	4	8
7	5	16	5	9
8	6	19	6	10

TEKS ★ TAKS Tune-Up and Mixed Review

TAKS Objective 5
TEKS (7.11)(B)

28. Which statement is NOT supported by the graph? **D**
  A Computer use increased in Japan from 2001 to 2004.
  B The United States had about 6 times as many computer users as the United Kingdom in 2001.
  C There were more U.S. computer users in 2004 than in all the other listed countries combined.
  D Germany had twice as many computer users as Japan in 2001.

Computer Use by Country

(bar graph with legend: 2001, 2004; y-axis: Millions of People; x-axis: United States, Japan, Germany, United Kingdom)

TAKS Objective 6
TEKS (7.15)(B)

29. In quadrilateral $FGHJ$, the measures of $\angle F$, $\angle G$, and $\angle H$ are 95°, 105°, and 45°. What is the measure of $\angle J$? Justify your reasoning. **F**
  F 115°; the sum of the angle measures of a quadrilateral is 360°.
  G 125°; the sum of the angle measures of a quadrilateral is 360°.
  H 135°; $\angle J$ is supplementary to $\angle H$.
  J 175°; the sum of the angle measures of a quadrilateral is 420°.

GO for Help

Lesson 8-9

Find the surface area of each prism. **30–32. See margin.**

30.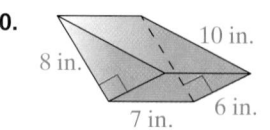
10 in.
8 in.
7 in.
6 in.

31.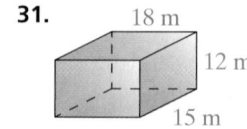
18 m
12 m
15 m

32.
16 ft
16 ft
16 ft

---

542 Chapter 11 Displaying and Analyzing Data

TEKS ★ TAKS Resources

• TAKS Strategies, p. 571
• TAKS Tune-Up, pp. 575–577

TAKS Tune-Up Kit

• TAKS Daily Review Transparencies
• TAKS Review and Preparation Workbook
• TAKS Strategies with Transparencies
• Texas Progress Monitoring Assessments

Alternative Assessment

Have students work in pairs. Each student writes a sample spreadsheet using real-world data. Partners exchange spreadsheets and make either a double bar or double line graph using the data in their partner's spreadsheets. Students check each other's graphs and share their results with the class.

(Enrichment/Reteaching side panel)

Enrichment 11-2 **L4**

Reteaching 11-2 Spreadsheets and Data **L2**

A **spreadsheet** is one way to organize data.

Columns are labeled A, B, C, and so on. Rows are numbered 1, 2, 3, and so on. The box where column B and row 3 meet is called **cell** B3. The *value* in cell B3 is 10.

You can use the data from this spreadsheet to make a **double bar graph**. A double bar graph compares two sets of data. The **legend**, or key, tells what kinds of data the graph is comparing.

Weekly Butter and Margarine Sales

	A	B	C
1	Day	Butter	Margarine
2	Monday	9	7
3	Tuesday	10	9
4	Wednesday	7	6
5	Thursday	9	6
6	Friday	10	6
7	Saturday	11	9

• Spreadsheet column A gives the labels for the horizontal axis.
• Spreadsheet column B gives the heights for one set of bars and one set of points.
• Spreadsheet column C gives the heights for another set of bars and another set of points.

You can compare changes over time of two sets of data with a double line graph.

Use the data in the spreadsheet for exercises 1–4.

1. What is the value in cell B4? cell C2?
78; 39

2. In which cell is the year 2000? 1997?
A5; A2

3. Make a double bar graph from the spreadsheet. Include a legend.
See Answers pages.

4. Make a double line graph from the spreadsheet. Include a legend.
See Answers pages.

Percents of Families Who Prefer Frozen and Fresh Vegetables

	A	B	C
1	Year	Frozen	Fresh
2	1997	61	39
3	1998	70	30
4	1999	78	22
5	2000	84	16

Graphing Using Spreadsheets

You can use spreadsheet software to graph data.

TEKS ★ TAKS

(7.11)(A) To select and use an appropriate representation for presenting and displaying relationships among collected data **TAKS** Obj. 5

(7.13)(D) To select technology to solve problems

(7.14)(B) To evaluate the effectiveness of different representations to communicate ideas

ACTIVITY

1. Enter the data in the table below into a spreadsheet. Use three column headings: Year, Men's Winning Time, and Women's Winning Time.

Olympic Winning Times in 400 Meters Freestyle (min)

Year	1980	1984	1988	1992	1996	2000	2004
Men	3.51	3.51	3.47	3.45	3.48	3.41	3.43
Women	4.09	4.07	4.04	4.07	4.07	4.06	4.05

1–2. Check students' work.

2. Use the graphing capability of the software. Show the data as a double bar graph. Label the horizontal scale "Year" and label the vertical scale "Men's and Women's Winning Times." Title the graph "Olympic Winning Times in 400 Meters Freestyle."

3. **Data Analysis** Use the graph to compare the winning times for men and women.

   3. It represents the differences between the winning times for men and for women.

4. Make a double line graph. Label the scales as you did in Exercise 2. **Check students' work.**

5. **Data Analysis** How is the double line graph similar to the double bar graph in Exercise 2? It compares the same information.

6. Which display, a double bar graph or a double line graph, do you prefer to use for this set of data? Explain. **See margin.**

Use the bar graph displayed at the right.

7. Use spreadsheet software to make the graph. **Check students' work.**

8. Use the software to convert the graph to a double line graph. **Check students' work.**

9. Which display, a double bar graph or a double line graph, do you prefer for this set of data? Explain. **See margin.**

10. (**Algebra**) Suppose 380 boys were surveyed. About how many boys chose tomatoes as their favorite burger topping? **about 228 boys**

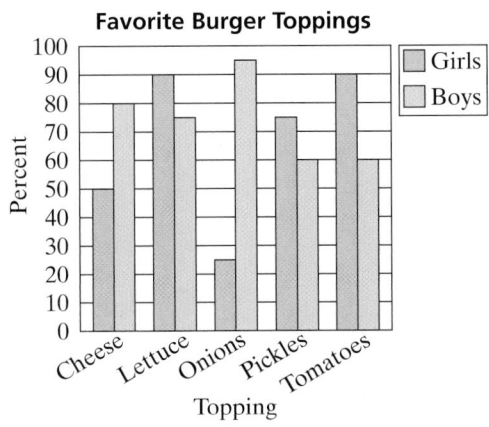

Favorite Burger Toppings

6. A double line graph better shows the differences between the winning times of men and of women for each year.

9. A double bar graph better shows the difference in topping preferences between girls and boys.

Graphing Using Spreadsheets

Students use spreadsheets to graph data. This will extend the work they did with spreadsheets in Lesson 11-2.

Guided Instruction

Review with students how spreadsheets display data. Conduct steps 1–6 of the Activity as a class and ask questions, such as:

- *How would it change the appearance of the bar graph if you labeled the axes the opposite way?* The bars would be horizontal instead of vertical.
- *What does each line on the line graph represent?* One line shows data for men and the other lines shows data for women.
- *How would both graphs show a third column for children?* as a third bar or line

Exercises

Have students work independently on the Exercises. Circulate and check students' work. Keep in mind, students may be unfamiliar with the software program.

Differentiated Instruction

Advanced Learners **L4**
Have students create their own set of data and represent it in all three forms, spreadsheet, double bar graph, and double line graph.

TEKS ★ TAKS Resources

- spreadsheet software with graphing capability

Dana Center TEKS Toolkit
   **Clarifying Activities (7.11)(A),
   (7.13)(D), (7.14)(B)**
Visit: PHSchool.com
Web Code: arq-9045

TEKS ⭐ TAKS

(7.11)(A) To select and use an appropriate representation for presenting and displaying relationships among data including stem-and-leaf plot **TAKS Obj. 5**

Also supports
(7.11)(B) TAKS Obj. 5, (7.12)(A) TAKS Obj. 5

Dana Center TEKS Toolkit Clarifying Activities (7.11)(A), (7.11)(B), (7.12)(A)
Visit: PHSchool.com
Web Code: arq-9045

TEKS Math Background

A stem-and-leaf plot separates each data value into a stem and a leaf. The leaf lists the values as often as they appear in the data. A *double stem-and-leaf plot* compares two sets of data in one diagram. Stem-and-leaf plots are much like line plots because each data value is represented in the plot.

More Math Background: p. 530C

Lesson Planning and Resources

See p. 530E for a list of the resources that support this lesson.

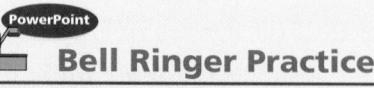
Bell Ringer Practice

☑ **Check Skills You'll Need**
Use student page, transparency, or PowerPoint.

TAKS Daily Review 84
Use transparency.

☑ Check Skills You'll Need

1. Vocabulary Review
What is a *median*?
1–4. See below.
Find the median of each set of data.

2. 24, 42, 51, 25, 63

3. 5.8, 6.9, 7.4, 3.9, 6.4

4. 110, 120, 130, 125

 for Help
Lesson 1-10

Check Skills You'll Need

1. the middle value of a set of data

2. 42

3. 6.4

4. 122.5

TEKS ⭐ TAKS

- **(7.11)(A)** To select and use an appropriate representation for presenting and displaying relationships among data, including stem-and-leaf plot **TAKS Obj. 5**
- **(7.11)(B)** To make inferences based on an analysis of data **TAKS Obj. 5**
- **(7.12)(A)** To describe a set of data using median and range **TAKS Obj. 5**

🔊 **New Vocabulary** stem-and-leaf plot

Why Learn This?

You can use a stem-and-leaf plot to compare measurements such as the different heights of teammates.

A **stem-and-leaf plot** is a graph that uses the digits of each number to show the data distribution. Each data value is broken into a "stem" (digit or digits on the left) and a "leaf" (digit or digits on the right).

EXAMPLE   Making a Stem-and-Leaf Plot

1 **Sports** The list gives the height in inches of each player on the San Antonio Spurs basketball team during a season. Make a stem-and-leaf plot of the data: 77 74 81 83 78 84 79 82 75 82 79 79.

Step 1 Write the stems. All the data values are in the 70s and 80s, so use 7 to represent 70 and 8 to represent 80. Draw a vertical line to the right of the stems.

stems →
| 7 |
| 8 |

Step 2 Write the leaves. For these data, the leaves are the values in the ones place.

| 7 | 7489599 | ← leaves |
| 8 | 13422 | |

Step 3 Make the stem-and-leaf plot with the leaves in order from least to greatest. Add a key to explain the leaves. Add a title.

San Antonio Spurs Heights of Players

| 7 | 4578999 |
| 8 | 12234 |

Key → **Key:** 7 | 4 means 74 in.

☑ Quick Check

1. Make a stem-and-leaf plot of the wind speeds (in miles per hour) recorded during a storm: 9, 14, 30, 16, 18, 25, 29, 25, 38, 34, 33.

See back of book.

Differentiated Instruction   Solutions for All Learners

Special Needs L1
Provide a copy of Example 1 to the students. Have them circle the digits that will represent the "stem" in the stem-and-leaf plot, and underline the digits that will be the "leaves."

learning style: visual

Below Level L2
Give students slips of paper with each player's height on them. Have them cut the slips in the appropriate place, discard all but one of the first halves and align the second halves appropriately to make a stem-and-leaf plot.

learning style: tactile

You can use a stem-and-leaf plot to compare two sets of data. From a stem, the leaves increase in value outward in each direction.

EXAMPLE Analyzing a Stem-and-Leaf Plot

② **Weather** Use the stem-and-leaf plot below. How many times did each city receive 3.5 in. of precipitation in a month?

Monthly Precipitation (in.)

Charlotte, N.C.		Portland, Me.
7	2	9
9 8 8 7 7 5 5 4 4 2	3	1 1 3 4 5 6 7 9
4	4	1 5
	5	2

← Find the values with a stem of 3 and leaves of 5.

Key: $4.3 \leftarrow 3 \mid 4 \mid 1 \rightarrow 4.1$

Charlotte twice received 3.5 in. of precipitation in a month. Portland received 3.5 in. of precipitation in a month only once.

✓ **Quick Check**

2. Which city had a higher median monthly precipitation? Explain.

See left.

2. Charlotte, N.C.; Charlotte had a median of 3.6 in., while Portland had a median of 3.55 in.

EXAMPLE Application: U.S. Presidential Elections

③ **TAKS Multiple Choice** The plot below shows the number of electoral votes for president each state (plus the District of Columbia) has.

Number of Electoral Votes by State

0	3 3 3 3 3 3 3 3 3 4 4 4 4 4 5 5 5 5 5 6 6 6 7 7 7 7 8 8 9 9 9
1	0 0 0 0 1 1 1 1 2 3 5 5 5 5 7
2	0 1 1 7
3	1 4
4	
5	5

Key: 0 | 3 means 3 votes

Which statement is best supported by the stem-and-leaf plot?

Ⓐ The mean is 2.5 votes. Ⓒ The mode is 8 votes.

Ⓑ The median is 8 votes. Ⓓ The range is 55 votes.

The middle value is 8, so the median is 8. The correct answer is choice B.

✓ **Quick Check**

3. Find the correct values for mean, mode, and range in Example 3.

10.5; 3; 52

TAKS Tip

List the data from the least to the greatest value. Then find the mean, median, mode, or range.

11-3 Stem-and-Leaf Plots **545**

2. Teach

Activity Lab
Use before the lesson.

All in One **Teaching Resources**
Activity Lab 11-3: Stem-and-Leaf Plots

Guided Instruction

Example 2
Point out that the double stem-and-leaf plot uses one set of stems for both sets of leaves.

PowerPoint
Additional Examples

① Use the table below. Draw a stem-and-leaf plot of the data.
High Temperatures (°F)

Week 1	81	73	67	81	77	79	73
Week 2	80	74	61	66	70	67	73

6	1 6 7 7
7	0 3 3 3 4 7 9
8	0 1 1

6|1 means 61

② Compare the two sets of data in the stem-and-leaf plot.

Waiting for the Doctor

Monday		Friday
2 1	0	5 6
0	1	1 1 4
6 1	2	3 4 6 6
3	3	5 5
9	4	7 8 8

1 min ← 1 | 0 | 5 → 5 min

a. Which day had the longest wait time? Monday

b. How long was the longest wait? 49 min

③ Does the data above support this statement? The average wait time for the doctor is about 24 minutes. yes

All in One **Teaching Resources**
• Daily Notetaking Guide 11-3 L3
• Adapted Notetaking 11-3 L1

Closure

• *What is a stem-and-leaf plot?*
a graph that uses the digits of each number to show the shape of the data

3. Practice

Assignment Guide

Check Your Understanding
Go over Exercises 1–5 in class before assigning the Homework Exercises.

Homework Exercises
A Practice by Example   6–13
B Apply Your Skills   14–16
C Challenge   17
TEKS ★ (TAKS) Tune-Up and
    Mixed Review   18–20

Homework Quick Check
To check students' understanding of key skills and concepts, go over Exercises 7, 9, 12, 15, and 16.

Differentiated Instruction Resources

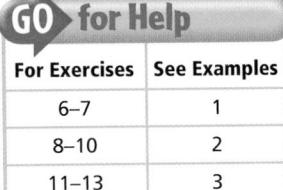

Check Your Understanding

1. **Vocabulary** In a stem-and-leaf plot, what is the difference between a stem and a leaf? **The stem is the digit or digits on the left and the leaf is the digit or digits on the right.**

Use the stem-and-leaf plot at the left.

```
4 | 3 6 7
5 | 1 2
6 | 1 7
7 | 1 8
8 | 2 6 8
```
Key: 8 | 2 means 82

2. **Number Sense** What does the number 6 represent when it is a stem? A leaf? **60; 6**

3. How many data values are in the set? **12**

4. What is the least value? The greatest value? **43; 88**

5. Copy and complete the graph with new data items 60 and 72.
   See margin.

Homework Exercises

For more exercises, see Extra Skills and Word Problems.

GO for Help

For Exercises	See Examples
6–7	1
8–10	2
11–13	3

Ⓐ **Draw a stem-and-leaf plot for each set of data.** 6–7. See margin.

6. sales of twelve companies (millions of dollars):
   1.3 1.4 2.3 1.4 2.4 2.5 3.9 1.4 1.3 2.5 3.6 1.4

7. high temperatures (°F) in a desert:
   99 113 112 98 100 103 101 111 104 108 109 112 113 118

Height Use the stem-and-leaf plot at the right to answer each question.

Student Height (in.)

Female		Male
7 4 3 1 0 0	5	6 7
8 5 4 1 0	6	2 3 5 5 6 7 9
0	7	1 2 3 4 6

Key: 61 ← 1 | 6 | 3 → 63

GPS 8. How many males are 65 in. tall? **2 males**

9. What is the height of the shortest male? The shortest female? **56 in.; 50 in.**

10. What is the tallest female's height? **70 in.**

Is the statement supported by the graph above? Explain.

11. The median height for females is 57 in.
    No; the median height for females is 58.5 in.

12. The mode of all heights is 65 in.
    Yes; 65 in. occurs the largest number of times.

13. The range of heights for males is 20 in.
    Yes; 76 − 56 = 20.

GPS Ⓑ 14. **Guided Problem Solving** Find the mean, median, and range of the data in the graph.
   - What is the place value of the leaves?
   - What is the order of the data from least to greatest?
   - How many data items are there?
     18, 18.4, 3.8

Distances Walked by Fundraisers (km)

```
16 | 1 1 2 3 5 5
17 | 0 2 2
18 | 4 5 8 9
19 | 3 6 7 9 9 9
```
Key: 19 | 3 means 19.3

5–7. See back of book.

Number of Counties in Western States

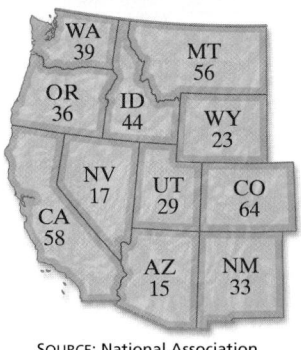

SOURCE: National Association of Counties

15. Multiple Choice Which graph best represents the data? C

(A)
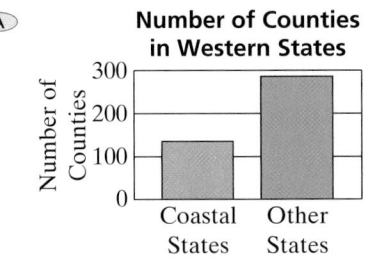
Number of Counties in Western States

(C)
Number of Counties in Western States

```
1 | 5 7
2 | 3 9
3 | 3 6 9
4 | 4
5 | 6 8
6 | 4
```
Key: 1 | 5 means 15 counties

(B)
Number of Counties in Western States
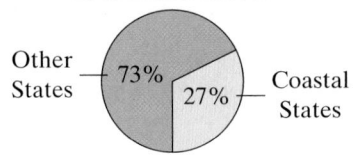
Other States 73%   27% Coastal States

(D)
Number of Counties in Western States

Number of Counties

GO Online
Homework Help
Visit: PHSchool.com
Web Code: are-1103

16. a. Data Collection Measure the width of the hands of at least 10 people. Use metric units. Make a stem-and-leaf plot of the data. 16a–b. Check students' work.

b. Writing in Math Write two true statements about the data.

(C) **17. Challenge** The median of a data set is 48. Find the value of the missing data item: 23 34 42 ■ 62 67. 54

TEKS ★ TAKS Tune-Up and Mixed Review

TAKS Objective 5
TEKS (7.11)(B)

18. The amount of iron in high-protein foods is shown. Which statement is NOT supported by the data? C

(A) There are three foods with 2.1 mg of protein or more.

(B) The modes are both 0.7 and 2.6 mg.

(C) The mean and median are the same.

(D) The median is 1.45 mg.

Iron in Three Ounces of High-Protein Foods (mg)

```
0 | 7 7 9
1 | 1 4 5 6
2 | 1 6 6
```
Key: 0 | 7 means 0.7

TAKS Objective 2
TEKS (7.3)(A)

19. A store is having a 30%-off sale. Hunter opens a store charge card and gets an additional 20% off his first purchase. What is the final cost of an item that was priced originally at $25? H

(F) $10.00   (G) $12.50   (H) $14.00   (J) $17.50

GO for Help
Lesson 10-7

20. A figure lies entirely in Quadrant I of a coordinate plane. In which quadrant will the figure lie after a 270° rotation about (0, 0)? IV

Alternative Assessment

Have students work in pairs to find data in almanacs, textbooks, or encyclopedias that can be displayed in a stem-and-leaf plot. Have pairs share their displays with the class.

TEKS ★ TAKS Resources

• TAKS Strategies, p. 571
• TAKS Tune-Up, pp. 575–577

TAKS Tune-Up Kit
• TAKS Daily Review Transparencies
• TAKS Review and Preparation Workbook
• TAKS Strategies with Transparencies
• Texas Progress Monitoring Assessments

4. Assess & Reteach

PowerPoint
Lesson Quiz

1. Make a stem-and-leaf plot for this set of data.
points scored by winning teams in the first fifteen Super Bowls:
35 33 16 23 16 24 14 24 16 21 32 27 35 31 27

```
1 | 4 6 6 6
2 | 1 3 4 4 7 7
3 | 1 2 3 5 5
```

2. Using the stem-and-leaf plot, find the mean, median, and mode scores. mean 24.9, median 24, mode 16

547

Choosing the Best Display

Students learn to choose the most appropriate method of displaying sets of data among all the methods they have learned.

Guided Instruction

Review all the methods of data display that students have learned so far: line plot, Venn diagram, stem-and-leaf plot, double line graph, circle graph, double bar graph. As you go over the Example with the class, ask:

- *Why should a Venn diagram be eliminated for the results of the survey?* People can only choose one use for the park so there will never be any overlapping responses.
- *What situation could you represent with a double line graph?* Sample: people who bike in the park and people who bring dogs to the park over a span of time
- *If you used a circle graph to represent the data, what would it look like?* The circle would be split into four sections, each proportional to a number of responses.

Exercises

Review the Exercises as a class, having volunteers give each answer and the reasoning for their choice. Have students evaluate the effectiveness of the different representations to communicate the data.

Differentiated Instruction

Advanced Learners L4
Have students create a set of data for one of the situations in the Exercises and represent the data with the appropriate display.

TEKS ★ TAKS Resources

Dana Center TEKS Toolkit Clarifying Activities (7.11)(A)
Visit: PHSchool.com
Web Code: arq-9045

11-3b Activity Lab

Data Analysis

TEKS ★ TAKS

(7.11)(A) To select and use an appropriate representation for presenting and displaying data and justify the selection
TAKS Obj. 5

Choosing the Best Display

When you display data, you should consider which type of display best represents the data.

EXAMPLE

A city council conducts a survey to decide how to develop a new public park. The council asks people to choose one of four park uses, as shown in the table. Choose the best display to represent the data. Explain your choice.

Step 1 Summarize the purpose of the data display.
The display must compare data for two age groups.

Step 2 Narrow down your options.
There are too many responses to use a line plot. Each person chose one use for the park. Since there is no overlap, you can eliminate a Venn diagram. You are not showing the distribution of data over a range, so you can eliminate a stem-and-leaf plot. There is no change over time, so you can eliminate a line graph.

Step 3 Choose one of the remaining displays.
Both a circle graph and a double bar graph can compare parts to wholes. In this situation, the table compares two sets of data across the same four categories, so the best option is a double bar graph.

City Park Use Survey Results

Use	18 and Under	Over 18
Tennis	72	86
Basketball	114	95
Skate Park	173	57
Garden	48	139

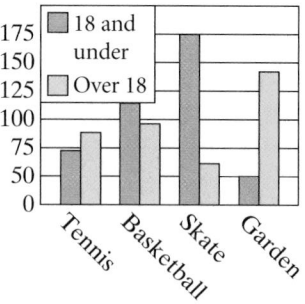

Exercises

Reasoning Match each data set at the left with the best type of data display at the right. Explain your choices. 1–6. See margin.

1. the number of students who hold part-time jobs, tutor, play sports, or do a combination of all three activities

2. favorite pizza topping, by percent of students in a class

3. the popularity of different bikes among boys and among girls

4. changes in desktop and laptop computer prices over time

5. the height in centimeters of each student in a class

6. the number of letters in the first names of students in your class

A. line plot
B. double line graph
C. double bar graph
D. stem-and-leaf plot
E. circle graph
F. Venn diagram

---

1. F; there is an overlap in the categories.

2. E; the data show parts of a whole.

3. C; the data compare categories of two groups.

4. B; a line graph shows change in data over time.

5. D; stem-and-leaf plots best show distribution of data.

6. A; a line plot compares frequency of the data.

✓ Checkpoint Quiz 1

Lessons 11-1 through 11-3

1. Make a frequency table and a line plot of the data below.
   5 7 8 3 5 4 6 7 8 9 1 2 5 4 2 1 3   See margin.

2. Graph the data below. Explain why you chose the graph you drew.
   See margin.

Art Show Attendance

Day	Sun.	Mon.	Tue.	Wed.	Thur.	Fri.	Sat.
Number of Adults	54	29	22	28	12	15	49
Number of Children	32	21	16	20	8	10	36

Give the content or value (millions of dollars) of each cell in the spreadsheet.

U.S. Service Industries Revenue 1998–2003

3. B3   4. A1   5. A3   6. B1
   $6,527 million   Industry   Health

Tell which cell has the given word or value in the spreadsheet.

7. 6,527 **B3**   8. Health **A3**   9. 983 **B2**

10. Make a stem-and-leaf plot of these 18-hole golf scores.
    93 120 112 89 87 124 117 95 117 121 113 95
    See margin.

	A	B	
1	Industry	Revenue (millions)	
2	Trucking	$983	
3	Health	$6,527	
4	Broadcasting	$2,734	

11-4a Activity Lab

Data Collection

Writing Survey Questions

1–5. Check students' work.

1. Choose a topic about which you would like people's opinions. Write five survey questions that do not influence the answer.

2. You want to survey people who will give you all kinds of responses. What group of people should you survey?

3. How many people should you survey?

4. **Data Collection** Conduct the survey. Display the results of your survey in a graph.

5. Consider the results of your survey. Do you think your questions influenced the answers? If so, how would you change the questions?

549

1–2. See back of book.
10. See back of book.

Math Background

Surveys are used to gather information about certain topics. A survey focuses on a certain group, or *population*. Since it is often difficult to survey each member of the population, a *random sample* is chosen. A random sample gives each member of the population an equal chance of being selected. If the sample is asked a *biased question*, or if the sample is not selected at random, the results of a survey may be misleading.

More Math Background: p. 530D

Lesson Planning and Resources

See p. 530E for a list of the resources that support this lesson.

Bell Ringer Practice

✓ **Check Skills You'll Need**
Use student page, transparency, or PowerPoint.

(TAKS) **Daily Review 85**
Use transparency.

Check Skills You'll Need

1. Vocabulary Review
A ___?___ is a ratio that compares a number to 100. **percent**

Write each ratio as a percent.

2. 4 out of 5 **80%**

3. 10 out of 40 **25%**

4. 14 out of 200 **7%**

 for Help
Lesson 6-1

What You'll Learn

To identify a random sample and to write a survey question

◀» **New Vocabulary** population, sample, random sample, biased question

Why Learn This?

You can use a survey to gather information from a group of people. Pollsters use surveys to understand group preferences.

A **population** is a group of objects or people. The population of an election is all the people who vote in that election. It is not practical to ask all the voters how they expect to vote. Pollsters select a **sample,** or a part of the population. A sample is called a **random sample** when each member of a population has the same chance of being selected.

EXAMPLE Identifying a Random Sample

1 You survey customers at a mall. You want to know which stores they shop at the most. Which sample is more likely to be random? Explain.

a. You survey shoppers in a computer store.

Customers that shop in a particular store may not represent all the shoppers in the entire mall. This sample is not random.

b. You walk around the mall and survey shoppers.

By walking around, you give everyone in the mall the same chance to be surveyed. This sample is more likely to be random.

1a. Answers may vary. Sample: Less likely to be random; you may get only people shopping after work.

b. More likely to be random; you won't just get people shopping after work.

✓ **Quick Check**

1. You survey a store's customers. You ask why they chose the store. Which sample is more likely to be random? Explain.
   a. You survey 20 people at the entrance from 5:00 P.M. to 8:00 P.M.
   b. You survey 20 people at the entrance throughout the day.

1a–b. See left.

Differentiated Instruction **Solutions for All Learners**

Special Needs L1
Ask student to work in pairs. Have them generate lists of adjectives that might make questions biased or unfair in the Homework Exercises. For example, they might list words such as *unhealthy* and *nutritious,* or *harsh* and *inspiring*.

learning style: verbal

Below Level L2
Have students make a list of words and phrases that may indicate a biased question, such as *all* or *never*. Students should also include double negatives.

learning style: verbal

When you conduct a survey, ask questions that do not influence the answer. A **biased question** is a question that makes an unjustified assumption or makes some answers appear better than others.

EXAMPLE Identifying Biased Questions

2 **Music** Is each question *biased* or *fair*? Explain.

a. "Do you think that soothing classical music is more pleasing than the loud, obnoxious pop music that teenagers listen to?"

This question is biased against pop music. It implies that all pop music is loud and that only teenagers listen to it. The adjectives "soothing" and "obnoxious" may also influence responses.

b. "Which do you think is the most common age group of people who like pop music?"

This question is fair. It does not assume that listeners of pop music fall into only one age group.

c. "Do you prefer classical music or pop music?"

This question is fair. It does not make any assumptions about classical music, pop music, or people.

2a. Biased; the question implies that meat is greasy and vegetables are healthy.

b. Fair; the question makes no assumptions about pizza toppings.

✓ **Quick Check**

2. Is each question *biased* or *fair*? Explain. 2a–b. See left.
   a. Do you prefer greasy meat or healthy vegetables on your pizza?
   b. Which pizza topping do you like best?

✓ **Check Your Understanding**

Vocabulary Match each statement with the appropriate term.

1. a group of objects or people **C**
2. makes some answers appear better **A**
3. gives members of a group the **B** same chance to be selected

   A. biased question
   B. random sample
   C. population

You want to determine the favorite spectator sport of seventh-graders at your school. You ask the first 20 seventh-graders who arrive at a soccer game, "Is soccer your favorite sport to watch?"

4. seventh-graders; seventh-graders attending a soccer game

4. What was the population of your survey? What was the sample?

5. The survey (was, was not) random. **was not**

6. You used a (biased, fair) question. **biased**

551

3. Practice

Assignment Guide

Check Your Understanding
Go over Exercises 1–6 in class before assigning the Homework Exercises.

Homework Exercises
A Practice by Example 7–15
B Apply Your Skills 16–21
C Challenge 22
TEKS ★ TAKS Tune-Up
and Mixed Review 23–27

Homework Quick Check
To check students' understanding of key skills and concepts, go over Exercises 9, 13, 17, 19, and 20.

Differentiated Instruction Resources

Adapted Practice 11-4 L1

Practice 11-4 L3
Random Samples and

You want to survey students in your school about their exercise habits. Tell whether the situations described in exercises 1 and 2 are likely to give a random sample of the population. Explain.

1. You select every tenth student on an alphabetical list of the students in your school. You survey the selected students in their first-period classes.
random sample; the selected students represent the population.

2. At lunchtime you stand by a vending machine. You survey every student who buys something from the vending machine.
Not a random sample; students that use the vending machine may not represent all types of students.

Is each question *biased* or *fair*? Rewrite biased questions as fair questions.

3. Do you think bike helmets should be mandatory for all bike riders?
Fair

4. Do you prefer the natural beauty of hardwood floors in your home?
Biased; do you prefer hardwood floors in your home?

5. Do you exercise regularly?
Fair

6. Do you eat at least the recommended number of servings of fruits and vegetables to ensure a healthy and long life?
Biased; how many servings of fruits and vegetables do you eat?

7. Do you prefer the look and feel of thick lush carpeting in your living room?
Biased; do you prefer thick carpeting?

8. Do you take a daily multiple vitamin to supplement your diet?
Fair

9. Do you read the newspaper to be informed about world events?
Fair

10. Do you feel that the TV news is a sensational portrayal of life's problems?
Biased; does TV news portray life accurately?

11-4 • Guided Problem Solving GPS L3

Student Page 553, Exercise 19:

Parks Suppose you are gathering information about visitors to Yosemite National Park. You survey every tenth person entering the park. Would you get a random sample of visitors? Explain.

Understand
1. What is a random sample?
In a random sample, each member of a population has an equal chance of being selected.

2. What are you being asked to do?
Determine if this sampling is random and explain the answer.

Plan and Carry Out
3. What is the population you are surveying?
people who visit Yosemite National Park

4. Does every person in the population have an equal chance of being surveyed? yes

5. Is this a random sample? Why or why not? yes; Each person has an equal chance of being surveyed.

Check
6. How else could you randomly survey the people at Yosemite National Park?
Sample answer: Survey visitors as they leave the park.

Solve Another Problem
7. You want to survey the people at the local pool about the food served in the snack shack. You decide to walk around the kiddy pool and survey parents. Why or why not?
No, this is not a random sample. People who are not parents might eat at the snack shack.

552

Homework Exercises

For more exercises, see Extra Skills and Word Problems.

GO for Help

For Exercises	See Examples
7–10	1
11–15	2

(A) **Which sample is more likely to be random? Explain.** 7–10. See margin.

7. You want to survey teens about their snacking habits.
   a. You ask people at a party to name their favorite snack.
   b. You ask several teens entering a grocery store.

8. You want to know the most popular book among all the students at your school.
   a. You ask students from different grades at your school.
   b. You ask a group of your friends.

9. You want to know which baseball team is regarded as the best.
   a. You ask everyone seated in your section of the ballpark.
   b. You ask several visitors at a tourist attraction.

10. You want to survey seventh-grade students about computer use.
    a. You ask seventh-graders leaving the cafeteria after lunch.
    b. You ask seventh-graders entering a library on Friday night.

Is each question *biased* or *fair*? Explain.

11. Do you prefer to exercise or to watch television?
    Fair; the question makes no assumptions.
12. Do you prefer rock music or jazz?
    Fair; the question makes no assumptions.
13. Do you prefer harsh rock music or inspiring jazz?
    Biased; the question uses the terms *harsh* and *inspiring*.
14. Do you prefer unhealthy snacks or nutritious snacks?
    Biased; the question uses the terms *nutritious* and *unhealthy*.
15. What type of snack do you prefer?
    Fair; the question makes no assumptions.

(B) GPS 16. **Guided Problem Solving** You are creating a survey to find out which weekend activity students prefer: shopping at the mall or watching a movie. Describe how you would find a random sample. Then write a question you could use for your survey.
   • What is the population you will need to survey?
   • Is your question fair or biased? Check students' work.

17. **Writing in Math** Which of the two surveys below would you use to determine attitudes about carnivals? Explain. See margin.

Survey	Question	Yes	No	Don't Know
A	Do you like going to noisy, overpriced carnivals?	53%	46%	1%
B	Do you like going to carnivals?	72%	27%	1%

18. Suppose you study the eating habits of college students. What question would you ask someone to determine whether he or she is a member of the population you want to study? See left.

18. Are you a college student?

GO Online
Homework Help
Visit: PHSchool.com
Web Code: are-1104

7–10. See back of book.
17. See back of book.
19–20. See back of book.
25–27. See back of book.

Careers A park ranger needs a college degree related to park management, natural history, forestry, or outdoor recreation.

19. **Parks** Suppose you are gathering information about visitors to Yosemite National Park. You survey every tenth person entering the park. Would you get a random sample of visitors? Explain.
GPS
See margin.

Clothes A clothing company surveys women ages 18 to 35 to decide the price of a suit. Is each method a random sample? Explain.

20. Select names at random from a national telephone directory. Call these people and survey the person that answers. See margin.

21. Select names from a national telephone directory. Call these people and survey any woman 18 to 35 who answers.
Yes; you will survey people in your population without any bias.

C 22. **Challenge** A newspaper surveys 3 out of every 100 people of voting age in a community. The community has 38,592 people of voting age. How many people are surveyed? about 1,158 people

---

TEKS ★ TAKS Tune-Up and Mixed Review

TAKS Objective 5
TEKS (7.11)(A)

23. A class is surveyed about computers and services. Which of the following gives the most detailed information about the results? **C**

 Home Computer Use

Activity	Number of Students
Internet	6
Printer	4
Both	4

C Home Computer Use

Internet: Bob, Trish, Asia Rey, Dixie, Yuko
Jose, Liz, Gavin, Manny
Printer: Kale, Tatum, Tyler, Brian

 B Home Computer Use

Printer 28%, Internet 44%, Both 28%

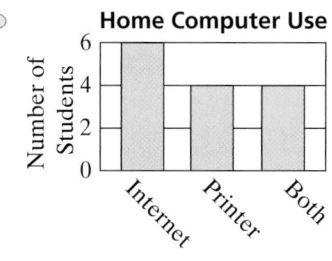 **D** Home Computer Use

TAKS Objective 6
TEKS (7.13)(C)

24. Ann, Betty, Cat, and Diane are married to Liem, Martin, Nate, and Pedro, but not in that order. Martin is Cat's brother. Cat is not married to Pedro. Ann and Nate are married. Diane's husband is an only child. Who is married to Betty? **G**

F Liem   **G** Martin   **H** Nate   **J** Pedro

25–27. See margin.

GO for Help Lesson 9-2

Write a rule for each sequence. Then find the next three terms.

25. 3, 8, 13, 18, . . .   26. −2, 1, 4, 7, . . .   27. 27, 16, 5, −6, . . .

Alternative Assessment

Have each student in a pair write a survey question. The question can be biased or fair. Partners exchange questions, rewrite them to be the opposite, and explain their changes. Pairs continue the activity as time permits.

TEKS ★ TAKS Resources

• TAKS Strategies, p. 571
• TAKS Tune-Up, pp. 575–577

TAKS Tune-Up Kit

• TAKS Daily Review Transparencies
• TAKS Review and Preparation Workbook
• TAKS Strategies with Transparencies
• Texas Progress Monitoring Assessments

---

4. Assess & Reteach

PowerPoint
Lesson Quiz

1. You want to survey people about their favorite exercise. Which sample below is more likely to be random? Explain.

   A. You ask people on a jogging track in a park to name their favorite exercise.

   B. You ask people on their lunch hour at a downtown intersection to name their favorite exercise. B; Sample: You are more likely to get a variety of answers by interviewing people away from an exercise site.

2. Explain why this question is either *biased* or *fair*. Do you prefer to play games on your computer or do boring homework? Biased. Sample: Homework is said to be boring, and games are assumed to be fun.

Enrichment 11-4 L4

Reteaching 11-4 Random Samples and L2

Carlos is curious about sports that students in his school like best. He cannot interview every student in the school. But he could interview a sample of the school **population.**

Carlos wants a **random sample.** A sample is random if everyone has an equal chance of being selected. How will Carlos get a random sample? He considers two possibilities:

• He can interview 30 students at a soccer game.
• He can interview 5 students in each of 6 class changes.

Carlos realizes that students at a soccer game probably like soccer better than other sports. That would not be a random sample. He decides to do the interviews during class changes.

What question will he ask? He considers two possibilities:

• "Which sport do you prefer, football, soccer, baseball, or tennis?"
• "Which do you enjoy most, the slow sport of baseball or one of the more exciting sports like football, soccer, or tennis?"

The second question is **biased.** It makes one answer seem better than another. Carlos decides to ask the first question.

1. You want to find how many people in your community are vegetarian. Where would be the best place to take a survey?
a shopping mall

Is each question biased or fair?

2. Will you vote for the young, inexperienced candidate, Mr. Soong, or the experienced candidate, Ms. Lopez? biased

3. Will you vote for Mr. Soong or Ms. Lopez? fair

You plan to survey people to see what percent own their home and what percent rent. Tell whether the following will give a random sample. Explain.

4. You interview people outside a pool supply store in the suburbs.
No; you are more likely to interview homeowners.

5. You interview people in the street near an apartment complex.
No; you are more likely to interview renters.

6. You mail a survey to every 20th person in the telephone book.
Yes; you can't tell if people own or rent.

553

1. Plan

TEKS ★ TAKS

(7.3)(B) To estimate and find solutions to application problems involving proportional relationships TAKS Obj. 2
Also supports (7.11)(B) TAKS Obj. 5

Dana Center TEKS Toolkit Clarifying Activities (7.3)(B), (7.11)(B)
Visit: PHSchool.com
Web Code: arq-9045

TEKS Math Background

See p. 530D for content support.

Lesson Planning and Resources

See p. 530E for a list of the resources that support this lesson.

PowerPoint
Bell Ringer Practice

✓ **Check Skills You'll Need**
Use student page, transparency, or PowerPoint.

TAKS **Daily Review 86**
Use transparency.

2. Teach

Activity Lab

Use before the lesson.

All in One **Teaching Resources**

Activity Lab 11-5: Using Random Samples

Guided Instruction

Error Prevention!

Students may place the data in the proportion incorrectly. Both ratios contain marked deer in the numerators. The left ratio is *counted;* the right is *actual.* The left ratio should be lesser.

554

✓ Check Skills You'll Need

1. Vocabulary Review
A *proportion* is an equation stating that two _?_ are equal. ratios

Solve each proportion.

2. $\frac{2}{3} = \frac{a}{15}$ 10

3. $\frac{n}{36} = \frac{11}{9}$ 44

4. $\frac{42}{63} = \frac{6}{k}$ 9

GO for Help
Lesson 5-5

Online active math

For: Population Activity
Use: Interactive Textbook, 11-5

TEKS ★ TAKS
- (7.3)(B) To estimate and find solutions to application problems involving proportional relationships TAKS Obj. 2
- (7.11)(B) To make inferences and convincing arguments based on an analysis of given or collected data TAKS Obj. 5

Why Learn This?

Researchers use the *capture/recapture method* to estimate animal population size. They collect, mark, and release animals. Then they capture another group of animals. The number of marked animals in the second group indicates the population size.

The following proportion is used to estimate a deer population.

$$\frac{\text{number of marked deer counted}}{\text{total number of deer counted}} = \frac{\text{total number of marked deer}}{\text{estimate of deer population}}$$

EXAMPLE   Using the Capture/Recapture Method

① TAKS **Griddable Item** Researchers count 48 marked deer and a total of 638 deer on a flight over an area. They know there are 105 marked deer. Write a proportion to estimate the deer population in the area.

$$\frac{\text{number of marked deer counted}}{\text{total number of deer counted}} = \frac{\text{total number of marked deer}}{\text{estimate of deer population}}$$

$\frac{48}{638} = \frac{105}{x}$ ← Write a proportion.

$48x = 105 \cdot 638$ ← Write the cross products.

$48x = 66{,}990$ ← Multiply.

$\frac{48x}{48} = \frac{66{,}990}{48}$ ← Divide each side by 48.

$x \approx 1{,}396$ ← Round to the nearest integer.

There are about 1,396 deer.

✓ Quick Check

about 1,914 deer

1. Suppose the researchers in Example 1 count 638 deer, but only 35 marked deer. Estimate the total deer population in the area.

Differentiated Instruction   Solutions for All Learners

Special Needs L1
Point out that in the Example in this lesson, since the tagged or marked animals are a subset of the total populations, the proportions will always have a greater number on the bottom, and a lesser number on top. This will help students set up the proportions accurately.

learning style: visual

Below Level L2
Have students use four different colors to represent each part of the proportion in words. They then color the numbers appropriately as they solve each proportion.

learning style: visual

Check Your Understanding

1. **Vocabulary** What is the capture/recapture method of estimating an animal population? **See margin.**

Use a proportion to estimate each animal population. Exercises 2 and 3 have been started for you. **2–3. See margin.**

2. about 12,917 trout

3. about 13,661 bass

2. total trout counted: 2,985
   tagged trout counted: 452
   total tagged trout: 1,956

$$\frac{\text{tagged trout counted}}{\text{total trout counted}} = \frac{\text{total tagged trout}}{x}$$

3. total bass counted: 3,102
   tagged bass counted: 198
   total tagged bass: 872

$$\frac{\text{tagged bass counted}}{\text{total bass counted}} = \frac{\text{total tagged bass}}{x}$$

4. total rabbits counted: 5,804
   marked rabbits counted: 3,214
   total marked rabbits: 5,398
   about 9,748 rabbits

5. total black bears counted: 218
   marked black bears counted: 25
   total marked black bears: 35
   about 305 bears

Homework Exercises

For more exercises, see Extra Skills and Word Problems.

GO for Help

For Exercises	See Examples
6–14	1

6. about 1,823 deer
7. about 2,010 deer
8. about 2,273 deer
9. about 2,048 deer
10. about 2,110 deer
11. about 2,535 deer
12. about 1,822 deer
13. about 2,081 deer
14. about 2,345 deer

Ⓐ **Estimate the total deer population for each year in the table.**

6. Year 1
7. Year 2
8. Year 3
9. Year 4
10. Year 5
11. Year 6
12. Year 7
13. Year 8
14. Year 9

Year	Total Deer Counted	Marked Deer Counted	Total Marked Deer
1	1,173	65	101
2	1,017	42	83
3	1,212	32	60
4	1,707	30	36
5	1,612	68	89
6	1,590	37	59
7	1,417	42	54
8	1,608	85	110
9	1,469	52	83

Ⓑ **GPS** 15. **Guided Problem Solving** In a study, a fish and game department worker catches, tags, and frees 124 catfish in a lake. A few weeks later, he catches and frees 140 catfish. Thirty-five have tags. Estimate the number of catfish in the lake. **about 496 catfish**
   - number of marked catfish counted = ▣
   - total number of catfish counted = ▣
   - total number of marked catfish = ▣

16. The population increased by about 522.

16. **Data Analysis** Use your answers to Exercises 6–14 above. Describe how the deer population changed over time. **See left.**

---

3. Practice

4. Assess & Reteach

555

Go Online

Homework Help
Visit: PHSchool.com
Web Code: are-1105

Use the report for Exercises 17 and 18.

17. 63 alligators

18. It may underestimate the population.

17. A biologist spilled juice on the report. Find the number of alligators that were caught, tagged, and set free. See left.

18. **Writing in Math** Explain how counting a high percent of the marked alligators affects your alligator estimate. See left.

Alligator Population	
Number caught, tagged, and set free	63
Number recaptured	105
Number recaptured with tags	50
Estimated total population	132

19. **Sharks** A biologist is studying the shark population off the Florida coast. He captures, tags, and sets free 38 sharks. A week later, 8 out of 25 sharks captured have tags. He uses the proportion $\frac{25}{8} = \frac{38}{x}$ to estimate that the population is about 12.
   a. **Error Analysis** Find the error in the biologist's proportion.
   b. Estimate the shark population. 19a–b. See margin.

20. **Reasoning** A class helps determine the squirrel population in a park. Students capture, tag, and free squirrels. A few squirrels lose their tags. How will this affect the population estimate? Explain. See left.

20. It would make the estimate appear too large.

21. **Challenge** In a capture/recapture program, 30% of the animals recaptured have tags. Suppose 70 animals were originally captured, tagged, and released. Estimate the population. about 233 animals

TEKS ★ TAKS Tune-Up and Mixed Review

GRIDDABLE ITEMS

TAKS Objective 5
TEKS (7.11)(B)

22. The table at the right shows the results of a biologist who captures, tags, and sets free lake trout. About what is the trout population in the lake? 250

Trout Population	
Number Tagged	150
Number Recaptured	100
Number Recaptured with Tags	60

TAKS Objective 3
TEKS (7.8)(C)

23. Alexandro needs 300 cubic inches of clay to make a sculpture. The clay comes in blocks that are 5 inches wide, 3 inches tall, and 4 inches deep. How many blocks does Alexandro need? 5

TAKS Objective 2
TEKS (7.3)(B)

24. Partners A and B split their profits in a ratio of 2 : 3. If Partner A makes a profit of $2,700, how much profit, in dollars, does Partner B make? Assume Partner B makes more than Partner A. 4,050

Go for Help

Lesson 10-1

Algebra Graph each point on the same coordinate plane.

25. $(3, 4)$ 26. $(0, 0)$ 27. $(-5, -2)$ 28. $(-1, -2)$ 29. $(4, -3)$
   25–29. See margin.

TEKS ★ TAKS Resources

- TAKS Strategies, p. 571
- TAKS Tune-Up, pp. 575–577

TAKS Tune-Up Kit
- TAKS Daily Review Transparencies
- TAKS Review and Preparation Workbook
- TAKS Strategies with Transparencies
- Texas Progress Monitoring Assessments

Alternative Assessment

Have students work in pairs. Each student writes a problem similar to Exercises 2–5. Partners exchange papers and use their partner's data to estimate each population. Partners explain their reasoning to each other.

Graphing Population Data

You can represent population data in different ways. The table below shows data about U.S. households.

U.S. Households

Year	Number of Households (millions)	People per Household
1950	42.9	3.38
1960	53.0	3.29
1970	63.4	3.11
1980	80.3	2.75
1990	91.9	2.63
2000	105.5	2.59

You can also represent the data above using a double line graph.

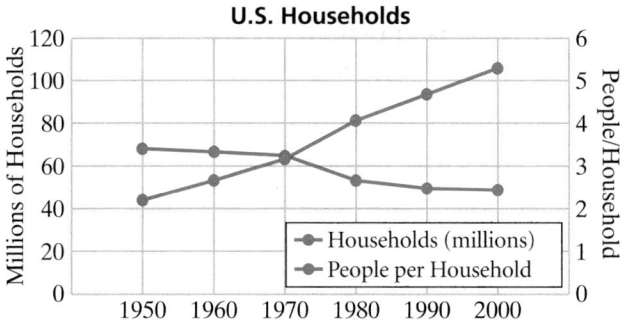

U.S. Households

ACTIVITY

Use the data in the table above for Exercises 1–3.

1. Make a line graph. Label the horizontal axis "Millions of Households." Label the vertical axis "People per Household." See margin.

2. Describe the relationship that the line graph in Exercise 1 shows between the number of people per household and the number of households. **As the number of households increases, the average number of people per household decreases.**

3. Use unit rates. Estimate the U. S. population for each year listed. **See above.**

4. Extend your graph in Exercise 1 to 2010. Estimate the number of households and the number of people per household in 2010. **about 118 million; about 2.5**

5. Use unit rates to estimate the U.S. population in 2010. **about 295 million**

3. 1950: 145 million

   1960: 174.4 million

   1970: 197.2 million

   1980: 220.8 million

   1990: 241.697 million

   2000: 273.2 million

4–5. Answers may vary. Samples are given.

19a–b. See back of book.
25–29. See back of book.

1. See back of book.

Activity Lab

Graphing Population Data

Students graph population data. This extends both their skills with population data and their skills with data display.

Guided Instruction

Explain to students that they can make a graph to show population data. Tell them to make the graph to scale to make the graph a reasonable size.
Ask:

- *What does each line in the double line graph represent?* number of households, number of people in a household

- *Why is a line graph the best choice to represent this data?* line graphs are useful to show change over time, as in this situation

- *What would change about the graph if you reversed the axis labels?* the slope of the line

Exercises
Have students work independently. Have them form small groups to compare their graphs and the answers to the questions.

Differentiated Instruction

Below Level L2
Rephrase the question to show the population of a small town for students who might have trouble visualizing millions of households.

TEKS ★ TAKS Resources

Dana Center TEKS Toolkit
   Clarifying Activities (7.11)(B),
   (7.11)(A)
Visit: PHSchool.com
Web Code: arq-9045

TEKS ★ TAKS

(7.11)(B) To make inferences and convincing arguments based on an analysis of given data TAKS Obj. 5

(7.11)(A) To select and use an appropriate representation for presenting and displaying data, including line graph, and justify the selection TAKS Obj. 5

557

Describing Data

In this feature, students interpret data to answer questions. They study and analyze data to find missing numbers and interpret whether statements about the data are valid.

Guided Instruction

Explain to students that data can often be confusing or misleading. They often need to analyze it in order to understand it. Have a volunteer read the problem aloud.

Ask:

- *Why do you multiply the number of students that gave a score by the score?* to find the total score for this plan
- *Why is the median or mode more appropriate to represent how the students feel?* More students objected to the change than supported the change. 4.5 and 4 are closer to 0, which represents students who oppose the change.
- *What makes this survey misleading?* Students who are for the change give a higher score than students who are against the change. If only a few students are for the change, the plan still gets a high score.

TEKS ★ TAKS Resources

Dana Center TEKS Toolkit Clarifying Activities (7.11)(B), (7.12)(B)
Visit: PHSchool.com
Web Code: arq-9045

TEKS ★ TAKS

(7.11)(B) To make inferences and convincing arguments based on an analysis of given data **TAKS** Obj. 5

(7.12)(B) To choose among mean, median, mode, or range to describe a set of data and justify the choice **TAKS** Obj. 5

Describing Data

Poll A middle-school class was polled on whether the school should change its mascot. A 0 rating meant the student was strongly against the change. A 10 rating meant the student was strongly in favor of the change. The line plot below shows the data. Whitney computed the mean. Was the mean a good descriptor of how the students felt?

Mascot Survey Result

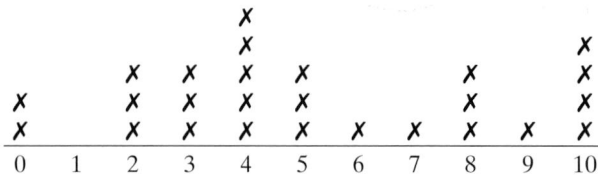

What You Might Think

> What do I know? What do I want to find out?

> What is the mean?

> Does the mean represent the students' feelings?

What You Might Write

I know the students' ratings. I need to find the mean, which is the sum of the ratings divided by 26. I need to find out whether the mean represents how the students felt.

total = $3 \times 2 + 3 \times 3 + 5 \times 4 + 3 \times 5 +$
$6 + 7 + 3 \times 8 + 9 + 4 \times 10$
$= 136$

mean = $136 \div 26$, or about 5.2

I do not think so. Thirteen students were against the change. Ten students were for the change. The median of 4.5 or mode of 4 would better show how students felt.

Think It Through

1. **Reasoning** How did Whitney know to divide by 26 to find the mean? Explain.

2. Explain how to find the median of 4.5 and the mode of 4.
   See margin.

1. There were 26 **X**s on the line, which represent 26 student responses.

2. Since there are 26 pieces of data, the median is the average of the 13th and 14th pieces of ordered data, which were 4 and 5. The mode was 4, since it was the most commonly reported piece of data.

Exercises

Solve each problem. For Exercises 3 and 4, answer the questions first.

3. Jax has a weekly test in math. His scores on the last five tests were 78, 92, 86, 94, and 95. What score does he need on his next exam to have an average of 90? **95**
   a. What do you know? What do you want to find out?
   b. How does a diagram like the one below help you understand what to do?

$600 \times 90\% = 540$					
78	92	86	94	95	■

4. Suppose a fox and a lizard compete in a 300-ft race. The fox runs at a rate of 30 ft/s. The lizard runs at a rate of 10 ft/s and starts 15 seconds before the fox. Who wins the race? Explain.
   a. What do you know? What do you want to find out?
   b. How does a table like the one below help you understand what to do?

Animal	Distance (ft)	Rate (ft/s)	Time (s)
Fox	300	30	■
Lizard	300	10	■

4. the fox; the lizard finishes the race in 30 s. After a 15 s head start, the lizard still runs for 15 s. The fox runs the entire race in 10 s, so the fox wins.

5. A tsunami is a big wave. A tsunami that struck land in 1883 was 120 ft high. An office building is about 12 ft high per floor. How many floors high was this wave? **10 floors**

6. Parents were asked in a survey, "Should the school require uniforms?" A 0 rating meant the parent was strongly against uniforms. A 5 rating meant the parent was strongly for uniforms. The frequency table below shows the survey results. Which measure—the mean, the median, or the mode—would best describe the data? Explain.

   6. Answers may vary. Sample: The mean of 2.03 and median of 2 best describe the data because they show there are parents who feel strongly both ways.

   Parent Survey Results

Rating	0	1	2	3	4	5
Tally	𝟳𝟰𝟰 𝟳𝟰𝟰 ///	/	///	///	//	𝟳𝟰𝟰 //

11-6

TEKS ★ TAKS

(7.11)(B) To make inferences and convincing arguments based on an analysis of given data
TAKS Obj. 5

Also supports
(7.11)(A) **TAKS** Obj. 5
(7.12)(B) **TAKS** Obj. 5

Dana Center TEKS Toolkit Clarifying Activities (7.11)(B), (7.11)(A), (7.12)(B)
Visit: PHSchool.com
Web Code: arq-9045

TEKS Math Background

Graphs can either intentionally or unintentionally be misleading. For example, some graphs are drawn with a vertical scale that skips over values instead of starting at zero. Others use uneven intervals that can exaggerate perceived differences and mislead a reader.

More Math Background: p. 530D

Lesson Planning and Resources

See p. 530E for a list of the resources that support this lesson.

✓ Check Skills You'll Need

1. **Vocabulary Review**
   An *outlier* mostly affects the __?__ of a data set. **mean**

2. Find the mean, median, and mode.
   122, 106, 113, 116, 120, 123, 119, 117, 123, 111
   117; 118; 123

GO for Help
Lesson 1-10

TEKS ★ TAKS

- (7.11)(B) To make inferences and convincing arguments based on an analysis of given data **TAKS** Obj. 5
- (7.11)(A) To select and use an appropriate representation for presenting and displaying relationships between collected data **TAKS** Obj. 5
- (7.12)(B) To choose among mean, median, mode, or range to describe a set of data and justify the choice for a particular situation **TAKS** Obj. 5

Why Learn This?

A graph can be a powerful way to present data. How you draw a graph can affect the impression you give about the data.

Time Spent on Homework

The graph above is misleading. It leads you to think that fourth-grade students spend almost no time on homework.

EXAMPLE   Redrawing Misleading Graphs

1. Redraw the graph above so it is not misleading.

   Method 1 Start the vertical scale at 0.

   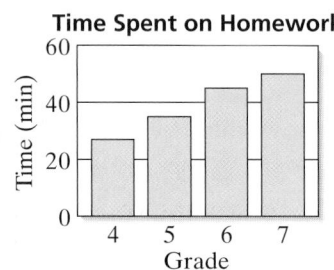

   Time Spent on Homework

   Method 2 Use a break in the vertical scale.

   Time Spent on Homework

✓ Quick Check

1. When is a break in a vertical scale especially useful?
   when space is limited or when you want to focus on a narrow range of data

PowerPoint

Bell Ringer Practice

✓ **Check Skills You'll Need**
Use student page, transparency, or PowerPoint.

TAKS **Daily Review 87**
Use transparency.

2a–b. See back of book.

560

Differentiated Instruction Solutions for All Learners

Special Needs L1
Some students might have a difficult time drawing or redrawing graphs. If so, have them work in pairs and make the decisions about intervals and breaks in the data, while their partner draws the graphs.

learning style: visual

Below Level L2
Have students brainstorm a list of ways data are used to mislead on television, such as "discounts up to 50% and more." Students can compare lists and refine them as needed.

learning style: verbal

Graphs can also mislead if the vertical or horizontal axes have unequal or very large intervals.

EXAMPLE Misleading Intervals

2 **Profit** Marketers use the graph below to show investors that annual profits increase steadily. Explain why the graph is misleading.

Annual Profit

The intervals of the horizontal axis are not equal. Annual profits increase $100,000 over the first 5 years. Profits then increase only $100,000 in 10 years. Annual profits increase at a slower rate.

✓ Quick Check 2a–b. See back of book.

2. a. Redraw the graph in Example 2. Use equal intervals on both axes.
   b. Redraw the graph at the right so it does not mislead.

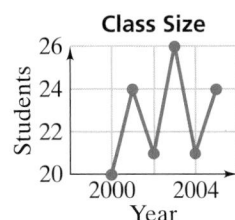
Class Size

Use of the mean, median, or mode of a data set can inform or mislead.

EXAMPLE Misleading Use of Data Measures

3 **TAKS Multiple Choice** You survey students in your class to find the number of pets per student. The results are shown. You want to convince your parents to let you have four pets. Which measure of the data should you use?

How Many Pets Do You Have?

0, 0, 0, 1, 1, 1,
1, 1, 1, 2, 2, 2,
3, 4, 7, 15, 27

  (A) Mean   (C) Mode
  (B) Median   (D) Range

The median and the mode are both 1 pet. Although these measures represent the typical number of pets, they are too low to convince your parents to let you have 4 pets. The range, 27 pets, is too large and only shows how much the number of pets varies. The mean is 4 pets. You can use this measure to influence your parents. The correct answer is A.

✓ Quick Check

3. Which two values in the data above would you consider outliers?
   15 and 27

Advanced Learners L4
Have students write sample scenarios and data sets that mislead by presenting only the mean, median, or mode as in Examples 3 and 4.

Pre-AP™

English Language Learners ELL
Have students work in pairs to talk about the words *misleading, impression,* and *influence.* Have them explain how each of these words relates to the kind of data displays people use in different situations.

learning style: verbal

2. Teach

Activity Lab

Use before the lesson.

All in One Teaching Resources
Activity Lab 11-6: Using Data to Persuade

Guided Instruction

Example 4
Have students find the mean, median, and mode to determine how the data can be displayed more accurately.

PowerPoint
Additional Examples

1 The graph shows the weekly earnings of four brothers.

Weekly Earnings

a. How is this graph misleading? **The graph starts at 4 instead of 0. It makes the lower values look lower than they are, and the difference between the high and low numbers is exaggerated.**

b. Redraw the graph so it is not misleading. **Check students' graphs.**

2 A television station presented this graph to its advertisers to show how viewership has increased. Explain how the graph is misleading.

Station Viewership 1990–2000

See back of book.

3 A salary survey of a television station is shown in the table. A reporter wants a raise, so he tells his boss, "The mean salary here is $55,000." How is this misleading?

Position	No.	Salary
Owner	1	$250,000
Anchor	4	$70,000
Reporter	6	$37,000
Producer	2	$35,000
Camera Operator	4	$29,000

See back of book.

4 The sign below is advertising for an auto dealership. Below are the data for the cars at the dealership. Explain whether or not the ad is misleading.

Cars Under $10,000!

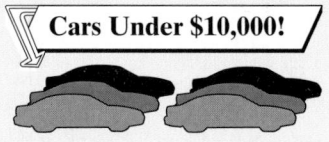

Model	Quantity	Price ($)
Pico	2	9,999
Toro	7	13,999
Enviro	9	15,999
Urban	4	22,999

See back of book.

All in One **Teaching Resources**
- Daily Notetaking Guide 11-6 L3
- Adapted Notetaking 11-6 L1

Closure

- *How can graphs be misleading?* Sample: The graph can start at a value other than zero or have uneven or broken intervals.
- *How can statistics be misleading?* Sample: by presenting only a part of the data or omitting important facts

---

You can mislead by showing part of the data or by leaving out facts.

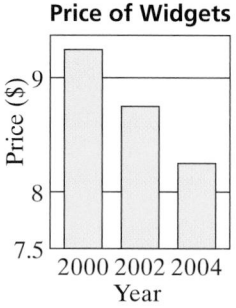

HARRY'S HAMBURGER LAND

"Home of the Under-500-Calorie Burger"

EXAMPLE Application: Advertising

4 Below are data about Harry's hamburgers. Is the advertisement at the left for Harry's Hamburger Land misleading?

Item	Calories	Fat (g)	Average Number Sold Daily
Kiddie Burger	480	35	80
Hamburger Plus	575	42	68
Health Burger	580	40	65
Golden Fries Hamburger	660	57	43
Burger Deluxe	700	55	75

Only one hamburger has less than 500 Calories. The ad is misleading.

Quick Check

4. How could you change the poster to better reflect the data?
Answers may vary. Sample: "Home of the under-500-Cal Kiddie Burger."

Check Your Understanding

Use the graph at the right.

Price of Widgets

1. Does the vertical scale start at 0? no

2. Are equal intervals used on both the horizontal and vertical axes? no

3. **Number Sense** The graph makes the price change seem (greater, less) than it really is.
greater

4. Redraw the graph so that it does not mislead.
See margin.

Homework Exercises

For more exercises, see Extra Skills and Word Problems.

GO for Help

For Exercises	See Examples
5–7	1–2
8–11	3–4

A 5. **Nutrition** Farnaz asks students at her school, "What's your favorite fruit?" She draws the graph below. Why is it misleading? See margin.

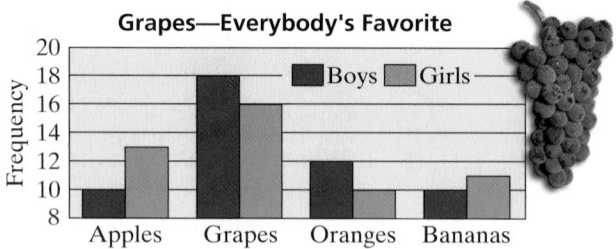

Grapes—Everybody's Favorite

4–7. See back of book.
12. See back of book.

6. The graph gives the impression that vehicle production in 2000 was about 5 times higher than in 1980. The vertical axis has a break in the scale.

7. The graph gives the impression that the largest group of students received the highest scores. There are uneven intervals on the *x*-axis.

For help with calculating the mean, median, or mode of a data set, go to Lesson 1-10, Examples 1–3.

8a. Mean; it is the highest.

b. Mode; it is the lowest.

10. Median; the $189 bike costs only $10 more than the median.

11. No; you have to subtract expenses of $15. You actually raised $113 for charity.

B **GPS**

For Exercises 6 and 7, tell what impression the graph gives and tell how the graph makes this impression. Then use the data to draw a graph that does not mislead. 6–7. See margin for graphs.

6.

Motor Vehicle Production

7.

Test Results

8. You score 93, 83, 76, 92, and 76 on five science exams.
   a. You want to show your parents how well you are doing in class. Should you use the mean, median, or mode? Explain. See left.
   b. Your teacher wants to encourage you to work harder. Which measure should your teacher use? Explain. See left.

9. **Bowling** The table shows the scores of two students in a bowling match.
   a. Bill says he won the match because he has a higher average. Is he correct? yes
   b. Kisha says she won the match. How can she justify this statement? She won two of three strings.

Bowling Scores

Game	1	2	3
Kisha	81	60	93
Bill	78	95	91

10. **Reasoning** You shop for bikes and find 7 types priced at $119, $139, $149, $179, $189, $199, and $209. You want to buy the $189 bike. Should you use the mean, median, or mode to convince your parents that this is a reasonable price for a bike? Explain.

11. **Number Sense** To raise money for charity, your class holds a car wash. You pay $15 for washing materials and collect $128 in donations. Can you say you raised $128 for charity? Explain.

12. **Guided Problem Solving** Use the data at the right to make two line graphs. The first graph should show great change in the winning times and the second graph should show little change. See margin.
    - **Make a Plan** Use a break for the vertical scale of the first graph. Use increments of 0.01 to 0.05 s. Start the vertical scale of the next graph at 0. Use increments of 0.5 to 2 s.
    - **Check the Answer** The first graph should suggest a greater variation in winning times than the second graph shows.

Men's 100-Meter Winning Times

Year	Time (s)
1988	9.92
1992	9.96
1996	9.84
2000	9.87
2004	9.85

SOURCE: *Sports Almanac*

13. **Open-Ended** Find a graph in a newspaper or magazine. Is the graph trying to mislead you? Explain. Check students' work.

---

3. Practice

Assignment Guide

Check Your Understanding
Go over Exercises 1–4 in class before assigning the Homework Exercises.

Homework Exercises
A Practice by Example 5–11
B Apply Your Skills 12–19
C Challenge 20
TEKS ★ TAKS Tune-Up and Mixed Review 21–25

Homework Quick Check
To check students' understanding of key skills and concepts, go over Exercises 6, 9, 16, 17, and 19.

Differentiated Instruction Resources

Lesson Quiz

Study the bar graph below.

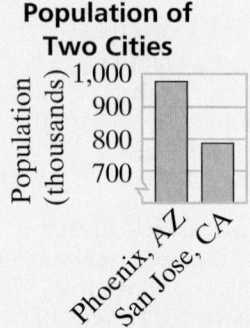

Population of Two Cities

1. What impression is given by this graph? **The population of Phoenix is double that of San Jose.**

2. How would you change the graph to better reflect the data? **Change the vertical scale by eliminating the break in the scale.**

3. Redraw the graph to accurately reflect the data. **Check students' graphs.**

16. See back of book.
18. See back of book.

GO Online

Homework Help
Visit: PHSchool.com
Web Code: are-1106

14. The graph gives the impression that profits have been increasing.

17. The company wants to give the impression that it is profitable even though it's not.

19. Yes; the 100 customers who did not respond may not be satisfied.

Business Use the graph below for Exercises 14–18.

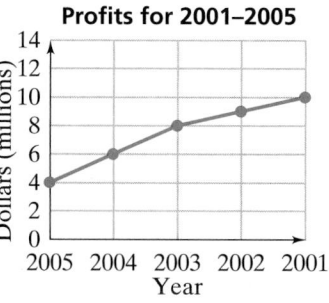

Profits for 2001–2005

14. What does the graph suggest? **See left.**

15. Why does the graph give the impression described in Exercise 14? **It reverses the scale on the x-axis.**

16. Use the data to draw a graph that does not mislead. **See margin.**

17. **Reasoning** Why would a company draw the misleading graph? Explain.

18. You want to show that the company is successful. Should you use the mean, median, or mode to suggest the greatest profit? Explain. **See margin.**

19. **Writing in Math** Spotless Cleaners sends out 200 customer surveys. The company gets 100 replies with 97 customers saying they are satisfied. In an ad, Spotless Cleaners says that 97% of its customers are satisfied. Is this statement misleading? Explain.

C 20. **Challenge** Research the cost of U.S. postage stamps for the past six years. Use your data to draw a graph that gives the impression of a large increase in stamp cost over time. **Check students' work.**

TEKS ★ TAKS Tune-Up and Mixed Review

TAKS Objective 5
TEKS (7.11)(B)

21. A town's population is shown. If the trend continues, which is the best prediction of the population in 2010? **B**
Ⓐ Fewer than 22,000 people
Ⓑ Between 22,000 and 29,000 people
Ⓒ Between 29,000 and 36,000 people
Ⓓ More than 36,000 people

Town's Population

TAKS Objective 3
TEKS (7.6)(C)

22. Which of the following can have a single base that is a hexagon? **J**
Ⓕ Prism   Ⓖ Cone   Ⓗ Cylinder   Ⓙ Pyramid

TAKS Objective 1
TEKS (7.2)(E)

23. What is the value of the expression $18 \div (9 - 6)^2 + 2 \times 6$? **A**
Ⓐ 14   Ⓑ 24   Ⓒ 30   Ⓓ 108

GO for Help Lesson 11-12

Estimation Use the graph.

24. Estimate the total amount spent on theater and opera from 1999 to 2003. **about 54 billion**

25. Estimate the total amount spent on movie tickets from 1999 to 2003. **about 45 billion**

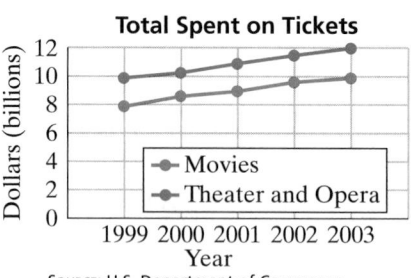

Total Spent on Tickets

SOURCE: U.S. Department of Commerce

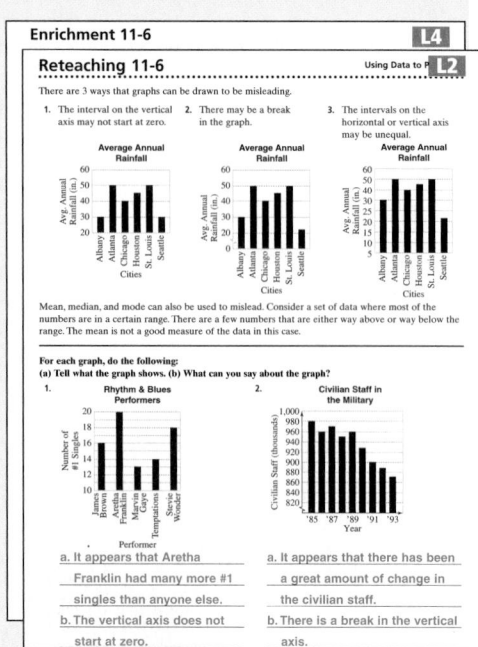

Enrichment 11-6   **L4**

Reteaching 11-6   Using Data to ... **L2**

TEKS ★ TAKS Resources
• TAKS Strategies, p. 571
• TAKS Tune-Up, pp. 575–577

TAKS Tune-Up Kit
• TAKS Daily Review Transparencies
• TAKS Review and Preparation Workbook
• TAKS Strategies with Transparencies
• Texas Progress Monitoring Assessments

Alternative Assessment

Have each student in a pair write a data set that has a very different mean, median, and mode. Partners exchange data sets and try to find which statistic best represents the data and which statistic is especially misleading. Students check each other's results.

1. Use the data at the right. Make a graph that would persuade filmmakers to make more movies in Georgia. **See margin.**

2. The data below show the class sizes at a school. Would you use the mean, the median, or the mode to convince the principal that there is a high number of students per class? Explain.

    27 29 34 24 29 19 30 19 25 22 27 19
    Median; it is a higher value than mean or mode.

3. **Open-Ended** Choose a survey topic and write a biased survey question and a fair survey question. **Check students' work.**

4. Which is the best way to survey a random sample of students from your school about their favorite radio station? Explain.

    Ⓐ Survey 5 students in each first-period class.

    Ⓑ Survey 12 students in the band.

    Ⓒ Call 25 friends.

    Ⓓ Survey each student in your math class.
      A; it is a more diverse sample.

Use a proportion to estimate each animal population.

5. total wild horses counted: 1,583
   marked wild horses counted: 496
   total marked wild horses: 1,213
   about 3,871 horses

6. total turtles counted: 51
   marked turtles counted: 32
   total marked turtles: 108
   about 172 turtles

Movies Filmed in Georgia

Year	Number
1997	10
1998	5
1999	4
2000	8
2001	4
2002	4
2003	6
2004	8

SOURCE: 2005 Georgia Film Sourcebook

MATH AT WORK

Pollsters

Pollsters interview people to find out their opinions and their preferences about specific topics. They must understand the topic of interest well in order to ask the right questions. If pollsters ask poor-quality questions, they will not get accurate responses.

Pollsters use math to analyze the data they collect. They find the mean, median, mode, and range of the data. Their analysis gives us an overall view of the data. They often graph data to display their findings.

 For: more information about pollsters
PHSchool.com **Web Code:** arb-2031

Checkpoint Quiz

Use this Checkpoint Quiz to check students' understanding of the skills and concepts of Lessons 11-4 through 11-6.

Resources

- All-in-One Teaching Resources Checkpoint Quiz 2
- Texas ExamView CD-ROM
- Success Tracker™ Online Intervention

MATH AT WORK

Pollsters

Students may not understand how the skills they have learned in this chapter can be applied to a career field. This feature should generate interest in applying math skills to real-world situations.

Guided Instruction

Define *pollster* for students. Discuss polls they have taken in class during the chapter and other polls they may have taken outside of class. Have volunteers read each paragraph. Ask questions, such as:

- *What kind of jobs might require data from a pollster?*
- *What skills that you have learned in this chapter are useful to a pollster?*
- *Do you think being a pollster would be an interesting job for you? Why or why not?*

565

1. See back of book.

Two-Variable Data Collection

Students study two sets of data in terms of how they affect each other. This will prepare them to study trends and scatter plots in Lesson 11-7.

Guided Instruction

Explain to students that sometimes two sets of data will affect each other. For example, the Number of Peanut Butter Sandwiches Eaten affects the Amount of Peanut Butter Remaining in the Jar.

Draw graphs to illustrate the changes in the wolf and moose populations. Ask:
- *What is the relationship between the populations?* As the wolf population increases, the moose population decreases.
- *What is a possible explanation for this relationship?* Sample: Wolves hunt the moose so there are fewer moose while the wolves thrive.

Exercises

Have students work in pairs on Exercises 1-4. When students have finished, have volunteers share their answers and discuss Exercise 4 as a class.
Repeat with Exercises 5-7.

Alternative Method

Allow students to make other kinds of graphs with which they are comfortable. For example, using a double bar graph in the Activity will display the same relationship, but may be easier for students to understand.

TEKS ★ TAKS Resources

- Activity Lab 11-7: Exploring Scatter Plots

Data Center TEKS Toolkit Clarifying Activities (7.11)(B), (7.11)(A)
Visit: PHSchool.com
Web Code: arq-9045

Two-Variable Data Collection

Isle Royale, the largest island in Lake Superior, is a favorable location for studying wolf and moose populations. The table shows wolf and moose population estimates during a 20-year period.

TEKS ★ TAKS

(7.11)(B) To make inferences and convincing arguments based on an analysis of given or collected data **TAKS** Obj. 5

(7.11)(A) To select and use an appropriate representation for presenting and displaying data, including line graph, and justify the selection **TAKS** Obj. 5

Moose and Wolf Populations on Isle Royale, Michigan

Year	Wolf	Moose	Year	Wolf	Moose
1985	22	1,115	1995	16	2,422
1986	20	1,192	1996	22	1,163
1987	16	1,268	1997	24	500
1988	12	1,335	1998	14	699
1989	12	1,397	1999	25	750
1990	15	1,216	2000	29	850
1991	12	1,313	2001	19	900
1992	12	1,590	2002	17	1,100
1993	13	1,879	2003	19	900
1994	17	1,770	2004	29	750

SOURCE: National Park Service

ACTIVITY

1. Describe the changes in the wolf population over the years.
   See above right.
2. Describe the changes in the moose population over the years.
   See above right.
3. Make a graph that shows the wolf population on the horizontal scale and the moose population on the vertical scale. Graph the ordered pairs (wolf, moose) for each year. See margin.

4. **Data Analysis** Do you see a relationship between the two populations? Explain.
   As the wolf population increases, the moose population decreases.

1. The wolf population tended to decrease from 1985 to 1993 and tended to increase after 1993.

2. The moose population tended to increase from 1985 to 1995. After dropping in 1997 and 1998, it began to increase again.

Exercises

5–7. Check students' work.
5. **Data Collection** Collect data on the length of your classmates' feet and the length of their forearms. Record the data in a table.

6. Display the data in an appropriate graph.

7. Do you see a relationship between the two lengths? Explain.

3. See back of book.

Exploring Scatter Plots

Prepares for TEKS (8.12)(B) To draw conclusions and make predictions by analyzing trends in scatter plots

Check Skills You'll Need

1. Vocabulary Review
Is the *x-axis* vertical or horizontal?
horizontal

Graph each point on the same coordinate plane.

2. (4, 0) **3.** (2, 5)

4. (0, 3) **5.** (1, 4)

6. (2, 3) **7.** (0, 0)

2–7. See back of book.

GO for Help
Lesson 10-1

What You'll Learn

To draw and interpret scatter plots and to analyze their trends

• Prepares for Grade 8 **TEKS (8.12)(B)** To draw conclusions and make predictions by analyzing trends in scatter plots

🔊 **New Vocabulary** scatter plot, positive trend, negative trend, no trend

Why Learn This?

You can graph data, such as the data shown below, as points in a coordinate plane. The graph may show an important pattern.

Book Bag Weights

Number of Books	3	3	4	4	5	6	6	7	7	8
Weight (lb)	6	8	6.5	9	10	7.5	12	9.5	11	12

A **scatter plot** is a graph that relates two sets of data. To make a scatter plot, graph the two sets of data as ordered pairs.

EXAMPLE Making Scatter Plots

① **Weights** Graph the data in the table above in a scatter plot.

Each column in the table represents a point on the scatter plot.

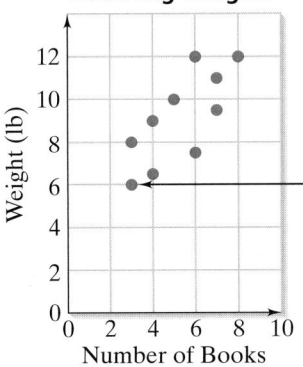

Book Bag Weights

This point is for the book bag that holds 3 books and weighs 6 lb.

✓ Quick Check

1. Graph the data in the table below in a scatter plot.

Height (in.)	58	64.5	67.5	65.5	63.5	64	71	62.5	69
Arm Span (in.)	57.5	64	68.5	66	62.5	66	72	63	70

Video Tutor Help
Visit: PHSchool.com
Web Code: are-0775

1.

Height and Arm Span

TEKS Math Background

A *scatter plot* is a set of points that shows a relationship between two sets of data by plotting them on a coordinate grid. Sometimes a scatter plot forms a pattern called a *trend*. *No trend* indicates that no relationship exists between the data. Note that the trend is independent of which variable is placed along the *x*-axis or *y*-axis. Because scatter plots are not functions, there can be multiple data points for any horizontal axis value.

More Math Background: p. 530D

Lesson Planning and Resources

See p. 530E for a list of the resources that support this lesson.

Bell Ringer Practice

✓ **Check Skills You'll Need**
Use student page, transparency, or PowerPoint.

Daily Review 88
Use transparency.

Differentiated Instruction Solutions for All Learners

Special Needs L1
Ask students to use their arms and hands to show you what a positive trend would look like on a scatter plot, emulating the general direction of the points. Repeat for a negative trend.

learning style: tactile

Below Level L2
Review with students positive-sloped lines and negative-sloped lines. Relate these lines to positive trends and negative trends.

learning style: verbal

567

Activity Lab

Use before the lesson.
Student Edition Activity Lab, Data Collection 11-7a, Two-Variable Data Collection, p. 566

 Teaching Resources

Activity Lab 11-7: Exploring Scatter Plots

Guided Instruction

Example 1
In Quick Check 1, watch for students who switch the *x*-coordinates and *y*-coordinates. Write the ordered pair as a guide.

PowerPoint

Additional Examples

1 Graph in a scatter plot the data from the table.

Height (in)	Test Scores
58	90
60	95
63	90
64	70
65	100
65	90
66	60
67	90
68	80
68	75
70	85
70	100
71	80
72	70

See back of book.

2 Describe the trend in the scatter plot for Exercise 1. no trend

 Teaching Resources

- Daily Notetaking Guide 11-7 **L3**
- Adapted Notetaking 11-7 **L1**

Closure

- *What is a scatter plot?* See back of book.
- *Identify a positive, negative, and no trend.* See back of book.

The scatter plot in Example 1 shows a relationship, or *trend*. As the number of books increases, the weight of the bag generally increases.

You can examine a scatter plot to see what kind of trend is shown.

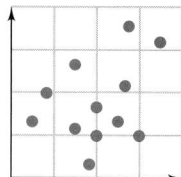

Positive trend
As one set of values increases, the other set tends to increase.

Negative trend
As one set of values increases, the other set tends to decrease.

No trend
There is no apparent relationship among the data.

EXAMPLE **Describing Trends in Scatter Plots**

2 Trees Describe the trend in the scatter plot.

As the age of a tree increases, the diameter of the tree tends to increase.

The scatter plot shows a positive trend.

✓ Quick Check

2. Suppose you draw a line that follows the trend shown in the scatter plot. Is the slope of the line positive or negative?
positive

Age and Diameter of Trees

SOURCE: USDA Forest Service

✓ Check Your Understanding

1. It illustrates what happens to one set of data when the other increases.

2. A tree that is 25 years old has a diameter of 8 inches.

1. Vocabulary How does a scatter plot relate two sets of data?

Use the scatter plot in Example 2 for Exercises 2–5.

2. What does the point at $(25, 8)$ represent? see left.

3. A tree that is 40 years old has a diameter of about 9 in. Is this data point shown on the scatter plot? yes

4. Estimation A tree is 28 years old. Estimate its diameter. about 7 in.

5. Estimation A tree has a diameter of 10 in. Estimate its age.
about 47 years

568 **Chapter 11** Displaying and Analyzing Data

Advanced Learners **L4**
Have students find the definition of *lines of best fit*. Students can fit lines to several scatter plots. Students can then speculate how the lines can help them make predictions.

Pre-AP™

English Language Learners ELL
Have students work in pairs to generate examples of relationships that would show up as positive, negative, or no trends in a scatter plot.

learning style: visual

For more exercises, see Extra Skills and Word Problems.

A Graph each set of data in a scatter plot. 6–8. See margin.

6.

Temperature (°F)	Weight of Clothing (lb)
60	5.5
58	5.2
50	6.2
42	6.8
36	7.8
32	7.4
30	8.4
26	9.9
22	10.9
20	12

7.

Hours Studying	Test Grade
0.5	68
0.75	70
1	82
1	78
1.25	78
1.25	86
1.25	94
1.5	82
1.75	90
2	88

8.

Price of CD ($)	14	13	7	10	18	12	23	17	12	19	15
Number of Songs	15	10	11	12	14	19	20	9	7	10	11

Describe the trend in each scatter plot.

9.
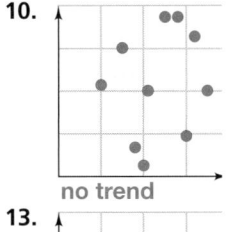
positive

10.
no trend

11.
negative

12.

no trend

13.
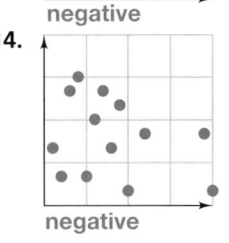
positive

14.
negative

B **GPS** **15. Guided Problem Solving** Use the data below. Predict the electrical use in a month that has an average temperature of 60°F.

about 190 kWh

Monthly Electrical Use

Average Temperature (°F)	77	72	68	45	39	50	35	30	47
Electricity Use (kWh)	170	143	168	236	260	196	244	309	266

- **Make a Plan** Make a scatter plot with °F on the horizontal axis. Draw a line that is close to most of the data points. Use the line to estimate the electricity use at 60°F.
- **Carry Out the Plan** The scatter plot shows a __?__ trend. The ordered pair (60, ■) represents the electricity use at 60°F.

6–8. See back of book.

Assignment Guide

Check Your Understanding
Go over Exercises 1–5 in class before assigning the Homework Exercises.

Homework Exercises
A Practice by Example   6–14
B Apply Your Skills   15–18
C Challenge   19
TEKS ★ **TAKS** Tune-Up and Mixed Review   20–23

Homework Quick Check
To check students' understanding of key skills and concepts, go over Exercises 7, 11, 16, 17, and 18.

Differentiated Instruction Resources

PowerPoint

Lesson Quiz

Time	Temperature
7 A.M.	13°F
8 A.M.	18°F
9 A.M.	25°F
10 A.M.	32°F

1. Make a scatter plot of the data in the table and describe the trend. **a positive trend**

Temperature

19. See back of book.

GO Online
Homework Help
Visit: PHSchool.com
Web Code: are-1107

16. **C;** as the temperature rises, more people will go to the beach.

17. Positive; the values are both increasing.

18. As ticket cost increased, admissions would also; no; as the values in one data set increase, so do values in the other.

---

16. Carmella made a scatter plot comparing the daily temperature and the number of people at a beach. Which of the three scatter plots below most likely represents the data? Explain your choice.

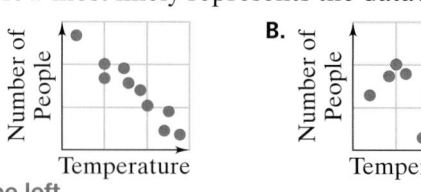

See left.

Make a scatter plot using the data in the table. Use the average ticket cost and the number of admissions.

17. **Data Analysis** What kind of trend do you see? Explain.

18. **Writing in Math** How would the scatter plot change if you switched the two axes? Would the trend change? Explain.

C 19. **Challenge** Make a scatter plot with "Year" as the horizontal scale and "Admissions" as the vertical scale. Predict the number of admissions in 2010. **See margin.**

Movie Attendance

Year	Average Ticket Cost (dollars)	Admissions (millions)
1997	4.59	1,388
1998	4.69	1,481
1999	5.08	1,465
2000	5.39	1,421
2001	5.66	1,487
2002	5.81	1,689
2003	6.03	1,574
2004	6.21	1,536

SOURCE: Motion Picture Association of America

TEKS ★ TAKS Tune-Up and Mixed Review

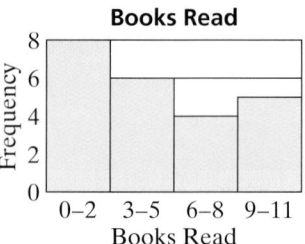

TAKS Objective 5
TEKS (7.11)(B)

20. The survey results of 23 students are shown. Which statement is supported by the graph? **B**
   - A Most students read 6–11 books.
   - B Most students read 0–5 books.
   - C The median was about 7 books.
   - D The mean was about 6 books.

TAKS Objective 2
TEKS (7.4)(C)

21. Which sequence follows the rule $3n + 1$, where n represents the position of a term in the sequence? **F**
   - F 4, 7, 10, 13, 16, . . .
   - G 4, 8, 13, 16, 20, . . .
   - H 1, 7, 10, 13, 19, . . .
   - J 4, 6, 7, 8, 9, . . .

TAKS Objective 3
TEKS (7.6)(B)

22. Which statement is always true about a right isosceles triangle? **D**
   - A It has 3 congruent sides.
   - B It has no congruent sides.
   - C It has three 60° angles.
   - D It has two acute angles.

Lesson 11-5

23. There are 35 marked seals in a region. Biologists count 36 seals, of which 8 are marked. About how many seals are in the region? **158 seals**

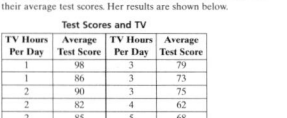

Enrichment 11-7 — L4

Reteaching 11-7 — Exploring Scatter — L2

Gilbert is investigating the relationship between the number of credit cards a person has and the amount of credit card debt.

First, he made a table from his data.

Then he plotted the data in a scatter plot.

Credit Cards and Credit Card Debt

Number of Cards	Amount of Debt
1	$0
1	$1,000
1	$5,000
2	$3,000
2	$5,000
3	$10,000
3	$5,000
3	$8,000
4	$10,000
5	$19,000

Gilbert's scatter plot shows a **positive trend** in the data. That means as the number of credit cards goes up, so does the amount of debt. As one value goes up, so does the other.

In a **negative trend**, one value goes up while the other goes down.

Complete the scatter plot for the data.

1. Dana surveyed her friends about how much TV they watch and their average test scores. Her results are shown below.

Test Scores and TV

TV Hours Per Day	Average Test Score	TV Hours Per Day	Average Test Score
1	98	3	79
1	86	3	73
2	90	3	75
2	82	4	62
2	85	5	68

2. Is the trend in the data negative or positive? Explain.
   Negative; as one value goes up, the other goes down.

3. Describe the relationship Dana likely found between test scores and TV time.
   The more TV students watch, the lower their test scores.

TEKS ★ TAKS Resources

- TAKS Strategies, p. 571
- TAKS Tune-Up, pp. 575–577

TAKS Tune-Up Kit

- TAKS Daily Review Transparencies
- TAKS Review and Preparation Workbook
- TAKS Strategies with Transparencies
- Texas Progress Monitoring Assessments

Alternative Assessment

Have students work in pairs. Each student writes a set of data for a scatter plot. Partners exchange papers, make a scatter plot using their partner's data, and describe any trends. Students check each other's scatter plot and descriptions.

Strategies

Interpreting Data

Before you answer a question that involves data, make sure you understand the information displayed in the graph. Then try to relate each of the answer choices to the data.

 EXAMPLE

The stem-and-leaf plot at the right shows the different costs of hair dryers. What is the mode hair dryer price?

  Ⓐ $4　　　　Ⓑ $20　　　　Ⓒ $24　　　　Ⓓ $25

The stems are tens digits. So the hair dryer prices range from $15 to $35. Choice A is the mode of the leaves, not of the data. Choice B is the range of the data. Choice D is the median. The correct answer is C.

Hair Dryer Prices

```
1 | 5 7
2 | 0 4 4 6
3 | 0 1 3 5
```

Key: 1 | 7 means $17.

Exercises

Use the double bar graph.

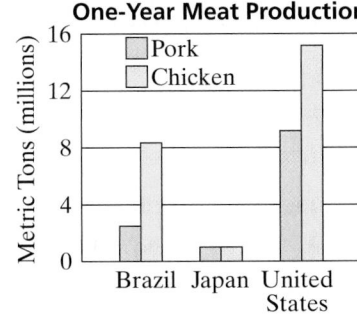

One-Year Meat Production

SOURCE: U.S. Department of Agriculture

Objective 5
TEKS (7.12)(A)

1. What is the approximate range of chicken production? **A**
  Ⓐ 14,000,000 metric tons　　　Ⓒ 7,000,000 metric tons
  Ⓑ 11,000,000 metric tons　　　Ⓓ 4,000,000 metric tons

Objective 5
TEKS (7.11)(B)

2. Which statement is NOT supported by the graph? **H**
  Ⓕ The mean of pork produced is about 4,000,000 metric tons.
  Ⓖ The mean of chicken produced is about 8,000,000 metric tons.
  Ⓗ All countries produced more chicken than pork.
  Ⓙ Brazil produced more pork than Japan.

Objective 5
TEKS (7.12)(A)

3. What is the approximate median of pork production? **B**
  Ⓐ 1,200,000 metric tons　　　Ⓒ 6,700,000 metric tons
  Ⓑ 2,600,000 metric tons　　　Ⓓ 9,300,000 metric tons

TAKS Strategies　Interpreting Data　**571**

 Strategies

Interpreting Data

Students learn to use and interpret data to answer questions. They learn to analyze the data that is presented and then relate it to the answer choices.

Guided Instruction

Explain to students that data can often help them choose the correct answer to a question. Remind them about misleading ways to present data and how they can redraw a graph to be more accurate.

Example

Look at the stem-and-leaf plot and make sure students understand what data it shows. Then ask:

• *How is the mode represented in the stem-and-leaf plot?* The number that repeats most often in the data is the mode.

TEKS ⭐ Resources

 Strategies with Transparencies
• Transparency 13
• Practice Sheet, p. 23

 Strategies with Transparencies

Test-Taking Strategies: Interpreting Data

Before you answer a question that involves interpreting data from a table, graph, or plot, make sure that you understand the information displayed.

Example The bar graph below shows the favorite fruit choices of a class of students. Which statement is best supported by the graph?

Favorite Fruits

A. More students chose grapes than chose apple and orange combined.

B. The fewest students chose apple.

C. The same number of students chose peach as chose watermelon.

D. More than half the students chose strawberry.

• 3 students chose grapes, 2 students chose apple, and 1 chose orange. Since 3 ≯ 2 + 1, eliminate choice A.

• 2 students chose apple. This is not the fewest, since only 1 student chose orange. Eliminate choice B.

• The total number of students choosing was 2 + 3 + 1 + 4 + 8 + 4 = 22. 8 is not more than half of 22, so eliminate choice D.

• 4 students chose peach, and 4 students chose watermelon. This is the same number, so the correct answer is choice C.

TEKS ★ TAKS Resources

Student Edition
Extra Skills and Word Problems
  Practice, Ch. 11, p. 650
English/Spanish Glossary, p. 675
Formulas and Properties, p. 673
Tables, p. 670
All in One Teaching Resources
- Vocabulary and Study
  Skills 11F   L3

TAKS Tune-Up Kit
- TAKS Daily Review
  Transparencies
- TAKS Review and Preparation
  Workbook
- TAKS Strategies with
  Transparencies
- Texas Progress Monitoring
  Assessments
- Texas ExamView CD-ROM
- MindPoint Quiz Show CD-ROM

Differentiated Instruction

Spanish Vocabulary Workbook
with Study Skills   ELL
Texas Interactive Textbook
- Audio Glossary
Online Vocabulary Quiz

Success Tracker™
Online at PHSchool.com

Vocabulary Review

- **biased question** (p. 551)
- **cell** (p. 538)
- **double bar graph** (p. 539)
- **double line graph** (p. 539)
- **frequency table** (p. 532)
- **histogram** (p. 533)
- **legend** (p. 539)
- **line plot** (p. 533)
- **negative trend** (p. 568)
- **no trend** (p. 568)
- **population** (p. 550)
- **positive trend** (p. 568)
- **random sample** (p. 550)
- **sample** (p. 550)
- **scatter plot** (p. 567)
- **spreadsheet** (p. 538)
- **stem-and-leaf plot** (p. 544)

Go Online
PHSchool.com
For: Online vocabulary quiz
Web Code: arj-1151

Choose the correct term to complete each sentence.

1. A (line, stem-and-leaf) plot separates the digits of the data. stem-and-leaf

2. A (negative, positive) trend involves a set of values that increases as another set of values decreases. negative

3. A (cell, legend) identifies the data being compared. legend

4. A (line plot, scatter plot) shows data by stacking ✗s above values. line plot

5. A (population, random sample) is a whole group. population

Skills and Concepts   TEKS ★ TAKS

Lesson 11-1

(7.11)(A) To use an appropriate representation for presenting and displaying relationships between collected data, including line plots
TAKS Obj. 5

(7.11)(B) To make inferences and convincing arguments based on an analysis of given data
TAKS Obj. 5

(7.14)(B) To evaluate the effectiveness of different representations to communicate ideas

A **frequency table** lists data items with the number of times each item occurs. A **line plot** shows data by stacking ✗'s above data values on a number line. A **histogram** is a bar graph with no spaces between bars.

6. Make a frequency table and a line plot for the number of hours of TV watched per person per week:
   5 7 9 5 3 6 8 6 5 7 6 8 7 7 6 5 4 4 5 6. See margin.

7. Use the table below to make a histogram. See margin.

How Many Pencils or Pens Are in Your Backpack?

Number of Pencils or Pens	0–4	5–9	10–14	15–19
Frequency	6	13	7	4

Airplanes The line plot at the right shows responses to a survey.

8. What do the numbers in the line plot represent?

9. How many people answered the survey? 14 people

8. the number of times a person has flown

How Many Times Have You Flown in an Airplane?

```
  ✗       ✗
  ✗   ✗   ✗
  ✗   ✗   ✗   ✗
  ✗   ✗   ✗   ✗           ✗
  1   2   3   4   5   6
```

6–7. See back of book.
13. See back of book.
17. The *y*-axis interval starts at 93, so it appears that the student who studied 6 h did twice as well as the student who studied 4 h.

Spanish Vocabulary/Study Skills   ELL

Vocabulary/Study Skills   L3

11F: Vocabulary Review   For use with the Chapter Review

Study Skill Take notes while you study. Use a highlighter to emphasize important material in your notes.

Circle the term that correctly completes each sentence.

1. A flip that creates symmetry is a (translation, reflection).
2. The first number in an ordered pair is the (x, y) coordinate.
3. Lines in a coordinate plane that are parallel to the y-axis are (horizontal, vertical).
4. A (line plot, frequency table) uses a number line with "x" marks to represent each data item.
5. You can use a (bar, circle) graph to easily compare amounts.
6. The (mean, median) is the middle number in a data set when the values are written in order from least to greatest.
7. The (mode, range) of a data set is the difference between the greatest and least data values.
8. A (line graph, scatter plot) can be used to investigate the relationship between two sets of data.
9. A sequence is (arithmetic, geometric) if each term is found by adding the same number to the previous term.
10. (Principal, Interest) is the amount of money borrowed or deposited.
11. The (area, surface area) of a prism is the sum of the areas of the faces.
12. (Circumference, Area) is the distance around a circle.
13. The opposite of squaring a number is finding its (square root, perfect square).
14. The (slope, bisector) of a line segment is a line, segment, or ray that goes through the midpoint of the segment.

Lessons 11-2, 11-3

(7.11)(A) To select and use an appropriate representation for displaying data, including bar graph, line graph, and stem-and-leaf plot **TAKS** Obj. 5

(7.11)(B) To make inferences based on an analysis of data **TAKS** Obj. 5

(7.12)(A) To describe a set of data using mean, median, mode, and range **TAKS** Obj. 5

A **double bar graph** compares two sets of data. A **double line graph** compares changes over time of two sets of data. A **stem-and-leaf plot** uses the digits of each number to show the shape of the data.

Education Use the double bar graph for Exercises 10–12.

10. In which skill did Group 2 excel the most?
counts to 20

11. In which skill did the two groups differ the most?
counts to 20

12. In which skill did the two groups differ the least? writes name

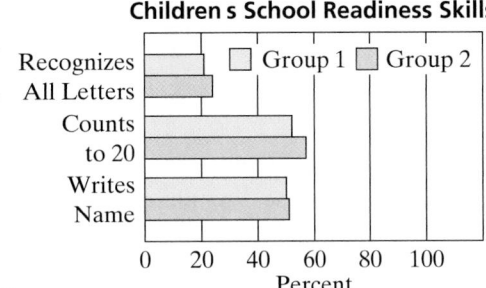

Children's School Readiness Skills

13. Draw a stem-and-leaf plot for the temperatures below. See margin.

48 54 45 60 50 70 66 69 40 61 50 60 58
47 40 27 23 60 47 40 29 16 55 36 19 27

Lessons 11-4, 11-5

(7.3)(B) To find solutions to application problems involving proportional relationships **TAKS** Obj. 2

(7.11)(B) To make inferences and convincing arguments based on an analysis of given or collected data **TAKS** Obj. 5

A **biased question** makes some answers appear better than others. You can use the capture/recapture method to estimate **population** size.

Tell whether each question is *biased* or *fair*. Explain.

14. What is your favorite activity after school?
Fair; the question makes no assumptions about the activity.

15. Do you like the calm, soothing ocean?
Biased; the question assumes the ocean is calm and soothing.

16. Biology Researchers know that there are 53 marked wolves in an area. On a flight over the area, they count 18 marked wolves and a total of 125 wolves. Estimate the total wolf population.
about 368 wolves

Lessons 11-6, 11-7

(7.11)(A) To select and use an appropriate representation for displaying data **TAKS** Obj. 5

(7.11)(B) To make inferences based on an analysis of given or collected data **TAKS** Obj. 5

(7.12)(B) To choose among mean, median, mode, or range to describe a set of data **TAKS** Obj. 5

Graphs can mislead if they use unequal intervals or improper breaks on an axis. A **scatter plot** relates two sets of data, showing whether the data have a **positive trend**, a **negative trend**, or **no trend**.

17. How is the graph at the right misleading?
See margin.

Describe the trend in each scatter plot.

18.

no trend

19.

negative

Chapter 11 Chapter Review **573**

Chapter 11 Test

Go Online
PHSchool.com
For: Online chapter test
Web Code: ara-1152

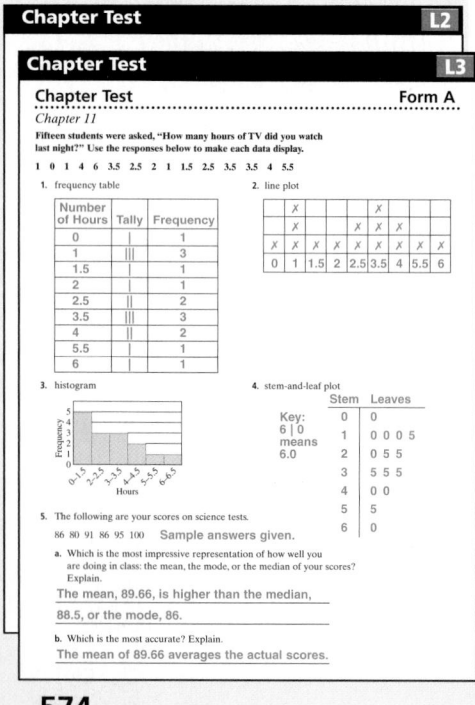

A pollster asks 20 people how many hours they sleep each night. Use the data below to draw each data display in Exercises 1–5.

8 7.5 9 7 8 7.5 6 6.5 9.5 7.5
8 7.5 8 7 8 6.5 8 8.5 8.5 7.5

1. frequency table   2. line plot

3. histogram   4. stem-and-leaf plot

5. **Reasoning** Explain how the stem-and-leaf plot in Exercise 4 would change if the person who said 9 had said 12.
1–5. See margin.

Use the spreadsheet below for Exercises 6–10.

	A	B	C	D
1	Student	Test 1	Test 2	Quiz
2	Alice	86	85	8
3	Xavier	91	89	9
4	Timotheo	79	84	8

6. What is the content of cell A3? Xavier

7. What is the content of cell C2? 85

8. In which cell is the word *Quiz?* D1

9. In which cell is the value 79? B4

10. In which cell is the word *Student?* A1

Is each question *biased* or *fair?* Explain.
11–14. See margin.
11. Do you prefer watching comedies or dramas?

12. Do you like watching violent sports or informative documentaries on TV?

13. Do you like sunny summers or dark winters?

14. Which season do you like best?

15. **Writing in Math** Explain how you can get a random sample of the people who use a town library. See margin.

Sales Use the double line graph below.

16. Estimate the year in which the sales were equal. 2001

17. In which year were sales lowest for each company? 1996

18. Redraw the graph to emphasize the highest sales for each company. See margin.

19. **Wages** Five students work at a store. Their hourly earnings are $8, $7.50, $12, $8.50, and $8. One student who earns $8 wants a raise. Should he use the mean, the median, or the mode to convince the boss? mean

Use a proportion to estimate each population.

20. total counted: 102   about 150
    tagged counted: 38
    total tagged: 56

21. total counted: 958   about 1,391
    tagged counted: 210
    total tagged: 305

22. a. Make a scatter plot of the data below.

Students' Ages and Heights

Age	12	13	12	14	14	13
Height (in.)	57	60	56	63	65	61

b. Describe the trend in the scatter plot.
22a–b. See margin.

1–5. See back of book.
11–15. See back of book.
18. See back of book.
22a–b. See back of book.

574

★ TAKS Tips

Some TAKS tests ask you to interpret a data display. This question asks you to interpret a Venn diagram.

Tip
The intersections in the diagram represent students who take more than one class.

The Venn diagram describes the number of students taking math, biology, and music. Which statement is NOT true?

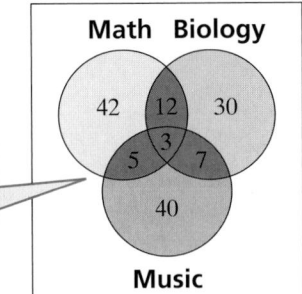

Math   Biology

42   12   30
5   3   7
40

Music

- Ⓐ Ten fewer students take biology than math.
- Ⓑ 109 students take math, music, or both.
- Ⓒ Five students take music and math but not biology.
- Ⓓ More students take both music and math than both biology and music.

Think It Through

47 students take math but not biology. Since 37 students take biology but not math, choice A is true. The students who take math, music, or both is 109. So choice B is true. The value 5 shows the intersection of the music and math circles. So choice C is true. Eight students take both music and math. Ten students take both biology and music. Since 8 is less than 10, choice D is false. The correct answer is D.

TEKS ★ TAKS Resources

TAKS Review and Preparation Workbook

Texas ExamView CD-ROM
- Instant TAKS Practice Test
- TAKS Practice Items

Differentiated Instruction

Spanish Assessment Resources
- Spanish Cumulative Review **ELL**

Texas ExamView CD-ROM
- Special Needs Practice Bank **L1**

Vocabulary Builder

As you solve test items, you must understand the meanings of mathematical terms. Match each term with its mathematical meaning.

A. circle graph **II**
B. line plot **I**
C. stem-and-leaf plot **III**

I. Shows the shape of a data set with stacked ✗s on a number line
II. Has wedges, or sections, to show parts
III. Uses the digits of each number to show data

Multiple Choice

Read each question. Then write the letter of the correct answer on your paper.

1. Which statement is always true about an obtuse isosceles triangle? **A**
   - Ⓐ It has two acute angles.
   - Ⓑ It has three congruent sides.
   - Ⓒ The sum of the angle measures is 90°.
   - Ⓓ It has no congruent angles.

2. Two angles of a triangle measure 102° and 48°. Which best describes the triangle? **H**
   - Ⓕ Right triangle
   - Ⓗ Obtuse triangle
   - Ⓖ Isosceles triangle
   - Ⓙ Acute triangle

3. Which of the following best
   describes the quadrilateral
   shown? **B**

   Ⓐ Rectangle
   Ⓑ Rhombus
   Ⓒ Trapezoid
   Ⓓ Square

4. Which solid can be
   formed from this net? **G**

   Ⓕ Cone
   Ⓖ Cylinder
   Ⓗ Rectangular prism
   Ⓙ Pyramid

5. Which net CANNOT be used to make
   a cube? **A**

   Ⓐ   Ⓒ

   Ⓑ   Ⓓ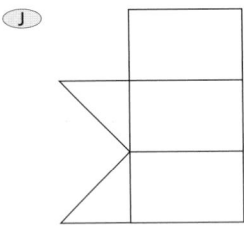

6. Which net can you use
   to find the amount
   of canvas you need
   for the tent shown
   at the right? **H**

   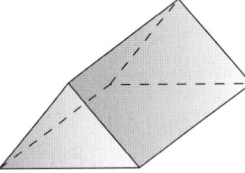

   Ⓕ   Ⓗ

   Ⓖ   Ⓙ

7. Which representation is NOT an
   appropriate way to display automobile
   traffic congestion in selected U.S. cities? **C**

   Ⓐ **Annual Delay Per Person**

City	Time (hours)
Los Angeles, CA	93
San Francisco, CA	72
Washington, D.C.	69
Seattle, WA	46
Houston, TX	63

   Ⓑ **Annual Delay Per Person (hours)**

   9 | 3
   7 | 2
   6 | 3 9
   4 | 6

   Key: 9 | 3 means 93 hours

   Ⓒ **Annual Delay Per Person**

   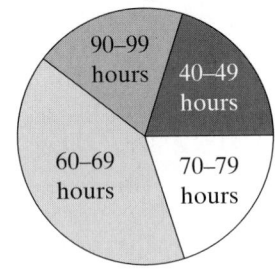

   90–99 hours
   40–49 hours
   60–69 hours
   70–79 hours

   Ⓓ **Annual Delay Per Person**

8. The graph shows the number of medals won by ten countries during one Olympics. Which statement is supported by these data? **H**

Number of Medals Won by 10 Countries

```
3 | 4 5
2 | 4
1 | 1 1 2 6 6 7
0 | 8
```

Key: 3 | 4 means 34 medals

Ⓕ There are three modes.
Ⓖ The range of medals won is 3.
Ⓗ 20% of the countries won 11 medals.
Ⓙ The median medals won is 12.

9. From the diagram, how many countries' citizens commonly speak Italian but not German or French? **A**

Languages Commonly Spoken

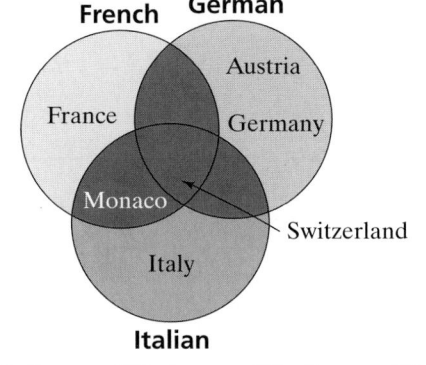

Ⓐ 0   Ⓑ 1   Ⓒ 2   Ⓓ 3

10. The graph below shows the Gross Domestic Product (GDP) in manufacturing. Which statement is NOT supported by the graph? **H**

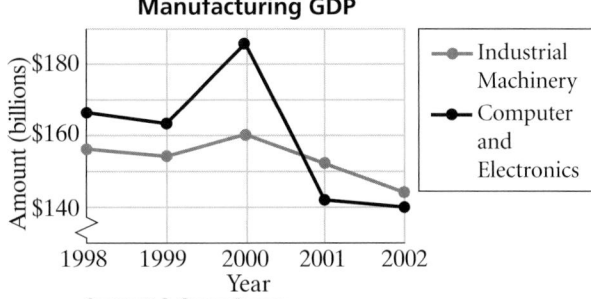

SOURCE: U.S. Census Bureau

Ⓕ In 1998, the difference between the computer/electronics and industrial GDPs was about $10 billion.
Ⓖ The industrial GDP first exceeded the computer/electronics GDP after 2000.
Ⓗ The range in the computer/electronics GDP was about $26 billion.
Ⓙ The industrial GDP in 2002 was about $140 billion.

Griddable Items

Record your answer in a grid.

11. Tracy can fit 12 books into a box with no space left over. Each book is 5 inches wide, 8 inches tall, and 1.5 inches thick. What is the volume of the box in cubic inches? **720**

12. A can has a radius of 3 cm and a height of 4 cm. To the nearest whole number, how many cubic centimeters does the can hold?
113

GO for Help Guide

TAKS Objective	Item Numbers	GO To	TAKS Objective	Item Numbers	GO To
Obj. 3: (7.6)(B)	1–2	Lesson 7-3	Obj. 5: (7.11)(B)	8	Lesson 11-3
	3	Lesson 7-4		9	Activity 11-1b
Obj. 3: (7.8)(B)	4–6	Lesson 8-9		10	Lesson 11-2
Obj. 5: (7.11)(A)	7	Lesson 11-3	Obj. 4: (7.9)(C)	11–12	Lesson 8-10

For additional TAKS practice, see the *TAKS Review and Preparation Workbook.*

Chapter at a Glance

Lesson Titles, Objectives, and Features	Assessment	NCTM Standards	TEKS ★ TAKS
12-1 Probability • To find the probability and complement of an event **Extension:** Odds	Lesson Quiz	1, 2, 5, 6, 7, 8, 9, 10	TEKS (7.1)(B) TAKS Obj. 1 TEKS (7.10)(B)
12-2a Activity Lab, Hands On: Exploring Probability **12-2 Experimental Probability** • To find the experimental probability and to use simulations **12-2b Activity Lab, Technology:** Random Numbers	Lesson Quiz	1, 2, 5, 6, 7, 8, 9, 10	TEKS (7.11)(B) TAKS Obj. 5 TEKS (7.10)(B), (7.13)(D)
12-3 Sample Spaces • To make and use sample spaces and to use the counting principle **12-3b Activity Lab, Data Analysis:** Using Data to Predict	Lesson Quiz Checkpoint Quiz 1	1, 2, 3, 5, 6, 7, 8, 9, 10	TEKS (7.10)(A), (7.11)(B) TAKS Obj. 5 TEKS (7.10)(B)
12-4a Activity Lab: Exploring Multiple Events **12-4 Compound Events** • To find the probability of independent and dependent events **Vocabulary Builder:** High-Use Academic Words **Guided Problem Solving:** Practice With Probability	Lesson Quiz	1, 2, 5, 6, 7, 8, 9, 10	TEKS (7.10)(A), (7.11)(B), (7.13)(A), (7.14)(A) TAKS Obj. 5, 6 TEKS (7.10)(B)
12-5 Permutations • To find permutations	Lesson Quiz	1, 2, 5, 6, 7, 8, 9, 10	
12-6 Combinations • To find combinations	Lesson Quiz Checkpoint Quiz 2	1, 2, 5, 6, 7, 8, 9, 10	
TAKS Practice Test			

NCTM Standards 2000

1 Number and Operations	2 Algebra	3 Geometry	4 Measurement	5 Data Analysis and Probability
6 Problem Solving	7 Reasoning and Proof	8 Communication	9 Connections	10 Representation

Correlations to Standardized Tests

All content for these tests is contained in *Prentice Hall Math,* Course 2. This chart reflects coverage in this chapter only.

	12-1	12-2	12-3	12-4	12-5	12-6
Terra Nova CAT6 (Level 17)						
Number and Number Relations	✔	✔	✔	✔	✔	✔
Computation and Numerical Estimation	✔	✔	✔	✔	✔	✔
Operation Concepts	✔	✔	✔	✔	✔	✔
Measurement						
Geometry and Spatial Sense						
Data Analysis, Statistics, and Probability	✔	✔	✔	✔	✔	✔
Patterns, Functions, Algebra	✔	✔	✔	✔	✔	✔
Problem Solving and Reasoning	✔	✔	✔	✔	✔	✔
Communication	✔	✔	✔	✔	✔	✔
Decimals, Fractions, Integers, and Percent	✔	✔	✔	✔	✔	✔
Order of Operations						
Terra Nova CTBS (Level 17)						
Decimals, Fractions, Integers, Percents	✔	✔	✔	✔	✔	✔
Order of Operations, Numeration, Number Theory	✔	✔	✔	✔	✔	✔
Data Interpretation	✔	✔	✔	✔	✔	✔
Pre-algebra	✔	✔	✔	✔	✔	✔
Measurement						
Geometry						
ITBS (Level 13)						
Number Properties and Operations	✔	✔	✔	✔	✔	✔
Algebra	✔	✔	✔	✔	✔	✔
Geometry						
Measurement						
Probability and Statistics	✔	✔	✔	✔	✔	✔
Estimation						
SAT10 (Int 3 Level)						
Number Sense and Operations	✔	✔	✔	✔	✔	✔
Patterns, Relationships, and Algebra	✔	✔	✔	✔	✔	✔
Data, Statistics, and Probability	✔	✔	✔	✔	✔	✔
Geometry and Measurement						
NAEP						
Number Sense, Properties, and Operations						
Measurement						
Geometry and Spatial Sense						
Data Analysis, Statistics, and Probability	✔	✔	✔	✔	✔	✔
Algebra and Functions						

CAT6 California Achievement Test, 6th Ed.   **CTBS** Comprehensive Test of Basic Skills   **ITBS** Iowa Test of Basic Skills, Form M
SAT10 Stanford Achievement Test, 10th Ed.   **NAEP** National Assessment of Educational Progress 2005 Mathematics Objectives

TEKS Math Background

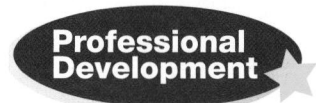

Focus on the TEKS

- At Grade 7, students convert between fractions, decimals, whole numbers, and percents (7.1)(B). Analysis of TAKS results shows that students struggle with this student expectation.

  In Lesson 12-1, students find the probability and complement of an event in the form of a fraction, decimal, and percent. Place special emphasis on this lesson because it focuses on (7.1)(B).

- New at Grade 7 is finding the probability of independent events (7.10)(B). Students work with theoretical and experimental probability in Lesson 12-1 and Lesson 12-2, respectively. In Lesson 12-4, students find probabilities of compound events involving dependent and independent events (7.10)(B).

12-1 Probability

TEKS ★ *TAKS* (7.1)(B) Obj. 1; (7.10)(B)

Math Understandings

- In mathematics, probability is expressed as a number that estimates how often an event will occur.
- Probabilities range from 0 (impossible) to 1 (certain).

An **outcome** is the result of an action. An **event** is an outcome or group of outcomes. If all the outcomes are equally likely, you can use a formula to find the theoretical probability.

Theoretical Probability
theoretical probability = $P(\text{event})$ = $\dfrac{\text{number of favorable outcomes}}{\text{total number of possible outcomes}}$

The probability of an impossible event is 0. The probability of a certain event is 1.

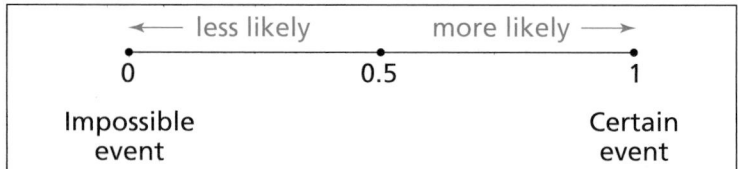

The **complement** of an event is the collection of outcomes not contained in the event.

Complement of an Event
For any event A, the complement is not A.
$P(A) + P(\text{not } A) = 1$ $\qquad$ $P(\text{not } A) = 1 - P(A)$

12-2 Experimental Probability

TEKS ★ *TAKS* (7.11)(B) Obj. 5; (7.10)(B), (7.13)(D)

Math Understandings

- Experimental probability is based on the results of an actual experiment; theoretical probability is based on the assumption that certain outcomes are equally likely.
- As the number of events increases, the ratio of the experimental results approaches the ratio that is the theoretical probability (the Law of Large Numbers).
- It is a fallacy that, when tossing a fair coin, you are more likely to get heads after tossing a series of tails. The probability remains one out of two.

Probability based on experimental data or observations is called **experimental probability**. Some events are too difficult or time-consuming to perform. You can simulate, or model, problems to find experimental probabilities.

Experimental Probability
$P(\text{event}) = \dfrac{\text{number of favorable outcomes}}{\text{total number of possible outcomes}}$

12-3 Sample Spaces

TEKS ★ (TAKS) (7.10)(A) Obj. 5; (7.10)(B)

Math Understandings
- To find the probability of an event, you need to know the total number of outcomes, or sample space.

The collection of all possible outcomes in an experiment is the **sample space.** You can use a tree diagram or the counting principle to find the total number of outcomes for an event.

The Counting Principle
Suppose there are *m* ways of making one choice and *n* ways of making a second choice. Then there are *m* × *n* ways to make the first choice followed by the second choice.

Example: If you can choose a shirt from 5 sizes and 7 colors, then you can choose 5 × 7, or 35 different shirts.

12-4 Compound Events

TEKS ★ (TAKS) (7.10)(A) Obj. 5; (7.10)(B)

Math Understandings
- Two events are independent if one event does not affect the sample space of the other event.
- Two events are dependent if one event affects the sample space of the other event.

A **compound event** consists of two or more events. These events either depend on or do not depend on each other. Two events are **independent events** if the occurrence of one event does not affect the probability of the occurrence of the other. Two events are **dependent events** if the occurrence of one event affects the probability of the occurrence of the other event.

Example: If you draw a letter from a set of alphabet cards and, without replacing, draw a second letter, the probability of drawing a Q followed by a U is $\frac{1}{26} \times \frac{1}{25}$ or $\frac{1}{650}$.

12-5 Permutations

Math Understandings
- Order makes a difference in permutations.

A **permutation** is an arrangement of objects in a particular order. The product of all positive integers less than or equal to a number is a **factorial**. You write 5 factorial as 5! The number of permutations of *n* items, using all *n* in each arrangement, is *n*! (read as "*n* factorial").

Example: Five students present reports to a class in 5! = 5 × 4 × 3 × 2 × 1, or 120 different ways.

The number of permutations of *n* items, using *r* of them at a time, is *n*! divided by (*n* − *r*)!

Example: Three out of five students present reports to a class in $\frac{5!}{2!}$ = 5 × 4 × 3, or 60 different ways.

12-6 Combinations

Math Understandings
- Order does not matter in combinations.

A **combination** is a grouping of objects in which the order of the objects does not matter. The number of combinations of *n* items, using *r* of them at a time, is the number of permutations of *n* items taken *r* at a time divided by *r*!

Example: The combination of 6 objects taken 4 at a time is 15.

$$\frac{6!}{(6-4)!} \div 4! = 15$$

Additional Professional Development Opportunities

Math Background Notes for Chapter 12: Every lesson has a Math Background in the PLAN section.

Research Overview, Mathematics Strands
Additional support for these topics and more is in the front of the Teacher's Edition.

LessonLab
LessonLab, a Pearson Education company, offers comprehensive, facilitated professional development designed to help teachers to improve student achievement. To learn more, please visit lessonlab.com.

Texas Chapter 12 Resources

	12-1	12-2	12-3	12-4	12-5	12-6	For the Chapter
Print Resources							
L3 Practice	●	●	●	●	●	●	
L1 Adapted Practice	●	●	●	●	●	●	
L3 Guided Problem Solving	●	●	●	●	●	●	
L2 Reteaching	●	●	●	●	●	●	
L4 Enrichment	●	●	●	●	●	●	
L3 Daily Notetaking Guide	●	●	●	●	●	●	
L1 Adapted Daily Notetaking Guide	●	●	●	●	●	●	
L3 Vocabulary and Study Skills Worksheets	●		●	●	●	●	●
L3 Daily Puzzles	●	●	●	●	●	●	
L3 Activity Labs	●	●	●	●	●	●	
L3 Checkpoint Quiz			●			●	
L3 Chapter Project							●
L2 Chapter Test							●
L3 Chapter Test							●
L4 Alternative Assessment							●
L3 Cumulative Review							●
Spanish Resources ELL							
L3 Practice	●	●	●	●	●	●	●
L3 Vocabulary and Study Skills Worksheets	●		●	●	●	●	
L3 Checkpoint Quiz			●			●	
L2 Chapter Test							●
L3 Chapter Test							●
L4 Alternative Assessment							●
L3 Cumulative Review							●
Transparencies							
Check Skills You'll Need	●	●	●	●	●	●	
Additional Examples	●	●	●	●	●	●	
Problem of the Day	●	●	●	●	●	●	
TAKS Daily Review	●	●	●	●	●	●	
Classroom Aid							
Student Edition Answers	●	●	●	●	●	●	●
Lesson Quiz	●	●	●	●	●	●	
TAKS Strategies							●
Technology							
Texas Interactive Textbook Online	●	●	●	●	●	●	●
Texas StudentExpress CD-ROM	●	●	●	●	●	●	●
Success Tracker™ Online Intervention	●	●	●	●	●	●	●
TeacherExpress CD-ROM	●	●	●	●	●	●	●
PresentationExpress CD-ROM	●	●	●	●	●	●	●
Texas ExamView CD-ROM with QuickTake	●	●	●	●	●	●	●
MindPoint Quiz Show CD-ROM	●	●	●	●	●	●	●
Prentice Hall Web Site: PHSchool.com	●	●	●	●	●	●	●

Also available: **Tune-Up Kit**
- TAKS Daily Review Transparencies
- TAKS Review and Preparation Workbook
- TAKS Strategies with Transparencies
- Texas Progress Monitoring Assessments
- Texas ExamView CD-ROM
- MindPoint Quiz Show CD-ROM

Other Resources
Algebra Readiness Tests
All-in-One Student Workbook
All-in-One Student Workbook, Adapted Version
Multilingual Handbook

Solution Key
Math Notes Study Folder
Spanish Cumulative Assessment

Where You Can Use the Lesson Resources

Here is a suggestion, following the four-step teaching plan, for how you can incorporate Differentiated Instruction Resources into your teaching.

	Instructional Resources `L3`	**Differentiated Instruction Resources**
1. Plan		
Preparation Read the Math Background in the Teacher's Edition to connect this lesson with students' previous experience. **Starting Class** **Check Skills You'll Need** Assign these exercises to review prerequisite skills. **TEKS ★ `TAKS`** Review the full text of the TEKS student expectations and TAKS objectives covered in this lesson. **New Vocabulary** Help students pre-read the lesson by pointing out the new terms introduced in the lesson.	**TEKS Math Background** **Math Understandings** **Transparencies & PresentationExpress CD-ROM** Check Skills You'll Need Problem of the Day TAKS Daily Review **Resources** Vocabulary and Study Skills	**Spanish Support** ELL Vocabulary and Study Skills
2. Teach		
`L3` **Guided Instruction** Use the Activity Labs to build conceptual understanding. Teach each Example. Use the Teacher's Edition side column notes for specific teaching tips, including Error Prevention notes. Use the Additional Examples found in the side column (and on transparency and PowerPoint) as an alternative presentation for the content. After each Example, assign the Quick Check exercise for that Example to get an immediate assessment of student understanding. Use the Closure activity in the Teacher's Edition to help students attain mastery of lesson content.	**Student Edition** Activity Lab **Resources** Daily Notetaking Guide Activity Lab **Transparencies & PresentationExpress CD-ROM** Additional Examples Classroom Aids **Texas ExamView CD-ROM with QuickTake**	**Teacher's Edition** Every lesson includes suggestions for working with students who need special attention. `L1` Special Needs `L2` Below Level `L4` Advanced Learners ELL English Language Learners **Resources** `L1` Adapted Daily Notetaking Guide **Multilingual Handbook**
3. Practice		

Assignment Guide
Check Your Understanding
Use these questions to check students' understanding before you assign homework.
Homework Exercises
Assign homework from these leveled exercises in the Assignment Guide.
  A Practice by Example
  B Apply Your Skills
  C Challenge
  `TAKS` Tune-Up and Mixed Review
Homework Quick Check
Use these key exercises to quickly check students' homework.
	Transparencies & PresentationExpress CD-ROM
	Student Answers
	Resources
	Practice
	Guided Problem Solving
	Vocabulary and Study Skills
	Activity Lab
	Daily Puzzles
	Texas ExamView CD-ROM with QuickTake
		Spanish Support
		ELL Practice
		ELL Vocabulary and Study Skills
		Resources
		`L1` Adapted Practice
		`L4` Enrichment

4. Assess & Reteach		
Lesson Quiz Assign the Lesson Quiz to assess students' mastery of the lesson content. **Checkpoint Quiz** Use the Checkpoint Quiz to assess student progress over several lessons.	**Transparencies & PresentationExpress CD-ROM** Lesson Quiz **Resources** Checkpoint Quiz	**Resources** `L2` Reteaching ELL Checkpoint Quiz Success Tracker™ Online Intervention **Texas ExamView CD-ROM with QuickTake**

KEY   `L1` Special Needs   `L2` Below Level   `L3` For All Students   `L4` Advanced, Gifted   ELL English Language Learners

Using Probability

Answers are in the back of the textbook.

For intervention, direct students to:

Writing Ratios
Lesson 5-1
Extra Skills and Word
  Problems Practice, Ch. 5

Using Proportional Reasoning
Lesson 5-4
Extra Skills and Word
  Problems Practice, Ch. 5

Percents, Fractions, and Decimals
Lesson 6-2
Extra Skills and Word
  Problems Practice, Ch. 6

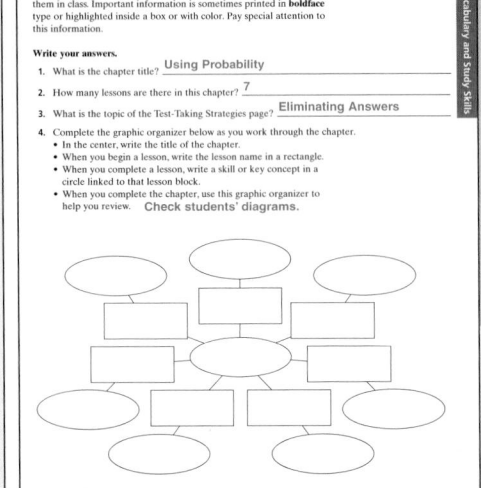

Spanish Vocabulary/Study Skills ELL

Vocabulary/Study Skills L3

12A: Graphic Organizer For use before Lesson 12-1

Study Skill Try to read new lessons before your teacher presents them in class. Important information is sometimes printed in **boldface** type or highlighted inside a box or with color. Pay special attention to this information.

Write your answers.
1. What is the chapter title? Using Probability
2. How many lessons are there in this chapter? 7
3. What is the topic of the Test-Taking Strategies page? Eliminating Answers
4. Complete the graphic organizer below as you work through the chapter.
  • In the center, write the title of the chapter.
  • When you begin a lesson, write the lesson name in a rectangle.
  • When you complete a lesson, write a skill or key concept in a circle linked to that lesson block.
  • When you complete the chapter, use this graphic organizer to help you review. Check students' diagrams.

578

CHAPTER 12 — Using Probability

 What You've Learned
TEKS ★ TAKS

- **(7.2)(D)** In Chapter 5, you used division to find unit rates and ratios in proportional relationships. **TAKS** Obj. 1

- **(7.14)(A)** In Chapter 9, you communicated mathematical ideas using graphical models. **TAKS** Obj. 6

- **(7.11)(A)** In Chapter 11, you selected and used an appropriate representation for presenting and displaying relationships among collected data. **TAKS** Obj. 5

 Check Your Readiness

For Exercises	See Lesson
1–6	5-1
7–12	5-4
13–22	6-2

GO for Help

Writing Ratios

Write each ratio in simplest form.

1. $\frac{9}{24}$ $\frac{3}{8}$
2. $\frac{20}{54}$ $\frac{10}{27}$
3. $\frac{15}{65}$ $\frac{3}{13}$
4. $\frac{16}{22}$ $\frac{8}{11}$
5. $\frac{21}{84}$ $\frac{1}{4}$
6. $\frac{18}{42}$ $\frac{3}{7}$

Using Proportional Reasoning

(Algebra) Solve each proportion.

7. $\frac{3}{10} = \frac{x}{30}$ 9
8. $\frac{n}{14} = \frac{25}{8}$ 43.75
9. $\frac{22}{c} = \frac{66}{15}$ 5
10. $\frac{16}{35} = \frac{20}{y}$ 43.75
11. $\frac{a}{24} = \frac{24}{9}$ 64
12. $\frac{19}{38} = \frac{f}{21}$ 10.5

Percents, Fractions, and Decimals

Write each decimal as a percent.

13. 0.46 46%
14. 0.265 26.5%
15. 0.07 7%
16. 0.256 25.6%
17. 0.82 82%

Write each fraction as a percent. When necessary, round to the nearest tenth of a percent.

18. $\frac{4}{5}$ 80%
19. $\frac{5}{11}$ 45.5%
20. $\frac{8}{14}$ 57.1%
21. $\frac{12}{30}$ 40%
22. $\frac{15}{32}$ 46.9%

Number, Operation, and Quantitative Reasoning
TEKS (7.1)(B) *TAKS* Obj. 1

Probability and Statistics
TEKS (7.10)(A), (7.11)(B)
TAKS Obj. 5; TEKS (7.10)(B)

Underlying Processes and Mathematical Tools
TEKS (7.13)(A), (7.14)(A)
TAKS Obj. 6; TEKS (7.13)(D)

Chapter 12 Overview

In this chapter, students work with both theoretical and experimental probability. They find the probability of both simple and compound events. They conclude the chapter by learning about permutations and combinations.

Activating Prior Knowledge

In this chapter, as they work with probability concepts, students will build on their knowledge of fractions, decimals, percents, ratios, and proportions. Ask questions such as:

• *How would you express the ratio $\frac{10}{16}$ in simplest form?* $\frac{5}{8}$

• *What is the value of x in the proportion $\frac{6}{x} = \frac{24}{8}$?* $x = 2$

• *What percent is equivalent to the fraction $\frac{7}{20}$?* 35%

What You'll Learn Next

TEKS ★ TAKS

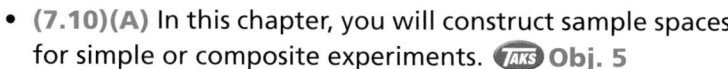

• **(7.10)(A)** In this chapter, you will construct sample spaces for simple or composite experiments. *TAKS* Obj. 5

• **(7.10)(B)** You will find the probability of independent events.

• **(7.11)(B)** You will make inferences based on an analysis of given or collected data. *TAKS* Obj. 5

TAKS **Tune-Up** On pages 619–623, you will review and practice the *TAKS* objectives you have learned.

🔊 Key Vocabulary

• combination (p. 610)
• complement (p. 581)
• compound event (p. 598)
• counting principle (p. 592)
• dependent events (p. 599)
• event (p. 580)
• experimental probability (p. 586)
• factorial (p. 606)
• independent events (p. 598)
• outcome (p. 580)
• permutation (p. 606)
• sample space (p. 591)
• theoretical probability (p. 580)

TEKS ★ TAKS

(7.10)(B) To find the probability of independent events
(7.1)(B) To convert between fractions, decimals, whole numbers, and percents
TAKS **Obj. 1**

Dana Center TEKS Toolkit Clarifying Activities (7.10)(B), (7.1)(B)
Visit: PHSchool.com
Web Code: arq-9045

TEKS Math Background

In the language of mathematical probability, the *theoretical probability* of an event, usually written as a fraction, is $P(\text{event}) =$
$\frac{\text{number of favorable outcomes}}{\text{total number of possible outcomes}}$.
The probability of any event can be represented by a rational number from 0 to 1, so $0 \le P(\text{event}) \le 1$ where 0 is $P(\text{impossible outcome})$ and 1 is $P(\text{certain outcome})$. The *complement* of an event, A, is the collection of unfavorable outcomes. This means that $P(A) + P(\text{not } A) = 1$.

More Math Background: p. 578C

Lesson Planning and Resources

See p. 578E for a list of the resources that support this lesson.

PowerPoint
Bell Ringer Practice

☑ **Check Skills You'll Need**
Use student page, transparency, or PowerPoint.

TAKS **Daily Review 89**
Use transparency.

☑ **Check Skills You'll Need**

1. Vocabulary Review
In what three forms can you write a *rational number*?
1–5. See below.
Write each fraction as a decimal and as a percent.

2. $\frac{31}{50}$ 3. $\frac{19}{20}$

4. $\frac{11}{40}$ 5. $\frac{11}{10}$

GO for Help
Lesson 6-2

Check Skills You'll Need

1. fraction, decimal, percent
2. 0.62; 62%
3. 0.95; 95%
4. 0.275; 27.5%
5. 1.1; 110%

Vocabulary Tip

You read $P(\text{vowel})$ as "the probability of a vowel."

TEKS ★ TAKS
• (7.10)(B) To find the probability of independent events
• (7.1)(B) To convert between fractions, decimals, whole numbers, and percents TAKS **Obj. 1**

🔊 **New Vocabulary** outcome, event, theoretical probability, complement

Why Learn This?

In sports, a coin toss often determines which team gets the ball first.

An **outcome** is the result of an action. For example, getting tails is a possible outcome of flipping a coin. An **event** is a collection of possible outcomes. If all the outcomes are equally likely, you can use a formula to find the theoretical probability.

KEY CONCEPTS **Theoretical Probability**

$$\text{theoretical probability} = P(\text{event}) = \frac{\text{number of favorable outcomes}}{\text{total number of possible outcomes}}$$

You can express probability as a fraction, a decimal, or a percent.

EXAMPLE **Finding Probability**

1 You select a letter at random from the letters shown. Find the probability of selecting a vowel. Express the probability as a fraction, a decimal, and a percent.

The event *vowel* has 2 outcomes, A and E, out of 5 possible outcomes.

$P(\text{vowel}) = \frac{2}{5}$ ← number of favorable outcomes
← total number of possible outcomes

$= \frac{2}{5}$, 0.4, or 40% ← **Write as a fraction, decimal, and percent.**

☑ **Quick Check**

1. Find $P(\text{consonant})$ as a fraction for the letters in Example 1. $\frac{3}{5}$

Differentiated Instruction Solutions for All Learners

Special Needs L1
For Quick Check 2, have students actually roll a number cube several times. Have them list the numbers they get, and think about the numbers they might get on any given roll.

learning style: tactile

Below Level L2
Have students convert these decimals to fractions:
0.25, 0.50, 0.75, 0.90. $\frac{1}{4}$, $\frac{1}{2}$, $\frac{3}{4}$, $\frac{9}{10}$

learning style: visual

All probabilities range from 0 to 1. The probability of rolling a 7 on a number cube is 0, so that is an *impossible* event. The probability of rolling a positive integer less than 7 is 1, so that is a *certain* event.

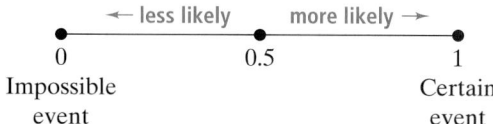

The **complement** of an event is the collection of outcomes not contained in the event. The sum of the probabilities of an event and its complement is 1. So $P(\text{event}) + P(\text{not event}) = 1$.

EXAMPLES **Finding Probabilities From 0 to 1**

2 **Clothes** The picture shows the jeans in Juanita's closet. She selects a pair of jeans with her eyes shut. Find $P(\text{dark color})$.

There are 8 possible outcomes. Since there are 3 black pairs and 2 blue pairs, the event *dark color* has 5 favorable outcomes.

$$P(\text{dark color}) = \frac{5}{8} \quad \leftarrow \text{number of favorable outcomes}$$
$$\leftarrow \text{total number of possible outcomes}$$

3 Refer to Juanita's closet. Find $P(\text{red})$.

The event *red* has no favorable outcome.

$$P(\text{red}) = \frac{0}{8}, \text{ or } 0 \quad \leftarrow \text{number of favorable outcomes}$$
$$\leftarrow \text{total number of possible outcomes}$$

4 Refer to Juanita's closet. Find $P(\text{not dark color})$.

$$P(\text{dark color}) + P(\text{not dark color}) = 1 \quad \leftarrow \begin{array}{l}\text{The sum of probabilities of an}\\ \text{event and its complement is 1.}\end{array}$$

$$\frac{5}{8} + P(\text{not dark color}) = 1 \quad \leftarrow \text{Substitute } \frac{5}{8} \text{ for } P(\text{dark color}).$$

$$\frac{5}{8} - \frac{5}{8} + P(\text{not dark color}) = 1 - \frac{5}{8} \quad \leftarrow \begin{array}{l}\text{Subtract } \frac{5}{8} \text{ from}\\ \text{each side.}\end{array}$$

$$P(\text{not dark color}) = \frac{3}{8} \quad \leftarrow \text{Simplify.}$$

For help with subtracting fractions, go to Lesson 3-2, Example 3.

✓ Quick Check

You roll a number cube once. Find each probability.

2. $P(\text{multiple of 3})$ $\frac{1}{3}$ **3.** $P(\text{not multiple of 2})$ $\frac{1}{2}$ **4.** $P(9)$ 0

Advanced Learners **L4**
Have students write a problem similar to Example 2, showing examples of no favorable outcomes and the sum of the probabilities of an event and its complement.

Pre-AP™

English Language Learners **ELL**
The notion of complements is conceptually and linguistically complex. Help students differentiate between the word *complement* here and the word *complement* in complementary angles.

learning style: verbal

Activity Lab
Use before the lesson.

 Teaching Resources
Activity Lab 12-1: Critical Thinking

Guided Instruction

Example 1
To learn the vocabulary of probability, have students define aloud the event (**selecting a letter at random from those shown**), the favorable outcome (**vowel**), and the unfavorable outcome (**consonant**).

Error Prevention!

Ask students to say "the probability of a vowel" for $P(\text{vowel})$ rather than using shortcuts such as "pea-vowel."

PowerPoint
Additional Examples

1 Find the probability of selecting a vowel from the letters F, G, H, I. Express the probability as a fraction, decimal, and a percent.
$\frac{1}{4}$, 0.25, 25%

2 Jacques has 1 blue shirt, 5 white shirts, 3 green shirts, and 2 brown shirts. He selects a shirt from his closet with his eyes shut. Find each probability.
a. $P(\text{white shirt})$ $\frac{5}{11}$
b. $P(\text{not green shirt})$ $\frac{8}{11}$
c. $P(\text{blue shirt})$ $\frac{1}{11}$

Teaching Resources
• Daily Notetaking Guide 12-1 **L3**
• Adapted Notetaking 12-1 **L1**

Closure

• *How do you find the theoretical probability of an event?* Divide the number of favorable outcomes by the total number of possible outcomes.
• *How do you find the probability of the complement of an event?* Subtract the probability of the event from 1.

581

Assignment Guide

Check Your Understanding
Go over Exercises 1–6 in class
before assigning the Homework
Exercises.

Homework Exercises
A Practice by Example   7–21
B Apply Your Skills   22–32
C Challenge   33
TEKS ★ TAKS Tune-Up and
Mixed Review   34–39

Homework Quick Check
To check students' understanding
of key skills and concepts, go over
Exercises 11, 18, 23, 29, and 32.

Differentiated Instruction **Resources**

✓ Check Your Understanding

1. Answers may vary.
   Sample: the result or
   group of results of an
   action

1. **Vocabulary** Define *event* without using the word *outcome*.

2. $P(A) = \frac{1}{3}$. Write an expression for $P(\text{not } A)$. $\frac{2}{3}$

**You select a marble from those shown.
Match each event with its probability.**

3. $P(\text{red})$ **B**   A. $\frac{5}{7}$

4. $P(\text{yellow})$ **C**   B. $\frac{2}{7}$

5. $P(\text{blue})$ **A**   C. 0

6. $P(\text{red or blue})$ **D**   D. 1

Homework Exercises

For more exercises, see Extra Skills and Word Problems.

GO for Help

For Exercises	See Examples
7–12	1
13–21	2

12. $\frac{1}{4}$; 0.25; 25%

18. $\frac{6}{10}$ or $\frac{3}{5}$

Ⓐ **You mix the letters A, C, Q, U, A, I, N, T, A, N, C, and E thoroughly.
Without looking, you select one letter. Find the probability of each event
as a fraction, a decimal, and a percent.** $\frac{1}{2}$; 0.5; 50%

7. $P(T)$ $\frac{1}{12}$; 0.08$\overline{3}$; about 8.3%   8. $P(A)$ $\frac{1}{4}$; 0.25; 25%   9. $P(\text{vowel})$

10. $P(\text{consonant})$ 11. $P(N)$ 12. $P(Q \text{ or } C)$
    $\frac{1}{2}$; 0.5; 50% $\frac{1}{6}$; 0.1$\overline{6}$; about 16.7%

You spin the spinner once. Find each probability.

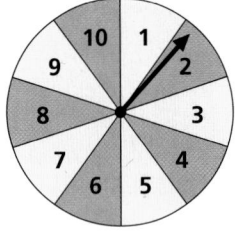

13. $P(12)$ 0   14. $P(2 \text{ or } 4)$ $\frac{2}{10}$ or $\frac{1}{5}$

15. $P(\text{multiple of 3})$ $\frac{3}{10}$ 16. $P(\text{even})$ $\frac{5}{10}$ or $\frac{1}{2}$

17. $P(\text{not 1})$ $\frac{9}{10}$ 18. $P(\text{not a factor of 10})$

19. $P(\text{less than 11})$ 20. $P(\text{not divisible by 3})$
    $\frac{10}{10}$ or 1 $\frac{7}{10}$

21. **Science** Six out of the 111 elements are noble gases. You write the
    names of all the elements on cards and select a card at random.
    What is the probability of *not* picking a noble gas? $\frac{105}{111}$

Ⓑ **GPS**

22. **Guided Problem Solving** The table shows
    data about a group of people's hair colors. You
    select a person at random from the group. What
    is $P(\text{not black hair})$? $\frac{122}{219}$
    - How many people are in the group?
    - How many people do *not* have black hair?

Hair Color

Color	Number
Blond	58
Brown	64
Black	97

GO Online
Homework Help
Visit: PHSchool.com
Web Code: are-1201

23. **Writing in Math** Describe a real-life situation where the probability
    of an event is 1. Then describe the complement of that situation.
    See margin.

582   **Chapter 12** Using Probability

23. Answers may vary. Sample: The
    probability that a female student will be
    chosen from an all-female school is 1.
    The complement is 0; it is impossible for
    a male student to be chosen.

You spin the spinner once. Find each probability.

24. $P(\text{not green})$ $\frac{3}{4}$

25. $P(\text{purple or blue})$ $\frac{3}{4}$

26. $P(\text{white})$ 0

27. $P(\text{not purple})$ $\frac{2}{4}$ or $\frac{1}{2}$

Government The U.S. House of Representatives has 435 members. Each member's name is put into a hat and one name is chosen at random. Find each probability as a decimal to the nearest hundredth.

28. $P(\text{Florida})$ 0.06

29. $P(\text{Texas})$ 0.07

30. $P(\text{not Illinois})$ 0.96

31. $P(\text{Pennsylvania})$ 0.04

U.S. House of Representatives

State	Number	State	Number
Florida	25	Illinois	19
Pennsylvania	19	Texas	32

SOURCE: U.S. Census Bureau. Go to **PHSchool.com** for a data update. Web Code arg-9041

32. a. Suppose $P(E) = 0.3$. Find $P(\text{not } E)$. 0.7

GPS **b.** Suppose $P(\text{not } E) = 65\%$. Find $P(E)$. 35%

C **33. Challenge** A bag contains an unknown number of marbles. You know that $P(\text{red}) = \frac{1}{4}$ and $P(\text{green}) = \frac{1}{4}$. What can you conclude about how many marbles are in the bag? Any positive integer divisible by 4 can be the number of marbles, since $\frac{1}{4}$ of that number must be a positive integer.

 TEKS **TAKS** **Tune-Up and Mixed Review**

TAKS Objective 2
TEKS (7.5)(A)

34. The model represents the equation $3x + 5 = 14$. What is the value of x? C

(A) $x = \frac{11}{5}$ (C) $x = 3$

(B) $x = 6$ (D) $x = \frac{19}{3}$

TAKS Objective 6
TEKS (7.14)(A)

35. Suppose 2 out of every 25 people in your state are 10 to 14 years old. Which equation can be used to find x, the percent of people in your state who are 10 to 14 years old? J

(F) $\frac{x}{100} = \frac{25}{2}$ (G) $\frac{100}{x} = \frac{10}{14}$ (H) $\frac{100}{25} = \frac{2}{x}$ (J) $\frac{x}{100} = \frac{2}{25}$

TAKS Objective 6
TEKS (7.13)(B)

36. Karl buys a pair of jeans that regularly costs $38. They are on sale for 25% off. Karl also buys a shirt that costs $23. The sales tax is 4.5%. What other information is necessary to find Karl's correct change? D

(A) The sale price of the jeans

(B) The total cost of the purchase

(C) The amount he paid for the sales tax

(D) The amount he gave the cashier

GO for Help **Lesson 9-8** **Algebra** Solve each equation for the variable in red.

37. $a = bc$ $\frac{a}{b}$

38. $n = \frac{g + w}{4}$ $4n - w$

39. $q = 2t + 8$ $\frac{q - 8}{2}$

Alternative Assessment

Each student in a pair writes a probability problem for a standard number cube, such as "find P(2 or 4)." Partners trade problems and find the probability as a decimal, fraction, and percent. Partners then find the complement. Partners discuss and agree on their results.

TEKS **TAKS** **Resources**

- TAKS Strategies, p. 615
- TAKS Practice Test, pp. 619–623

TAKS Tune-Up Kit

- TAKS Daily Review Transparencies
- TAKS Review and Preparation Workbook
- TAKS Strategies with Transparencies
- Texas Progress Monitoring Assessments

4. Assess & Reteach

PowerPoint
Lesson Quiz

In a stack are several number cards: three 1s, four 2s, three 3s, two 4s, two 6s, and six 7s. You pick a card at random.

1. Write $P(3)$ as a fraction, a decimal, and a percent.
$\frac{3}{20}$, 0.15, 15%

2. Write $P(\text{not } 7)$ as a fraction, a decimal, and a percent.
$\frac{7}{10}$, 0.7, 70%

Reteaching 12-1   **L2**

To find a **theoretical probability**, first list all possible **outcomes**. Then use the formula:

$P(\text{event}) = \frac{\text{number of favorable outcomes}}{\text{total number of possible outcomes}}$

A letter is selected at random from the letters of the word FLORIDA. What is the probability that the letter is an A?

- There are 7 letters (possible outcomes).
- There is one A, which represents a favorable outcome.

$P(A) = \frac{\text{number of favorable outcomes}}{\text{total number of outcomes}} = \frac{1}{7}$

The probability that the letter is an A is $\frac{1}{7}$.

Selecting a letter other than A is called *not A* and is the **complement** of the event A. The sum of the probabilities of an event and its complement equals 1, or 100%.

What is the probability of the event "*not A*"?

$P(A) + P(\text{not } A) = 1$

$\frac{1}{7} + P(\text{not } A) = 1$

$P(\text{not } A) = 1 - \frac{1}{7} = \frac{6}{7}$

The probability of the event "*not A*" (selecting F, L, O, R, I, or D) is $\frac{6}{7}$.

Spin the spinner shown once. Find each probability as a fraction, a decimal, and a percent.

1. $P(5)$
$\frac{\text{number of favorable outcomes}}{\text{total number of outcomes}}$
$= \frac{1}{5}$; 0.2; 20%

2. $P(\text{odd number})$
$\frac{\text{number of favorable outcomes}}{\text{total number of outcomes}}$
$= \frac{2}{5}$; 0.4; 40%

You select a card at random from a box that contains cards numbered from 1 to 10. Find each probability as a fraction, a decimal, and a percent.

3. $P(\text{even number})$ $\frac{1}{2}$, 0.5; 50%

4. $P(\text{number less than 4})$ $\frac{3}{10}$, 0.3; 30%

5. $P(\text{not 5})$ $\frac{9}{10}$, 0.9; 90%

The letters H, A, P, P, I, N, E, S, and S are written on pieces of paper. Select one piece of paper. Find each probability.

6. $P(\text{not vowel})$ $\frac{2}{3}$

7. $P(\text{not } E)$ $\frac{8}{9}$

A number is selected at random from the numbers 1 to 50. Find the odds in favor of each outcome.

8. selecting a multiple of 5 $\frac{1}{4}$

9. selecting a factor of 50 $\frac{3}{22}$

Enrichment 12-1   **L4**
Critical Thinking

Odds The probability ratio compares favorable outcomes to total outcomes. When outcomes are equally likely, you can write ratios, called *odds*, that compare favorable outcomes to unfavorable outcomes.

Odds in favor of an event = the ratio of the number of favorable outcomes to the number of unfavorable outcomes

Odds against an event = the ratio of the number of unfavorable outcomes to the number of favorable outcomes

Suppose a bag contains ten slips with classroom math challenge tasks you can do for extra credit. The tasks include problems related to probability, geometry, and algebra. The number of tasks related to probability is twice the number of tasks related to algebra. There is at least one task devoted to each type of problem.

1. If the odds of choosing an algebra task are 1 : 9, how many slips for each task will there be?
2 probability tasks, 1 algebra task, 7 geometry tasks

2. If the odds of choosing an algebra task are 1 : 4, how many slips for each task will there be?
4 probability tasks, 2 algebra tasks, 4 geometry tasks

3. If the odds of choosing a probability task are 3 : 2, how many slips for each task will there be?
6 probability tasks, 3 algebra tasks, 1 geometry task

Suppose a bag contains 15 slips, each listing one of these sports: basketball, baseball, football, volleyball. There are three times as many slips for basketball as baseball and twice as many slips for football as for volleyball. There is at least one slip for each sport.

4. What are the odds of drawing a slip that shows each of the following sports?
basketball $\frac{9}{6}$ or 3 : 2   baseball $\frac{3}{12}$ or 1 : 4
football $\frac{2}{13}$ volleyball $\frac{1}{14}$

5. Which sport is most likely to be picked in a random drawing? Explain.
Basketball, since 9 chances out of 15 is more likely to happen than 3 out of 15, 2 out of 15, or 1 out of 15.

583

Odds

Students learn about odds and how to write them. This will extend the work they did with probability in Lesson 12-1.

Guided Instruction

Define *odds* for students. Explain that this is a common way of stating a probability ratio. Ask volunteers for examples of odds in everyday life. Make sure students understand the difference between odds and probability. Ask questions such as:

- *Can odds be even?* yes *How?* If there are an equal number of favorable and unfavorable events, the odds are even. It is equally likely that either will happen.
- *How are the odds in favor and the odds against the same event related?* They are reciprocals.
- *If you are given the odds in favor of an event, how can you find the total number of possible outcomes?* Add both terms. For example, if the odds are 2 : 3, the total number of possible outcomes is 5.

Exercises

Have students work independently on the Exercises. When they have finished, have them compare answers with a partner and discuss any differences.

Odds

The probability ratio compares favorable outcomes to all possible outcomes. When outcomes are equally likely, you can write ratios, called *odds*, that compare favorable outcomes to unfavorable outcomes.

Odds in favor of an event = the ratio of the number of favorable outcomes to the number of unfavorable outcomes

Odds against an event = the ratio of the number of unfavorable outcomes to the number of favorable outcomes

EXAMPLE **Finding Odds**

Coins Five quarters are shown below. Find the odds that a quarter you select at random shows at least one musical instrument.

odds in favor = 2 to 3 or 2 : 3   ← Two have an instrument. Three do not.

The odds that a quarter shows at least one musical instrument are 2 to 3 in favor.

Exercises

1. Refer to the example above. Find the odds that a quarter selected at random shows a race car. 1 : 4

You roll a number cube once. Find the odds in favor of each outcome.

2. rolling a 5 1 : 5   3. rolling a multiple of 3 2 : 4   4. rolling an odd number 3 : 3

5. You spin a spinner with equal sections lettered A–Z once. The spinner lands on the first letter of your name. Calculate the odds for and against this event. 1 : 25; 25 : 1

Hands On

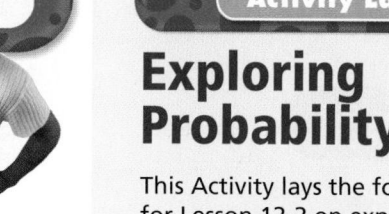

TEKS ★ Taks

(7.10)(B) To find the probability of independent events

(7.13)(D) To select tools such as real objects to solve problems

Exploring Probability

If you toss one coin 100 times, you might expect to get heads and tails about the same number of times. What happens when you toss *two* coins 100 times?

EXAMPLE

Toss two coins 10 times. Record the results. Use the results to determine which event is most likely: two heads (HH), two tails (TT), or one head and one tail (HT).

The table below shows one set of results.

Toss	1	2	3	4	5	6	7	8	9	10
Result	HH	HT	HT	TT	HH	HT	TT	HT	HH	HT

In all, there are three outcomes of HH, two outcomes of TT, and five outcomes of HT. One head and one tail is the most likely event.

Exercises

1. Conduct an experiment in which you use two coins, such as a penny and a nickel. Place them in a small paper cup. Cover the top, and shake the cup before each coin toss. Toss both coins 100 times. Make a table to record each result. **Check students' work.**

2. Are your results similar to other students' results? Explain.
   Check students' work.

3. **Reasoning** Are the three outcomes all equally likely? Or is one outcome more likely to occur than the others? Explain. **See right.**

Three students play the game at the right.

4. Is a game with these rules fair? Explain why or why not? **See right.**

5. **Open-Ended** How might you change the rules to make the game fair? **See right.**

6. Conduct an experiment to test your new game. Do you still think your game is fair? Explain.
   Check students' work.

3. Answers may vary. Sample: The HT event includes two outcomes: H penny and T nickel, and H nickel and T penny. So the HT event is twice as likely as HH and TT.

4. Not fair; player C will score about twice as many points as player A or player B.

5. Answers may vary. Sample: players A and B get two points for HH or TT.

GAME RULES

❶ Player A receives 1 point if two heads (HH) are tossed.

❷ Player B receives 1 point if two tails (TT) are tossed.

❸ Player C receives 1 point if one head and one tail (HT) are tossed.

Exploring Probability

This Activity lays the foundation for Lesson 12-2 on experimental probability. Students investigate the idea of doing an experiment to observe the frequency of events occurring. They explore the concept of equally likely outcomes.

Guided Instruction

Example
Review and discuss the theoretical probability of an event, *P(E)*. Then discuss the meaning of *equally likely events.* Explain that the events occur with the same relative frequency. Challenge students to give examples.

Special Needs L1
Point out that the outcomes—two tails, a head and a tail, and two heads—are not equally likely. *P*(two heads) is $\frac{1}{4}$, as is *P*(two tails). But the probability of getting a head and a tail is $\frac{1}{2}$.

Exercises
Have one partner shake and toss, while the other records results.
Exercises 4–6 Elicit from students that for a game to be fair, each player must have an equal chance of success according to its rules.

Alternative Method
Students may prefer to draw from a bag containing equal numbers of two different colored marbles.

TEKS ★ Taks Resources

- Activity Lab 12-2: Experimental and Theoretical Probability
- coins
- paper cup
- equal numbers of two different colors of marbles
- small bag

Dana Center TEKS Toolkit Clarifying Activities (7.10)(B), (7.13)(D)
Visit: PHSchool.com
Web Code: arq-9045

TEKS ★ TAKS

(7.10)(B) To find the probability of independent events

Also supports
(7.11)(B) TAKS Obj. 5
(7.13)(D)

Dana Center TEKS Toolkit
Clarifying Activities (7.10)(B),
(7.11)(B), (7.13)(D)
Visit: PHSchool.com
Web Code: arq-9045

TEKS Math Background

Experimental probability is used to monitor the quality of manufacturing processes and products. These processes have small but acceptable variations. Probability is used to monitor and correct variations beyond acceptable measures. Such "quality control" methods rely on finding experimental probability by sampling and simulations. *Simulations* are models used to calculate probabilities for experimental situations that are too difficult or costly to perform.

More Math Background: p. 578C

Lesson Planning and Resources

See p. 578E for a list of the resources that support this lesson.

Bell Ringer Practice

✓ **Check Skills You'll Need**
Use student page, transparency, or PowerPoint.

TAKS Daily Review 90
Use transparency.

586

✓ Check Skills You'll Need

1. Vocabulary Review
Explain the difference between an *event* and an *outcome*.
See below.
You roll a number cube once. Find each probability.

2. $P(4)$ $\frac{1}{6}$

3. $P(\text{multiple of } 2)$ $\frac{1}{2}$

4. $P(8)$ 0

for Help
Lesson 12-1

Check Skills You'll Need

1. Answers may vary.
   Sample: An outcome is a single result, but an event can be a group of results.

Online

Video Tutor Help
Visit: PHSchool.com
Web Code: are-0775

TEKS ★ TAKS

• (7.10)(B) To find the probability of independent events
• (7.11)(B) To make inferences and convincing arguments based on an analysis of given or collected data TAKS Obj. 5
• (7.13)(D) To select tools such as real objects to solve problems

🔊 **New Vocabulary** experimental probability

Why Learn This?

Manufacturers collect data on the quality of their products. They use experimental probability to determine how many defective items they can expect to produce.

Probability based on experimental data or observations is called **experimental probability.**

KEY CONCEPTS **Experimental Probability**

$$P(\text{event}) = \frac{\text{number of times an event occurs}}{\text{total number of trials}}$$

EXAMPLE **Finding Experimental Probability**

1 You attempt 16 free throws in a basketball game. Your results are shown. What is the experimental probability of making a free throw?

Results of Free Throw Attempts

0 = miss				1 = make			
0	0	1	1	1	0	1	0
0	1	0	1	1	1	0	0	1

$P(\text{free throw}) = \frac{8}{16}$ ← number of throws made
              ← total number of attempted free throws

$= \frac{1}{2}$ ← Simplify.

The experimental probability of making a free throw is $\frac{1}{2}$.

✓ Quick Check

1. In 60 coin tosses, 25 are tails. Find the experimental probability. $\frac{5}{12}$

586 Chapter 12 Using Probability

Differentiated Instruction **Solutions for All Learners**

Special Needs L1
For Example 3, provide students with coins, and let them act out the simulation by tossing the coins 20 times. Let them try this several times. Have them record their results.

learning style: tactile

Below Level L2
Have students write these fractions in simplest form:
$\frac{4}{6}, \frac{10}{15}, \frac{8}{16}, \frac{7}{21}, \frac{2}{3}, \frac{2}{3}, \frac{1}{2}, \frac{1}{3}$

learning style: visual

2. Teach

EXAMPLE Application: Manufacturing

② **TAKS Multiple Choice** A bicycle company checks a random sample of bikes. The results are shown. If the trend continues, which is the best prediction of the number of defective bikes in a batch of 1,300?

Quality Control Results

Defective Bikes	Bikes Checked
12	400

Ⓐ 430 bikes   Ⓑ 390 bikes   Ⓒ 43 bikes   Ⓓ 39 bikes

The experimental probability that a bike is defective is $\frac{12}{400}$, or $\frac{3}{100}$.

Let x represent the predicted number of defective bikes.

$$\begin{array}{l} \text{defective bikes} \to \\ \text{bikes checked} \to \end{array} \frac{3}{100} = \frac{x}{1,300} \begin{array}{l} \leftarrow \text{defective bikes} \\ \leftarrow \text{bikes checked} \end{array} \quad \leftarrow \textbf{Write a proportion.}$$

$$3(1,300) = 100x \quad \leftarrow \textbf{Write the cross products.}$$

$$3,900 = 100x \quad \leftarrow \textbf{Simplify.}$$

$$\frac{3,900}{100} = \frac{100x}{100} \quad \leftarrow \textbf{Divide each side by 100.}$$

$$39 = x \quad \leftarrow \textbf{Simplify.}$$

You can predict that 39 bikes are defective. The correct answer is D.

✓ Quick Check

● **2.** Predict the number of defective bikes in a batch of 3,500. **105 bikes**

You can simulate, or model, events to find experimental probabilities.

EXAMPLE Simulating an Event

③ Find the experimental probability that 2 of 3 children in a family are girls. Assume that girls and boys are equally likely.

Simulate the problem by tossing three coins. Let "heads" represent a girl and "tails" represent a boy. A sample of 20 coin tosses is shown.

T T H	T T T	(H T H)	H T T	(H T H)
T T H	(H H T)	H T T	T H T	H H H
(H H T)	T T H	(T H H)	(H T H)	T H T
T H T	T H T	T H T	H H H	H H H

$$P(\text{two girls}) = \frac{6}{20}, \text{ or } \frac{3}{10} \quad \begin{array}{l} \leftarrow \text{number of times } \textit{two heads} \text{ occur} \\ \leftarrow \text{total number of tosses} \end{array}$$

The experimental probability that 2 of 3 children are girls is $\frac{3}{10}$.

✓ Quick Check

● **3.** What is the experimental probability that 3 children are all boys? $\frac{1}{20}$

12-2 Experimental Probability **587**

587

Assignment Guide

Check Your Understanding
Go over Exercises 1–5 in class before assigning the Homework Exercises.

Homework Exercises
A Practice by Example   6–12
B Apply Your Skills   13–22
C Challenge   23
TEKS ★ (TAKS) Tune-Up and
  Mixed Review   24–29

Homework Quick Check
To check students' understanding of key skills and concepts, go over Exercises 7, 10, 14, 15, and 22.

Differentiated Instruction Resources

Adapted Practice 12-2   **L1**

Practice 12-2   Experimental P **L3**

Suppose you observe the color of socks worn by students in your class: 12 have white, 4 have black, 3 have blue, and 1 has red. Find each experimental probability as a fraction in simplest form.

1. $P(\text{white})$ $\frac{3}{5}$ 2. $P(\text{red})$ $\frac{1}{20}$ 3. $P(\text{blue})$ $\frac{3}{20}$
4. $P(\text{black})$ $\frac{1}{5}$ 5. $P(\text{yellow})$ 0 6. $P(\text{black or red})$ $\frac{1}{4}$

Use the data in the table at the right for Exercises 7–12. Find each experimental probability as a percent.

Favorite Snack Survey Results	
Snack	Number of Students
Fruit	8
Granola	2
Pretzels	3
Chips	7
Carrots	5

7. $P(\text{fruit})$ 32%   8. $P(\text{granola})$ 8%
9. $P(\text{pretzels})$ 12%   10. $P(\text{carrots})$ 20%
11. $P(\text{not fruit})$ 68%   12. $P(\text{granola or chips})$ 36%
13. Do an experiment to find the probability that a word chosen randomly in a book is the word *the*. How many words did you look at to find $P(\text{the})$? What is $P(\text{the})$?
Check students' answers.

14. Suppose the following is the result of tossing a coin 5 times:
heads, tails, heads, tails, heads
What is the experimental probability for heads?
60%

Solve.

15. The probability that a twelve-year-old has a brother or sister is 25%. Suppose you survey 300 twelve-year-olds. About how many do you think will have a brother or sister?   about 75

16. **a.** A quality control inspector found flaws in 13 out of 150 sweaters. Find the probability that a sweater has a flaw. Round to the nearest tenth of a percent.   8.7%
b. Suppose the company produces 500 sweaters a day. How many will not have flaws?   457 sweaters
c. Suppose the company produces 600 sweaters a day. How many will have flaws?   52 sweaters

---

12-2 • Guided Problem Solving **GPS**   **L3**

GPS Student Page 588, Exercise 14:

a. Science The probability that a male human is colorblind is 8%. Suppose you interview 1,000 males. About how many would you expect to be colorblind?
b. Reasoning Will you always get the same number? Explain.

Understand
1. What does it mean to be colorblind?
It means a person cannot see certain colors.
2. What are you being asked to do in part (a)?
Find how many males will be colorblind out of 1,000.

Plan and Carry Out
3. Find 8% of 1,000   80
4. How many males out of 1,000 would you expect to be colorblind?
80 men
5. Will you always get exactly this number? Explain.
Sample answer: Not necessarily; the 8% colorblind percent is based on experimental results. The results of other experiments may differ.

Check
6. How could you find the answer another way?
Sample answer: Use a proportion; $\frac{x}{1,000} = \frac{8}{100}$.

Solve Another Problem
7. The probability of a person being left-handed is about 11%. Suppose you interview 500 people. About how many would you expect to be left-handed?
$500 \times 0.11 = 55$ people

---

1. **Vocabulary** What is the difference between theoretical probability and experimental probability? Explain. **See margin.**

You toss a coin 40 times and get 18 tails. Find each experimental probability.

2. $P(\text{heads}) = \frac{22}{\blacksquare}$ 40   3. $P(\text{tails}) = \frac{\blacksquare}{40}$ 18

4. **Mental Math** In a bird sanctuary, the experimental probability that any bird you see is a robin is about $\frac{1}{8}$. Suppose this trend continues. There are 48 birds. Predict the number of robins you see.   **6 robins**

5. You want to find the probability that three out of five babies are boys. You decide to toss coins to simulate the problem. How many coins would you use? Explain.   **5 coins; one for each baby**

Homework Exercises

For more exercises, see Extra Skills and Word Problems.

GO for Help

For Exercises	See Examples
6–8	1–2
9–12	3

A **Find each experimental probability.**

6. tosses: 80; tails: 40; $P(\text{tails}) = \underline{\ ?\ }$ $\frac{1}{2}$
7. tosses: 250; heads: 180; $P(\text{heads}) = \underline{\ ?\ }$ $\frac{18}{25}$

8. **Manufacturing** The quality-control engineer of Top Notch Tool Company finds flaws in 8 of 60 wrenches examined. Predict the number of flawed wrenches in a batch of 2,400.   **320 wrenches**

Baseball A baseball team averages one win to every one loss. Use a simulation to find each experimental probability for three games.

9. $P(\text{three wins})$ 10. $P(\text{1 win and 2 losses})$
11. $P(\text{2 wins and 1 loss})$ 12. $P(\text{three losses})$
    9–12. Check students' work.

B **GPS** 13. **Guided Problem Solving** During hockey practice, Yuri blocked 19 out of 30 shots and Gene blocked 17 out of 24 shots. For the first game, the coach wants to choose the goalie with the greater probability of blocking a shot. Which player should he choose?   **Gene**
  • **Make a Plan** Find the experimental probability that each player will block the shot.

14b. Not necessarily; the 8% colorblind percent is based on experimental results. The results of other experiments may differ.

14. **a. Science** The probability that a male human is colorblind is 8%. **GPS** Suppose you interview 1,000 males. About how many would you expect to be colorblind?   **80 males**
b. Reasoning Will you always get the same number? Explain.
See left.

1. Theoretical probability is computed by the formula
$$P(\text{event}) = \frac{\text{number of favorable outcomes}}{\text{total number of possible outcomes}}.$$
Experimental probability is based on experimental data or observation.

22. Answers may vary. Sample: Toss six coins, record data, and repeat several times. Calculate the experimental probability of two coins being heads.

15. A company checks washers at four plants and records the number of defective washers. Find each experimental probability.

Plant	Number of Washers	Number Defective	P(Defective)	
1	2,940	588	■	$\frac{1}{5}$
2	1,860	93	■	$\frac{1}{20}$
3	640	26	■	$\frac{13}{320}$
4	3,048	54	■	$\frac{9}{508}$

Data Analysis Use the data shown. Find each experimental probability.

Students' Birthdays

16. $P(\text{Sunday})$ $\frac{3}{25}$ **17.** $P(\text{Monday})$ $\frac{6}{25}$

18. $P(\text{Tuesday})$ $\frac{1}{5}$ **19.** $P(\text{Friday})$ $\frac{2}{25}$

20. $P(\text{weekday})$ $\frac{18}{25}$ **21.** $P(\text{weekend})$ $\frac{7}{25}$

22. **Writing in Math** Describe a possible simulation to solve the following problem. You guess on six true-or-false questions. What is the probability that you guess exactly two answers correctly?
See margin.

C 23. Challenge On any day, a company has x torn posters in stock. On Monday, the total number of torn posters is 252. Express $P(\text{torn})$ on Monday in terms of x. If $P(\text{torn}) = \frac{1}{42}$, what is x? $\frac{x}{252}$; 6

TEKS ★ TAKS Tune-Up and Mixed Review

TAKS Objective 5
TEKS (7.11)(B)

24. The picture shows the number of colored shirts sold this week at Joan's Clothing Shop. If the trend continues, which is the best prediction of the number of orange shirts sold in one year? **C**

10 Blue Shirts   3 Gray Shirts   5 Orange Shirts   8 Green Shirts

Ⓐ 20　　Ⓑ 130　　Ⓒ 260　　Ⓓ 1,362

TAKS Objective 2
TEKS (7.3)(B)

25. The scale on a map of Texas is 1 in. : 31 mi. Which distance on the map should represent the 420 mi from Amarillo to El Paso? **G**

Ⓕ 1.25 in.　　Ⓖ 13.5 in.　　Ⓗ 135 in.　　Ⓙ 13,824 in.

 GO for Help **Lesson 12-1**

27. $\frac{3}{9}$ or $\frac{1}{3}$

You spin the spinner once. Find each probability.

26. $P(\text{purple})$ $\frac{2}{9}$

27. $P(\text{blue})$

28. $P(\text{blue or yellow})$ $\frac{7}{9}$

29. $P(\text{not yellow})$ $\frac{5}{9}$

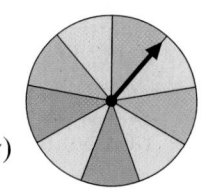

Alternative Assessment

Have pairs of students survey twenty classmates or friends to find the month of each person's birthday. Pairs record the data in a line plot. They then find the experimental probability of a birthday occurring in each month.

TEKS ★ TAKS Resources

- TAKS Strategies, p. 615
- TAKS Practice Test, pp. 619–623

TAKS Tune-Up Kit

- TAKS Daily Review Transparencies
- TAKS Review and Preparation Workbook
- TAKS Strategies with Transparencies
- Texas Progress Monitoring Assessments

---

4. Assess & Reteach

PowerPoint
Lesson Quiz

A manufacturer makes computer circuit boards. A random check of 5,000 circuit boards shows that 25 are defective.

1. What is the experimental probability that a circuit board is defective? $\frac{1}{200}$

2. Predict the number of defective circuit boards per month if the company manufactures 41,000 circuit boards in July. **205 defective circuit boards**

Reteaching 12-2 Experimental Pr **L2**

Probability measures how likely it is that an event will occur. For an **experimental probability**, you collect data through observations or experiments and use the data to state the probability.

The jar contains red, green, and blue chips. You shake the jar, draw a chip, note its color, and then put it back. You do this 20 times with these results: 7 blue chips, 5 red chips, and 8 green chips. The experimental probability of drawing a green chip is

$P(\text{green chip}) = \frac{\text{number of times "green chips" occur}}{\text{total number of trials}}$

$P(\text{green chip}) = \frac{8}{20} = \frac{2}{5} = 0.4 = 40\%$

The probability of drawing a green chip is $\frac{2}{5}$, or 0.4, or 40%.

Sometimes a model, or simulation, is used to represent a situation. Then, the simulaton is used to find the experimental probability. For example, spinning this spinner can simulate the probability that 1 of 3 people is chosen for president of the student body.

Use the 20 draws above to complete each exercise.

1. What is the experimental probability of drawing a red chip? Write the probability as a fraction. $P(\text{red chip}) = \frac{5}{20} = \frac{1}{4}$

2. What is the experimental probability of drawing a blue chip? Write the probability as a percent. $P(\text{blue chip}) = \frac{7}{20} = 35\%$

Suppose you have a bag with 30 chips: 12 red, 8 white, and 10 blue. You shake the jar, draw a chip, note its color, and then put it back. You do this 30 times with these results: 10 blue chips, 12 red chips, and 8 white chips. Write each probability as fraction in simplest form.

3. $P(\text{red}) \frac{2}{5}$　　4. $P(\text{white}) \frac{4}{15}$　　5. $P(\text{blue}) \frac{1}{3}$

Describe a probability simulation for each situation.

6. You guess the answers on a true/false test with 20 questions. Sample answer: Flip a coin 20 times.

7. One student out of 6 is randomly chosen to be the homeroom representative. Sample answer: Spin a spinner divided into six equal sections.

Enrichment 12-2 Experimental P **L4**

Applications of Probability

A speck of dust lands on the grid shown. What is the probability that it

1. lands on the dark-shaded area? $\frac{12}{25} = 48\% = 0.48$
2. lands on the light-shaded area? $\frac{8}{25} = 32\% = 0.32$
3. lands on the unshaded area? $\frac{1}{5} = 20\% = 0.2$
4. lands on the 4 center squares? $\frac{1}{25} = 4\% = 0.04$
5. does not land on the unshaded area? $\frac{4}{5} = 80\% = 0.80$
6. does not land on the dark-shaded area? $\frac{13}{25} = 52\% = 0.52$

In a coin toss game, you earn points for landing on the shaded figures. Assume coins land randomly in the large square. What is the probability that a coin

7. lands on the trapezoid? $\frac{9}{125} = 7.2\% = 0.072$
8. lands on the circle? $\approx 6.75\% = 0.0675$
9. lands on the L-shape? $\frac{7}{100} = 7\% = 0.07$
10. does not land on the trapezoid? $92.8\% = 0.928$
11. does not land on the circle or the L-shape? $86.25\% = 0.8625$
12. lands in the unshaded area? $79.05\% = 0.7905$
13. lands in the square? 100%

589

Random Numbers

Students worked with simulations in Lesson 12-2. This Activity introduces them to random number generation using spreadsheet software as a useful tool for simulating events.

Guided Instruction

Technology Tip

Elicit what the advantages are of using computer simulation to do a probability experiment. Guide students to appreciate that spreadsheets can generate random numbers rapidly and can keep track of the results.

Exercises

Have students work in pairs. Then pairs can discuss their results with the class. For the Writing in Math activity, have students ask classmates for their predictions before presenting those results.

Differentiated Instruction

Advanced Learners **L4**

Have students generate their own spreadsheet of random numbers and write problems. Have them trade papers with a partner and solve each other's problems.

TEKS ★ TAKS Resources

- spreadsheet software

Dana Center TEKS Toolkit Clarifying Activities (7.10)(B), (7.13)(D)
Visit: PHSchool.com
Web Code: arq-9045

12-2b Activity Lab

Technology

TEKS ★ TAKS
(7.10)(B) To find the probability of independent events
(7.13)(D) To select technology to solve problems

Random Numbers

You can use a random number table to simulate some problems. To generate a random number table in a spreadsheet, follow these steps.

Step 1 Highlight the group of cells to use for your table.

Step 2 Select the Format Cells menu.

Step 3 Choose the category Custom and enter 0000. Click OK.

Step 4 Use the formula RAND()*10,000. This will make a group of 4 digits in each cell of a spreadsheet. (*Note:* Each time you generate a random number table, you will get a different group of digits.)

	A	B	C	D
1	2260	1927	7807	0912
2	8879	6235	5897	8068
3	8121	4646	8368	1613
4	0821	8911	3022	0307
5	9393	5403	4930	4898

EXAMPLE

A rare lily bulb has a 50% chance of growing. You plant four bulbs. What is the experimental probability that all four will grow?

Use the random number table. Let even digits represent *grows,* and let odd digits represent *does not grow.* Then a 4-digit number of all even digits represents the event *all four grow.* Of 20 groups, 3 consist entirely of even digits. So the experimental probability of four bulbs growing is $\frac{3}{20}$, or 15%.

2260 1927 7807 0912
8879 6235 5897 8068
8121 4646 8368 1613
0821 8911 3022 0307
9393 5403 4930 4898

← Any group of 4 even digits represents *all four grow.*

Exercises

Use the random number table above or generate your own.

1. Suppose there is a 30% probability of being stopped by a red light at each of four stoplights. What is the experimental probability of being stopped by at least two red lights? Let 0, 1, and 2 represent red lights. $\frac{9}{20}$

2. **Reasoning** Suppose there is a 60% chance of a red light at each stoplight. How many digits would you use to represent getting a red light? Explain. 6 digits; 6 out of 10 digits represent 60%.

3. **Writing in Math** Write a probability problem you can solve using a random number table. Solve your problem. Check students' work.

12-3 Sample Spaces

Check Skills You'll Need

1. Vocabulary Review
What diagram can you use to find the *prime factors* of a number? factor tree

Write the prime factorization of each number.

2. 15 3 · 5 **3.** 14 2 · 7

4. 26 2 · 13 **5.** 55 5 · 11

GO for Help
Lesson 2-2

TEKS ★ (TAKS)
• **(7.10)(A)** To construct sample spaces for simple or composite experiments
(TAKS) **Obj. 5**
• **(7.10)(B)** To find the probability of independent events

🔊 **New Vocabulary** sample space, counting principle

Why Learn This?

When you are at a salad bar, you can choose from different vegetables, fruits, and dressings. You may want to know all the possible combinations of ingredients you can use.

The collection of all possible outcomes in an experiment is the **sample space**. You can use the sample space to find the probability of an event.

TEKS ★ (TAKS)

(7.10)(A) To construct sample spaces for simple or composite experiments
(TAKS) **Obj. 5**
(7.10)(B) To find the probability of independent events

Dana Center TEKS Toolkit Clarifying Activities (7.10)(A), (7.10)(B)
Visit: PHSchool.com
Web Code: arq-9045

TEKS Math Background

The counting principle states that when *m* choices can be made for the first place and *n* choices can be made for the second place, then the total number of choices is the product, *mn*. The *sample space* of an event is all possible outcomes that can be shown in a table, tree diagram, and set of ordered pairs.

More Math Background: p. 578D

Lesson Planning and Resources

See p. 578E for a list of the resources that support this lesson.

★ (TAKS) Tip

When you construct a sample space for two events, pair each possible outcome for the first event with each possible outcome for the second event.

EXAMPLE Finding a Sample Space

1 a. Make a table to find the sample space for rolling two number cubes colored red and blue. Write the outcomes as ordered pairs.

	1	2	3	4	5	6
1	(1, 1)	(2, 1)	(3, 1)	(4, 1)	(5, 1)	(6, 1)
2	(1, 2)	(2, 2)	(3, 2)	(4, 2)	(5, 2)	(6, 2)
3	(1, 3)	(2, 3)	(3, 3)	(4, 3)	(5, 3)	(6, 3)
4	(1, 4)	(2, 4)	(3, 4)	(4, 4)	(5, 4)	(6, 4)
5	(1, 5)	(2, 5)	(3, 5)	(4, 5)	(5, 5)	(6, 5)
6	(1, 6)	(2, 6)	(3, 6)	(4, 6)	(5, 6)	(6, 6)

← There are 36 possible outcomes.

b. Find the probability of rolling at least one 3.

There are 11 outcomes with at least one 3. There are 36 possible outcomes. So the probability of rolling at least one 3 is $\frac{11}{36}$.

✓ Quick Check

1. Give the sample space for tossing two coins. Find the probability of getting two heads. See left.

1.
	H	T	$;\frac{1}{4}$
H	HH	HT	
T	TH	TT	

PowerPoint
Bell Ringer Practice

✓ **Check Skills You'll Need**
Use student page, transparency, or PowerPoint.

(TAKS) **Daily Review 91**
Use transparency.

Differentiated Instruction Solutions for All Learners

Special Needs L1
Students may have a difficult time drawing tree diagrams. Provide them with rulers, or graph paper to help them. If they still have trouble, have them work with a partner who can draw the tree diagram while they label the outcomes from each branch.

learning style: visual

Below Level L2
Review the sample space for rolling a standard number cube and the probability of various outcomes, such as rolling an even number.

$P(\text{even}) = \frac{3}{6}$ or $\frac{1}{2}$

learning style: verbal

Activity Lab

Use before the lesson.

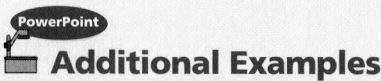 **Teaching Resources**

Activity Lab 12-3: Decision Making

Guided Instruction

Example 2
Ask a volunteer to explain the differences between a kayak, a canoe, and a rowboat.

Example 3
Explain that since the Commutative Property states that $5 \times 6 = 6 \times 5$, you could choose the meat first, followed by the bread, with the same results.

PowerPoint

Additional Examples

1 **a.** Make a table to show the sample space for tossing two coins. Write the outcomes as ordered pairs. {(H, H), (H, T), (T, H), (T, T)}

b. Find P(T, T), the probability of tossing two tails. $\frac{1}{4}$

2 Suppose you can go west or northwest by train, bus, or car.

a. Draw a tree diagram to show the sample space. {(w, t), (w, b), (w, c), (nw, t), (nw, b), (nw, c)}

b. What is the probability of a random selection that results in a bus trip west? $\frac{1}{6}$

3 How many kinds of coin purses are available if the purses come in small or large sizes and colors red, blue, yellow, and black? 8

You can also show a sample space by using a tree diagram. Each branch of the tree represents one choice.

EXAMPLE **Using a Tree Diagram**

2 **River Travel** Suppose you are going to travel on a river. You have two choices of boats—a kayak or a rowboat. You can go upstream on three smaller streams, to the north, northwest, and northeast.

a. What is the sample space for your journey?

Make a tree diagram for the possible outcomes.

Boat	Stream	Outcome
Kayak	North	Kayak, North
	Northwest	Kayak, Northwest
	Northeast	Kayak, Northeast
Rowboat	North	Rowboat, North
	Northwest	Rowboat, Northwest
	Northeast	Rowboat, Northeast

← There are six possible outcomes.

b. Suppose you select a trip at random. What is the probability of selecting a kayak and going directly north?

There is one favorable outcome (kayak, north) out of six possible outcomes. The probability is $\frac{1}{6}$.

✓ Quick Check

2. a. Suppose a canoe is added as another choice of boats in Example 2. Draw a tree diagram to show the sample space. See back of book.

b. Find the probability of selecting a canoe at random for the trip. $\frac{1}{3}$

In Example 2 above, there are 2 choices of boats and 3 choices of direction. There are 2×3, or 6, total possible choices. This suggests a simple way to find the number of outcomes—using the **counting principle.**

KEY CONCEPTS **The Counting Principle**

Suppose there are m ways of making one choice and n ways of making a second choice. Then there are $m \times n$ ways to make the first choice followed by the second choice.

Example
If you can choose a shirt in 5 sizes and 7 colors, then you can choose among 5×7, or 35, shirts.

Advanced Learners **L4**
Have students find the number of sandwich choices if there are 4 kinds of bread, 5 kinds of meat, and 3 kinds of cheese. 60 choices

Pre-AP™

English Language Learners **ELL**
For Example 1, make sure to point out that the ordered pairs are formed by using the intersection of the outcomes for each pair of number cubes. Students may have a difficult time understanding why 1, 3 and 3, 1 are different outcomes. Show them using number cubes.

learning style: visual

EXAMPLE Using the Counting Principle

3 **Griddable Item** How many different sandwiches can you order when you choose one bread and one meat from the menu?

Use the counting principle.

Bread		Meat
number of choices	×	number of choices
5	×	6 = 30

There are 30 different sandwiches available.

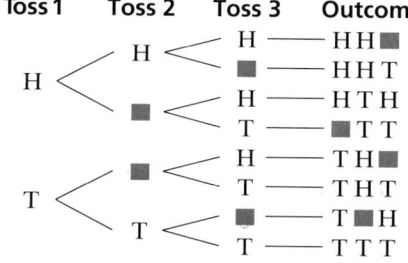

THE
DELI COUNTER
SANDWICHES

FRESH BREADS	DELI MEATS
Rye	Roast Beef
Wheat	Turkey
White	Ham
Pita	Pastrami
Wrap	Salami
	Liverwurst

✓ Quick Check

3. A manager at the Deli Counter decides to add chicken to the list of meat choices. How many different sandwiches are now available?
35 sandwiches

Check Your Understanding

1. **Vocabulary** What is a sample space? the collection of all possible outcomes in an experiment

2. Complete the tree diagram for tossing a coin three times.
See margin.

Toss 1	Toss 2	Toss 3	Outcome
H	H	H	H H ■
		■	H H T
	■	H	H T H
		T	■ T T
T	■	H	T H ■
		T	T H T
	T	■	T ■ H
		T	T T T

Use your completed diagram from Exercise 2 to find each probability.

3. $P(\text{HHH}) = \frac{■}{8}$ 1

4. $P(\text{TTT}) = \frac{1}{■}$ 8

5. $P(\text{at least one H}) = \frac{■}{8}$ 7

6. $P(\text{exactly 2 T's}) = \frac{■}{8}$ 3

7. If you toss 4 coins, how many possible outcomes are there? 16

8. Find the number of different couches that you can make using 16 different fabrics and 8 patterns. 128 couches

9. **Multiple Choice** An architect has 3 different widths he can use for a rectangular building design. He also has 4 different lengths to use for the design. How many different designs are possible? D
   Ⓐ 3   Ⓑ 4   Ⓒ 7   Ⓓ 12

2. See back of book.

All in One Teaching Resources
- Daily Notetaking Guide 12-3 **L3**
- Adapted Notetaking 12-3 **L1**

Closure

- *What is the sample space?* all possible outcomes of an event
- *What is the counting principle?* The number of ways to make *m* choices followed by *n* choices is *m* × *n*.

Assignment Guide

Check Your Understanding
Go over Exercises 1–9 in class before assigning the Homework Exercises.

Homework Exercises
A Practice by Example   10–16
B Apply Your Skills   17–27
C Challenge   28
TEKS ★ TAKS Tune-Up and
        Mixed Review   29–32

Homework Quick Check
To check students' understanding of key skills and concepts, go over Exercises 13, 16, 23, 24, and 27.

Differentiated Instruction **Resources**

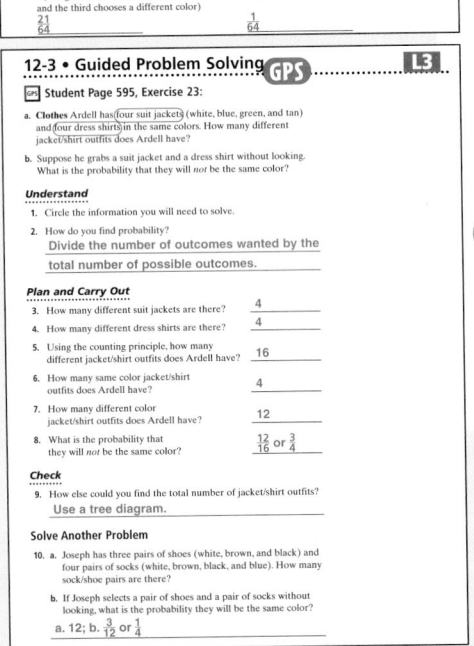

594

For more exercises, see Extra Skills and Word Problems.

GO for Help

For Exercises	See Examples
10–12	1
13–14	2
15–16	3

10.

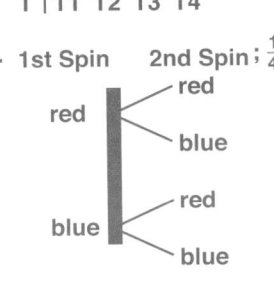

H   T ; $\frac{1}{2}$

	H	T
H	HH	HT
T	TH	TT

12.   1   2   3   4 ; $\frac{1}{8}$

	H1	H2	H3	H4
H	H1	H2	H3	H4
T	T1	T2	T3	T4

13. 1st Spin   2nd Spin ; $\frac{1}{4}$

red
  red
  blue

blue
  red
  blue

GO Online
Homework Help
Visit: PHSchool.com
Web Code: are-1203

A **Make a table to show the sample space for each situation and find the number of outcomes. Then find the probability.**

10. You toss two coins. What is the probability of getting one tail and one head? See left.

11. You roll a number cube once. What is the probability of rolling a number less than 4? 1 2 3 4 5 6; $\frac{3}{6}$ or $\frac{1}{2}$

12. You toss a coin and spin a spinner. The spinner has four equal sections that are numbered from 1 to 4. Find the probability of getting tails and spinning a 4. See left.

Make a tree diagram. Then find the probability of each event.

13. A spinner is half red and half blue. If you spin the spinner twice, what is the probability that you will get red both times? See left.

14. You choose at random from the letters A, B, C, and D, and you roll a number cube once. What are the chances you get A and 5? See margin.

Use the counting principle.

15. **Cooking** You make a recipe with herbs and spices for a party. You have four herbs—basil, bay leaves, chives, and dill. You also have three spices—paprika, pepper, and garlic powder. How many different recipes with one herb and one spice can you make?
12 recipes

16. **Education** A school has four art teachers, three music teachers, and eight history teachers. In how many ways can a student be assigned an art teacher, a music teacher, and a history teacher? 96 ways

B **GPS** 17. **Guided Problem Solving** A traveler chooses one city tour at random from buses D, E, and F. He then chooses one harbor tour at random from boats 1, 2, and 3. What is the probability that he takes tours with bus D and boat 2? $\frac{1}{9}$
• Draw a diagram of all the possible outcomes.
• How many outcomes include tours with bus D and boat 2?

A spinner has four equal sections numbered 1 through 4. You spin it twice. Use the sample space below to find each probability.

18. $P(1, 2)$ $\frac{1}{16}$

19. $P(1, \text{odd})$ $\frac{2}{16}$ or $\frac{1}{8}$

20. $P(\text{even, odd})$ $\frac{4}{16}$ or $\frac{1}{4}$

		Second Spin		
	1	2	3	4
First Spin 1	(1, 1)	(1, 2)	(1, 3)	(1, 4)
2	(2, 1)	(2, 2)	(2, 3)	(2, 4)
3	(3, 1)	(3, 2)	(3, 3)	(3, 4)
4	(4, 1)	(4, 2)	(4, 3)	(4, 4)

14. See back of book.

Find the number of outcomes for each situation.

21. Pick one of 7 boys and one of 12 girls. **84**

22. Toss five coins once each. **32**

23. a. **Clothes** Ardell has four suit jackets (white, blue, green, and tan)
     and four dress shirts in the same colors. How many different jacket-and-shirt outfits does Ardell have? **16 outfits**
    b. Suppose he grabs a suit jacket and a dress shirt without looking. What is the probability that they will *not* be the same color? $\frac{12}{16}$ or $\frac{3}{4}$

24. **Writing in Math** Explain how to use the counting principle to find the number of outcomes in a sample space. **See left.**

Careers Tailors fit designer clothes for important events.

24. Multiply the number of choices for each part of the sample space.

Use the menu for Exercises 25–28.

25. List all the possible drink orders. **See margin.**

26. You order lemonade and popcorn. Draw a tree diagram to show the sample space. **See margin.**

27. **Reasoning** A manager uses the counting principle to find $P(\text{small popcorn, medium lemonade}) = \frac{1}{24}$. Do you agree? Explain. **See margin.**

C 28. **Challenge** Find the probability that you randomly select the same size popcorn and drink. $\frac{6}{24}$ or $\frac{1}{4}$

CITY CINEMA

POPCORN
small $3.00
medium . .$4.00
large $5.00

FRUIT PUNCH or LEMONADE
small $2.75
medium . .$3.00
large $3.25
jumbo . . . $3.75

TEKS ★ TAKS Tune-Up and Mixed Review

GRIDDABLE ITEMS

TAKS Objective 5
TEKS (7.12)(A)

29. The data in the stem-and-leaf plot at the right show the lengths of principal rivers in Africa. What is the median length, in miles, of the rivers? **1,100**

African River Lengths (hundreds of miles)

```
0 | 6 7 7
1 | 0 0 0 1 2 3 7
2 | 6 7
4 | 1
```

Key: 2 | 6 means 2,600 miles

TAKS Objective 1
TEKS (7.1)(B)

30. Suppose $\frac{21}{25}$ of your classmates can attend your birthday party. What is this fraction expressed as a decimal? **0.84**

TAKS Objective 5
TEKS (7.10)(A)

31. Trista has purple, yellow, and red wrapping paper. She can use blue or white ribbon. She has four shapes of gift tags. In how many different ways can she choose one wrapping paper, one ribbon, and one gift tag? **24**

 GO for Help Lesson 12-2

32. A hockey player makes 3 goals out of 9 shots in a game. What is the experimental probability that he does not make a goal? $\frac{6}{9}$ or $\frac{2}{3}$

Alternative Assessment

Each student in a pair writes a problem that can be solved by either making a tree diagram or using the counting principle. Partners exchange papers and solve each other's problem. Have students share their problems and solutions with the class.

TEKS ★ TAKS Resources

• TAKS Strategies, p. 615
• TAKS Practice Test, pp. 619–623

TAKS Tune-Up Kit
• TAKS Daily Review Transparencies
• TAKS Review and Preparation Workbook
• TAKS Strategies with Transparencies
• Texas Progress Monitoring Assessments

---

4. Assess & Reteach

PowerPoint
Lesson Quiz

You pick a card at random from cards labeled 1, 2, or 3 and then spin a spinner divided into thirds, each of which is labeled with a number 1, 2, or 3.

1. Make a table showing the sample space. {(1, 1), (1, 2), (1, 3), (2, 1), (2, 2), (2, 3), (3, 1), (3, 2), (3, 3)}

2. How many possible outcomes are there? **9**

3. What is the probability of two 3s? $\frac{1}{9}$

4. What is the probability of picking a card and spinning the same number? $\frac{1}{3}$

25. small fruit punch, small lemonade, medium fruit punch, medium lemonade, large fruit punch, large lemonade, jumbo fruit punch, jumbo lemonade

26. See back of book.

27. No; there are 12 possible orders, so the probability for each order is $\frac{1}{12}$.

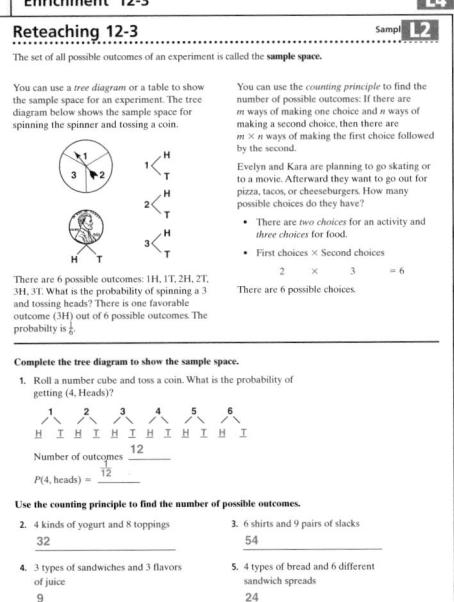

595

Using Data to Predict

Students use data from tables to predict outcomes. This will extend their work with sample spaces from Lesson 12-3.

Guided Instruction

Explain to students that they study the data in a table to find a trend and make predictions about the data. Have a volunteer read the problem aloud. Then ask questions, such as:

* *What is the probability of Katie mowing the lawn?* $\frac{2}{5}$

* *What are the odds in favor of Tim mowing the lawn?* 9 to 6

* *What conclusion can you draw about how often Tim will mow the lawn compared to how often Katie will mow the lawn?* Tim will mow the lawn $1\frac{1}{2}$ times as often as Katie will.

Activity

Have students work in pairs on the Activity. When they have completed the Activity, review students' conclusions as a class.

Differentiated Instruction

Advanced Learners **L4**
Have students estimate how many times each Tim and Katie will mow the lawn in 75 trials, 105 trials, and 135 trials. Ask them what trend they notice.

TEKS ★ **TAKS** Resources

Dana Center TEKS Toolkit Clarifying Activities (7.11)(B), (7.10)(A), (7.10)(B)
Visit: PHSchool.com
Web Code: arq-9045

 12-3b **Activity Lab**

Data Analysis

TEKS ★ **TAKS**
(7.11)(B) To make inferences and convincing arguments based on an analysis of given data **TAKS** Obj. 5
(7.10)(A) To construct sample spaces for simple or composite experiments **TAKS** Obj. 5
(7.10)(B) To find the probability of independent events

Using Data to Predict

Katie and Tim play the following game to decide who should mow the lawn each week.

* Katie or Tim places three black marbles and three white marbles into a bag.
* Tim pulls out two marbles.
* If the marbles match, Katie mows the lawn. Otherwise, Tim mows the lawn.

The table below shows the results of the first 15 trials.

Marble Selection Results

Event	Number of Times
Marbles matched	6
No match	9

ACTIVITY

1. **Estimation** Use the data from the table above. Assume the data trend continues. For Katie and Tim, estimate the number of times that each one mows the lawn in 45 trials. **Katie: 18; Tim: 27**

2. **Data Collection** Simulate the game with three red cubes and three yellow cubes. Put the cubes in a bag. Select two cubes at random. Record whether or not they match. Return the cubes to the bag, and repeat until you have recorded 45 trials. **Check students' work.**

3. **Reasoning** Describe how the results of your experiment compare to your predictions. Is the game fair? Explain. **Check students' work.**

4. Tim thinks the probability that the marbles match equals the probability that they do not match. Use diagrams and what you have learned to show why the probabilities are not equal. Find the probability that the two marbles match and the probability that they do not match. **See margin.**

5. Add a fourth cube of each color into the bag. Find the probability of selecting two cubes that match. Predict the number of matches in 49 trials. $\frac{3}{7}$; 21 matches

6. **Data Analysis** Test your prediction. Record the results of 49 trials. Compare your results to your prediction. Is this game more fair or less fair than the original game? Explain. **Check students' work.**

4. See back of book.

You spin the spinner at the right once. Write each probability as a fraction, a decimal, and a percent.

1. P(2 or 3) **2.** P(even) **3.** P(not 4) **4.** P(not even)
$\frac{2}{5}$; 0.4; 40% $\frac{2}{5}$; 0.4; 40% $\frac{4}{5}$; 0.8; 80% $\frac{3}{5}$; 0.6; 60%

You spin the spinner twice.

5. Give the sample space.

6. Find P(green, then green)

7. Find P(purple, then blue) $\frac{1}{16}$

5. PP, PB, PR, PG

BB, BR, BG, BP

GG, GP, GB, GR

RR, RB, RP, RG

6. $\frac{1}{16}$

8. Forestry The table shows a sample of the number of spruce trees counted in a forest area. Find the experimental probability of selecting a Serbian spruce. $\frac{20}{119}$

9. A true-or-false quiz has five questions. Use a simulation or a sample space to find the probability of guessing at random and getting exactly three correct answers. $\frac{5}{16}$

Spruce Trees

Tree Type	Number
Norway spruce	32
Serbian spruce	20
Colorado spruce	67

12-4a Activity Lab

Exploring Multiple Events

You want to make a necklace using two colors of beads. You decide which colors to use by selecting from the beads at the right. You select the first bead at random. You put the bead back and make another selection at random.

TEKS ★ TAKS

(7.10)(A) To construct sample spaces for composite experiments **TAKS** Obj. 5

1. Give the sample space for the colors of the two beads. Write the outcomes as ordered pairs. See margin.

2. What is the probability of selecting a red bead first? $\frac{4}{16}$ or $\frac{1}{4}$

3. What is the probability of selecting red beads twice? $\frac{1}{16}$

4. Suppose you now select a red bead and do not replace it. How many beads of each color are left? 1 red, 2 green, 2 blue, 2 yellow

5. Reasoning Does the probability of selecting a red bead second depend on whether you replace the first red bead? Explain. See margin.

597

---

1. RR, RB, RG, RY, BR, BB, BG, BY, GR, GB, GG, GY, YR, YB, YG, YY

5. Yes; if you replace the first red bead, then P(red for second draw) $= \frac{2}{8}$, or $\frac{1}{4}$, but if you do not replace the first red bead, then P(red for second draw) $= \frac{1}{7}$.

TEKS ★ TAKS

(7.10)(B) To find the probability of independent events

(7.10)(A) To construct sample spaces for simple or composite experiments
TAKS Obj. 5

Dana Center TEKS Toolkit Clarifying Activities (7.10)(B), (7.10)(A)
Visit: PHSchool.com
Web Code: arq-9045

TEKS Math Background

A *compound event* consists of two or more events. If the probability of the second event is not affected by the first event, the two events are *independent events*. The probability of independent events, $P(A$ and $B)$, is the product of the probabilities for each separate event, $P(A) \times P(B)$.

Two events are *dependent events* if the occurrence of the first event changes the probability of the second event. The probability of dependent events is also the product of the separate probabilities.

More Math Background: p. 578D

Lesson Planning and Resources

See p. 578E for a list of the resources that support this lesson.

Bell Ringer Practice

✓ **Check Skills You'll Need**
Use student page, transparency, or PowerPoint.

TAKS **Daily Review 92**
Use transparency.

598

✓ Check Skills You'll Need

1. **Vocabulary Review**
Describe multiplying fractions using the terms *denominator* and *numerator*.
1–5. See below.
Find each product.

2. $\frac{3}{4} \cdot \frac{3}{4}$ 3. $\frac{3}{5} \cdot \frac{2}{5}$

4. $\frac{1}{5} \cdot \frac{1}{4}$ 5. $\frac{3}{7} \cdot \frac{2}{7}$

 for Help
Lesson 3-4

Check Skills You'll Need

1. To multiply fractions, multiply the numerators and multiply the denominators.

2. $\frac{9}{16}$

3. $\frac{6}{25}$

4. $\frac{1}{20}$

5. $\frac{6}{49}$

TEKS ★ TAKS

- (7.10)(B) To find the probability of independent events
- (7.10)(A) To construct sample spaces for simple or composite experiments TAKS **Obj. 5**

🔊 **New Vocabulary** compound event, independent events, dependent events

Why Learn This?

You can find the probability of more than one event, such as winning a game twice.

A **compound event** consists of two or more events. Two events are **independent events** if the occurrence of one event does not affect the probability of the occurrence of the other.

KEY CONCEPTS **Probability of Independent Events**

If A and B are independent events, then $P(A$, then $B) = P(A) \times P(B)$.

EXAMPLE **Probability of Independent Events**

❶ **Multiple Choice** You and a friend play a game twice. What is the probability that you win both games? Assume $P(\text{win})$ is $\frac{1}{2}$.

   Ⓐ $\frac{1}{2}$ Ⓑ $\frac{4}{9}$ Ⓒ $\frac{1}{4}$ Ⓓ $\frac{1}{8}$

$P(\text{win, then win}) = P(\text{win}) \times P(\text{win})$ ← Winning is the first and second event.

$\qquad\qquad\qquad\quad = \frac{1}{2} \times \frac{1}{2}$ ← Substitute $\frac{1}{2}$ for $P(\text{win})$.

$\qquad\qquad\qquad\quad = \frac{1}{4}$ ← Multiply.

The probability of winning both games is $\frac{1}{4}$. The correct answer is C.

✓ Quick Check

● 1. Find $P(\text{win, then lose})$. $\frac{1}{4}$

Differentiated Instruction **Solutions for All Learners**

Special Needs L1
To model the idea of *with* and *without replacement*, place some counters or marbles, in two colors, in a bag. Have students do experiments in which they take some marbles out and do not replace them. Then repeat the experiment, taking some out and replacing them. They should record their data.

learning style: tactile

Below Level L2
Review multiplication of fractions. Using a calculator will help students multiply fractions with greater denominators, as in $\frac{1}{26} \cdot \frac{1}{26} \cdot \frac{1}{676}$

learning style: visual

First Draw

| 1 | 2 | 3 | 4 | 5 |

Select a card
at random. → 4

Second Draw

| 1 | 2 | 3 | 5 |

Select again. → ?

Suppose you play a game with cards numbered 1–5. You draw two cards at random. You draw the first card and do not replace it. The probability in the second draw depends on the result of the first draw.

Two events are **dependent events** if the occurrence of one event affects the probability of the occurrence of the other event.

> **KEY CONCEPTS** **Probability of Dependent Events**
>
> If event B depends on event A, then
> $P(A, \text{then } B) = P(A) \times P(B \text{ after } A)$.

EXAMPLES **Probability of Dependent Events**

2 You select a card at random from those below. The card has the letter M. Without replacing the M card, you select a second card. Find the probability that you select a card with the letter A after you select M.

| M | A | T | H | E | M | A | T | I | C | S |

There are 10 cards remaining after you select an M card.

$P(A) = \dfrac{2}{10}$ ← number of cards with the letter A
← number of cards remaining

$= \dfrac{1}{5}$ ← Simplify.

The probability of selecting an A for the second card is $\frac{1}{5}$.

Online
active math

For: Probability Activity
Use: Interactive
Textbook, 12-4

3 You select a card from a bucket that contains 26 cards lettered A–Z without looking. Without replacing the first card, you select a second one. Find the probability of choosing C and then M.

The events are dependent. After the first selection, 25 letters remain.

$P(C, \text{then } M) = P(C) \times P(M \text{ after } C)$ ← Use the formula for dependent events.

$= \dfrac{1}{26} \times \dfrac{1}{25}$ ← Substitute.

$= \dfrac{1}{650}$ ← Multiply.

The probability of choosing C and then M is $\frac{1}{650}$.

✓ Quick Check

2. Use the cards in Example 2. You select a T card at random. Without replacing the T card, you select a second card. Find $P(S)$. $\frac{1}{10}$

3. Suppose another 26 cards lettered A–Z are put in the bucket in Example 3. Find $P(J, \text{then } J)$. $\frac{1}{1,326}$

2. Teach

Activity Lab

Use before the lesson.
Student Edition Activity Lab 12-4a, Exploring Multiple Events, p. 597

All in One Teaching Resources
Activity Lab 12-4: Compound Events

Guided Instruction

Error Prevention!

Note that dependent events must have a change in sample space.

Example 3
Ask: *What words in the problem make it clear that these two selections are dependent events?*
"without" and "replacing"

Additional Examples

1 A box contains the same number of green marbles, orange marbles, and blue marbles. You draw one marble, replace it, and draw a second marble. What is the probability that both marbles you draw are blue? $\frac{1}{9}$

2 You select a card at random from those having A, E, I, O, U, P, C. The card has the letter E. Without replacing the E card, you select a second card. Find the probability of selecting a card that does not have a vowel. $\frac{1}{3}$

3 A bag contains 3 red marbles, 4 white marbles, and 1 blue marble. You draw one marble. Without replacing it, you draw a second marble. What is the probability that the two marbles you draw are red and white? $\frac{3}{14}$

Differentiated Instruction Solutions for All Learners

Advanced Learners L4
In Example 3, if you replaced the first card before drawing the second, what would the probability of winning be? $\frac{1}{676}$

English Language Learners ELL
Relate the phrase *compound* event to compound words, which are composed of more than one word. Likewise, relate *independent events* to independent people, who do not depend on others to do their tasks.

Pre-AP™

learning style: verbal

599

Closure

• *How do you find the probability of a compound event?* Find the product of the probability of each event.

• *Explain the difference between independent and dependent events.* **Sample: For independent events, the occurrence of one event does not affect the probability of the other event; for dependent events, one event does affect the probability of the other event.**

● More Than One Way

You toss a coin three times. What is the probability of getting three heads?

Brianna's Method

Each toss of a coin is an independent event. The probability of getting heads for one coin toss is $\frac{1}{2}$. I can multiply the probabilities of the three coin tosses.

$$P(\text{three heads}) = \frac{1}{2} \times \frac{1}{2} \times \frac{1}{2} = \frac{1}{8}$$

The probability of three heads is $\frac{1}{8}$.

Chris's Method

I can make a tree diagram for the coin tosses. A favorable outcome is one with 3 heads.

The tree diagram shows 1 favorable outcome out of 8 possible outcomes. The probability of three heads is $\frac{1}{8}$.

Toss 1	Toss 2	Toss 3	Outcome
H	H	H	H H H
		T	H H T
	T	H	H T H
		T	H T T
T	H	H	T H H
		T	T H T
	T	H	T T H
		T	T T T

Choose a Method

You toss a coin four times. What is the probability of getting tails all four times? Describe your method and explain why you chose it.

$\frac{1}{16}$; **answers may vary. Sample: It is quicker to find the product of probabilities.**

✓ Check Your Understanding

1. **Vocabulary** How do independent and dependent events differ?
   See margin.

2. **Multiple Choice** Two independent events A and B both have a probability of $\frac{1}{3}$. Which expression represents $P(A, \text{then } B)$? **B**

   Ⓐ $\frac{1}{3} + \frac{1}{3}$ Ⓑ $\frac{1}{3} \times \frac{1}{3}$ Ⓒ $\frac{1}{3} + \frac{1}{2}$ Ⓓ $\frac{1}{3} \times \frac{1}{2}$

Are the two events *independent* or *dependent*?

3. You toss a nickel. Then you toss a dime. **independent**

4. **dependent**   4. You select a card. Then you select again without replacement.

600   **Chapter 12** Using Probability

1. **Two events are independent if the occurrence of one does not affect the probability of the other occurring; two events are dependent if the occurrence of one does affect the probability of the other occurring.**

For more exercises, see Extra Skills and Word Problems.

GO for Help

For Exercises	See Examples
5–10	1
11–19	2
20–22	3

(A) **You roll a number cube twice. Find each probability.**

5. $P(1, \text{then } 2)$ $\frac{1}{36}$

6. $P(3, \text{then even})$ $\frac{3}{36}$ or $\frac{1}{12}$

7. $P(\text{less than 4, then 1})$ $\frac{3}{36}$ or $\frac{1}{12}$

8. $P(\text{odd, then even})$ $\frac{9}{36}$ or $\frac{1}{4}$

9. $P(\text{divisible by 2, then 5})$ $\frac{3}{36}$ or $\frac{1}{12}$

10. $P(\text{greater than 2, then odd})$ $\frac{12}{36}$ or $\frac{1}{3}$

An arrangement of 8 students is shown below. The numbers of all the students are in a basket. The teacher selects a number and replaces it. Then the teacher selects a second number. Find each probability.

11. $P(\text{student 1, then student 8})$ $\frac{1}{64}$

12. $\frac{16}{64}$ or $\frac{1}{4}$

12. $P(\text{student in row A, then student in row B})$

13. $P(\text{student in row A, then student 6, 7, or 8})$ $\frac{12}{64}$ or $\frac{3}{16}$

Row	Student			
A	1	2	3	4
B	5	6	7	8

You select the letter A from the group. Without replacing the A, you select a second letter. Find each probability.

14. $P(Z)$ $\frac{1}{7}$

15. $P(\text{vowel})$ $\frac{2}{7}$

16. $P(\text{red})$ $\frac{2}{7}$

17. $P(\text{blue})$ $\frac{5}{7}$

18. $P(\text{consonant})$ $\frac{5}{7}$

19. $P(\text{not } K)$ $\frac{6}{7}$

A box contains 20 cards numbered 1–20. You select a card. Without replacing the first card, you select a second card. Find each probability.

20. $P(1, \text{then } 20)$ $\frac{1}{380}$

21. $P(3, \text{then even})$ $\frac{10}{380}$ or $\frac{1}{38}$

22. $P(\text{even, then } 7)$ $\frac{10}{380}$ or $\frac{1}{38}$

(B) **23. Guided Problem Solving** Five girls and seven boys want to be the two broadcasters for a school show. To be fair, a teacher puts their names in a hat and selects two. Find $P(\text{girl, then boy})$. $\frac{35}{132}$
- **Make a Plan** The selections of the two names are (dependent, independent) events. Find the probability of selecting a girl first. Then find the probability of selecting a boy after selecting a girl.
- **Carry Out the Plan** $P(\text{girl first}) = \frac{5}{\boxed{}}$; $P(\text{boy after girl}) = \frac{7}{\boxed{}}$

Two coins are dropped at random into the boxes in the diagram below.

24. What is the theoretical probability that both coins fall into a shaded box? $\frac{1}{25}$

25. In 50 trials, both coins land in a shaded box twice. What is the experimental probability that both coins fall into a shaded box? $\frac{1}{25}$

PowerPoint

Lesson Quiz

Find each probability.

1. You roll a number cube twice. What is $P(2 \text{ and even})$? $\frac{1}{12}$

2. You draw a card at random from a stack of ten cards, each labeled with a number from 1 through 10. Then you draw a second card. What is $P(5, \text{ then } 3)$? $\frac{1}{90}$

29–30. See back of book.

35. See back of book.

GO Online

Homework Help

Visit: PHSchool.com

Web Code: are-1204

26. Events with no outcomes in common are called *disjoint events* or *mutually exclusive events*. To find the probability of mutually exclusive events, add the probabilities of the individual events. Suppose you select a number from 21 to 30 at random. What is the probability of selecting a number that is even or prime? $\frac{7}{10}$

Choose a Method A bag contains 3 blue marbles, 4 red marbles, and 2 white marbles. Three times you draw a marble and return it. Find each probability.

27. $P(\text{red, then white, then blue})$ 28. $P(\text{all white})$ $\frac{8}{729}$
$\frac{24}{729}$ or $\frac{8}{243}$

29. **Reasoning** Events are complementary if they cover all possibilities with no overlap. Are the following sets of events *complementary*, *mutually exclusive*, or *neither*? Explain. **29a–b. See margin.**
   a. A traffic light shows red, yellow, or green or is broken.
   b. A student receives an A, B, or C on a test.

30. **Writing in Math** When you select marbles without replacing them, are the events *independent* or *dependent*? Explain. See margin.

31. **Challenge** You have two spinners with colors on them. The probability of spinning green on both spinners is $\frac{5}{21}$. The probability of spinning green on the first one alone is $\frac{1}{3}$. What is the probability of spinning green on the second spinner alone? $\frac{5}{7}$

TEKS ★ TAKS Tune-Up and Mixed Review

TAKS Objective 5
TEKS (7.10)(A)

32. Dominica rolls a number cube once and spins the spinner at the right once. Which choice shows all the possible outcomes when she rolls an odd number and spins an odd number? **C**
   Ⓐ $(1, 1), (1, 3), (3, 1), (3, 3), (5, 1)$
   Ⓑ $(1, 1), (2, 2), (3, 3), (4, 3), (5, 3), (6, 3)$
   Ⓒ $(1, 1), (1, 3), (3, 1), (3, 3), (5, 1), (5, 3)$
   Ⓓ $(1, 1), (3, 3), (5, 5)$

TAKS Objective 3
TEKS (7.6)(A)

33. Which two angles are NOT complementary? **J**
   Ⓕ $1°, 89°$ Ⓖ $33°, 57°$ Ⓗ $22°, 68°$ Ⓙ $42°, 56°$

TAKS Objective 1
TEKS (7.2)(B)

34. William worked $2\frac{3}{4}$ hours on Saturday and $3\frac{3}{4}$ hours on Sunday. On Monday, he worked half as many hours as he did on Saturday and Sunday combined. How many hours did he work Monday? **C**
   Ⓐ $1\frac{3}{8}$ hours   Ⓑ $1\frac{7}{8}$ hours   Ⓒ $3\frac{1}{4}$ hours   Ⓓ $6\frac{1}{2}$ hours

GO for Help   Lesson 12-3

35. Make a table to show the sample space for one spin of a spinner with equal sections numbered from 1 to 3 and one toss of a coin.
See margin.

TEKS ★ TAKS Resources

- TAKS Strategies, p. 615
- TAKS Practice Test, pp. 619–623

TAKS Tune-Up Kit

- TAKS Daily Review Transparencies
- TAKS Review and Preparation Workbook
- TAKS Strategies with Transparencies
- Texas Progress Monitoring Assessments

Alternative Assessment

Have students work in small groups. Provide groups with coins, index cards, spinners, and/or number cubes. Groups write one problem dealing with dependent events and one problem dealing with independent events. Then groups challenge other groups to solve their problems.

Vocabulary Builder

High-Use Academic Words

TEKS ★ TAKS
(7.14)(A) To communicate mathematical ideas using language TAKS Obj. 6

High-use academic words are words that you will see often in textbooks and on tests. These words are not math vocabulary terms, but knowing them will help you succeed in mathematics.

Direction Words

Some words tell what to do in a problem. I need to understand what these words are asking so that I give the correct answer.

Word	Meaning
Analyze	To examine in detail to determine relationships
List	To present information in some order or to give examples
Persuade	To cause someone to do or believe something, especially by reasoning

Exercises

Match each situation with the correct word.

1. You do a survey in which you write the types of cereal people prefer and the number of times people choose each type of cereal. **B**

2. You convince the manager of a diner to serve a certain type of cereal based on a survey. **C**

3. You determine the cereal preferences of people based on a survey. **A**

    A. analyze
    B. list
    C. persuade

4. List all the possible outcomes of flipping a coin and rolling a number cube. Then find the probability that an outcome is heads and even. **See margin.**

5. Analyze the data at the right. How would you use the data to persuade a disc jockey to play hip-hop music? Explain. **See margin.**

6. **Word Knowledge** Think about the word *outcome*.
   a. Choose the letter for how well you know the word.
      A. I know its meaning.   **6a–c. Check students' work.**
      B. I've seen it, but I don't know its meaning.
      C. I don't know it.
   b. **Research** Look up and write the definition of *outcome*.
   c. Use the word in a sentence involving mathematics.

Music Preference Survey

Type of Music	Frequency
Hip-hop	|||| |||| ||||
House	|||
Country	||||
Rock	|||| ||||

4. **H1, H2, H3, H4, H5, H6, T1, T2, T3, T4, T5, T6;** P(heads and even) $= \frac{3}{12}$, or $\frac{1}{4}$

5. **When asked about music preference, there is the greatest probability that the response is hip-hop.**

Vocabulary Builder

High-Use Academic Words

In this feature, students are introduced to words that are not strictly mathematical but appear frequently in their texts.

Guided Instruction

Explain that the vocabulary words in this feature have multiple meanings and some can apply to math problems. Have volunteers read each word and its definition aloud. Ask:
- *Which word is the closest synonym for study?* **analyze**
- *How would you use list as it relates to probability?* **Sample: List all the potential outcomes to form a sample space.**
- *How could you use persuade in a math problem?* **Sample: The experimental probability of a coin flip landing heads is $\frac{93}{100}$. Would this persuade you to predict heads or tails on the next flip?**

Exercises

Have students work independently, review the answers as a class, and discuss any differences.

Differentiated Instruction

Advanced Learners   **L4**
Have students create their own fill-in-the-blank questions for the vocabulary words. Have them trade papers with a partner and answer their partner's questions.

TEKS ★ TAKS Resources

Dana Center TEKS Toolkit Clarifying Activities (7.14)(A)
Visit: PHSchool.com
Web Code: arq-9045

Practice With Probability

In this feature, students practice solving problems involving probability. They find the probability of independent and dependent events.

Guided Instruction

Explain to students that they can use probability to make predictions in everyday life. Ask volunteers for examples of using probability in their lives. Then have a volunteer read the problem aloud.
Ask:

- *What kind of probability is this question asking you to find?* **dependent probability**

- *Why do we multiply the three probabilities?* **Dependent probability is the product of the probability of the first event and all subsequent events.**

- *How would you find the probability of Anna winning first place and Cole winning second place?* **Multiply $\frac{60}{300}$ by $\frac{51}{240}$.**

- *How would you express the probability of Anna winning first place as a percent?* **20%** *The probability of Anna winning first place and Cole winning second place?* **4.3%**

TEKS ★ TAKS Resources

Dana Center TEKS Toolkit Clarifying Activities (7.11)(B), (7.13)(A)
Visit: PHSchool.com
Web Code: arq-9045

TEKS ★ TAKS
(7.11)(B) To make inferences and convincing arguments based on an analysis of given data **TAKS** Obj. 5
(7.13)(A) To identify and apply mathematics to activities in and outside of school **TAKS** Obj. 6

Practice With Probability

Members of a math club solve problems worth 1 to 4 points. Then the club has a drawing for three prizes based on the number of points members have earned.

Each student's name is put in a hat once for every point he or she earns. A student can win only one prize. Based on the table below, what are the chances that Anna wins first prize, Cole wins second prize, and Dillon wins third prize?

Points Earned

Name	Frequency	Name	Frequency
Anna	~~IIII~~ ~~IIII~~ ~~IIII~~ ~~IIII~~ ~~IIII~~ ~~IIII~~ ~~IIII~~ ~~IIII~~ ~~IIII~~ ~~IIII~~ ~~IIII~~ ~~IIII~~	Cole	~~IIII~~ ~~IIII~~ ~~IIII~~ ~~IIII~~ ~~IIII~~ ~~IIII~~ ~~IIII~~ ~~IIII~~ ~~IIII~~ ~~IIII~~ I
Dillon	~~IIII~~ ~~IIII~~ ~~IIII~~ ~~IIII~~ ~~IIII~~ ~~IIII~~ ~~IIII~~ ~~IIII~~ ~~IIII~~ ~~IIII~~ III	Raja	~~IIII~~ ~~IIII~~ ~~IIII~~ ~~IIII~~ ~~IIII~~ ~~IIII~~ ~~IIII~~ ~~IIII~~ II
Bailey	~~IIII~~ ~~IIII~~ ~~IIII~~ ~~IIII~~ ~~IIII~~ ~~IIII~~ ~~IIII~~ I	Rosa	~~IIII~~ ~~IIII~~ ~~IIII~~ ~~IIII~~ ~~IIII~~ ~~IIII~~ ~~IIII~~ ~~IIII~~ ~~IIII~~ III

What You Might Think

> What do I know? What do I want to find out?

> How can I solve the problem?

> What is the answer?

What You Might Write

I know each person's number of points. I want to know the chances that Anna wins first, Cole wins second, and Dillon wins third.

Anna's chances are $\frac{60}{300}$. After Anna wins first prize, she cannot win again. So Cole's chances are $\frac{51}{240}$. Then Dillon's chances are $\frac{53}{189}$.

The chances of the three winning in that order are $\frac{60}{300} \times \frac{51}{240} \times \frac{53}{189}$. This is about 0.01, or 1%.

Think It Through

1. Why are Anna's chances $\frac{60}{300}$? Why are Cole's chances $\frac{51}{240}$ if Anna wins first? Why are Dillon's chances $\frac{53}{189}$ if Cole wins second? See margin.

2. How can you use a calculator to verify $\frac{60}{300} \times \frac{51}{240} \times \frac{53}{189} \approx 0.01$?
   Type in (60 × 51 × 53) ÷ (300 × 240 × 189).

1. Anna's chances to win are $\frac{60}{300}$ because she has earned 60 of the total 300 points; Cole's chances to win are $\frac{51}{240}$ because he has earned 51 out of the remaining 240 points (after Anna's are removed); Dillon's chances to win are $\frac{53}{189}$ because he has earned 53 of the remaining 189 points (after Anna's and Cole's are removed).

Word Problem Practice

Exercises
Have students work independently on the Exercises. When they have finished, they can form small groups to compare answers and elect a representative to report their results to the class.

Exercises

Solve each problem. For Exercise 3, answer the questions first.

3. Fran's chances of making free throws in basketball are 80% based on her performance this season. If the trend continues, what are the chances she will make both of her next two free throws? **64%**
  a. What do you know? What do you want to find out?
  b. How can you solve the problem? Explain.

4. You play the card game In Between with the following rules.
  • Use 30 cards numbered 1–30.
  • You turn over two cards at random.
  • You win if the next card turned over is between the two cards. $\frac{6}{28}$ or $\frac{3}{14}$

For the cards displayed at the right, what is the probability you will win?

5. Janice agrees to work for her neighbor for a year. In return, her neighbor will pay her $480 and give her a car. Janice has to stop working after 9 months. Since she does not work the full year, she gets only $60 and the car. How much is the car worth? **$1,200**

6. George participates in a 3-mile walk for hunger. He averages 6 miles per hour for the first mile, 5 miles per hour for the next mile, and 4 miles per hour for the last mile. How long does it take him to walk the 3 miles? **37 min**

7. Students study the advantages and disadvantages of year-round schools (YRS). They then express their opinions in a poll. A "0" means the student is strongly against YRS. A "10" means the student is strongly for YRS.

7. About 5.23; 4.5; 4; answers may vary. Sample: the median, because half the students are on either side of that response

YRS Survey Results

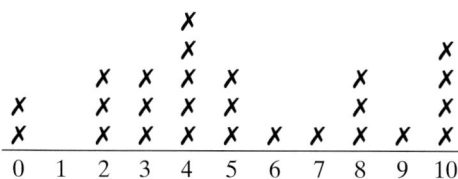

The line plot shows the data collected. Find the mean, median, and mode of the data. Which measure best represents how the students feel about YRS? Explain.

Differentiated Instruction

Below Level   L2

Provide students with problems involving multiple independent events, such as repeatedly spinning a spinner to get a certain result, to allow them to practice simpler problems.

Objectives

To find permutations

Examples

1 Finding Permutations
2 Finding Permutations Using Factorials
3 Application: Olympics

Math Background

The simplest permutation that students have used is the ordered pair that name the coordinates of a point on a plane. In this case, the other possible permutations, (y, x), (y, y), and (x, x) are not generally used. The letters in MATH have, for example, $4 \cdot 3 \cdot 2 \cdot 1$, or 24, permutations. The total number of permutations of n objects is $n!$ while the number of permutations of n objects taken r at a time is

$$\frac{n!}{(n-r)!}$$

More Math Background: p. 578D

Lesson Planning and Resources

See p. 578E for a list of the resources that support this lesson.

Bell Ringer Practice

✓ **Check Skills You'll Need**
Use student page, transparency, or PowerPoint.

TAKS Daily Review 93
Use transparency.

606

 Check Skills You'll Need

1. Vocabulary Review
What is a *product?*
See below.
Find each product.

2. $10 \cdot 9$ 90

3. $20 \cdot 19$ 380

4. $8 \cdot 7 \cdot 6$ 336

5. $10 \cdot 9 \cdot 8$ 720

6. $5 \cdot 4 \cdot 3$ 60

 for Help
Lesson 1-8

For: Permutations Activity
Use: Interactive Textbook, 12-5

Check Skills You'll Need

1. the result of multiplication

What You'll Learn

To find permutations

🔊 **New Vocabulary** permutation, factorial

Why Learn This?

Sometimes the order of the outcomes is important, such as the order of letters in words.

A **permutation** is an arrangement of items in a particular order. Suppose you arrange the four letters O, P, S, and T in two ways. The permutation STOP is different from the permutation POTS because the order of the letters is different.

EXAMPLE Finding Permutations

1 Find the number of permutations of the letters L, I, K, and E. The first letter can be any of the four letters. You have three choices for the second, two for the third, and one for the fourth letter.

$$4 \quad \times \quad 3 \quad \times \quad 2 \quad \times \quad 1 \quad = \quad 24 \leftarrow \text{Use the counting principle.}$$

first letter   second letter   third letter   fourth letter

There are 24 different permutations.

✓ Quick Check

1. Find the number of permutations of the letters H, A, N, D, L, and E.
720

There are $4 \times 3 \times 2 \times 1$ permutations of the letters C, A, R, and E. The product of all positive integers less than or equal to a number is the **factorial** for that number. You write 4 factorial as 4!.

$$4! = 4 \times 3 \times 2 \times 1$$

Differentiated Instruction Solutions for All Learners

Special Needs L1
Provide students with square paper tiles. Have them write the letters listed in Example 1, and arrange them, recording their arrangement each time. This will let them see the counting principle in action.

learning style: visual

Below Level L2
Allow students to use calculators to find factorials. Many calculators have a factorial key.

learning style: tactile

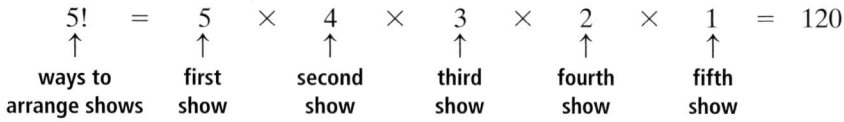 **EXAMPLE** Finding Permutations Using Factorials

 Calculator Tip

To evaluate 5!, press 5 `MATH`. Scroll right to option PRB. Select option 5—"!". Press `ENTER`.

2 **Television** A TV station has five shows to broadcast on a weeknight. How many different arrangements of the shows can they make?

$$5! \quad = \quad 5 \quad \times \quad 4 \quad \times \quad 3 \quad \times \quad 2 \quad \times \quad 1 \quad = \quad 120$$

↑	↑	↑	↑	↑	↑
ways to arrange shows	first show	second show	third show	fourth show	fifth show

The station can make 120 different arrangements of the shows.

✓ Quick Check

2. Write the number of permutations for the letters G, R, A, V, I, E, and S in factorial form. Then multiply. **7! = 5,040**

The sample space below shows the two-letter permutations of the 4 letters in STOP. There are 4 possible choices for the first letter and 3 possible choices for the second letter. The number of permutations is 4 × 3 = 12.

ST	OP	TP	TS	PO	PT
TO	PS	OS	OT	SP	SO

EXAMPLE Application: Olympics

3 Suppose a men's Olympic ice hockey tournament has 12 teams. Find the number of different ways that teams can win the gold, silver, and bronze medals.

There are 12 possible teams that can win the gold medal. After that, there are 11 teams that can win the silver medal. Finally, there are 10 teams that can win the bronze medal.

$$12 \quad \times \quad 11 \quad \times \quad 10 \quad = \quad 1,320 \quad \leftarrow \text{Use the counting principle.}$$

↑	↑	↑
gold medal	silver medal	bronze medal

There are 1,320 different ways that teams can win the three medals.

✓ Quick Check

3b. The example selects only 3 teams from the 12 choices, so the answer is 12 × 11 × 10, not 12!.

3. **a.** Women's Olympic ice hockey tournaments have eight teams. Find the number of different ways that teams can win the gold, silver, and bronze medals. **336**

   b. Reasoning In Example 3, the number is not found by finding 12!. Explain why. **See left.**

12-5 Permutations **607**

2. Teach

Activity Lab
Use before the lesson.

All in One Teaching Resources
Activity Lab 12-5: Exploring Order

Guided Instruction

Example 1
Have students model the Example by making four cards or pieces of paper with the letters on them.

Example 3
Discuss why the number decreases by one each time.

PowerPoint
Additional Examples

1 Find the number of permutations of the letters T, I, G, E, and R. **120**

2 How many different ways can you arrange a nickel, a dime, a penny, and a quarter in a row? **24**

3 Find the number of permutations for the blue, red, and green ribbons for 12 horses at a show. **1,320**

All in One Teaching Resources
• Daily Notetaking Guide 12-5 **L3**
• Adapted Notetaking 12-5 **L1**

Closure

• *What is a permutation?* an arrangement of objects in a particular order
• Explain how to use factorial form to find the permutations of the letters in F, R, O, and G. **4! = 4 · 3 · 2 · 1 = 24**

Advanced Learners **L4**
Have students explore with examples whether $a! + b!$ has the same value as $(a + b)!$. **The values are not always the same.**

English Language Learners **ELL**
Have students explain when they use factorials to find permutations and when they do not. In Example 3, there are not 12 medal choices, there are only 3.

Pre-AP™

learning style: verbal

Assignment Guide

Check Your Understanding
Go over Exercises 1–6 in class before assigning the Homework Exercises.

Homework Exercises
A Practice by Example   7–25
B Apply Your Skills   26–39
C Challenge   40
TEKS ★ TAKS Tune-Up and Mixed Review   41–45

Homework Quick Check
To check students' understanding of key skills and concepts, go over Exercises 9, 16, 33, 34, and 39.

Differentiated Instruction Resources

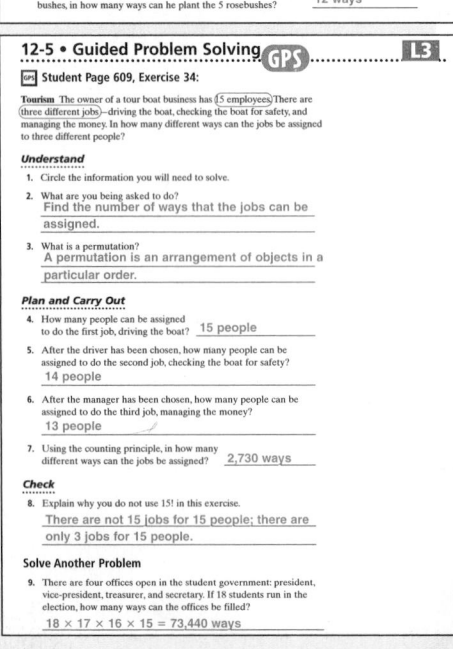

Adapted Practice 12-5   L1

Practice 12-5   Per. L3

Find the number of permutations of each group of letters.
1. C, H, A, I, R   120
2. L, I, G, H, T, S   720
3. C, O, M, P, U, T, E, R   40,320

Write the number of permutations in factorial form. Then simplify.
4. S, P, A, C, E   5! = 120
5. P, L, A, N   4! = 24
6. S, A, M, P, L, E   6! = 720

Find the number of three-letter permutations of the letters.
7. A, P, Q, M   24
8. L, S, U, V, R   60
9. M, B, T, O, D, K   120

Find the value of each factorial expression.
10. 9!   362,880
11. 7!   5,040
12. 6!   720

Solve.
13. Suppose that first-, second-, and third-place winners of a contest are to be selected from eight students who entered. In how many ways can the winners be chosen?   336
14. Antonio has nine different sweat shirts that he can wear for his job doing yardwork. He has three pairs of jeans and two pairs of sweat pants. How many different outfits can Antonio wear for the yardwork?   45
15. Ramona has a combination lock for her bicycle. She knows the numbers are 20, 41, and 6, but she can't remember the order. How many different arrangements are possible?   6 arrangements
16. Travis is planting 5 rosebushes along a fence. Each rosebush has a different flower color: red, yellow, pink, peach, and white. If he wants to plant 3 rosebushes in between white and yellow rosebushes, in how many ways can he plant the 5 rosebushes?   12 ways

12-5 • Guided Problem Solving GPS   L3

Student Page 609, Exercise 34:

Tourism The owner of a tour boat business has 5 employees. There are three different jobs—driving the boat, checking the boat for safety, and managing the money. In how many ways can the jobs be assigned to three different people?

Understand
1. Circle the information you will need to solve.
2. What are you being asked to do? Find the number of ways that the jobs can be assigned.
3. What is a permutation? A permutation is an arrangement of objects in a particular order.

Plan and Carry Out
4. How many people can be assigned to do the first job, driving the boat?   15 people
5. After the driver has been chosen, how many people can be assigned to do the second job, checking the boat for safety?   14 people
6. After the manager has been chosen, how many people can be assigned to do the third job, managing the money?   13 people
7. Using the counting principle, in how many different ways can the jobs be assigned?   2,730 ways

Check
8. Explain why you do not use 15! in this exercise. There are not 15 jobs for 15 people; there are only 3 jobs for 15 people.

Solve Another Problem
9. There are four offices open in the student government: president, vice-president, treasurer, and secretary. If 18 students run in the election, how many ways can the offices be filled? $18 \times 17 \times 16 \times 15 = 73,440$ ways

---

✓ Check Your Understanding

1. **Vocabulary** What is a permutation? an arrangement of items in a particular order
2. **Multiple Choice** How many permutations are there of the words *star*, *square*, and *triangle*? C
   - Ⓐ 1   Ⓑ 3   Ⓒ 6   Ⓓ 9

Match each set of digits to the correct number of permutations.

3. even digits 2 through 8   B
4. odd digits 1 through 9   A
5. all digits 1 through 9   C

   A. 120
   B. 24
   C. 362,880

6. **Reasoning** Does 3! + 2! = 5!? Justify your answer. No, 3! = 6 and 2! = 2, so 3! + 2! = 8, but 5! = 120.

Homework Exercises

For more exercises, see Extra Skills and Word Problems.

GO for Help

For Exercises	See Examples
7–12	1
13–19	2
20–25	3

Ⓐ **Find the number of permutations of each group of letters.**

7. W, O, R, L, D   120
8. H, U, M, A, N   120
9. T, O, Y   6
10. P, I, C, K, L, E   720
11. L, U, N, C, H, E, S   5,040
12. M, A, R, S   24

Write the number of permutations in factorial form. Then simplify.

13. C, A, T   3! = 6
14. R, A, T, E, S
15. P, A, C, K   4! = 24
16. D, E, P, A, R, T   6! = 720
17. I, N, C, L, U, D, E   7! = 5,040
18. L, U, C, K, Y   5! = 120

19. **Planning** You plan to shop, call a friend, study, and exercise, all in one day. How many arrangements of activities can you plan?
   24 arrangements

Find the number of two-letter permutations of the letters.

20. R, E, P, S   12
21. Q, I, E, R, T, Y, U   42
22. G, D, X, Z, C   20
23. A, E, I, O, U, Y   30
24. M, A, P, L, E   20
25. L, A, P   6

Ⓑ **GPS**

26. **Guided Problem Solving** Two sisters and a brother line up for movie tickets. Find the probability that they line up boy-girl-girl. $\frac{1}{3}$
    - **Make a Plan** Make a sample space. Remember, each sister counts separately, so use B, G, and g for the three siblings. Use the sample space to find the probability.
    - **Carry Out the Plan** Write a ratio to find probability.

Find the value of each factorial expression.
   3,628,800
27. 4!   24
28. 6!   720
29. 7!   5,040
30. 8!   40,320
31. 10!

33. 6 MATH ! = or 6 ✕ 5 ✕ 4 ✕ 3 ✕ 2 ✕ 1 =

39a. BS, GS, RS, BD, GD, RD, BP, GP, RP

   b. 3 × 3 = 9 possibilities

44. $\frac{64}{256}$ or $\frac{1}{4}$

45. $\frac{8}{256}$ or $\frac{1}{32}$

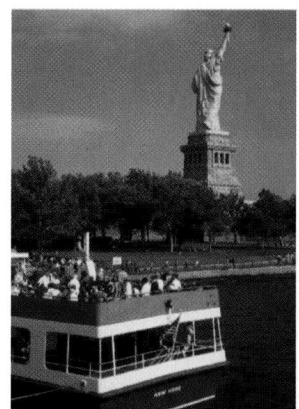

32. The password to access a computer consists of 3 lower-case letters. You do not have the password. What is the greatest number of passwords you can try before you have access? **17,576 passwords**

33. <u>Writing in Math</u> Describe two different ways you can use a calculator to find the value of 6!. **See margin.**

34. **Tourism** The owner of a tour boat business has 15 employees. There are three different jobs—driving the boat, checking the boat for safety, and managing the money. In how many different ways can the jobs be assigned to three different people? **2,730 ways**

Find the value of each expression.

35. $5! \div 2!$ **60**   **36.** $4! \div 3!$ **4**   **37.** $6! \div 4!$ **30**   **38.** $7! \div 3!$ **840**

39. **Soccer** The team names and uniform colors for a soccer league are shown.
  a. Show the sample space of the different name-color possibilities.
  b. Use the counting principle to support your answer to part (a). **39a–b. See margin.**

Team Name	Uniform Color
Scorers	Blue
Defenders	Green
Passers	Red

C 40. **Challenge** Write an algebraic expression to show how many two-letter permutations are possible with $(n - 2)$ different letters.
$(n - 2)(n - 3)$

TEKS ★ TAKS Tune-Up and Mixed Review

TAKS Objective 5
TEKS (7.10)(A)

41. You can play one sport and join one music group. The sports are football, soccer, and tennis. The groups play rock or hip-hop. Which list shows all possible arrangements of a sport and a music group? **A**
  Ⓐ (football, rock), (football, hip-hop), (soccer, rock), (soccer, hip-hop), (tennis, rock), (tennis, hip-hop)
  Ⓑ (football, rock), (football, soccer), (football, tennis), (soccer, rock), (tennis, hip-hop)
  Ⓒ (football, rock), (soccer, rock), (tennis, rock)
  Ⓓ (football, rock), (football, hip-hop), (soccer, tennis), (tennis, rock), (tennis, hip-hop)

TAKS Objective 1
TEKS (7.2)(F)

42. A Fahrenheit temperature is 32° more than $\frac{9}{5}$ of a Celsius temperature C. Which algebraic expression represents the Fahrenheit temperature for a given Celsius temperature? **G**
  Ⓕ $32 + \frac{9}{5}$ Ⓖ $\frac{9}{5}C + 32$ Ⓗ $(32)\frac{9}{5} + C$ Ⓙ $\frac{9}{5}C - 32$

GO for Help   **Lesson 12-4**

You have a set of 16 cards numbered 1–16. You select a card and put it back into the set. Then you select another card. Find each probability.
44–45. See margin.
43. $P(2, \text{ then } 6)$ $\frac{1}{256}$ **44.** $P(\text{even, then odd})$ **45.** $P(16, \text{ then odd})$

Alternative Assessment

Have students work in pairs or small groups. Each student writes a word with four to eight letters in which no letters are repeated. Students exchange words with members of their group and find the number of permutations of the letters.

TEKS ★ TAKS Resources

• TAKS Strategies, p. 615
• TAKS Practice Test, pp. 619–623

TAKS Tune-Up Kit
• TAKS Daily Review Transparencies
• TAKS Review and Preparation Workbook
• TAKS Strategies with Transparencies
• Texas Progress Monitoring Assessments

---

4. Assess & Reteach

PowerPoint
Lesson Quiz

1. Find the number of permutations for the letters A, B, C, and D. **24**

2. Find the value of 5!. **120**

3. Write the number of permutations in factorial form of the letters U, N, I, T, E, and D. **6!**

4. Find the number of three-letter permutations of the letters E, N, O, U, G, and H. **120**

Objectives
To find combinations

Examples
1 Application: Clothing
2 Application: Careers

Math Background

In the permutations of the letters in BLACK, for example, the order makes a difference because BLAKC is not the same as BLKAC. A *combination* is the grouping of objects in which the order of the objects does not matter; so BLAKC is considered the same combination as BLKAC. You can find the number of combinations by finding the number of permutations and eliminating duplicates.

More Math Background: p. 578D

Lesson Planning and Resources

See p. 578E for a list of the resources that support this lesson.

PowerPoint

Bell Ringer Practice

☑ **Check Skills You'll Need**
Use student page, transparency, or PowerPoint.

TAKS Daily Review 94
Use transparency.

☑ **Check Skills You'll Need**

1. **Vocabulary Review** Explain why CAT and ACT are not the same *permutations*. See below.

   Find the number of permutations of each group of letters.

2. G, I, R, L **24**

3. H, I, K, E, R, S **720**

GO for Help
Lesson 12-5

Check Skills You'll Need

1. The letters are not in the same order.

Vocabulary Tip

Combination comes from a Latin word that means "together."

What You'll Learn

To find combinations

◀)) **New Vocabulary** combination

Why Learn This?

Sometimes the order of objects does not matter. You may only care about the combination of objects.

Whether you pack your hat before your scarf, or your scarf before your hat, you have still packed the two items. A **combination** is a grouping of objects in which the order of the objects does not matter.

EXAMPLE Application: Clothing

① The colors of four scarves are listed. You decide to pack two scarves. How many different combinations of two scarves are possible?

Step 1 Let letters represent the scarves. Make a list of all the possible permutations.

Color	Letter
Blue	b
Yellow	y
Green	g
Red	r

(b, y) (y, b) (g, b) (r, b) (b, g) (y, g)
(g, y) (r, y) (b, r) (y, r) (g, r) (r, g)

Step 2 Cross out any group containing the same letters as another group.

(b, y) ~~(y, b)~~ (g, b) (r, b) ~~(b, g)~~ (y, g)
~~(g, y)~~ (r, y) ~~(b, r)~~ ~~(y, r)~~ (g, r) ~~(r, g)~~

Six different combinations of two colors are possible.

☑ **Quick Check**

1. How many different combinations of two seashells can you make from three seashells? **3**

Differentiated Instruction Solutions for All Learners

Special Needs **L1**
Provide students with a copy of Example 1. Have them color-code the pairs of letters, matching the color of their marker or crayon to the letter (blue, yellow, green, and red.) This will let them visualize why certain pairs of letters are crossed out.

learning style: visual

Below Level **L2**
Review how to simplify fractions, such as

$$\frac{120}{6} = \frac{120 \div 6}{6 \div 6} = \frac{20}{1} = 20.$$

learning style: visual

In Example 1, the total number of permutations for four scarves taken two at a time is 4 × 3. The number of permutations of the smaller group, two scarves, is 2 × 1. You can find the number of combinations by dividing the total number of permutations by the number of permutations for the smaller group.

$$\text{combinations} = \frac{\text{total number of permutations}}{\text{number of permutations of smaller group}} = \frac{4 \times 3}{2 \times 1} = 6$$

 EXAMPLE   **Application: Careers**

On career day, an architect, an engineer, a carpenter, and a journalist speak at your school. You plan to attend three presentations. How many different combinations of presentations can you choose from?

Step 1 Find the total number of permutations.

$$\underset{\substack{\uparrow \\ \text{first} \\ \text{choice}}}{4} \times \underset{\substack{\uparrow \\ \text{second} \\ \text{choice}}}{3} \times \underset{\substack{\uparrow \\ \text{third} \\ \text{choice}}}{2} = 24 \text{ permutations} \quad \leftarrow \text{Use the counting principle.}$$

Step 2 Find the number of permutations of the smaller group.

$$3 \times 2 \times 1 = 6 \text{ permutations} \quad \leftarrow \text{Use the counting principle.}$$

Step 3 Find the number of combinations.

$$\frac{\text{total number of permutations}}{\text{number of permutations of smaller group}} = \frac{24}{6} \quad \leftarrow \text{Divide.}$$

$$= 4 \quad \leftarrow \text{Simplify.}$$

You can attend 4 combinations of presentations.

 Quick Check

2. If you go to two presentations, how many different combinations of presentations can you choose from? 6

✓ Check Your Understanding

1. **Vocabulary** Why is order not important in finding combinations?
   In a combination, only the grouping of the items matters.

   Would you solve Exercises 2–4 using a *combination* or a *permutation*?

2. choosing three pieces of fruit from seven pieces combination

3. giving first and second place awards permutation

4. choosing five books from a list of ten books combination

5. $\frac{7 \times 6 \times 5}{3 \times 2 \times 1}, \frac{10 \times 9 \times 8 \times 7 \times 6}{5 \times 4 \times 3 \times 2 \times 1}$ 5. Write an expression for each combination in Exercises 2–4.

---

2. Teach

Activity Lab

Use before the lesson.

All in One Teaching Resources
Activity Lab 12-6: Arranging Items

Guided Instruction

Example 1
Verify students' understanding of "number of permutations of the smaller group" by having them work through the pattern for Quick Check 1, three shells taken two at a time.

PowerPoint
 Additional Examples

1 You have one pen in each of these colors: red, green, blue, and purple. You lend three to a friend. How many combinations of colors are possible in the pens you lend? 4

2 The county fair has 10 rides. You have time for 3 of them. How many different combinations of rides are available to you? 120

All in One Teaching Resources
• Daily Notetaking Guide 12-6 **L3**
• Adapted Notetaking 12-6 **L1**

Closure

• *How do you find the combinations of four shirts taken two at a time?* Sample: Make an organized list and cross out duplicates; or divide the total number of permutations, 4 × 3 or 12, by the number of permutations of the smaller group, 2 × 1 or 2, which is $\frac{12}{2}$ or 6.

Advanced Learners **L4**
How many basketball teams of 5 players each can you select from 12 players? 792

English Language Learners **ELL**
In Example 1, point out that the pairs of letters being crossed out are duplicates of pairs of letters that are not crossed out. The pairs of letters crossed out, which correspond to colors, are the same letters but in different order than the ones remaining.

Pre-AP™

learning style: verbal

3. Practice

Assignment Guide

Check Your Understanding
Go over Exercises 1–5 in class before assigning the Homework Exercises.

Homework Exercises
A Practice by Example   6–16
B Apply Your Skills   17–30
C Challenge   31
TEKS ★ TAKS Tune-Up and
   Mixed Review   32–36

Homework Quick Check
To check students' understanding of key skills and concepts, go over Exercises 8, 15, 22, 24, and 27.

Differentiated Instruction **Resources**

Homework Exercises

For more exercises, see Extra Skills and Word Problems.

Ⓐ **For Exercises 6 and 7, use the table to make an organized list.**

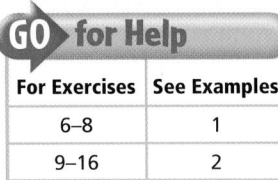

For Exercises	See Examples
6–8	1
9–16	2

Swimmer	Letter
Noah	N
Olivia	O
Kevin	K
Chloe	C

6. **Swimming** The four swimmers listed at the right are trying out for the swim team. Two will make the team. How many different combinations of two swimmers are possible? **6**

7. If 3 swimmers will make the team, how many combinations of 3 swimmers are possible? **4**

8. Five campers want to go on a hiking trip. A camp counselor will choose three of them. How many different combinations are possible? **10**

Find the number of combinations.

9. Choose two people from three. **3**

10. Choose three people from five. **10**

11. Choose two people from six. **15**

12. Choose four people from six. **15**

Sports Use the poster for Exercises 13–16. Find the number of combinations for each situation.

13. Participate in 2 track events. **6**

14. Participate in 2 games. **1**

15. Participate in 2 field events. **3**

16. Participate in 3 track events. **4**

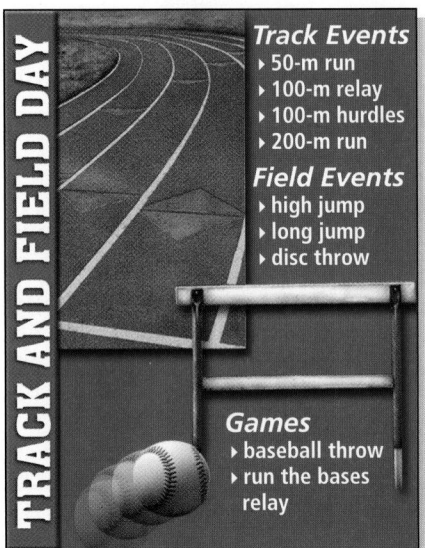

Track Events
▸ 50-m run
▸ 100-m relay
▸ 100-m hurdles
▸ 200-m run

Field Events
▸ high jump
▸ long jump
▸ disc throw

Games
▸ baseball throw
▸ run the bases
▸ relay

TRACK AND FIELD DAY

Ⓑ **GPS** 17. **Guided Problem Solving**
You have six pizza toppings. How many different 3-topping pizzas can you make? **20 pizzas**
- total permutations:
  $6 \times \blacksquare \times \blacksquare$
- permutations of smaller group: $\blacksquare \times 2 \times 1$

GO Online
Homework Help
Visit: PHSchool.com
Web Code: are-1206

Evaluate each expression.

18. $\frac{4!}{3!}$ **4**

19. $\frac{5!}{2!}$ **60**

20. $\frac{6!}{4!}$ **30**

21. $\frac{7!}{3!}$ **840**

22. **Music** You have 5 different CDs to play. Your CD player can hold
GPS 3 CDs. How many different combinations of 3 CDs can you select?
10 combinations

23. Twelve students organize a trip. Two of them are assigned to collect money. In how many ways can these two students be chosen? **66 ways**

24. Reasoning To open a combination lock, you must dial the numbers in the right order. Explain why "permutation lock" might be more appropriate than "combination lock" as a name for the lock shown at the left. Answers may vary. Sample: If the lock's combination is 5-10-15, you cannot open the lock with the combination 10-15-5.

Determine whether each situation involves a combination or a permutation. Then answer the question.

25. You select three books from a bookshelf that holds eight books. How many different sets of books can you choose? combination; 56 sets

26. Four students stand beside one another for a photograph. How many different orders are possible? permutation; 24 orders

27. Writing in Math Use your own words and an example to explain the difference between a permutation and a combination.
Check students' work.

Calculator Tip

To find $_4C_2$, press 4 MATH. Scroll right to option PRB. Select option 4—*nCr*. Press 2 ENTER.

You can use a graphing calculator to find the number of combinations. Use $_nC_r$ where n is the total number of items, C is combinations, and r is the number of items in a grouping. Evaluate each combination.

28. $_7C_3$ 35   **29.** $_6C_3$ 20   **30.** $_8C_5$ 56

C 31. Challenge You want to mix two of the paint colors below. Use the number of possible combinations to find P(blue and green). $\frac{1}{6}$

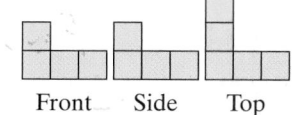

TEKS ★ TAKS Tune-Up and Mixed Review

TAKS Objective 5
TEKS (7.12)(A)

32. Julia sold magazine subscriptions for a fundraiser. The numbers of subscriptions she sold in the last seven days were 5, 2, 3, 2, 7, 1, and 4. Which measure of data is represented by 2 subscriptions? **B**
Ⓐ Mean   Ⓑ Mode   Ⓒ Median   Ⓓ Range

TAKS Objective 3
TEKS (7.8)(A)

33. The top, side, and front views of an object are shown at the right. Which solid matches the views? **G**

Front   Side   Top

 Ⓕ   Ⓖ   Ⓗ   Ⓙ

 GO for Help   **Lesson 12-5**

Write the number of permutations in factorial form. Then simplify.

36. 5! = 120

34. D, O, G   3! = 6   **35.** S, H, O, E   4! = 24   **36.** D, R, U, M, S

Alternative Assessment

Have students work in pairs or small groups. Each student makes up a situation similar to those in Exercises 6–8. Students exchange papers and solve each others' problems. Students can challenge other groups to solve their problems.

TEKS ★ TAKS Resources

- TAKS Strategies, p. 615
- TAKS Practice Test, pp. 619–623

TAKS Tune-Up Kit

- TAKS Daily Review Transparencies
- TAKS Review and Preparation Workbook
- TAKS Strategies with Transparencies
- Texas Progress Monitoring Assessments

---

4. Assess & Reteach

PowerPoint
Lesson Quiz

Find the number of combinations.

1. You choose 3 out of 6 people. 20

2. Choose any two letters from the set of letters C, D, S, T, and U. 10

3. Choose any three letters from the set of letters A, B, C, and D. 4

613

Use this Checkpoint Quiz to check students' understanding of the skills and concepts of Lessons 12-4 through 12-6.

Resources

- All-in-One Teaching Resources Checkpoint Quiz 2
- Texas ExamView CD-ROM
- Success Tracker™ Online Intervention

MATH GAMES

Products of Winners

In this game, students test probability. They roll two number cubes, multiply the products and get points based on whether the product is odd or even.

Guided Instruction

Before students play the game, have a volunteer read the rules. Have students predict whether Player A or Player B is more likely to win. Pair students who predict opposite letters with each other and have them test their theories by playing. When they have finished playing, discuss the results.

Resources

- two number cubes

614

✓ Checkpoint Quiz 2 Lessons 12-4 through 12-6

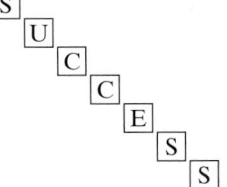

You select a letter at random from the group at the right. You replace the letter and make another selection. Find each probability.

1. P(vowel, then S) $\frac{6}{49}$ 2. P(vowel, then C) $\frac{4}{49}$

3. P(C, then E) $\frac{2}{49}$ 4. P(T, then S) 0

5. P(U, then consonant) $\frac{5}{49}$

You have 4 blue cards, 1 red card, and 3 green cards. You select a card at random, do not replace it, and select a second card. Find each probability.

6. P(green, then red) $\frac{3}{56}$ 7. P(blue, then green) $\frac{12}{56}$ or $\frac{3}{14}$ 8. P(red, then blue) $\frac{4}{56}$ or $\frac{1}{14}$

9. You decide to put the pictures of six friends in a row on a bulletin board. In how many different ways can you arrange the pictures? **720 ways**

10. How many different combinations of four flowers can you make from six different flowers? **15 combinations**

Teams A, B, C, and D enter a cheerleading competition.

11. Give the sample space of the different orders in which the teams can perform. **See margin.**

12. The two best teams will advance to the next round. How many different combinations of two best teams are possible? **6 combinations**

MATH GAMES Products of Winners

What You'll Need

- two number cubes

How To Play

- Take turns rolling two number cubes. Find the product of the two numbers. If the product is even, Player A scores a point. If the product is odd, Player B scores a point.
- After 15 rolls each, the player with more points wins. Who would you rather be, Player A or Player B?

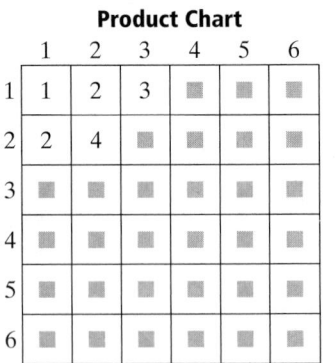

Product Chart

	1	2	3	4	5	6
1	1	2	3	■	■	■
2	2	4	■	■	■	■
3	■	■	■	■	■	■
4	■	■	■	■	■	■
5	■	■	■	■	■	■
6	■	■	■	■	■	■

614

11. ABCD, ABDC, ACBD, ACDB, ADBC, ADCB, BACD, BADC, BCAD, BCDA, BDAC, BDCA, CABD, CADB, CBAD, CBDA, CDAB, CDBA, DABC, DACB, DBAC, DBCA, DCAB, DCBA

Eliminating Answers

Before you try to answer a multiple-choice question, you may be able to save time by eliminating some answer choices. Then you can choose your answer carefully from the remaining options.

EXAMPLE

A bag contains ten blue, six red, and four green pens. You select a pen at random. What is the probability of not choosing a green pen?

$\text{(A) } \dfrac{1}{5}$ $\text{(B) } \dfrac{4}{5}$ $\text{(C) } \dfrac{5}{6}$ $\text{(D) } \dfrac{9}{11}$

Look at the denominator of each choice. The number of possible outcomes is $10 + 6 + 4$, or 20. The denominator of the answer must be 20 or a factor of 20. Eliminate choices C and D because they have denominators of 6 and 11.

Estimate the magnitude of the answer. Since most of the pens are not green, the probability of *not* choosing a green pen is a fraction greater than $\frac{1}{2}$. Since choice A is less than $\frac{1}{2}$, you can eliminate choice A.

The correct answer is choice B.

Exercises

Objective 5
TEKS (7.11)(B)

1. A school has 1,060 students. The results of a survey are shown.

Students Surveyed	Students Who Produced Computer Art
40	24

If the trend in the table continues, which is the best prediction of the total number of students who produced computer art? C

    (A) 260 students   (C) 640 students
    (B) 480 students   (D) 790 students

Objective 5
TEKS (7.10)(A)

2. A wheel is divided evenly into three sections labeled A, B, and C. You spin it twice. Which list shows all the possible outcomes? H

    (F) (A, B), (B, A), (A, C), (C, A), (B, C), (C, B)
    (G) (A, A), (A, B), (B, A), (A, C), (C, A), (B, C), (C, C)
    (H) (A, A), (A, B), (B, A), (A, C), (C, A), (B, B), (B, C), (C, B), (C, C)
    (J) (A, B), (B, A), (A, C), (C, A), (B, C), (C, B), (A, A), (B, B)

Eliminating Answers

When students take multiple-choice tests, they can improve their chances of success, by the laws of probability, every time they are able to eliminate an answer choice. This feature focuses on the strategy of eliminating answer choices.

Guided Instruction

To convince students of the effectiveness of the strategy of eliminating answer choices on multiple-choice tests, present the following situation and questions:

- *You take a multiple-choice test with five answer choices. You have no idea at all which answer is correct. What is the probability that you guess the correct answer?* $\frac{1}{5}$

- *Suppose that you know one answer choice is wrong and you eliminate it. Now what is the probability that you guess the correct answer?* $\frac{1}{4}$

TEKS ★ **Resources**

 Strategies with Transparencies
- Transparency 6
- Practice Sheet, p. 24

Strategies with Transparencies

Test-Taking Strategies: Eliminating Answers

When solving a multiple choice problem, first try to eliminate some of the answer choices.

Be sure to cross out answers you eliminate in the test booklet—*not* on the answer sheet.

> *Example* The original price of a coat was $65. It was discounted 20% the day you bought it. How much money did you save?
> A. $78   B. $52   C. $13   D. $5

Since $78 is more than the original amount, you can immediately eliminate choice A.

By estimating you can determine that $60 times 0.20 is greater than $5, so you can eliminate choice D.

Since the question is asking for how much you saved, you can eliminate choice B because you know by estimating that you did not save more than 50% of the original price.

The answer is choice C.

Identify two answer choices you can immediately eliminate. Then solve the problem.
1. There are 32 students in Wyatt's class. At least 75% of the students have been vaccinated against chicken pox. About how many students have not had this vaccination?
   A. 40 students   B. 28 students
   C. 16 students   D. 8 students

Eliminate choice A: There are only 32 students in the class.
Eliminate choice B: By estimating you know that less than half the class has not had the vaccination. The answer is choice D.

Chapter 12 Review

Chapter 12 Review

TEKS ★ TAKS Resources

Student Edition
Extra Skills and Word
  Problems Practice, Ch. 12, p. 652
English/Spanish Glossary, p. 675
Formulas and Properties, p. 673
Tables, p. 670

All in One Teaching Resources
- Vocabulary and Study
  Skills 12F   L3

TAKS Tune-Up Kit
- TAKS Daily Review
  Transparencies
- TAKS Review and Preparation
  Workbook
- TAKS Strategies with
  Transparencies
- Texas Progress Monitoring
  Assessments
- Texas ExamView CD-ROM
- MindPoint Quiz Show CD-ROM

Differentiated Instruction

Spanish Vocabulary Workbook
with Study Skills   ELL
Texas Interactive Textbook
- Audio Glossary
Online Vocabulary Quiz

Success ✂ Tracker™
Online at PHSchool.com

Spanish Vocabulary/Study Skills ELL

Vocabulary/Study Skills L3

12F: Vocabulary Review Puzzle — For use with the Chapter Review

Study Skill When using a word bank, read the words first. Then answer the questions.

Complete the crossword puzzle. Use the words from the following list.

parallelogram	conjecture	decagon	equation	mode
combination	symmetry	variable	discount	prime
independent	permutation	dependent	outcome	slope

ACROSS
2. Events are _____ if the occurrence of
one event affects the probability of the
occurrence of another event.
4. A figure has _____ if one side of the
figure is the mirror image of the other side.
6. four-sided figure with two sets of parallel lines
8. possible result of an action
11. Events are _____ if the occurrence of
one event does not affect the probability of the
occurrence of another event.

DOWN
1. prediction that suggests what you
expect will happen
2. difference between the original
price and the sale price
3. letter that stands for a number
5. ratio that describes the steepness of
a line
6. arrangement of objects in a
particular order
7. number that occurs most often in a
data set
9. grouping of objects in which order
does not matter
10. mathematical statement with an
equal sign
12. polygon with ten sides
13. whole number with only two
factors, itself and the number one

Vocabulary Review

 combination (p. 610)
complement (p. 581)
compound event (p. 598)
counting principle (p. 592)
dependent events (p. 599)

event (p. 580)
experimental probability
  (p. 586)
factorial (p. 606)
independent events (p. 598)

outcome (p. 580)
permutation (p. 606)
sample space (p. 591)
theoretical probability (p. 580)

Go Online
PHSchool.com
For: Online vocabulary quiz
Web Code: arj-1251

Choose the correct term to complete each sentence.

1. A (combination, permutation) is a grouping of objects in which the
order of the objects does not matter. combination

2. An outcome or a group of outcomes is called a(n) (event, factorial).
event

3. Two events are (dependent, independent) if the occurrence of one
event does not affect the probability of the occurrence of the other.
independent

4. The (odds in favor of, odds against) an event is the ratio of the
number of favorable outcomes to the number of unfavorable
outcomes. odds in favor of

5. (Theoretical, Experimental) probability is based on observations.
Experimental

Skills and Concepts   TEKS ★ TAKS

Lesson 12-1
(7.10)(B) To find the
probability of independent
events
(7.1)(B) To convert between
fractions, decimals, whole
numbers, and percents
TAKS Obj. 1

You can find the **theoretical probability** of an event using this formula.

$$P(\text{event}) = \frac{\text{number of favorable outcomes}}{\text{total number of possible outcomes}}$$

**You select a card at random from the cards
shown at the right. Find each probability.**

$$\boxed{T}\,\boxed{R}\,\boxed{U}\,\boxed{M}\,\boxed{P}\,\boxed{E}\,\boxed{T}$$

6. $P(\text{P})$ $\frac{1}{7}$ 7. $P(\text{vowel})$ $\frac{2}{7}$ 8. $P(\text{not P})$ $\frac{6}{7}$

Lesson 12-2
(7.10)(B) To find the
probability of independent
events
(7.11)(B) To make
inferences and convincing
arguments based on an
analysis of given or collected
data **TAKS Obj. 5**
(7.13)(D) To select tools
such as real objects to solve
problems

You find the **experimental probability** of an event using this formula.

$$P(\text{event}) = \frac{\text{number of times an event occurs}}{\text{total number of trials}}$$

**Games A computer game company makes random checks of its
games. Of 200 games, 4 are found to be defective.**

9. Find the experimental probability that a game is defective. $\frac{1}{50}$

10. If the trend continues, predict the number of defective games in a
batch of 1,600. 32

616   Chapter 12 Chapter Review

11. See back of book.

Lesson 12-3

(7.10)(A) To construct sample spaces for simple or composite experiments

TAKS Obj. 5

(7.10)(B) To find the probability of independent events

The collection of all possible outcomes in a probability experiment is called a **sample space.** You can use the **counting principle** to find the number of outcomes of an event.

Use the menu below for Exercises 11–13.

Appetizers	Soups
Egg Rolls	Won-ton
Fried Won-tons	Sizzling Rice

Main Dishes
Almond Chicken
Sweet & Sour Pork
Beef with Broccoli

11. At the China Panda, if you order the family dinner, you choose one appetizer, one soup, and one main dish from the menu. Draw a tree diagram to show the sample space. See margin.

12. You ask the restaurant to choose the meal for you at random. What is the probability of getting the egg roll, won-ton soup, and almond chicken for your meal? $\frac{1}{12}$

13. Use the counting principle to find the number of possible dinners.

12 dinners

Lesson 12-4

(7.10)(B) To find the probability of independent events

(7.10)(A) To construct sample spaces for simple or composite experiments

TAKS Obj. 5

A **compound event** consists of two or more events. Two events are **independent events** if the occurrence of one event does not affect the probabilty of the occurrence of the other. Two events are **dependent events** if the occurrence of one event affects the probability of the occurrence of the other.

A hat contains the names of eight girls and six boys. You select two names without replacing the first name. Find each probability.

14. $P(\text{boy, then boy})$
$\frac{30}{182}$ or $\frac{15}{91}$

15. $P(\text{girl, then boy})$
$\frac{48}{182}$ or $\frac{24}{91}$

16. (girl, then girl)
$\frac{56}{182}$ or $\frac{4}{13}$

17. Two independent events A and B both have a probability of $\frac{1}{4}$. Find $P(A, \text{then } B)$. $\frac{1}{16}$

Lessons 12-5, 12-6

- To find permutations
- To find combinations

A **permutation** is an arrangement of objects in a particular order. A **combination** is a grouping of objects in which order does not matter.

18. Five students compete on a relay team. Only four of them can race at a time. How many different teams are possible? **5 teams**

19. Four students are selected for a relay team. In how many ways can they line up for the race? **24 ways**

TEKS ★ TAKS Resources

- Texas ExamView CD-ROM
  - Ch. 12 Ready-Made Test
  - Make your own Ch. 12 test
- MindPoint Quiz Show CD-ROM
  - Chapter 12 Review

Differentiated Instruction

All in One Teaching Resources

Chapter 12 Test **L2**
- Chapter 12 Test **L3**
- Chapter 12 Alternative Assessment **L4**

Spanish Assessment Resources **ELL**
- Chapter 12 Test **L2**
- Chapter 12 Test **L3**
- Chapter 12 Alternative Assessment **L4**

Texas ExamView CD-ROM
- Special Needs Test **L1**
- Special Needs Practice Bank **L1**

Online Chapter 12 Test at www.PHSchool.com **L3**

1. $\frac{3}{8}$; 0.375; 37.5%

2. $\frac{1}{8}$; 0.125; 12.5%

Chapter Test **L2**

Chapter Test **L3**

Chapter Test   Form A
Chapter 12

Use the data below. Find the experimental probability of each event as a fraction, a decimal, and a percent.

Toss	1	2	3	4	5	6	7	8	9	10	11	12	13	14	15	16	17	18
Heads	X		X	X	X		X	X	X			X	X	X		X	X	
Tails		X				X				X	X				X			X

1. P(heads) $\frac{2}{3}$; 0.6̄; 66$\frac{2}{3}$%   2. P(tails) $\frac{1}{3}$; 0.3̄; 33$\frac{1}{3}$%

You work at a T-shirt printing business. Of the 4,700 T-shirts shipped, 564 are printed improperly.

3. What is the experimental probability that a T-shirt is printed improperly?
   12%

4. Predict the number of improperly printed T-shirts in a batch of 2,000.
   240 T-shirts

Use the spinner at the right to find the probability of each event.

5. P(△) $\frac{3}{8}$ 6. P(□) $\frac{3}{8}$
7. P(△) $\frac{1}{4}$ 8. P(△ or □) $\frac{3}{4}$
9. P(△ or △) $\frac{5}{8}$ 10. P(neither △ nor □) $\frac{1}{4}$

Suppose you have a bag that contains 4 black, 3 green, 1 red, and 2 orange marbles. Find each probability.

11. P(green) $\frac{3}{10}$ 12. P(green or red) $\frac{2}{5}$
13. P(not orange) $\frac{4}{5}$ 14. P(green or black) $\frac{7}{10}$
15. P(red, then orange when red is not replaced) $\frac{1}{45}$ 16. P(black) $\frac{2}{5}$

The letters G E O M E T R Y are written on a set of cards. You mix the cards thoroughly. Without looking, you draw one letter, replace it, then draw another. Find each probability.

17. P(E, T) $\frac{1}{32}$ 18. P(M, Y) $\frac{1}{64}$

618

Use the data. Find the experimental probability of each event as a fraction, a decimal, and a percent.
1–2. See margin.

1. P(purple)

2. P(green)

3. P(orange) 0; 0; 0%

Marker Color	Frequency
Purple	6
Green	2
White	3
Black	5

4. a. **Quality Control** Factory workers test 80 batteries. Four batteries are defective. What is the experimental probability that a battery is defective? $\frac{1}{20}$

   b. Assume this trend continues. Predict the number of defective batteries in a batch of 1,600. **80 defective batteries**

There are six open containers arranged as shown. You toss a ball and it falls into one of the containers. Find each probability. 5. $\frac{2}{6}$ or $\frac{1}{3}$

5. P(number greater than 4)

6. P(even number) $\frac{3}{6}$ or $\frac{1}{2}$

7. P(4) $\frac{1}{6}$

8. P(7) 0

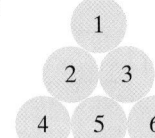

You have a bag that contains 6 blue, 2 green, 3 red, and 1 white marble. You select a marble at random. Find each probability. 13. $\frac{6}{144}$ or $\frac{1}{24}$

9. P(blue) $\frac{6}{12}$ or $\frac{1}{2}$ 10. P(white) $\frac{1}{12}$

11. P(not green) $\frac{10}{12}$ or $\frac{5}{6}$ 12. P(red) $\frac{3}{12}$ or $\frac{1}{4}$

13. P(green, then red when green is replaced)

14. P(red, then blue when red is not replaced)
$\frac{18}{132}$ or $\frac{3}{22}$

15. a. Find the number of two-letter permutations of the letters M, A, T, H. **12**

   b. Find the number of two-letter combinations of the letters M, A, T, H. **6**

---

16. Each of the letters D E T E R M I N E D is written on a card. You mix the cards thoroughly. What is the probability of selecting an E and then an M, if the first card is replaced before selecting the second card? $\frac{3}{100}$

17. **Writing in Math** Suppose you toss a coin several times and record the results. Out of 20 trials, you get tails 9 times. What is the experimental probability of getting heads? Explain why this may differ from the theoretical probability. **See margin.**

A car comes in the colors and models listed in the table below. Assume there is the same chance of selecting any color or model.

Colors	Models
Silver	Hatchback
Gray	Coupe
Black	Sedan

18. Give the sample space. **See margin.**

19. Find the probability that a car selected at random is a silver hatchback. $\frac{1}{9}$

20. Find the probability that a car selected at random is a yellow coupe. **0**

21. You have the same chance of getting any one of four prizes when you buy Good Morning Cereal. You want to use a simulation to find the probability of getting all four prizes when you buy four boxes of cereal. Which statement is *not* true? **B**

   Ⓐ You can simulate the problem by using a spinner divided into four equal sections.

   Ⓑ A possible answer is four boxes.

   Ⓒ The more trials you perform, the better your results should be.

   Ⓓ The result of your simulation is an experimental probability.

---

17. $\frac{11}{20}$; although the theoretical and experimental probabilities are not always the same, you expect the experimental probability to be close to the theoretical probability.

18. (Silver, Hatchback); (Silver, Coupe); (Silver, Sedan); (Gray, Hatchback); (Gray, Coupe); (Gray, Sedan); (Black, Hatchback); (Black, Coupe); (Black, Sedan)

Practice Test

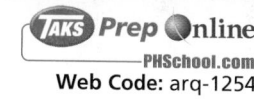
Web Code: arq-1254

Read each question. Then write the letter of the correct answer or the answer you would grid on your paper.

1. The table below shows running times from the Summer Olympics.

2004 Summer Olympics

Athlete	Event (meters)	Time (seconds)
Nesterenko	100	11
Campbell	200	21
Williams-Darling	400	49
Holmes	800	116

Which athlete had the fastest speed? **C**

Ⓐ Holmes; she ran the farthest.

Ⓑ Nesterenko; she had the shortest time.

Ⓒ Campbell; she ran more than 9 m/s.

Ⓓ Williams-Darling; she ran more than 8 m/s.

2. The cost of Dave and Michelle's dinner was $32.45. They want to leave a 20% tip. Which of the following is closest to the amount of the tip they want to leave? **G**

Ⓕ $6.00 Ⓖ $6.50 Ⓗ $7.00 Ⓙ $7.50

3. Bananas are on sale at $0.39 per pound. Jill buys 3.25 pounds of bananas. About how much does she pay for the bananas? **B**

Ⓐ Less than $1.00

Ⓑ Between $1.00 and $2.00

Ⓒ Between $2.50 and $3.00

Ⓓ More than $3.25

4. Which statement is NOT true of a cylinder? **F**

Ⓕ It has six edges.

Ⓖ The bases are not polygons.

Ⓗ It has two parallel bases.

Ⓙ It has no vertices.

5. $\angle P$ and $\angle N$ are complementary. The measure of $\angle P$ is 27°. What is the measure of $\angle N$? **B**

Ⓐ 27° Ⓑ 63° Ⓒ 90° Ⓓ 53°

6. The corresponding sides of two similar triangles are __?__ . **H**

Ⓕ equal Ⓗ proportional

Ⓖ rays Ⓙ congruent

7. Which sequence follows the rule $3n + 2$, where n represents the position of a term in the sequence? **C**

Ⓐ 11, 15, 19, 23, 27, . . .

Ⓑ 7, 10, 13, 16, 19, . . .

Ⓒ 5, 8, 11, 14, 17, . . .

Ⓓ 5, 7, 9, 11, 13, . . .

8. The fraction $\frac{4}{5}$ is found between which pair of fractions on a number line? **G**

Ⓕ $\frac{7}{10}$ and $\frac{11}{15}$ Ⓗ $\frac{3}{4}$ and $\frac{3}{5}$

Ⓖ $\frac{3}{4}$ and $\frac{17}{20}$ Ⓙ $\frac{8}{10}$ and $\frac{17}{20}$

9. Hannah spent $\frac{1}{2}$ of the class budget on food and $\frac{1}{4}$ of the remaining amount on raffle prizes. After she spent $50.25 on decorations, she had $24.75 left. What was the amount of the class budget? **D**

Ⓐ $75.00 Ⓒ $125.00

Ⓑ $100.00 Ⓓ $200.00

10. In the first baseball game of the season, Aman was at bat 5 times and hit the ball 3 times. If the pattern continues and he is at bat 40 times during the season, what is the best prediction of the number of times he will hit the ball? **G**

Ⓕ 6 times Ⓗ 38 times

Ⓖ 24 times Ⓙ 67 times

11. The model at the right represents $\sqrt{25} = 5$. Which arrangement of small squares can you use to model a large square that represents $\sqrt{144}$? **A**

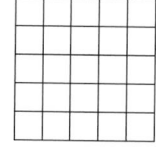

Ⓐ 12 rows of 12 squares

Ⓑ 8 rows of 18 squares

Ⓒ 9 rows of 16 squares

Ⓓ 13 rows of 13 squares

TAKS GO for Help Guide

Item	TAKS Objective	GO to
1	Obj. 6: (7.15)(B)	Lesson 5-2
2	Obj. 2: (7.3)(A)	Lesson 6-7
3	Obj. 1: (7.2)(G)	Lesson 1-3
4	Obj. 3: (7.6)(C)	Lesson 8-8
5	Obj. 3: (7.6)(A)	Lesson 7-2
6	Obj. 3: (7.6)(D)	Lesson 5-6
7	Obj. 2: (7.4)(C)	Lesson 9-4
8	Obj. 1: (7.1)(A)	Lesson 3-6
9	Obj. 6: (7.13)(C)	Lesson 3-4
10	Obj. 6: (7.15)(A)	Lesson 9-1
11	Obj. 1: (7.1)(C)	Lesson 8-6
12	Obj. 3: (7.7)(A)	Lesson 10-1
13	Obj. 5: (7.12)(A)	Lesson 1-10
14	Obj. 5: (7.11)(B)	Lesson 11-1
15	Obj. 2: (7.4)(A)	Lesson 7-3
16	Obj. 4: (7.9)(A)	Lesson 8-5
17	Obj. 5: (7.12)(A)	Lesson 1-10
18	Obj. 6: (7.13)(B)	Lesson 5-3
19	Obj. 5: (7.12)(A)	Lesson 1-10
20	Obj. 2: (7.5)(A)	Lesson 4-3
21	Obj. 3: (7.8)(A)	Lesson 8-8a
22	Obj. 6: (7.14)(A)	Lesson 4-4
23	Obj. 1: (7.2)(C)	Lesson 1-10
24	Obj. 2: (7.4)(C)	Lesson 9-4
25	Obj. 4: (7.9)(A)	Lesson 8-5
26	Obj. 2: (7.3)(B)	Lesson 5-7
27	Obj. 2: (7.4)(A)	Lesson 8-5
28	Obj. 6: (7.13)(A)	Lesson 8-10
29	Obj. 3: (7.6)(B)	Lesson 7-3
30	Obj. 1: (7.2)(E)	Lesson 2-1
31	Obj. 6: (7.13)(A)	Lesson 1-7
32	Obj. 1: (7.1)(B)	Lesson 6-2
33	Obj. 2: (7.3)(B)	Lesson 5-4
34	Obj. 2: (7.3)(A)	Lesson 6-4
35	Obj. 5: (7.12)(A)	Lesson 1-10
36	Obj. 6: (7.14)(A)	Lesson 4-6
37	Obj. 1: (7.2)(A)	Lesson 3-6
38	Obj. 6: (7.13)(A)	Lesson 4-4
39	Obj. 2: (7.3)(A)	Lesson 6-8
40	Obj. 5: (7.12)(B)	Lesson 1-10
41	Obj. 5: (7.10)(A)	Lesson 12-3
42	Obj. 4: (7.9)(C)	Lesson 8-5
43	Obj. 3: (7.6)(C)	Lesson 8-8
44	Obj. 4: (7.9)(C)	Lesson 8-10
45	Obj. 2: (7.4)(A)	Lesson 8-5
46	Obj. 2: (7.3)(A)	Lesson 6-4
47	Obj. 1: (7.2)(F)	Lesson 1-3
48	Obj. 4: (7.9)(C)	Lesson 8-10

12. Which of the following coordinates lie within the triangle? **H**

- Ⓕ (−2, 4)
- Ⓖ (−4, 7)
- Ⓗ (−4, 2)
- Ⓙ (2, 4)

13. Six giraffes at the zoo have the following heights: 19 ft, 16.5 ft, 17.5 ft, 18.5 ft, 18 ft, and 18.5 ft. A seventh giraffe is brought to the zoo. Its height makes the median and mode of the heights equal. What is the height of the seventh giraffe? **C**
- Ⓐ Exactly 18 feet
- Ⓑ Between 18 feet and 18.5 feet
- Ⓒ 18.5 feet or more
- Ⓓ Less than 18 feet

14. The graph below shows the populations of various towns and the areas of the towns. If the trend continues, which is the best prediction of the population of a town that has an area of 35 square miles? **G**

Population and Area

- Ⓕ Fewer than 40,000 people
- Ⓖ Between 41,000 and 65,000 people
- Ⓗ Between 66,000 and 80,000 people
- Ⓙ More than 100,000 people

15. Which of the following CANNOT be used to find the perimeter of an equilateral triangle with side length s? **D**
- Ⓐ $3s$
- Ⓒ $s + s + s$
- Ⓑ $2s + s$
- Ⓓ $s \times s \times s$

16. Lulu drew a circle with a radius of 25 inches and another circle with a radius of 15 inches. What is the approximate difference between the areas of the two circles? **J**
- Ⓕ 63 in.^{2}
- Ⓗ 400 in.^{2}
- Ⓖ 942 in.^{2}
- Ⓙ 1,256 in.^{2}

17. Mr. Song paid $120.00 for four tickets. He later bought another ticket for $45.00. What was the mean cost of all the tickets? **C**
- Ⓐ $30.00
- Ⓒ $33.00
- Ⓑ $75.00
- Ⓓ $165.00

18. Tammy has 7.5 lb of ground beef. What should Tammy do to find how many four-ounce hamburgers she can make? **G**
- Ⓕ Change 7.5 lb to ounces by dividing by 16. Then divide the result by 4.
- Ⓖ Change 7.5 lb to ounces by multiplying by 16. Then divide the result by 4.
- Ⓗ Change 7.5 lb to ounces by dividing by 16. Then multiply the result by 4.
- Ⓙ Change 7.5 lb to ounces by multiplying by 16. Then multiply the result by 4.

19. Abe collected the data below to see how many minutes he used his phone each day.

22, 13, 15, 18, 20

What number could be added to the set of data in order for the median and mode of the set to be equal? **C**
- Ⓐ 14
- Ⓑ 15
- Ⓒ 18
- Ⓓ 20

20. The model represents the equation $x + 4 = -1$. What is the value of x? **J**

Key

$\bigoplus = +1$

$\ominus = -1$

- Ⓕ $x = 4$
- Ⓗ $x = 5$
- Ⓖ $x = -1$
- Ⓙ $x = -5$

21. The top, front, and side views of a solid figure made of cubes are shown below.

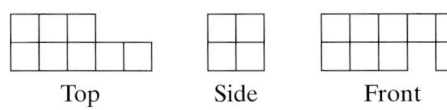

Top   Side   Front

Which figure matches the views above? **D**

Ⓐ   Ⓒ

Ⓑ   Ⓓ

22. The diameter of Jupiter is about 143,000 km, or about 11 times the diameter of Earth. Which expression can be used to find d, the diameter of Earth? **G**

Ⓕ $d = \dfrac{11}{143{,}000}$

Ⓖ $d = \dfrac{143{,}000}{11}$

Ⓗ $d = 143{,}000 \times 11$

Ⓙ $11 = d \times 143{,}000$

23. The average minimum temperatures in Amarillo, Texas, from January to June are $-5°C$, $-3°C$, $1°C$, $5°C$, $11°C$, and $16°C$. Which expression can be used to find the range of temperatures? **D**

Ⓐ $-5 + 16$ Ⓒ $16 - 5$

Ⓑ $-3 + 11$ Ⓓ $16 - (-5)$

24. Which description shows the relationship between a term and n, its position in the sequence? **J**

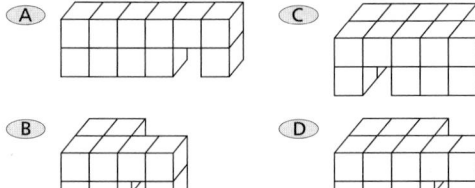

Position	1	2	3	4	5	n
Value of Term	3	5	7	9	11	

Ⓕ Add 2 to n.

Ⓖ Multiply n by 4 and then subtract 3.

Ⓗ Multiply n by 4 and then subtract 1.

Ⓙ Multiply n by 2 and then add 1.

25. Alison traces a circle with a radius of 10 centimeters, like the one shown at the right. What is the approximate area of the shaded region? **A**

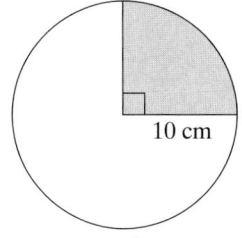

10 cm

Ⓐ 78.5 cm^2 Ⓒ 314 cm^2

Ⓑ 90 cm^2 Ⓓ 400 cm^2

26. Dan drew a map of his campus. He used a scale in which 1 inch represents 5 miles. What distance on Dan's map should represent the 2.5 miles between his dorm and the library? **G**

Ⓕ 0.25 in.   Ⓗ 2.5 in.

Ⓖ 0.5 in.   Ⓙ 5 in.

27. Kristin walked the 3-km circumference of the Tidal Basin in Washington, D.C. Which expression can be used to find the diameter of the basin? **B**

Ⓐ 3π Ⓑ $\dfrac{3}{\pi}$ Ⓒ -3π Ⓓ $\dfrac{\pi}{3}$

28. Paul wants to put a crystal cube with a side length of 9 inches into a rectangular box. The box has a base length of 10 inches and a base width of 11 inches. Which of the following does he need to know to see whether he can fit the cube into the box? **F**

Ⓕ The height of the box

Ⓖ The base area of the crystal cube

Ⓗ The surface area of the crystal cube

Ⓙ The base area of the box

29. Which statement is always true about an isosceles triangle? **B**

Ⓐ It has three congruent angles.

Ⓑ It has at least two congruent sides.

Ⓒ It has one right angle.

Ⓓ Every angle measure is different.

30. What is the value of the expression $(4 - 2)^2 + 6 \times 3 - 1$? **H**

Ⓕ 16   Ⓖ 17   Ⓗ 21   Ⓙ 29

31. The table below shows the women golfers who have won the most tournaments.

Golfer	Career Wins
Whitworth	88
Suggs	58
Lopez	48
Zaharias	41
Sheehan	35

Which statement is NOT supported by the information in the table? **D**

- (A) Whitworth had fewer than three times the career wins of Sheehan.
- (B) Whitworth and Suggs had more combined wins than the combined wins of Lopez, Zaharias, and Sheehan.
- (C) Suggs had less than twice the wins of Zaharias.
- (D) Lopez and Sheehan together had more wins than Whitworth.

32. Colleen needed to complete $\frac{3}{5}$ of her project by noon. What percent of the project did Colleen need to complete by noon? **G**

- (F) 25%　(G) 60%　(H) 40%　(J) 75%

33. Justin can ride his bike 10 miles in 36 minutes. At this rate, about how many minutes will it take him to ride 25 miles? **D**

- (A) 25 minutes
- (B) 61 minutes
- (C) 77 minutes
- (D) 90 minutes

34. Thirty-three out of sixty teachers vote for a new teacher's lounge. Which best represents the percent of the teachers who did NOT vote for the new lounge? **G**

- (F) 33%　(G) 45%　(H) 55%　(J) 60%

35. In which data set are the mean, median, mode, and range all the same number? **A**

- (A) {2, 3, 1, 3, 2, 1, 2}
- (B) {1, 1, 1, 2, 3, 1, 2}
- (C) {2, 2, 2, 3, 2, 1, 3}
- (D) {1, 2, 1, 2, 2, 1, 2}

36. Which expression can be used to solve the problem below? **H**
Luis charges $3.00 per gallon of gasoline for his lawn mower plus $8.00 per hour for mowing a lawn. How much will Luis earn if he uses 2 gal of gas and mows for 3.5 h?

- (F) $3 \times 8 + 2 \times 3.5$
- (G) $3 + 8 \times 2 + 3.5$
- (H) $3 \times 2 + 8 \times 3.5$
- (J) $3 \times 3.5 + 8 \times 2$

37. Which model represents $\frac{2}{3} \times \frac{1}{4}$? **C**

38. A strawberry cake requires $2\frac{1}{3}$ cups of flour. A fruitcake requires $\frac{1}{4}$ cup less flour than the strawberry cake. Which equation can be used to find *n*, the number of cups of flour needed for the fruitcake? **H**

- (F) $n = 2\frac{1}{3} + \frac{1}{4}$
- (G) $n = 2\frac{1}{3} \cdot \frac{1}{4}$
- (H) $n = 2\frac{1}{3} - \frac{1}{4}$
- (J) $n = 2\frac{1}{3} \div \frac{1}{4}$

39. Which of the following represents the greatest percent of change? **D**

- (A) A mountain lion's shoulder height grows from 1.5 feet to 2 feet.
- (B) A car goes from 25 miles per hour to 30 miles per hour.
- (C) A cruise-ship company increases the number of cruises it provides from 35 to 40.
- (D) A student increases his study time from 35 min per night to 1 h per night.

40. The following data represent the number of students who bought school lunches this week: 38, 53, 42, 24, 53. Which measure of data is represented by 29? **J**

- (F) Mean
- (G) Mode
- (H) Median
- (J) Range

41. Sokunthea has 1 quarter, 3 dimes and 3 nickels in her pocket. Which list shows all the possible unique outcomes if she chooses 3 coins at one time from her pocket? **C**

A

Quarter	Dime	Nickel
Quarter	Dime	Dime
Quarter	Nickel	Nickel
Dime	Dime	Nickel
Dime	Nickel	Nickel
Nickel	Nickel	Nickel

B

Quarter	Dime	Nickel
Dime	Dime	Nickel
Dime	Nickel	Nickel
Nickel	Nickel	Nickel

C

Quarter	Dime	Nickel
Quarter	Dime	Dime
Quarter	Nickel	Nickel
Dime	Dime	Nickel
Dime	Nickel	Nickel
Dime	Dime	Dime
Nickel	Nickel	Nickel

D

Quarter	Quarter	Dime
Dime	Dime	Nickel
Nickel	Nickel	Nickel

42. You build a piece of scenery that is 9 feet tall, 3 feet wide, and 11 feet long. It is a rectangular prism. What is the volume of the piece? **G**
 F 318 ft^3 H 252 ft^3
 G 297 ft^3 J 46 ft^3

43. Which of the following has exactly one base that is a polygon? **C**
 A Cone C Pyramid
 B Sphere D Cylinder

44. What is the volume of the gift box below? **H**

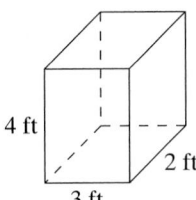

4 ft 2 ft 3 ft

 F 9 ft^3 H 24 ft^3
 G 12 ft^3 J 76 ft^3

45. Fred has a circular coaster with a circumference of 7 inches. Which expression could be used to find the radius of the coaster? **B**
 A $7 + 2\pi$ C $7 - 2\pi$
 B $\dfrac{7}{2\pi}$ D $\dfrac{7}{\pi}$

46. In the school orchestra, 30 students play string instruments, 22 students play brass instruments, and 3 students play percussion. What percent of the students in the orchestra play brass instruments? **G**
 F 22% H 55%
 G 40% J 60%

47. Vicky bought 3 dozen cookies at 6 cookies for $2.99, and 20 pints of milk at 4 pints for $2.25. What is the total amount she spent, not including tax, on cookies and milk? **D**
 A $5.24 C $17.97
 B $9.00 D $29.19

48. Christine built a wooden case.

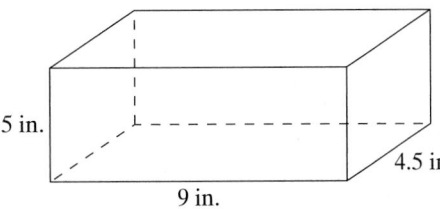

5 in. 4.5 in. 9 in.

The case was 5 inches high by 4.5 inches wide by 9 inches long. What was the volume of the case in cubic inches? **202.5**

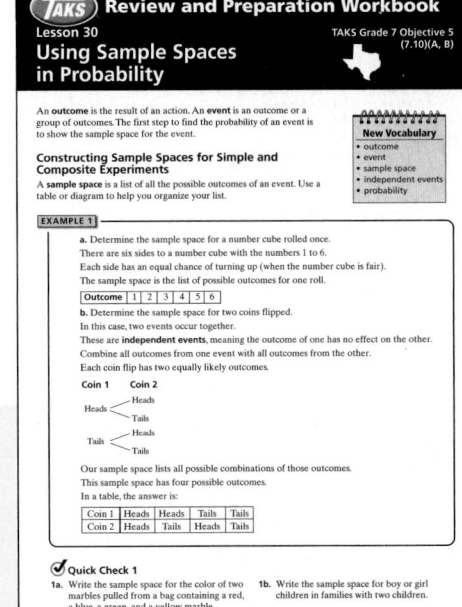

Board Walk

Students apply their knowledge of integers to create a board game.

Resources

All in One Teaching Resources
- Chapter 1 Project Support

Guided Instruction

Activating Prior Knowledge
Have students talk about board games that they have played. Ask them to share the strengths and weaknesses of the games. Ask:
- *What makes a board game something you would play repeatedly?* Sample: You can make strategy choices.

Making the Measure

Students apply their knowledge of measurement to create their own system for measuring distance.

Resources

All in One Teaching Resources
- Chapter 2 Project Support

Guided Instruction

Activating Prior Knowledge
Review common measurements of customary length. Ask students to suggest benchmarks for each. Ask:
- *What distance will you use for your ruler? Why?* Have students justify their answers.

Social Studies Connection
Invite students to learn more about other ancient measures, like the "cubit." Have them report on their findings.

624

Chapter Projects

Chapter 1 *Decimals and Integers*

What makes a board game so much fun? You have challenges like road blocks or false paths that make you backtrack. Then you land on a lucky square that lets you leap forward past your opponent. Best of all, you are with your friends as you play!

Create a Board Game For this chapter project, you will use integers to create a game. Then you will play your game with friends or family for a trial run. Finally you will decorate your game and bring it to class to play.

Go Online
PHSchool.com
For: Information to help you complete your project
Web Code: ard-0161

Chapter 2 *Exponents, Factors, and Fractions*

In the high jump, as in most sports, a consistent system of measurement allows athletes to make comparisons. It took the decree of a king to create one such system!

Back in the 12th century, King Henry I of England decided that a yard was the distance from the tip of his nose to the end of his thumb. How far is it from the tip of your nose to the end of your thumb? Is it more than a yard or less? Is it the same distance for everyone?

Invent Your Own Ruler For the chapter project, you will design a new system for measuring distance. Your final project will be a new ruler, together with a report on its usefulness.

Go Online
PHSchool.com
For: Information to help you complete your project
Web Code: ard-0261

624 Chapter Projects

Chapter 3 Operations With Fractions

Did you ever make pancakes? The recipe can be pretty simple—an egg, some pancake mix, milk, and maybe some oil. Or forget the mix and start from scratch! Either way, you can vary the ingredients to suit your tastes. Do you want to include some wheat germ? How about some pecans, or maybe some fruit? Bananas are always in season!

Write Your Own Recipe For the chapter project, you will write your own recipe for pancakes. Your final project will be a recipe that will feed everyone in your class.

Go Online
PHSchool.com
For: Information to help you complete your project
Web Code: ard-0361

READ ALL ABOUT IT!

Chapter 4 Equations and Inequalities

Flexible hours! Great pay! Work before or after school! Newspaper deliverers needed! Suppose to earn extra money you get a job delivering newspapers in your neighborhood. You plan to save the money you make so that you can buy yourself brand new snow skiing gear.

Make a Savings Plan In this chapter, you will figure out how much time you can commit to your job, how much money you can earn per week, and how much money you need to make per week in order to reach your savings goal. As part of your final project, you will write a letter to your boss at the newspaper office describing your level of commitment as a newspaper deliverer.

Go Online
PHSchool.com
For: Information to help you complete your project
Web Code: ard-0461

Chapter Projects **625**

Chapter Projects

Toss and Turn

Students apply their knowledge of fractions to make and then adjust a recipe.

Resources

All in One Teaching Resources
• Chapter 3 Project Support

Guided Instruction

Activating Prior Knowledge
Tell students that chefs constantly adjust recipes to create new dishes and to feed different numbers of diners. Ask:
• When creating a recipe, what must you think about in addition to the ingredients and how much of each to use? **Sample: Deciding where and when to buy what you need, figuring out cooking times, and so on.**

Read All About It!

Students apply their knowledge of equations and inequalities to make savings plans for themselves.

Resources

All in One Teaching Resources
• Chapter 4 Project Support

Guided Instruction

Activating Prior Knowledge
Ask students to share experiences they have had trying to save money over time. Ask:
• *Suppose you could save $5 each week. How could you figure out how many weeks you would have to save in order to have enough money for a $45 baseball bat and a $19 baseball?* **Sample: Write and solve an inequality: $5n \geq (45 + 19)$**

Careers

Invite students to interview bankers to find out the responsibilities, skills, and background required.

625

Weighty Matters

Students apply their knowledge of ratios and proportions to create a table of animal weights.

Resources

All in One Teaching Resources
• Chapter 5 Project Support

Guided Instruction

Activating Prior Knowledge
Brainstorm a list of common pets and their approximate weights. Then have volunteers adjust the guesses by researching typical weights for certain breeds of dogs and cats and other pets. Ask:
• *How could you find the cost of the statue of the 35-pound dog cast in gold?* One way: Use the newspaper to find the price of gold in oz. Convert it to lb by multiplying it by 16 oz.

Art Connection
Invite students to look through art books or other sources to find examples of sculptures of animals.

Chills and Thrills

Students apply their knowledge of percents and data collection to find out what amusement park rides people prefer.

Resources

All in One Teaching Resources
• Chapter 6 Project Support

Guided Instruction

Activating Prior Knowledge
Have students work together to create a list of favorite amusement park rides that they can use in their surveys. Ask:
• *How might your survey measure people's preferences?* One way: have people use a simple point system (i.e., 3 pts for favorite, 2 pts for 2nd favorite, and so on).

Chapter 5 *Ratios, Rates, and Proportions*

Have you ever loved a pet so much that you wanted a statue made of it? Imagine a statue of your pet on the front steps of your home. "Gee, what a wise way to spend hard-earned money," your admiring neighbors would say. Or maybe not. In addition to being expensive, these statues would also be heavy. For instance, a 35-lb dog cast in gold would weigh about 670 lb.

Using Specific Gravity For the chapter project, you will find the weight of different animals and the weight of different metals. Your final project will be a table of animals with their weights, the weight of their statues in different materials, and the cost of the statues.

Go Online
PHSchool.com
For: Information to help you complete your project
Web Code: ard-0561

Chapter 6 *Percents*

Your world is spinning. You are screaming. And you are loving every minute of it! Even though you are scared, you know that you will come to a safe stop at the end of the ride.

A successful amusement park attraction must be both fun and safe. Planners of amusement parks use a lot of math to create thrills but avoid any spills.

Take a Survey For the chapter project, you will decide which rides are most likely to be most popular. Your final product will be a recommendation about which rides to include in a proposed amusement park for your town.

PHSchool.com
For: Information to help you complete your project
Web Code: ard-0661

Raisin'
the **Roof**

Chapter 7 Geometry

Look around you. Triangles are everywhere in construction! You see them in bridges, in buildings, in scaffolding; even in bicycle frames! This project will give you a greater appreciation of the importance of triangles in construction. You might also develop a taste for raisins!

Build a Tower For the chapter project, you will use toothpicks and raisins to build geometric shapes. Your final product will be a tower strong enough to support a baseball.

Go Online
PHSchool.com

For: Information to help you complete your project
Web Code: ard-0761

Chapter 8 Measurement

Space is money! So before cargo is prepared for shipment in large containers, it is packaged in smaller containers based on its size and shape.

Cans of tuna are examples of items you buy in cylindrical containers. Would you pack two cylinders side-by-side or one above the other? One arrangement wastes cardboard! But which one?

Design Boxes for Shipping Cylinders For the chapter project, you will design boxes to hold cylindrical items. Your final product will be a model of a box that holds six cylinders.

Go Online
PHSchool.com

For: Information to help you complete your project
Web Code: ard-0861

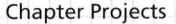

Raisin' the Roof

Students apply their knowledge of geometric shapes to build a tower.

Resources

All in One Teaching Resources

• Chapter 7 Project Support

Guided Instruction

Activating Prior Knowledge
Discuss with students that the triangle is a key structural concept that is applied to the construction of most structures. Ask:

• *How might you use the idea of triangles as supports to build your tower?* One way: build a cube, each side of which is a square formed by four congruent right triangles.

Shape Up and Ship Out

Students apply their knowledge of volume to design a box to hold cylinders.

Resources

All in One Teaching Resources

• Chapter 8 Project Support

Guided Instruction

Activating Prior Knowledge
Initiate a discussion of what food manufacturers consider when designing packages for their products. Ask:

• *Which is a more important design consideration, the package's size or its shape? Explain.* Accept all reasonable responses students can justify.

Diversity
Discuss the many different ways that people store, package, and transport goods in different cultures around the world.

627

Happy Landings

Students apply their knowledge of patterns and rules to create a graph showing how fast water empties from a container.

Resources

All in One Teaching Resources
- Chapter 9 Project Support

Guided Instruction

Activating Prior Knowledge
Discuss why different kinds of graphs are better suited than others to display certain kinds of data. Ask:
- *What graph do you think would work best to show the speed at which water empties from a container? Why?* line graph; shows changes over time

Science Connection
Have students research the speed an object falls to earth, ignoring air resistance, and report to the class.

People's Choice

Students apply their knowledge of sampling and percents to make a prediction.

Resources

All in One Teaching Resources
- Chapter 10 Project Support

Guided Instruction

Activating Prior Knowledge
Initiate a discussion in which students share their experiences with polling and sampling. Ask:
- *You wish to poll a sample of students in our school to find out how the full student body would react to a later start time. How would you constitute that sample?* Sample: a mix of boys and girls, a mix of ages, a mix of classes

happy landings

Imagine this—you have just opened your parachute and you are floating through the air. Exciting, huh? How long it takes you to come to the ground can be predicted because the change in height versus time occurs in a predictable pattern. Many other things change in a predictable pattern, for instance, the height of a burning candle and the growth of money in a bank account.

Graphing Data For the chapter project, you will find how fast a container of water will empty if there is a hole in it. Your final project will be a graph of the data you collect.

Go Online PHSchool.com
For: Information to help you complete your project
Web Code: ard-0961

People's choice

You're an advertising executive, and you want to know which of three television shows is the most popular. So you plan to conduct a poll of viewers.

But how many viewers do you survey? Polling is expensive, so you don't want to poll too many. Polling too few viewers might give you the wrong information. Here's your chance to explore the process!

Finding a Sample Size Fill a container with three different kinds of beans. Use the beans to find the sample size that best predicts the percent of each kind of bean in the container.

Go Online PHSchool.com
For: Information to help you complete your project
Web Code: ard-1061

Chapter **11** *Displaying and Analyzing Data*

Chances are there's at least one person in a large crowd who has the same birthday as you! How many people do you think have the same favorite food? How many like the same television show? What kinds of cars do the people in the crowd have? Pollsters face questions like these all the time, and they take surveys to help answer them.

Estimate the Size of a Crowd and Take a Survey For the chapter project, you will use averages to estimate the size of a crowd. You will also take a survey and present your results in a graph.

For: Information to help you complete your project
Web Code: ard-1161

Chapter Projects

Everybody Wins

Chapter **12** *Using Probability*

Remember the game "Rock, Paper, Scissors"? It is an unusual game because paper wins over rock, rock wins over scissors, and scissors win over paper. You can use mathematics to create and investigate a situation with similar characteristics.

Make Three Number Cubes For this chapter project, you will design three number cubes A, B, and C, which have a surprising property: A usually beats B, B usually beats C, and C usually beats A. Your final step will be to construct your cubes.

For: Information to help you complete your project
Web Code: ard-1261

Chapter Projects **629**

Too Many to Count

Students apply their knowledge of data analysis to estimate the size of a crowd and then graph the results.

Resources

All in One Teaching Resources
• Chapter 11 Project Support

Guided Instruction

Activating Prior Knowledge
Ask students to think about times when they were part of a large crowd, such as at a parade or at a ballgame. Ask:
• *How could you estimate the size of a large crowd?* Sample: Use benchmarks—seating sections of a stadium, city blocks for a parade, and so on.

Visual Learners
Have pairs of students spill a large container of counters, like coins or centimeter cubes, on a table. Ask them to find ways to divide up the counters in order to estimate how many there are.

Everybody Wins

Students apply their knowledge of probability to design a game with given attributes.

Resources

All in One Teaching Resources
• Chapter 12 Project Support

Guided Instruction

Activating Prior Knowledge
Have students talk about ways to design number cubes to meet the requirements of this project. Ask:
• *What do you think is meant by "usually"?* Sample: That a win is more likely than not, or > 50%.

629

Exercises 1–4. Answers may vary. Samples:

1. 2
2. 3
3. 10
4. 70
5. 8.28
6. 5.23
7. 9.107
8. 2.699
9. 4.93
10. 7.917
11. 3.072
12. 46.8
13. 8.5
14. 6.6
15. 5.3
16. 23.1
17. 0.09
18. 0.0006
19. 0.0000027
20. 0.62
21. >
22. =
23. >
24. <
25. −100
26. 0
27. −6
28. −4
29. 0
30. −3
31. 28
32. −21
33. 45
34. −33
35. 5
36. −11

CHAPTER 1 Extra Practice

Skills

● **Lesson 1-1** Use any estimation strategy to estimate.

1. $2.7236 - 0.6512$
2. $2.4 + 0.86$
3. $106.3 \div 7.92$
4. 7.06×9.23

● **Lesson 1-2** Find each sum or difference.

5. $5.87 + 2.41$
6. $9.31 - 4.08$
7. $7.2 + 1.907$
8. $4.86 - 2.161$

● **Lessons 1-3 and 1-4** Find each product or quotient.

9. 2.9×1.7
10. $6.09 \cdot 1.3$
11. $7.68 \cdot 0.4$
12. $(5.2 \cdot 1.5) \cdot 6$
13. $30.6 \div 3.6$
14. $44.856 \div 7.12$
15. $17.172 \div 3.24$
16. $62.37 \div 2.7$

● **Lesson 1-5** Write the number that makes each statement true.

17. $\blacksquare\,L = 90\ mL$
18. $0.6\ mL = \blacksquare\,L$
19. $\blacksquare\,mg = 2.7\ kg$
20. $\blacksquare\,km = 620{,}000\ m$

● **Lesson 1-6** Compare using <, =, or >.

21. $|-3|\ \blacksquare\ |-2|$
22. $|10|\ \blacksquare\ |-10|$
23. $|-19|\ \blacksquare\ |9|$
24. $|-11|\ \blacksquare\ |-12|$

● **Lesson 1-7** Find the value of each expression.

25. $-110 + 5 - (-5)$
26. $3 - 6 + 3$
27. $(-3) + (-2) + (-1)$
28. $2 - 2 - 4$
29. $(-9) + 8 - (-1)$
30. $-7 + (12 - 8)$
31. $4 + 11 - (-13)$
32. $-14 + (-7)$

● **Lesson 1-8** Find each product or quotient.

33. $-5 \cdot (-9)$
34. $11 \cdot (-3)$
35. $-45 \div (-9)$
36. $\dfrac{-121}{11}$

● **Lesson 1-9** Find the value of each expression.

37. $2(8 - 45)$
38. $24 - (3 + 19)$
39. $3(21 + 7)$
40. $3(61 + 9)$
41. $(18 - 24)(7)$
42. $8 \cdot 6 - 47$
43. $(53 - 9) \div 11$
44. $27 \cdot (31 - 7)$

● **Lesson 1-10** Find the mean, median, and mode for each situation.

45. prices of different brands of cameras:
    $150, $100, $240, $220, $195, $225

46. number of seconds to run the 100-meter dash:
    9, 13, 14, 11, 12, 12, 15, 14, 10, 13, 9, 12

Word Problems

● **Lesson 1-1**

47. **Weather** In Chicago, Illinois, the average wind speed is 10.3 mi/h. In Great Falls, Montana, the average wind speed is 12.5 mi/h. What is the difference in wind speeds?

● **Lessons 1-2 and 1-3**

48. The weight of your kitten is 4.5 kg. The weight of your friend's kitten is 2.7 kg. How much more does your kitten weigh?

49. **Estimation** Your new job pays $8.20 per hour. Estimate how much you will earn if you work for 4 hours.

● **Lesson 1-4**

50. You buy four packages of shoe laces. You pay with a $10 bill and receive $3.24 in change. What is the price of each package?

● **Lesson 1-5**

51. You are making a banner. You have a sheet of paper that is 2 m wide and want to leave a 35-cm blank margin on either side. How many centimeters can you use for text?

● **Lessons 1-6 through 1-8**

52. Scores for a local golf tournament vary from 6 under par (−6) to 51 over par. Find the range of the scores.

53. **Fitness** Your pulse rate tells how fast your heart beats. Suppose your pulse after running is 160 beats per minute (bpm). After 4 min of rest, your pulse is 84 bpm. At what rate did your pulse decrease?

● **Lesson 1-9**

54. You go with 5 friends to an art museum. The admission fee is $5.25 per person. A special exhibition costs an additional $4.75 per person. Use mental math to find the total cost.

● **Lesson 1-10**

55. Find the mean of 2.4, 3.4, 6.1, 4.7, 2.9, 2.6, 3.3, 3.6, 2.7, and 3.2. Identify the outlier. Then find the mean without the outlier.

Chapter 1 Extra Practice **631**

37. −74
38. 2
39. 84
40. 210
41. −42
42. 1
43. 4
44. 648
45. 188.$\overline{3}$; 207.5; no mode
46. 12; 12; 12
47. 2.2 mi/h
48. 1.8 kg
49. $32.80
50. $1.69
51. 130 cm
52. 57
53. 19 bpm
54. $60
55. 3.49; 6.1; 3.2

Extra Skills and Word Problems

Extra Skills and Word Problems

Skills

● **Lesson 2-1**   Simplify. Use paper and pencil, a model, or a calculator.

1. 100^1 **2.** 5^3 **3.** $(-5)^4$ **4.** -6^2 **5.** $(12-5)^3$

● **Lesson 2-2**   Find the GCF of each pair of numbers.

6. 35, 49   **7.** 11, 12   **8.** 28, 40   **9.** 17, 34   **10.** 16, 26   **11.** 16, 86

● **Lesson 2-3**   Write each fraction in simplest form.

12. $\frac{21}{24}$ **13.** $\frac{65}{100}$ **14.** $\frac{15}{75}$ **15.** $\frac{40}{80}$ **16.** $\frac{72}{108}$ **17.** $\frac{110}{225}$

● **Lesson 2-4**   Compare each pair of fractions. Use <, =, or >.

18. $\frac{1}{4}$ ▪ $\frac{2}{9}$ **19.** $\frac{3}{7}$ ▪ $\frac{1}{2}$ **20.** $\frac{2}{5}$ ▪ $\frac{4}{10}$ **21.** $\frac{5}{6}$ ▪ $\frac{7}{8}$ **22.** $\frac{3}{5}$ ▪ $\frac{2}{3}$

● **Lessons 2-5 and 2-6**   Write each mixed number as an improper fraction.

23. $7\frac{7}{8}$ **24.** $3\frac{5}{7}$ **25.** $3\frac{1}{4}$ **26.** $4\frac{2}{5}$ **27.** $10\frac{1}{6}$ **28.** $2\frac{2}{5}$

Write each fraction as a decimal.

29. $\frac{4}{5}$ **30.** $\frac{1}{9}$ **31.** $\frac{7}{8}$ **32.** $\frac{13}{4}$ **33.** $\frac{28}{8}$ **34.** $\frac{100}{6}$

● **Lesson 2-7**   Order from least to greatest.

35. $\frac{9}{12}$, 0.35, $\frac{3}{6}$, −1.0   **36.** −1.8, $\frac{1}{4}$, $\frac{1}{3}$, 3.5   **37.** $\frac{10}{11}$, $0.\overline{6}$, $\frac{1}{2}$, 0.375

● **Lesson 2-8**   Write in scientific notation.

38. 5,000   **39.** 160,000   **40.** 4,700,000   **41.** 7,900,000,000

Word Problems

● **Lesson 2-1**

42. Your class is collecting pennies to give to a charity. You donate 2¢ on the first day. Each day, you double the amount you donate. How many pennies will you donate on the tenth day?

43. Geometry Let m represent the side length of one square. Let n represent the side length of another square. Find the total area of $m^2 + n^2$ for $m = 3$ and $n = 2$.

● **Lessons 2-2 and 2-3**

44. Suppose you just fed your cat and bird. You feed your cat every 5 hours and your bird every 12 hours. In how many hours will you feed them at the same time again?

45. The shutter of a camera opens and closes quickly. For each exposure time of $\frac{1}{4}$ s, $\frac{1}{125}$ s, and $\frac{1}{150}$ s, write an equivalent fraction with a denominator of 1,000.

● **Lesson 2-4**

46. The same number of oranges, apples, and pears are in a fruit basket. After one week, $\frac{3}{8}$ of the oranges, $\frac{1}{5}$ of the apples, and $\frac{1}{2}$ of the pears have not been eaten. Which fruit is most popular? Explain.

● **Lesson 2-5**

47. Baking You can make a loaf of challah bread by braiding 6 strands of dough together. What is the number of loaves of bread you can make with 40 strands of dough? Write your answer as a mixed number.

48. The distance from your house to the mall is $18\frac{1}{2}$ miles. Write the distance as an improper fraction in fourths of a mile.

● **Lessons 2-6 and 2-7**

49. Surveys When students are asked which enrichment class they prefer, 0.25 choose sign language, $\frac{10}{48}$ choose starting a business, $\frac{5}{12}$ choose robotics, and 0.125 choose origami. List their choices in increasing order of preference.

50. A plant measures $6\frac{1}{12}$ in. Write this value as a decimal.

51. The amount of water in three different barrels is $3.\overline{6}$ gal, $\frac{16}{5}$ gal, and $3\frac{5}{6}$ gal. Which barrel contains the most water?

52. A baseball player has a batting average of .305. Write this decimal as a fraction in simplest form.

53. A stock price changes each day. The following list shows the daily price change for 7 days: 0.09, −0.70, −0.11, 0.3, 0.67, −0.28, 0.54. Order the price changes from least to greatest.

39. 1.6×10^5

40. 4.7×10^6

41. 7.9×10^9

42. $20.46

43. 13

44. 60 h

45. $\frac{250}{1,000}$ s, $\frac{8}{1,000}$ s, $\frac{4}{1,000}$ s

46. Apples; since $\frac{1}{5} < \frac{3}{5} < \frac{1}{2}$, the fruit with the least amount left is apples. So apples are most popular.

47. $6\frac{2}{3}$ loaves

48. $\frac{74}{4}$ mi

49. robotics, sign language, starting a business, study time

50. $6.08\overline{3}$ in.

51. $3\frac{5}{6}$-gal barrel

52. $\frac{61}{200}$

53. −0.70, −0.28, −0.11, 0.09, 0.3, 0.54, 0.67

Exercises 1–8. Answers may vary. Samples:

1. about 1

2. about 2

3. about 1

4. about $1\frac{1}{2}$

5. about 18

6. about 10

7. about 65

8. about 99

9. $1\frac{1}{3}$

10. $\frac{2}{5}$

11. $\frac{1}{3}$

12. $\frac{11}{12}$

13. 7

14. $3\frac{3}{5}$

15. $7\frac{7}{8}$

16. $10\frac{13}{20}$

17. $\frac{3}{20}$

18. $\frac{1}{5}$

19. 25

20. $2\frac{3}{10}$

21. 3

22. 12

23. $2\frac{2}{9}$

24. $1\frac{7}{15}$

25. 12

26. $2\frac{1}{4}$

27. 660

28. $202\frac{2}{3}$

29. 13,000

30. $2\frac{1}{3}$

31. 25 g

32. $5\frac{1}{4}$ lb

33. 28 pt

34. 35.95 mL

35. 1.000 mg

36. 120 min

CHAPTER 3 — Extra Practice

Skills

● **Lesson 3-1**   Use benchmarks to estimate each sum or difference.

1. $\frac{2}{5} + \frac{7}{9}$

2. $\frac{3}{4} + \frac{5}{6}$

3. $\frac{3}{4} - \frac{1}{5}$

4. $\frac{8}{9} + \frac{7}{15}$

5. $9\frac{8}{10} + 8\frac{2}{10}$

6. $15\frac{2}{5} - 5\frac{4}{7}$

7. $71\frac{1}{5} - 5\frac{2}{3}$

8. $99\frac{9}{19} + \frac{1}{5}$

● **Lessons 3-2 and 3-3**   Find each sum or difference.

9. $\frac{2}{3} + \frac{2}{3}$

10. $\frac{7}{10} - \frac{3}{10}$

11. $\frac{7}{12} - \frac{1}{4}$

12. $\frac{1}{6} + \frac{3}{4}$

13. $4\frac{3}{8} + 2\frac{5}{8}$

14. $5\frac{2}{5} - 1\frac{4}{5}$

15. $11 - 3\frac{1}{8}$

16. $7\frac{2}{5} + 3\frac{1}{4}$

● **Lessons 3-4 and 3-5**   Find each product or quotient.

17. $\frac{3}{8} \cdot \frac{2}{5}$

18. $\frac{1}{4}$ of $\frac{4}{5}$

19. $\frac{5}{6}$ of 30

20. $2\frac{7}{8} \cdot \frac{4}{5}$

21. $\frac{3}{5} \div \frac{1}{5}$

22. $9 \div \frac{3}{4}$

23. $\frac{5}{6} \div \frac{3}{8}$

24. $3\frac{2}{3} \div 2\frac{1}{2}$

● **Lesson 3-6**   Complete.

25. $\frac{3}{4}$ gal = ▇ c

26. 4,500 lb = ▇ t

27. $\frac{3}{8}$ mi = ▇ yd

28. $12\frac{2}{3}$ lb = ▇ oz

29. $6\frac{1}{2}$ t = ▇ lb

30. 2 yd, 1 ft = ▇ yd

● **Lesson 3-7**   Choose the more precise measurement.

31. 25 g, 2.55 kg

32. 2 t, $5\frac{1}{4}$ lb

33. 28 pt, 15 qt

34. 7 L, 35.95 mL

35. 0.75 g, 1,000 mg

36. 120 min, 2 h

Word Problems

● **Lesson 3-1**

37. **Estimation**   Use benchmarks to estimate the total weight of two bags of cheese that weigh $\frac{1}{8}$ lb and $\frac{2}{5}$ lb.

38. **Estimation**   From the following daily mileages, estimate the median number of miles a runner jogged: $9\frac{3}{5}$, $5\frac{1}{4}$, $7\frac{5}{10}$, $1\frac{7}{8}$, $6\frac{3}{4}$, $3\frac{2}{8}$.

Lessons 3-2 and 3-3

39. Write a number sentence for the model at the right.

40. Geometry A side of a square is $\frac{4}{5}$ cm long. What is the perimeter of the square?

41. The Grand Canyon in Arizona has a maximum depth of $1\frac{1}{8}$ mi. The Black Canyon in Colorado has a maximum depth of $\frac{1}{2}$ mi. Find the difference between the depths.

42. You want to build a fence that has twice the perimeter of a triangular plot of land. The land plot has dimensions $1\frac{1}{2}$ yd, 2 yd, and $3\frac{1}{4}$ yd. What is the perimeter of the fence?

Lessons 3-4 and 3-5

43. At an apple orchard, you pick $10\frac{2}{5}$ lb of apples. You give $\frac{3}{8}$ of the apples to your friend. How many pounds of apples do you give your friend?

For each serving size in the table below, find the number of ounces and the number of Calories.

Nonfat Yogurt

	Servings	$\frac{1}{4}$	$\frac{1}{2}$	$\frac{3}{4}$	1	$1\frac{1}{2}$	2
44.	Ounces	a. ■	b. ■	c. ■	8	d. ■	e. ■
45.	Calories	a. ■	b. ■	c. ■	160	d. ■	e. ■

46. During a $2\frac{3}{4}$-hour assembly, each speaker spoke for $\frac{1}{4}$ of an hour. How many speakers were there?

47. Suppose you have $6\frac{4}{5}$ cantaloupes. How many fifths of a cantaloupe can you cut?

Lesson 3-6

48. A woman is 66 in. tall. What is her height in feet?

49. A marathon runner needs to run 137,280 feet to complete the race. How many miles is the race?

Lesson 3-7

50. Measurement You measure the length of a book to be 12 in. Your friend measures the same book to be 1 ft long. You know that 12 in. equals 1 ft. Does this mean that the two measurements are equally precise? Explain.

---

37. about $\frac{1}{2}$ lb

38. 6 mi

39. $\frac{1}{2} + \frac{1}{4} = \frac{3}{4}$

40. $3\frac{1}{5}$ cm

41. $\frac{5}{8}$ mi

42. $13\frac{1}{2}$ yd

43. $3\frac{9}{10}$ lb

44a. 2

 b. 4

 c. 6

 d. 12

 e. 16

45a. 40

 b. 80

 c. 120

 d. 240

 e. 320

46. 11 speakers

47. 34 fifths

48. $6\frac{1}{2}$ ft

49. 21,120,000 ft

50. No; an inch is a smaller unit of measure.

1. $n - 3$

2. $s + 17$

3. $d - 5$

4. $n \div 2 + 6$

5.

x	3(x − 1)	3x − 1	3x + 1
5	12	14	16
2	3	5	7

6. 6

7. 12

8. 23

9. 27

10. −16

11. −24

12. 47

13. 162

14. −75

15. 6

16. 40

17. −96

18. 5

19. 15

20. 5

21. 40

22. 6

23. −2

24. −4

25. 54

26.

27.

28.

29.

30.

31.

32.

CHAPTER 4 Extra Practice

Skills

● **Lesson 4-1** Write an algebraic expression and draw a diagram for each word phrase.

1. The difference of a number n and 3

2. 17 more than s students

3. 5 fewer than d days

4. 6 more than the quotient of n and 2

5. Copy and complete the table at the right. Substitute the value on the left for the variable in the expression at the top of each column. Then evaluate.

x	3(x − 1)	3x−1	3x + 1
5	■	■	■
2	■	■	■

● **Lesson 4-2** Use mental math to solve each equation.

6. $5b = 30$

7. $n + 5 = 17$

8. $m - 8 = 15$

9. $\frac{z}{3} = 9$

● **Lesson 4-3** Solve each equation. Check your answer.

10. $t - 13 = -29$

11. $17 + d = -7$

12. $d + 112 = 159$

13. $y - 68 = 94$

● **Lesson 4-4** Solve each equation. Check your answer.

14. $\frac{m}{5} = -15$

15. $-7y = -42$

16. $0.4t = 16$

17. $\frac{x}{12} = -8$

● **Lesson 4-5** Solve each equation using number sense.

18. $7t + 5 = 40$

19. $2d - 12 = 18$

20. $5w - 18 = 7$

21. $\frac{z}{4} + 5 = 15$

● **Lesson 4-6** Solve each equation. Check your answer.

22. $\frac{r}{-6} + 4 = 3$

23. $12m + 24 = 0$

24. $-6g - 9 = 15$

25. $\frac{k}{-3} - 2 = -20$

● **Lessons 4-7 through 4-9** Solve each inequality. Graph the solution.

26. $y + 5 \geq 11$

27. $p + 7 < -3$

28. $a - 9 \leq 1$

29. $d - 3 > -13$

30. $3y \geq 33$

31. $\frac{p}{7} < -2$

32. $\frac{a}{-8} \leq -7$

33. $4d > -36$

Word Problems

● **Lesson 4-1**

34. A dance club spends $20 on advertising to promote its fall show. Write an algebraic expression for the amount of money left in the budget if the club starts with d dollars.

Extra Skills and Word Problems

● Lesson 4-2

35. Kobayashi set a world record for hot dog eating when he ate 50 hot dogs in 720 seconds. Write an equation and estimate the number of seconds it took him to eat one hot dog.

36. You mail a package at the post office. The postage costs $12.18. You pay with a $20 bill. Write an equation and estimate the amount of change you receive.

● Lessons 4-3 through 4-6 Write and solve an equation for each situation.

37. A peregrine falcon can fly as fast as 220 mi/h. This speed is 150 mi/h faster than the maximum running speed of a cheetah. What is the speed of a cheetah?

38. A snorkeler looks at coral 4.5 feet below sea level, or at −4.5 ft. A scuba diver looks at coral located at 10 times that depth. How far below sea level does the scuba diver descend?

39. An auto rental agency offers a rate of $38 per day plus $.30/mile. After a one-day rental, Misha's bill was $74. How many miles did Misha drive?

40. A pair of running shoes costs $37 less than twice the cost of a pair of basketball sneakers. The sneakers cost $48.50. How much do the running shoes cost?

● Lesson 4-7 Write an inequality for each statement.

41. The space shuttle can carry more than 38,000 pounds.

42. Today your break will be shorter than 15 minutes.

43. A song is less than 5 minutes long.

44. A shelf can hold at most 250 pounds.

● Lessons 4-8 and 4-9 Write and solve an inequality for each problem.

45. A ride at an amusement park requires a rider to be at least 48 in. tall. Your little brother is 37 in. tall. How many inches must he grow in order to ride?

46. For your party, you plan a game where each player needs three spoons. You buy a box of 50 spoons. At most, how many people can play the game?

33.

34. $d - 20$

35. about 14 s

36. about $8

37. Let s = speed of cheetah; $s + 150 = 220$; 70 mi/h.

38. Let d = depth of scuba diver; $\frac{d}{10} = -4.5$; −45 ft.

39. Let m = miles Misha drives; $38 + 0.3m = 74$; $120.

40. Let c = cost of running shoes; $2c - 37 = 48.50$; $42.75.

41. $f > 38,000$

42. $b < 15$

43. $d < 5$

44. $p \le 250$

45. $h + 37 \ge 48$; at least 11 in.

46. $3p \le 50$; at most 16 people

1. 2 : 3; 2 to 3

2. $\frac{3}{5}$; 3 to 5

3. $\frac{4}{7}$; 4 : 7

4. 15 to 5; $\frac{15}{5}$

5. 25 to 50; 25 : 50

6. 48 fl oz for $3.19

7. 16 oz for $4.80

8. 6 pt for $7.14

9. 3 gal for $5.69

10. 32 oz for $4.99

11. 3 lb for $17.97

12. 5 yd for $20.30

13. 8 lb for $6.79

14. 0.5 L for $1.25

15. yes

16. no

17. yes

18. no

19. no

20. 20

21. 3

22. 3.5

23. 20

24. 2

25. $x = 8.56$, $y = 7.5$

26. $1.\overline{6}$

27. 450 ft

28. 600 ft

29. 300 ft

30. 1,200 ft

31. 465 ft

32. 37.5 ft

33. Yes; 15 out of 120 equals $\frac{1}{8}$, which is less than $\frac{3}{10}$.

CHAPTER 5 — Extra Practice

Skills

● **Lesson 5-1** Write each ratio in two other ways.

1. $\frac{2}{3}$
2. 3 : 5
3. 4 to 7
4. 15 : 5
5. $\frac{25}{50}$

● **Lesson 5-2** Find each unit price. Then determine the better buy.

6. soap: 32 fl oz for $2.29 — 48 fl oz for $3.19

7. cereal: 12 oz for $3.95 — 16 oz for $4.80

8. cider: 2 pt for $2.49 — 6 pt for $7.14

9. milk: 1 gal for $1.99 — 3 gal for $5.69

10. pasta: 8 oz for $1.29 — 32 oz for $4.99

11. fish: 2 lb for $13.98 — 3 lb for $17.97

12. fabric: 3 yd for $12.48 — 5 yd for $20.30

13. rice: 2 lb for $1.89 — 8 lb for $6.79

14. juice: 2 L for $5.99 — 0.5 L for $1.25

● **Lesson 5-3** By using cross products, tell whether the ratios can form a proportion.

15. $\frac{4}{3}$, $\frac{12}{9}$
16. $\frac{8}{5}$, $\frac{11}{7}$
17. $\frac{21}{6}$, $\frac{7}{2}$
18. $\frac{6}{24}$, $\frac{2}{4}$
19. $\frac{50}{6}$, $\frac{3}{2}$

● **Lesson 5-4** Solve each proportion using cross products.

20. $\frac{12}{a} = \frac{3}{5}$
21. $\frac{n}{12} = \frac{4}{16}$
22. $\frac{7}{8} = \frac{n}{4}$
23. $\frac{7}{10} = \frac{14}{a}$
24. $\frac{7}{n} = \frac{17.5}{5}$

● **Lesson 5-5** Each pair of figures is similar. Find the value of each variable.

25.

26.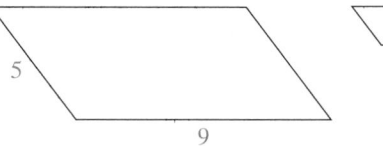

● **Lesson 5-6** The scale on a drawing is 0.5 in. : 15 ft. Find the actual length for each drawing length. Round to the nearest tenth, if necessary.

27. 15 in.
28. 20 in.
29. 10 in.
30. 40 in.
31. 15.5 in.
32. 1.25 in.

Word Problems

● **Lesson 5-1**

33. **Nutrition** The U.S. Department of Agriculture (USDA) recommends that no more than $\frac{3}{10}$ of your Calories come from fat. In a bowl of Tasty Crunch cereal, 15 out of 120 Calories are from fat. Is this within the USDA recommendation? Explain.

Lesson 5-2

34. Suppose you swim 500 yd in 3 min 20 s. What is your unit rate in seconds?

35. A bottle of 250 multivitamins costs $14.99. A bottle of 500 multivitamins costs $32.99. Which bottle is the better buy?

Lesson 5-3

36. For a game, you need 3 yellow marbles for every 8 red marbles. If you have 42 yellow marbles and 112 red marbles, do you have the appropriate numbers of marbles for the game? Explain.

Lesson 5-4

37. Business You sell packs of 12 pens for $3.48. At this rate, how much should you charge for a pack of 20 pens?

38. There are 385 mosquitoes in 11 ft^3 of a room. Predict the number in 15 ft^3.

39. There are 144 tulips in 8 m^2 of a garden. Predict the number in 25 m^2.

40. A recipe for fruit salad serves 4 people. It calls for 2 oranges and 16 grapes. You want to serve 10 people. How many oranges and grapes will you need?

Lesson 5-5

41. Geometry The ratio of the corresponding sides of two similar rectangles is 5 : 7. The smaller rectangle has a length of 3 cm and a width of 5 cm. Find the perimeter of the larger rectangle.

42. Indirect Measurement A student is 4 ft tall and his shadow is 3 ft long. A nearby building has a shadow 51 ft long. How tall is the building?

43. A woman stands near a telephone pole. She is 150 cm tall and her shadow is 3 m long. The shadow of the telephone pole is 30 m long. How tall is the telephone pole?

Lesson 5-6

44. The scale of a map is $\frac{1 \text{ cm}}{3.75 \text{ km}}$. Find the actual distance for a map distance of 8 cm.

45. The scale of a drawing is $\frac{1}{2}$ in. : 12 ft. Find the length of a drawing for an actual length of 84 ft.

34. 2.5 yd/s

35. The bottle with 250 multivitamins is a better buy.

36. Yes; $\frac{3}{8}$ and $\frac{42}{112}$ are proportional because $3 \cdot 112 = 8 \cdot 42$.

37. $5.80

38. 525 mosquitoes

39. 450 tulips

40. 5 oranges and 40 grapes

41. $22\frac{2}{5}$ cm

42. 68 ft

43. 1,500 cm or 15 m

44. 30 km

45. $3\frac{1}{2}$ in.

CHAPTER 6 Extra Practice

Skills

● **Lesson 6-1** Write each ratio as a percent.

1. $\frac{4}{5}$ 2. $\frac{11}{5}$ 3. $\frac{3}{25}$ 4. $\frac{19}{20}$ 5. $\frac{1}{10}$ 6. $\frac{3}{2}$

● **Lesson 6-2** Write each percent as a decimal.

7. 37.5% 8. 11.375% 9. 2.55% 10. 9% 11. 1.111% 12. 97.05%

● **Lesson 6-3** Write each percent as a fraction in simplest form.

13. 225% 14. 0.1% 15. 0.07% 16. 398% 17. 156% 18. 0.2%

● **Lesson 6-4** Find each answer using mental math.

19. 30% of 285 20. 51% of 326 21. 9% of 1,250 22. 49% of 88 23. 101% of 150

● **Lesson 6-5** Write a proportion and solve.

24. 54 is what percent of 135? 25. What percent of 48 is 2.4? 26. What percent of 200 is 120?

27. 8 is what percent of 20? 28. 32.5 is what percent of 130? 29. What percent of 150 is 27?

● **Lesson 6-6** Write and solve an equation to find the part of a whole.

30. 30% of 250 is what number? 31. What number is 90% of 70? 32. 45% of 200 is what number?

33. What number is 7% of 88? 34. 4% of 200 is what number? 35. What number is 22% of 1?

● **Lesson 6-7** Find each payment.

36. $75 with a 5% sales tax 37. $219 with a 3.5% sales tax 38. $85.65 with a 3% sales tax

● **Lesson 6-8** Find each percent of change. Round to the nearest tenth. State whether the change is an increase or a decrease.

39. 25 to 40 40. 95 to 45 41. 108 to 110 42. 50 to 95 43. 125 to 75

44. 8.5 to 10 45. 100 to 15 46. 63.5 to 20 47. 111 to 150 48. 25.9 to 30.2

Word Problems

● **Lesson 6-1**

49. **Art** Draw and shade the first letter of your name on a 10-by-10 grid. Determine what percent of the grid is shaded.

**Answers **

1. 80%
2. 220%
3. 12%
4. 95%
5. 10%
6. 150%
7. 0.375
8. 0.11375
9. 0.0255
10. 0.09
11. 0.01111
12. 0.9705
13. $2\frac{1}{4}$
14. $\frac{1}{10}$
15. $\frac{7}{100}$
16. $3\frac{49}{50}$
17. $1\frac{14}{25}$
18. $\frac{1}{500}$
19. 85.5
20. 166.26
21. 112.5
22. 43.12
23. 151.5
24. 40%
25. 5%
26. 60%
27. 40%
28. 25%
29. 18%
30. 75
31. 63
32. 90
33. 6.16
34. 8
35. .22
36. $78.75
37. $226.67
38. $88.22

Extra Skills and Word Problems

Extra Skills and Word Problems

● **Lesson 6-2** The table shows the percent of the Recommended Daily Allowance for some of the nutrients in a 6-oz baked potato.

Potato Facts

Nutrient	RDA
Magnesium	14%
Iron	34%
Vitamin B6	35%

SOURCE: National Institutes of Health

50. Write each percent as a fraction and as a decimal.

51. Nutrition Suppose you eat a 6-oz baked potato. What percent of each nutrient do you still need to meet the Recommended Daily Allowance?

● **Lessons 6-3 through 6-6**

52. Environment A study has suggested that desert areas throughout the world could increase as much as 185% in the next 100 years due to global warming. Write the percent as a decimal and a fraction.

53. Four hundred students attended a school dance. If 35% of the students were boys, how many boys attended the dance?

54. The regular price of a backpack is $34. A store sells the backpack at 30% off. What is the sale price?

55. An awards banquet is attended by 120 people. Ribbons are awarded for first, second, and third place in each of 25 categories. No one gets more than one ribbon. What percent of the people attending the banquet receive a ribbon?

56. A frozen yogurt shop sold 45 strawberry cones on Friday. This is 30% of the number of strawberry cones they sold that week. How many strawberry cones did they sell that week?

● **Lesson 6-7**

57. You go to a stylist for a haircut. The cost of the haircut is $12.50. Find the amount of a 15% tip for the stylist.

58. A salesperson earns a salary of $2,500, plus 4% commission on sales of $1,500. What are the salesperson's total earnings?

● **Lesson 6-8**

59. If the cost of a dozen eggs rises from $.99 to $1.34, what is the percent of the increase?

60. A television is on sale for $449.95. This is $30 off the original price. Find the percent of the discount.

61. A bookstore pays $4.25 for paperback books and charges $9.95. What is the maximum percent of discount the store can offer, while making a profit of $2 on each book? Check your answer.

39. 60% increase

40. 52.6% decrease

41. 1.9% increase

42. 90% increase

43. 40% decrease

44. 17.6% increase

45. 85% decrease

46. 68.5% decrease

47. 35.1% increase

48. 16.6% increase

49. Check students' work.

50. $\frac{7}{50}$, 0.14; $\frac{17}{50}$, 0.34; $\frac{7}{20}$, 0.35

51. Magnesium: 86%; Iron: 66%; Vitamin B6: 65%

52. 1.85; $\frac{37}{20}$

53. 140 boys

54. $23.80

55. 62.5%

56. 150 cones

57. $1.88

58. $2,560

59. 35.$\overline{35}$%

60. 6.25%

61. $6.25

1. $\overrightarrow{YZ}$
2. $\overline{SW}$
3. $\overleftrightarrow{CR}$
4. 65°; 155°
5. 75°; 165°
6. 5°; 95°
7. 44°; 134°
8. 115°
9. 90°
10. 67°
11. parallelogram; $\overline{AB}$ and $\overline{CD}$, $\overline{BC}$ and $\overline{AD}$; $\angle B$ and $\angle D$, $\angle A$ and $\angle C$
12. rectangle; $\overline{PS}$ and $\overline{QR}$, $\overline{PQ}$ and $\overline{RS}$; $\angle P$, $\angle Q$, $\angle R$, and $\angle S$
13. pentagon; $\overline{EF}$, $\overline{FG}$, $\overline{GH}$, $\overline{HJ}$, and $\overline{JE}$; $\angle E$, $\angle F$, $\angle G$, $\angle H$, and $\angle J$
14. rhombus; $\overline{LM}$, $\overline{MN}$, $\overline{NK}$, and $\overline{KL}$; $\angle L$ and $\angle N$, $\angle K$ and $\angle M$
15. $\angle C$
16. $\angle D$
17. $\overline{CD}$
18. $\overline{CE}$
19. 61.92°
20.

21.

Extra Practice

Skills

● **Lesson 7-1**   Name each segment, ray, or line.

1.

2.

3.

● **Lesson 7-2**   Find the measures of the complement and the supplement of each angle.

4. $m\angle A = 25°$
5. $m\angle U = 15°$
6. $m\angle T = 85°$
7. $m\angle C = 46°$

● **Lesson 7-3**   Find x in each triangle.

8.

9.

10.

● **Lesson 7-4**   Classify each polygon. Then name the congruent sides and angles.

11.

12.

13.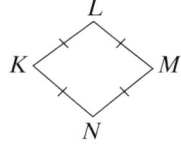

14.

● **Lesson 7-5** $\triangle ABD \cong \triangle CED$. Complete each congruence statement.

15. $\angle A \cong$ ▨
16. $\angle D \cong$ ▨
17. $\overline{AD} \cong$ ▨
18. $\overline{AB} \cong$ ▨

● **Lessons 7-6 and 7-7**

19. **Surveys** In a survey of 500 people, 86 preferred Brand A. Find the measure of the central angle that you would draw to represent Brand A in a circle graph.

● **Lesson 7-8**   Copy each segment. Then construct its perpendicular bisector.

20.

21.

Lesson 7-1

22. Draw $\overline{AB}$, with $\overline{AC}$ on $\overline{AB}$.

23. Why are two lines drawn on a chalkboard *not* skew?

Lessons 7-2 and 7-3

24. Geography On a map, the measure of one of the angles formed by two intersecting roads is 79°. Find the measures of the complement and the supplement of the angle.

25. A triangular window has two angles that measure 32° and 116°. Find the measure of the third angle. Then classify the triangle.

Lesson 7-4

26. A frame for a house has two pairs of opposite sides that are parallel. What shapes can the frame be?

Lesson 7-5

27. Manufacturing Workers make sure that the same parts for a product manufactured on an assembly line are all congruent. To do this, they compare each part to a sample part. Are the triangles congruent?

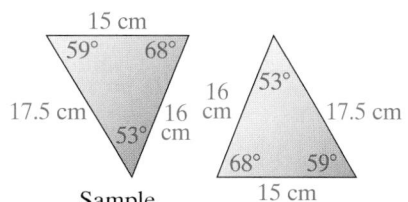

Sample

Lesson 7-6

28. Suppose your watch says 12:15 P.M. What kind of angle is the central angle formed by the two hands of your watch?

Lesson 7-7

29. Survey The data show the results of a survey on the preferred day for grocery shopping. Use the data to draw a circle graph.

Day	Percent	Day	Percent
Monday	4	Friday	17
Tuesday	5	Saturday	29
Wednesday	12	Sunday	7
Thursday	13	No preference	13

Lesson 7-8

30. Draw $\overline{CD}$ at least 3 in. long. Construct and label a segment that is one half as long as $\overline{CD}$.

23. A chalkboard is a plane, so all lines on the chalkboard would be in the same plane.

24. 11°; 101°

25. 32°; obtuse isosceles triangle

26. parallelogram, rhombus, rectangle

27. yes

28. acute angle

29.

30.

CHAPTER 8

1. 1,400 ft²

2. 1,300 ft²

3. 1,500 ft²

4. 84 cm²

5. 250 km²

6. 3,600 m²

7. 2,400 in.²

8. 40 m²

9. 240 ft²

10. 26 mi²

11. 4.71 km; 1.77 km²

12. 37.7 cm; 113.04 cm²

13. 56.5 m; 254.34 m²

14. 62.8 in.; 314 in.²

15. 1

16. 2

17. 7

18. 9

19. 30

20. 60

21. 8 m

22. 13 yd

23. 8 cm

24. triangular prism; 36 in.²

25. cylinder; about 471 m²

26. rectangular prism; 202 ft²

CHAPTER 8 **Extra Practice**

Skills

● **Lesson 8-1** Estimate the area of each shaded region. Each square represents 100 ft².

1.

2.

3.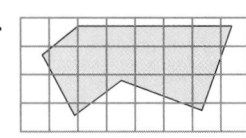

● **Lesson 8-2** Find each area for a triangle with base *b* and height *h*.

4. $b = 7$ cm
$h = 12$ cm

5. $b = 10$ km
$h = 25$ km

6. $b = 100$ m
$h = 3.6$ m

7. $b = 60$ in.
$h = 40$ in.

● **Lessons 8-3 and 8-4** Find the area of each parallelogram or trapezoid.

8.

9.

10.

● **Lesson 8-5** Use $\pi \approx 3.14$ to estimate the circumference and area for each circle.

11. $d = 1.5$ km

12. $r = 6$ cm

13. $r = 9$ m

14. $d = 20$ in.

● **Lesson 8-6** Simplify each square root.

15. $\sqrt{1}$

16. $\sqrt{4}$

17. $\sqrt{49}$

18. $\sqrt{81}$

19. $\sqrt{900}$

20. $\sqrt{3,600}$

● **Lesson 8-7** Find each missing length.

21.

22.

23.

● **Lessons 8-8 and 8-9** Name each figure and find its surface area.

24.

25.

26.

Lesson 8-10

27. Find the volume of the figures in Exercises 25 and 26.

Word Problems

Lessons 8-1 and 8–2

28. Which is a reasonable estimate for the perimeter of a school building—600 ft or 600 yd? Explain your choice.

29. Patterns Copy and complete the table by finding the perimeter and area of each rectangle. What happens to the perimeter and area of a rectangle when you double, triple, or quadruple the dimensions?

ℓ	w	P	A
3 in.	1 in.	■	■
6 in.	2 in.	■	■
9 in.	3 in.	■	■
12 in.	4 in.	■	■

Lessons 8-3 and 8-4

30. A triangular mirror is 12 in. wide and 37 in. tall. Find its area.

31. A park wall is designed to have the irregular shape shown. Use familiar figures to find the area of the park.

12 m   8 m   12 m

16 m

Lesson 8-5

32. A circular pool has a diameter of 20 ft. What area needs to be covered? Round to the nearest square foot.

Lessons 8-6 and 8-7

33. Science The distance that an object falls is given by the formula $d = 16t^2$, where d is the distance in feet and t is the time in seconds. A stone falls 1,600 ft into water. How long does it take for the stone to reach the water?

34. A ladder leans against a building. The bottom of the ladder is 5 ft from the building. The ladder reaches a window that is 17 ft from the ground. How long is the ladder? Round your answer to the nearest tenth.

Lesson 8-8

35. Use graph paper to draw a trapezoidal prism.

Lessons 8-9 and 8-10   A jewelry box is 12 in. long, 7 in. wide, and 3 in. tall.

36. Find the surface area of the jewelry box.

37. Find the volume of the jewelry box.

27. 785 m³; 180 ft³

28. Check students' work.

29. The perimeter doubles, triples, or quadruples; the area gets 4 times, 9 times, or 16 times as large.

30. 222 in.²

31. 160 m²

32. 314 ft²

33. 10 s

34. 17.7 ft

35. Check students' work.

36. 282 in.²

37. 252 in.³

CHAPTER 9

1.

Test Score / Hours of Study

2.

Savings ($) / Time (mo)

3.

Height (in.) / Age (yr)

4. arithmetic

5. geometric

6. neither

7. $y = 6x$

8. $y = x - 2$

9. $y = 3x + 1$

10. $y = 10 - 2x$

11.

12.

646

Skills

● **Lessons 9-1 and 9-3** Graph the data in each table. In Exercise 3, first find the values of the variables.

1.

Hours of Study	Science Test Score
1	72
2	77
3	89
4	92

2.

Time (mo)	Savings (dollars)
2	125
4	295
6	420
8	625

3.

A	B
15	45
17	51
19	57
23	q
p	81

● **Lesson 9-2** Identify each sequence as *arithmetic, geometric,* or *neither.*

4. 7, 10, 13, 16, . . .

5. 800, 400, 200, 100, . . .

6. 50, 25, 48, 24, . . .

● **Lesson 9-4** Write a rule for the function represented by each table.

7.

x	y
0	0
1	6
2	12
3	18

8.

x	y
0	−2
1	−1
2	0
3	1

9.

x	y
0	1
1	4
2	7
3	10

10.

x	y
0	10
1	8
2	6
3	4

● **Lesson 9-5** Graph each function. Use input values of 1, 2, 3, 4, and 5.

11. $y = x + 5$

12. $y = 8 - x$

13. $y = 2x$

● **Lesson 9-6**

14. On her trip to the library, Arlene walked two blocks to the bus stop in five minutes. She rode the bus for 15 min. The bus stopped three times for one minute each time. Sketch a graph to represent Arlene's trip.

● **Lesson 9-7** Find the balance in each compound interest account.

15. $1,000 principal
5% annual interest rate
4 years

16. $700 principal
4% annual interest rate
12 years

17. $1,500 principal
5.5% annual interest rate
7 years

● **Lesson 9-8** Solve each equation for the variable in red.

18. $v = \ell w h$

19. $y = mx + b$

20. $p = 2\ell + 2w$

Word Problems

● **Lesson 9-1**

21. Publishing The table shows costs of printing books. Estimate the cost of printing 2,500 books and the cost of printing 7,500 books.

Number of Books	Cost ($)
5,000	175,000
10,000	290,000

● **Lesson 9-2**

22. A boss pays new employees $8/h the first year, $9/h the second year, $10/h the third year, and $15/h the fourth year. Is the pattern *arithmetic, geometric, both,* or *neither*?

● **Lesson 9-3**

23. There are 12 eggs in a dozen. Use this relationship to make a table that shows the number of eggs you have in 10, 20, 30, and 50 dozen eggs.

● **Lesson 9-4**

24. Write a function rule that relates the number of miles *m* you travel in *h* hours if you drive at an average speed of 50 mi/h.

● **Lesson 9-5**

25. Geometry The area of a square is a function of its side length. Write and graph a function rule to represent this concept. Describe the shape of your graph.

● **Lesson 9-6**

26. Sketch a graph for the following situation. You run 3 blocks from the library and then walk 5 more blocks to your home. Show the distance on the vertical axis and time on the horizontal axis.

● **Lesson 9-7**

27. Finance You invest $1,000 at 5% for 9 months. How much simple interest do you earn?

● **Lesson 9-8**

28. Sports The formula for a batting average a is $a = \frac{h}{n}$, where h is the number of hits and n is the number of times at bat. The highest major-league lifetime batting average was .366 by Ty Cobb, who had 4,189 hits. About how many times at bat did he have?

13.

14.

15. $1,215.51

16. $1,120.72

17. $2,182.02

18. $h = \dfrac{V}{\ell w}$

19. $x = \dfrac{y - b}{m}$

20. $\ell = \dfrac{P - 2w}{2}$

21. about $120,000; about $235,000

22. neither

23.

Dozens	Number of Eggs
10	120
20	240
30	360
50	600

24. $m = 50h$

25. $A = s^2$

The graph is a curve that goes upward.

26.

27. $37.50

28. about 11,445 at-bats

647

CHAPTER 10

1. *G*

2. *E*

3. *B*

4. $-\frac{3}{4}$

5. $\frac{2}{3}$

6. -3

7. yes

8. no

9. no

10.

x	y
−3	9
−2	4
−1	1
0	0
1	1
2	4
3	9

11.

x	y
−3	5
−2	0
−1	−3
0	−4
1	−3
2	0
3	5

12.

x	y
−3	27
−2	12
−1	3
0	0
1	3
2	12
3	27

13.

x	y
−3	12
−2	8
−1	4
0	0
1	4
2	8
3	12

14. $(x, y) \rightarrow (x + 5, y)$

15. $(x, y) \rightarrow (x + 6, y + 2)$

16. $(x, y) \rightarrow (x + 5, y - 3)$

17. reflection over the *x*-axis

648

Skills

● **Lessons 10-1 and 10-3**   Use the graph for Exercises 1–6.

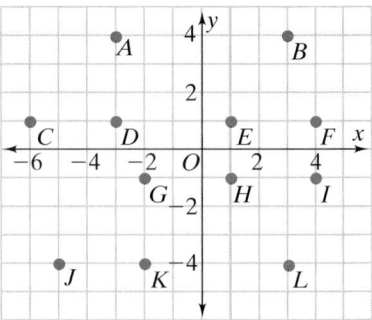

Name the point with the given coordinates.

 1. $(-2, -1)$ **2.** $(1, 1)$ **3.** $(3, 4)$

Find the slope of the line through the points.

 4. *A* and *E*   **5.** *G* and *E*   **6.** *B* and *F*

● **Lesson 10-2**   Tell whether each ordered pair is a solution of $y = x + 18$.

 7. $(2, 20)$ **8.** $(22, 4)$ **9.** $(36, -18)$

● **Lesson 10-4**   Make a table of solutions for each equation. Use integer values of *x* from −3 to 3. Then graph each equation.

 10. $y = x^2$ **11.** $y = x^2 - 4$ **12.** $y = 3x^2$ **13.** $y = 4|x|$

● **Lesson 10-5**   Write a rule for the translation shown in each graph.

 14.   **15.**   **16.**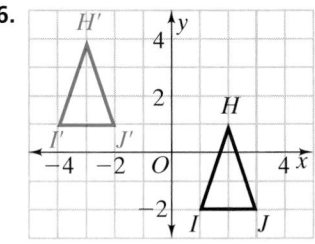

● **Lesson 10-6**   Use the graph from Exercises 1–6 to answer Exercise 17.

 17. Is the triangle formed by points *E*, *B*, and *F* a reflection, a rotation, or a translation of the image formed by points *H*, *L*, and *I*? Explain.

● **Lesson 10-7**   Graph the square *ABCD* with vertices *A*(2, −3), *B*(4, −5), *C*(6, −3), and *D*(4, −1). Then connect the vertices in order.

 18. Draw the image of *ABCD* after a rotation of 180° about point *A*.

 19. Write the coordinates of the image of *ABCD*.

Word Problems

● **Lessons 10-1 and 10–2**

20. **Geometry** Graph the points $G(1, 4)$, $H(-2, 4)$, $J(-2, -5)$, and $K(1, -5)$. Connect the points to form a polygon. Classify the polygon by its angles and its sides.

21. **Finance** You have $35 saved. You plan to save $5 each week from now on. The plan is modeled by $y = 5x + 35$. Graph the equation to find the amount of money you will have saved after 8 weeks.

22. **Aviation** A Learjet aircraft can travel at a speed of 400 mi/h. The equation $y = 400x$ represents the distance y traveled during x hours in flight. Graph the equation to find the distance traveled in 5 hours.

● **Lessons 10-3 and 10-4**

23. Find the slopes of j and k in the graph at the right. Which line has a negative slope?

24. The slope of a piece of land is its grade. If the grade of a piece of land is 12%, what is its slope?

25. **Physics** An object falls from an initial height of 6,000 ft. The equation $h = -16t^2 + 6,000$ represents the height of the object, in feet, after t seconds. Make a table of values to find the height of the object after 0, 2, 4, and 10 seconds. Then graph the equation.

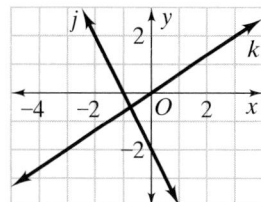

● **Lessons 10-5 through 10-7**

26. You show a friend that the path you take to school can be seen as a translation on a coordinate plane. The point $M(3, 5)$ represents your house. The point $M'(2, -3)$ represents your school. Write a rule to describe your path to school.

27. Trace the figure at the right and draw the line(s) of symmetry. If there are no lines of symmetry, write *none*.

Figure II is the image of Figure I. Identify each transformation as a *translation*, a *reflection*, or a *rotation*.

28.

29.

18.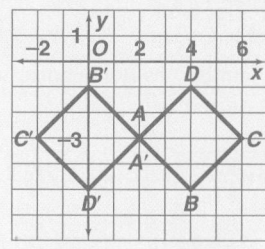

19. $A'(2, -3)$ $C'(-2, -3)$
    $B'(0, -1)$ $D'(0, -5)$

20.

    rectangle

21. $75

22.

    2,000 mi

23. line j

24. $\frac{3}{25}$

25.

t	h
0	6,000
2	5,936
4	5,744
10	4,400

26. $(x, y) \rightarrow (x - 1, y - 8)$

27.

28. reflection

29. rotation

649

CHAPTER 11

1.

Temp.	Tally	Frequency
84	II	2
85	IIII	4
86	II	2
87		0
88	III	3
89		0
90	II	2
91	I	1
92	I	1

2.

```
        X
        X           X
    X   X   X       X           X
    X   X   X       X       X   X   X
    ←———————————————————————————————→
    84  85  86  87  88  89  90  91  92
```

3. A

4. D

5. 18

6.
```
4 | 0  4  8
5 | 1  5  7  7
6 | 0  0  4
7 | 2  3  7
8 | 0  2
```

8 | 0 means 80

7. 42

8. Check students' work.

9. about 658 seagulls

10. Misleading; it is misleading because the graph appears to show that sales have doubled from year 1 to year 5.

11.

The scatter plot shows a positive trend.

Skills

● **Lesson 11-1**   Use the data below for Exercises 1 and 2.
high temperatures (°F): 85, 88, 91, 84, 90, 85, 84, 90, 88, 86, 85, 92, 85, 86, 88

    1. Make a frequency table.   **2.** Make a line plot.

● **Lesson 11-2**   Use the graph for Exercises 3–5.

    3. Which team has won the most matches?

    4. Which team has won the fewest matches?

    5. About how many more matches has Team A won than Team D?

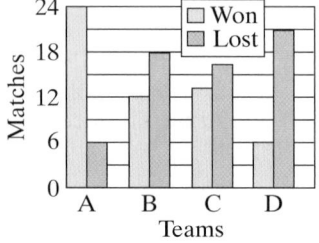

● **Lesson 11-3**   The table shows the number of stories of some tall buildings in the United States. Use the table to answer Exercises 6 and 7.

    6. Draw a stem-and-leaf plot for the data.

    7. What is the range of the data?

Number of Stories				
73	44	57	64	48
60	55	51	77	40
80	72	60	82	57

● **Lesson 11-4**

    8. Write a fair survey question and a biased survey question.

● **Lesson 11-5**

    9. Suppose 25 sea gulls were marked in a nesting area. Later, 500 sea gulls were counted, 19 of which were marked. Estimate the population.

● **Lesson 11-6**   The graph shows the growth of a company's DVD sales.

    10. Decide whether the graph appears misleading. If so, explain how the graph makes the misleading impression.

Company DVD Sales

● **Lesson 11-7**   The data show the heights and weights of some 7-year-olds.

Height	40 in.	39 in.	42 in.	45 in.	48 in.	43 in.	41 in.
Weight	56 lb	52 lb	62 lb	75 lb	72 lb	67 lb	62 lb

    11. Make a scatter plot of the data. Describe any trend you see in the data.

Word Problems

● **Lesson 11-1**

12. You survey students about how many times they ate at a restaurant last month. The results are shown. Make a histogram of the data.

How Many Meals Did You Eat Out Last Month?

Number of Meals	0–3	4–7	8–11	12–15
Frequency	8	12	3	7

13. You record the daily temperature (°F) for the month of June, Make a frequency table of the temperatures below.

82 81 88 88 87 92 91 85 92 83 82 84 86 89 90
87 86 84 83 84 87 86 90 91 87 86 80 84 91 90

● **Lesson 11-2**   **Use the double bar graph.**

14. Which fundraisers had incomes of more than $4,000?

15. Which fundraiser made the most profit? The least profit?

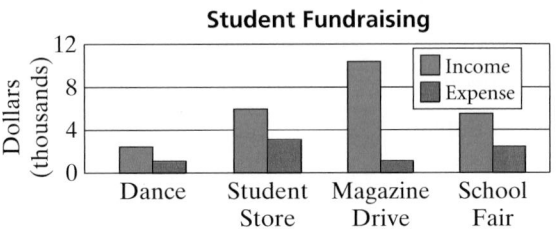
Student Fundraising

● **Lessons 11-3 through 11-5**

16. Science A botanist measures the heights of giant sunflowers in inches. Draw a stem-and-leaf plot for the height data below.
98 99 94 87 83 74 69 88 78 99 100 87 77.

17. An urban planner wants to know how road construction affects bus drivers. How can the planner survey a random sample of bus drivers?

18. Ecology Marine biologists are studying the otter population in a coastal region. There are 20 marked sea otters in the region. In a survey, the biologists count 42 sea otters, of which 12 are marked. About how many sea otters are in the area?

● **Lessons 11-6 and 11-7**   **For Exercises 19 and 20, use the graph at right showing measles cases in the United States.**

19. What does the graph suggest about the occurrence of measles in 1990?

20. Use the data to draw a graph that does not mislead.

21. What trend do you expect to see in a scatter plot in which the horizontal axis represents hours spent watching television and the vertical axis represents hours spent studying? Explain.

12.

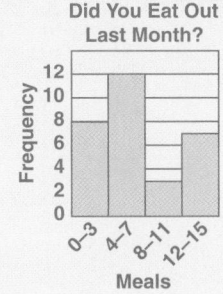
How Many Meals Did You Eat Out Last Month?

13.

Temp (F)	Tally	Frequency
80	I	1
81	I	1
82	II	2
83	II	2
84	IIII	4
85	I	1
86	IIII	4
87	IIII	4
88	II	2
89	I	1
90	III	3
91	III	3
92	II	2

14. student store, magazine drive, school fair

15. magazine drive, dance

16.   **Heights of Giant Sunflowers (in.)**

```
 6 | 9
 7 | 4 7 8
 8 | 3 7 7 8
 9 | 4 8 9 9
10 | 0
```

Key: 6 | 9 means 69

17. Get a list of bus drivers from each company and call every 10th driver.

18. about 70 sea otters

19. The graph suggests that the outbreak was not significant.

20.

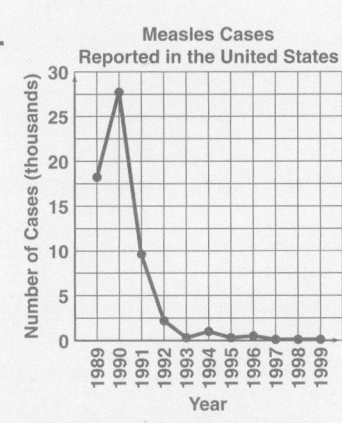
Measles Cases Reported in the United States

21. Negative; as the number of hours watching TV increases, the time spent studying will probably decrease.

651

CHAPTER 12

1. $\frac{1}{6}$

2. $\frac{1}{3}$

3. $\frac{1}{2}$

4. $\frac{1}{20}$

5. $\frac{37}{41}$

6. $\frac{3}{28}$

7. Answers may vary.
Sample: HHH, HHT, HTH, THH, TTT, TTH, THT, HTT

8. Answers may vary.
Sample:

	1	2	3	4	5	6
H	1H	2H	3H	4H	5H	6H
T	1T	2T	3T	4T	5T	6T

12

9. Answers may vary.
Sample:

	E	F	G	H
A	EA	FA	GA	HA
B	EB	FB	GB	HB
C	EC	FC	GC	HC

12

10.

$\frac{1}{12}$

Skills

● **Lesson 12-1** **You roll a number cube. Find the odds in favor.**

1. rolling a 2

2. rolling a 3 or 5

3. rolling a 2, 4, or 6

● **Lesson 12-2**

4. A quality control engineer at a factory inspected 300 glow sticks for quality. The engineer found 15 defective glow sticks. What is the experimental probability that a glow stick is defective?

The number of wins and losses for basketball teams are shown. Find each experimental probability.

5. Kingwood, Humble, Texas
Wins: 37, Losses: 4
Find $P(\text{Win})$.

6. Westchester, Los Angeles, Calif
Wins: 25 Losses: 3
Find $P(\text{Loss})$.

● **Lesson 12-3** **Make a table to show the sample space for each situation. Then find the number of outcomes.**

7. You toss three coins.

8. You spin a number 1 to 6 and toss a coin.

9. You choose one letter from each of the two sets of letters E, F, G, H and A, B, C.

10. You toss two coins and spin a spinner with three congruent sections colored red, white, and blue. Draw a tree diagram to find the sample space. Then find $P(2 \text{ heads, then blue})$.

● **Lesson 12-4** **A bag contains 6 green marbles, 8 blue marbles, and 3 red marbles. Find $P(B)$ after A has happened.**

11. A: Draw a green marble. Keep it.
B: Draw a red marble.

12. A: Draw a blue marble. Replace it.
B: Draw a red marble.

● **Lessons 12-5 and 12-6** **State whether the situation is a *permutation* or a *combination*. Then answer the question.**

13. In how many ways can a committee of 2 be chosen from 5 members?

14. In how many ways can a president and a treasurer be selected from a club of 5 members?

● **Lessons 12-1 and 12-2**

15. You write the letters M, I, S, S, I, S, S, I, P, P, and I on cards and mix them in a hat. You select one card without looking. Find the probability of selecting an I.

16. Suppose you have 3 red, 3 black, and 3 blue marbles in your pocket. Does the probability of randomly selecting a black marble equal the probability of randomly selecting a blue one? Explain.

17. A quality-control inspector finds flaws in 6 of 45 tools examined. If the trend continues, what is the best prediction of the number of defective tools in a batch of 540?

18. Crispy Cereal offers one free prize in every box: a baseball card, a keychain, or a bracelet. You buy 3 boxes. Find the experimental probability of *not* getting a baseball card. Simulate the problem.

● **Lessons 12-3 and 12-4**

19. Make a tree diagram for choosing one letter at random from each of two sets of letters: A, B, and C and W, X, Y, and Z. Then find the probability of choosing an A and a W.

20. A spinner has equal sections numbered 1 to 3. You spin the spinner 4 times. How many different outcomes are possible?

21. You drop a coin twice inside the rectangle. Estimate the probability that the coin lands in one of the circles both times. Use 3 for π.

22. A volleyball team won 31 games and lost 4 games in one season. The coach has a summary sheet for each game. The coach selects two sheets at random to compare. Find P(win, then loss) without replacement.

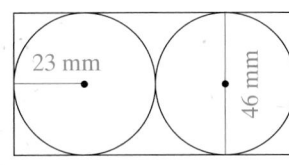

● **Lessons 12-5 and 12-6**

23. There are 20 teams that compete in a tournament. Find the number of different ways that two teams can finish in first and second place.

24. You scramble the letters P, A, and N. Make an organized list of the sample space. Then find the number of the groups that form real words. What are they?

25. You have six toppings to use for a pizza. How many different three-topping pizzas can you make?

26. A club of 50 people wants to select 4 members as representatives. How many different combinations of 4 people are possible?

11. $\frac{3}{16}$

12. $\frac{3}{17}$

13. combination; 10

14. permutation; 20

15. $\frac{4}{11}$

16. Yes; since you have the same number of blue marbles as black marbles, the number of favorable outcomes for each is the same.

17. about 72 defective tools

18. $\frac{8}{27}$

19. $\frac{1}{12}$

20. 81 outcomes

21. $\frac{9}{16}$

22. $\frac{62}{595}$

23. 380 ways

24. ANP, APN, NAP, NPA, PAN, PNA; 2; NAP, PAN

25. 20 pizzas

26. 5,527,200 combinations

1. >
2. >
3. >
4. >
5. <
6. <
7. <
8. <
9. >
10. <
11. 3,347; 3,474; 3,734; 3,747; 3,774
12. 70,309; 70,903; 73,090; 73,909
13. 30,256,403; 30,265,403; 32,056,403; 302,056,403
14. 881,472; 881,872; 884,172; 887,142

Skills Handbook

Comparing and Ordering Whole Numbers

The numbers on a number line are in order from least to greatest.

```
   +----+----+----+----+----+----+----+----+---->
  298  299  300  301  302  303  304  305  306
```

You can use a number line to compare whole numbers. Use the symbols > (is greater than) and < (is less than).

EXAMPLE

1 Use > or < to compare the whole numbers.

a. 303 ■ 299

303 is to the right of 299.

303 > 299

b. 301 ■ 305

301 is to the left of 305.

301 < 305

The value of a digit depends on its place in a number. Compare digits starting from the left.

EXAMPLE

2 Use > or < to compare the whole numbers.

a. 12,060,012,875 ■ 12,060,012,675

8 hundreds > 6 hundreds, so
12,060,012,875 > 12,060,012,675

b. 465,320 ■ 4,653,208

0 millions < 4 millions, so
465,320 < 4,653,208

Exercises

Use > or < to compare the whole numbers.

1. 3,660 ■ 360
2. 74,328 ■ 74,238
3. 88,010 ■ 8,101
4. 87,524 ■ 9,879
5. 295,286 ■ 295,826
6. 829,631 ■ 842,832
7. 932,401 ■ 932,701
8. 60,000 ■ 500,000
9. 1,609,372,002 ■ 609,172,002
10. 45,248,315,150 ■ 45,283,718,150

Order the numbers from least to greatest.

11. 3,747; 3,474; 3,774; 3,347; 3,734
12. 70,903; 70,309; 73,909; 73,090
13. 32,056,403; 302,056,403; 30,265,403; 30,256,403
14. 884,172; 881,472; 887,142; 881,872

Rounding Whole Numbers

You can use number lines to help you round numbers.

EXAMPLE

1 **a.** Round 7,510 to the nearest thousand.

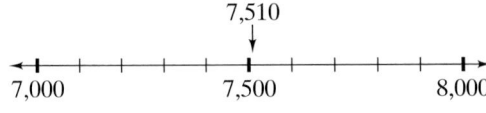

7,510 is between 7,000 and 8,000.

7,510 rounds to 8,000.

b. Round 237 to the nearest ten.

237 is between 230 and 240.

237 rounds to 240.

To round a number to a particular place, look at the digit to the right of that place. If the digit is less than 5, round down. If the digit is 5 or more, round up.

EXAMPLE

2 Round to the place of the underlined digit.

a. 3,4<u>6</u>3,280

The digit to the right of the 6 is 3, so 3,463,280 rounds down to 3,460,000.

b. 28<u>9</u>,543

The digit to the right of the 9 is 5, so 289,543 rounds up to 290,000.

Exercises

Round to the nearest ten.

| **1.** 42 | **2.** 89 | **3.** 671 | **4.** 3,482 | **5.** 7,029 | **6.** 661,423 |

Round to the nearest thousand.

| **7.** 5,800 | **8.** 3,100 | **9.** 44,500 | **10.** 9,936 | **11.** 987 | **12.** 313,591 |
| **13.** 5,641 | **14.** 37,896 | **15.** 82,019 | **16.** 808,155 | **17.** 34,501 | **18.** 650,828 |

Round to the place of the underlined digit.

19. 68,<u>8</u>52	**20.** <u>4</u>51,006	**21.** 3,40<u>6</u>,781	**22.** 2<u>8</u>,512,030	**23.** 71,2<u>2</u>5,003
24. 96,<u>3</u>59	**25.** 4<u>0</u>1,223	**26.** <u>8</u>,902	**27.** 3,6<u>7</u>7	**28.** 2,551,<u>7</u>50
29. 6<u>8</u>,663	**30.** 70<u>1</u>,803,229	**31.** 56<u>5</u>,598	**32.** 32,<u>8</u>10	**33.** 1,<u>0</u>46,300

Skills Handbook

Skills Handbook

Multiplying Whole Numbers

When you multiply by a two-digit number, first multiply by the ones and then multiply by the tens. Add the products.

EXAMPLE

1 Multiply 62×704.

Step 1

$$\begin{array}{r} 704 \\ \times\ 62 \\ \hline 1408 \end{array}$$

Step 2

$$\begin{array}{r} 704 \\ \times\ 62 \\ \hline 1408 \\ 42240 \end{array}$$

Step 3

$$\begin{array}{r} 704 \\ \times\ 62 \\ \hline 1408 \\ +\ 42240 \\ \hline 43,648 \end{array}$$

EXAMPLE

2 Find each product.

a. 93×6

$$\begin{array}{r} 93 \\ \times\ 6 \\ \hline 558 \end{array}$$

b. 25×48

$$\begin{array}{r} 48 \\ \times\ 25 \\ \hline 240 \\ +\ 960 \\ \hline 1,200 \end{array}$$

c. 80×921

$$\begin{array}{r} 921 \\ \times\ 80 \\ \hline 73,680 \end{array}$$

Exercises

Find each product.

1. $\begin{array}{r}74\\ \times\ 6\end{array}$	**2.** $\begin{array}{r}35\\ \times\ 9\end{array}$	**3.** $\begin{array}{r}53\\ \times\ 7\end{array}$	**4.** $\begin{array}{r}80\\ \times\ 8\end{array}$	**5.** $\begin{array}{r}98\\ \times\ 4\end{array}$	**6.** $\begin{array}{r}65\\ \times\ 8\end{array}$
7. $\begin{array}{r}512\\ \times\ 3\end{array}$	**8.** $\begin{array}{r}407\\ \times\ 9\end{array}$	**9.** $\begin{array}{r}225\\ \times\ 6\end{array}$	**10.** $\begin{array}{r}340\\ \times\ 5\end{array}$	**11.** $\begin{array}{r}816\\ \times\ 7\end{array}$	**12.** $\begin{array}{r}603\\ \times\ 3\end{array}$
13. $\begin{array}{r}70\\ \times\ 36\end{array}$	**14.** $\begin{array}{r}41\\ \times\ 55\end{array}$	**15.** $\begin{array}{r}38\\ \times\ 49\end{array}$	**16.** $\begin{array}{r}601\\ \times\ 87\end{array}$	**17.** $\begin{array}{r}271\\ \times\ 34\end{array}$	**18.** $\begin{array}{r}450\\ \times\ 67\end{array}$

19. 6×82 **20.** 405×5 **21.** 81×9 **22.** 3×274 **23.** 553×4

24. 60×84 **25.** 52×17 **26.** 31×90 **27.** 78×52 **28.** 43×66

29. 826×3 **30.** 702×4 **31.** 5×128 **32.** 6×339 **33.** 781×7

656 Skills Handbook

Dividing Whole Numbers

First estimate the quotient by rounding the divisor, the dividend, or both. When you divide, after you bring down a digit, you must write a digit in the quotient.

EXAMPLE

Find each quotient.

a. $741 \div 8$

Estimate:
$720 \div 8 \approx 90$

$$
\begin{array}{r}
92 \ \text{R5} \\
8\overline{)741} \\
-72 \\
\hline
21 \\
-16 \\
\hline
5
\end{array}
$$

b. $838 \div 43$

Estimate:
$800 \div 40 \approx 20$

$$
\begin{array}{r}
19 \ \text{R21} \\
43\overline{)838} \\
-43 \\
\hline
408 \\
-387 \\
\hline
21
\end{array}
$$

c. $367 \div 9$

Estimate:
$360 \div 9 \approx 40$

$$
\begin{array}{r}
40 \ \text{R7} \\
9\overline{)367} \\
-360 \\
\hline
7
\end{array}
$$

Exercises

Divide.

1. $4\overline{)61}$
2. $8\overline{)53}$
3. $7\overline{)90}$
4. $3\overline{)84}$
5. $6\overline{)81}$

6. $6\overline{)469}$
7. $3\overline{)653}$
8. $8\overline{)645}$
9. $9\overline{)231}$
10. $4\overline{)415}$

11. $60\overline{)461}$
12. $40\overline{)213}$
13. $70\overline{)517}$
14. $30\overline{)432}$
15. $80\overline{)276}$

16. $43\overline{)273}$
17. $52\overline{)281}$
18. $69\overline{)207}$
19. $38\overline{)121}$
20. $81\overline{)433}$

21. $94\overline{)1,368}$
22. $62\overline{)1,147}$
23. $55\overline{)2,047}$
24. $85\overline{)1,450}$
25. $46\overline{)996}$

26. $94 \div 4$
27. $66 \div 9$
28. $90 \div 5$
29. $69 \div 6$
30. $58 \div 8$

31. $323 \div 5$
32. $849 \div 7$
33. $404 \div 8$
34. $934 \div 3$
35. $619 \div 6$

36. $777 \div 50$
37. $528 \div 20$
38. $443 \div 40$
39. $312 \div 40$
40. $335 \div 60$

41. $382 \div 72$
42. $580 \div 68$
43. $279 \div 43$
44. $232 \div 27$
45. $331 \div 93$

46. $614 \div 35$
47. $423 \div 28$
48. $489 \div 15$
49. $1,134 \div 51$
50. $1,103 \div 26$

1. 15 R1
2. 6 R5
3. 12 R6
4. 28
5. 13 R3
6. 78 R1
7. 217 R2
8. 80 R5
9. 25 R6
10. 103 R3
11. 7 R41
12. 5 R13
13. 7 R27
14. 14 R12
15. 3 R36
16. 6 R15
17. 5 R21
18. 3
19. 3 R7
20. 5 R28
21. 14 R52
22. 18 R31
23. 37 R12
24. 17 R5
25. 21 R30
26. 23 R2
27. 7 R3
28. 18
29. 11 R3
30. 7 R2
31. 64 R3
32. 121 R2
33. 50 R4
34. 311 R1
35. 103 R1
36. 15 R27
37. 26 R8
38. 11 R3
39. 7 R32
40. 5 R35
41. 5 R22
42. 8 R36
43. 6 R21
44. 8 R16
45. 3 R52
46. 17 R19
47. 15 R3
48. 32 R9
49. 22 R12
50. 42 R11

Place Value and Decimals

Each digit in a decimal has both a place and a value. The value of any place is one tenth the value of the place to its left. In the chart below, the digit 5 is in the hundredths place. So its value is 5 hundredths.

thousands	hundreds	tens	ones	.	tenths	hundredths	thousandths	ten-thousandths	hundred-thousandths
2	8	3	6	.	7	5	0	1	4

EXAMPLE

a. In what place is the digit 8?

hundreds

b. What is the value of the digit 8?

8 hundreds

Exercises

Use the chart above. Write the place of each digit.

1. 3
2. 4
3. 6
4. 7
5. 1
6. 0

Use the chart above. Write the value of each digit.

7. 3
8. 4
9. 6
10. 7
11. 1
12. 0

Write the value of the digit 6 in each number.

13. 0.162
14. 0.016
15. 13.672
16. 1,640.8
17. 62.135

18. 26.34
19. 6,025.9
20. 0.6003
21. 2,450.65
22. 615.28

23. 3.16125
24. 1.20641
25. 0.15361
26. 1.55736
27. 10.0563

Write the value of the underlined digit.

28. 24.0026
29. 14.931
30. 5.7894
31. 0.87
32. 10.0563

1. 0.03
2. 21,000,000
3. 6.02
4. 2,000,000,000.6
5. 2.05
6. 5,012
7. 0.000007
8. 0.0041
9. 0.011
10. 1.000025
11. 0.304
12. five thousand seven hundred and four tenths
13. three million and nine hundredths
14. twelve and sixty-nine millionths
15. nine hundred and two hundredths
16. twenty-five and seven hundred-thousandths
17. fifteen hundred-thousandths

Reading and Writing Decimals

A place value chart can help you read and write decimals. When there are no ones, write a zero before the decimal point.

billions	hundred millions	ten millions	millions	hundred thousands	ten thousands	thousands	hundreds	tens	ones	.	tenths	hundredths	thousandths	ten-thousandths	hundred-thousandths	millionths	Read
									0	.	0	7					7 hundredths
								2	3	.	0	1	4				23 and 14 thousandths
3	0	0	0	0	0	0	0	0	0	.	8						3 billion and 8 tenths
									5	.	0	0	0	1	0	2	5 and 102 millionths

EXAMPLE

a. Write thirteen ten-thousandths in numerals.

Ten-thousandths is 4 places after the decimal point. So the decimal will have 4 places after the decimal point. The number is 0.0013.

b. Write 1.025 in words.

The digit 5 is in the thousandths place. So 1.025 is one and twenty-five thousandths.

Exercises

Write a number for the given words.

1. three hundredths

2. twenty-one millions

3. six and two hundredths

4. two billion and six tenths

5. two and five hundredths

6. five thousand twelve

7. seven millionths

8. forty-one ten-thousandths

9. eleven thousandths

10. one and twenty-five millionths

11. three hundred four thousandths

Write each number in words.

12. 5,700.4

13. 3,000,000.09

14. 12.000069

15. 900.02

16. 25.00007

17. 0.00015

Rounding Decimals

You can use number lines to help you round decimals.

EXAMPLE

1 **a.** Round 1.627 to the nearest tenth.

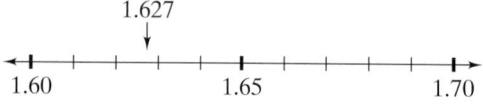

1.627 is between 1.6 and 1.7.

1.627 rounds to 1.6.

b. Round 0.248 to the nearest hundredth.

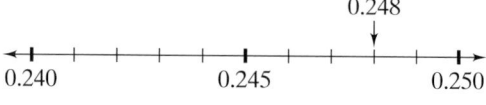

0.248 is between 0.24 and 0.25.

0.248 rounds to 0.25.

To round a number to a particular place, look at the digit to the right of that place. If the digit is less than 5, round down. If the digit is 5 or more, round up.

EXAMPLE

2 **a.** Round 2.4301 to the nearest whole number.

The digit to the right of 2 is 4, so 2.4301 rounds down to 2.

b. Round 0.0515 to the nearest thousandth.

The digit to the right of 1 is 5, so 0.0515 rounds up to 0.052.

Exercises

Round to the nearest tenth.

1. 2.75	**2.** 3.816	**3.** 19.72	**4.** 401.1603	**5.** 499.491	**6.** 3.949
7. 4.67522	**8.** 20.397	**9.** 399.956	**10.** 129.98	**11.** 96.4045	**12.** 125.66047

Round to the nearest hundredth.

13. 31.723	**14.** 14.869	**15.** 1.78826	**16.** 0.1119	**17.** 736.941	**18.** 9.6057
19. 0.699	**20.** 4.231	**21.** 12.09531	**22.** 5.77125	**23.** 0.9195	**24.** 4.0033

Round to the nearest thousandth.

25. 0.4387	**26.** 0.0649	**27.** 3.4953	**28.** 8.07092	**29.** 0.6008	**30.** 6.0074

Round to the nearest whole number.

31. 3.942	**32.** 10.4	**33.** 79.52	**34.** 105.3002	**35.** 431.23	**36.** 0.4962

Multiplying Decimals

When you multiply decimals, first multiply as if the factors were whole numbers. Then, count the decimal places in both factors to find how many places are needed in the product.

EXAMPLE

1 Multiply 2.5×1.8.

$$
\begin{array}{r}
1.8 \quad \leftarrow \textbf{ one decimal place} \\
\times\ 2.5 \quad \leftarrow \textbf{ one decimal place} \\
\hline
90 \\
+\ 360 \\
\hline
4.50 \quad \leftarrow \textbf{ two decimal places}
\end{array}
$$

EXAMPLE

2 Find each product.

a. 0.7×1.02

$$
\begin{array}{r}
1.02 \\
\times\ 0.7 \\
\hline
0.714
\end{array}
$$

b. 0.03×407

$$
\begin{array}{r}
407 \\
\times\ 0.03 \\
\hline
12.21
\end{array}
$$

c. 0.62×2.45

$$
\begin{array}{r}
2.45 \\
\times\ 0.62 \\
\hline
490 \\
+\ 14700 \\
\hline
1.5190
\end{array}
$$

d. 75×3.06

$$
\begin{array}{r}
3.06 \\
\times\ 75 \\
\hline
1530 \\
+\ 21420 \\
\hline
229.50
\end{array}
$$

Exercises

Multiply.

1. $\begin{array}{r} 0.3 \\ \times\ 8 \\ \hline \end{array}$
2. $\begin{array}{r} 5 \\ \times\ 0.06 \\ \hline \end{array}$
3. $\begin{array}{r} 0.04 \\ \times\ 7 \\ \hline \end{array}$
4. $\begin{array}{r} 6 \\ \times\ 0.8 \\ \hline \end{array}$
5. $\begin{array}{r} 3.1 \\ \times\ 0.05 \\ \hline \end{array}$
6. $\begin{array}{r} 14 \\ \times\ 0.2 \\ \hline \end{array}$

7. $\begin{array}{r} 3.1 \\ \times\ 6 \\ \hline \end{array}$
8. $\begin{array}{r} 0.05 \\ \times\ 43 \\ \hline \end{array}$
9. $\begin{array}{r} 0.27 \\ \times\ 5 \\ \hline \end{array}$
10. $\begin{array}{r} 72 \\ \times\ 0.6 \\ \hline \end{array}$
11. $\begin{array}{r} 0.8 \\ \times\ 312 \\ \hline \end{array}$
12. $\begin{array}{r} 4.56 \\ \times\ 7 \\ \hline \end{array}$

13. 5×2.41
14. 704×0.3
15. 9×1.35
16. 1.2×0.3

17. 0.04×2.5
18. 6.6×0.3
19. 15.1×0.02
20. 0.8×31.3

21. 0.07×25.1
22. 42.2×0.9
23. 0.6×30.02
24. 0.05×11.8

25. 71.13×0.4
26. 48×2.1
27. 6.3×85
28. 0.42×98

29. 76×3.3
30. 0.77×51
31. 5.2×4.8
32. 0.12×6.1

1. 2.4
2. 0.3
3. 0.28
4. 4.8
5. 0.155
6. 2.8
7. 18.6
8. 2.15
9. 1.35
10. 43.2
11. 249.6
12. 31.92
13. 12.05
14. 211.2
15. 12.15
16. 0.36
17. 0.1
18. 1.98
19. 0.302
20. 25.04
21. 1.757
22. 37.98
23. 18.012
24. 0.59
25. 28.452
26. 100.8
27. 535.5
28. 41.16
29. 250.8
30. 39.27
31. 24.96
32. 0.732

Zeros in the Product

When you multiply with decimals, start at the right of the product to count the number of decimal places. Sometimes you need to write extra zeros to the left of a product before you can place the decimal point.

EXAMPLE

1 Multiply 0.03×0.51.

Step 1

$$\begin{array}{r} 0.51 \quad \leftarrow \text{ two decimal places} \\ \times\ 0.03 \quad \leftarrow \text{ two decimal places} \\ \hline 153 \quad \leftarrow \text{ four decimal places} \end{array}$$

Step 2

$$\begin{array}{r} 0.51 \\ \times\ 0.03 \\ \hline 0.0153 \end{array}$$ $\leftarrow$ Put extra zeros to the left. Then place the decimal point.

EXAMPLE

2 Find each product.

a. 0.2×0.3

$$\begin{array}{r} 0.3 \\ \times\ 0.2 \\ \hline 0.06 \end{array}$$

b. 0.5×0.04

$$\begin{array}{r} 0.04 \\ \times\ 0.5 \\ \hline 0.020 \end{array}$$

c. 4×0.02

$$\begin{array}{r} 0.02 \\ \times\ 4 \\ \hline 0.08 \end{array}$$

d. 0.02×0.45

$$\begin{array}{r} 0.45 \\ \times\ 0.02 \\ \hline 0.0090 \end{array}$$

Exercises

Multiply.

1. $\begin{array}{r} 0.1 \\ \times\ 0.6 \\ \hline \end{array}$

2. $\begin{array}{r} 0.4 \\ \times\ 0.2 \\ \hline \end{array}$

3. $\begin{array}{r} 0.05 \\ \times\ 0.06 \\ \hline \end{array}$

4. $\begin{array}{r} 0.01 \\ \times\ 8 \\ \hline \end{array}$

5. $\begin{array}{r} 0.7 \\ \times\ 0.02 \\ \hline \end{array}$

6. $\begin{array}{r} 0.03 \\ \times\ 0.4 \\ \hline \end{array}$

7. $\begin{array}{r} 0.03 \\ \times\ 0.9 \\ \hline \end{array}$

8. $\begin{array}{r} 0.06 \\ \times\ 0.5 \\ \hline \end{array}$

9. $\begin{array}{r} 0.2 \\ \times\ 0.02 \\ \hline \end{array}$

10. $\begin{array}{r} 7 \\ \times\ 0.01 \\ \hline \end{array}$

11. $\begin{array}{r} 0.05 \\ \times\ 0.05 \\ \hline \end{array}$

12. $\begin{array}{r} 0.6 \\ \times\ 0.06 \\ \hline \end{array}$

13. 0.4×0.08

14. 0.07×0.05

15. 0.03×0.03

16. 0.09×0.05

17. 0.5×0.08

18. 0.06×0.7

19. 0.07×0.01

20. 0.16×0.2

21. 0.01×0.74

22. 0.47×0.08

23. 0.76×0.1

24. 0.19×0.3

25. 0.5×0.17

26. 0.31×0.08

27. 0.14×0.05

28. 0.07×0.85

29. 0.45×0.06

30. 0.4×0.23

31. 0.17×0.06

32. 0.3×0.24

Dividing a Decimal by a Whole Number

When you divide a decimal by a whole number, first divide as if the numbers were whole numbers. Then put a decimal point in the quotient directly above the decimal point in the dividend.

EXAMPLE

1 Divide $0.256 \div 8$.

Step 1

$$
\begin{array}{r}
32 \\
8)\overline{0.256} \\
-24 \\
\hline
16 \\
-16 \\
\hline
0
\end{array}
$$

Step 2

$$
\begin{array}{r}
0.032 \\
8)\overline{0.256} \\
-24 \\
\hline
16 \\
-16 \\
\hline
0
\end{array}
$$

← Put extra zeros to the left. Then place the decimal point.

EXAMPLE

2 Find each quotient.

a. $12.6 \div 6$

$$
\begin{array}{r}
2.1 \\
6)\overline{12.6} \\
-12 \\
\hline
06 \\
-6 \\
\hline
0
\end{array}
$$

b. $37.26 \div 81$

$$
\begin{array}{r}
0.46 \\
81)\overline{37.26} \\
-324 \\
\hline
486 \\
-486 \\
\hline
0
\end{array}
$$

c. $0.666 \div 9$

$$
\begin{array}{r}
0.074 \\
9)\overline{0.666} \\
-63 \\
\hline
36 \\
-36 \\
\hline
0
\end{array}
$$

Exercises

Divide.

1. $4)\overline{28.56}$ **2.** $5)\overline{16.5}$ **3.** $9)\overline{6.984}$ **4.** $6)\overline{91.44}$ **5.** $4)\overline{35.16}$

6. $81)\overline{33.291}$ **7.** $22)\overline{2.42}$ **8.** $26)\overline{1,723.8}$ **9.** $83)\overline{15.272}$ **10.** $39)\overline{26.91}$

11. $17.52 \div 2$ **12.** $10.53 \div 9$ **13.** $14.49 \div 7$ **14.** $37.14 \div 6$

15. $0.0324 \div 9$ **16.** $0.1352 \div 8$ **17.** $0.0882 \div 6$ **18.** $0.8682 \div 6$

19. $79.599 \div 13$ **20.** $45.918 \div 18$ **21.** $59.7 \div 15$ **22.** $74.664 \div 12$

23. $12.342 \div 22$ **24.** $29.792 \div 32$ **25.** $22.568 \div 26$ **26.** $11.340 \div 36$

Skills Handbook   **663**

Skills Handbook

1. 7.14
2. 3.3
3. 0.776
4. 15.24
5. 8.79
6. 0.411
7. 0.11
8. 66.3
9. 0.184
10. 0.69
11. 8.76
12. 1.17
13. 2.07
14. 6.19
15. 0.0036
16. 0.00169
17. 0.0147
18. 0.1447
19. 6.123
20. 2.551
21. 3.98
22. 6.222
23. 0.561
24. 0.931
25. 0.868
26. 0.315

Skills Handbook

Powers of Ten

You can use shortcuts when multiplying and dividing by powers of ten.

When you multiply by...	move the decimal point...	When you divide by...	move the decimal point...
1,000	3 places to the right.	1,000	3 places to the left.
100	2 places to the right.	100	2 places to the left.
10	1 place to the right.	10	1 place to the left.
0.1	1 place to the left.	0.1	1 place to the right.
0.01	2 places to the left.	0.01	2 places to the right.

EXAMPLE

Multiply or divide.

a. 0.3×0.01

b. $0.18 \div 1,000$

0.00.3 ← Move the decimal point 2 places to the left.

0.000.18 ← Move the decimal point 3 places to the left.

$0.3 \times 0.01 = 0.003$

$0.18 \div 1,000 = 0.00018$

Exercises

Multiply.

1. 3.2×0.01 **2.** $1,000 \times 0.12$ **3.** 0.7×0.1 **4.** 0.01×6.2

5. 0.09×100 **6.** 23.6×0.01 **7.** 5.2×10 **8.** $0.08 \times 1,000$

9. 100×0.05 **10.** 0.1×0.24 **11.** 18.03×0.1 **12.** 6.1×100

Divide.

13. $82.3 \div 0.1$ **14.** $0.4 \div 1,000$ **15.** $5.02 \div 0.01$ **16.** $16.5 \div 100$

17. $236.7 \div 0.1$ **18.** $45.28 \div 10$ **19.** $0.9 \div 1,000$ **20.** $1.03 \div 0.01$

21. $42.6 \div 0.1$ **22.** $203.05 \div 0.01$ **23.** $4.7 \div 10$ **24.** $0.07 \div 100$

Multiply or divide.

25. 0.32×0.1 **26.** $0.03 \div 100$ **27.** $2.6 \div 0.1$ **28.** $12.6 \times 1,000$

29. $0.8 \div 1,000$ **30.** 0.01×6.7 **31.** 100×0.15 **32.** $23.5 \div 10$

Zeros in Decimal Division

When you are dividing by a decimal, sometimes you need to use extra zeros in the dividend, the quotient, or both.

EXAMPLE

Find each quotient.

a. $0.14 \div 0.04$

Multiply by 100.

$$
\begin{array}{r}
3.5 \\
0.04.\overline{)0.14.0} \\
-12 \\
\hline
20 \\
-20 \\
\hline
0
\end{array}
$$

b. $0.00434 \div 0.07$

Multiply by 100.

$$
\begin{array}{r}
0.062 \\
0.07.\overline{)0.00.434} \\
-42 \\
\hline
14 \\
-14 \\
\hline
0
\end{array}
$$

c. $0.045 \div 3.6$

Multiply by 10.

$$
\begin{array}{r}
0.0125 \\
3.6.\overline{)0.0.4500} \\
-36 \\
\hline
90 \\
-72 \\
\hline
180 \\
-180 \\
\hline
0
\end{array}
$$

Exercises

Divide.

1. $0.4\overline{)0.001}$

2. $0.05\overline{)0.0023}$

3. $0.02\overline{)0.000162}$

4. $0.6\overline{)0.0015}$

5. $1.2\overline{)0.078}$

6. $0.34\overline{)0.00119}$

7. $0.12\overline{)0.009}$

8. $2.5\overline{)0.021}$

9. $0.0017 \div 0.02$

10. $0.003 \div 0.6$

11. $0.01099 \div 0.7$

12. $0.104 \div 0.05$

13. $0.0945 \div 0.09$

14. $0.00045 \div 0.3$

15. $0.052 \div 0.8$

16. $0.142 \div 0.04$

17. $0.034 \div 0.05$

18. $0.0019 \div 0.2$

19. $0.9 \div 0.2$

20. $0.000175 \div 0.07$

21. $0.0084 \div 1.4$

22. $0.259 \div 3.5$

23. $0.00468 \div 0.52$

24. $0.00056 \div 0.16$

25. $0.0612 \div 7.2$

26. $0.17701 \div 3.1$

27. $0.00063 \div 0.18$

28. $0.011 \div 0.25$

29. $0.3069 \div 9.3$

30. $0.000924 \div 0.44$

31. $0.03234 \div 0.35$

32. $0.00123 \div 8.2$

33. $0.03225 \div 0.75$

34. $0.006 \div 0.75$

35. $0.73 \div 0.25$

36. $0.68 \div 0.002$

37. $0.398 \div 0.05$

38. $0.0004 \div 0.002$

39. $0.125 \div 0.005$

1. 0.0025
2. 0.046
3. 0.0081
4. 0.0025
5. 0.065
6. 0.0035
7. 0.075
8. 0.0084
9. 0.085
10. 0.005
11. 0.0157
12. 2.08
13. 1.05
14. 0.0015
15. 0.065
16. 3.55
17. 0.68
18. 0.0095
19. 4.5
20. 0.0025
21. 0.006
22. 0.074
23. 0.009
24. 0.0035
25. 0.0085
26. 0.0571
27. 0.0035
28. 0.044
29. 0.033
30. 0.0021
31. 0.0924
32. 0.00015
33. 0.043
34. 0.008
35. 2.92
36. 340
37. 7.96
38. 0.2
39. 25

Adding and Subtracting Fractions With Like Denominators

When you add or subtract fractions with the same denominator, first add or subtract the numerators. Write the answer over the denominator.

EXAMPLE

1 Add or subtract. Write the answer in simplest form.

a. $\frac{5}{16} + \frac{3}{16}$

$$\begin{array}{r} \frac{5}{16} \\ + \frac{3}{16} \\ \hline \frac{8}{16} = \frac{1}{2} \end{array}$$

b. $\frac{7}{8} - \frac{1}{8}$

$$\begin{array}{r} \frac{7}{8} \\ - \frac{1}{8} \\ \hline \frac{6}{8} = \frac{3}{4} \end{array}$$

c. $\frac{3}{5} + \frac{2}{5}$

$$\frac{3}{5} + \frac{2}{5} = \frac{5}{5} = 1$$

To add or subtract mixed numbers, add or subtract the fractions first. Then add or subtract the whole numbers.

EXAMPLE

2 Add or subtract. Write the answer in simplest form.

a. $2\frac{5}{8} + 3\frac{1}{8}$

$$\begin{array}{r} 2\frac{5}{8} \\ + 3\frac{1}{8} \\ \hline 5\frac{6}{8} = 5\frac{3}{4} \end{array}$$

b. $4\frac{3}{4} - 1\frac{1}{4}$

$$\begin{array}{r} 4\frac{3}{4} \\ - 1\frac{1}{4} \\ \hline 3\frac{2}{4} = 3\frac{1}{2} \end{array}$$

c. $5\frac{5}{6} + 2\frac{5}{6}$

$$5\frac{5}{6} + 2\frac{5}{6} = 7\frac{10}{6}$$
$$= 7 + 1 + \frac{4}{6}$$
$$= 8\frac{2}{3}$$

Exercises

Add or subtract. Write the answers in simplest form.

1. $\begin{array}{r} \frac{2}{5} \\ + \frac{2}{5} \\ \hline \end{array}$
2. $\begin{array}{r} \frac{2}{6} \\ - \frac{1}{6} \\ \hline \end{array}$
3. $\begin{array}{r} \frac{2}{7} \\ + \frac{2}{7} \\ \hline \end{array}$
4. $\begin{array}{r} 9\frac{1}{3} \\ - 8\frac{1}{3} \\ \hline \end{array}$
5. $\begin{array}{r} 8\frac{6}{7} \\ - 4\frac{2}{7} \\ \hline \end{array}$
6. $\begin{array}{r} 3\frac{1}{10} \\ + 1\frac{3}{10} \\ \hline \end{array}$

7. $\frac{3}{8} + \frac{2}{8}$
8. $\frac{3}{6} - \frac{1}{6}$
9. $\frac{6}{8} - \frac{3}{8}$
10. $\frac{2}{9} + \frac{1}{9}$
11. $\frac{4}{5} - \frac{1}{5}$
12. $\frac{3}{4} + \frac{1}{4}$

13. $8\frac{7}{10} + 2\frac{3}{10}$
14. $1\frac{4}{5} + 3\frac{3}{5}$
15. $2\frac{2}{9} + 3\frac{4}{9}$
16. $8\frac{5}{8} - 3\frac{3}{8}$
17. $9\frac{7}{10} - 2\frac{3}{10}$
18. $9\frac{3}{4} + 1\frac{3}{4}$

Metric Units of Length

The basic unit of length in the metric system is the meter. All the other units are based on the meter. In the chart below, each unit is 10 times the value of the unit to its left.

Unit	Millimeter	Centimeter	Decimeter	Meter	Decameter	Hectometer	Kilometer
Symbol	mm	cm	dm	m	dam	hm	km
Value	0.001 m	0.01 m	0.1 m	1 m	10 m	100 m	1,000 m

To change a measure from one unit to another, start by using the chart to find the relationship between the two units.

EXAMPLE

Complete each equation.

a. $0.8 \text{ km} = \blacksquare \text{ m}$

$1 \text{ km} = 1,000 \text{ m}$

$0.8 \times 1,000 = 800$ ← To change km to m, multiply by 1,000.

$0.8 \text{ km} = 800 \text{ m}$

b. $17.2 \text{ mm} = \blacksquare \text{ cm}$

$1 \text{ mm} = 0.1 \text{ cm}$

$17.2 \times 0.1 = 1.72$ ← To change mm to cm, multiply by 0.1.

$17.2 \text{ mm} = 1.72 \text{ cm}$

c. $\blacksquare \text{ cm} = 2.1 \text{ km}$

$1 \text{ km} = 100,000 \text{ cm}$

$2.1 \times 100,000 = 210,000$ ← To change km to cm, multiply by 100,000.

$210,000 \text{ cm} = 2.1 \text{ km}$

d. $\blacksquare \text{ m} = 5,200 \text{ cm}$

$1 \text{ cm} = 0.01 \text{ m}$

$5,200 \times 0.01 = 52$ ← To change cm to m, multiply by 0.01.

$52 \text{ m} = 5,200 \text{ cm}$

Exercises

Complete each equation.

1. $1 \text{ mm} = \blacksquare \text{ cm}$

2. $1 \text{ m} = \blacksquare \text{ km}$

3. $1 \text{ mm} = \blacksquare \text{ m}$

4. $1 \text{ cm} = \blacksquare \text{ m}$

5. $1.2 \text{ cm} = \blacksquare \text{ km}$

6. $\blacksquare \text{ km} = 45,000 \text{ mm}$

7. $\blacksquare \text{ m} = 30 \text{ km}$

8. $6.2 \text{ cm} = \blacksquare \text{ mm}$

9. $3.3 \text{ km} = \blacksquare \text{ m}$

10. $0.6 \text{ mm} = \blacksquare \text{ cm}$

11. $72 \text{ cm} = \blacksquare \text{ m}$

12. $180 \text{ m} = \blacksquare \text{ mm}$

13. $\blacksquare \text{ cm} = 13 \text{ km}$

14. $\blacksquare \text{ m} = 530 \text{ cm}$

15. $4,900 \text{ mm} = \blacksquare \text{ m}$

16. $\blacksquare \text{ cm} = 24 \text{ m}$

17. $\blacksquare \text{ km} = 106,000 \text{ cm}$

18. $259,000 \text{ mm} = \blacksquare \text{ m}$

19. $1,200,000 \text{ mm} = \blacksquare \text{ km}$

1. 0.1
2. 0.001
3. 0.001
4. 0.01
5. 0.000012
6. 0.045
7. 30,000
8. 62
9. 3,300
10. 0.06
11. 0.72
12. 180,000
13. 1,300,000
14. 5.3
15. 4.9
16. 2,400
17. 1.06
18. 259
19. 1.2

Skills Handbook

Metric Units of Capacity

The basic unit of capacity in the metric system is the liter. All the other units are based on the liter. In the chart below, each unit is 10 times the value of the unit on the left. Note that we use a capital L as the abbreviation for *liter* to avoid confusion with the number 1.

Unit	Milliliter	Centiliter	Deciliter	Liter	Decaliter	Hectoliter	Kiloliter
Symbol	mL	cL	dL	L	daL	hL	kL
Value	0.001 L	0.01 L	0.1 L	1 L	10 L	100 L	1,000 L

To change a measure from one unit to another, start by using the chart to find the relationship between the two units.

EXAMPLE

Complete each equation.

a. 245 mL = ■ L

   1 mL = 0.001 L

   245 × 0.001 = 0.245 ← To change mL to L, multiply by 0.001.

   245 mL = 0.245 L

b. ■ mL = 4.5 kL

   1 kL = 1,000,000 mL

   4.5 × 1,000,000 = 4,500,000 ← To change kL to mL, multiply by 1,000,000.

   4,500,000 mL = 4.5 kL

Exercises

Complete each equation.

1. 1 L = ■ mL
2. 1 mL = ■ kL
3. 1 kL = ■ L
4. 1 kL = ■ mL
5. 200 L = ■ kL
6. 1.3 kL = ■ mL
7. ■ kL = 240 L
8. 0.6 mL = ■ L
9. ■ kL = 106,000 L
10. 72 kL = ■ mL
11. ■ mL = 1.5 kL
12. ■ kL = 450,000 mL
13. 4,900 L = ■ kL
14. ■ kL = 200,000 mL
15. ■ L = 8 mL
16. 4.2 L = ■ mL
17. 57,000,000 mL = ■ L
18. 28,000 kL = ■ L
19. ■ mL = 9,000 L
20. 4,000 L = ■ mL
21. 870 L = ■ kL

Metric Units of Mass

The basic unit of mass in the metric system is the gram. All the other units are based on the gram. In the chart below, each unit is 10 times the value of the unit to its left.

Unit	Milligram	Centigram	Decigram	Gram	Decagram	Hectogram	Kilogram
Symbol	mg	cg	dg	g	dag	hg	kg
Value	0.001 g	0.01 g	0.1 g	1 g	10 g	100 g	1,000 g

To change a measure from one unit to another, start by using the chart to find the relationship between the two units.

EXAMPLE

Complete each equation.

a. $2.3 \text{ kg} = \blacksquare \text{ g}$

$1 \text{ kg} = 1,000 \text{ g}$

$2.3 \times 1,000 = 2,300$ ← To change kg to g, multiply by 1,000.

$2.3 \text{ kg} = 2,300 \text{ g}$

b. $\blacksquare \text{ g} = 250 \text{ mg}$

$1 \text{ mg} = 0.001 = 0.25$

$250 \times 0.001 = 0.25$ ← To change mg to g, multiply by 0.001.

$0.25 \text{ g} = 250 \text{ mg}$

Exercises

Complete each equation.

1. $1 \text{ mg} = \blacksquare \text{ g}$

2. $1 \text{ g} = \blacksquare \text{ kg}$

3. $1 \text{ mg} = \blacksquare \text{ kg}$

4. $1 \text{ g} = \blacksquare \text{ mg}$

5. $1 \text{ kg} = \blacksquare \text{ g}$

6. $1 \text{ kg} = \blacksquare \text{ mg}$

7. $\blacksquare \text{ g} = 8 \text{ mg}$

8. $1,500 \text{ mg} = \blacksquare \text{ kg}$

9. $\blacksquare \text{ kg} = 200,000 \text{ g}$

10. $\blacksquare \text{ mg} = 3.7 \text{ g}$

11. $0.6 \text{ mg} = \blacksquare \text{ g}$

12. $370 \text{ g} = \blacksquare \text{ kg}$

13. $\blacksquare \text{ kg} = 300,000 \text{ mg}$

14. $900 \text{ g} = \blacksquare \text{ mg}$

15. $\blacksquare \text{ kg} = 5.7 \text{ mg}$

16. $120 \text{ g} = \blacksquare \text{ kg}$

17. $\blacksquare \text{ kg} = 440 \text{ g}$

18. $\blacksquare \text{ kg} = 1,006,000 \text{ mg}$

19. $0.009 \text{ kg} = \blacksquare \text{ mg}$

20. $0.2 \text{ mg} = \blacksquare \text{ g}$

21. $8.6 \text{ kg} = \blacksquare \text{ g}$

Skills Handbook

Skills Handbook

Table 1 Measures

Metric	Customary
Length	**Length**
10 millimeters (mm) = 1 centimeter (cm)	12 inches (in.) = 1 foot (ft)
100 cm = 1 meter (m)	36 in. = 1 yard (yd)
1,000 mm = 1 m	3 ft = 1 yd
1,000 m = 1 kilometer (km)	5,280 ft = 1 mile (mi)
	1,760 yd = 1 mi
Area	**Area**
100 square millimeters (mm^2) =	144 square inches (in.^{2}) =
$\quad$ 1 square centimeter (cm^2)	$\quad$ 1 square foot (ft^2)
10,000 cm^2 = 1 square meter (m^2)	9 ft^2 = 1 square yard (yd^2)
	4,840 yd^2 = 1 acre
Volume	**Volume**
1,000 cubic millimeters (mm^3) =	1,728 cubic inches (in.^{3}) =
$\quad$ 1 cubic centimeter (cm^3)	$\quad$ 1 cubic foot (ft^3)
1,000,000 cm^3 = 1 cubic meter (m^3)	27 ft^3 = 1 cubic yard (yd^3)
Mass	**Mass**
1,000 milligrams (mg) = 1 gram (g)	16 ounces (oz) = 1 pound (lb)
1,000 g = 1 kilogram (kg)	2,000 lb = 1 ton (t)
Liquid Capacity	**Liquid Capacity**
1,000 milliliters (mL) = 1 liter (L)	8 fluid ounces (fl oz) = 1 cup (c)
	2 c = 1 pint (pt)
	2 pt = 1 quart (qt)
	4 qt = 1 gallon (gal)

Time

1 minute (min) = 60 seconds (s)
1 hour (h) = 60 min
1 day (d) = 24 h
1 year (yr) = 365 d

Table 2 Reading Math Symbols

$\approx$	is approximately equal to	p. 4	$\overline{AB}$	segment AB	p. 324
$-$	minus (subtraction)	p. 4	$\parallel$	is parallel to	p. 325
$=$	is equal to	p. 4	$\angle ABC$	angle with sides BA and BC	p. 330
$+$	plus (addition)	p. 5	$m\angle ABC$	measure of angle ABC	p. 330
$\div$	divide (division)	p. 5	$\cong$	is congruent to	p. 346
( )	parentheses for grouping	p. 9	$\overset{\frown}{AB}$	arc AB	p. 351
$\times, \cdot$	times (multiplication)	p. 13	d	diameter	p. 353
$\lvert a \rvert$	absolute value of a	p. 31	r	radius	p. 353
$-a$	opposite of a	p. 31	$\perp$	is perpendicular to	p. 362
$>$	is greater than	p. 32	P	perimeter	p. 375
$<$	is less than	p. 32	ℓ	length	p. 375
$\circ$	degrees	p. 34	w	width	p. 375
[ ]	brackets for grouping	p. 48	A	area	p. 380
a^n	nth power of a	p. 68	b	base length	p. 380
$\wedge$	raise to a power		h	height	p. 380
	(calculator key)	p. 69	b_1, b_2	base lengths of a trapezoid	p. 388
$\ldots$	and so on	p. 97	C	circumference	p. 394
$\neq$	is not equal to	p. 136	π	pi, an irrational number	
$\frac{1}{a}$	reciprocal of a	p. 141		approximately equal to 3.14	p. 394
$\overset{?}{=}$	Is the statement true?	p. 174	$\sqrt{x}$	nonnegative square root of x	p. 400
$\geq$	is greater than or equal to	p. 205	V	volume	p. 421
$\leq$	is less than or equal to	p. 205	B	area of base	p. 422
$a : b$	ratio of a to b	p. 228	(a, b)	ordered pair with	
$\angle A$	angle with vertex A	p. 251		x-coordinate a and	
AB	length of segment $\overline{AB}$	p. 251		y-coordinate b	p. 486
$\sim$	is similar to	p. 252	$F \rightarrow F'$	F maps onto F'	p. 510
$\triangle ABC$	triangle with vertices ABC	p. 252	A'	image of A, A prime	p. 510
%	percent	p. 274	$P(\text{event})$	probability of the event	p. 580
$\overleftrightarrow{AB}$	line AB	p. 324	$n!$	n factorial	p. 606
$\overrightarrow{AB}$	ray AB	p. 324			

Table 3 Squares and Square Roots

Number n	Square n^2	Positive Square Root $\sqrt{n}$	Number n	Square n^2	Positive Square Root $\sqrt{n}$
1	1	1.000	51	2,601	7.141
2	4	1.414	52	2,704	7.211
3	9	1.732	53	2,809	7.280
4	16	2.000	54	2,916	7.348
5	25	2.236	55	3,025	7.416
6	36	2.449	56	3,136	7.483
7	49	2.646	57	3,249	7.550
8	64	2.828	58	3,364	7.616
9	81	3.000	59	3,481	7.681
10	100	3.162	60	3,600	7.746
11	121	3.317	61	3,721	7.810
12	144	3.464	62	3,844	7.874
13	169	3.606	63	3,969	7.937
14	196	3.742	64	4,096	8.000
15	225	3.873	65	4,225	8.062
16	256	4.000	66	4,356	8.124
17	289	4.123	67	4,489	8.185
18	324	4.243	68	4,624	8.246
19	361	4.359	69	4,761	8.307
20	400	4.472	70	4,900	8.367
21	441	4.583	71	5,041	8.426
22	484	4.690	72	5,184	8.485
23	529	4.796	73	5,329	8.544
24	576	4.899	74	5,476	8.602
25	625	5.000	75	5,625	8.660
26	676	5.099	76	5,776	8.718
27	729	5.196	77	5,929	8.775
28	784	5.292	78	6,084	8.832
29	841	5.385	79	6,241	8.888
30	900	5.477	80	6,400	8.944
31	961	5.568	81	6,561	9.000
32	1,024	5.657	82	6,724	9.055
33	1,089	5.745	83	6,889	9.110
34	1,156	5.831	84	7,056	9.165
35	1,225	5.916	85	7,225	9.220
36	1,296	6.000	86	7,396	9.274
37	1,369	6.083	87	7,569	9.327
38	1,444	6.164	88	7,744	9.381
39	1,521	6.245	89	7,921	9.434
40	1,600	6.325	90	8,100	9.487
41	1,681	6.403	91	8,281	9.539
42	1,764	6.481	92	8,464	9.592
43	1,849	6.557	93	8,649	9.644
44	1,936	6.633	94	8,836	9.695
45	2,025	6.708	95	9,025	9.747
46	2,116	6.782	96	9,216	9.798
47	2,209	6.856	97	9,409	9.849
48	2,304	6.928	98	9,604	9.899
49	2,401	7.000	99	9,801	9.950
50	2,500	7.071	100	10,000	10.000

Table 4 For Use With Problem Solving Applications

Chapter 1
Temperature Extremes and Annual Precipitation

Location	High Temperature (°F)	Low Temperature (°F)	Annual Precipitation (in.)
Anchorage, Alaska	86	-38	14.7
El Paso, Tex.	109	-8	8.0
Indianapolis, Ind.	107	-25	39.2
Miami, Fla.	100	28	59.9
Pago Pago, Amer. Samoa	98	67	193.6
San José, Costa Rica	92	49	70.8
South Pole Station	6	-107	0.1

SOURCE: *The Weather Almanac*

Chapter 9
Animal Longevity

Animal	Birth Weight (Male) (g)	Maximum Life Span (yr)
Dragonfly	1	0.1
Rat	6	3.3
Salmon	15	13
Spoonbill	45	10
Rabbit	65	13
Cat	98	28
Dog (cocker spaniel)	240	20

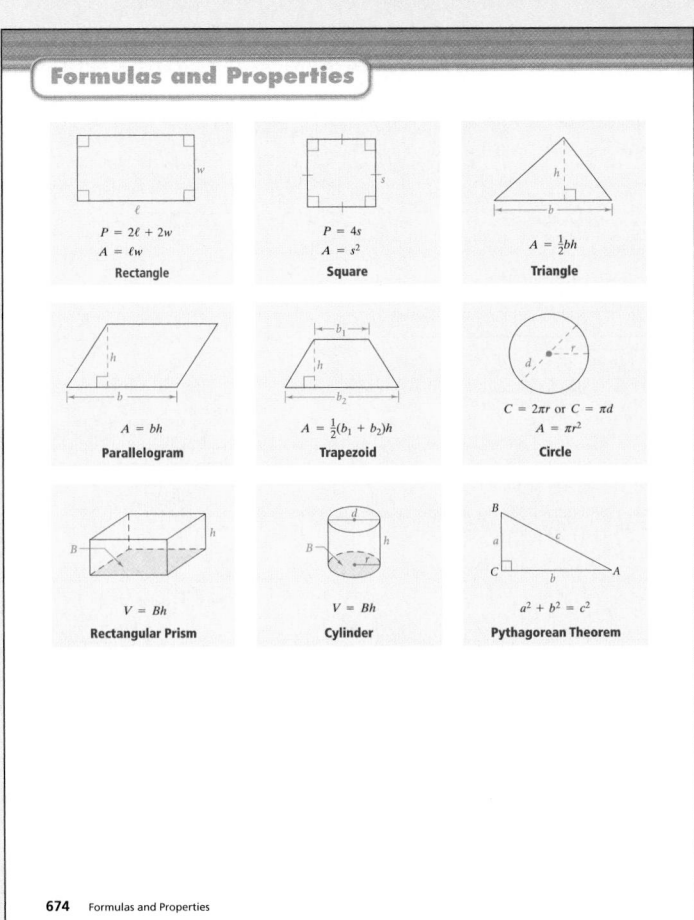

$P = 2\ell + 2w$
$A = \ell w$
Rectangle

$P = 4s$
$A = s^2$
Square

$A = \frac{1}{2}bh$
Triangle

$A = bh$
Parallelogram

$A = \frac{1}{2}(b_1 + b_2)h$
Trapezoid

$C = 2\pi r$ or $C = \pi d$
$A = \pi r^2$
Circle

$V = Bh$
Rectangular Prism

$V = Bh$
Cylinder

$a^2 + b^2 = c^2$
Pythagorean Theorem

Properties of Real Numbers

Unless otherwise stated, the variables a, b, c, and d used in these properties can be replaced with any number represented on a number line.

Identity Properties
Addition $a + 0 = a$ and $0 + a = a$
Multiplication $a \cdot 1 = a$ and $1 \cdot a = a$

Commutative Properties
Addition $a + b = b + a$
Multiplication $a \cdot b = b \cdot a$

Associative Properties
Addition $(a + b) + c = a + (b + c)$
Multiplication $(a \cdot b) \cdot c = a \cdot (b \cdot c)$

Inverse Properties
Addition
$a + (-a) = 0$ and $-a + a = 0$
Multiplication
$a \cdot \frac{1}{a} = 1$ and $\frac{1}{a} \cdot a = 1$ $(a \neq 0)$

Distributive Properties
$a(b + c) = ab + ac$ $(b + c)a = ba + ca$
$a(b - c) = ab - ac$ $(b - c)a = ba - ca$

Properties of Equality
Addition   If $a = b$, then $a + c = b + c$.
Subtraction   If $a = b$, then $a - c = b - c$.
Multiplication   If $a = b$, then $a \cdot c = b \cdot c$.
Division   If $a = b$, and $c \neq 0$, then $\frac{a}{c} = \frac{b}{c}$.
Substitution   If $a = b$, then b can replace a in any expression.
Reflexive $a = a$
Symmetric   If $a = b$, then $b = a$.
Transitive   If $a = b$ and $b = c$, then $a = c$.

Cross Products Property
$\frac{a}{c} = \frac{b}{d}$ is equivalent to $ad = bc$.

Zero Product Property
If $ab = 0$, then $a = 0$ or $b = 0$.

Closure Property
$a + b$ is a unique real number.
ab is a unique real number.

Density Property
Between any two rational numbers, there is at least one other rational number.

Properties of Inequality
Addition   If $a > b$, then $a + c > b + c$.
                    If $a < b$, then $a + c < b + c$.
Subtraction   If $a > b$, then $a - c > b - c$.
                    If $a < b$, then $a - c < b - c$.
Multiplication
If $a > b$ and $c > 0$, then $ac > bc$.
If $a < b$ and $c > 0$, then $ac < bc$.
If $a > b$ and $c < 0$, then $ac < bc$.
If $a < b$ and $c < 0$, then $ac > bc$.
Division
If $a > b$ and $c > 0$, then $\frac{a}{c} > \frac{b}{c}$.
If $a < b$ and $c > 0$, then $\frac{a}{c} < \frac{b}{c}$.
If $a > b$ and $c < 0$, then $\frac{a}{c} < \frac{b}{c}$.
If $a < b$ and $c < 0$, then $\frac{a}{c} > \frac{b}{c}$.
Transitive   If $a > b$ and $b > c$, then $a > c$.

English/Spanish Illustrated Glossary

A

Absolute value (p. 31) The absolute value of a number is its distance from 0 on a number line.

Valor absoluto (p. 31) El valor absoluto de un número es su distancia del 0 en una recta numérica.

-7 is 7 units from 0, so $|-7| = 7$.

Acute angle (p. 330) An acute angle is an angle with a measure between 0° and 90°.

Ángulo agudo (p. 330) Un ángulo agudo es un ángulo que mide entre 0° y 90°.

$0° < m\angle 1 < 90°$

Acute triangle (p. 337) An acute triangle has three acute angles.

Triángulo acutángulo (p. 337) Un triángulo acutángulo tiene tres ángulos agudos.

$\angle 1, \angle 2,$ and $\angle 3$ are acute.

Addition Property of Equality (p. 180) The Addition Property of Equality states that if the same value is added to each side of an equation, the results are equal.

Propiedad aditiva de la igualdad (p. 180) La propiedad aditiva de la igualdad establece que si se suma el mismo valor a cada lado de una ecuación, los resultados son iguales.

Since $\frac{20}{2} = 10$, $\frac{20}{2} + 3 = 10 + 3$.
If $a = b$, then $a + c = b + c$.

Addition Property of Inequality (p. 210) The Addition Property of Inequality states that if you add the same value to each side of an inequality, the relationship between the two sides does not change.

Propiedad aditiva de la desigualdad (p. 210) La propiedad aditiva de la desigualdad establece que si sumas el mismo valor a cada lado de una desigualdad, la relación entre los dos lados no cambia.

If $a > b$, then $a + c > b + c$.
Since $4 > 2$, $4 + 11 > 2 + 11$.
If $a < b$, then $a + c < b + c$.
Since $4 < 9$, $4 + 11 < 9 + 11$.

Additive inverse (p. 38) Two numbers whose sum is 0 are additive inverses.

Inverso aditivo (p. 38) Dos números cuya suma es 0 son inversos aditivos.

$(-5) + 5 = 0$

Adjacent angles (p. 331) Adjacent angles share a vertex and a side but have no interior points in common.

Ángulos adyacentes (p. 331) Los ángulos adyacentes comparten un vértice y un lado, pero no tienen puntos interiores en común.

$\angle 1$ and $\angle 2$ are adjacent angles.

Algebraic expression (p. 169) An algebraic expression is a mathematical phrase that uses variables, numbers, and operation symbols.

Expresión algebraica (p. 169) Una expresión algebraica es un enunciado matemático que usa variables, números y símbolos de operaciones.

$2x - 5$ is an algebraic expression.

Angle (p. 330) An angle is formed by two rays with a common endpoint called a vertex.

Ángulo (p. 330) Un ángulo está formado por dos rayos que tienen un punto final común llamado vértice.

$\angle 1$ is made up of $\overrightarrow{GP}$ and $\overrightarrow{GS}$ with common endpoint G.

Angle of rotation (p. 520) The angle of rotation is the number of degrees that a figure rotates.

Ángulo de rotación (p. 520) El ángulo de rotación es el número de grados que se rota una figura.

$\triangle RST$ has been rotated 180° to $\triangle R'S'T'$.

Arc (p. 351) An arc is part of a circle.

Arco (p. 351) Un arco es parte de un círculo.

$\overarc{AB}$ is an arc of circle O. $\overarc{ABC}$ is a semicircle of circle O.

Area (p. 375) The area of a figure is the number of square units it encloses.

Área (p. 375) El área de una figura es el número de unidades cuadradas que contiene.

The area of each square is 1 ft^2. $\ell = 6$ ft and $w = 4$ ft, so the area is 24 ft^2.

Arithmetic sequence (p. 442) In an arithmetic sequence, each term is the result of adding a fixed number (called the common difference) to the previous term.

Progresión aritmética (p. 442) En una progresión aritmética, cada término es el resultado de sumar un número fijo al término anterior.

The sequence 4, 10, 16, 22, 28, . . . is an arithmetic sequence. You add 6 to each term to find the next term.

Associative Property of Addition (p. 9) The Associative Property of Addition states that changing the grouping of the addends does not change the sum.

Propiedad asociativa de la suma (p. 9) La propiedad asociativa de la suma establece que cambiar la agrupación de los sumandos no cambia la suma.

$(2 + 3) + 7 = 2 + (3 + 7)$
$(a + b) + c = a + (b + c)$

Associative Property of Multiplication (p. 15) The Associative Property of Multiplication states that changing the grouping of factors does not change the product.

Propiedad asociativa de la multiplicación (p. 15) La propiedad asociativa de la multiplicación establece que cambiar la agrupación de los factores no altera el producto.

$(3 \cdot 4) \cdot 5 = 3 \cdot (4 \cdot 5)$
$(a \cdot b) \cdot c = a \cdot (b \cdot c)$

B

Balance (p. 469) The balance of an account is the principal plus the interest earned.

Saldo (p. 469) El saldo de una cuenta es el capital más los intereses ganados.

You deposit $100 and earn $5 interest. Your balance is $105.

Base (p. 68) When a number is written in exponential form, the number that is used as a factor is the base.

Base (p. 68) Cuando un número se escribe en forma exponencial, el número que se usa como factor es la base.

$5^4 = 5 \times 5 \times 5 \times 5$
└ base

Bases of three-dimensional figures (pp. 410, 411) See *Cone*, *Cylinder*, *Prism*, and *Pyramid*.

Bases de figuras tridimensionales (pp. 410, 411) Ver *Cone*, *Cylinder*, *Prism* y *Pyramid*.

Bases of two-dimensional figures (pp. 380, 384, 388) See *Parallelogram*, *Triangle*, and *Trapezoid*.

Bases de figuras bidimensionales (pp. 380, 384, 388) Ver *Parallelogram*, *Triangle* y *Trapezoid*.

Benchmark (p. 120) A benchmark is a convenient number used to replace fractions that are less than 1.

Punto de referencia (p. 120) Un punto de referencia es un número conveniente que se usa para reemplazar fracciones menores que 1.

Using benchmarks, you would estimate $\frac{5}{6} + \frac{4}{9}$ as $1 + \frac{1}{2}$.

Biased question (p. 551) A biased question is a question that makes one answer appear better than another.

Pregunta tendenciosa (p. 551) Una pregunta tendenciosa es una pregunta que hace que una respuesta parezca mejor que otra.

"Do you prefer good food or junk food?"

Box-and-whisker plot (p. 58) A box-and-whisker plot is a graph that summarizes a data set along a number line. There is a box in the middle and whiskers at either side.

Gráfica de caja y brazos (p. 58) Una gráfica de caja y brazos es un diagrama que resume un conjunto de datos usando una recta línea. Hay una caja en el centro y extensiones a cada lado.

The box-and-whisker plot uses these data: 16 19 26 26 27 29 30 31 34 34 38 39 40.
The lower quartile is 26. The median is 30. The upper quartile is 36.

C

Capture/recapture (p. 554) Capture/recapture is a sampling technique that uses proportions to estimate animal populations.

Captura/recaptura (p. 554) Captura/recaptura es una técnica de muestreo que usa las proporciones para estimar poblaciones animales.

Cell (p. 538) A cell is a box where a row and a column meet.

Celda (p. 538) Una celda es una caja donde se unen una fila y una columna.

	A	B	C	D	E
1	0.50	0.70	0.60	0.50	2.30
2	1.50	0.50	2.75	2.50	7.25

Column C and row 2 meet at the shaded box, cell C2.

Center of a circle (p. 350) A circle is named by its center.

Centro de un círculo (p. 350) Un círculo es denominado por su centro.

Circle O

Center of a sphere (p. 411) See *Sphere*.

Centro de una esfera (p. 411) Ver *Sphere*.

Center of rotation (p. 519) The center of rotation is a fixed point about which a figure is rotated.

Centro de rotación (p. 519) El centro de rotación es un punto fijo alrededor del cual rota una figura.

O is the center of rotation.

Central angle (p. 350) A central angle is an angle with its vertex at the center of a circle.

Ángulo central (p. 350) Un ángulo central es un ángulo que tiene el vértice en el centro de un círculo.

∠*AOB* is a central angle of circle *O*.

Chord (p. 350) A chord is a segment that has both endpoints on the circle.

Cuerda (p. 350) Una cuerda es un segmento que tiene ambos extremos sobre el círculo.

$\overline{CB}$ is a chord of circle *O*.

Circle (p. 350) A circle is the set of points in a plane that are all the same distance from a given point called the center.

Círculo (p. 350) Un círculo es el conjunto de puntos de un plano que están a la misma distancia de un punto dado llamado centro.

Circle graph (p. 354) A circle graph is a graph of data where a circle represents the whole.

Gráfica circular (p. 354) Una gráfica circular es una gráfica de datos donde un círculo representa el todo.

Histories 26%   Tragedies 26%
Romances 13%   Comedies 35%
The circle graph represents the types of plays William Shakespeare wrote.

Circumference (p. 394) Circumference is the distance around a circle. You calculate the circumference of a circle by multiplying the diameter by π.

Circunferencia (p. 394) La circunferencia es la distancia alrededor de un círculo. La circunferencia de un círculo se calcula multiplicando el diámetro por π.

The circumference of a circle with a diameter of 10 cm is 10π, or approximately 31.4 cm.

Combination (p. 610) A combination is a grouping of objects in which the order of the objects does not matter.

Combinación (p. 610) Una combinación es una agrupación de objetos en que el orden de los objetos no tiene importancia.

You choose two vegetables from carrots, peas, and spinach. The possible combinations are carrots and peas, carrots and spinach, and peas and spinach.

Commission (p. 305) A commission is pay that is equal to a percent of sales.

Comisión (p. 305) Una comisión es un pago que es igual a un porcentaje de las ventas.

A salesperson receives a 6% commission on sales of $200. Her commission is $12.

Commutative Property of Addition (p. 9) The Commutative Property of Addition states that changing the order of the addends does not change the sum.

Propiedad conmutativa de la suma (p. 9) La propiedad conmutativa de la suma establece que al cambiar el orden de los sumandos no se altera la suma.

$3 + 1 = 1 + 3$
$a + b = b + a$

Commutative Property of Multiplication (p. 15) The Commutative Property of Multiplication states that changing the order of the factors does not change the product.

Propiedad conmutativa de la multiplicación (p. 15) La propiedad conmutativa de la multiplicación establece que al cambiar el orden de los factores no se altera el producto.

$6 \cdot 3 = 3 \cdot 6$
$a \cdot b = b \cdot a$

Compass (p. 361) A compass is a geometric tool used to draw circles or arcs.

Compás (p. 361) Un compás es una herramienta que se usa en geometría para dibujar círculos o arcos.

Compatible numbers (p. 5) Compatible numbers are numbers that are easy to compute mentally.

Números compatibles (p. 5) Los números compatibles son números con los que se puede calcular mentalmente con facilidad.

Estimate $151 \div 14.6$.
$151 \approx 150, 14.6 \approx 15$
$150 \div 15 = 10$
$151 \div 14.6 \approx 10$

Complement (p. 581) The complement of an event is the collection of outcomes not contained in the event.

Complemento (p. 581) El complemento de un suceso es la colección de resultados que el suceso no incluye.

The event *no rain* is the complement of the event *rain*.

Complementary (p. 331) Two angles are complementary if the sum of their measures is 90°.

Complementario (p. 331) Dos ángulos son complementarios si la suma de sus medidas es 90°.

∠*BCA* and ∠*CAB* are complementary angles.

Composite number (p. 75) A composite number is a whole number greater than 1 that has more than two factors.

Número compuesto (p. 75) Un número compuesto es un número entero mayor que 1, que tiene más de dos factores.

24 is a composite number. Its factors are 1, 2, 3, 4, 6, 8, 12, and 24.

Compound event (p. 598) A compound event is an event that consists of two or more events. The probability of a compound event can be found by multiplying the probability of one event by the probability of a second event.

Suceso compuesto (p. 598) Un suceso compuesto es un suceso que está formado por dos o más sucesos. La probabilidad de un suceso compuesto se puede hallar al multiplicar la probabilidad de un suceso por la probabilidad de un segundo suceso.

If $P(A) = \frac{1}{3}$ and $P(B) = \frac{1}{2}$, then $P(A, \text{then } B) = \frac{1}{6}$.

Compound interest (p. 469) Compound interest is interest paid on the original principal and on any interest that has been left in the account. You can use the formula $B = p(1 + r)^t$ where *B* is the balance in the account, *p* is the principal, *r* is the annual interest rate, and *t* is the time in years that the account earns interest.

Interés compuesto (p. 469) El interés compuesto es el interés que se paga sobre el principal original y sobre cualquier interés que ha quedado en la cuenta. Se puede usar la fórmula $B = p(1 + r)^t$ donde *B* es el saldo en la cuenta, *p* es el principal, *r* es la tasa de interés anual y *t* es el tiempo en años en que la cuenta gana interés.

You deposit $500 in an account earning 5% annual interest.
The balance after six years is $500(1 + 0.05)^6$, or $670.05.

Cone (p. 411) A cone is a three-dimensional figure with one circular base and one vertex.

Cono (p. 411) Un cono es una figura tridimensional con una base circular y un vértice.

base

Congruent angles (p. 331) Congruent angles are angles that have the same measure.

Ángulos congruentes (p. 331) Los ángulos congruentes son ángulos que tienen la misma medida.

∠*B* ≅ ∠*C*

Congruent polygons (p. 346) Congruent polygons are polygons with the same size and shape.

Polígonos congruentes (p. 346) Los polígonos congruentes son polígonos que tienen el mismo tamaño y forma.

△*ABC* ≅ △*QSR*

Congruent sides (p. 336) Congruent sides have the same length.

Lados congruentes (p. 336) Los lados congruentes tienen la misma longitud.

△*EFG* is an equilateral triangle.
$\overline{EF} \cong \overline{FG} \cong \overline{GE}$

Conjecture (p. 443) A conjecture is a prediction that suggests what can be expected to happen.

Conjetura (p. 443) Una conjetura es una predicción que sugiere lo que se puede esperar que ocurra.

Every clover has three leaves.

Coordinate plane (p. 486) A coordinate plane is formed by a horizontal number line called the *x*-axis and a vertical number line called the *y*-axis.

Plano de coordenadas (p. 486) Un plano de coordenadas está formado por una recta numérica horizontal llamada eje de *x* y por una recta numérica vertical llamada eje de *y*.

Corresponding parts (p. 346) Corresponding parts of congruent polygons are congruent.

Partes correspondientes (p. 346) Las partes correspondientes de los polígonos congruentes son congruentes.

$\overline{AB} \cong \overline{ED}, \overline{BC} \cong \overline{DF}, \overline{CA} \cong \overline{FE}$
∠*A* ≅ ∠*E*, ∠*B* ≅ ∠*D*, ∠*C* ≅ ∠*F*
△*ABC* ≅ △*EDF*

EXAMPLES

Counting principle (p. 592) If there are *m* ways of making one choice from a first situation and *n* ways of making a choice from a second situation, then there are *m* × *n* ways to make the first choice followed by the second.

Toss a coin and roll a standard number cube. The total number of possible outcomes is 2 × 6 = 12.

Principio de conteo (p. 592) Si hay *m* maneras de hacer una elección para una primera situación y *n* maneras de hacer una elección para una segunda situación, entonces hay *m* × *n* maneras de hacer la primera elección seguida de la segunda.

Cross products (p. 239) For two ratios, the cross products are found by multiplying the denominator of one ratio by the numerator of the other ratio.

In the proportion $\frac{2}{5} = \frac{10}{25}$, the cross products are $2 \cdot 25$ and $5 \cdot 10$.

Productos cruzados (p. 239) En dos razones, los productos cruzados se hallan al multiplicar el denominador de una razón por el numerador de la otra razón.

Cube (p. 410) A cube is a rectangular prism whose faces are all squares.

Cubo (p. 410) Un cubo es un prisma rectangular cuyas caras son todas cuadradas.

Cubic unit (p. 421) A cubic unit is a cube whose edges are one unit long.

Unidad cúbica (p. 421) Una unidad cúbica es un cubo cuyos lados tienen una unidad de longitud.

Cylinder (p. 410) A cylinder is a three-dimensional figure with two congruent parallel bases that are circles.

Cilindro (p. 410) Un cilindro es una figura tridimensional con dos bases congruentes paralelas que son círculos.

D

Decagon (p. 340) A decagon is a polygon with 10 sides.

Decágono (p. 340) Un decágono es un polígono que tiene 10 lados.

EXAMPLES

Dependent events (p. 599) Two events are dependent events if the occurrence of one event affects the probability of the occurrence of the other event.

Suppose you draw two marbles, one after the other, from a bag. If you do *not* replace the first marble before drawing the second marble, the events are dependent.

Sucesos dependientes (p. 599) Dos sucesos son dependientes si el acontecimiento de uno afecta la probabilidad de que el otro ocurra.

Diameter (p. 350) A diameter is a segment that passes through the center of a circle and has both endpoints on the circle.

Diámetro (p. 350) Un diámetro es un segmento que pasa por el centro de un círculo y que tiene ambos extremos sobre el círculo.

$\overline{RS}$ is a diameter of circle *O*.

Discount (p. 311) The difference between the original price and the sale price of an item is called the discount.

A $20 book is discounted by $2.50 to sell for $17.50.

Descuento (p. 311) Se llama descuento a la diferencia entre el precio de un artículo y su precio de venta.

Distributive Property (p. 49) The Distributive Property shows how multiplication affects an addition or subtraction: $a(b + c) = ab + ac$.

$2(3 + \frac{1}{2}) = 2 \cdot 3 + 2 \cdot \frac{1}{2}$
$8(5 - 3) = 8 \cdot 5 - 8 \cdot 3$

Propiedad distributiva (p. 49) La propiedad distributiva muestra cómo la multiplicación afecta a una suma o a una resta: $a(b + c) = ab + ac$.

Divisible (p. 73) A whole number is divisible by a second whole number if the first number can be divided by the second number with a remainder of 0.

16 is divisible by 1, 2, 4, 8, and 16.

Divisible (p. 73) Un número entero es divisible por un segundo número entero si el primer número se puede dividir por el segundo número y el residuo es 0.

Division Property of Equality (p. 186) The Division Property of Equality states that if both sides of an equation are divided by the same nonzero number, the sides remain equal.

Since $3(2) = 6$, $3(2) \div 2 = 6 \div 2$.
If $a = b$ and $c \neq 0$, then $\frac{a}{c} = \frac{b}{c}$.

Propiedad de división de la igualdad (p. 186) La propiedad de división de la igualdad establece que si ambos lados de una ecuación se dividen por el mismo número distinto de cero, los dos lados se mantienen iguales.

EXAMPLES

Division Property of Inequality (p. 214) The Division Property of Inequality states that if you divide an inequality by a positive number, the direction of the inequality is unchanged. If you divide an inequality by a negative number, *reverse* the direction of the inequality sign.

If $a > b$ and $c > 0$, then $\frac{a}{c} > \frac{b}{c}$.
Since $2 > 1$ and $3 > 0$, $\frac{2}{3} > \frac{1}{3}$.
If $a < b$ and $c > 0$, then $\frac{a}{c} < \frac{b}{c}$.
Since $2 < 4$ and $3 > 0$, $\frac{2}{3} < \frac{4}{3}$.
If $a > b$ and $c < 0$, then $\frac{a}{c} < \frac{b}{c}$.
Since $2 > 1$ and $-4 < 0$, $\frac{2}{-4} < \frac{1}{-4}$.
If $a < b$ and $c < 0$, then $\frac{a}{c} > \frac{b}{c}$.
Since $2 < 4$ and $-4 < 0$, $\frac{2}{-4} > \frac{4}{-4}$.

Propiedad de división de la desigualdad (p. 214) La propiedad de división de la desigualdad establece que si se divide una desigualdad por un número positivo, la dirección de la desigualdad no cambia. Si se divide una desigualdad por un número negativo, se *invierte* la dirección del signo de desigualdad.

Double bar graph (p. 539) A double bar graph is a graph that uses bars to compare two sets of data.

Gráfica de doble barra (p. 539) Una gráfica de doble barra es una gráfica que usa barras para comparar dos conjuntos de datos.

This double bar graph shows class size for grades 6, 7, and 8 for boys and girls.

Double line graph (p. 539) A double line graph is a graph that compares changes over time for two sets of data.

Gráfica de doble línea (p. 539) Una gráfica de doble línea es una gráfica que compara los cambios de dos conjuntos de datos a través del tiempo.

This double line graph represents seasonal air conditioner and snow blower sales (in thousands of dollars) for a large department-store chain.

E

Edge (p. 410) An edge is a segment formed by the intersection of two faces of a three-dimensional figure.

Arista (p. 410) Una arista es un segmento formado por la intersección de dos caras de una figura tridimensional.

EXAMPLES

Equation (p. 174) An equation is a mathematical sentence with an equal sign.

$27 \div 9 = 3$ and $x + 10 = 8$ are examples of equations.

Ecuación (p. 174) Una ecuación es una oración matemática con un signo igual.

Equilateral triangle (p. 336) An equilateral triangle is a triangle with three congruent sides.

Triángulo equilátero (p. 336) Un triángulo equilátero es un triángulo que tiene tres lados congruentes.

$\overline{SL} \cong \overline{LW} \cong \overline{WS}$

Equivalent fractions (p. 82) Equivalent fractions are fractions that name the same number.

$\frac{1}{2}$ and $\frac{25}{50}$ are equivalent fractions.

Fracciones equivalentes (p. 82) Las fracciones equivalentes son fracciones que indican la misma cantidad.

Equivalent ratios (p. 229) Equivalent ratios name the same number. Equivalent ratios written as fractions are equivalent fractions.

The ratios $\frac{4}{7}$ and $\frac{8}{14}$ are equivalent.

Razones equivalentes (p. 229) Las razones equivalentes indican el mismo número. Las razones equivalentes escritas como fracciones son fracciones equivalentes.

Evaluating expressions (p. 170) To evaluate an expression, replace each variable with a number. Then follow the Order of Operations.

To evaluate the expression $3x + 2$ for $x = 4$, substitute 4 for *x*.
$3x + 2 = 3(4) + 2 = 14$

Evaluación de una expresión (p. 170) Para evaluar una expresión, se reemplaza cada variable con un número. Luego se sigue el orden de las operaciones.

Event (p. 580) A collection of possible outcomes is an event.

When you toss a coin, "heads" and "tails" are possible events.

Suceso (p. 580) Un suceso es un grupo de resultados posibles.

Experimental probability (p. 586) For a series of trials, the experimental probability of an event is the ratio of the number of times an event occurs to the total number of trials.
$P(\text{event}) = \frac{\text{number of times an event occurs}}{\text{total number of trials}}$

A basketball player makes 19 baskets in 28 attempts. The experimental probability that the player makes a basket is $\frac{19}{28} \approx 68\%$.

Probabilidad experimental (p. 586) En una serie de pruebas, la probabilidad experimental de un suceso es la razón del número de veces que ocurre un suceso al número total de pruebas.
$P(\text{suceso}) = \frac{\text{número de veces que ocurre un suceso}}{\text{número total de pruebas}}$

Exponent (p. 68)   An exponent tells how many times a number, or base, is used as a factor.

Exponente (p. 68)   Un exponente dice cuántas veces se usa como factor un número, o base.

exponent

$3^4 = 3 \times 3 \times 3 \times 3$

Read 3^4 as *three to the fourth power.*

Face (p. 410)   A face is a flat surface of a three-dimensional figure that is shaped like a polygon.

Cara (p. 410)   Una cara es una superficie plana de una figura tridimensional que tiene la forma de un polígono.

face

Factor (p. 75)   A factor is a whole number that divides another whole number with a remainder of 0.

Divisor (p. 75)   Un divisor es un número entero que divide a otro número entero y el residuo es 0.

1, 2, 3, 4, 6, 12, 18, and 36 are factors of 36.

Factorial (p. 606)   A factorial is the product of all positive integers less than or equal to a number. The symbol for factorial is an exclamation point.

Factorial (p. 606)   Una factorial es el producto de todos los enteros positivos menores o iguales que un número. El símbolo de factorial es un signo de cierre de exclamación.

$5! = 5 \times 4 \times 3 \times 2 \times 1 = 120$

Formula (p. 472)   A formula is a rule that shows the relationship between two or more quantities.

Fórmula (p. 472)   Una fórmula es una regla que muestra la relación entre dos o *más* cantidades.

The formula $P = 2\ell + 2w$ gives the perimeter of a rectangle in terms of its length and width.

Frequency table (p. 532)   A frequency table is a table that lists each item in a data set with the number of times the item occurs.

Tabla de frecuencia (p. 532)   Una tabla de frecuencia es una tabla que registra todos los elementos de un conjunto de datos y el número de veces que ocurre cada uno.

Household Telephones

Phones	Tally	Frequency
1	✝✝✝ |||	8
2	✝✝✝		6
3						4

This frequency table shows the number of household telephones for a class of students.

Function (p. 452)   A function is a relationship that assigns exactly one output value for each input value.

Función (p. 452)   Una función es una relación que asigna exactamente un valor resultante a cada valor inicial.

Wages s are a function of the number of hours worked w. If you earn \$6/h, then your wages can be expressed by the function $s = 6w$.

Geometric sequence (p. 442)   In a geometric sequence, each term is the result of multiplying the previous term by a fixed number (called the common ratio).

Progresión geométrica (p. 442)   En una progresión geométrica, cada término es el resultado de la multiplicación del término anterior por un número fijo llamado rayón común.

The sequence 1, 3, 9, 27, 81, . . . is a geometric sequence. You multiply each term by 3 to find the next term.

Graph of an equation (p. 492)   The graph of an equation is the graph of all the points that are solutions of the equation.

Gráfica de una ecuación (p. 492)   La gráfica de una ecuación es la gráfica de todos los puntos cuyas coordenadas son soluciones a la ecuación.

The coordinates of all the points on the graph satisfy the equation $y = |x| - 1$.

Greatest common factor (GCF) (p. 75)   The greatest common factor of two or more numbers is the greatest number that is a factor of all of the numbers.

Máximo común divisor (MCD) (p. 75)   El máximo común divisor de dos o más números es el mayor número que es divisor de todos los números.

The GCF of 12 and 30 is 6.

Height of three-dimensional figures (p. 410)   See *Cylinder* and *Prism.*

Altura de figuras tridimensionales (p. 410)   Ver *Cylinder* y *Prism.*

Height of two-dimensional figures (pp. 380, 384, 388)   See *Parallelogram, Triangle,* and *Trapezoid.*

Altura de figuras bidimensionales (pp. 380, 384, 388)   Ver *Parallelogram, Triangle* y *Trapezoid.*

Hexagon (p. 340)   A hexagon is a polygon with six sides.

Hexágono (p. 340)   Un hexágono es un polígono que tiene seis lados.

Histogram (p. 533)   A histogram is a bar graph with no spaces between the bars. The height of each bar shows the frequency of data within that interval.

Histograma (p. 533)   Un histograma es una gráfica de barras sin espacio entre las barras. La altura de cada barra muestra la frecuencia de los datos dentro del intervalo.

Board Game Purchases

1–2 3–4 5–6 7–8
Games Bought

The histogram gives the frequency of board game purchases at a local toy store.

Horizontal (p. 499)   Horizontal lines are parallel to the *x*-axis.

Horizontal (p. 499)   Las rectas horizontales son paralelas al eje de *x*.

Hypotenuse (p. 405)   In a right triangle, the hypotenuse is the longest side, which is opposite the right angle.

Hipotenusa (p. 405)   En un triángulo rectángulo, la hipotenusa es el lado más largo, que es el lado opuesto al ángulo recto.

$\overline{AC}$ is the hypotenuse of $\triangle ABC$.

Identity Property of Addition (p. 9)   The Identity Property of Addition states that the sum of 0 and *a* is *a*.

Propiedad de identidad de la suma (p. 9)   La propiedad de identidad de la suma establece que la suma de cero y *a* es *a*.

$7 + 0 = 7$
$a + 0 = a$

Identity Property of Multiplication (p. 15)   The Identity Property of Multiplication states that the product of 1 and *a* is *a*.

Propiedad de identidad de la multiplicación (p. 15)   La propiedad de identidad de la multiplicación establece que el producto de 1 y *a* es *a*.

$7 \cdot 1 = 7$
$a \cdot 1 = a$

Image (p. 510)   An image is the result of a transformation of a point, line, or figure.

Imagen (p. 510)   Una imagen es el resultado de una transformación de un punto, una recta o una figura.

$A'B'C'D'$ is the image of $ABCD$.

Improper fraction (p. 91)   An improper fraction has a numerator that is greater than or equal to its denominator.

Fracción impropia (p. 91)   Una fracción impropia tiene un numerador mayor o igual que su denominador.

$\frac{24}{15}$ and $\frac{16}{16}$ are improper fractions.

Independent events (p. 598)   Two events are independent events if the occurrence of one event does not affect the occurrence of the other.

Sucesos independientes (p. 598)   Dos sucesos son independientes si el acontecimiento de uno no afecta la probabilidad de que el otro suceso ocurra.

Suppose you draw two marbles, one after the other, from a bag. If you replace the first marble before drawing the second marble, the events are independent.

Indirect measurement (p. 253)   Indirect measurement uses proportions and similar triangles to measure distances that would be difficult to measure directly.

Medición indirecta (p. 253)   La medición indirecta usa proporciones y triángulos semejantes para medir las distancias que serían difíciles de medir directamente.

5 ft
4 ft   10 ft

A 5-ft-tall person standing near a tree has a shadow 4 ft long. The tree has a shadow 10 ft long. The height of the tree is 12.5 ft.

Inductive reasoning (p. 443)   Inductive reasoning involves looking for a pattern and writing a rule to describe the pattern in a sequence.

Razonamiento inductivo (p. 443)   El razonamiento inductivo implica buscar un patrón y escribir una regla para describir el patrón en una secuencia.

By inductive reasoning, the next number in the pattern 2, 4, 6, 8, . . . is 10.

Inequality (p. 205) An inequality is a mathematical sentence that contains one of the signs <, >, ≤, ≥, or ≠.

Desigualdad (p. 205) Una desigualdad es una oración matemática que contiene uno de los signos <, >, ≤, ≥ o ≠.

$x < -5, x > 8, x \leq 1, x \geq -11, x \neq 7$

Integers (p. 31) Integers are the set of positive whole numbers, their opposites, and 0.

Enteros (p. 31) Los enteros son el conjunto de números enteros positivos, sus opuestos y el 0.

$\ldots -3, -2, -1, 0, 1, 2, 3, \ldots$

Intersecting lines (p. 325) Intersecting lines have exactly one point in common.

Rectas que se intersecan (p. 325) Las rectas que se intersecan tienen exactamente un punto en común.

Inverse operations (p. 181) Inverse operations are operations that undo each other.

Operaciones inversas (p. 181) Las operaciones inversas son las operaciones que se anulan entre ellas.

Addition and subtraction are inverse operations.

Irrational number (p. 401) An irrational number is a number that cannot be written as the ratio of two integers. In decimal form, an irrational number cannot be written as a terminating or repeating decimal.

Número irracional (p. 401) Un número irracional es un número que no se puede escribir como una razón de dos enteros. Como decimal, un número irracional no se puede escribir como decimal finito o periódico.

The numbers π and $2.41592653\ldots$ are irrational numbers.

Irregular polygon (p. 340) An irregular polygon is a polygon with sides that are not all congruent and/or angles that are not all congruent.

Polígono irregular (p. 340) Un polígono irregular es un polígono que tiene lados que no son todos congruentes y/o ángulos que no son todos congruentes.

KLMN is an irregular polygon.

Isosceles triangle (p. 336) An isosceles triangle is a triangle with at least two congruent sides.

Triángulo isósceles (p. 336) Un triángulo isósceles es un triángulo que tiene al menos dos lados congruentes.

$\overline{LM} \cong \overline{LB}$

L

Least common denominator (LCD) (p. 87) The least common denominator of two or more fractions is the least common multiple (LCM) of their denominators.

Mínimo común denominador (MCD) (p. 87) El mínimo común denominador de dos o más fracciones es el mínimo común múltiplo (MCD) de sus denominadores.

The LCD of the fractions $\frac{3}{8}$ and $\frac{7}{10}$ is 40.

Least common multiple (LCM) (p. 74) The least common multiple of two or more numbers is the least multiple that is common to all of the numbers.

Mínimo común múltiplo (MCM) (p. 74) El mínimo común múltiplo de dos o más números es el menor múltiplo que es común con todos los números.

The LCM of 15 and 6 is 30.

Legend (p. 539) A legend, or key, identifies data that are compared.

Leyenda (p. 539) Una leyenda, o clave, identifica categorías en una gráfica.

Legs of a right triangle (p. 405) The legs of a right triangle are the two shorter sides of the triangle.

Catetos de un triángulo rectángulo (p. 405) Los catetos de un triángulo rectángulo son los dos lados más cortos del triángulo.

$\overline{AB}$ and $\overline{BC}$ are the legs of $\triangle ABC$.

Line (p. 324) A line is a series of points that extends in two opposite directions without end.

Recta (p. 324) Una recta es una serie de puntos que se extiende indefinidamente en dos direcciones opuestas.

$\overrightarrow{CG}$ is shown.

Linear equation (p. 492) An equation is a linear equation when the graph of its solutions lies on a line.

Ecuación lineal (p. 492) Una ecuación es lineal cuando la gráfica de sus soluciones es una línea.

$y = \frac{1}{2}x + 3$ is a linear equation because the graph of its solutions is a line.

Line of reflection (p. 515) A line of reflection is a line over which a figure is reflected.

Eje de reflexión (p. 515) Un eje de reflexión es una recta sobre la cual se refleja una figura.

KLMN is reflected over the *y*-axis.

Line of symmetry (p. 514) A line of symmetry divides a figure into mirror images.

Eje de simetría (p. 514) Un eje de simetría divide una figura en imágenes reflejas.

Line plot (p. 533) A line plot is a graph that shows the shape of a data set by stacking ✗'s above each data value on a number line.

Diagrama de puntos (p. 533) Un diagrama de puntos es una gráfica que muestra la forma de un conjunto de datos agrupando ✗ sobre cada valor de una recta numérica.

Pets Owned by Students

The line plot shows the number of pets owned by each of 12 students.

Line symmetry (p. 514) A figure has line symmetry when one side is the mirror image of the other side.

Simetría lineal (p. 514) Una figura tiene simetría lineal cuando un lado es la imagen refleja del otro lado.

The left and right sides of the mask are mirror images of each other.

M

Markup (p. 311) The markup is the difference between the selling price and the original cost.

Sobrecosto (p. 311) El sobrecosto es la diferencia entre el precio de venta y el costo original.

A store buys a shirt for $15 and sells it for $25. The markup is $10.

Mean (p. 53) The mean of a set of data values is the sum of the data divided by the number of data items.

Media (p. 53) La media de un conjunto de valores de datos es la suma de los datos dividida por el número de datos.

The mean temperature (°F) for the set of temperatures 44, 52, 48, 55, 61, and 67 is $\frac{44 + 52 + 48 + 55 + 61 + 67}{6} = 54.5$.

Median (p. 54) The median of a data set is the middle value when the data are arranged in numerical order. When there is an even number of data values, the median is the mean of the two middle values.

Mediana (p. 54) La mediana de un conjunto de datos es el valor del medio cuando los datos están organizados en orden numérico. Cuando hay un número par de valores de datos, la mediana es la media de los dos valores del medio.

Temperatures (°F) for five days arranged in order are 44, 48, 52, 55, and 58. The median temperature is 52°F because it is the middle number in the set of data.

Midpoint (p. 362) The midpoint of a segment is the point that divides the segment into two segments of equal length.

Punto medio (p. 362) El punto medio de un segmento es el punto que divide el segmento en dos segmentos de igual longitud.

$XM = YM$. M is the midpoint of $\overline{XY}$.

Mixed number (p. 91) A mixed number is the sum of a whole number and a fraction.

Número mixto (p. 91) Un número mixto es la suma de un número entero y una fracción.

$3\frac{11}{16}$ is a mixed number.
$3\frac{11}{16} = 3 + \frac{11}{16}$

Mode (p. 54) The mode of a data set is the item that occurs with the greatest frequency.

Moda (p. 54) La moda de un conjunto de datos es el dato que sucede con mayor frecuencia.

The mode of the set of prices $2.50, $2.75, $3.60, $2.75, and $3.70 is $2.75.

Multiple (p. 74) A multiple of a number is the product of that number and any nonzero whole number.

Múltiplo (p. 74) Un múltiplo de un número es el producto de ese número y cualquier número entero diferente de cero.

The number 39 is a multiple of 13.

Multiplication Property of Equality (p. 188) The Multiplication Property of Equality states that if each side of an equation is multiplied by the same number, the results are equal.

Propiedad multiplicativa de la igualdad (p. 188) La propiedad multiplicativa de la igualdad establece que si cada lado de una ecuación se multiplica por el mismo número, los resultados son iguales.

Since $\frac{12}{2} = 6$, $\frac{12}{2} \cdot 2 = 6 \cdot 2$.
If $a = b$, then $a \cdot c = b \cdot c$.

Multiplication Property of Inequality (p. 216) The Multiplication Property of Inequality states that if you multiply an inequality by a positive number, the direction of the inequality is unchanged. If you multiply an inequality by a negative number, *reverse* the direction of the inequality sign.

Propiedad multiplicativa de la desigualdad (p. 216) La propiedad multiplicativa de la desigualdad establece que cuando se multiplica una desigualdad por un número positivo, la dirección de la desigualdad no cambia. Si se multiplica una desigualdad por un número negativo, se *invierte* la dirección del signo de la desigualdad.

If $a > b$ and $c > 0$, then $ac > bc$.
If $a < b$ and $c > 0$, then $ac < bc$.
Since $3 < 5$ and $7 > 0$, $3 \cdot 7 > 2 \cdot 7$.
If $a > b$ and $c < 0$, then $ac < bc$.
Since $3 > 2$ and $-6 < 0$,
$3 \cdot (-6) < 2 \cdot (-6)$.
If $a < b$ and $c < 0$, then $ac > bc$.
Since $3 < 5$ and $-6 < 0$,
$3 \cdot (-6) > 5 \cdot (-6)$.

N

Negative trend (p. 568) There is a negative trend between two sets of data if one set of values tends to increase while the other set tends to decrease.

Tendencia negativa (p. 568) Hay una tendencia negativa entre dos conjuntos de datos si un conjunto de valores tiende a aumentar, mientras el otro conjunto tiende a disminuir.

Net (p. 414) A net is a two-dimensional pattern that can be folded to form a three-dimensional figure.

Plantilla (p. 414) Una plantilla es un patrón bidimensional que se puede doblar para formar una figura tridimensional.

These are nets for a cube.

Nonlinear equation (p. 504) The graph of a nonlinear equation is not a straight line.

Ecuación no lineal (p. 504) La gráfica de una ecuación no lineal no es una recta.

$y = x^2$ is an example of a nonlinear equation.

No trend (p. 568) There is no trend between two sets of data if the points show no relationship to each other.

Sin tendencia (p. 568) Sin tendencia entre dos conjuntos de datos significa que no hay relación alguna entre los puntos.

696 Glossary

O

Obtuse angle (p. 330) An obtuse angle is an angle with a measure greater than 90° and less than 180°.

Ángulo obtuso (p. 330) Un ángulo obtuso es un ángulo que mide más de 90° y menos de 180°.

Obtuse triangle (p. 337) An obtuse triangle is a triangle with one obtuse angle.

Triángulo obtusángulo (p. 337) Un triángulo obtusángulo es un triángulo que tiene un ángulo obtuso.

Octagon (p. 340) An octagon is a polygon with eight sides.

Octágono (p. 340) Un octágono es un polígono que tiene ocho lados.

Odds (p. 584) When outcomes are equally likely, odds are expressed as the following ratios:

odds *in favor* of an event = the ratio of the number of favorable outcomes to the number of unfavorable outcomes
odds *against* an event = the ratio of the number of unfavorable outcomes to the number of favorable outcomes

Posibilidades (p. 584) Cuando los resultados son igualmente posibles, las posibilidades se expresan como las siguientes razones:

posibilidades *en favor* de un suceso = la razón del número de resultados favorables al número de resultados desfavorables
posibilidades *en contra* de un suceso = la razón del número de resultados desfavorables al número de resultados favorables

You roll a standard number cube. The odds in favor of getting a 4 are 1 : 5.

Open sentence (p. 174) An open sentence is an equation with one or more variables.

Proposición abierta (p. 174) Una proposición abierta es una ecuación con una o más variables.

$b - 7 = 12$

Opposites (p. 31) Opposites are two numbers that are the same distance from 0 on a number line, but in opposite directions.

Opuestos (p. 31) Opuestos son dos números que están a la misma distancia del 0 en una recta numérica, pero en direcciones opuestas.

17 and -17 are opposites.

Glossary **697**

Ordered pair (p. 486) An ordered pair identifies the location of a point. The x-coordinate shows a point's position left or right of the y-axis. The y-coordinate shows a point's position up or down from the x-axis.

Par ordenado (p. 486) Un par ordenado identifica la ubicación de un punto. La coordenada x muestra la posición de un punto a la izquierda o derecha del eje de y. La coordenada y muestra la posición de un punto arriba o abajo del eje de x.

The x-coordinate of the point $(-2, 1)$ is -2, and the y-coordinate is 1.

Order of operations (pp. 48, 69)
1. Work inside grouping symbols.
2. Do all work with exponents.
3. Multiply and divide in order from left to right.
4. Add and subtract in order from left to right.

Orden de las operaciones (pp. 48, 69)
1. Trabaja dentro de los signos de agrupación.
2. Trabaja con los exponentes.
3. Multiplica y divide en orden de izquierda a derecha.
4. Suma y resta en orden de izquierda a derecha.

$2^3(7 - 4) = 2^3 \cdot 3 = 8 \cdot 3 = 24$

Origin (p. 486) The origin is the point of intersection of the x- and y-axes on a coordinate plane.

Origen (p. 486) El origen es el punto de intersección de los ejes de x y de y en un plano de coordenadas.

The ordered pair that describes the origin is $(0, 0)$.

Outcome (p. 580) An outcome is any of the possible results that can occur in an experiment.

Resultado (p. 580) Un resultado es cualquiera de los posibles desenlaces que pueden ocurrir en un experimento.

The outcomes of rolling a standard number cube are 1, 2, 3, 4, 5, and 6.

Outlier (p. 53) An outlier is a data item that is much higher or much lower than the other items in a data set.

Valor extremo (p. 53) Un valor extremo es un dato que es mucho más alto o más bajo que los demás datos en un conjunto de datos.

An outlier in the data set 6, 7, 9, 10, 11, 12, 14, and 52 is 52.

698 Glossary

P

Parallel lines (p. 325) Parallel lines are lines in the same plane that never intersect.

Rectas paralelas (p. 325) Las rectas paralelas son rectas en el mismo plano que nunca se intersecan.

$\overleftrightarrow{EF}$ is parallel to $\overleftrightarrow{HI}$.

Parallelogram (p. 341) A parallelogram is a quadrilateral with both pairs of opposite sides parallel.

Paralelogramo (p. 341) Un paralelogramo es un cuadrilátero cuyos pares de lados opuestos son paralelos.

$\overline{KV}$ is parallel to $\overline{AD}$ and $\overline{AK}$ is parallel to $\overline{DV}$, so $KVDA$ is a parallelogram.

Pentagon (p. 340) A pentagon is a polygon with five sides.

Pentágono (p. 340) Un pentágono es un polígono que tiene cinco lados.

Percent (p. 274) A percent is a ratio that compares a number to 100.

Porcentaje (p. 274) Un porcentaje es una razón que compara un número con 100.

$\frac{25}{100} = 25\%$

Percent of change (p. 310) The percent of change is the percent a quantity increases or decreases from its original amount.

Porcentaje de cambio (p. 310) El porcentaje de cambio es el porcentaje que aumenta o disminuye una cantidad a partir de su cantidad original.

The number of employees increases from 14 to 21. The percent of change is $\frac{21 - 14}{14} = 50\%$.

Perfect square (p. 400) A perfect square is a number that is the square of an integer.

Cuadrado perfecto (p. 400) Un cuadrado perfecto es un número que es el cuadrado de un entero.

Since $25 = 5^2$, 25 is a perfect square.

Perimeter (p. 375) The perimeter of a figure is the distance around the figure.

Perímetro (p. 375) El perímetro de una figura es la distancia alrededor de la figura.

The perimeter of rectangle $ABCD$ is 12 ft.

Glossary **699**

T677

Permutation (p. 606) A permutation is an arrangement of objects in a particular order.

Permutación (p. 606) Una permutación es un arreglo de objetos en un orden particular.

The permutations of the letters W, A, and X are WAX, WXA, AXW, AWX, XWA, and XAW.

Perpendicular bisector (p. 362) A perpendicular bisector is a segment bisector that is perpendicular to the segment.

Mediatriz (p. 362) Una mediatriz es una bisectriz de un segmento que es perpendicular a ese segmento.

$\overleftrightarrow{MK} \perp \overline{AB}$, $AM = MB$. $\overleftrightarrow{MK}$ is the perpendicular bisector of $\overline{AB}$.

Perpendicular lines (p. 362) Perpendicular lines intersect to form right angles.

Rectas perpendiculares (p. 362) Las rectas perpendiculares se intersecan para formar ángulos rectos.

$\overleftrightarrow{DE} \perp \overleftrightarrow{RS}$

Pi (p. 394) Pi (π) is the ratio of the circumference C of any circle to its diameter d.

Pi (p. 394) Pi (π) es la razón de la circunferencia C de cualquier círculo a su diámetro d.

$\pi = \dfrac{C}{d}$

Plane (p. 325) A plane is a flat surface that extends indefinitely in all directions.

Plano (p. 325) Un plano es una superficie plana que se extiende indefinidamente en todas las direcciones.

$DEFG$ is a plane.

Point (p. 324) A point is a location that has no size.

Punto (p. 324) Un punto es una ubicación que no tiene tamaño.

• A

A is a point.

Polygon (p. 252) A polygon is a closed figure formed by three or more line segments that do not cross.

Polígono (p. 252) Un polígono es una figura cerrada que está formada por tres o más segmentos de recta que no se cruzan.

Population (p. 550) A population is a group of objects or people about which information is wanted.

Población (p. 550) Una población es un grupo de objetos o personas sobre el que se busca información.

A class of 25 students is a sample of the population of a school.

Positive trend (p. 568) There is a positive trend between two sets of data if one set of values tends to increase while the other set tends to increase.

Tendencia positive (p. 568) Existe una tendencia positiva entre dos conjuntos de datos si un conjunto de valores tiende a aumentar mientras el otro conjunto también tiende a aumentar.

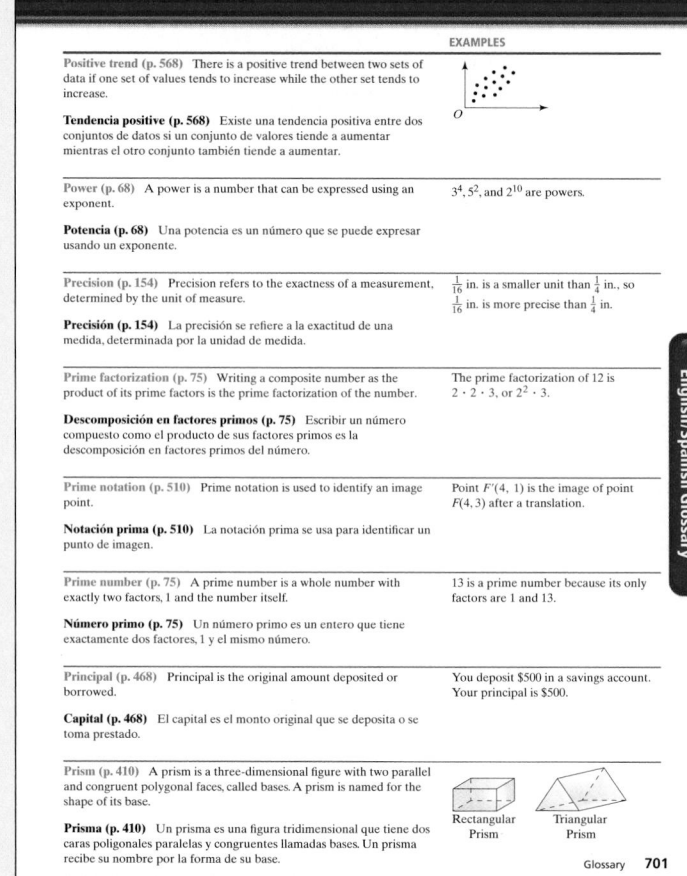

Power (p. 68) A power is a number that can be expressed using an exponent.

Potencia (p. 68) Una potencia es un número que se puede expresar usando un exponente.

3^4, 5^2, and 2^{10} are powers.

Precision (p. 154) Precision refers to the exactness of a measurement, determined by the unit of measure.

Precisión (p. 154) La precisión se refiere a la exactitud de una medida, determinada por la unidad de medida.

$\frac{1}{16}$ in. is a smaller unit than $\frac{1}{4}$ in., so $\frac{1}{16}$ in. is more precise than $\frac{1}{4}$ in.

Prime factorization (p. 75) Writing a composite number as the product of its prime factors is the prime factorization of the number.

Descomposición en factores primos (p. 75) Escribir un número compuesto como el producto de sus factores primos es la descomposición en factores primos del número.

The prime factorization of 12 is $2 \cdot 2 \cdot 3$, or $2^2 \cdot 3$.

Prime notation (p. 510) Prime notation is used to identify an image point.

Notación prima (p. 510) La notación prima se usa para identificar un punto de imagen.

Point $F'(4, 1)$ is the image of point $F(4, 3)$ after a translation.

Prime number (p. 75) A prime number is a whole number with exactly two factors, 1 and the number itself.

Número primo (p. 75) Un número primo es un entero que tiene exactamente dos factores, 1 y el mismo número.

13 is a prime number because its only factors are 1 and 13.

Principal (p. 468) Principal is the original amount deposited or borrowed.

Capital (p. 468) El capital es el monto original que se deposita o se toma prestado.

You deposit $500 in a savings account. Your principal is $500.

Prism (p. 410) A prism is a three-dimensional figure with two parallel and congruent polygonal faces, called bases. A prism is named for the shape of its base.

Prisma (p. 410) Un prisma es una figura tridimensional que tiene dos caras poligonales paralelas y congruentes llamadas bases. Un prisma recibe su nombre por la forma de su base.

Rectangular Prism   Triangular Prism

Probability (pp. 580, 586) Probability is used to describe the likeliness that an event will happen. See *Experimental probability* and *Theoretical probability*.

Probabilidad (pp. 580, 586) La probabilidad se usa para describir la posibilidad de que ocurra un suceso. Ver *Experimental probability* y *Theoretical probability*.

Proportion (p. 238) A proportion is an equation stating that two ratios are equal.

Proporción (p. 238) Una proporción es una ecuación que establece que dos razones son iguales.

$\frac{3}{12} = \frac{9}{36}$ is a proportion.

Pyramid (p. 410) A pyramid is a three-dimensional figure with triangular faces that meet at a vertex and a base that is a polygon. A pyramid is named for the shape of its base.

Pirámide (p. 410) Una pirámide es una figura tridimensional que tiene caras triangulares que coinciden en un vértice y una base que es un polígono. Una pirámide recibe su nombre por la forma de su base.

Triangular Pyramid   Rectangular Pyramid

Pythagorean Theorem (p. 405) In any right triangle, the sum of the squares of the lengths of the legs (a and b) is equal to the square of the length of the hypotenuse (c): $a^2 + b^2 = c^2$.

Teorema de Pitágoras (p. 405) En cualquier triángulo rectángulo, la suma del cuadrado de la longitud de los catetos (a y b) es igual al cuadrado de la longitud de la hipotenusa (c): $a^2 + b^2 = c^2$.

The right triangle has leg lengths 3 and 4 and hypotenuse length 5. $3^2 + 4^2 = 5^2$

Q

Quadrants (p. 486) The x- and y-axes divide the coordinate plane into four regions called quadrants.

Cuadrantes (p. 486) Los ejes de x y de y dividen el plano de coordenadas en cuatro regiones llmadas cuadrantes.

The quadrants are labeled I, II, III, and IV.

Quadrilateral (p. 340) A quadrilateral is a polygon with four sides.

Cuadrilátero (p. 340) Un cuadrilátero es un polígono que tiene cuatro lados.

R

Radius (p. 350) A radius of a circle is a segment that connects the center of a circle to the circle.

Radio (p. 350) Un radio de un círculo es un segmento que conecta el centro del círculo con el círculo.

$\overline{OA}$ is a radius of circle O.

Random sample (p. 550) In a random sample, each member of the population has an equal chance of being selected.

Muestra aleatoria (p. 550) En una muestra aleatoria, cada miembro de la población tiene la misma posibilidad de ser elegido.

For the population *customers at a mall*, a random sample would be every 20th customer entering in a 2-hour period.

Range (p. 55) The range of a data set is the difference between the greatest and the least values.

Rango (p. 55) El rango de un conjunto de datos es la diferencia entre los valores mayor y menor.

Data set: 62, 109, 234, 35, 96, 49, 201
Range: $201 - 35 = 166$

Rate (p. 232) A rate is a ratio that compares two quantities measured in different units.

Tasa (p. 232) Una tasa es una razón que compara dos cantidades medidas en diferentes unidades.

You read 116 words in 1 min. Your reading rate is $\frac{116 \text{ words}}{1 \text{ min}}$.

Ratio (p. 228) A ratio is a comparison of two quantities by division.

Razón (p. 228) Una razón es una comparación de dos cantidades mediante la división.

There are three ways to write a ratio: 9 to 10, 9 : 10, and $\frac{9}{10}$.

Rational number (p. 102) A rational number is a number that can be written as a quotient of two integers, where the divisor is not 0.

Número racional (p. 102) Un número racional es un número que se puede escribir como cociente de dos enteros, donde el divisor es diferente de cero.

$\frac{1}{3}$, -5, 6.4, $0.666\ldots$, $-2\frac{4}{5}$, 0, and $\frac{7}{3}$ are rational numbers.

Ray (p. 324) A ray is part of a line, with one endpoint and all the points of the line on one side of the endpoint.

Rayo (p. 324) Un rayo es una parte de una recta que tiene un extremo y todos los puntos de la recta a un lado del extremo.

endpoint of $\overrightarrow{CG}$

$\overrightarrow{CG}$ represents a ray.

Reciprocal (p. 141) Two numbers are reciprocals if their product is 1.

Recíproco (p. 141) Dos números son recíprocos si su producto es 1.

The numbers $\frac{4}{9}$ and $\frac{9}{4}$ are reciprocals.

Rectangle (p. 341) A rectangle is a parallelogram with four right angles.

Rectángulo (p. 341) Un rectángulo es un paralelogramo que tiene cuatro ángulos rectos.

Reflection (p. 515) A reflection, or flip, is a transformation that flips a figure over a line of reflection.

Reflexión (p. 515) Una reflexión es una transformación que voltea una figura sobre un eje de reflexión.

$K'L'M'N'$ is a reflection of $KLMN$ over the y-axis.

Regular polygon (p. 340) A regular polygon is a polygon with all sides congruent and all angles congruent.

Polígono regular (p. 340) Un polígono regular es un polígono que tiene todos los lados y todos los ángulos congruentes.

$ABDFEC$ is a regular hexagon.

Repeating decimal (p. 97) A repeating decimal is a decimal that repeats without end. The repeating block can be one or more digits.

Decimal periódico (p. 97) Un decimal periódico es un decimal que repite los mismos dígitos interminablemente. El bloque que se repite puede ser un dígito o más de un dígito.

$0.888\ldots = 0.\overline{8}$
$0.272727\ldots = 0.\overline{27}$

Rhombus (p. 341) A rhombus is a parallelogram with four congruent sides.

Rombo (p. 341) Un rombo es un paralelogramo que tiene cuatro lados congruentes.

Right angle (p. 330) A right angle is an angle with a measure of 90°.

Ángulo recto (p. 330) Un ángulo recto es un ángulo que mide 90°.

$m\angle D = 90°$

Right triangle (p. 337) A right triangle is a triangle with one right angle.

Triángulo rectángulo (p. 337) Un triángulo rectángulo es un triángulo que tiene un ángulo recto.

Since $\angle B$ is a right angle, $\triangle ABC$ is a right triangle.

Rise (p. 498) The rise of a line is a vertical change in a line. See *Slope*.

Distancia vertical (p. 498) La distancia vertical de una recta es el cambio vertical de la recta. Ver *Pendiente de una recta*.

Rotation (p. 519) A rotation is a transformation that turns a figure about a fixed point O, called the center of rotation.

Rotación (p. 519) Una rotación es una transformación que gira una figura sobre un punto fijo O, llamado centro de rotación.

$\triangle RST$ has been rotated about the origin O to $\triangle R'S'T'$.

Rotational symmetry (p. 519) A figure has rotational symmetry if it can be rotated 180° or less and match the original figure.

Simetría rotacional (p. 519) Una figura tiene simetría rotacional si se puede rotar 180° o menos y calzar sobre la figura original.

This figure has 60° rotational symmetry.

Run (p. 498) The run of a line is a horizontal change in a line. See *Slope*.

Distancia horizontal (p. 498) La distancia horizontal de una recta es el cambio horizontal de la recta. Ver *Pendiente de una recta*.

S

Sample (p. 550) A sample is a part of the population.

Muestra (p. 550) Una muestra es una parte de la población.

A class of 25 students is a sample of a school population. The sample size is 25.

Sample space (p. 591) Sample space is the collection of all possible outcomes in a probability experiment.

Espacio muestral (p. 591) El espacio muestral es el total de todos los resultados posibles en un experimento de probabilidad.

The sample space for tossing two coins is HH, HT, TH, TT.

Scale (p. 259) A scale is the ratio that compares a length in a drawing to the corresponding length in the actual object.

Escala (p. 259) Una escala es la razón que compara la longitud en un dibujo con la longitud correspondiente en el objeto real.

A 25-mi road is 1 in. long on a map. The scale can be written three ways:
1 in. : 25 mi, $\frac{1\text{ in.}}{25\text{ mi}}$, 1 in. = 25 mi.

Scale drawing (p. 259) A scale drawing is an enlarged or reduced drawing of an object that is similar to the actual object.

Dibujo a escala (p. 259) Un dibujo a escala es un dibujo aumentado o reducido de un objeto que es semejante al objeto real.

Maps and floor plans are scale drawings.

Scalene triangle (p. 336) A scalene triangle is a triangle with no congruent sides.

Triángulo escaleno (p. 336) Un triángulo escaleno es un triángulo cuyos lados no son congruentes.

Scatter plot (p. 567) A scatter plot is a graph that relates two sets of data.

Diagrama de dispersión (p. 567) Un diagrama de dispersión es una gráfica que relaciona dos conjuntos de datos.

Sales and Advertising

The scatter plot shows amounts spent by several companies on advertising (in dollars) versus product sales (in thousands of dollars).

Scientific notation (p. 107) A number in scientific notation is written as the product of two factors. The first factor is a number greater than or equal to 1 and less than 10; the second factor is a power of 10.

Notación científica (p. 107) Un número en notación científica se escribe como el producto de dos factores. El primer factor es un número mayor o igual a 1 y menor que 10; el segundo factor es una potencia de 10.

37,000,000 is written as 3.7×10^7 in scientific notation.

Segment (p. 324) A segment has two endpoints and all the points of the line between the points.

Segmento (p. 324) Un segmento tiene dos extremos y todos los puntos de la recta entre los puntos extremos.

endpoints of $\overline{EF}$

$\overline{EF}$ represents the segment shown.

Segment bisector (p. 362) A segment bisector is a line, segment, or ray that goes through the midpoint of a segment.

Mediatriz de un segmento (p. 362) Una mediatriz de un segmento es una recta, segmento o rayo que pasa por el punto medio de un segmento.

$GM = MH$. $\overleftrightarrow{FD}$ is a bisector of $\overline{GH}$.

Semicircle (p. 351) A semicircle is half a circle. See *Arc*.

Semicírculo (p. 351) Un semicírculo es la mitad de un círculo. Ver *Arco*.

Sequence (p. 442) A sequence is a set of numbers that follow a pattern.

Secuencia (p. 442) Una secuencia es un conjunto de números que sigue un patrón.

$3, 6, 9, 12, 15, \ldots$ is a sequence.

Similar polygons (p. 252) Two polygons are similar if their corresponding angles have the same measure and the lengths of their corresponding sides are proportional.

Polígonos semejantes (p. 252) Dos polígonos son semejantes si sus ángulos correspondientes tienen la misma medida y las longitudes de sus lados correspondientes son proporcionales.

$\triangle ABC \sim \triangle RTS$

Simple interest (p. 468) Simple interest is interest calculated only on the principal. Use the formula $I = prt$ where I is the interest, p is the principal, r is the annual interest rate, and t is time in years.

Interés simple (p. 468) El interés simple se calcula sólo en relación al principal. Se usa la fórmula $I = prt$ donde I es el interés, p es el principal, r es la tasa de interés anual y t es el tiempo en años.

The simple interest earned on $200 invested at 5% annual interest for three years is $200 \cdot 0.05 \cdot 3$, or $30.

Simplest form (p. 82) A fraction is in simplest form when the numerator and denominator have no common factors other than 1.

Mínima expresión (p. 82) Una fracción está en su mínima expresión cuando el numerador y el denominador no tienen otro factor común más que el uno.

The simplest form of $\frac{3}{9}$ is $\frac{1}{3}$.

Skew lines (p. 325) Skew lines lie in different planes. They are neither parallel nor intersecting.

Rectas cruzadas (p. 325) Las rectas cruzadas están en planos diferentes. No son paralelas ni se intersecan.

$\overleftrightarrow{MT}$ and $\overleftrightarrow{QR}$ are skew lines.

Slope of a line (p. 498) Slope is a ratio that describes the steepness of a line.

$$\text{slope} = \frac{\text{rise}}{\text{run}}$$

Pendiente de una recta (p. 498) La pendiente es la razón que describe la inclinación de una recta.

$$\text{pendiente} = \frac{\text{cambio vertical}}{\text{cambio horizontal}}$$

The slope of the given line is $\frac{2}{4} = \frac{1}{2}$.

Solution (pp. 174, 205) A solution is any value or values that make an equation or inequality true.

Solución (pp. 174, 205) Una solución es cualquier valor o valores que hacen que una ecuación o una desigualdad sea verdadera.

4 is the solution of $x + 5 = 9$.
7 is a solution of $x < 15$.

Sphere (p. 411) A sphere is the set of all points in space that are the same distance from a center point.

Esfera (p. 411) Una esfera es el conjunto de todos los puntos en el espacio que están a la misma distancia de un punto central.

Spreadsheet (p. 538) A spreadsheet is a tool used for organizing and analyzing data. Spreadsheets are arranged in numbered rows and lettered columns.

Hoja de cálculo (p. 538) Una hoja de cálculo es una herramienta que se usa para organizar y analizar datos. Las hojas de cálculo se organizan en filas numeradas y columnas en orden alfabético.

	A	B	C	D	E
1	0.50	0.70	0.60	0.50	2.30
2	1.50	0.50	2.75	2.50	7.25

In the spreadsheet, column C and row 2 meet at the shaded box, cell C2.

Square (p. 341) A square is a parallelogram with four right angles and four congruent sides.

Cuadrado (p. 341) Una cuadrado es un paralelogramo que tiene cuatro ángulos rectos y cuatro lados congruentes.

$QRST$ is a square. $\angle Q$, $\angle R$, $\angle S$, and $\angle T$ are right angles, and $\overline{QR} \cong \overline{RS} \cong \overline{ST} \cong \overline{TQ}$.

Square root (p. 400) Finding the square root of a number is the inverse of squaring a number.

Raíz cuadrada (p. 400) Hallar la raíz cuadrada de un número es el inverso de elevar un número al cuadrado.

$\sqrt{9} = 3$ because $3^2 = 9$.

Stem-and-leaf plot (p. 544) A stem-and-leaf plot is a graph that uses the digits of each number to show the shape of the data. Each data value is broken into a "stem" (digit or digits on the left) and a "leaf" (digit or digits on the right).

Diagrama de tallo y hojas (p. 544) Un diagrama de tallo y hojas es una gráfica en la que se usan los dígitos de cada número para mostrar la forma de los datos. Cada valor de los datos se divide en "tallo" (dígito o dígitos a la izquierda) y "hojas" (dígito o dígitos a la derecha).

stem	leaves
27	7
28	5 6 8
29	6 9
30	8

Key: 27 | 7 means 27.7

This stem-and-leaf plot displays recorded times in a race. The stem represents the whole number of seconds. The leaves represent tenths of a second.

Straight angle (p. 330) A straight angle is an angle with a measure of 180°.

Ángulo llano (p. 330) Un ángulo llano es un ángulo que mide 180°.

$m\angle TPL = 180°$

Subtraction Property of Equality (p. 180) The Subtraction Property of Equality states that if the same number is subtracted from each side of an equation, the results are equal.

Propiedad sustractiva de la igualdad (p. 180) La propiedad sustractiva de la igualdad establece que si se resta el mismo número a cada lado de una ecuación, los resultados son iguales.

Since $\frac{20}{2} = 10$, $\frac{20}{2} - 3 = 10 - 3$.
If $a = b$, then $a - c = b - c$.

Subtraction Property of Inequality (p. 211) When you subtract the same number from each side of an inequality, the relationship between the two sides does not change.

Propiedad sustractiva de la desigualdad (p. 211) Cuando se resta el mismo número a cada lado de una desigualdad, la relación entre los dos lados no cambia.

If $a > b$, then $a - c > b - c$.
Since $9 > 6$, $9 - 2 > 6 - 2$.
If $a < b$, then $a - c < b - c$.
Since $9 < 13$, $9 - 2 < 13 - 2$.

Supplementary (p. 331) Supplementary angles are two angles whose measures add to 180°.

Suplementario (p. 331) Los ángulos suplementarios son dos ángulos cuyas medidas suman 180°.

$\angle A$ and $\angle D$ are supplementary angles.

Surface area of a prism (p. 415) The surface area of a prism is the sum of the areas of its faces.

Área total de un prisma (p. 415) El área total de un prisma es la suma de las áreas de sus caras.

Each square = 1 in.²

$4 \cdot 12 \text{ in.}^2 + 2 \cdot 9 \text{ in.}^2 = 66 \text{ in.}^2$

T

Terminating decimal (p. 96) A terminating decimal is a decimal that stops, or terminates.

Decimal finito (p. 96) Un decimal finito es un decimal que termina.

Both 0.6 and 0.7265 are terminating decimals.

Theoretical probability (p. 580) The formula used to compute the theoretical probability of an event is
$$P(\text{event}) = \frac{\text{number of favorable outcomes}}{\text{total number of possible outcomes}}$$

Probabilidad teórica (p. 580) La fórmula que se usa para calcular la probabilidad teórica de un suceso es
$$P(\text{suceso}) = \frac{\text{número favorable de resultados}}{\text{número total de resultados posibles}}$$

Suppose you select a letter from the letters H, A, P, P, and Y. The theoretical probability of selecting a P is $\frac{2}{5}$.

Three-dimensional figure (p. 410) Three-dimensional figures are figures that do not lie in a plane.

Figura tridimensional (p. 410) Las figuras tridimensionales son figuras que no están en un solo plano.

face

edge

Tip (p. 304) A tip is a percent of a bill given to a person providing a service.

Propina (p. 304) Una propina es un porcentaje de una cuenta que se le da a una persona por el servicio prestado.

A lunch bill is $18. You leave a 20% tip of $3.60.

Transformation (p. 510) A transformation is a change of the position, shape, or size of a figure. Three types of transformations that change position only are translations, reflections, and rotations.

Transformacion (p. 510) Una transformación es un cambio de posición, forma o tamaño de una figura. Tres tipos de transformaciones que cambian la posición son las traslaciones, las reflexiones y las rotaciones.

$K'L'M'N'$ is a reflection, or flip, of $KLMN$ across the y-axis.

Translation (p. 510) A translation is a transformation that moves every point of a figure the same distance and in the same direction.

Traslación (p. 510) Una traslación es una transformación que mueve cada punto de una figura la misma distancia y en la misma dirección.

$A'B'C'D'$ is a translation image of $ABCD$.

Trapezoid (p. 341) A trapezoid is a quadrilateral with exactly one pair of parallel sides.

Trapecio (p. 341) Un trapecio es un cuadrilátero que tiene exactamente un par de lados paralelos.

$\overline{UV}$ is parallel to $\overline{WY}$.

Trend (p. 568) A trend is a relationship between two sets of data. See *Positive trend*, *Negative trend*, and *No trend*.

Tendencia (p. 568) Una tendencia es una relación entre dos conjuntos de datos. Ver *Positive trend*, *Negative trend* y *No trend*.

Triangle (p. 340) A triangle is a polygon with three sides.

Triángulo (p. 340) Un triángulo es un polígono que tiene tres lados.

U

Unit cost (p. 233) A unit rate that gives the cost per unit is a unit cost.

Costo unitario (p. 233) Un costo unitario es una tasa unitaria que da el costo por unidad.

$\frac{\$5.98}{10.2 \text{ fl oz}} = \$.59/\text{fl oz}$

Unit rate (p. 232) The rate for one unit of a given quantity is called the unit rate.

Tasa unitaria (p. 232) La tasa para una unidad de una cantidad dada se llama tasa unitaria.

If you drive 130 mi in 2 h, your unit rate is $\frac{65 \text{ mi}}{1 \text{ h}}$, or 65 mi/h.

V

Variable (p. 169) A variable is a letter that stands for a number. The value of an algebraic expression varies, or changes, depending upon the value given to the variable.

Variable (p. 169) Una variable es una letra que representa un número. El valor de una expresión algebraica varía, o cambia, dependiendo del valor que se le dé a la variable.

x is a variable in the equation $9 + x = 7$.

Variable expression (p. 169) A variable expression is a group of numbers, variables, and operations.

Expresión variable (p. 169) Una expresión variable es un grupo de números, variables y operaciones.

$7 + x,\ 2y - 4,\ \frac{3}{5}g,\ \frac{7}{k}$

Vertex of an angle (p. 330) The vertex of an angle is the point of intersection of two sides of an angle.

Vértice de un ángulo (p. 330) El vértice de un ángulo es el punto de intersección de dos lados de un ángulo.

Vertex of a polygon (p. 330) The vertex of a polygon is any point where two sides of a polygon meet.

Vértice de un polígono (p. 330) El vértice de un polígono es cualquier punto donde se encuentran dos lados de un polígono.

Vertical (p. 499) Vertical lines are parallel to the y-axis.

Vertical (p. 499) Las rectas verticales son paralelas al eje de y.

Vertical angles (p. 331) Vertical angles are formed by two intersecting lines. Vertical angles are opposite each other.

Ángulos verticales (p. 331) Los ángulos verticales están formados por dos rectas que se intersecan. Los ángulos verticales son opuestos entre sí.

$\angle 1$ and $\angle 2$ are vertical angles, as are $\angle 3$ and $\angle 4$.

Volume (p. 421) The volume of a three-dimensional figure is the number of cubic units needed to fill the space inside the figure.

Volumen (p. 421) El volumen de una figura tridimensional es el número de unidades cúbicas que se necesitan para llenar el espacio dentro de la figura.

The volume of the rectangular prism is 36 cubic units.

X

x-axis (p. 486) The x-axis is the horizontal number line that, together with the y-axis, forms the coordinate plane.

Eje de x (p. 486) El eje de x es la recta numérica horizontal que, junto con el eje de y, forma el plano de coordenadas.

---

x-coordinate (p. 486) The x-coordinate is the first number in an ordered pair. It tells the number of horizontal units a point is from the origin, O.

Coordenada x (p. 486) La coordenada x es el primer número en un par ordenado. Indica el número de unidades horizontales a las que un punto está del orígen, O.

The x-coordinate is -2 for the ordered pair $(-2, 1)$.
The point is 2 units to the left of the origin.

Y

y-axis (p. 486) The y-axis is the vertical number line that, together with the x-axis, forms the coordinate plane.

Eje de y (p. 486) El eje de y es la recta numérica vertical que, junto con el eje de x, forma el plano de coordenadas.

y-coordinate (p. 486) The y-coordinate is the second number in an ordered pair. It tells the number of vertical units a point is from the origin, O.

Coordenada y (p. 486) La coordenada y es el segundo número en un par ordenado. Indica el número de unidades verticales a las que un punto está del orígen, O.

The y-coordinate is 1 for the ordered pair $(-2, 1)$. The point is 1 unit up from the x-axis.

Z

Zero pair (p. 36) The pairing of one "$+$" chip with one "$-$" chip is called a zero pair.

Par cero (p. 36) El emparejamiento de una ficha "$+$" con una ficha "$-$" se llama par cero.

a zero pair

Zero Product Property (p. 15) The Zero Product Property states that the product of 0 and any number is 0.

Propiedad del cero (p. 15) La propiedad del cero establece que el producto de cero y cualquier número es cero.

$6 \cdot 0 = 0$
$a \cdot 0 = 0$

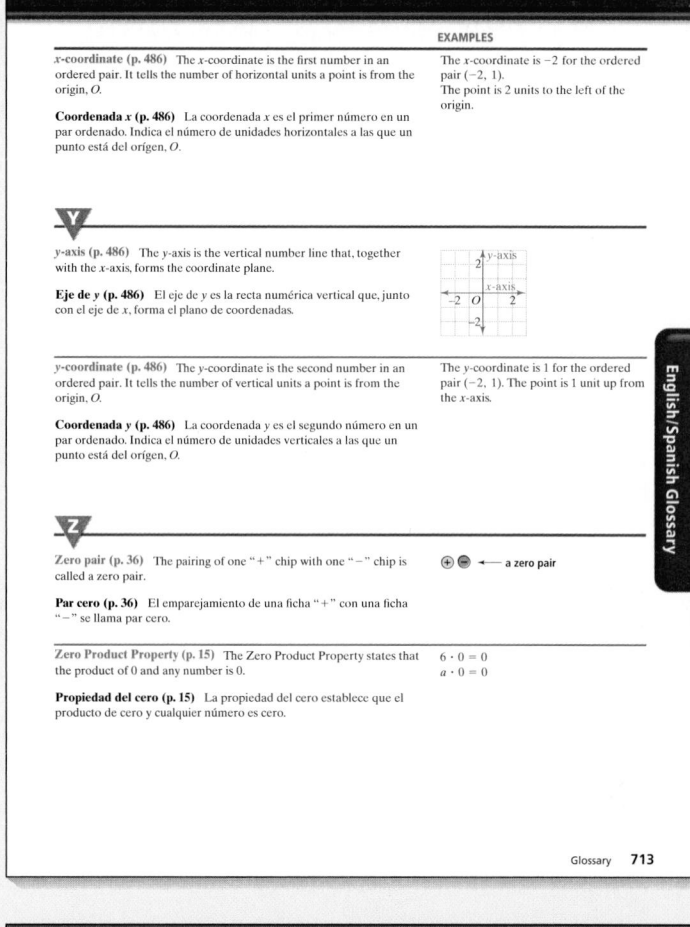

English/Spanish Glossary

✓ Answers to Instant Check System™

Chapter 1

Check Your Readiness   p. 2

1. < 2. > 3. 37 4. 76 5. 216 6. 214 7. tenths 8. thousandths 9. ones 10. hundredths 11. ten-thousandths 12. four hundred twenty-one and five tenths 13. five thousand six and four hundredths 14. fifteen and four thousandths 15. three hundred twenty-nine thousandths 16. seven hundred ten and four hundred thirteen thousandths 17. 34.12 18. 278.79 19. 3.60 20. 81.80 21. 17.00

Lesson 1-1   pp. 4–5

Check Skills You'll Need 1. An estimate is an answer with a calculation; a guess is an answer without a calculation. **2.** 83,000 **3.** 400 **4.** 24,110 **5.** 3,500

Quick Check 1 a. 3 **b.** 6 **c.** 30 **2.** about $14 Yes; you can buy about 48 ÷ 16, or 3, DVDs from category B. This is half the number of DVDs you can buy from category D.

Lesson 1-2   pp. 8–9

Check Skills You'll Need 1. Place value is the position and value of a digit in a decimal. **2.** 8 hundredths **3.** 8 tenths **4.** 8 hundreds **5.** 8 thousandths

Quick Check 1. 8.02 min **2.** 11.89 **3.** 10.3

Lesson 1-3   pp. 14–15

Check Skills You'll Need 1. Estimating gives an approximate answer. **2.** 15 **3.** 28 **4.** 10

Quick Check 1. 11.583 **2.** 63

Checkpoint Quiz 1 1. $10 **2.** $11 **3.** Answers may vary. Sample: about 6 **4.** Answers may vary. Sample: about 13 **5.** 24.57 **6.** 14.321 **7.** 2.92 **8.** 21.86 **9.** 12.1584 **10.** 0.096 **11.** 51.072 **12.** 11.118 **13.** = **14.** 487.5 words **15.** 6.45 lb

Lesson 1-4   pp. 20–21

Check Skills You'll Need 1. Numbers that are easy to compute mentally. **2.–4.** Answers may vary. Samples are given. **2.** 8 **3.** 13 **4.** 7

Quick Check 1 a. 2.3 **b.** 106 **c.** 14.7 **2.** 5.2 smoothies

Lesson 1-5   pp. 26–27

Check Skills You'll Need 1. Commutative Property **2.** 5 **3.** 4,567 **4.** 3. 5. 70

Quick Check 1 a. 180 mL **b.** 500 mg **2.** 34,000 mL **3.** 4.690 kg

Lesson 1-6   pp. 31–32

Check Skills You'll Need 1. Associative **2.** 4,244.8 **3.** 0.5397 **4.** 6,425.1

Quick Check 1 a. 8 **b.** −13 **c.** 22 **2.** 8 **3.** −8 < −2 **4.** −4, −1, 2, 3

Checkpoint Quiz 2 1. 1.2 **2.** 3.15 **3.** 1.7 **4.** 500 **5.** 4.1 **6.** 1,700 **7.** > **8.** < **9.** = **10.** 240 mL

Lesson 1-7   pp. 38–40

Check Skills You'll Need 1. the same distance from zero as the number **2.** −73 **3.** 49 **4.** −22 **5.** −13 **6.** 424 **7.** 13

Quick Check 1 a. −7 **b.** −8 **c.** 0 **2 a.** −162 **b.** −18 **c.** 0 **3.** −7 **4.** 21 **5 a.** −137 − (−155) **b.** 18 ft

Lesson 1-8   pp. 44–45

Check Skills You'll Need 1. zero **2.** 4 **3.** 5 **4.** −35 **5.** 0

Quick Check 1. 28 **2.** −524 ft/h

Lesson 1-9   pp. 48–49

Check Skills You'll Need 1. Comm. Prop. of Add. **2.** 12.1 **3.** 18.2 **4.** 20

Quick Check 1 a. −15 **b.** 0 **c.** −9 **2.** $23.93 **3.** 126

Lesson 1-10   pp. 53–55

Check Skills You'll Need 1. division **2.** 13 **3.** −4 **4.** −2

Quick Check 1. 224 **2.** −1.5 **3 a.** 17 **b.** no mode **c.** pen **4.** 143°F

Chapter 2

Check Your Readiness   p. 66

1. 5 5. 2 1.423 3. 3.89 4. 677.447 5. < 6. < 7. = 8. < 9. < 10. > 11. −27 12. 9 13. −9 14. 4 15. 28 16. 2 17. 1

Lesson 2-1   pp. 68–69

Check Skills You'll Need 1. before **2.** 2 **3.** 12 **4.** −10 **5.** 1

Quick Check 1 a. 44^4 **b.** $(-2)^2$ **2 a.** 243 **b.** 1,000,000,000 **c.** 9.61 **3 a.** −27 **b.** −27 **c.** 62

Lesson 2-2   pp. 74–76

Check Skills You'll Need 1. 0 **2.** 24 **3.** 21 **4.** 12

Quick Check 1 a. 20 **b.** 35 **c.** 60 **2.** Composite; the factors of 15 are 1, 3, 5, and 15. Since 15 has more than two factors, 15 is composite. **3.** $72 = 2^3 \cdot 3^2$ **4.** 8

Checkpoint Quiz 1 1. 75 **2.** 1 **3.** 54 **4.** 12 **5.** 70 **6.** 60 **7.** 1, 3, 13, 39 **8.** 1, 2, 4, 13, 26, 52 **9.** 1, 2, 5, 10, 11, 22, 55, 110 **10.** 1, 2, 4, 5, 8, 10, 20, 25, 40, 50, 100, 200 **11.** $2^5 \cdot 3$ **12.** $2 \cdot 3 \cdot 5^2$ **13.** $3^2 \cdot 5^2$ **14.** $3^2 \cdot 37$ **15.** 12 ft

Lesson 2-3   pp. 82–83

Check Skills You'll Need 1. It is the greatest factor that divides both numbers. **2.** 2 **3.** 12 **4.** 5 **5.** 1

Quick Check 1. Answers may vary. Sample: $\frac{8}{10}$, $\frac{12}{15}$ **2.** Answers may vary. Sample: $\frac{9}{15}$, $\frac{3}{5}$ **3.** $\frac{4}{5}$ **4.** $\frac{2}{5}$

Lesson 2-4   pp. 87–88

Check Skills You'll Need 1. least common multiple **2.** 12 **3.** 20 **4.** 8 **5.** 45

Quick Check 1 a. < **b.** < **c.** > **2.** $\frac{5}{32}$ in., $\frac{1}{4}$ in., $\frac{5}{16}$ in., $\frac{3}{8}$ in.

Lesson 2-6   pp. 96–98

Check Skills You'll Need 1. The numerator and denominator have no common factors other than 1. **2.** $\frac{3}{5}$ **3.** $\frac{5}{6}$ **4.** $\frac{5}{12}$

Quick Check 1. $\frac{21}{4}$ **2.** 3

Lesson 2-6   pp. 96–98

Check Skills You'll Need 1. In simplest form, they are the same. **2.–5.** Answers may vary. Samples are given. **2.** $\frac{4}{5}$, $\frac{8}{10}$ **3.** $\frac{3}{4}$, $\frac{6}{8}$ **4.** $\frac{2}{3}$, $\frac{4}{12}$ **5.** $\frac{1}{2}$, $\frac{5}{10}$

Quick Check 1. 0.625 **2.** 0.5 **3 a.** $1\frac{91}{250}$ **b.** $2\frac{12}{25}$ **c.** $3\frac{3}{5}$ **4.** 1.862, $1\frac{7}{15}$, $1\frac{3}{5}$ **5.** cats, dogs, fish, birds

Checkpoint Quiz 2 1. $1\frac{2}{7}$ **2.** $\frac{5}{12}$ **3.** $\frac{3}{5}$ **4.** > **5.** < **6.** = **7.** $4\frac{5}{6}$ **8.** $\frac{37}{9}$ **9.** $16\frac{2}{5}$ **10.** 0.00015, 0.004, 0.0112

Lesson 2-7   pp. 102–103

Check Skills You'll Need 1. Terminating decimal stops; the decimal **2.** 0.75 **3.** −0.7 **4.** 1.3 **5.** 0.25

Quick Check 1. $-\frac{2}{3} < -\frac{1}{6}$ **2.** −4.2 > −4.9 **3.** $-6\frac{1}{4}$, −4, 6.55, $12\frac{1}{2}$

Lesson 2-8   pp. 106–107

Check Skills You'll Need 1. factor **2.** 27 **3.** 16 **4.** 100,000 **5.** 16

Quick Check 1. 1.69×10^5 **2.** 640,000

Chapter 3

Check Your Readiness   p. 118

1. −40 2. −24 3. 100 4. 18 5. −45 6. 60 7. −3 8. 20 9. 9 10. 21 11. 12 12. 9 13. $\frac{3}{4}$ 14. $\frac{1}{2}$ 15. $\frac{7}{8}$ 16. $\frac{3}{8}$ 17. $\frac{1}{3}$ 18. $\frac{5}{9}$ 19. $\frac{2}{3}$ 20. $\frac{5}{7}$

Lesson 3-1   pp. 120–121

Check Skills You'll Need 1. When you estimate by rounding, you round a number to the nearest unit. When you use compatible numbers, you look for numbers that are easy to compute mentally. **2.** 7 **3.** 4 **4.** 8 **5.** 6 **6.** 2

Quick Check 1. about $\frac{1}{2}$ **2.** about 6 in. **3 a.** about 20 **b.** about 48 **c.** about 14 **4 a.** about 6 **b.** about 6 **c.** about 9

Lesson 3-2   pp. 126–127

Check Skills You'll Need 1. equivalent **2.** 4 **3.** 8 **4.** 25

Quick Check 1 a. $\frac{4}{5}$ **b.** $\frac{1}{4}$ **c.** 1 **2 a.** $\frac{7}{12}$ **b.** $\frac{11}{14}$ **3.** $\frac{7}{8}$ mi

Lesson 3-3   pp. 130–131

Check Skills You'll Need 1. When two fractions have the same denominator, you can compare them by looking at the numerators. **2.** < **3.** <

Quick Check 1 a. $4\frac{1}{3}$ **b.** $4\frac{4}{5}$ **c.** 1 **2 a.** 1 **b.** $12\frac{1}{24}$ **c.** $4\frac{3}{10}$ **3.** $1\frac{1}{2}$ ft

Checkpoint Quiz 1 1. $5\frac{1}{2}$ in. **2.** $13\frac{1}{2}$ in. **3.** 5 in. **4.** $\frac{1}{6}$ **5.** 2 **6.** $5\frac{5}{9}$ **7.** $8\frac{19}{20}$ **8.** $\frac{9}{2}$ **9.** $11\frac{5}{6}$ **10.** $21\frac{5}{8}$ in.

Lesson 3-4   pp. 136–137

Check Skills You'll Need 1. The numerator is greater than the denominator. **2.** $\frac{13}{3}$ **3.** $\frac{13}{2}$ **4.** $\frac{5}{2}$ **5.** $\frac{19}{4}$

Instant Check System™ Answers

Page 716

Quick Check 1 a. $\frac{3}{20}$ b. $\frac{2}{5}$ c. $\frac{8}{15}$ 2. 63 members
3 a. $10\frac{19}{24}$ b. $4\frac{17}{25}$ c. $15\frac{3}{32}$

Lesson 3-5 — pp. 141–142
Check Skills You'll Need 1. multiplication 2. $\frac{2}{7}$ 3. $\frac{5}{18}$
4. 45 5. 4
Quick Check 1 a. $3\frac{1}{6}$ b. $\frac{5}{6}$ c. 20 2 a. $1\frac{25}{44}$ b. $\frac{3}{4}$
c. $1\frac{3}{16}$ 3. $\frac{19}{30}$ cans

Lesson 3-6 — pp. 148–149
Check Skills You'll Need 1. It consists of a whole
number and a fraction. 2. $1\frac{1}{12}$ 3. 5 4. $12\frac{1}{8}$ 5. $4\frac{1}{4}$
Quick Check 1. $1\frac{7}{12}$ 2. $6\frac{1}{4}$ c 3. 74 oz
Checkpoint Quiz 1 1. $\frac{5}{8}$ 2. $\frac{1}{3}$ 3. $\frac{1}{5}$ 4. $9\frac{11}{32}$ 5. $\frac{11}{15}$
6. $11\frac{1}{9}$ yd² 7. $\frac{2}{5}$ 8. $6\frac{5}{9}$ 9. 2 10. $\frac{4}{5}$ 11. 13
12. $45\frac{3}{4}$ min 13. $3\frac{1}{3}$ 14. $2\frac{1}{4}$ 15. $8\frac{1}{2}$

Lesson 3-7 — pp. 154–155
Check Skills You'll Need 1. meter; liter; gram 2. 100
3. 0.001 4. 10 5. 1,000 6. 0.001
Quick Check 1. 13 in. 2. 12.5 g 3. $10\frac{1}{8}$ mi
4 a. $\frac{1}{8}$ in. b. $\frac{1}{16}$ in. 5. 14.1 g 6. 44 m

Chapter 4
Check Your Readiness — p. 166
1. 4.414 2. 8.6 3. 0.79 4. 15.21 5. −36 6. 1
7. 42 8. −6 9. 20 10. 1 11. 1 12. 6 13. 7
14. 38 15. > 16. = 17. > 18. <

Lesson 4-1 — pp. 169–170
Check Skills You'll Need 1. order of operations 2. 11
3. 10 4. −10 5. 3
Quick Check 1. $p - 16$ 2. $9t$ 3. Answers may vary.
Sample: a number decreased by 50, 50 less than a
number, 50 subtracted from a number 4. 56

Lesson 4-2 — pp. 174–175
Check Skills You'll Need 1. variable 2. $y + 4$
3. $v - 6$ 4. $\frac{k}{9}$
Quick Check 1 a. 5 b. 8 2 a. 10 b. −16.1 c. 8.8
d. −9 3. about 26 boxes

Lesson 4-3 — pp. 180–182
Check Skills You'll Need 1. equation 2. about 9
3. about 18 4. about 25

Quick Check 1. 168 2. $7.95 3 a. Check students'
work. b. 116

Lesson 4-4 — pp. 186–188
Check Skills You'll Need 1. simplest form 2. $\frac{1}{4}$ 3. 4
4. 1 5. a
Quick Check 1 a. −7.2 b. 9 c. 3 2. $5c = 110$; $22
3. −390
Checkpoint Quiz 1 1. $x - 4$ 2. $3x$ 3. $\frac{3}{4}$ 4. $x + 9$
5. −4.4 6. 1.8 7. −9.1 8. 48
9. $y + 18 = 1825$; $y = 1807$ 10. 24 years
8 months

Lesson 4-5 — pp. 194–196
Check Skills You'll Need 1. algebraic expression 2. 1
3. 7 4. −12 5. −2
Quick Check 1. Let s = son's age; $3s - 2$ 2. 37
3 a. 4 b. 5 c. 11 4. Let b = number of 3-point
baskets; $8 + 3b = 23$; 5 baskets.

Lesson 4-6 — pp. 200–201
Check Skills You'll Need 1. Multiplication Property of
Equality 2. 6 3. −5 4. −64 5. −18
Quick Check 1. 2 200 3. Let m = number of
markers; $0.79m + 1.25 = 7.57$; 8 markers

Lesson 4-7 — pp. 205–206
Check Skills You'll Need 1. opposites 2. > 3. > 4. <
5. >
Quick Check 1. −2, 1.4 2. [number line]
3. $x < 4$ 4. $t \le 62$ [number line] −7 −6 −5 −4 −3 −2
Checkpoint Quiz 1 1. 5 2. 40 3. 24 4. −9 5. −2
6. −5 7. Let c = the cost of a skirt;
$12 + 2c = 38$; $13. 8. [number line] −5 −4 −3 −2 −1 0
9. [number line] −5 −4 −3 −2 −1 0
10. [number line] −4 −3 −2 −1 0 1

Lesson 4-8 — pp. 210–211
Check Skills You'll Need 1. because they "undo" each
other 2. −6 3. 14 4. 9 5. 7
Quick Check 1. $y < 7$; [number line] 4 5 6 7 8 9
2 a. $x > -4$; [number line] −6 −5 −4 −3 −2 −1
b. $y < 1$; [number line] −2 −1 0 1 2 3
c. $w \le -9$; [number line] −11 −9 −7

Page 717

3. Let p = number of points;
$p + 104 > 200$; $p > 91$; you need more than
91 points.

Lesson 4-9 — pp. 214–216
Check Skills You'll Need 1. You can add to each side of
an equation or inequality without changing the
relationship. 2. 5 3. −10 4. 40 5. 16
Quick Check 1 a. $p > -9$;
−11 −10 −9 −8 −7 −6
b. $m \le 3$; 0 1 2 3 4 5
c. $n > -3$; −5 −4 −3 −2 −1 0 2. 416 min
3. $k > 20$; 18 20 22

Chapter 5
Check Your Readiness — p. 226
1. 14.4 2. 114.66 3. 47.7 4. 1.12 5. 2.6
6. 10.52 7. −8 8. 60 9. −2 10. 75 11. >
12. < 13. = 14. > 15. $\frac{3}{4}$ 16. $\frac{1}{2}$ 17. $\frac{3}{8}$ 18. $\frac{1}{8}$
19. $2\frac{7}{9}$

Lesson 5-1 — pp. 228–229
Check Skills You'll Need 1. Equivalent fractions are
fractions that name the same amount. 2. $\frac{1}{2}$
3. $\frac{7}{9}$ 4. $\frac{7}{5}$ 5. $\frac{1}{3}$
Quick Check 1. 7 to 12, 7 : 12, $\frac{7}{12}$ b. 7 to 5;
7 : 5; $\frac{7}{5}$ 2. Answers may vary. Samples: $\frac{14}{18}$, $\frac{35}{45}$
3. $\frac{6}{5}$ 4 a. not equivalent b. not equivalent
c. equivalent

Lesson 5-2 — pp. 232–233
Check Skills You'll Need 1. division 2. $\frac{3}{5}$ 3. $\frac{3}{4}$ 4. $\frac{11}{8}$
5. $\frac{1}{9}$
Quick Check 1. 70 heartbeats per min 2. $7.00
3. $.064/fl oz, $.056/fl oz; the 64-fl-oz bottle is the
better buy.
Checkpoint Quiz 1 1. 7 to 52, $\frac{7}{52}$ 2. $\frac{2}{3}$ 3. $\frac{1}{4}$ 4. 12 to 7
5. 2 : 3 6. 42 words/min 7. 9 points/game
8. $.2633, $.2475; the second item is the better
buy. 9. $7.80, $6.57; the second item is the better
buy. 10. 15 pizzas

Lesson 5-3 — pp. 238–239
Check Skills You'll Need 1. LCM 2. > 3. = 4. <
5. >

Quick Check 1. no; $\frac{5}{6} \ne \frac{5}{7}$ 2 a. yes; 48 = 48 b. yes;
36 = 36 c. no; 36 ≠ 40

Lesson 5-4 — pp. 244–245
Check Skills You'll Need 1. A ratio is a unit rate when
you are finding the rate for one unit of something.
2. 8 km/d 3. 62 mi/h 4. 25 push-ups/min
5. 60 words/min
Quick Check 1 a. $6.37 b. $119.51 2 a. 9 b. 2
c. 16.8 3. 27.2 c. 192.5

Lesson 5-5 — pp. 250–251
Check Skills You'll Need 1. proportion 2. 6 3. 12
4. 42 5. 9.5
Quick Check 1. 20 2. 36 ft
Checkpoint Quiz 1 1. no 2. yes 3. no 4. yes
5. $8.40 6. $16.50 7. 120° 8. 26° 9. 9 10. 12

Lesson 5-6 — pp. 259–261
Check Skills You'll Need 1. For two ratios, the cross
products are found by multiplying the
denominator of each ratio by the numerator of the
other ratio. 2. 8 3. 15 4. 1 5. 7
Quick Check 1. 104 m 2. about 206 km
3. 1 in. : 16 in. 4. 5 in.

Chapter 6
Check Your Readiness — p. 272
1. 5 2. 14 3. 5 4. 10 5. $\frac{17}{25}$ 6. $\frac{2}{5}$ 7. $\frac{17}{25}$ 8. $\frac{5}{7}$
9. $\frac{1}{100}$ 10. 30 11. 800 12. 8.4 13. 3 14. 80
15. 2.16 16. 200

Lesson 6-1 — pp. 274–275
Check Skills You'll Need 1. Equivalent ratios have
the same value. 2–5. Answers may vary. Samples
are given.
2. $\frac{4}{10}$, $\frac{6}{15}$ 3. $\frac{26}{100}$, $\frac{39}{150}$ 4. $\frac{6}{50}$, $\frac{9}{75}$ 5. $\frac{2}{20}$, $\frac{3}{30}$
Quick Check 1. $\frac{54}{100}$; 54% 2.

3 a. $\frac{3}{4}$; 75% b. $\frac{1}{2}$; 50% c. $\frac{7}{10}$; 70% 4. 80%

Page 718

Lesson 6-2 — pp. 279–281
Check Skills You'll Need 1. A repeating decimal is a
decimal that repeats without end. 2. 0.3125
3. 0.275 4. 0.4 5. 0.13
Quick Check 1. 60.7% 2 a. 0.35 b. 0.125 c. 0.078
3. 52.5% 4. $\frac{3}{50}$ 5 a. 29%, $\frac{3}{10}$, $\frac{7}{25}$, 0.74
b. 0.08, 15%, $\frac{7}{20}$, 50%

Lesson 6-3 — pp. 284–285
Check Skills You'll Need 1. 100 2. 1% 3. 98%
4. 95% 5. 8%
Quick Check 1. 1.25; $\frac{5}{4}$ or $1\frac{1}{4}$ 2. 0.0035; $\frac{7}{2,000}$
3. 280% 4. 0.46%
Checkpoint Quiz 1 1. 0.45; $\frac{9}{20}$ 2. 1.35; $1\frac{7}{20}$
3. 0.0098; $\frac{49}{5,000}$ 4. 56% 5. $\frac{1}{5}$, 20%, 0.245, $\frac{1}{4}$
6. $\frac{16}{25}$; 64% 7.
8. about 0.6% 9. 35% 10. 75%

Lesson 6-4 — pp. 290–291
Check Skills You'll Need 1. multiplication 2. 1,200
3. 1,350 4. 70.2 5. 29.7
Quick Check 1. 105 2. 960 3 a. about 60 b. about
100 c. about 600

Lesson 6-5 — pp. 294–295
Check Skills You'll Need 1. ratios 2. 8 3. 15 4. 87.5
Quick Check 1. 25% 2. 17 3. 15 problems

Lesson 6-6 — pp. 298–299
Check Skills You'll Need 1. If both sides of an equation
are divided by the same nonzero number, the
results are equal. 2. 17 3. 48
Quick Check 1. 150 seats 2. 16.2 3. about 20.5%

Lesson 6-7 — pp. 304–305
Check Skills You'll Need 1. left 2. 0.065 3. 0.0425
4. 0.15 5. 0.2
Quick Check 1. $195.18 2 a. about $8.70 b. about
$9.30 c. about $7.50 3. $192 4. $849

Checkpoint Quiz 1 1. 58.3% 2. 16 3. 84% 4. 45%
5. 68.4 6. 222 7. $313.95 8. $82.45 9. $35.50
10. $77

Lesson 6-8 — pp. 310–311
Check Skills You'll Need 1. 500 and $16n$ 2. 10 3. 12.5
4. 50
Quick Check 1. 1.9% 2. 99.4% 3. 40%

Chapter 7
Check Your Readiness — p. 322
1. < 2. > 3. > 4. < 5. 6 7. 12 8. 105
9. 5 10. 94 11. 80 12. 16 13. 111 14. 46
15. 108 16. 86.4 17. 16.2 18. 64.8

Lesson 7-1 — pp. 324–325
Check Skills You'll Need 1. <, >, ≤, ≥, ≠

Quick Check 1 a. $\overrightarrow{PD}$ b. $\overline{RS}$ c. $\overrightarrow{AV}$ 2 a. EF, HD
b. EB, CB, AB, GH, DH c. FC, EF, BC, HD

Lesson 7-2 — pp. 330–332
Check Skills You'll Need 1. equation 2. 70 3. 140
4. 74 5. 158
Quick Check 1. obtuse 2. 53° 3. 108°; 72°; 108°

Lesson 7-3 — pp. 336–337
Check Skills You'll Need 1. an angle with a measure
greater than 0° and less than 90° 2. right
3. obtuse
Quick Check 1. isosceles 2 a. right b. acute
3. 22°

Lesson 7-4 — pp. 340–342
Check Skills You'll Need 1. an equilateral triangle
2. equilateral 3. isosceles 4. scalene

Page 719

Quick Check 1 a. The octagon is irregular because
the sides are not all congruent. b. The triangle is
regular because all sides and all angles are
congruent. c. Multiply the side length by the
number of sides the polygon has. 2 a. hexagons,
triangles b. squares, triangles, rhombuses
3. Answers may vary. An example is given.

[trapezoid figure]

Checkpoint Quiz 1 1. $\overline{XZ}$ 2. $\overline{NM}$ 3. $\overline{KV}$ 4.
78°; 168° 5. 43°; 133° 6. 25°; 115° 7. 70°
8. equilateral 9. obtuse isosceles 10. right
scalene 11. Equilateral △PQT is regular, square
QRST is regular, and pentagon PQRST is irregular.

Lesson 7-5 — pp. 346–347
Check Skills You'll Need 1. Two polygons are similar if
corresponding angles are congruent and
corresponding side lengths have the same
proportion. 2. 5 3. 56° 4. 52°
Quick Check 1. Congruent; the sides and angles all
have the same measure. 2. No; the sides are
different lengths. 3 a. $\overline{AB} \cong \overline{FG}$; $\overline{BC} \cong \overline{GH}$;
$\overline{CD} \cong \overline{HI}$; $\overline{DA} \cong \overline{IF}$;
$\angle A \cong \angle F$; $\angle B \cong \angle G$;
$\angle C \cong \angle H$; $\angle D \cong \angle I$
b. 15.5; 139°

Lesson 7-6 — pp. 350–351
Check Skills You'll Need 1. 2 2. $\overline{FR}$ 3. $\overline{ZJ}$ 4. $\overline{NK}$
Quick Check 1. $\angle AOB$, $\angle AOC$, $\angle AOD$,
$\angle BOC$, $\angle BOD$, $\angle COD$
2. ZY, ZYX, YZX 3. CDE, CE

Lesson 7-7 — pp. 354–355
Check Skills You'll Need 1. Every percent can be
written as a decimal by moving the decimal point
two places to the left. Thus 25% becomes 0.25.
So taking the percent of a number is the same as
multiplying by a decimal. 2. 90 3. 216 4. 259.2
Quick Check 1. about 470 million 2 a. 144°
b.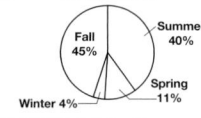

Favorite Season — Summer 40%, Spring 11%, Winter 4%, Fall 45%

Checkpoint Quiz 1 1. Yes. The square root of the
area is the side length. Since both squares have
the same area, they have the same side length.

Being squares, they both have four right angles.
Congruent sides and congruent angles means the
squares are congruent.
2. Town Middle School — Grade 6 25%, Grade 7 33.3%, Grade 8 41.7%
25% (90°) for 6th grade 33.3% (120°) for
7th grade, and 41.7% (150°) for 8th grade.
3. $\overline{RS}$ and $\overline{ST}$ 4. $\overline{TR}$
5. $\angle RPS$, $\angle SPT$, $\angle TPQ$, and $\angle QPR$

Lesson 7-8 — pp. 361–362
Check Skills You'll Need 1. a common point 2. $\overline{VW}$
3. $\overline{FG}$ 4. $\overline{CL}$
Quick Check 1. [figure: T 25 mm R, S, V]
2.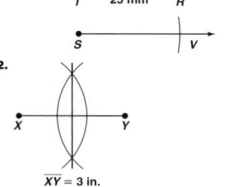
XY = 3 in.

Chapter 8
Check Your Readiness — p. 372
1. 3.14 2. 123 3. 108 4. 5 5. 97 6. 24 7. 144
8. 3 9. 8 10. 58° 11. 63° 12. 50°

Lesson 8-1 — pp. 374–375
Check Skills You'll Need 1. inch, foot, yard, mile 2. 12
3. 4 4. 204
Quick Check 1. 400 mi; driving distances are usually
measured in miles. 2–4. Answers may vary.
Samples are given.
2. about 24 units 3. about 92 yd² 4. area: about
60 ft²; perimeter: about 90 ft

Lesson 8-2 — pp. 380–381
Check Skills You'll Need 1. Changing the order of the
factors does not change the product. 2. 450
3. 28.08 4. 57.12 5. 2.04

Quick Check 1. 90 cm² **2.** 22 cm

Lesson 8-3 pp. 384–385
Check Skills You'll Need 1. $\frac{1}{2}$ **2.** 3 **3.** 2 **4.** 5 **5.** 4.5
Quick Check 1. 24 cm **2a.** 216 m² **b.** 48 cm²

Lesson 8-4 pp. 388–389
Check Skills You'll Need 1. It is one of a pair of opposite sides. **2.** 75 cm³ **3.** 135 m²
Quick Check 1a. 34.1 m² **b.** 81 m² **2.** 8.75 in.²
Checkpoint Quiz 1 1. 420 km² **2.** 360 km² **3.** 54 m² **4.** 240 in.² **5.** 90 m²

Lesson 8-5 pp. 394–395
Check Skills You'll Need 1. radius **2.** $\overline{OA}$ or $\overline{OB}$ **3.** $\overline{DC}$ or $\overline{AB}$ **4.** $\overline{AB}$
Quick Check 1. 28.3 m **2.** 452 m²

Lesson 8-6 pp. 400–401
Check Skills You'll Need 1. Multiply the number by itself. **2.** 64 **3.** 144 **4.** 4 **5.** 49
Quick Check 1a. 8 **b.** 9 **c.** 15 **2.** about 9 ft × 9 ft **3a.** irrational **b.** rational **c.** rational **d.** rational

Lesson 8-7 pp. 405–406
Check Skills You'll Need 1. an integer **2.** 2 **3.** 4 **4.** 6 **5.** 7
Quick Check 1. 17 in. **2.** 24 mi **3.** 65 m

Lesson 8-8 pp. 410–411
Check Skills You'll Need 1. regular polygon

2. **3.**
4.
Quick Check 1. triangular prism; cone
2.

Lesson 8-9 pp. 414–416
Check Skills You'll Need 1. The height of a triangle is the length of the perpendicular segment from a vertex to the base opposite the vertex or to an extension of the base. **2.** 48 m² **3.** 6 ft²
Quick Check 1. Answers may vary. Sample:

2. 328 ft²
3. 3,455.8 m²
Checkpoint Quiz 1 1. $8 < \sqrt{77} < 9$ **2.** 18 cm **3.** 39 cm **4.** 4 yd **5.** 8 m **6.** sphere **7.** cone **8.** rectangular prism **9.** 36 in.² **10.** 2,884 m²

Lesson 8-10 pp. 421–423
Check Skills You'll Need 1. $\pi = \frac{C}{d}$ **2.** 113 m² **3.** 177 in.²
Quick Check 1. 120 in.³ **2.** 72 cm³ **3a.** about 6,000 cm³; 6,107 cm³ **b.** The estimate will be a little large.

Chapter 9

Check Your Readiness p. 434
1. 0 **2.** 32 **3.** -3 **4.** 65 **5.** 6.9 **6.** -40.8 **7.** 52.4 **8.** 1.5 **9.** 15 **10.** 5 **11.** $4\frac{3}{4}$ **12.** 36 **13.** 343 **14.** $24\frac{3}{8}$ **15.** 0.04 **16.** 0.12 **17.** 0.0358 **18.** 0.0405 **19.** 0.103

Lesson 9-1 pp. 437–438
Check Skills You'll Need 1. Yes; it can be written as a fraction. **2-5.**
0.8 2.3 $3\frac{1}{2}$ 7
Quick Check 1.
[graph: Price ($) vs. Amount of Yogurt (c)]

2. about $125 **3.** about 175°

Lesson 9-2 pp. 442–443
Check Skills You'll Need 1. 8 **2.** 0 **3.** -1 **4.** -2 **5.** -3
Quick Check 1. Start with 44 and add -9 repeatedly; -1, -10, -19. **2.** Start with 1,000 and multiply by $\frac{1}{10}$ repeatedly; 1, $\frac{1}{10}$, $\frac{1}{100}$ **3a.** neither **b.** neither **c.** arithmetic

Lesson 9-3 pp. 446–447
Check Skills You'll Need 1. addition **2.** -10 **3.** 4 **4.** -8 **5.** 14
Quick Check 1.

Amount of Gas (gal)	Miles Driven
1	18.1
2	36.2
3	54.3
4	72.4
5	90.5

271.5 miles **2.** 5, 7, 9, 11 **3.** $n - 9$; 1
Checkpoint Quiz 1 1.
[graph: Teaspoons vs. Tablespoons]
2. 30 teaspoons **3.** 3 tablespoons **4.** Start with 7 and add 7 repeatedly; 35, 42, 49. **5.** Start with 250 and add -30 repeatedly; 130, 100, 70. **6.** Start with 2, then add 3, 6, 12, 24 and so on; 47, 95, 191. **7.** Start with -4 and multiply by -3 repeatedly; -324, 972, -2,916. **8.** arithmetic; arithmetic; neither; geometric **9.** $50n$; 500

Lesson 9-4 pp. 452–453
Check Skills You'll Need 1. The expression has no variable. **2.** 9 **3.** 1 **4.** 0 **5.** 2
Quick Check 1. $d = 62t$ **2.** $y = 4x + 1$ **3.**

x	y
0	-4
1	-2
2	0
3	2

Lesson 9-5 pp. 456–457
Check Skills You'll Need 1. a set of numbers that follow a pattern **2.** $5n$ **3.** $2n - 9$ **4.** $101n$

Quick Check 1.

2. $d = 60t$; 270 mi
[graph: Distance (mi) vs. Time (h)]

Lesson 9-6 pp. 461–462
Check Skills You'll Need 1. Answers will vary. **2.** 100 mi **3.** 140 mi **4.** 10 mi **5.** 20 mi
Quick Check 1. You walk two blocks at a fast pace and then stop for 12 min. Then you walk 2 blocks at a slower pace and 2 blocks at the faster pace.
2.
[graph: Distance from Home vs. Time — Walking to school, At school, Bus trip home, Waiting for friend, Ride with mom (distance increases quickly), Arrive at home]
3.
[graph: Number of Cans vs. Time (A.M.)]
Checkpoint Quiz 1 1. $y = 5x$ **2.** $y = 3x - 3$

3. $y = x + 9$ **4.** [graph] **5.** Edwin **6.** 1 s
7.
[graph: Speed vs. Time (h)]

Lesson 9-7 pp. 468–469
Check Skills You'll Need 1. A percent is a ratio that compares a number to 100. **2.** 0.04 **3.** 0.09 **4.** 0.020 **5.** 0.065
Quick Check 1. $44.00 **2.**
[graph: Interest ($) vs. Time (yr)]
3. $4,943.49

Lesson 9-8 pp. 472–473
Check Skills You'll Need 1. If you divide each side of an equation by the same nonzero number, the two sides remain equal. **2.** $\frac{9}{5}$ **3.** $2\frac{2}{3}$ **4.** -32
Quick Check 1a. $x = \frac{y+4}{2}$ **b.** $x = y - 3$ **c.** $x = 2y - 5$ **2.** 6%

Chapter 10

Check Your Readiness p. 484
1. [number line -8-6-4-2 0 2 4 6 8]
2. [number line -8-6-4-2 0 2 4 6 8]
3. [number line -4-3-2-1 0 1 2 3 4]
4. [number line -8-6-4-2 0 2 4 6 8]
5. 63 **6.** -10 **7.** 6 **8.** 0.9 **9.** 125 **10.** 64 **11.** 1,331 **12.** 10,000 **13.** acute **14.** right **15.** obtuse **16.** straight **17.** obtuse **18.** acute

Lesson 10-1 pp. 486–487
Check Skills You'll Need 1. They are the same distance from zero, but in opposite directions.

2. [number line -8-6-4-2 0 2 4 6 8]
3. [number line -4-3-2-1 0 1 2 3 4]
4. [number line -2-1 0 1 2]
5. [number line -12-9-6-3 0 3 6 9 12]
6. [number line -12-9-6-3 0 3 6 9 12]
7. [number line -8-6-4-2 0 2 4 6 8]

Lesson 9-7 pp. 468–469
Quick Check 1. (4, 2), (1, -2), (-5, -3)
2. [graph: R, Quadrant II]
3. Answers may vary. Sample:
[graph: (0, 9), (6, 9), (0, 0), (0, 6)]

Lesson 10-2 pp. 491–492
Check Skills You'll Need 1. an equal sign **2.** 9 **3.** 6 **4.** 1 **5.** 10
Quick Check 1a. (-2, 6), (0, 8), (2, 10) **b.** (-2, -3), (0, -1), (2, 1) **c.** (-2, 4), (0, 0), (2, -4) **2.** no
3a. [graph] **b.** [graph]

c. [graph]
Lesson 10-3 pp. 498–499
Check Skills You'll Need 1. The numerator and denominator have no common factors other than 1. **2.** $\frac{3}{4}$ **3.** $-\frac{2}{3}$ **4.** $\frac{1}{3}$ **5.** -5
Quick Check 1. $\frac{1}{2}$ **2.** $\frac{1}{4}$ **3.**
[graph: P]
Checkpoint Quiz 1 1-3.
[graph: Q, D, K]
1. III **2.** II **3.** **4.** [graph]
5. [graph] **6.** [graph]

7. [graph: d]
8. $-\frac{3}{2}$ **9.** [graph: P]
10. [graph: A]
Lesson 10-4 pp. 504–505
Check Skills You'll Need 1. An equation is linear when the graph of its solutions is a line. **2-4.** Answers may vary. Samples are given. **2.** (0, 12), (-2, 10), (3, 15) **3.** (0, -20), (5, -15), (-10, -30) **4.** (0, 0), (1, 15), (-2, -30)
Quick Check 1.

x	-3	-2	-1	0	1	2	3
y	18	8	2	0	2	8	18

[graph]
2.

x	-2	-1	0	1	2
y	4	2	0	2	4

[graph]

Lesson 10-5 pp. 510–511
Check Skills You'll Need 1. The x-coordinate is 2, and the y-coordinate is -5.
2-5.

[graph: E, R, S, G]

T683

Page 724

Quick Check 1. (−3, −3)
2. A(−4, 3), B(−1, 4), C(−3, 1) → A'(−7, 4), B'(−4, 5), C'(−6, 2)
3. (x, y) → (x + 6, y + 1)

Lesson 10-6 pp. 514–515
Check Skills You'll Need 1. image **2.** (−3, 3) **3.** (1, 5) **4.** (−3, 5)
Quick Check 1. yes
2 a–b. [graph] a. (4, 1)   b. (−4, −1)
3. A(−1, 4), B(−4, 2), C(−2, 1) → A'(−1, −4), B'(−4, −2), C'(−2, −1)
Checkpoint Quiz 2 1. [graph] **2.** [graph] **3.** [graph]

4. [graph]
5. No; $3^2 − 4 ≠ −5$. **6.** (−3, 9) **7.** (12, 6) **8.** (3, 0) **9.** (1, 4) **10.** 3 and 8

Lesson 10-7 pp. 519–520
Check Skills You'll Need 1. 90°
2. acute 60°
3. obtuse 120°
4. right 90°
5. straight 180°
Quick Check 1 a. Yes; it looks the same as you move each point to another point. **b.** No; it does not match the original figure after any rotation of 180° or less. **c.** Yes; it looks the same as the original when it is rotated 180°. **2.** 60°
3. [graph] T'(0, 0), R'(−3, −3), G'(−5, −1)

Page 725

Chapter 11
Check Your Readiness p. 530
1. −31, −30, 13, 32, 33, 34 **2.** 10.2, 10.9, 11.1, 11.3, 11.5 **3.** 12 **4.** 32 **5.** 67 **6.** 8.5 **7.** 18 **8.** 14 **9.** 68 **10.** 108 **11–14.** [graph] **11.** II **12.** y-axis **13.** I **14.** x-axis

Lesson 11-1 pp. 532–533
Check Skills You'll Need 1. An integer is a positive or negative whole number, or 0. **2.** 16, 22, 23, 45, 52, 61, 87, 91 **3.** −47, −43, −41, 42, 43, 45
Quick Check 1. U.S. Representatives for 22 States

Number of Representatives	Tally	Frequency
1	ЖΙ	5
2	II	2
3	IIII	4
4	I	1
5	III	3
6		0
7	II	2
8	II	2
9	II	2

2. Number of Students in Math Classes [dot plot] 20 22 24 26 28
3. Ages of Employees [bar graph] Number of Employees vs Age (years) 20-29, 30-39, 40-49, 50-59, 60-69, 70-79

Lesson 11-2 pp. 538–539
Check Skills You'll Need 1. interval
2. [scatter plot: Height (in.) vs Age (yr)]
Quick Check 1 a. 95; 95 million households with VCRs in 2001 **b.** C6 **2.** 2001 **3.** Answers may vary. Sample: about 130 million

Lesson 11-3 pp. 544–545
Check Skills You'll Need 1. the middle value of a set of data **2.** 42 **3.** 6.4 **4.** 122.5
Quick Check 1. Wind Speeds Recorded During Storm (mph)

```
0 | 9
1 | 4 6 8
2 | 5 5 9
3 | 0 3 4 8
Key: 0 | 9 means 9
```

2. Charlotte, N.C.; Charlotte had a median of 3.6 in., while Portland had a median of 3.55 in. **3.** 10.5; 3; 52
Checkpoint Quiz 1 1.

Number	Tally	Frequency
1	II	2
2	II	2
3	II	2
4	II	2
5	III	3
6	I	1
7	II	2
8	II	2
9	I	1

[dot plot 1–9]

Page 726

2. Graphs and explanations may vary. Sample graph: Art Show Attendance [bar graph] Adults, Children; Attendance vs Day: S M Tu W Th F S
3. $6,527 million **4.** Industry **5.** Health **6.** Revenue (millions) **7.** B3 **8.** A3 **9.** B2
10.

```
 8 | 7 9
 9 | 3 5 5
10 |
11 | 2 3 7 7
12 | 0 1 4
Key: 8 | 7 means 87
```

Lesson 11-4 pp. 550–551
Check Skills You'll Need 1. percent **2.** 80% **3.** 25% **4.** 7%
Quick Check 1 a. Answers may vary. Sample: Less likely to be random; you may get only people shopping after work. **b.** More likely to be random; you won't just get people shopping after work. **2 a.** Biased; the question implies that meat is greasy and vegetables are healthy. **b.** Fair; the question makes no assumptions about pizza toppings.

Lesson 11-5 p. 554
Check Skills You'll Need 1. ratios **2.** 10 **3.** 44 **4.** 9
Quick Check 1. about 1,914 deer

Lesson 11-6 pp. 560–562
Check Skills You'll Need 1. mean **2.** 117; 118; 123
Quick Check 1. when space is limited or when you want to focus on a narrow range of data

2 a. Annual Profits [graph] Profits (100,000 dollars) vs Years
Class Size [graph] Students vs Year 2000 2001 2002 2003 2004
3. 15 and 27 **4.** Answers may vary. Sample: "Home of the under-500-Cal Kiddie Burger."
Checkpoint Quiz 2 1. Movies Filmed in Georgia [graph] Movies vs Year 2004–1997
2. Median; it is a higher value than mean or mode. **3.** Answers will vary. **4.** A; it is a more diverse sample. **5.** about 3,871 horses **6.** about 172 turtles

Page 727

Lesson 11-7 pp. 567–568
Check Skills You'll Need 1. horizontal
2-7. [graph]
Quick Check 1. [scatter plot: Arm Span (in.) vs Height (in.)] Height and Arm Span **2.** positive

Chapter 12
Check Your Readiness p. 578
1. $\frac{3}{8}$ **2.** $\frac{10}{27}$ **3.** $\frac{3}{13}$ **4.** $\frac{8}{11}$ **5.** $\frac{1}{4}$ **6.** $\frac{3}{7}$ **7.** 9 **8.** 43.75 **9.** 5 **10.** 43.75 **11.** 64 **12.** 10.5 **13.** 46% **14.** 26.5% **15.** 7% **16.** 25.6% **17.** 82% **18.** 80% **19.** 45.5% **20.** 57.1% **21.** 40% **22.** 46.9%

Lesson 12-1 pp. 580–581
Check Skills You'll Need 1. fraction, decimal, percent **2.** 0.62; 62% **3.** 0.95; 95% **4.** 0.275; 27.5% **5.** 1.1; 110%
Quick Check 1. $\frac{3}{5}$ **2.** $\frac{1}{3}$ **3.** $\frac{1}{2}$ **4.** 0

Lesson 12-2 pp. 586–587
Check Skills You'll Need 1. Answers may vary. Sample: An outcome is a single result, but an event can be a group of results. **2.** $\frac{1}{6}$ **3.** $\frac{1}{2}$ **4.** 0
Quick Check 1. $\frac{5}{12}$ **2.** 105 bikes **3.** $\frac{1}{20}$

Lesson 12-3 pp. 591–593
Check Skills You'll Need 1. factor tree **2.** 3 · 5 **3.** 2 · 7 **4.** 2 · 13 **5.** 5 · 11

Quick Check 1.

	H	T	; $\frac{1}{4}$
H	HH	HT	
T	TH	TT	

2 a. Vessel — Stream — Outcome **b.** $\frac{1}{3}$
Kayak: N → K, N; NW → K, NW; NE → K, NE
Canoe: N → C, N; NW → C, NW; NE → C, NE
Rowboat: N → R, N; NW → R, NW; NE → R, NE
3. 35 sandwiches
Checkpoint Quiz 1 1. $\frac{2}{5}$; 0.4; 40% **2.** $\frac{2}{5}$; 0.4; 40% **3.** $\frac{4}{5}$; 0.8; 80% **4.** $\frac{3}{5}$; 0.6; 60% **5.** PP, PB, PR, PG, BB, BR, BG, BP GG, GP, GB, GR, RR, RB, RP, RG **6.** $\frac{1}{16}$ **7.** $\frac{1}{16}$ **8.** $\frac{20}{119}$ **9.** $\frac{5}{16}$

Lesson 12-4 pp. 598–599
Check Skills You'll Need 1. To multiply fractions, multiply the numerators and multiply the denominators. **2.** $\frac{9}{16}$ **3.** $\frac{9}{25}$ **4.** $\frac{20}{49}$ **5.** $\frac{4}{49}$
Quick Check 1. $\frac{1}{4}$ **2.** $\frac{1}{10}$ **3.** $\frac{1}{1,326}$

Lesson 12-5 pp. 606–607
Check Skills You'll Need 1. the result of multiplication **2.** 90 **3.** 380 **4.** 336 **5.** 720 **6.** 60
Quick Check 1. 720 **2.** 7! = 5,040 **3 a.** 336 **b.** The example selects only 3 teams from the 12 choices, so the answer is 12 × 11 × 10, not 12!

Lesson 12-6 pp. 610–611
Check Skills You'll Need 1. The letters are not in the same order. **2.** 24 **3.** 720
Quick Check 1. 3 **2.** 12
Checkpoint Quiz 2 1. $\frac{6}{49}$ **2.** $\frac{3}{49}$ **3.** $\frac{4}{49}$ **4.** 0 **5.** $\frac{5}{49}$ **6.** $\frac{3}{56}$ **7.** $\frac{1}{56}$ or $\frac{3}{14}$ **8.** $\frac{4}{56}$ or $\frac{1}{14}$ **9.** 720 ways **10.** 15 combinations **11.** ABCD, ABDC, ACBD, ACDB, ADBC, ADCB, BACD, BADC, BCAD, BCDA, BDAC, BDCA, CABD, CADB, CBAD, CBDA, CDAB, CDBA, DABC, DACB, DBAC, DBCA, DCAB, DCBA **12.** 6 combinations

Chapter 1

Lesson 1-1
pp. 6–7

EXERCISES 1. Rounded numbers are numbers rounded to the nearest whole number, whereas compatible numbers are chosen because they are easy to compute mentally. **3.** C **5.** B **7.** 11 **9.** 90 **13.** 19 **15.** 14 **19.** 4 **21.** 10 **29.** about $2.10 **33.** about $26; (390 ÷ 30) × $2 **37.** 706.8, 761.8, 768.0, 768.1

Lesson 1-2
pp. 10–11

EXERCISES 1. Assoc. Prop. of Add. **3.** 40 **5.** 19 **7.** 0 **9.** 105.8 **11.** 7.582 **19.** 5.26 **21.** 0.0645 **27.** 43.5 **29.** 39.5 **35.** > **37.** 122.4 m **39.** 4.67 in. **41.** sailfish: 0.008 mi/h **45.** 136

Lesson 1-3
pp. 16–17

EXERCISES 1. Comm. Prop. of Mult. **3.** The product is divided by 10. **5.** 2 **7.** 0; zero property **9.** 3; commutative property **13.** 0.15 **15.** 3.915 **21.** 0 **23.** 21.5 **33.** 0.432 **13.52 million **41.** $11.04 **45.** 1.643

Lesson 1-4
pp. 22–23

EXERCISES 1. dividend **3.** 4 **5.** 400 **7.** 6 **9.** 12 **17.** 0.75 **19.** 740 **27.** 4,490 **29.** 3.02 **33.** 14 yd **35.** The quotient is greater than the divisor; dividing by a number less than one is the same as multiplying by a whole number. **37.** 1.45 in. **41.** 6.7

Lesson 1-5
pp. 28–30

EXERCISES 1. 1,000 **3.** 0.01 **5.** 0.064 **7.** 0.00849 **9.** 22 m **11.** 900 **13.** 58,000 **23.** C **25.** D **29.** millimeters **33.** 1,250 g **35.** 5 mugs **37.** No; a double batch needs 2.02 L. **41.** 6.35

Lesson 1-6
pp. 33–34

EXERCISES 1. Whole numbers do not include negative numbers. **3 a.** sometimes true **b.** sometimes true **c.** sometimes true **d.** sometimes true **5.** −4 **7.** 2 **9.** 5 **11.** −12 **13.** 8 **15.** −11 **23.** 11 **25.** 1 **33.** < **35.** < **41.** −5, −2, −1, 0, 7 **45 a.** Omaha, Nebr. Bismarck, N. Dak. **47.** −3551, −3515, −3155, −3151 **49.** No; there are no integers between the integers −3 and −4. **53.** 453

Lesson 1-7
pp. 41–42

EXERCISES 1. A; always **3.** C; never **5.** 8 **7.** −1 **9.** 1 **13.** 38 **15.** 0 **19.** 13 **21.** 25 **29.** −1 + 4 = 3 **31.** −2 **33.** 8:00 A.M. **41.** >

Lesson 1-8
pp. 46–47

EXERCISES 1. B **3.** 4 **5.** 80 **7.** −2 **9.** −5 **11.** 36 **13.** 21 **19.** 3 **21.** −14 **31.** −1 **35.** 6 min **37 a.** 278 − 5(15) **b.** $203 **41.** 1.42

Lesson 1-9
pp. 50–51

EXERCISES 1. multiplication **3.** 11(2) should be 11(0.2). **5.** 20; 4 **7.** 30; 2; 160 **9.** 7 **11.** 3 **17.** 145 **19.** 19.8 **27.** (4 + 4) ÷ 4 − 4 = −2 **29.** 1,840 ft² **31.** 3,348 ft **39.** −60

Lesson 1-10
pp. 55–57

EXERCISES 1. outlier **3.** 5 **5.** Median; the outlier 45 greatly affects the mean. **7.** 3.5; 3.5; no mode; 1 **9.** 8 **13.** 8 **17.** 51 and 58 **21.** 10 **29.** Answers may vary. Samples are given. 1, 2, 3, 5, 5 **33.** 87 cartons **37.** 123, 213, 231, 312, 321

Chapter Review
pp. 60–61

1. Distr. Prop. **2.** Assoc. Prop. of Add. **3.** absolute value **4.** mode **5.** order of operations

Exercises 6–9. Answers may vary. Samples are given.

6. 7; compatible numbers **7.** 52, rounding **8.** 63, rounding **9.** 6; front-end estimation **10.** 3.7 **11.** 0.567 **12.** 0.73 **13.** 16.875 **14.** 7.31 lb **15.** 0.456 **16.** 14,200 **17.** 340 **18.** 71.47 m **19.** < 20. = **21.** > **22.** > **23.** 6 **24.** 29 **25.** −30 **26.** −25 **27.** 3.425 **28.** 13.13 **29.** 19 **30.** 162.4 **31.** 2; 2; 2; 2

Chapter 2

Lesson 2-1
pp. 70–71

EXERCISES 1. The exponent tells you how many times the base is used as a factor. **3.** −625 **7.** B **9.** 2⁶ **11.** 6³ **15.** 81 **17.** 0.000064 **25.** 39

27. 39 **31.** 60 · 60 · 60; 6³

33.

Power of 10	Value	Number of Zeros
10^1	10	1
10^2	100	2
10^3	1,000	3
10^4	10,000	4
10^5	100,000	5

35. 12 **37.** Positive; $(-672)^2$ is positive and larger than 192. **45.** 40

Lesson 2-2
pp. 77–78

EXERCISES 1. A factor is a whole number that divides another whole number with a remainder of 0. A multiple of a number is the product of the number and another whole number. **3.** 2 **5.** Composite; the factors are 1, 2, 4, 7, 14 and 28. **7.** Composite; the factors are 1, 2, 13 and 26. **9.** 36 **11.** 10 **17.** 1, 2, 4, 5, 10, 20 **21.** prime **25.** $3^2 \cdot 5$ **27.** $2^2 \cdot 3 \cdot 7$ **33.** 2 **35.** 16 **43.** 1 **45.** 50 **47.** 6 boxes **49.** Yes; both can be written as $2^3 \cdot 3$. **55.** −5, −4, 3, 6

Lesson 2-3
pp. 84–85

EXERCISES 1. No; the GCF of the numerator and denominator of a fraction in simplest form is 1. **3.** No; the student added 4 instead of multiplying by 4 **7.** $\frac{10}{12}$, $\frac{15}{18}$, $\frac{1}{8}$, $\frac{6}{48}$ **21.** $\frac{9}{5}$, $\frac{7}{3}$ **23.** $\frac{3}{4}$ **31.** Answers may vary. Sample: $\frac{5}{8}$, $\frac{10}{16}$ **33.** D **37.** Answers may vary. Sample: $\frac{2a}{2b}$, $\frac{3a}{3b}$ **41.** 17.09

Lesson 2-4
pp. 89–90

EXERCISES 1. The LCM of the denominators of two or more fractions is the LCD. **3.** 63 **5.** 24 **7.** > **9.** < **11.** < **19.** $\frac{1}{9}$, $\frac{4}{8}$, $\frac{1}{6}$ **21.** $\frac{5}{9}$, $\frac{7}{12}$, $\frac{1}{3}$ **29.** $\frac{3}{4}$ in.; the $\frac{3}{4}$-in. nail is not long enough to go all the way through the board. **31.** = **33.** > **35.** what they say **37.** $\frac{3}{4} > \frac{7}{10}$ **45.** 72

Lesson 2-5
pp. 93–94

EXERCISES 1. Both are larger than 1. **3.** proper fraction **5.** improper fraction **7.** 8 **9.** It is a whole number because 72 is divisible by 12. **11.** $\frac{23}{4}$ **13.** $\frac{23}{4}$ **21.** $8\frac{1}{3}$ **23.** $\frac{13}{2}$ **33.** $\frac{7}{12}$ **35.** 1 **37.** $1\frac{5}{8}$, $\frac{13}{8}$ **39.** $4\frac{3}{8}$ mi **41.** $3\frac{2}{8}$, $3\frac{1}{4}$, $\frac{26}{8}$ **45.** −12

Lesson 2-6
pp. 99–100

EXERCISES 1. A terminating decimal stops, whereas a repeating decimal has a block of digits that repeat without end. **3.** $1\frac{3}{8}$ **5.** $3\frac{9}{100}$ **7.** 0.5, $1\frac{1}{3}$, 1.9, 2 **9.** 0.8 **11.** 0.6 **17.** $\frac{33}{50}$ **19.** $\frac{3}{4}$ **25.** 3.84, $3\frac{41}{50}$, 3.789, 2 **31.** < **33.** > **35.** when the numerator is not a multiple of 3 **37.** N.Y.: $\frac{4,572}{19,227}$ Tex.: $\frac{6,267}{22,490}$ Calif.: $\frac{9,596}{33,893}$ Fla.: $\frac{4,003}{17,397}$ Ohio: $\frac{2,779}{11,459}$ **39.** Fla., N.Y., Ohio, Tex., Calif. **41.** The quotients are 0.5, 5, 50, 500, 5,000, and 50,000. As the divisor gets smaller, the quotient gets larger because divisor × quotient = dividend. **45.** 0.36

Lesson 2-7
pp. 104–105

EXERCISES 1. Answers may vary. Sample: A rational number is a number that can be written as a quotient of two integers. **3.** > **5.** −236, $-7\frac{1}{7}$, −3.3, 0, $\frac{41}{99}$ **7.** > **9.** < **19.** −1.0, $-\frac{3}{5}$, 0.25, $\frac{3}{4}$ **25.** > **27.** > **29.** frog **31.** $\frac{3}{4}$ **35.** $\frac{1}{2}$

Lesson 2-8
pp. 108–109

EXERCISES 1. It is written as the product of two factors, one greater than or equal to 1 and less than 10, and the other a power of 10. **3.** 5 **5.** B **7.** A **9.** 7.5×10^7 **11.** 4.4×10^4 **17.** 3,400 **27.** 1,600 lb **31.** 3.5×10^5 **33.** about 3.3×10^2 h **37.** 60

Chapter Review
pp. 112–113

1. exponent **2.** prime **3.** factors **4.** equivalent fraction **5.** GCF **6.** −16 **7.** −64 **8.** 125 **9.** 60 **10.** $2^2 \cdot 3 \cdot 7$ **11.** $2 \cdot 3 \cdot 13$ **12.** $2 \cdot 3^2 \cdot 5$ **13.** 27 **14.** 5 **15.** 210 days from now **16.** $\frac{1}{6}$, $\frac{1}{4}$ **17.** $\frac{1}{2}$, $\frac{3}{8}$ **18.** $\frac{3}{4}$, $\frac{1}{3}$ **19.** $\frac{7}{12}$, $\frac{3}{2}$ **20.** store B **21.** $5\frac{3}{4}$ h **22.** 6 **23.** $2\frac{1}{4}$ **24.** $6\frac{2}{3}$ **25.** 26 **26.** 7 **27.** 0.3 **28.** 0.5 **29.** 2.5 **30.** 0.8 **31.** 0.08 **32.** $-\frac{1}{4}$, 0.3, $\frac{3}{4}$ **33.** $-\frac{4}{11}$, −0.3, 2.7 **34.** $-\frac{5}{6}$, −0.5, 2.2 **35.** 7.123×10^6 **36.** 906,000 **37.** 8.19×10^4 **38.** 601,500,000

Chapter 3

Lesson 3-1
pp. 122–123

EXERCISES 1. Answers may vary. Sample: A benchmark is a convenient number used to replace a fraction. Examples are 0, $\frac{1}{2}$, and 1 for fractions between 0 and 1. **3.** 1 **5.** $\frac{1}{2}$ **7.** 1 **9.** 7 **11.** about $\frac{1}{2}$ **13.** about $\frac{1}{2}$ **21.** about 10 **23.** about 5 **29.** about 4 **35.** about 29 **37.** 2 h **39.** about $\frac{1}{2}$ t **41.** about $4\frac{1}{2}$ t **49.** $11\frac{1}{8}$

Lesson 3-2
pp. 128–129

EXERCISES 1. Answers may vary. Sample: It doesn't make sense to add fractions with different denominators. For example, $\frac{1}{2} + \frac{1}{3} \neq \frac{2}{5}$. **3.** 16 **5.** 1 **7.** 9 **9.** $\frac{7}{40}$ **11.** $\frac{23}{40}$ **13.** $\frac{1}{16}$ **15.** $1\frac{1}{2}$ **17.** $\frac{7}{8}$ **27.** $1\frac{5}{8}$ **29.** $1\frac{10}{21}$ **37.** positive **41.** $\frac{1}{2}$ **43.** $\frac{7}{10}$, $\frac{45}{52}$ **51.** −2.4, 1.34, $\frac{7}{3}$, $\frac{25}{4}$

Lesson 3-3
pp. 132–133

EXERCISES 1. $3\frac{3}{4}$ **3.** $2\frac{2}{5}$ **5.** $3\frac{5}{7}$ **7.** $\frac{19}{10}$ **9.** $8\frac{1}{5}$ **15.** $18\frac{5}{6}$ **19.** $1\frac{1}{3}$ **25.** $29\frac{3}{20}$ **29.** $7\frac{7}{8}$ mi **31.** $4\frac{1}{2}$ in.² **33.** $10\frac{3}{8}$ c.i. **37.** 115

Lesson 3-4
pp. 138–139

EXERCISES 3. $2\frac{1}{4} \cdot 1\frac{3}{2} = \frac{9}{4} \cdot \frac{3}{4}$ **5.** No; you do not need to find a common denominator, since you reduce the product anyway. **7.** $\frac{1}{3}$ **9.** $\frac{5}{18}$ **15.** 12 **17.** 26 **25.** 12 **27.** $3\frac{3}{8}$ **33.** $8\frac{1}{3}$ c **35.** 0 **39.** $\frac{7}{8}$ mi **41.** 28 games **43.** 2 mi²; $6\frac{3}{8}$ mi **47.** 76

Lesson 3-5
pp. 143–145

EXERCISES 1. $1\frac{1}{3}$ **3.** $\frac{1}{2}$ **5.** $4\frac{2}{7}$ **7.** A **9.** 8 **11.** $\frac{5}{8}$ **21.** $\frac{6}{23}$ **23.** $1\frac{1}{3}$ **35.** Your friend found the reciprocal of $\frac{3}{8}$ without changing $5\frac{3}{8}$ to an improper fraction; $\frac{8}{43}$. **37.** 800 nails **39.** 6 costumes **41.** 1 **47.** 12 ft **53.** 2,564

Lesson 3-6
pp. 150–151

EXERCISES 1. multiply **3.** multiply **5.** divide **7.** It takes more smaller units to equal the larger unit. **9.** $4\frac{1}{2}$ **11.** $6\frac{1}{6}$ **17.** 3 **19.** $\frac{1}{2}$ **21.** 12 **25.** 5,000 **31.** 9,560 ft **33.** 2,400 **35.** $3\frac{1}{2}$ **39.** 4 ft **41.** no; quarter pound = 4 oz **47.** 3

Lesson 3-7
pp. 156–157

EXERCISES 1. 4 in., $3\frac{1}{2}$ in., $3\frac{6}{8}$ in. **3.** $3\frac{12}{16}$ in. **5.** $4\frac{1}{2}$ ft **7.** $1\frac{15}{16}$ in. **9.** 56 lb **17.** 2 lb **19.** 4 ft **21.** 8.9 oz **25.** 2 cm **27.** $4\frac{3}{16}$ in. **29.** ft **31.** cm **35.** 541 ft **41.** about 6

Chapter Review
pp. 160–161

1. reciprocal **2.** benchmark **3.** precision **4.** benchmark; precision **5.** about 1 **6.** about $\frac{1}{2}$ **7.** about 1 **8.** about $\frac{1}{2}$ **9.** about 3 **10.** about 25 **11.** about 14 **12.** about 10 **13.** about 8 mi **14.** $1\frac{7}{12}$ **15.** $6\frac{13}{16}$ **16.** $\frac{5}{13}$ **17.** $\frac{1}{12}$ **18.** $11\frac{5}{20}$ min **19.** $\frac{1}{4}$ **20.** $\frac{9}{16}$ **21.** 9 **22.** $94\frac{23}{24}$ **23.** $39\frac{7}{12}$ m² **24.** $\frac{1}{2}$ **25.** 6 **26.** $3\frac{3}{8}$ **27.** $\frac{5}{18}$ **28.** $3\frac{1}{2}$ ft **29.** $3\frac{1}{2}$ **30.** $1\frac{1}{2}$ **31.** 6 **32.** 22 **33.** 4,000 **34.** 7 **35.** about 9 ft **36.** 12 c **37.** 5.5 L **38.** 8.75 m **39.** 23 h **40.** 25 g **41.** $11\frac{3}{16}$ **42.** 7 g **43.** 13 yd **44.** 11.6 cm **45.** 21.00 lb **46.** 5 L **47.** 5.13 m

Chapter 4

Lesson 4-1
pp. 171–172

EXERCISES 1. An algebraic expression differs from a numerical expression because it contains at least one variable, and the value changes. **3.** addition

5–7. Answers may vary. Samples are given:

5. the product of 5 and w **7.** the quotient of w and 4 **9.** 6 **11.** 6 **13.** $\frac{5}{12}$ **15–17.** Answers may vary. Samples are given. **17.** two more than a number **19.** nine and one tenth less than a number **25.** 42 **27.** 3 **33.** 10n **35.** Answers may vary. Sample: Multiply 24(60) to find the number of minutes in 24 h. Then multiply the answer by 1,260, the number of beats per minute. The heart beats 1,814,400 times in 24 h. **39.** Answers may vary. Sample: The second student charges $15 to start and $3/h. **43.** 45

Lesson 4-2
pp. 176–177

EXERCISES 1. solution **3.** yes **5.** no **7.** −3 **9.** −4 **11.** 288 **15.** −8 **17.** −4 **21.** about 19 **27.** 54 **29.** 20 **33.** 4d = 360 **31.** 31.89 in. **37.** 4c = 67.80; about $17; no; the total should be about 4($12.95), or $51.80. **41.** 1

Lesson 4-3
pp. 183–184

EXERCISES 1. Inverse **3.** 12 **5.** −49 **7.** 205.4 **19.** 9 **25.** B **31.** 119 **33.** −0.9 **37.** p − 8.45 = 21.50; $29.95 **39.** Let r = the number of runs needed; 3 + 4 + 2 + 6 + 8 + r = 30; 7 runs. **43.** 33

Lesson 4-4
pp. 188–190

EXERCISES 1. Multiplication Property of Equality **3.** Division Property of Equality **5.** Division Property of Equality **7.** C **9.** 12 **11.** −5 **23.** −24 **25.** 100.8 **39.** 50 **41.** 85 **45.** 15 yr **47.** b is the reciprocal of a and $b \neq 0$. **55.** $\frac{23}{28}$

Lesson 4-5
pp. 196–198

EXERCISES 1. A one-step expression uses only one operation, while a two-step expression uses two. **3.** B **5.** C **7.** 70 **9.** Let h = your height; 6h + 1. **13.** 1.5 **15.** −0.9 **21.** 15.2 **23.** 7 **33.** 11.5 **35.** 45 **39.** 9 min **41.** Answers may vary. Sample: You need to keep the equation "balanced." **47.** =

Lesson 4-6
pp. 202–204

EXERCISES 1. Let m = number of miles; 2.00 + 0.50m = 5.00; 6 mi **3.** 12 **5.** −3 **7.** 8 **31.** Let h = number of additional hours; 3.95 + 1.25h = 7.70; 3 h. **35.** 11 **39.** 15 credits

Lesson 4-7
pp. 207–208

EXERCISES 1. inequality **3.** C **5.** −1 **7.** −2
11.
13.
19. $x \leq 6$
25. $a \geq 17$;
31. $w \leq 3$
33. −3, −2, or −1 **39.** −4, −2, −1, 2, 4, 7

Lesson 4-8
pp. 212–214

EXERCISES 1. Addition Property of Equality **3.** C **5.** B **7.** $g \leq -6$;
9. $y \geq 16$;
17. $n \geq 1$;

19. $p \leq -4$; **29.** $w > -\frac{1}{2}$
31. $j \geq -5$ **35.** No; the solution of $x + 5 \leq -2$ is $x \leq -7$, and the solution of $-2 \leq x + 5$ is $x \geq -7$. **39.** no more than 1,240 Cal **43.** $\frac{1}{5}$

Lesson 4-9
pp. 216–218

EXERCISES 1. The inequality symbol is reversed. **3.** > **5.** >
7. $p > 12$;
9. $x < -8$;
19. $p < -15$;
21. $w \leq -21$;
35. $4x \leq -44$; $x \leq -11$ **41.** $50.2 < t$ **43.** at most 3 hot dogs **45.** 4 bags of peanuts; $.50 **47.** The student should not have reversed the inequality symbol. **49.** −3x + 10 > 19; $x < -3$;
53. −3.83; 3.6; 2.2

Chapter Review
pp. 220–221

1. variable **2.** inequality **3.** equation **4.** algebraic expression **5.** solution of an inequality **6.** 5 **7.** 6.3 **8.** 10 **9.** −10 **10.** −7 **11.** 20 **12.** 4 **13.** 72 **14.** 24 **15.** 84 **16.** 99 **17.** −12 **18.** 52 **19.** 5 **20.** 43 **21.** −54 **22.** 114 tickets **23.** 1 **24.** 12 **25.** −3 **26.** 140 + 35w = 1.050; 26 wk
27. $t \leq 10$;
28. $r < 5$;
29. $h < -22$;
31. 9 > 17;
32. $m \geq -7$;
33. $x \geq 20$;

CHAPTER 5

Lesson 5-1 pp. 230–231
EXERCISES 1. Equivalent ratios name the same amount, as do equivalent fractions.
3–5. Answers may vary. Samples are given.
3. 2 to 16 5. 20 to 18 7. $\frac{17}{24}$ 9. equivalent
11. equivalent 21 to 25, 21 : 25, $\frac{21}{25}$
14–16. Answers may vary. Samples are given.
15. 12 to 14 17. $\frac{1}{2}$ 19. $\frac{3}{200}$ 23. equivalent
31 a. 8 : 4, 7.5 : 3, 3.5 : 1 b. 10 qt antifreeze, 5 qt water 37. 45

Lesson 5-2 pp. 234–235
EXERCISES 1. Answers may vary. Sample: It gives the cost of one item. 3. 147; 7 5. 8 g
7. 16 points/game 11. $30 15. $.93/oz
17. $.06/fl oz, $.05/fl oz; the 50-fl-oz detergent is the better buy. 23. $.75/pt 25. $.60/lb
27 a. 1 person/mi² b. No; answers may vary. Sample: Some regions of the state are more densely populated than others. 29. about 39,421,000 times; about 108,000 times; about 75 times 33. 29

Lesson 5-3 pp. 240–241
EXERCISES 1. ratios 3. 8 5. 9 7. 12 9. No; you need to multiply the numerator of one by the denominator of the other. They do form a proportion.
$$\frac{3}{4} \:⟋\: \frac{12}{16}$$
$$3 \cdot 16 \:⟋\: 4 \cdot 12$$
$$48 = 48$$
11. no 13. yes 31. no 33. no 35. Yes; the weight ratios $\frac{174}{29}$ and $\frac{102}{17}$ are proportional because 174 · 17 = 102 · 29. 37. yes; $\frac{26}{4} = \frac{104}{4}$
39. $\frac{4n}{3}$ and $\frac{9}{9}$ will always form a proportion because 36n = 36n for all values of n. 43. 105

Lesson 5-4 pp. 246–248
EXERCISES 1. Answers may vary. Sample: Finding a unit rate gives you a denominator of 1, so you only need to multiply to solve the proportion. $\frac{5}{8} = \frac{x}{x}$, x = 40 3. 4 5. 12 7. $7.90
9. $59.00 11. 6 13. 6 17. 20 19. 85.75 31. 5
33. 6.9
35. 240 should be the numerator. $\frac{2}{8} = \frac{240}{n}$
43. −6, −3, −2, 1, 8

Lesson 5-5 pp. 254–255
EXERCISES 1. Two polygons are similar if corresponding angles have the same measure and the lengths of the corresponding sides form equivalent ratios. 5. $\overline{AB}$ 7. 11.2 ft 15. 6
17. 2.88 km 19. 99 cm 23. 5

Lesson 5-6 pp. 261–263
EXERCISES 1. ratio; length 3. No; the scale should be written as model : actual, or 8 ft : 6 ft.
5. 7 in. 7. 165 ft 9. 495 ft 13. about 38 mi
23. Answers may vary. Sample: 1 cm : 1.9 m
25a. 1 in. : 4 ft b. 0.5 in.

Chapter Review pp. 266–267
1. a scale drawing 2. unit cost 3. rate 4. scale
5. similar 6. $\frac{3}{5}$ 7. $\frac{1}{5}$
11. $\frac{39}{97}$, 39 to 97, 39 : 97 12. 6 passengers/car
13. 75 Cal/serving 14. 23 students/classroom
15. $4/kg 16. $0.28/oz, $0.31/oz; the 10-oz size is the better buy. 17. 3 ft² per minute 18. 12
19. 25 20. 3 21. 136 22. $\frac{5}{?} = \frac{?}{250,000}$; 417,000 board feet 23. 7.5 ft 24. 15 ft 25. 45
26. x = 45, y = 36 27. 6,300 mi 28. 0.75 in.

Chapter 6

Lesson 6-1 pp. 276–277
EXERCISES 1. $\frac{32}{100}$; 32% 3. 67% 5. 90%
7. $\frac{64}{100}$; 64% 11. 15. $\frac{4}{5}$, 80%

21. 60% 23. 84% 25. 55% 27. 70% 29. 52%
31. about 19% 33. about 28% 39. −2, −3

Lesson 6-2 pp. 282–283
EXERCISES 1. 62%, $\frac{62}{100}$, 0.62 3. $\frac{1}{5}$, 0.54, 55%
5. 57% 7. yes 9. 11. 0.88 15. 90% 17. 8.3%
21. $\frac{3}{5}$ 23. $\frac{1}{5}$ 27. 12%, 0.25, $\frac{1}{5}$
33.

Topping	With Olives	Plain	With Onions and Green Peppers
Percent of the Pizza	37.5%	12.5%	50%
Number of Slices	3	1	4

35 a. 79%, $\frac{16}{20}$, $\frac{21}{25}$, 85%, $\frac{9}{10}$, 92% b. 85%
39. −0.9 ≤ x

Lesson 6-3 pp. 286–287
EXERCISES 1. 1.5; $\frac{3}{2}$ or $1\frac{1}{2}$ 3. 825% 5. 4
7. Answers may vary. Sample: A decimal that is less than 1% has zeros in the tenths and hundredths place, such as 0.009. A decimal that is greater than 100% has a number other than zero before the decimal point, such as 1.01.
9. 1.3; $1\frac{3}{10}$ 11. 3.45; $3\frac{9}{20}$ 21. 160% 23. 258%
35. 270% 37. 1,001% 39. 1.66; $1\frac{33}{50}$
41. 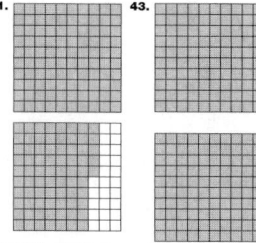 43.

45. 0.26% 47. No; it cannot be more than 100% fat. 49. Yes; it is reasonable that $\frac{1}{2}$ of 1% of the seeds will not grow. 53. $\frac{7}{25}$

Lesson 6-4 pp. 292–293
EXERCISES 1. 29 3. 58.08 5. $\frac{1}{6} \cdot 60 = 12$
7. $\frac{3}{20} \cdot 40 = 6$ 9. Answers may vary. Sample: You would probably use a fraction when the percent can be written as a fraction that is compatible with the other number. You would use a decimal for all other cases. 11. 16 13. 27.6 19. 57.2
21. 474 29. about 30 31. about 80 37. 160.38
39. 42.38 41. 6,800 forest fires 45. 26 students
49. 60

Lesson 6-5 pp. 296–297
EXERCISES 1. percent; 25% 3. whole; 16 5. C
7. B 9. 10% 11. 2% 15. 5 17. 2.25 21. 18.75
23. 80 27. $\frac{90}{n} = \frac{40}{100}$; 225 29. $\frac{54}{144} = \frac{n}{100}$; 37.5
31. 37.5% 35. The number 100 always appears as the denominator of one of the ratios, since percent means "out of 100." 41. $\frac{1}{3}$

Lesson 6-6 pp. 300–301
EXERCISES 1. No; "20% of 40" asks for a part, "20 is what percent of 40" asks for a percent, and "20 is 40% of what number" asks for a whole.
3. C 5. 625p = 500; 80% 7. 0.96x = 24; 25
13. x = 0.41 · 800; 328 17. 18 = 48x; 37.5%
23. 69% 27. 49% 29. about 190 people
31. 45 members 37. yes

Lesson 6-7 pp. 306–307
EXERCISES 1. You earn 8% of the amount you sell. 3. $3.60 5. $27 7. $.71 9. $77.12
11. about $10.35 15. $96 21. $23 23. 5%
25. $6,800 33. $2.35/lb

Lesson 6-8 pp. 312–314
EXERCISES 1. Answers may vary. Sample: They both involve the difference between the original price and the selling price. Percent of markup is a percent of increase and percent of discount is a percent of decrease. 3. $\frac{15}{35}$; 43% increase
5. $\frac{374}{748}$, 50% decrease 7. A 9. 13% 11. 50%
17. 50% 23. 56% 29. 25% decrease
33. $53.30
35.

	A	B	C Change ($)	D Change (%)
1	Yr	Sales	Change ($)	Change (%)
2	1	200,000	—	—
3	2	240,000	40,000	20%
4	3	300,000	60,000	25%
5	4	330,000	30,000	10%

41. $471.30

Chapter Review pp. 316–317
1. C 2. E 3. D 4. B 5. A 6. 0.65; $\frac{13}{20}$
7. 0.02; $\frac{1}{50}$ 8. 0.018; $\frac{9}{500}$ 9. 0.625; $\frac{5}{8}$ 10. 37.5%
11. 16% 12. 44.82 13. 0.64 14. 97.2 15. 70%
16. 47.5 17. 252 18. 12 19. 72 20. 20%
21. $57.60 22. about $10.52 23. $268 24. $63
25. $216 26. $275 27. $225 28. 16.7% decrease 29. 20% increase 30. 15% increase
31. 40% increase 32. 72% decrease 33. 16.7% decrease 34. 31% decrease

Chapter 7

Lesson 7-1 pp. 326–327
EXERCISES 1. Skew lines 3. $\overline{LC}$ 5. $\overleftrightarrow{KE}$
7. $\overline{BC}$, $\overline{FE}$ 9. $\overline{LC}$ 11. $\overline{ZV}$ 15. $\overline{AE}$, $\overline{EF}$, $\overline{DH}$, $\overline{GH}$
21. yes 25.
29. $\overleftrightarrow{EF}$ and $\overleftrightarrow{GH}$ do not lie in the same plane.
31. $\overline{UV}$, $\overline{UV}$, $\overline{UV}$, $\overline{VU}$, $\overline{VW}$, $\overline{VY}$, $\overline{WY}$, $\overline{WX}$, $\overline{WX}$, $\overline{XW}$, $\overline{WX}$, $\overline{YZ}$, $\overline{YZ}$
35. about 9% increase

Lesson 7-2 pp. 333–334
EXERCISES 1. Vertical angles lie opposite each other, while adjacent angles lie next to each other. 3. acute, 45°, 135° 5. acute, 15°, 105°
7. obtuse 9. 11°; 101° 11. 78°; 168° 19. 57°
23. 159.8° and 69.8° 25. The student used the wrong scale on the protractor. 27. about 65°
29. Answers may vary. Sample:
∠JHK and ∠BHC, ∠HCD and ∠BCL 31. ∠HCB

Lesson 7-3 pp. 338–339
EXERCISES 1. no 3. obtuse scalene 5. acute isosceles 7. scalene 9. obtuse 13. 64°
17. isosceles 21. 44° 23. An equilateral triangle is always isosceles because it has 3 congruent sides. An isosceles triangle is not always equilateral because it has at least 2 congruent sides. 27. 1.16; $\frac{29}{25}$

Lesson 7-4 pp. 342–344
EXERCISES 1. A trapezoid is a quadrilateral with only one pair of parallel sides. A parallelogram is a quadrilateral with two pairs of parallel sides.
3. quadrilateral, parallelogram 5. quadrilateral, parallelogram, rhombus, rectangle, square 7. The parallelogram is irregular because the sides are not all congruent. 9. rectangles, trapezoids 11.

15. Trapezoid; $\overline{PQ}$ is parallel to $\overline{RS}$.
17. JN = 5 in.; m∠J = m∠K = m∠L = m∠N = 90°
19.

23. No; it would be a rectangle.

25. 29. 1.6

Lesson 7-5 pp. 348–349
EXERCISES 1. Yes. Similar polygons have congruent angles and sides in proportion. If the proportion is 1 to 1, then the polygons are not just similar, but congruent. 3. Congruent; all corresponding sides and angles are congruent.
5. Not congruent; not all corresponding sides and angles are congruent.
7. $\overline{CV} \cong \overline{JP}$; $\overline{VR} \cong \overline{PX}$; 11. △SRT 15. $\overline{BD}$
$\overline{RC} \cong \overline{XJ}$; ∠C ≅ ∠J;
∠V ≅ ∠P; ∠R ≅ ∠X
VR = 9; m∠V = 83°;
∠X = 41°; m∠J = 56°
17. ∠C 21. $\overline{XY} \cong \overline{BA}$; $\overline{YZ} \cong \overline{AD}$;
25. 25% $\overline{ZW} \cong \overline{DC}$; $\overline{WX} \cong \overline{CB}$;
∠Y ≅ ∠A; ∠Z ≅ ∠D; ∠W ≅ ∠C; ∠X ≅ ∠B
YZ = 11; ZW = 18;
m∠Y = 127°; m∠D = 83°;
m∠B = 83°

Lesson 7-6 pp. 352–353
EXERCISES 1. A radius is a line from the center of a circle to a point on the circle. A diameter is a line between two points on a circle that passes through the center of the circle. 3. M 5. $\overline{JL}$
7. ∠JMK, ∠KML, ∠JML 9. $\overline{OC}$, $\overline{OK}$, $\overline{OD}$
13. $\overline{TR}$, $\overline{RS}$, $\overline{ST}$ 15. $\overline{CD}$, $\overline{DB}$, $\overline{CB}$
19–21. Answers may vary. Samples are given.
19. ∠FDG, ∠GDH 21. △FDG 27. 22.6 cm
31. 400 m 35. acute

Lesson 7-7 pp. 356–357
EXERCISES 1. the whole circle, 360°, 100%
3. 90° 5. 36° 7. sleeping
11.

Movies Rentals — Other 24%, Action 33%, Comedy 43%

13. Mexico 15. 11.7 million people
17.

Students Volunteering — 5 days 8%, 4 days 8%, 1 day 44%, 3 days 20%, 2 days 20%

19. 140 students 23. $1\frac{1}{4}$

Lesson 7-8 pp. 363–364
EXERCISES 1. Answers may vary. Sample: Since Q is the midpoint of $\overline{PR}$, $\overline{PQ}$ and $\overline{QR}$ are congruent.
3. 8 in. 5. $3\frac{1}{2}$ m 17.

$\overline{AB}$ = 5 in.

21. 4.2 cm 23. 34 mm 27.
31. $\frac{5}{7}$, 5 : 7

Chapter Review pp. 366–367
1. parallel 2. pentagon 3. supplementary
4. scalene 5. acute 6. 35°, 125° 7. 63°, 153°
8. 3°, 93° 9. 78°, 168°
10. 120°; isosceles; obtuse

11. 60°; equilateral; acute
12. 31°; scalene; right 13. pentagon; regular
14. square, regular 15. octagon, irregular
16. m∠M = 30°, m∠C = m∠P = 46°, m∠B = 104°, AC = 22, BC = 12, MN = 17
17. $\overline{TW}$, $\overline{TY}$, $\overline{TK}$, $\overline{TM}$
18. $\overline{MY}$ 19. T 20. $\overline{WY}$; $\overline{KY}$
21. ∠WYM, ∠YKW, ∠KMY, ∠MWK, ∠WYK
22.
23.

Chapter 8

Lesson 8-1 pp. 376–378
EXERCISES 1. square 3. C 5. A 7. 6 in.; it is less than a foot. 11. about 20 ft 13. about 875 mi² 15. area: about 198 yd²; perimeter: about 81 yd 19. about $\frac{1}{2}$ in. 23. Answers may vary. Sample: about 500 yd² 27 a. about 7,840,000 ft²
b. about 136 31. 150% increase

Lesson 8-2 pp. 382–383
EXERCISES 1. right 3. True; A = bh, so if the bases are equal and the heights are equal, the areas will be equal. 5. 3 7. 25 m² 9. 12 ft² 13. 625 mi² 19. 9 m; 26.4 m 21. 10.5 cm; 21 cm²
23. They have the same bases, but the height of the parallelogram must be less than the height of the rectangle because a leg is shorter than the hypotenuse.
25. area = 161 in.²; perimeter = 62 in.
29. 2; 2 31. 1.52; $1\frac{13}{25}$

Selected Answers

Lesson 8-3 — pp. 386–387

EXERCISES 1. right **3.** 6 cm **5.** 10 cm² **7.** 17.5 m² **9.** 12.5 ft **13.** 1,440 yd² **15.** 72 km² **19.** 50,000 yd² **21.** 102 m² **23.** 10,000 km² **25.** 27.68 km² **27.** 3 ft; if $b = 4$ and $h =$ the corresponding height, then the area of the triangle is $\frac{1}{2}(4)h$, or $2h$. Since the area is 6 ft², $2h = 6$. So $h = 3$. **31.** 28

Lesson 8-4 — pp. 391–392

EXERCISES 1. height **3.** $b_1 = 2.7$ in., $b_2 = 8$ in., $h = 10$ in. **5.** 144 m² **11.** 500 km² **13.** 121.5 in.² **15.** $5\frac{3}{4}$ ft² **17.** 448 in.² **19.** 104 m²; 45.6 m **23.** $480.18

Lesson 8-5 — pp. 396–397

EXERCISES 1. No; π is nonrepeating and nonterminating. **3.** 2; 4π **5.** $\frac{1}{2}$; $\frac{1}{2}$; 2 **7.** 53.4 m **9.** 251.3 in. **13.** 314 m² **15.** 707 ft² **21.** 88 m; 616 m² **23.** 69.1 in.; 380.3 in.² **25.** about 188 in.; about 2,827 in.² **31.** ∠O

Lesson 8-6 — pp. 402–403

EXERCISES 1. area **3.** yes **5.** no **7.** 10 **9.** 5 **17.** about 2 **19.** about 7 **23.** irrational **25.** rational **31.** 12 ft **35.** rational **37.** rational **39.** irrational
41.

8 km
8 km
1 square = 1 km²

43.

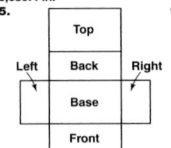
11 ft
11 ft
1 square = 1 ft²

45. about 26.9 **49.** 2

Lesson 8-7 — pp. 407–408

EXERCISES 1. hypotenuse **3.** 13.6 m **5.** 23.3 ft **7.** 17.5 m **9.** 12 ft **11.** 9 m **17.** 0.5 m **19.** 21.4 m **21.** 10 ft **23.** 7 km **25.** 3 **29.** $n = 0.60 \cdot 40$; 24

Lesson 8-8 — pp. 412–413

EXERCISES 1. cylinder **3.** rectangle; rectangular prism **5.** pentagon; pentagonal prism **7.** cone **9.** hexagonal pyramid **13.**

17. rectangular prism **19.** cone **21.** none **23.** 64 m² **25.** 7 faces; 12 edges; 7 vertices **29.** 11 m

Lesson 8-9 — pp. 416–418

EXERCISES 1. surface area **3.** cylinder; about 5,089.4 in.²
5.

	Top	
Left	Back	Right
	Base	
	Front	

9. 264 m²

13. 785.4 cm² **17.** 528 in.² **19.** 1,407 ft² **21.** 2,890 in.² **23.** 1960.4 in.² **27.** 990 ft² **31.** rational

Lesson 8-10 — pp. 424–425

EXERCISES 1. volume **3.** 60 in.³ **5.** 166.375 in.³ **9.** 31.5 in.³ **11.** about 84 in.³; 88 in.³ **15.** 6.5 cm **17.** 18 in. **21.** about 6 million gal **23.** Yes; the height of the can is less than the height of the case. Since $3(2.5) < 7.6$, 3 cans will fit along the width of the case. Since $4(2, 5) < 11$, 4 cans will fit along the length of the case. Then the case can hold 3×4, or 12 cans. **27.** 50°; 140°

Chapter Review — pp. 428–429

1. edge **2.** hypotenuse **3.** prism **4.** circumference **5.** cone **6.** about 400 in.² **7.** 7 in.; the width is less than a foot. **8.** 10.5 m² **9.** 38 cm² **10.** 160 ft² **11.** 25.1 in.; 50.3 in.² **12.** 44 mi; 153.9 mi² **13.** 22 km; 38.5 km² **14.** 6 in. **15.** 39 yd **16.** cylinder **17.** rectangular pyramid **18.** pentagonal pyramid **19.** 22 in.²; 6 in.³ **20.** 288 m²; 324 m³ **21.** 747.7 yd²; 1,539.4 yd³

Chapter 9

Lesson 9-1 — pp. 439–440

EXERCISES 1. A graph shows how the data are changing. **3.** Answers may vary. Sample: 0–8; 4 intervals of 2 **5.** 0–5,000; 10 intervals of 50
7.

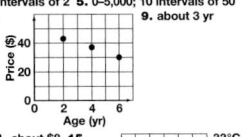
Price ($) / Age (yr)

9. about 3 yr

11. about $8 **15.**

33°C
Temp. (°C) / Time (h)

17 a.

Perimeter (in.) / Side Length (in.)

b. 2.4 in. **c.** 14 in.
d. Check students' work.
19 a.

Number of Weeks	Pay ($)		Number of Weeks	Pay ($)
1	10		1	47
2	20		2	54
3	30		3	61
4	40		4	68
5	50		5	75

b.

c. first neighbor: $100; second neighbor: $110; working for the second neighbor **23.** 0.05

Lesson 9-2 — pp. 444–445

EXERCISES 1. Yes; dividing by −4 is the same as multiplying by −$\frac{1}{4}$. **3.** −6 **5.** 12.5 **7.** Start with 25 and add −4 repeatedly; 9, 5, 1. **9.** Start with 2 and multiply by −3 repeatedly; 162, −486, 1,458. **15.** neither **17.** both **21.** Answers may vary. Sample: He may be correct, but he cannot keep decreasing his time by 15 s indefinitely. **23.** 1 **25.** 1 **27 a.** 17; 16 **b.** Blue tiles: start with 0, add 0, 4, 0, 4 and so on; yellow tiles: start with 0, add 4, 0, 4, 0 and so on. **29.** $123,456 \times 9 = 1,111,104$ **35.** 12.5 mi

Lesson 9-3 — pp. 448–449

EXERCISES 1. 10; 50 **3.** 324; 972; 2,916
5.

Cans of Soup	Number of Servings
3	9
4	12
5	15
6	18
7	21

7. 4, 5, 6, 7 **9.** 5, 10, 15, 20 **13.** $11n$; 110 **15.** $\frac{n}{2}$; 5 **21.**

Miles	Time (h)
10	0.4
20	0.8
30	1.2
40	1.6
50	2.0

23.

Celsius	Kelvin
0	273
10	283
20	293
40	313
80	353
120	393

25.

Side Length (in.)	Area (in.²)
2	4
3	9
5	25
8	64
10	100
12	144

---

27 a.

x	y
−4	−6
−2	−3
2	3
4	6

b. 0 **31.** 7

Lesson 9-4 — pp. 454–455

EXERCISES 1. exactly one **3.** Each output is 5 times the input. **5.** $d = 30t$ **9.** $y = 3x + 5$
13.

x	y
0	9
1	8
2	7
3	6

15.

x	y
0	0
1	$\frac{1}{2}$
2	1
3	$1\frac{1}{2}$

21. $y = (0.50)n$ **23.** $d = 48h$ **25.** Answers may vary. Sample: The y-values increase by $\frac{1}{2}$ when the x-values increase by 1. **27.** −3.875, −3.5, −0.875 **31.** 1 mm; it is less than 1 m.

Lesson 9-5 — pp. 457–459

EXERCISES 1. a table showing the relationship between the input and output of a function
3.

Output y / Input x

5.

Output y / Input x

7. $d = 320t$; 3,200 mi

Distance (mi) / Time (h)

9. 750 Calories **11.** A

Lesson 9-6 — pp. 463–464

EXERCISES 1. C **3.** B **5.** You travel at a steady pace for 2 h, stop for $\frac{1}{2}$ h, and then travel at the same steady pace for 2 h. **7.** You should not connect the points because you sell only whole-number glasses of lemonade.

Income / Cups Sold

11 a. The graph shows that Josh caught up to Rafael after about 11 s. **b.** Josh **13.** The ball is 20 ft high on the way up and on the way down. It reaches that height after about 0.4 s and about 2.4 s. **15.** Answers may vary. Sample: A person threw a ball into the air. It left the person's hand 5 feet above the ground and landed on the ground about 2.75 seconds later. **19.** >

Lesson 9-7 — pp. 470–471

EXERCISES 1. Simple interest is calculated only on the principal. Compound interest is calculated on the principal and any interest left in the account. **3.** $1,543.12 **5.** $71.40
9.

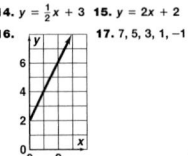
Interest ($) / Time (yr)

11.
Interest ($) / Time (yr)

15. $1,643.94 **21.** $543.14 **25.** C **27.** E **29.** $4,370.91 **35.**

15.

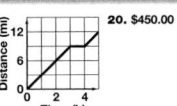

17.

25. 15 ft²

Lesson 9-8 — pp. 474–475

EXERCISES 1. No; it cannot be used to show the relationship between two quantities. **3.** No; it cannot be used to show the relationship between two quantities. **5.** multiplication **7.** $y = \frac{x}{z}$ **9.** $r = \frac{p+5}{3}$ **21.** $F = \frac{9}{5}C + 32$ **23.** $w = \frac{v}{\ell \cdot h}$ **25.** $r = 2t$ **27.** 7 ft **29.** 5 cm **33.** 14.4 m

Chapter Review — pp. 478–479

1. arithmetic **2.** function **3.** principal **4.** compound **5.** conjecture
6.

Calories / Servings

7.

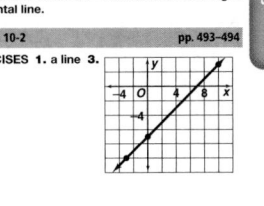
Pay ($) / Time (days)

8. $82.50 **9.** arithmetic **10.** geometric **11.** neither **12.** −6n; −60 **13.**

x	y
0	3
2	4
4	5
6	6

14. $y = \frac{1}{2}x + 3$ **15.** $y = 2x + 2$
16.
y

17. 7, 5, 3, 1, −1

18. Answers may vary. Sample: You travel for 2 h at a constant rate of 50 mi/h. You stop for 4 h, and then return to your starting place at a constant rate of 50 mi/h.

19.
Distance (mi) / Time (h)

20. $450.00

21. $3,298.49 **22.** $x = \frac{z - y}{3}$ **23.** $x = -\frac{k}{4yz}$ **24.** $x = 9\left(\frac{z}{3} + 4\right)$, or $x = 3z + 36$ **25.** $9.00

Chapter 10

Lesson 10-1 — pp. 488–489

EXERCISES 1. (0, 0) **3.** A **5.** D **7.** (−2, 2) **9.** (3, 0) **15.** IV **17.** III

23–26. Answers may vary. Samples are given.
23.
(0, 3) (3, 3)
(0, 2) (3, 0)
O

29. IV

31.
(2, 5)
(6, 3)
(2, 1)
O
acute
isoceles

33. Answers may vary. Sample: (−3, −3), (0, −3), (4, −3); if the x-coordinate is 37, the y-coordinate would be −3 because it is a straight horizontal line.

Lesson 10-2 — pp. 493–494

EXERCISES 1. a line **3.**
y

5. The point (5, −2) lies on the line.
7. (0, 9), (2, 11), (−3, 6) **9.** (0, 4), (2, 2), (−1, 5)
15. yes **17.** yes **23.**

25. **37.** I, III

39. The student thought the product of −3 and −1 was −3; it is 3. **43.** No; for x < 0, the y-values are negative. **45.** $604.66

Lesson 10-3 pp. 500–501
EXERCISES 1. rise; run **3.** −2 **5.** −1 **7.** 2
11. **15.** $-\frac{1}{4}$

17. Roof A; the slope of roof A is $\frac{5}{3}$, and the slope of roof B is $\frac{3}{3}$. Since $\frac{5}{3} > \frac{3}{3}$, roof A is steeper.
19 a. $24,000 **b.** −2 **c.** Every year, the value of the car decreases $2,000. **25.** No; an isosceles triangle has two equal angles, but △XYZ does not.

Lesson 10-4 pp. 506–507
EXERCISES 1. If the solutions of an equation form a line, it is linear. If the graph of the solutions is not a line, it is nonlinear.

3.

x	−3	−2	−1	0	1	2	3
y	3	2	1	0	1	2	3

5. Answers may vary. Sample: Squaring a positive or a negative number always results in a positive number. So for all values of x, x^2 is positive, and y is always positive. **7.** no

9.

x	−3	−2	−1	0	1	2	3
y	−27	−12	−3	0	−3	−12	−27

11.

x	−3	−2	−1	0	1	2	3
y	7	2	−1	−2	−1	2	7

17.

x	−3	−2	−1	0	1	2	3
y	6	4	2	0	2	4	6

19.

x	−3	−2	−1	0	1	2	3
y	−3	−2	−1	0	−1	−2	−3

27. A **29.** F **31.** yes; $6.5^2 = 42.25$ **35.** 7 cm

Lesson 10-5 pp. 512–513
EXERCISES 1. transformation
3. P(−3, −3) → P'(1, 1)
Q(−1, −1) → Q'(3, 3)
R(−1, −3) → R'(3, 1)
5. (1, −2) **7.** (−5, −3)
11.

A(−1, −2), B(2, 0),
C(−2, 2) → A'(−1, 0),
B'(2, 2), C'(−2, 4)
13.
A(−1, −2), B(2, 0),
C(−2, 2) → A'(−1, −4),
B'(2, −2), C'(−2, 0)
15. (x, y) → (x − 5, y)
19. right 4 units, up 1 unit

21. left 1 unit, up 4 units

23. (x, y) → (x + 3, y − 1)
25. (x, y) → (x − 1, y + 4)
27. Answers may vary. Sample: up 2, right 1; right 2, up 1; up 1, right 2; right 1, up 2
31. (−1, −6); (0, −2); (1, 2)

Lesson 10-6 pp. 516–517
EXERCISES 1. A line of reflection produces a mirror image of the figure, and a line of symmetry divides a figure into mirror images.
3. A(−1, 1), B(−3, 4),
C(−5, −2) → A'(1, 1),
B'(3, 4), C'(5, −2)
5. The x-coordinates are opposites; the y-coordinates are the same. **7.** none **11.** (1, 5)
13. (2, 6) **17.**

21. (−3, 4), (3, −4) **23.** (7, −2), (−7, 2)
27. reflection; y-axis; (x, y) → (−x, y)
29. rhombus

33. (0, 2), (1, 5), (2, 8), (3, 11)

Lesson 10-7 pp. 521–522
EXERCISES 1. line symmetry and rotational symmetry **3.** yes; 120° **5.** 90° **7.** No; it does not match the original figure after any rotation of 180° or less. **11.** 180°

13.

P'(0, 0), Q'(−2, 0), R'(−2, −6), S'(0, −6)
19. III **21.** I **23 a.** 90°; 180°; 270° **b.** Yes; the image stays the same after rotation.
27. square **31.** equilateral

Chapter Review pp. 524–525
1. reflection **2.** center of rotation **3.** slope **4.** ordered pair **5.** linear equation
6–8.

6. IV **7.** III **8.** II

9–11. Answers may vary. Samples are given.
9. (0, 3), (−2, 1), (5, 8)
10. (0, −5), (5, 0), (−1, −6)
11. (0, 1), (2, 5), (−3, −5)
12. (0, −2), (4, −6), (−3, 1)
13.

14.
15.

x	−3	−2	−1	0	1	2	3
y	8	3	0	−1	0	3	8

16.

x	−3	−2	−1	0	1	2	3
y	4	3	2	1	2	3	4

17.

x	−3	−2	−1	0	1	2	3
y	16	6	0	−2	0	6	16

18.

x	−3	−2	−1	0	1	2	3
y	12	8	4	0	4	8	12

19. A(3, −1), B(1, 1),
C(4, 4) → A'(3, −3),
B'(1, −1), C'(4, 2)
20. A(3, −1), B(1, 1),
C(4, 4) → A'(0, −1),
B'(−2, 1), C'(1, 4)
21. A(3, −1), B(1, 1),
C(4, 4) → A'(6, −6),
B'(4, −4), C'(7, −1)

22.

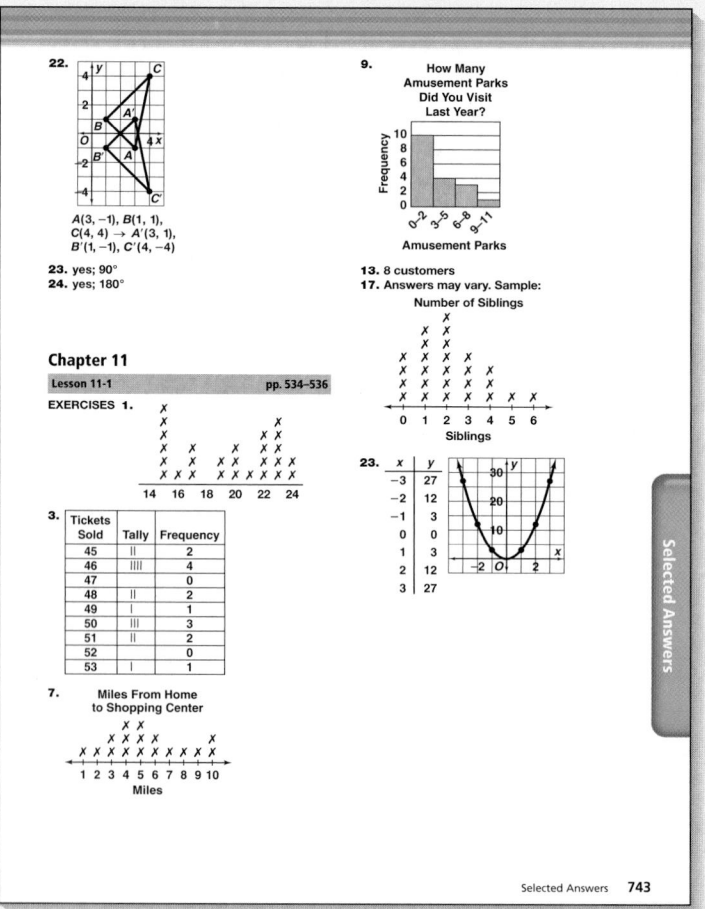

A(3, −1), B(1, 1),
C(4, 4) → A'(3, 1),
B'(1, −1), C'(4, −4)
23. yes; 90°
24. yes; 180°

Chapter 11

Lesson 11-1 pp. 534–536
EXERCISES 1.

14 16 18 20 22 24

3.

Tickets Sold	Tally	Frequency
45	II	2
46	IIII	4
47		0
48	II	2
49	I	1
50	III	3
51	II	2
52		0
53	I	1

7. Miles From Home to Shopping Center

1 2 3 4 5 6 7 8 9 10
Miles

9. How Many Amusement Parks Did You Visit Last Year?
Frequency
0–2 3–5 6–8 9–11
Amusement Parks

13. 8 customers
17. Answers may vary. Sample:
Number of Siblings
0 1 2 3 4 5 6
Siblings

23.

x	y
−3	27
−2	12
−1	3
0	0
1	3
2	12
3	27

Page 744

Lesson 11-2   pp. 540–542

EXERCISES 1. lawn mowing **3.** yes **5.** 26
9. A1 **11.** B3 **13.** Corpus Christi, Texas **15.** all
of them **19.** 1975–2000 **25.** Double line graph;
line graphs are best for showing change over
time.
27 a.

B3 = 4, B4 = 7,
D4 = 6, D5 = 7

b. (1.5, 5.5) **31.** 1,332 m²

Lesson 11-3   pp. 546–547

EXERCISES 1. The stem is the digit or digits on
the left, and the leaf is the digit or digits on the
right. **3.** 12 **5.**

```
4 | 3 6 7
5 | 1 2
6 | 0 1 7
7 | 1 2 8
8 | 2 6 8
```
Key: 8 | 2 means 82

7. High Temperatures
in the Desert (°F)
```
 9 | 8 9
10 | 0 1 3 4 8 9
11 | 1 2 2 3 3 8
```
Key: 9 | 8 means 98

9. 56 in.; 50 in. **11.** No; the median height for
females is 58.5 in. **13.** Yes; 76 − 56 = 20.
15. C **17.** 54

Lesson 11-4   pp. 551–553

EXERCISES 1. C **3.** B **5.** was not **7.** Part (b);
the sample is more diverse. **11.** Fair; the
question makes no assumptions. **13.** Biased; the
question uses the terms *harsh* and *inspiring*.
19. Yes; surveying every 10th person is random,
and you should get a mix of ages and genders.
21. Yes; you will survey people in your population
without any bias. **25.** Start with 3 and add 5
repeatedly; 23, 28, 33

Lesson 11-5   pp. 555–556

EXERCISES 1. Researchers capture, mark, and
release animals, and then capture another group
of animals. The number of marked animals in the
second group indicates population size. **3.** about
13,661 bass **5.** about 305 bears **7.** about
2,010 deer **9.** about 2,048 deer **17.** 63 alligators
19 a. The proportion should be $\frac{8}{25} = \frac{38}{x}$.
b. 119 sharks **21.** about 233 animals

Lesson 11-6   pp. 562–564

EXERCISES 1. no **3.** greater **5.** The vertical axis
starts with 8 instead of 0. The title is also
misleading since grapes are not everyone's
favorite. **7.** The graph gives the impression that
the largest group of students received the highest
scores. There are uneven intervals on the x-axis.

Test Results

15. It reverses the scale on the x-axis. **17.** The
company wants to give the impression that it is
profitable even though it's not. **25.** about
45 billion

Lesson 11-7   pp. 568–570

EXERCISES 1. It illustrates what happens to one
set of data when the other increases. **3.** yes
5. about 47 years

Page 745

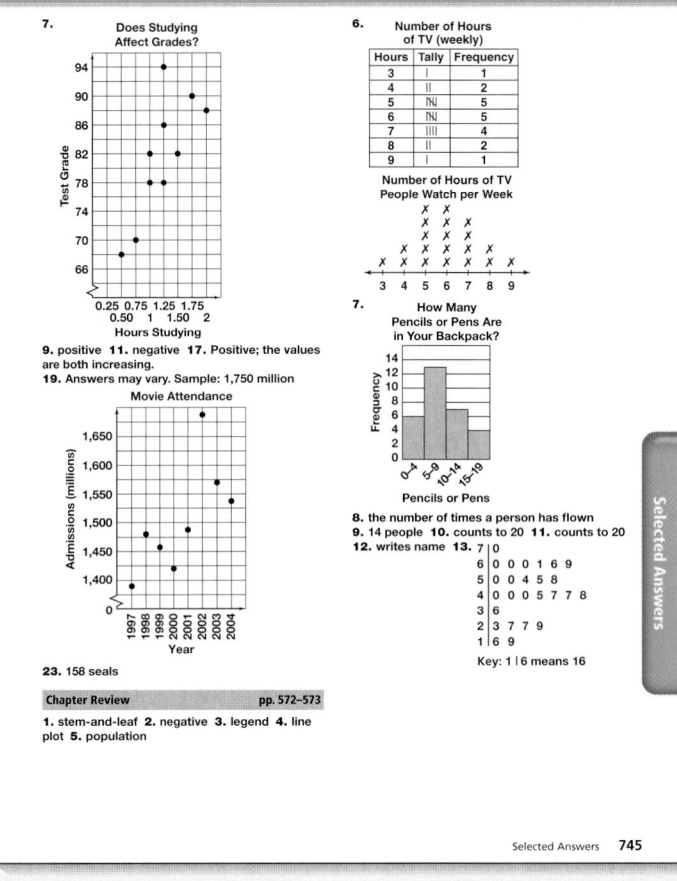

7. Does Studying Affect Grades?

9. positive **11.** negative **17.** Positive; the values
are both increasing.
19. Answers may vary. Sample: 1,750 million

Movie Attendance

23. 158 seals

6. Number of Hours of TV (weekly)

Hours	Tally	Frequency
3		1
4	II	2
5	⌿	5
6	⌿	5
7	IIII	4
8	II	2
9	I	1

Number of Hours of TV
People Watch per Week

7. How Many Pencils or Pens Are in Your Backpack?

8. the number of times a person has flown
9. 14 people **10.** counts to 20 **11.** counts to 20
12. writes name **13.**
```
7 | 0
6 | 0 0 0 1 6 9
5 | 0 0 4 5 8
4 | 0 0 0 5 7 7 8
3 | 6
2 | 3 7 7 9
1 | 6 9
```
Key: 1 | 6 means 16

Chapter Review   pp. 572–573

1. stem-and-leaf **2.** negative **3.** legend **4.** line
plot **5.** population

Page 746

14. Fair; the question makes no assumptions
about the activity. **15.** Biased; the question
assumes the ocean is calm and soothing.
16. about 368 wolves **17.** The y-axis interval
starts at 93, so it appears that the student who
studied 6 h did twice as well as the student who
studied 4 h. **18.** no trend **19.** negative

Chapter 12

Lesson 12-1   pp. 582–583

EXERCISES 1. Answers may vary. Sample: the
result or group of results of an action **3.** B **5.** A
7. $\frac{7}{12}$; 0.083; about 8.3% **9.** $\frac{1}{2}$; 0.5; 50% **13.** 0
15. $\frac{3}{10}$ **25.** $\frac{3}{4}$ **27.** $\frac{2}{3}$ or $\frac{1}{2}$ **37.** $\frac{a}{b}$

Lesson 12-2   pp. 588–589

EXERCISES 1. Theoretical probability is
computed by the formula
$P(\text{event}) = \frac{\text{number of favorable outcomes}}{\text{total number of possible outcomes}}$;
Experimental probability is based on experimental
data or observation.
3. 18 **5.** 5 coins; one for each baby **7.** $\frac{18}{25}$
15. $\frac{1}{5}$; $\frac{1}{20}$; $\frac{13}{320}$ **17.** $\frac{6}{25}$ **19.** $\frac{9}{508}$ **21.** $\frac{7}{25}$
23. $\frac{x}{252}$; 6 **27.** $\frac{3}{9}$ or $\frac{1}{3}$

Lesson 12-3   pp. 593–595

EXERCISES 1. the collection of all possible
outcomes in an experiment **3.** 1 **5.** 7 **7.** 16
9. D **11.** 1 2 3 4 5 6; $\frac{3}{6}$ or $\frac{1}{2}$
13.

1st Spin   2nd Spin; $\frac{1}{4}$

15. 12 recipes **19.** $\frac{2}{16}$ or $\frac{1}{8}$ **23 a.** 16 outfits
b. $\frac{12}{16}$ or $\frac{3}{4}$ **25.** small fruit punch, small lemonade,
medium fruit punch, medium lemonade, large fruit
punch, large lemonade, jumbo fruit punch, jumbo
lemonade **27.** No; there are 12 possible orders,
so the probability for each order is $\frac{1}{12}$.

Lesson 12-4   pp. 600–602

EXERCISES 1. Two events are independent if the
occurrence of one does not affect the probability
of the other occurring; two events are dependent
if the occurrence of one does affect the
probability of the other occurring.
3. independent **5.** $\frac{1}{36}$ **7.** $\frac{3}{36}$ or $\frac{1}{12}$ **11.** $\frac{1}{64}$ **15.** $\frac{1}{7}$
17. $\frac{5}{7}$ **21.** $\frac{10}{380}$ **25.** $\frac{1}{25}$ **27.** $\frac{24}{729}$ or $\frac{8}{243}$
29 a. Complementary; red, yellow, green, or
broken are all the possible events of a traffic
light. **b.** Mutually exclusive; since a student can
only receive one grade on a test, the events have
no outcomes in common.
31. $\frac{5}{7}$ **35.**

	1	2	3
H	H1	H2	H3
T	T1	T2	T3

Lesson 12-5   pp. 608–609

EXERCISES 1. an arrangement of items in a
particular order **3.** B **5.** C **7.** 120 **9.** 6
13. 3! = 6 **15.** 4! = 24 **21.** 42 **23.** 30 **27.** 24
29. 5,040 **31.** 3,628,800 **35.** 60 **37.** 30
39 a. BS, GS, RS, BD, GD, RD, BP, GP, RP
b. 3 × 3 = 9 possibilities **43.** $\frac{1}{256}$

Lesson 12-6   pp. 611–613

EXERCISES 1. In a combination, only the
grouping of the items matters. **3.** permutation
5. $\frac{7 \times 6 \times 5}{3 \times 2 \times 1}$, $\frac{10 \times 9 \times 8 \times 7 \times 6}{5 \times 4 \times 3 \times 2 \times 1}$ **7.** 4 **9.** 3 **13.** 6
19. 60 **21.** 840 **23.** 66 ways **25.** combination;
56 sets **29.** 20 **31.** $\frac{1}{6}$ **35.** 4! = 24

Page 747

Chapter Review   pp. 616–617

1. combination **2.** event **3.** independent
4. odds in favor of **5.** Experimental **6.** $\frac{1}{7}$ **7.** $\frac{2}{7}$
8. $\frac{6}{7}$ **9.** $\frac{1}{50}$ **10.** 32
11.

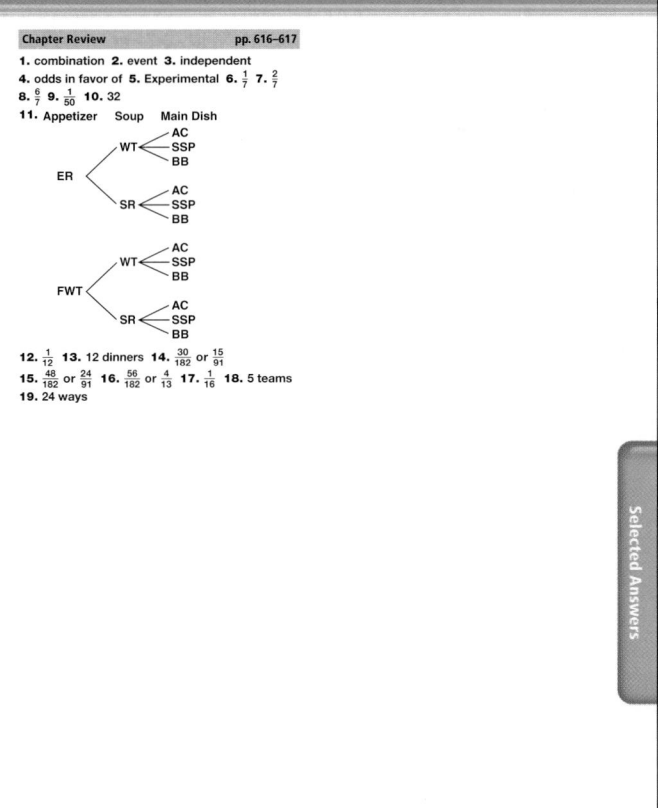

Appetizer   Soup   Main Dish

12. $\frac{1}{12}$ **13.** 12 dinners **14.** $\frac{30}{182}$ or $\frac{15}{91}$
15. $\frac{48}{182}$ or $\frac{24}{91}$ **16.** $\frac{56}{182}$ or $\frac{4}{13}$ **17.** $\frac{1}{16}$ **18.** 5 teams
19. 24 ways

Additional Answers

CHAPTER 2

Lesson 2-6

page 101   Activity Lab

1.

Seed Type	Fraction
A	$\frac{5}{16}$
B	$\frac{1}{4}$
C	$\frac{1}{2}$
D	$\frac{17}{35}$
E	$\frac{9}{26}$
F	$\frac{1}{3}$
G	$\frac{14}{55}$
H	$\frac{18}{35}$
I	$\frac{8}{15}$

3.

Seed Type	Number Sprouted	Number Planted
I	8	15
H	18	35
C	22	44
D	17	35
E	18	52
F	21	63
A	15	48
G	14	55
B	5	20

page 114   Chapter Test

28. Write the numerator and denominator in prime factorization form. Find the product of the common factors and divide the numerator and denominator by that product.

29. Answers may vary. Sample:

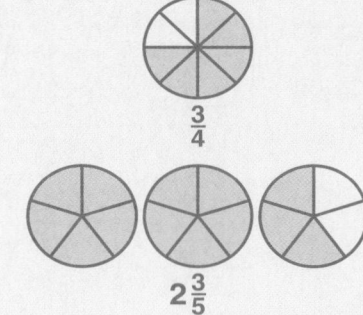

$\frac{3}{4}$

$2\frac{3}{5}$

CHAPTER 3

Lesson 3-1

page 125   Activity Lab

3. $\frac{3}{4}$,

4. $\frac{2}{3}$,

5. $\frac{9}{10}$,

6. $\frac{1}{2}$,

Lesson 3-3

page 135   Activity Lab

4. $\frac{2}{15}$,

5. $\frac{5}{12}$,

6. $\frac{1}{8}$,

7. $\frac{6}{12}$,

8. $\frac{3}{24}$,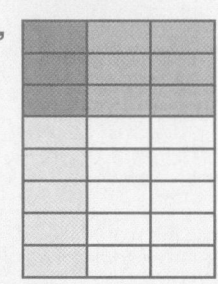

CHAPTER 4

page 168   Activity Lab

1.

A	B
1	8
2	9
5	12
10	17
30	37
50	57
n	$n + 7$

Each value in column B is 7 more than its corresponding value in column A.

2.

C	D
1	−4
2	−3
5	0
10	5
25	20
45	40
n	n − 5

Each value in column D is 5 less than its corresponding value in column C.

3.

E	F
1	40
2	80
5	200
10	400
100	4,000
500	20,000
n	40n

Each value in column F is 40 times its corresponding value in column E.

4. n represents any number in columns A, C, and E. Different operations can be applied to n to get any value in columns B, D, and F.

Lesson 4-7

pages 207–208   Homework Exercises

25. a ≥ 17;
15 16 17 18 19 20

26. n > 100;
98 99 100 101 102 103

27. p ≤ 0;
−3 −2 −1 0 1 2

28. s ≤ 65;
50 60 70

Lesson 4-8

pages 212–214   Homework Exercises

10. x > −4;
−6 −5 −4 −3 −2 −1

11. n ≤ 27;
25 27 29

12. p < 0;
−3 −2 −1 0 1 2

13. y ≥ 17;
15 16 17 18 19

14. q < 6;
4 5 6 7 8

15. b > −2;
−4 −2 0

16. h < −21;
−23 −21 −19

17. n ≥ 1;
−1 0 1 2 3 4

18. r > −5;
−7 −6 −5 −4 −3 −2

19. p ≤ −4;
−7 −6 −5 −4 −3 −2

20. b > −23;
−25 −23 −21

21. f ≥ −5;
−7 −6 −5 −4 −3 −2

22. m > 1;
−1 0 1 2 3

23. x < 1;
−1 0 1 2 3

24. k ≤ −11;
−13 −11 −9

Lesson 4-9

pages 217–218   Homework Exercises

9. x < −8;
−11 −10 −9 −8 −7 −6

10. b ≤ 3;
0 1 2 3 4 5

11. w ≥ −6;
−8 −7 −6 −5 −4 −3

12. d ≤ 7;
4 5 6 7 8 9

13. t < −5;
−8 −7 −6 −5 −4 −3

14. g < −7;
−9 −7 −5

15. p ≥ −5;
−7 −5 −3

16. y < −6.1;
−6.4 −6.2 −6

17. w ≥ 6.5;
6 6.5 7

19. p < −15;
−17 −15 −13

20. k ≥ 24;
22 23 24 25 26 27

21. w ≤ −21;
−23 −21 −19

22. y > −56;
−58 −56 −54

23. n < 10;
7 8 9 10 11 12

24. m ≥ −30;
−32 −30 −28

25. x < −40;
−42 −40 −38

26. c ≤ 10;
7 8 9 10 11 12

27. x > −80;
−85 −80 −75

28. g ≥ −8.4
−8.6 −8.4 −8.2

29. p > −16.8
−17 −16.8 −16.6

30. f ≤ −27.5
−28 −27.5 −27

48. −18 ≥ −2y, y ≥ 9;
−2y < −18; y > 9; no; y = 9 is not a solution to the second inequality.

7 8 9 10 11 12

7 8 9 10 11 12

49. −3x + 10 > 19; x < −3;
−6 −5 −4 −3 −2 −1

pages 220–221   Chapter Review

27. t ≤ 10;
7 8 9 10 11 12

28. r < 5;
2 3 4 5 6 7

29. h < −22;
−24 −22 −20

30. p ≥ −15;
−17 −15 −13

31. g > 17;
15 17 19

32. $m \geq -7$;

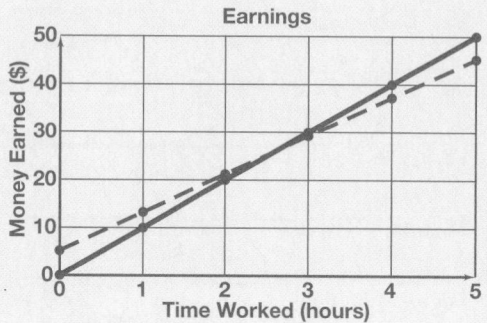
(number line: $-9\ -8\ -7\ -6\ -5\ -4$, filled circle at -7)

33. $x \geq 20$;

(number line: $18\quad 20\quad 22$, filled circle at 20)

page 222   Chapter Test

19. Let b = number of bricks; $6b = 72$; 12 bricks.

20. Let a = cost per apple; $12a + 3.35 = 8.75$; $0.45.

21. Let b = cost per button; $322b = 483$; $1.50.

22. Let d = daily distance; $4d = 1{,}145$; 286.25 mi.

23. Let n = number of players; $\frac{n}{12} = 13$; 156 players.

24. Let c = the cost of the party; $\frac{c}{6} + 65 = 160$; $570.

30. $n \geq 3$;

(number line: $1\ 2\ 3\ 4\ 5\ 6$, filled circle at 3)

31. $y > 24$;

(number line: $22\quad 24\quad 26$, open circle at 24)

32. $m \leq -9$;

(number line: $-11\quad -9\quad -7$, filled circle at -9)

33. $w < -8$;

(number line: $-10\quad -8\quad -6$, open circle at -8)

34. $x < -4$;

(number line: $-7\ -6\ -5\ -4\ -3\ -2$, open circle at -4)

35. $h \geq 9$;

(number line: $7\ 8\ 9\ 10\ 11\ 12\ 13$, filled circle at 9)

36. $v < -48$;

(number line: $-50\quad -48\quad -46$, open circle at -48)

37. $p \leq -66$;

(number line: $-68\quad -66\quad -64$, filled circle at -66)

38. $k \geq 12$;

(number line: $10\quad 12\quad 14$, filled circle at 12)

39. $x > 60$;

(number line: $58\quad 60\quad 62$, open circle at 60)

40. Let m = number of additional people allowed aboard; $143 + m \leq 220$; $m \leq 77$; at most 77 people.

41. Let b = number of bottles; $1.49b \leq 12$; $b \leq 8.05$; at most 8 bottles.

42. Let m = amount Alex's mother spent; $52 + m \geq 130$; $m \geq 78$; at least $78.

43. Answers may vary. Sample: You use inverse operations to solve both equations and inequalities. With inequalities, you sometimes have to reverse the sign when solving.

CHAPTER 5

Lesson 5-3

page 242   Activity Lab

1.

Earnings

	1 hour	2 hours	3 hours	4 hours	5 hours
Manny	10	20	30	40	50
Ilene	13	21	29	37	45

2.

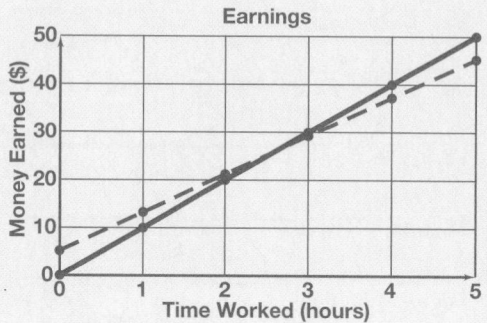

Earnings (graph: Money Earned ($) vs Time Worked (hours))

Lesson 5-4

page 251   Activity Lab

1.

Fig. 1	Angle Measure	Fig. 2	Angle Measure
∠A	90°	∠P	90°
∠B	32°	∠Q	32°
∠C	58°	∠R	58°

Angle measures are the same.

2.

Fig. 1	Side Length (cm)	Fig. 2	Side Length (cm)
AB	5	PQ	2.5
BC	6	QR	3
CA	3	RP	1.5

Lengths of Fig. 2 are all 0.5 times the lengths of Fig. 1.

3.

Fig. 3	Angle Measure	Fig. 4	Angle Measure
∠A	40°	∠P	40°
∠B	120°	∠Q	120°
∠C	20°	∠R	20°

Angle measures are the same.

Fig. 3	Side Length (cm)	Fig. 4	Side Length (cm)
AB	2	PQ	3
BC	4	QR	6
CA	5	RP	7.5

Lengths of Fig. 4 are all 1.5 times the lengths of Fig. 3.

4. Check students' work. Sample: Similar figures have the same corresponding angle measures and proportional side lengths.

Lesson 5-6

page 259   Check Skills You'll Need

1. For two ratios, the cross products are found by multiplying the denominator of each ratio by the numerator of the other ratio.

CHAPTER 6

Lesson 6-1

page 276   Homework Exercises

10.

11.

(grid figure)

12.

13.

14.

Lesson 6-2

page 283   Homework Exercises

33.

Topping	With Olives	Plain	With Onions and Green Peppers
Percent of the Pizza	37.5%	12.5%	50%
Number of Slices	3	1	4

Lesson 6-3

page 287   Homework Exercises

41.

42.

43.

44.

Lesson 6-4

page 289   Activity Lab

3.

Language	Percent	Number of Students
English	78%	~789
Spanish	58%	~587
Chinese	34%	~344
French	26%	~263
German	10%	~101

Lesson 6-8

page 314   Homework Exercises

35.

	A	B	C	D
1	Yr	Sales	Change ($)	Change (%)
2	1	200,000	—	—
3	2	240,000	40,000	20%
4	3	300,000	60,000	25%
5	4	330,000	30,000	10%

page 318   Chapter Test

14.

15.

16.

CHAPTER 7

Lesson 7-1

page 324   Check Skills You'll Need

2.

3.

4.

5.

6.

7.

page 327   Homework Exercises

Exercises 24–28. Answers may vary. Samples are given.

24.

25. Q

26.

27.

28.

Lesson 7-2

page 334   Homework Exercises

32.

$m\angle A = 90 - m\angle B = 90 - 51 = 39$
$m\angle A = 39 = (3x - 12)$
$51 = 3x$
$17 = x$

Lesson 7-3

page 337   TE Closure

Scalene triangles have no congruent sides; isosceles triangles have at least two congruent sides; equilateral triangles have three congruent sides.

Acute triangles have three acute angles; obtuse triangles have one obtuse angle; right triangles have one right angle.

Write an equation using "the sum of the angle measures equals 180°." Then solve for the missing angle.

Lesson 7-5

page 347   TE Additional Examples

1. Congruent: All corresponding sides and angles are congruent.

3a. $\overline{DE} \cong \overline{OP}$,
$\overline{DF} \cong \overline{OQ}, \overline{EF} \cong \overline{PQ}$,
$m\angle Q \cong m\angle F$,
$m\angle P \cong m\angle E$,
$m\angle O \cong m\angle D$

3b. $OP = 24; m\angle Q = 53°$

page 348   Homework Exercises

7. $\overline{CV} \cong \overline{JP}; \overline{VR} \cong \overline{PX}$;
$\overline{RC} \cong \overline{XJ}; \angle C \cong \angle J$;
$\angle V \cong \angle P; \angle R \cong \angle X$
$VR = 9; m\angle V = 83°$;
$m\angle X = 41°; m\angle J = 56°$

8. $\overline{ED} \cong \overline{KJ}; \overline{DC} \cong \overline{JI}$;
$\overline{CB} \cong \overline{IH}; \overline{BA} \cong \overline{HG}$;
$\overline{AF} \cong \overline{GL}; \overline{FE} \cong \overline{LK}$;
$\angle E \cong \angle K; \angle D \cong \angle J$;
$\angle C \cong \angle I; \angle B \cong \angle H$;
$\angle A \cong \angle G; \angle F \cong \angle L$;
$m\angle E = 135°$;
$m\angle A = 117; \overline{BC} = 6$;
$LK = 11; m\angle J = 90°$;
$m\angle I = m\angle H = 135°$;
$m\angle L = 108°$

Lesson 7-6

page 353   Homework Exercises

29. Check students' work for diagrams. All the quadrilaterals are rectangles.

30. Check students' work for diagrams. All the triangles are scalene or isosceles right triangles.

Lesson 7-7

page 355   Quick Check

2b.

TE Additional Examples

2.

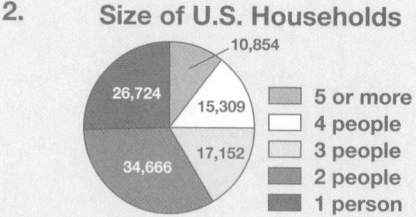

TE Closure

Add the parts to find the total; use a proportion to find the central angle for each part; draw a circle and mark each angle; and label each section and write a title.

pages 356–357   Homework Exercises

10. **Frozen Yogurt Sales**

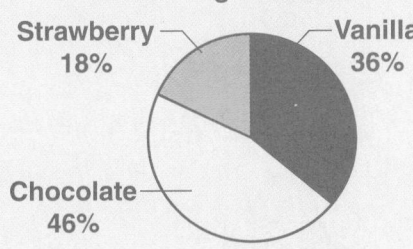

Strawberry 18%
Vanilla 36%
Chocolate 46%

11. **Movies Rentals**

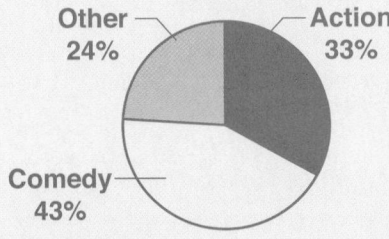

Other 24%
Action 33%
Comedy 43%

12. 900; 900; 900; 360°;
     81; 900; 360°

Mode of Transportation

Bicycle
Walk 28%
15%
Bus 48%
9% Car

17. **Students Volunteering**

5 days 8%
1 day 44%
4 days 8%
3 days 20%
2 days 20%

18. Answers may vary. Sample: A
     circle graph would be a good
     choice for showing an ice cream
     store's customers' favorite flavors
     among a selection of five. A circle
     graph would be a bad choice if you
     were trying to show the number of
     customers who like a flavor,
     because they can like more than
     one. A circle graph shows parts of
     a whole. When there is overlap, a
     Venn diagram might be more
     appropriate.

page 358   Checkpoint Quiz 2

2. **Town Middle School**

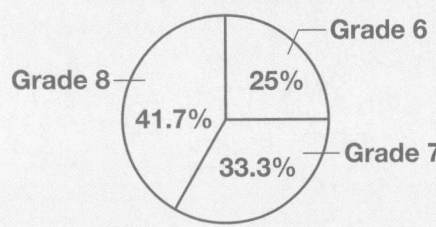

Grade 8
Grade 6
41.7%
25%
33.3%
Grade 7

25% (90°) for 6th grade 33.3%
(120°) for 7th grade, and 41.7%
(150°) for 8th grade.

page 360   Guided Problem Solving

4. **U.S. Blood Type Percentages**

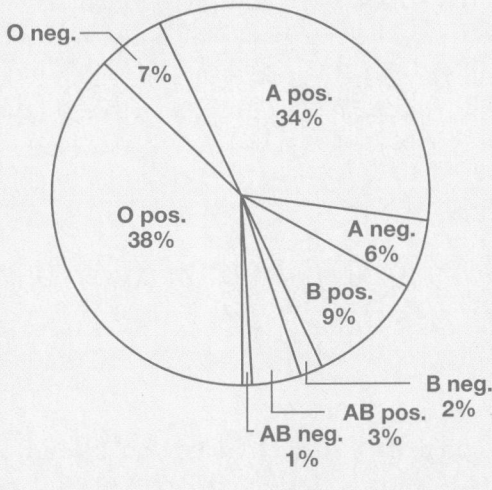

O neg.
7%
A pos. 34%
O pos. 38%
A neg. 6%
B pos. 9%
B neg. 2%
AB pos. 3%
AB neg. 1%

U.S. Blood Type (millions of people)

Type	Positive	Negative
O	106.8	19.7
A	95.5	16.9
B	25.3	5.6
AB	8.4	2.8

page 363   Homework Exercises

15.

C   F   E   D

16.

J
M   N   K

17.

A   B

$\overline{AB}$ = 5 in.

18.

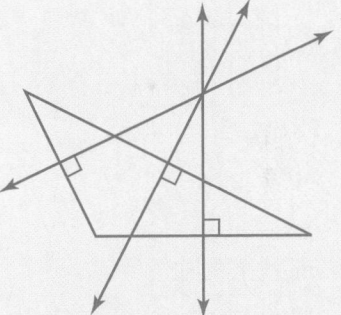

The perpendicular bisectors
of the sides of any triangle
will intersect in one point.

page 368   Chapter Test

12. Check students' work. An
     example is given.

13.

32. Student Earnings

33. All are quadrilaterals. A rhombus and a square both have four congruent sides. A rectangle and a square both have four congruent angles. A square is a rectangle and a rhombus.

CHAPTER 8

Lesson 8-6

page 403   Homework Exercises

41.

8 km

8 km

1 square = 1 km²

42.

9 m

9 m

1 square = 1 m²

43.

11 ft

11 ft

1 square = 1 ft²

44.

2 mi

2 mi

1 square = 1 mi²

Lesson 8-8

page 409   Activity Lab

1.   Top   Front   Right

2.   Top   Front   Right

3.   Top   Front   Right

4.

5.

page 410   Check Skills You'll Need

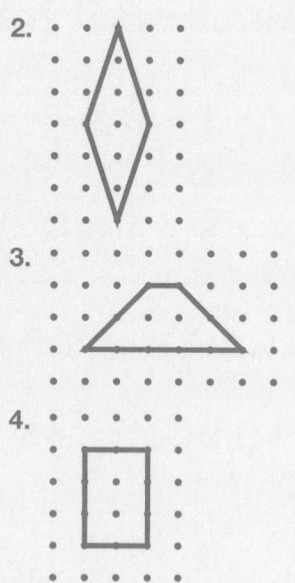

2.

3.

4.

pages 412   Homework Exercises

12.

13.

14.

Lesson 8-9

page 414   Quick Check

1. Answers may vary. Sample:

pages 417–418   Homework Exercises

5–8. Nets may vary. Samples are given.

5.

	Top	
Left	Back	Right
	Base	
	Front	

6.

7.

8.

25. Doubling the radius of the base has more effect on the surface area of a cylinder because the radius is doubled and then squared.

If $r = 1$ and $h = 1$, then
$$SA = 2\pi(1)^2 + 2 \cdot 1\pi \cdot 1 = 4\pi.$$
If $r = 2$ and $h = 1$, then
$$SA = 2\pi(2)^2 + 2 \cdot 2\pi \cdot 1 = 8\pi + 4\pi = 12\pi.$$
If $r = 1$ and $h = 2$, then
$$SA = 2\pi(1)^2 + 2(1)\pi(2) = 2\pi + 4\pi = 6\pi.$$

26. Answers may vary. Sample:

OR

page 419   Extension

1.

Number of Unit Cubes on an Edge	Total Number of Unit Cubes	Total Number Expressed as a Power	Number of Unit Cubes With Given Number of Sides Painted			
			0	1	2	3
2	8	2^3	0	0	0	8
3	27	3^3	1	6	12	8
4	64	4^3	8	24	24	8
5	125	5^3	27	54	36	8
6	216	6^3	64	96	48	8
7	343	7^3	125	150	60	8

CHAPTER 9

page 436   Activity Lab

1b.

Travel Speed

2a.

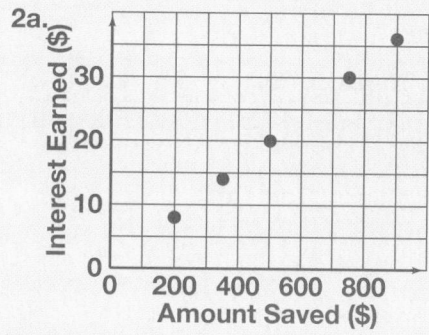

Lesson 9-1

page 437   Check Skills You'll Need

1. Yes; it can be written as a fraction.

2–5.

page 437   Quick Check

1.

page 438   TE Additional Examples

1.

pages 439–440   Homework Exercises

14.

a score of 69

15.

33°C

16.

12 qt.

Additional Answers

17a.

18.

Answers may vary. Sample: About 6:25; the trend in the data may not continue between ages 14 and 18.

19a.

Number of Weeks	Pay ($)		Number of Weeks	Pay ($)
1	10		1	47
2	20		2	54
3	30		3	61
4	40		4	68
5	50		5	75

b.

Lesson 9-2

page 444   Homework Exercises

6. Start with −8 and add 7 repeatedly; 20, 27, 34.

7. Start with 25 and add −4 repeatedly; 9, 5, 1.

8. Start with 1 and multiply by 2 repeatedly; 16, 32, 64.

9. Start with 2 and multiply by −3 repeatedly; 162, −486, 1,458.

10. Start with 600 and multiply by $-\frac{1}{2}$ repeatedly; −75, 37.5, −18.75.

11. Start with $\frac{1}{2}$ and multiply by $\frac{1}{2}$ repeatedly; $\frac{1}{32}$, $\frac{1}{64}$, $\frac{1}{128}$.

12. Start with −2 and multiply by −2 repeatedly; −32, 64, −128.

13. Start with $\frac{1}{4}$ and multiply by $\frac{1}{3}$ repeatedly; $\frac{1}{324}$, $\frac{1}{972}$, $\frac{1}{2,916}$

Lesson 9-3

page 446   Quick Check

1.

Amount of Gas (gal)	Miles Driven
1	18.1
2	36.2
3	54.3
4	72.4
5	90.5

271.5 miles

pages 448–449   Homework Exercises

20.

Time (h)	0.5	1	1.5	2
Cost ($)	12.50	25	37.50	50

21.

Miles	Time (h)
10	0.4
20	0.8
30	1.2
40	1.6
50	2.0

22.

Change in a Parking Meter ($)	Time Allowed to Park (h)
0.25	0.5
0.50	1
0.75	1.5
1.25	2.5

23.

Celsius	Kelvin
0	273
10	283
20	293
40	313
80	353
120	393

24a.

x	0	1	2	3	4	5
y	−1	2	5	8	11	14

b. Multiply x by 3 and subtract 1.

25.

Side Length (in.)	Area (in.^{2})
2	4
3	9
5	25
8	64
10	100
12	144

26.

Group	Blue Squares	Yellow Squares
1	2	2
2	3	3
3	4	4

11 blue squares

27a.

x	y
−4	−6
−2	−3
2	3
4	6

b. 0

Lesson 9-4

page 454   Homework Exercises

12.

x	y
0	2
1	3
2	4
3	5

13.

x	y
0	9
1	8
2	7
3	6

14.

x	y
0	0
1	4
2	8
3	12

15.

x	y
0	0
1	$\frac{1}{2}$
2	1
3	$\frac{3}{2}$

16.

x	y
0	0
1	−3
2	−6
3	−9

17.

x	y
0	1
1	3
2	5
3	7

18.

x	y
0	−2
1	2
2	6
3	10

19.

x	y
0	1
1	2
2	5
3	10

Lesson 9-5

page 457   Quick Check

2. $d = 60t$; 270 mi

TE Additional Examples

1.

$h = 2w + 1$; 9 in.

2.

pages 458–459   Homework Exercises

4.

5.

6. $S = 6t$; $60

7. $d = 320t$; 3,200 mi

14a.

x	y
1	3
2	4
3	5
4	6

b. $y = x + 2$

15.

16.

17.

18.

T699

20a. $d = 181t$

b. 181 mi/h; if you divide any of the distances by time, you get 181 mi/h.

c. about 10.4 h

d.

21. Answers may vary. Sample:

s	A
1	0.433
2	1.732
3	3.897
4	6.928

The graph is a curve.

page 460   Activity Lab

1–6. Students' graphs may vary from these calculator screens.

1.

X	Y₁
0	0
1	2
2	4
3	6
4	8
5	10
6	12

X=

2.

X	Y₁
0	−3
1	−2
2	−1
3	0
4	1
5	2
6	3

X=

3.

X	Y₁
0	13
1	11
2	9
3	7
4	5
5	3
6	1

X=

4.

X	Y₁
0	1
1	2
2	3
3	4
4	5
5	6
6	7

X=

5.

X	Y₁
0	−4
1	−1
2	2
3	5
4	8
5	11
6	14

X=

6.

X	Y₁
0	6
1	6.5
2	7
3	7.5
4	8
5	8.5
6	9

X=

7. Answers may vary. Sample: If you use a window of 0 to 10 for x, your window for y should go from 0 to 1,000 with increments of 100.

Lesson 9-6

page 462   Quick Check

2.

TE Additional Examples

1. Sample: Nancy walked for five min. She stopped for one min. She walked home at the same speed she started out.

2.

3.

pages 463–464   Exercises

6.

T700

7. You should not connect the points because you sell only whole-number cups of lemonade.

8. You can connect the points because time is continuous.

9.

10. A; the bowl has a diameter that varies with height, so the relationship between height and time will not be constant.

11a. The graph shows that Josh caught up to Rafael after about 11 s.

b. Josh

c. If the lines were parallel, then Rafael would have covered the 100 m in the same time, so he would have won the race.

Lesson 9-7

pages 470–471 Homework Exercises

9.

10.

11.

12.

13.

14.

34–35. Answers may vary. Samples are given.

34.

35.

Lesson 9-8

page 476 Activity Lab

1.

6.

7. 126 inches represents 6 inches above the rim, or the height the ball needs to reach to be slam-dunked.

8. The formula accounts for the length of a person's arm above his or her head while dunking.

9. $h = \frac{4}{5}(126 - v)$

page 479 Chapter Review

13.

x	y
0	3
2	4
4	5
6	6

16.

page 480 Chapter Test

1. Start with 1 and multiply by 3 repeatedly; 81, 243, 729.

2. Start with 4 and add 5 repeatedly; 24, 29, 34.

3. Start with 3, then add 1, 2, 3, 4, and so on; 13, 18, 24.

4. Start with 10 and add −2 repeatedly; 2, 0, −2.

5. Start with −23 and add 4 repeatedly; −11, −7, −3.

6. Start with 6 and multiply by 0.5 repeatedly; 0.375, 0.1875, 0.09375.

7. geometric; arithmetic; neither; arithmetic; arithmetic; geometric

8a.

9.

Books	Cost ($)
1	2.95
2	5.90
3	8.85
4	11.80
5	14.75

10.

Side Length (in.)	Perimeter (in.)
5	20
6	24
7	28
8	32
9	36

11. $y = -5x - 2$

12. $y = 2x + 1$

13. $y = 3x$

14.

20.

Earnings ($)	Savings ($)
10	2
20	4
30	6
40	8

23.

24. Answers may vary. Sample: The oven temperature is high, and then it cools down and stabilizes.

CHAPTER 10

Lesson 10-1

page 486   Check Skills You'll Need

1. They are the same distance from zero, but in opposite directions.

2.

3.

4.

5.

6.

7.

page 487   Quick Check

3. Answers may vary. Sample:

TE Additional Examples

3.

15–22.

23–26. Answers may vary. Samples are given.

23.

24.

25.

26.

31.

acute isoceles

32.

33. Answers may vary. Sample:
(−3, −3), (0, −3), (4, −3)
If the x-coordinate is 37, the y-coordinate would be −3 because it is a straight horizontal line.

35. If both are positive, then the point is in quadrant I. If both are negative, then the point is in quadrant III. If the x-coordinate is positive and the y-coordinate is negative, then the point is in quadrant IV. If the x-coordinate is negative and the y-coordinate is positive, then the point is in quadrant II.

36. Answers may vary. Sample is given.

page 490   Activity Lab

2.

24 units²

3.

130 units²

Lesson 10-2

page 492   Quick Check

3a.

b.

c.

pages 493–494   Exercises

2.

x	x − 7	y	(x, y)
0	0 − 7	−7	(0, −7)
−3	−3 − 7	−10	(−3, −10)
10	10 − 7	3	(10, 3)

3.

6–13. Answers may vary. Samples are given.

6. (0, −2), (3, 1), (−4, −6)

7. (0, 9), (2, 11), (−3, 6)

8. (0, 0), (8, 8), (−1, −1)

9. (0, 4), (2, 2), (−1, 5)

10. (0, 0), (1, 5), (−2, −10)

11. (0, 0), (1, −8), (−1, 8)

12. (0, 1), (1, 4), (−2, −5)

13. (0, −5), (1, −1), (−1, −9)

22.

23.

24.

25.

26.

27.

28.

29.

30.

31.

32.

33.

34.

Shipping Costs

$30

35.

Fence Dimensions

12 ft

40.

x	50x	y	(x, y)
0	50(0)	0	(0, 0)
2	50(2)	100	(2, 100)
4	50(4)	200	(4, 200)
8	50(8)	400	(8, 400)
12	50(12)	600	(12, 600)
16	50(16)	800	(16, 800)

yes

42.

$y = \frac{1}{12}x$

Lesson 10-3

page 499   TE Additional Examples

3.

pages 500–501   Homework Exercises

13.

Answers may vary. Sample: Since (1, 3) and (2, 3) are both points on the line, the slope is $\frac{3-3}{2-1}$, or $\frac{0}{1}$, which is equal to 0.

17. Roof A; the slope of roof A is $\frac{5}{3}$, and the slope of roof B is $\frac{3}{5}$. Since $\frac{5}{3} > \frac{3}{5}$, roof A is steeper.

18. No; the slope of the ramp is $\frac{33}{80}$, whereas the slope in the guidelines is $\frac{1}{12}$. Since $\frac{33}{80} > \frac{1}{12}$, the ramp does not meet the guidelines.

25. No; an isoceles triangle has two equal angles, but $\triangle XYZ$ does not.

page 503   Checkpoint Quiz 1

1–3.

4.

5.

6.

7.

9.

10.

Lesson 10-4

page 504 Check Skills You'll Need

1. An equation is linear when the graph of its solutions is a line.

2–4. Answers may vary. Samples are given.

2. (0, 12), (−2, 10), (3, 15)

3. (0, −20), (5, −15), (−10, −30)

4. (0, 0), (1, 15), (−2, −30)

Quick Check

1.

x	−3	−2	−1	0	1	2	3
y	18	8	2	0	2	8	18

2.

x	−3	−2	−1	0	1	2	3
y	9	4	1	0	1	4	9

3.

x	−3	−2	−1	0	1	2	3
y	3	2	1	0	1	2	3

4.

x	−3	−2	−1	0	1	2	3
y	27	8	1	0	−1	−8	−27

8.

x	−3	−2	−1	0	1	2	3
y	36	16	4	0	4	16	36

9.

x	−3	−2	−1	0	1	2	3
y	−27	−12	−3	0	−3	−12	−27

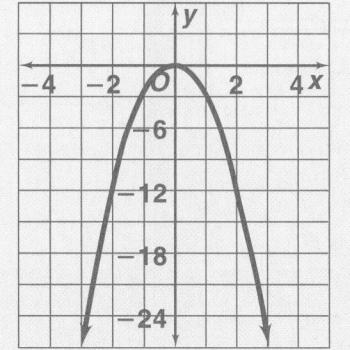

10.

x	−3	−2	−1	0	1	2	3
y	$4\frac{1}{2}$	2	$\frac{1}{2}$	0	$\frac{1}{2}$	2	$4\frac{1}{2}$

11.

x	−3	−2	−1	0	1	2	3
y	7	2	−1	−2	−1	2	7

12.

x	−3	−2	−1	0	1	2	3
y	11	6	3	2	3	6	11

13.

x	−3	−2	−1	0	1	2	3
y	−6	−1	2	3	2	−1	−6

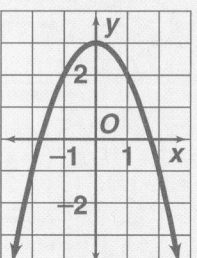

14.

x	−3	−2	−1	0	1	2	3
y	−13	−8	−5	−4	−5	−8	−13

15.

x	−3	−2	−1	0	1	2	3
y	4	1	0	1	4	9	16

16.

x	-3	-2	-1	0	1	2	3
y	16	9	4	1	0	1	4

17.

x	-3	-2	-1	0	1	2	3
y	6	4	2	0	2	4	6

18.

x	-3	-2	-1	0	1	2	3
y	1	$\frac{2}{3}$	$\frac{1}{3}$	0	$\frac{1}{3}$	$\frac{2}{3}$	1

19.

x	-3	-2	-1	0	1	2	3
y	-3	-2	-1	0	-1	-2	-3

20.

x	-3	-2	-1	0	1	2	3
y	-1	0	1	2	1	0	1

21.

x	-3	-2	-1	0	1	2	3
y	4	3	2	1	0	1	2

22.

x	-3	-2	-1	0	1	2	3
y	2	1	0	1	2	3	4

23.

t	$16t^2$	d	(t, d)
0	$16(0)^2$	0	(0, 0)
1	$16(1)^2$	16	(1, 16)
3	$16(3)^2$	144	(3, 144)
5	$16(5)^2$	400	(5, 400)

24.

25. Absolute value is always nonnegative, so the opposite of absolute value will always be nonpositive. Since y is always nonpositive, the points will always be in Quadrants III and IV.

26.

30a.

t	$-16t^2 + 12,000$	h	(t, h)
0	$-16(0)^2 + 12,000 = 0 + 12,000$	12,000	(0, 12,000)
5	$-16(5)^2 + 12,000 = -400 + 12,000$	11,600	(5, 11,600)
10	$-16(10)^2 + 12,000 = -1,600 + 12,000$	10,400	(10, 10,400)
20	$-16(20)^2 + 12,000 = -6,400 + 12,000$	5,600	(20, 5,600)

b.

about 9,700 ft

32.

r	$S = 4\pi r^2$	$V = \frac{4}{3}\pi r^3$
0	0	0
1	12	4
2	48	32
3	108	108
4	192	256
5	300	500

3

Lesson 10-5

page 510 Check Skills You'll Need

1. The x-coordinate is 2, and the y-coordinate is −5.

2–5.

2.

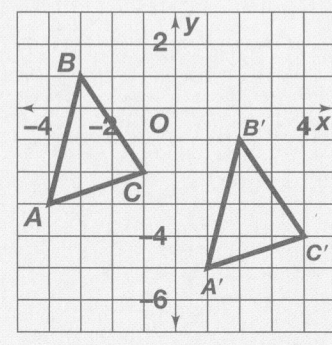

$A(-4, 3)$, $B(-1, 4)$,
$C(-3, 1) \rightarrow A'(-7, 4)$,
$B'(-4, 5)$, $C'(-6, 2)$

TE Additional Examples

2.

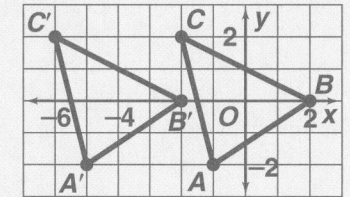

$A(-4, -3)$, $B(-3, 1)$, $C(-1, -2)$
$\rightarrow A'(1, -5)$, $B'(2, -1)$, $C'(4, -4)$

pages 512–513 Homework Exercises

10.

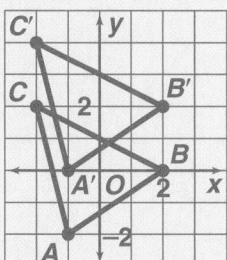

$A(-1, -2)$, $B(2, 0)$,
$C(-2, 2) \rightarrow A'(-5, -2)$,
$B'(-2, 0)$, $C'(-6, 2)$

11.

$A(-1, -2)$, $B(2, 0)$,
$C(-2, 2) \rightarrow A'(-1, 0)$,
$B'(2, 2)$, $C'(-2, 4)$

12.

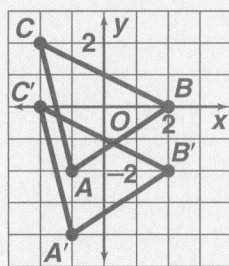

$A(-1, -2)$, $B(2, 0)$,
$C(-2, 2) \rightarrow A'(5, -1)$,
$B'(8, 1)$, $C'(4, 3)$

13.

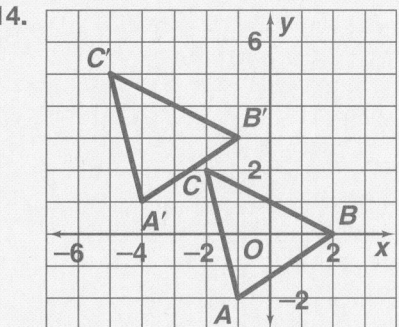

$A(-1, -2)$, $B(2, 0)$,
$C(-2, 2) \rightarrow A'(-1, -4)$,
$B'(2, -2)$, $C'(-2, 0)$

14.

$A(-1, -2)$, $B(2, 0)$,
$C(-2, 2) \rightarrow A'(-4, 1)$,
$B'(-1, 3)$, $C'(-5, 5)$

18.

right 3 units, down 1 unit

19.

right 4 units, up 1 unit

20.

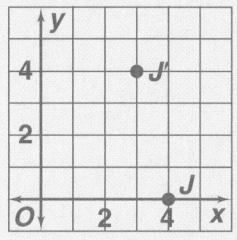

right 1 unit, up 2 units

21.

left 1 unit, up 4 units

22. $P'(4, -3)$, $L'(-1, 4)$, $N'(2, 1)$;
$(x, y) \rightarrow (x + 4, y + 3)$

26. Answers may vary. Sample:
Stating the horizontal change
first fits with the format of a
coordinate pair (x, y).

Lesson 10-6

pages 514–515 Quick Check

1.

yes

2a–b.

3.

$A(-1, 4)$, $B(-4, 2)$,
$C(-2, 1) \rightarrow A'(-1, -4)$,
$B'(-4, -2)$, $C'(-2, -1)$

TE Additional Examples

2–3.

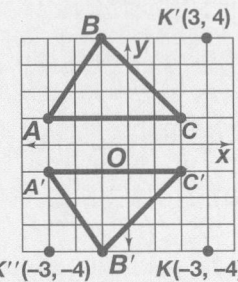

pages 516–517   Homework Exercises

6.

7. none

8.

9.

16.

17.

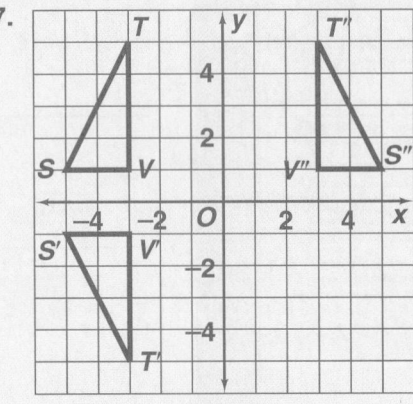

18. $A(-3, 3) \rightarrow A'(3, 3)$,
$B(-1, 3) \rightarrow B'(1, 3)$,
$C(-1, -1) \rightarrow C'(1, -1)$,
$D(-3, -1) \rightarrow D'(3, -1)$

29.

33. $(0, 2)$, $(1, 5)$, $(2, 8)$, $(3, 11)$

34. $(0, 4)$, $(1, 3)$, $(2, 2)$, $(3, 1)$

35. $(0, -1)$, $(1, -3)$, $(2, -5)$, $(3, -7)$

page 518   Checkpoint Quiz 2

10. 3 and 8

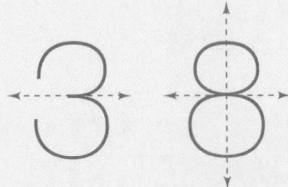

Lesson 10-7

page 519   Check Skills You'll Need

2.

acute

3.

obtuse

4.

right

5.

straight

page 520   Quick Check

3.

$T'(0, 0)$, $R'(-3, -3)$, $G'(-5, -1)$

pages 521–522   Homework Exercises

13.

$P'(0, 0)$, $Q'(-2, 0)$, $R'(-2, -6)$, $S'(0, -6)$

14.

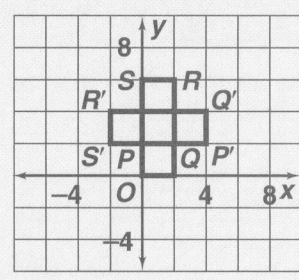

$P'(4, 2)$, $Q'(4, 4)$, $R'(-2, 4)$, $S'(-2, 2)$

15.

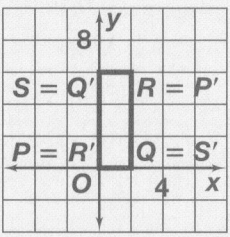

$P'(2, 6)$, $Q'(0, 6)$, $R'(0, 0)$, $S'(2, 0)$

16.

$P'(-2, 4)$, $Q'(-2, 2)$, $R'(4, 2)$, $S'(4, 4)$

27.

square

pages 524–525   Chapter Review

6–8.

13.

14.

15.

x	−3	−2	−1	0	1	2	3
y	8	3	0	−1	0	3	8

16.

x	−3	−2	−1	0	1	2	3
y	4	3	2	1	2	3	4

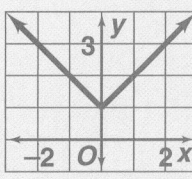

17.

x	−3	−2	−1	0	1	2	3
y	16	6	0	−2	0	6	16

18.

x	−3	−2	−1	0	1	2	3
y	12	8	4	0	4	8	12

19. $A(3, -1)$, $B(1, 1)$,
$C(4, 4) \rightarrow A'(3, -3)$,
$B'(1, -1)$, $C'(4, 2)$

20. $A(3, -1)$, $B(1, 1)$,
$C(4, 4) \rightarrow A'(0, -1)$,
$B'(-2, 1)$, $C'(1, 4)$

---

21. $A(3, -1)$, $B(1, 1)$,
$C(4, 4) \rightarrow A'(6, -6)$,
$B'(4, -4)$, $C'(7, -1)$

22.

$A(3, -1)$, $B(1, 1)$,
$C(4, 4) \rightarrow A'(3, 1)$,
$B'(1, -1)$, $C'(4, -4)$

page 526   Chapter Test

1–4.

5–6. Answers may vary. Samples are given.

5.

6.

11.

T709

12.

13.

14.

19.

20.

21.

x	−3	−2	−1	0	1	2	3
y	7	2	−1	−2	−1	2	7

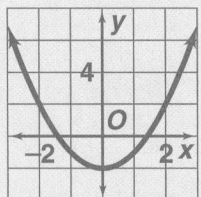

22.

x	−3	−2	−1	0	1	2	3
y	7	5	3	1	3	5	7

23.

x	0.25x + 2	y	(x, y)
2	0.25 (2) + 2	2.5	(2, 2.5)
4	0.25 (4) + 2	3	(4, 3)
6	0.25 (6) + 2	3.5	(6, 3.5)

24.

25.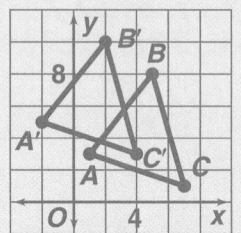

$A(1, 3)$, $B(5, 8)$, $C(7, 1)$ →
$A'(2, 0)$, $B'(6, 5)$, $C'(8, −2)$

26.

$A(1, 3)$, $B(5, 8)$, $C(7, 1)$ →
$A'(−2, 5)$, $B'(2, 10)$,
$C'(4, 3)$

27.

$A(1, 3)$, $B(5, 8)$, $C(7, 1)$ →
$A'(−1, 3)$, $B'(−5, 8)$,
$C'(−7, 1)$

30.

CHAPTER 11

Lesson 11-1

pages 532–533   Quick Check

1.

U.S. Representatives for 22 States

Number of Represen- tatives	Tally	Frequency
1	⦀⦀	5
2	‖	2
3	‖‖	4
4	‖	2
5	‖‖	3
6		0
7	‖	2
8	‖	2
9	‖	2

2.   **Number of Students in Math Classes**

T710

3.

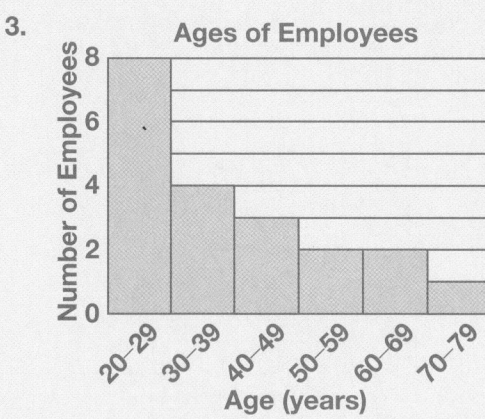

Ages of Employees

page 534   More Than One Way

Answers may vary. Sample:

Number of Hours
Worked per Week

pages 534–536   Exercises

2.

3.

Tickets Sold	Tally	Frequency
45	II	2
46	IIII	4
47		0
48	II	2
49	I	1
50	III	3
51	II	2
52		0
53	I	1

4.

Number of TVs	Tally	Frequency
1	NN I	6
2	NN I	6
3	NN	5
4	I	1

5.

Student Ages	Tally	Frequency
11	IIII	4
12	NN	5
13	NN	5
14	III	3

6.

Plants Sold
per Person

7.

Miles From Home
to Shopping Center

8.

Blocks Walked
From Home to School

9.

How Many
Amusement Parks
Did You Visit
Last Year?

Amusement Parks

10.

How Many Hours
Do You Sleep
Each Night?

11.

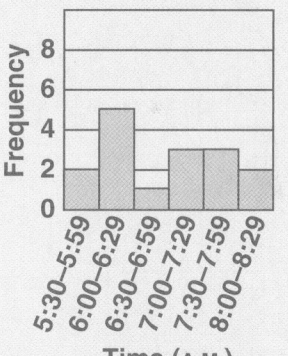

What Time
Do You Wake
in the Morning?

17. Answers may vary. Sample:

Number of Siblings

18.

Home Prices

Home Prices

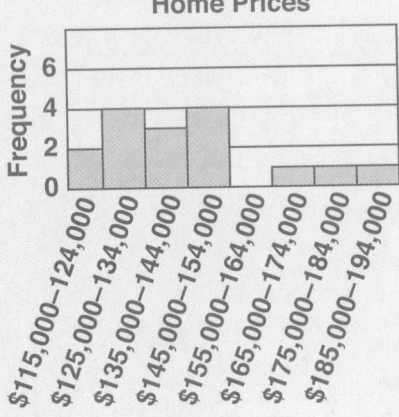

22.

x	y
−3	8
−2	3
−1	0
0	−1
1	0
2	3
3	8

23.

x	y
−3	27
−2	12
−1	3
0	0
1	3
2	12
3	27

24.

x	y
−3	−27
−2	−12
−1	−3
0	0
1	−3
2	−12
3	−27

Lesson 11-2

page 538   Check Skills You'll Need

2.

Height (in.) vs Age (yr)

page 542   Homework Exercises

27.

a. B3 = 4, B4 = 7,
   D4 = 6, D5 = 7

b. (1.5, 5.5)

page 544   Quick Check

1.

1	56		5	31
2	80		6	10
3	40 60 78		7	25
4	22 50
5	31
6	10
7	25

Key: 156 means $1.56

page 546   Homework Exercises

5.

4	3 6 7
5	1 2
6	0 1 7
7	1 2 8
8	2 6 8

Key: 8 | 2 means 82

6. Sales of Twelve Companies
   (millions of dollars)

1	3 3 4 4 4 4
2	3 4 5 5
3	6 9

Key: 1 | 3 means 1.3

7. High Temperatures
   in the Desert (°F)

9	8 9
10	0 1 3 4 8 9
11	1 2 2 3 3 8

Key: 9 | 8 means 98

page 549   Checkpoint Quiz 1

1.

Number	Tally	Frequency
1	II	2
2	II	2
3	II	2
4	II	2
5	III	3
6	I	1
7	II	2
8	II	2
9	I	1

2. Graphs and explanations may vary. Sample graph:

10.

```
 8 | 7 9
 9 | 3 5 5
10 |
11 | 2 3 7 7
12 | 0 1 4
```

Key: 8 | 7 means 87

Lesson 11-4

pages 552–553   Homework Exercises

7. Part (b); the sample is more diverse.

8. Part (a); the sample is more diverse.

9. Part (b); the sample is more diverse.

10. Part (a); the sample is more diverse.

---

17. Survey B; survey A is biased because it uses the terms *noisy* and *overpriced*; survey B is not biased because it makes no assumptions.

19. Yes; surveying every 10th person is random, and you should get a mix of ages and genders.

20. No; you will include people outside of your population in the survey.

25. Start with 3 and add 5 repeatedly; 23, 28, 33

26. Start with −2 and add 3 repeatedly; 10, 13, 16

27. Start with 27 and subtract 11 repeatedly; −17, −28, −39

Lesson 11-5

page 555   Homework Exercises

1. Researchers capture, mark, and release animals, and then capture another group of animals. The number of marked animals in the second group indicates population size.

2. about 12,917 trout

3. about 13,661 bass

TE Closure

Use the proportion:

$$\frac{\text{number of marked animals counted}}{\text{total number of animals counted}} = \frac{\text{number of marked animals}}{\text{estimate of animal population}}.$$

pages 556   Homework Exercises

19a. The proportion should be $\frac{8}{25} = \frac{38}{x}$.

  b. 119 sharks

25–29.

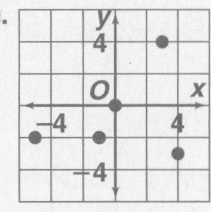

---

page 557   Activity Lab

1.

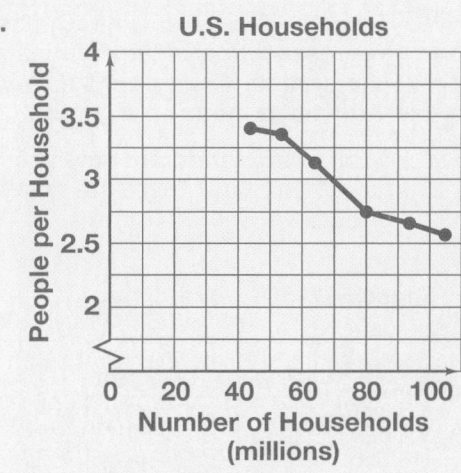

Lesson 11-6

page 561   Quick Check

2a.

  b.

TE Additional Examples

2. The intervals on the horizontal axis are uneven. The number of viewers may not have increased as sharply as the graph illustrates.

page 562   TE   Additional Examples

3. Sample: The mean is not the best representation of the salaries at the station. The owner's salary skews the mean.

4. Misleading; there are only two cars under $10,000. There are many more over that amount.

pages 562–564   Exercises

4.

Price of Widgets

5. The vertical axis starts with 8 instead of 0. The title is also misleading since grapes are not everyone's favorite.

6. The graph gives the impression that vehicle production in 2000 was about 5 times higher than in 1980. The vertical axis has a break in the scale.

World Motor Vehicle Production

7. The graph gives the impression that the largest group of students received the highest scores. There are uneven intervals on the x-axis.

Test Results

12.

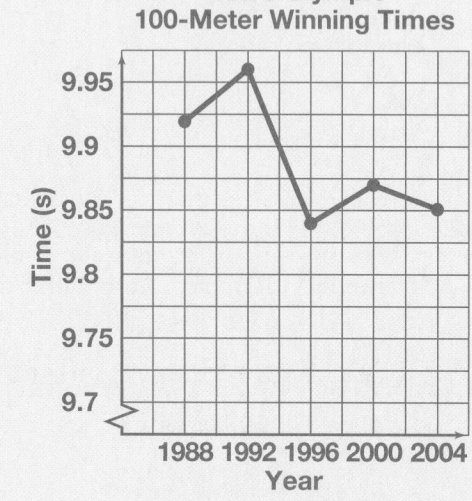

Men's Olympic 100-Meter Winning Times

Men's Olympic 100-Meter Winning Times

16.

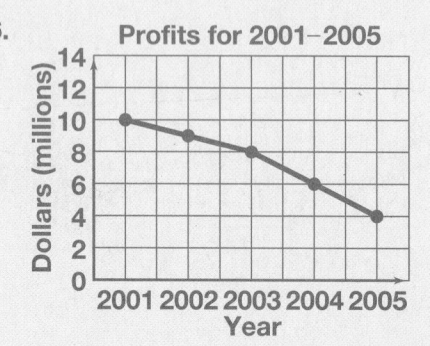

Profits for 2001–2005

18. Answers may vary. Sample: The median; it does not reflect the lower profits.

page 565   Checkpoint Quiz 2

1.

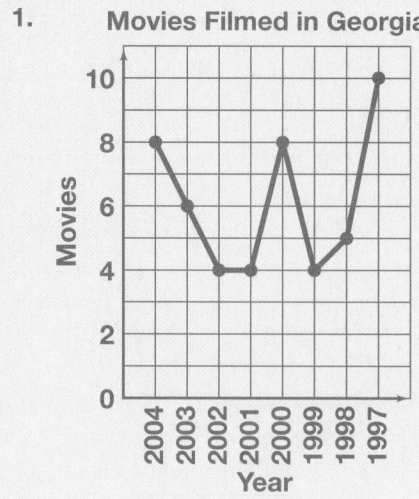

Movies Filmed in Georgia

page 566   Activity Lab

3.

Moose and Wolf Populations on Isle Royale, Michigan

T714

Lesson 11-7

page 567 Check Skills You'll Need

2–7.

page 568 TE Additional Examples

1.

Height Compared to Test Scores

TE Closure

a graph that relates two sets of data by plotting the two sets of data as ordered pairs

A positive trend has one set of values increasing as the others increase. A negative trend has one set of values decreasing as the others increase. No trend has no relationship between the sets of data.

pages 569–570 Homework Exercises

6.

Temperature and Clothing

7.

Does Studying Affect Grades?

8.

CD Prices

19.

Movie Attendance

Answers may vary. Sample: 1,750 million

---

pages 572–573 Chapter Review

6.

Number of Hours of TV (weekly)

Hours	Tally	Frequency
3	I	1
4	II	2
5	NN	5
6	NN	5
7	IIII	4
8	II	2
9	I	1

Number of Hours of TV People Watch per Week

7.

How Many Pencils or Pens Are in Your Backpack?

Pencils or Pens

13.
```
7 | 0
6 | 0 0 0 1 6 9
5 | 0 0 4 5 8
4 | 0 0 0 5 7 7 8
3 | 6
2 | 3 7 7 9
1 | 6 9
```

Key: 1 | 6 means 16

page 574 Chapter Test

1.

Hours of Sleep

Hours	Tally	Frequency
6	I	1
6.5	II	2
7	II	2
7.5	NN	5
8	NN I	6
8.5	II	2
9	I	1
9.5	I	1

Chapter 17
(read section
17.1 – 17.3)
Pg. 675 – 677

2. **Hours of Sleep**

3. How Many Hours of Sleep Do You Get per Night?

4. Hours of Sleep

```
6 | 0 5 5
7 | 0 0 5 5 5 5 5
8 | 0 0 0 0 0 0 5 5
9 | 0 5
```

Key: 6 | 0 means 6.0

5. There would no longer be a zero after 9, and there would be three new rows ending with 12 in the stem and 0 in the leaf.

11. Fair; the question makes no assumptions about the types of shows on TV.

12. Biased; the question makes assumptions about sports being violent and documentaries being informative.

13. Biased; the question makes assumptions that summers are preferable to winters.

14. Fair; the question makes no assumptions about the seasons.

15. Answers may vary. Sample: Get a list of the people who live in the town. Call every 10th person and ask if he or she uses the library.

18. Sales for Two Computer Companies

22a. Student Ages and Heights

b. positive

CHAPTER 12

Lesson 12-2

page 587   TE Additional Examples

3. Results will vary, but, in a large number of trials, will approach the theoretical probability of $\frac{1}{16}$.

TE Closure

the ratio of the number of times an event occurs to the total number of trials

Sample: Decide what coins to use and what outcomes they represent; toss the coins and record each result; count how many times the successful outcome occurred; write the ratio for the experimental probability.

Lesson 12-3

page 592   Quick Check

2a.

pages 593–595   Exercises

2.

14.

26. Popcorn   Lemonade

Small — Small, Medium, Large, Jumbo

Medium — Small, Medium, Large, Jumbo

Large — Small, Medium, Large, Jumbo

4. $P(\text{match}) = \frac{12}{30}$ or $\frac{2}{5}$;

    $P(\text{do not match}) = \frac{18}{30}$ or $\frac{3}{5}$

    Diagrams may vary. Sample is given.

		Second Choice				
		B	B	B	W	W	W
First Choice	B	—	BB	BB	BW	BW	BW
	B	BB	—	BB	BW	BW	BW
	B	BB	BB	—	BW	BW	BW
	W	WB	WB	WB	—	WW	WW
	W	WB	WB	WB	WW	—	WW
	W	WB	WB	WB	WW	WW	—

Lesson 12-4

29a. Complementary; red, yellow, green, or broken are all the possible events of a traffic light.

  b. Mutually exclusive; since a student can only receive one grade on a test, the events have no outcomes in common.

30. Dependent; answers may vary. Sample: $P(\text{red}) = \frac{4}{9}$ and $P(\text{white}) = \frac{2}{9}$. When you pick without replacement, $P(\text{red, then white}) = \frac{4}{9} \cdot \frac{2}{8}$. The probability of the second event is affected by the occurrence of the first.

35.
	1	2	3
H	H1	H2	H3
T	T1	T2	T3

11.
Appetizer   Soup   Main Dish

ER
- WT
  - AC
  - SSP
  - BB
- SR
  - AC
  - SSP
  - BB

FWT
- WT
  - AC
  - SSP
  - BB
- SR
  - AC
  - SSP
  - BB

Index

Teacher's Edition entries appear in blue type.

defined, 410
height of, 410
surface area of, 416, 417, 418, 429
volume of, 423, 424, 425, 429

D

Data
collecting, 243, 532–537, 549–553, 566, 572, 573
displaying. *See* Displaying data
graphing, 437, 439, 462, 463, 478
interpreting, 571
using to persuade, 560–564
using to predict results, 596

Data analysis, 129
box-and-whisker plots, 58
circle graphs, 354–357, 367
describing data, 558
double bar graph, 539–542, 543, 573
double line graph, 539, 541, 542, 557, 573
exercises that use, 56–57, 177, 293, 476, 543, 555, 557, 566, 570, 589, 596
frequency table, 532–536, 572, 603, 604
histogram, 533–536, 572
interpreting data, 571
line plot, 533–535, 558, 572
mean. *See* Mean
median. *See* Median
misleading graphs, 560–564, 573
misleading statistics, 558, 561, 563
mode. *See* Mode
outlier, 53
population size, 554–557, 573
quartiles, 58
random samples, 550, 552
range. *See* Range
scatter plots, 567–570, 573
stem-and-leaf plot, 544–547, 573
survey, 54, 98, 238, 289, 293, 294, 549–553, 573, 626, 629
trends, 568, 569, 573
using data to persuade, 560–564, 573
using spreadsheets, 173, 314, 538, 539, 540, 543, 590
Venn diagrams, 537, 575

Data Analysis Activity Lab
Box-and-Whisker Plots, 58
Choosing Scales and Intervals, 436
Choosing the Best Display, 548
Exploring Percent of Change, 309
Graphing Population Data, 557
Inequalities in Bar Graphs, 209
Representing Data, 495
Using Data to Predict, 596
Using Percent Data in a Graph, 289
Using Tables to Compare Data, 101

Data Collection
exercises that use, 537, 542, 547, 549, 596

Data Collection Activity Lab
Making a Circle Graph, 358
Two-Variable Data Collection, 566
Using Proportions With Data, 243
Writing Survey Questions, 549

Decagons, 340, 343
Decameter (dam), 27
Decimal(s)
adding, 8–11, 17, 62, 66, 166
annexing zeros to divide, 21, 22
changing to fractions, 97, 99
changing to, from fractions, 95–97, 99, 113
comparing, 11, 103, 104, 113, 530
dividing, 6, 19–23, 30, 120, 226, 663, 665
dividing decimal by decimal, 20, 62
estimating with, 4–5, 8, 14, 60
modeling, 13, 19, 20, 103, 278, 279
multiplying, 13–17, 26, 31, 226, 372, 661
ordering, 98, 99, 113
place value and, 2, 658
reading and writing, 659
repeating, 97, 98, 99, 113, 401
rounding, 660
Skills Handbook, 658–665
subtracting, 9, 10–11, 17, 62, 66, 166
terminating, 96, 99, 113, 401
writing as percents, 279, 282, 578
writing percents as, 280, 282, 316, 434

Decimal points, aligning, 8, 9
Decimeter (dm), 27
Decrease, percent of, 310, 311, 313, 378
Deductive reasoning. *See* Reasoning
Defects, 587, 588, 589, 617
Denominator
common, 126, 128, 130, 666
different, 127, 131
simplifying fractions, 82, 83, 113
See also Least Common Denominator (LCD)

Dependent event, 599, 600–601, 617
Diagnostic Test, xlvi–xlvii
Diagonal, 344
Diagram
drawing, 404
for ratios, 228, 232, 233
for solving equations, 185, 186, 192, 196
tree, 592, 593, 594, 600, 617
Venn, 537, 575
for writing algebraic expressions, 169, 170

Diameter
of circle, 351, 352, 367
defined, 350
finding circumference and area of circle, 394–397

Difference. *See* Subtraction
Differentiated Instruction, 2F, 66F, 118F, 166F, 226F, 272F, 322F, 372F, 434F, 484F, 530F, 578F, Teacher's Edition pages 4–5, 6, 8–9, 10, 12, 13, 14–15, 16, 19, 20–21, 22, 25, 26–27, 29, 31–32, 33, 36, 38–39, 41, 44–45, 46, 48–49, 50, 52, 53–54, 56, 58, 60, 62, 63, 68–69, 70, 72, 74–75, 77, 81, 82–83, 84, 87–88, 89, 91–92, 93, 96–97, 99, 101, 102–103, 104, 106–107, 108, 110, 112, 114, 115, 120–121, 122, 124, 126–127, 128, 130–131, 132, 136–137, 138, 141–142, 144, 147, 148–149, 150, 152, 153, 154–155, 156, 158, 160, 162, 163, 168, 169–170, 171, 173, 174–175, 176, 178, 179, 180–181, 183, 185, 186–187, 189, 193, 194–195, 197, 200–201, 203, 205–206, 207, 209, 210–211, 212, 214–215, 217, 220, 222, 223, 228–229, 230, 232–233, 234, 238–239, 240, 242, 244–245, 247, 250, 252–253, 254, 259–260, 262, 264, 266, 268, 269, 270, 274–275, 276, 279–280, 282, 284–285, 286, 290–291, 292, 294–295, 296, 298–299, 300, 303, 304–305, 306, 308, 309, 310–311, 313, 316, 318, 319, 324–325, 326, 328, 330–331, 333, 335, 336–337, 338, 340–341, 343, 346–347, 348, 350–351, 352, 354–355, 356, 360, 361–362, 363, 366, 368, 369, 374–375, 377, 380–381, 382, 384–385, 386, 388–389, 391, 393, 394–395, 396, 399, 400–401, 402, 405–406, 407, 410–411, 412, 414–415, 417, 419, 420, 421–422, 424, 426, 428, 430, 431, 437–438, 439, 442–443, 444, 446–447, 448, 452–453, 454, 456–457, 458, 460, 461–462, 463, 467, 468–469, 470, 472–473, 474, 476, 478, 480, 481, 486–487, 488, 490, 491–492, 493, 495, 497, 498–499, 500, 502, 504–505, 506, 508, 510–511, 512, 514–515, 516, 519–520, 521, 524, 526, 527, 532–533, 535, 537, 538–539, 541, 543, 544–545, 546, 548, 549, 550–551, 552, 554–555, 556, 557, 559, 560–561, 563, 567–568, 569, 572, 574, 575, 580–581, 582, 584, 586–587, 588, 590, 591–592, 594, 596, 597, 598–599, 601, 603, 605, 606–607, 608, 610–611, 612, 616, 618, 619

Dilation, 256
Direction Words, 124, 185
Discounts
finding discounted price, 312
percent of, 311, 313, 317

Discrete Mathematics
combination, 610–613, 617
counting principle, 592–593, 594, 606, 607, 611, 617
factorial, 606–607, 609
permutation, 606–609, 611, 617
tree diagram, 592, 593, 594, 617

Disjoint events, 602
Displaying data
choosing best display, 548
circle graph, 354–359
double bar graph, 539–542, 543, 573
double line graph, 539, 541, 542, 557, 573
graphing population data, 557
line plot, 533–535, 558, 572
reporting frequency, 532–536, 572, 603, 604
in spreadsheet. *See* Spreadsheet
stem-and-leaf plot, 544–547, 573
using data to persuade, 560–564, 573
Venn diagram, 537, 575

Distributive Property, 49–51, 61, 62, 66, 133
Diversity, 627
Dividend, 20

Index

of whole numbers, 656
Zero Property, 15

Multiplication Property
  of Equality, 188
  of Inequality, 216

Multiplier, common, 253

N

Negative exponent, 110

Negative rational numbers, 102–105, 113

Negative slope, 498–499

Negative trend, 568, 573

Net, 414–418, 429
  defined, 414
  drawing, 414, 416–417, 429
  finding surface area, 415–416, 429

New Vocabulary, 4, 8, 14, 31, 38, 48, 53, 68, 74, 82,
  87, 91, 96, 102, 141, 154, 169, 174, 180, 186,
  205, 210, 214, 228, 232, 238, 252, 259, 274,
  304, 310, 324, 330, 336, 340, 346, 350, 354,
  361, 374, 380, 384, 388, 394, 400, 405, 410,
  414, 421, 442, 452, 468, 472, 486, 491, 498,
  504, 514, 519, 532, 538, 544, 550, 580, 586,
  591, 598, 606, 610

No trend, 568, 573

Nonlinear equation, 504–507, 525

Notation
  arrow, 511, 512, 525
  prime (9), 510
  scientific, 106–109, 113

Number(s)
  classifying, 401, 402, 403
  compatible, 5–6, 9, 15, 121, 122
  composite, 75, 77, 112
  finding percent of, 289–293, 316, 322
  irrational, 401, 402, 403, 429
  modeling, 4, 12, 13, 19, 20, 24, 27, 31, 32, 36–40,
    43–44, 49, 52, 53, 56, 58, 69, 74, 75, 76, 80, 87,
    91, 98, 102, 103, 120, 125, 127, 135, 136, 140,
    141, 206, 210, 210–211, 215, 221, 281, 294–
    295, 302, 308, 400, 401, 443, 466, 484, 581
  prime, 75–78, 112
  random, 590
  rational, 102–105, 113, 401
  in scientific notation, 106–107, 108, 110, 113
  in standard form, 107, 108, 110, 113
  writing with exponents, 68, 70
  See also Integers; Mixed numbers; Whole
    numbers

Number line
  adding integers on, 12, 38–42
  box-and-whisker plots, 58
  comparing and ordering integers on, 32
  comparing decimals on, 98, 102

comparing fractions on, 87, 91, 102
estimating fractions using, 120
estimating percents using, 308
estimating square roots using, 400
exercises that use, 41, 42, 47, 65, 90, 145, 177,
  183, 198, 207, 208, 212, 217, 218, 221, 222,
  241, 287
finding absolute value on, 32
finding LCM using, 74
finding opposites on, 31, 484
graphing inequalities on, 206, 210–211, 215, 221
identifying outliers on, 53
modeling using, 4, 12, 27, 31, 32, 38–40, 44, 53,
  56, 58, 74, 87, 91, 98, 102, 103, 120, 206, 210–
  211, 215, 221, 281, 308, 400, 484, 581
multiplying integers on, 44
ordering rational numbers on, 103, 281
probability on, 581
rounding on, 4
subtracting integers on, 40

Number patterns, 442–445, 446–447

Number properties, 9, 48–51, 61, 62, 66, 133, 136,
  141, 166, 180, 186, 188, 210, 211, 214, 216,
  228, 239, 674

Number Sense, 10, 16, 24, 33, 46, 77, 100, 122, 132,
  138, 140, 143, 145, 150, 156, 176, 202, 230,
  240, 246, 286, 306, 312, 356, 396, 402, 419,
  436, 441, 466, 506, 546, 562, 563, 588
  choosing appropriate units, 153
  solving equations using, 174–177, 195–198, 221

Number sequences
  arithmetic sequence, 442, 444–445, 478
  Fibonacci sequence, 445
  geometric sequence, 442–445, 478

Number theory, 74, 75, 76

Numerator, 82, 83, 113. *See also* Fraction(s)

O

Obtuse angle, 330, 333

Obtuse triangle, 337, 338, 367

Octagons, 340

Odds, 584

Online Active Math, 32, 40, 70, 92, 137, 142, 170,
  216, 229, 253, 280, 294, 337, 342, 405, 423,
  462, 469, 498, 520, 554, 599, 606

Online Chapter Projects, 624–629

Online Chapter Test, 62, 114, 162, 222, 268, 318,
  368, 430, 480, 526, 574, 618

Online Homework Help, 7, 11, 17, 22, 30, 42, 47,
  51, 57, 71, 78, 85, 90, 94, 100, 105, 108, 123,
  128, 133, 139, 144, 151, 157, 172, 176, 184,
  190, 198, 203, 212, 217, 231, 235, 241, 248,
  254, 262, 277, 287, 293, 297, 301, 306, 327,
  339, 344, 349, 352, 357, 364, 378, 383, 392,
  397, 403, 408, 413, 418, 425, 440, 445, 449,
  455, 458, 464, 471, 474, 489, 494, 501, 506,
  513, 517, 522, 536, 541, 547, 552, 556, 564,
  570, 582, 589, 594, 602, 609, 612

Online Intervention. See Success Tracker

Online Lesson Quiz, 7, 11, 17, 23, 29, 33, 41, 47,
  51, 57, 71, 77, 85, 89, 93, 99, 105, 109, 123,

129, 133, 139, 145, 151, 157, 171, 177, 183,
189, 197, 203, 207, 213, 217, 231, 235, 241,
247, 255, 263, 277, 283, 287, 293, 297, 301,
307, 313, 327, 333, 339, 343, 349, 353, 357,
363, 377, 383, 387, 391, 397, 403, 407, 413,
417, 425, 439, 445, 449, 455, 459, 463, 471,
475, 489, 493, 501, 507, 513, 517, 521, 535,
541, 547, 553, 555, 563, 569, 583, 589, 595,
601, 609, 613

Online Math at Work, 18, 134, 237, 345, 450, 565

Online TAKS Prep, 63, 115, 163, 223, 269, 319,
  369, 431, 481, 527, 575, 619

Online Video Tutor Help, 8, 53, 68, 87, 126, 141,
  180, 187, 228, 238, 298, 305, 331, 354, 380,
  421, 468, 473, 492, 505, 567, 581, 586

Online Vocabulary Quizzes, 60, 112, 160, 220, 266,
  316, 366, 428, 478, 524, 572, 616

Open sentence, 174, 221

Open-ended, 47, 190, 197, 204, 222, 254, 256, 297,
  307, 338, 349, 352, 357, 378, 402, 418, 459,
  489, 509, 522, 563, 585

Operations
  inverse, 181, 186, 188, 210, 221
  order of. *See* Order of operations

Opposites, 31, 38, 39–40, 61
  finding, 31, 33
  graphing, 31, 484

Order of operations, 48–51, 61
  defined, 48, 69
  simplifying expressions, 53, 66, 72, 166, 169,
    172, 372
  simplifying expressions that use exponents,
    69–70, 112, 434
  using scientific calculator, 72

Ordered pair, 486, 487, 488, 491, 492, 493, 524

Ordering
  data sets, 53–55
  decimals, 7, 98, 99, 113
  exercises that use, 7, 33, 34, 57, 89, 99, 104, 282,
    283
  fractions, 98, 99, 113
  integers, 31–34, 61, 208, 322, 654
  rational numbers, 87, 91, 101, 103, 104, 113,
    281, 282, 283
  whole numbers, 2, 654

Origin, 486

Outcome, 580–581, 584

Outlier, 53, 61

Overviews. See Chapter Overviews

P

Pacing Chart. See Leveled Pacing Chart

Parabola, 504, 506

Parallel lines, 325, 326, 327, 328, 366

Parallelogram
  area of, 379–383, 385, 428
  base of, 379, 380–383
  defined, 341
  height of, 379, 380–383

Parentheses and order of operations, 48–51, 72

314, 332, 390, 391, 473, 474, 505, 507, 534, 536, 600, 602

choosing a process, 219

Draw a Picture or Diagram, l, 24, 25, 80, 81, 93, 146, 147, 171, 192, 193, 253, 302, 303, 365, 386, 407, 488, 497, 559, 594

Guided Problem Solving. *See* Guided Problem Solving

high-use academic words, 124, 185, 328, 508, 603

Look for a Pattern, li, 404, 441, 466, 467

Make a Table, liv, 376, 448, 506, 559

More Than One Way, 28, 76, 143, 202, 246, 312, 332, 390, 473, 505, 534, 600

practice solving problems, 146, 192, 496

reading for understanding, 159

selecting appropriate operations, 152

Systematic Guess and Check, lii, 217, 338, 402

TAKS Strategies. *See* TAKS Strategies

Think It Through, 24, 63, 80, 115, 146, 163, 192, 223, 249, 269, 302, 319, 359, 369, 398, 431, 466, 481, 496, 527, 558, 575, 604

Word Problem Practice, 25, 81, 147, 193, 249, 303, 360, 399, 466, 467, 497, 559, 605

Work a Simpler Problem, lv

Work Backward, lvi, 200, 315, 473

Write an Equation, lvii, 176, 183, 192, 202, 203, 249, 250, 333, 458, 467, 474

Product, 141

zeros in, 662

See also Cross product; Multiplication

Professional Development, 2C–D, 66C–D, 118C–D, 166C–D, 226C–D, 272C–D, 322C–D, 372C–D, 434C–D, 484C–D, 530C–D, 578C–D, Teacher's Edition pages 4, 8, 14, 20, 26, 31, 38, 44, 48, 53, 68, 74, 82, 87, 91, 96, 102, 106, 120, 126, 130, 136, 141, 148, 154, 169, 174, 180, 186, 194, 200, 205, 210, 214, 228, 232, 238, 244, 252, 259, 274, 279, 284, 290, 294, 298, 304, 310, 324, 330, 336, 340, 346, 350, 354, 361, 374, 380, 384, 388, 394, 400, 405, 410, 414, 421, 437, 442, 446, 452, 456, 461, 468, 472, 486, 491, 498, 504, 510, 514, 519, 532, 538, 544, 550, 554, 560, 567, 580, 586, 591, 598, 606, 610

Program Resources, 2E, 66E, 118E, 166E, 226E, 272E, 322E, 372E, 434E, 484E, 530E, 578E

Proper fractions, 132

writing percents, 285, 316

Properties, 674

of addition, 9, 52, 180

associative property, 9, 15, 60

commutative property, 9, 15, 60

Cross-Products, 239

distributive, 49–51, 61, 62, 66, 133

of equality, 52, 180, 186, 188

identifying, 62

Identity Property, 9, 15

of Inequality, 210, 211, 214, 216

modeling, 52

of multiplication, 15, 60

validating conclusions using, 9, 15, 52

Proportion

defined, 238, 267

estimating population size, 554–556

finding a part, 295, 296

finding part and the whole using percent and, 317

modeling, 294–295, 317

ratios. *See* Ratio

solving, 238–241, 243, 249, 267, 322, 530

solving percent problems using, 294–297, 317

solving using cross products, 239–240, 267

solving using mental math, 245

solving using unit rates, 244, 247

solving using variables, 245, 272, 322

Proportional reasoning, 244–248, 272, 578

Proportional relationships

circle graphs, 354–360, 367

geometry, 251–256, 267, 354–360, 367

maps and scale drawings, 259–263, 267

in measurement, 26–30, 61, 148–151, 161

modeling, 27, 228, 232, 233, 234, 239, 249, 251, 253, 258, 260, 261, 264

number, 26–30, 61, 148–151, 161, 228–235, 238–241, 243, 249, 259–263, 266–267

probability, 580–583, 5 84, 586–589, 598, 599, 616

proportions, 238–241

proportions and equations, 244–248, 249–250, 265

ratios, 228–231, 238, 266

for similar figures, 251–256, 267, 269, 271

unit rates and proportional reasoning, 232–235, 266–267

using proportions with data, 243

using to predict results, 554, 587

using to solve percent problems, 294–297, 301, 310–314, 317

writing ratios in simplest form, 229, 230, 238, 266

Protractor, 251, 329, 335, 358

Pyramid, 410, 412, 429

Pythagorean Theorem, 404–408, 429

Q

Quadrant, 486–489, 524, 530

Quadrilaterals, 340–344

defined, 340

special, identifying, 341

Quartiles, 58

Question, biased, 551, 552, 573

Quick Check, 4, 5, 8, 9, 14, 15, 20, 21, 26, 27, 31, 32, 39, 40, 45, 48, 49, 53, 54, 55, 68, 69, 74, 75, 82, 83, 88, 92, 96, 97, 98, 102, 103, 107, 120, 121, 126, 127, 130, 131, 136, 137, 141, 142, 148, 149, 154, 155, 169, 170, 175, 176, 181, 182, 187, 188, 194, 195, 196, 200, 201, 205, 206, 210, 211, 215, 216, 228, 229, 232, 233, 238, 239, 244, 245, 253, 259, 260, 261, 274, 275, 279, 280, 281, 284, 285, 290, 291, 294, 295, 298, 299, 304, 305, 310, 311, 324, 325, 331, 332, 336, 337, 341, 342, 346, 347, 351, 354, 355, 361, 362, 374, 375, 376, 381, 384, 385, 389, 395, 400, 401, 405, 406, 411, 414,

415, 422, 423, 437, 438, 442, 443, 446, 447, 452, 453, 456, 457, 461, 462, 468, 469, 472, 473, 486, 487, 491, 492, 498, 499, 504, 505, 510, 511, 514, 515, 519, 520, 532, 533, 538, 539, 544, 545, 550, 551, 554, 560, 561, 562, 567, 568, 580, 581, 586, 587, 591, 592, 593, 598, 599, 606, 607, 610, 611

Quotient, 20

estimating, 5, 6

See also Division

R

Radical sign, 400

Radius

of circle, 351, 352, 353, 367

defined, 350

finding circumference and area of circle, 394–397

Random number, 590

Random sample, 549–553

Range

defined, 55

describing data, 558

finding, 55, 56, 57, 61

misleading use of, 561, 563

from stem-and-leaf plots, 545, 546, 571

Rate(s), 232–235, 242, 243, 266

modeling, 232, 233, 242

unit, 232, 266

Ratio, 228–231, 266

comparing, 229, 230

of corresponding sides, 252–253

defined, 228, 266

equivalent, 229, 230, 266, 275, 276

modeling, 228

odds, 584

writing, 228, 230

writing as percents, 275, 276, 316

writing in simplest form, 229, 230, 238, 266, 578

Rational numbers, 102–105

classifying, 401, 402, 403

Cubes Activity Lab, 278

defined, 102, 113

negative, 102–103, 104, 113

ordering, 87, 91, 98, 101, 102–105, 113, 281, 282, 283

See also Decimal(s); Fraction(s)

Rays, 324, 326, 328

Reading for understanding, 159

Real-world applications

advertising, 526, 562

air travel, 458

airplanes, 572

amusement parks, 351

animals, 105

animation, 511

aquariums, 425

avalanches, 499

aviation, 513

baking, 35, 138, 217

ballooning, 108, 268

banking, 469

Index

Acknowledgements

Staff Credits

The people who make up the **Prentice Hall Math** team—representing design services, editorial, editorial services, educational technology, marketing, market research, photo research and art development, production services, publishing processes, and rights & permissions—are listed below. Bold type denotes core team members.

Dan Anderson, Carolyn Artin, Nick Blake, **Stephanie Bradley,** Kyla Brown, Patrick Culleton, Kathleen J. Dempsey, **Frederick Fellows, Suzanne Finn,** Paul Frisoli, Ellen Granter, **Richard Heater,** Betsy Krieble, Lisa LaVallee, Christine Lee, Kendra Lee, Cheryl Mahan, **Carolyn McGuire,** Eve Melnechuk, Terri Mitchell, Jeffrey Paulhus, Mark Roop-Kharasch, Marcy Rose, Rashid Ross, Irene Rubin, Siri Schwartzman, Vicky Shen, **Dennis Slattery,** Elaine Soares, Dan Tanguay, Tiffany Taylor, Mark Tricca, Paula Vergith, Kristin Winters, Helen Young

Additional Credits

Paul Astwood, Sarah J. Aubry, Jonathan Ashford, Peter Chipman, Patty Fagan, Tom Greene, Kevin Keane, Mary Landry, Jon Kier, Dan Pritchard, Sara Shelton, Jewel Simmons, Ted Smykal, Steve Thomas, Michael Torocsik, Maria Torti

TE Design

Susan Gerould/Perspectives

Illustration

Additional Artwork

Rich McMahon; Ted Smykal

Kenneth Batelman: 580; Joel Dubin: 601; John Edwards, Inc.: 184, 263, 265, 589; Das Grup: 593, 594; Kelly Graphics: 351, 354; Carla Kiwior: 132, 142; Brucie Roche: 7, 195, 235, 415, 424, 582; John Schreiner: 218, 307, 597; Wilkinson Studios: 423, 613; JB Woolsey: 233, 253; XNR Productions, Inc.: 32, 43, 55, 260, 262, 264, 383, 386, 389, 390

Photography

Front Cover: Paul Frankian/Index Stock Imagery, Inc.
Back Cover: Corbis/Picture Quest

Title page: tl, Bob Daemmrich Photography; **tr,** Williamson Edwards/The Image Bank; **bl,** David Muench; **br,** Bob Daemmrich Photography.

Front matter Pages x, Tom Brakefield/Corbis; **xi,** Jim Craigmyle/Corbis; **xii,** Robert Tyrell; **xiii,** Joe Gemignani/Corbis; **xiv,** Getty Images, Inc; **xv,** Mitch Windham/The Image Works; **xvi,** Roger Ressmeyer/Corbis; **xvii,** Rudi Von Briel/Photo Edit; **xviii,** Jeff Greenberg/PhotoEdit; **xix,** Andersen Ross/Getty Images, Inc; **xx,** David Young-Wolff/PhotoEdit; **xxi,** Andre Jenny/Alamy; **xlviii,** Richard Haynes; **xlix,** Richard Haynes; **l,** Bryan Peterson/Getty Images, Inc.; **lii,** Cindy Charles/PhotoEdit; **liii,** Randall Hyman; **liv,** Jeff Lepore/Photo Researchers, Inc.; **lvi,** Photonica/Getty Images; **lvii,** Brian Bailey/Getty Images, Inc.; **xlviii,** Richard Haynes.

Chapter 1 Pages 3, Art Wolfe/Photo Researchers, Inc; **4,** Tom Brakefield/Corbis; **5,** Russ Lappa; **8,** Mary Kate Denny/Photo Edit; **8 ml,** Richard Haynes; **11 ml,** Gallo Images/Corbis; **11 mr,** Andrew McKim/Masterfile; **14,** Robin Nelson/Photo Edit; **16,** Robert Rathe/Getty Images; **17,** Terry Oakley/Alamy; **18,** Frank Siteman/Monkmeyer; **19,** Richard Haynes; **20,** Spencer Grant/Photo Edit; **21,** Eyewire/Getty Images, Inc. **23,** Rachel Epstein/PhotoEdit, **26 tr,** Prentice Hall photo by Jane Latta; **26 mr,** Guy Ryecart/

Dorling Kindersley; **26 br,** Dorling Kindersley; **28,** Russ Poole Photography; **28 tl,** Richard Haynes; **28 mr,** Richard Haynes; **31,** Age Fotostock/SuperStock; **32,** Wayne R. Blenduke/Getty Images; **34,** Reuters NewMedia, Inc./Corbis; **35,** Richard Haynes; **37,** Richard Haynes; **41,** Keith Kent/Peter Arnold, Inc.; **43,** Richard Haynes; **44,** G. Kalt/Zefa/Corbis; **45,** Philip & Karen Smith/SuperStock; **47,** Peter Pinnock/Getty Images, Inc.; **51,** Doug Wilson/Alamy Images, **53,** Richard Haynes; **54 bl,** Clive Boursnel/Dorling Kindersley; **54 br,** Kevin Summers/Getty Images; **55,** Arthur Tilley/Getty Images, Inc.; **56,** Tim Davis/Getty Images; **57,** Gordon Clayton/Dorling Kindersley.

Chapter 2 Pages 67, Steve Satushek/Getty Images; **68,** Richard Haynes; **71,** Andrew Syred/Photo Researchers, Inc.; **74,** D. J. Peters/AP/Wide World Photos, **76 ml,** Richard Haynes; **76 br,** Richard Haynes; **78,** G.D.T./Getty Images, Inc.; **79 b,** Richard Haynes; **79 t,** Russ Lappa; **83,** Hans Halberstadt/Corbis; **84,** Rubberball/SuperStock; **86,** Richard Haynes; **87 mr,** A. & J. Visaoe/Peter Arnold, Inc.; **87 bl,** Richard Haynes; **88,** Jim Pickerell, **91,** Associated Press/THE HAWK EYE/AP Wide World; **92,** Tony Savino/The Image Works; **94,** The Image Works; **96,** Spencer Grant/PhotoEdit; **98,** Jeff Greenberg/PhotoEdit; **100,** Janet Foster/Masterfile; **102,** Rhoda Sidney/PhotoEdit; **105,** David Aubrey/Corbis; **106,** Jim Craigmyle/Corbis; **107,** NASA/Finley Holiday Films; **109,** *FOXTROT*©1992 Bill Amend. Reprinted with permission of Universal Press Syndicate. All rights reserved.

Chapter 3 Pages 119, Andrew Syred/SPL/Photo Researchers; **121,** Jump Run Productions/Getty Images; **123,** Peter Vanderwarker/Stock Boston; **124,** Richard Haynes; **125,** Richard Haynes; **126 mr,** David Kelly Crow/Photo Edit; **126 bl,** Richard Haynes; **127,** Addison Geary/Stock Boston; **129 ml,** Tom Stewart/Corbis; **129 mr,** John A. Rizzo/Getty Images, Inc.; **130,** Earl Carter/Southeastern Sports Photos; **131,** Marnie Burkhart/Masterfile; **133,** Tom Stewart/Corbis; **134,** Tom Stewart/Corbis; **135,** Richard Haynes; **136,** Richard Hutchings/PhotoEdit; **138,** Robert Tyrell; **139,** Kwame Zikomo/SuperStock, Inc.; **140,** Richard Haynes; **141,** Richard Haynes; **142,** Pierre Arsenault/Masterfile; **143 tl,** Richard Haynes; **143,** Richard Haynes; **145,** Douglas Faulkner/Corbis; **149,** Karl Weatherly/PhotoDisc/Getty Images, Inc.; **151,** Gallo Images/Corbis; **155 tl,** David C. Ellis/Getty Images; **155 tr,** Russ Lappa; **157,** Friedrich Von Horsten/Animals Animals/Earth Scenes

Chapter 4 Pages 167, Bruce M. Herman/Photo Researchers, Inc.; **169,** Eddy Lemaistre/For Picture/Corbis; **170,** David Young-Wolff/PhotoEdit; **172,** Francois Gohier/Ardea; **174,** Keren Su/Corbis; **175,** Ariel Skelley/Corbis Stock Market; **177,** Joe Gemignani/Corbis; **180,** Richard Haynes; **181,** Lee Cohen/Getty Images; **182,** Janeart/Getty Images; **183,** Dr. Jeremy Burgess/Photo Researchers, Inc.; **185,** Richard Haynes; **187,** Richard Haynes; **189,** Will Hart; **191,** Prentice Hall; **194,** age fotostock/Superstock; **197,** Stuart Westmorland/Getty Images; **198,** David Young-Wolff/PhotoEdit; **199 t,** Richard Haynes; **200,** Ron Sachs/Corbis; **201,** Alan Thornton/Getty Images, Inc.; **202 tl,** Richard Haynes; **202 mr,** Richard Haynes; **203,** Reuters/Corbis; **204,** Patrick Clark/PhotoDisc/Getty Images, Inc.; **205,** D&J Heaton/Stock Boston; **206,** Russ Lappa; **208 tl,** SuperStock, Inc.; **208 tr,** Michael Newman/PhotoEdit; **210,** Bill Bachmann/Photo Edit **211,** Stephen Simpson/Getty Images; **213,** Kevin R. Morris/Corbis; **214,** Frances Roberts/Alamy; **215,** Jose Luis Pelaez, Inc./Corbis; **217,** Antonio Mo/Getty Images, Inc.

Chapter 5 Pages 227, Dave G. Houser/Corbis; **228,** Richard Haynes; **229,** AP Photo/Paul Sakuma; **231,** LWA-Dann Tardif/CORBIS; **232,** David Young-Wolff/Photo Edit; **235,** Andy Lyons/Getty Images, Inc.; **236,** BIOS/Peter Arnold, Inc.; **237 t,** Alan Levenson/Getty Images; **237 b,** Ron Kimball/Ron Kimball Stock; **238,** Richard Haynes; **241,** Johnson Space Center/NASA; **246 tl & mr,** Richard Haynes; **247,** Franklin D. Roosevelt Library; **248,** Photodisc Green/Getty Images; **251,** Richard Haynes; **252,** Alaska Stock LLC/Alamy; **255,** Brian Sytnyk/Masterfile; **257,** Richard Haynes; **258,** Richard Haynes; **259,** Getty Images, Inc.; **264,** AP/Wide World Photos

Chapter 6 Pages 273, Omni Photo Communications, Inc./Index Stock; 276, Mitsuaki Iwago/Minden Pictures; 278, Richard Haynes; 280, Kelly Mooney Photography/Corbis; 281, Peter Johnson/Corbis; 283, Hillary Price; 284, Robin Nelson/Photo Edit; 285, David Young-Wolff/PhotoEdit; 287, Tom McHugh/Photo Researchers, Inc.; 288, Richard Haynes; 290, Rhoda Sidney/Photo Edit; 291, Richard Haynes; 293, UNEP/Rougier/The Image Works; 294, IML Image Group Ltd./Alamy; 297, Bob Daemmrich/Stock Boston; 298 tr, Mitch Windham/The Image Works; 298 bl, Richard Haynes; 299, David Young-Wolff/PhotoEdit; 301, Bob Daemmrich/The Image Works 304, Bernard Wolf/PhotoEdit; 305 tl, Adamsmith Productions/Corbis; 305 bl, Richard Haynes; 307, Lawrence Migdale/Photo Researchers, Inc.; 310, Mark Reinstein/The Image Works; 312 tl & mr, Richard Haynes; 313, Photo Researchers, Inc.

Chapter 7 Pages 323, William A. Bake/Corbis; 325, Rafeal Macia/Photo Researchers, Inc.; 326 mr, Design by Jean-Charles Guillois and Ines Levy; 326 br, James Marshall/Corbis; 328 mr, Kevin Mallet/Dorling Kindersley; 328 tr, Richard Haynes; 329, Richard Haynes; 330, Richard Pasley/Stock Boston; 331, Richard Haynes; 332 mr & bl, Richard Haynes; 333, William Taufic/Corbis; 334, Spencer Grant/PhotoEdit; 335, Richard Haynes; 336, Russ Lappa; 339, Paul Hermansen/Getty Images, Inc.; 340, 2007 Mondrian/Holtzman Trust. c/o hcr@hcrinternational.com/Erich Lessing/Art Resource, NY; 342, Bill Aron/PhotoEdit; 343 tl, Max Alexander/DK Picture Library; 343 tr, Felicia Martinez/PhotoEdit; 343 br, Paul Trummer/Getty Images, Inc.; 343 bl, Cavagnaro/Visuals Unlimited; 344, 1995 by NEA, Inc. Thaves 6–13; 345, Peter Beck/Corbis; 346, Roger Ressmeyer/Corbis; 347, 2004 AFP/Getty Images; 350, Spencer Grant/PhotoEdit; 351, Lawrence Migdale; 353, James L. Amos/Corbis; 354, Richard Haynes; 355, NASA; 357, Spencer Grant/Photo Edit; 361, Andreas Pollok/Getty Images; 362, Courtesy of Wellesley College Library, Special Collections, photo by George McLean

Chapter 8 Pages 373, Michael Grecco/Stock Boston; 374, Getty Images; 375, Jacques Descloitres, MODIS Rapid Response Team, NASA/GSFC; 379, Richard Haynes; 380, Janis Daemmrich/Daemmrich Photography; 380 bl, Richard Haynes; 381, Rudi Von Briel/Photo Edit; 384, Bob Daemmrich/The Image Works; 387, U.S. Coast Guard; 388, Photo by Randy Varga; 389, Buddy Mays/Corbis; 390 tl & br, Richard Haynes; 392, C Squared Studios/Getty Images, Inc.; 393, Richard Haynes; 395, Larry Lilac/Alamy; 397, Lawrence Migdal/Stock Boston; 400, Myrleen Ferguson Cate/PhotoEdit; 403, FOXTROT ©1992 Bill Amend. Reprinted with permission of Universal Press Syndicate. All rights reserved. 406, Jeff Greenberg/PhotoEdit; 408, Michael J. Howell/Stock Boston; 409 mr & bm, Russ Lappa; 409 tr, Richard Haynes; 409 bl, Russ Lappa; 410, David Parker/Photo Researchers, Inc.; 413, Davies & Starr/Getty Images, Inc.; 413, John Lei/Stock Boston; 413, Spike Mafford/Getty Images, Inc.; 416, Richard Haynes; 418, Amy Etra/PhotoEdit; 420, Richard Haynes; 421 mr, George & Monserrate Schwartz/Alamy; 421, Richard Haynes

Chapter 9 Pages 435, Charles Bush; 438, George Shelley/Masterfile; 440, Bob Daemmrich/Stock Boston; 441 bl, Russ Lappa; 441 bm, Russ Lappa; 441 br, Russ Lappa; 441 tr, Richard Haynes; 442, Hal Horwitz/Corbis; 445, Kaz Chiba/Getty Images; 446, SuperStock; 449 ml, Cheryl Hogue/Visuals Unlimited; 449 mr, Russ Lappa; 450, Chris Marona/Photo Researchers, Inc.; 455, Michael Newman/PhotoEdit; 456, Royalty Free/Corbis; 457, Mark Bernett/Stock Boston; 459, Bettmann/Corbis; 461, Bob Daemmrich/The Image Works; 462, Jeff Greenberg/PhotoEdit; 464, Lowe Art Museum, University of Miami/SuperStock, Inc.; 466, Russ Lappa; 468 mr, Ariel Skelley/Corbis; 468 bl, Richard Haynes; 470, Superstock/Alamy; 472, AP/Wide World Photos; 473 mr & br, Richard Haynes; 473 tl, Richard Haynes; 475, Richard Hutchings/Photo Researchers, Inc.

Chapter 10 Pages 485, NASA/Masterfile; 487, David R. Frazier/The Image Works; 489, John R. Bracegirdle/Getty Images, Inc.; 491, Dave Nagel/Getty Images, Inc.; 492, Richard Haynes; 493, Andersen Ross/Getty Images, Inc.; 494, Lynda Richardson/Corbis; 498, AP Wide World Photos; 499, Corbis; 500 ml, Peter Guttman/Corbis; 500 mr, Adam Jones/Photo Researchers, Inc.; 501, Prentice Hall; 503, Richard Haynes; 504, Colorsport; 505 ml, tl, & br, Richard Haynes; 506, Getty Images; 507, Steve Fitchett/Getty Images, Inc.; 508, Richard Haynes; 510, Victoria & Albert Museum, London/Art Resource, NY; 513, George Hall/Corbis; 514 br, Charles Kennard/Stock Boston; 514 bl, Jerome Wexler/Photo Researchers, Inc.; 514 mr, Nuridsany et Perennou/Photo Researchers, Inc.; 517, Sturgis McKeever/Photo Researchers, Inc.; 519, Jonathan Nourok/Photo Edit; 519 br, Foto World/Getty Images, Inc.

Chapter 11 Pages 531, John Hickey/The Buffalo News; 532, Jose Luis Pelaez, Inc./Corbis; 534 tr & ml, Richard Haynes; 535, Dennis MacDonald/PhotoEdit; 537, Siede Preis/Getty Images, Inc.; 538, Bill Aron/Photo Edit; 544, David Young-Wolff/PhotoEdit; 546, Jeff Greenberg/PhotoEdit; 550, Andy King/Reuters/Landov; 552, Anton Vengo/SuperStock, Inc.; 553, Karen Preuss/The Image Works; 554, Jim Brandenburg/ Minden Pictures; 556, Amos Nachuom/Corbis; 560, Tony Freeman/PhotoEdit; 562, Patricia Brabant/Getty Images, Inc.; 565, Michael Newman/PhotoEdit; 567, Richard Haynes; 568, David Weintraub/Photo Researchers, Inc.

Chapter 12 Pages 579, Pictor International, Ltd./PictureQuest; 580, Jim Cummins/Getty Images; 581, Richard Haynes; 583, Andre Jenny/Alamy; 584, Prentice Hall; 585, Richard Haynes; 586, Andy Sacks/Getty Images, Inc.; 586, Richard Haynes; 587, Paul Barton/Corbis; 589, David Young-Wolff/PhotoEdit; 591, Burke/Triolo Productions/Foodpix; 592, Hughes Martin/Corbis; 595, TRBPhoto/Getty Images, Inc.; 596, Bob Daemmrich/The Image Works; 598, Emely/Zefa/Corbis; 600 tr & ml, Richard Haynes; 602, Comstock/Alamy; 603, Richard Haynes; 606, Getty Images, Inc.; 607, Robert Laberge/Getty Images, Inc.; 609, Joseph Sohm; ChromoSohm Inc./Corbis; 610, Todd Warnock/Getty Images; 611, David Hiller/Getty Images; 613, Russ Lappa

Teacher's Edition

Editorial Services: Pearson Education Development Group
Production Services: Argosy Publishing

T740

Grade 7

LENGTH

Metric	Customary
1 centimeter = 10 millimeters	1 foot = 12 inches
1 meter = 100 centimeters	1 yard = 3 feet
1 kilometer = 1000 meters	1 mile = 5280 feet
	1 mile = 1760 yards

CAPACITY AND VOLUME

Metric	Customary
1 liter = 1000 milliliters	1 cup = 8 ounces
	1 pint = 2 cups
	1 quart = 2 pints
	1 gallon = 128 ounces
	1 gallon = 4 quarts

MASS AND WEIGHT

Metric	Customary
1 gram = 1000 milligrams	1 pound = 16 ounces
1 kilogram = 1000 grams	1 ton = 2000 pounds

TIME

1 minute = 60 seconds

1 hour = 60 minutes

1 day = 24 hours

1 week = 7 days

1 year = 365 days

1 year = 52 weeks

1 year = 12 months

Continued on the following page

Inches

0

1

2

3

4

5

6

Perimeter	square	$P = 4s$
	rectangle	$P = 2l + 2w$ or $P = 2(l + w)$
Pi	π	$\pi \approx 3.14$ or $\pi \approx \frac{22}{7}$
Circumference	circle	$C = 2\pi r$ or $C = \pi d$
Area	square	$A = s^2$
	rectangle	$A = lw$ or $A = bh$
	triangle	$A = \frac{1}{2}bh$ or $A = \frac{bh}{2}$
	trapezoid	$A = \frac{1}{2}(b_1 + b_2)h$ or $A = \frac{(b_1 + b_2)h}{2}$
	circle	$A = \pi r^2$
Volume	cube	$V = s^3$
	rectangular prism	$V = lwh$ or $V = Bh*$
	cylinder	$V = \pi r^2 h$ or $V = Bh*$

B represents the area of the Base of a solid figure.

Centimeters